THE SADTLER HANDBOOK OF ULTRAVIOLET SPECTRA

Editor:
William W. Simons
Spectroscopist
Sadtler Research Laboratories, Inc.

SADTLER | HEYDEN

Published by
Sadtler Research Laboratories
Division of Bio-Rad Laboratories, Inc.
3316 Spring Garden Street
Philadelphia, Pennsylvania 19104

ISBN 0-8456-0033-8

Library of Congress Catalog Card Number: 79-65539

Co-published for exclusive distribution in Europe by
Heyden & Son Ltd.
Spectrum House, Hillview Gardens
London N.W. 4, England 2JQ

ISBN 0-8550-1443-1

Printed in the United States of America

THE SADTLER HANDBOOK OF ULTRAVIOLET SPECTRA

PREFACE

The purpose of this abridged edition of the Sadtler Standard Ultraviolet Spectra collection is two-fold. First, it is intended to satisfy the academic need for a small, convenient collection of reference spectra of organic compounds relevant to introductory courses on organic chemistry and the supplementary laboratory classes on experimental organic chemistry and qualitative organic chemistry. Second, this collection is intended to serve as a desk reference to those employed in industry who resort to ultraviolet spectroscopy for the qualitative or quantitative characterization of organic compounds when comprehensive spectra collections are not available.

Although the Sadtler Handbook of Ultraviolet Spectra has been designed to stand alone, many chemists will find its greatest usefulness in the complementary data it provides to that found in the Handbooks of Infrared and NMR Spectra. All three volumes contain spectral data for the same compounds and they utilize an identical spectra numbering system providing ready access to the IR, NMR and UV spectra of those compounds that have been included in the set.

With regard to the spectra printed in this volume, consideration should be given to the spectrometer and solvent employed in its preparation. The earliest UV spectra contained in the Sadtler Standard UV spectra collection (1960 - 1962) were prepared with a Perkin-Elmer Spectracord 4000A ® spectrometer. The vertical absorbance scales for these spectra are inverted by more modern standards, i.e., the bottom of the chart represents an absorbance of 2.0 decreasing to 0.0 at the top of chart, whereas the presentation of spectra recorded on the Cary 15 ® and the Beckman model 25 ® spectrometers possess absorbance scales increasing from 0.0 at the bottom of the chart to 1.0 at the top.

The horizontal wavelength scales of the spectra of all three instruments are consistent in that they increase from a nominal 200 mμ on the left to 350 mμ on the right. Several of the spectra prepared after 1962 may have wavelength scales ranging out to 500 mμ or 800 mμ for those compounds that display absorption bands in the visible region of the spectrum.

The majority of the spectra were examined as solutions in methanol although some of the earlier spectra and those compounds which react with methanol have been scanned using isooctane, dioxane, hexane or water as the solvent. The comparison of UV spectra prepared using solvents of widely different polarities should be avoided due to significant differences in the observed wavelength and intensities of the maxima that may be observed.

This volume contains over 2000 spectra representing the neutral, base and acid scans for 1600 compounds. There are no spectra for the remaining compounds for a variety of reasons. Firstly, many of the compounds do not produce maxima in the near UV region. These groups of compounds are usually the aliphatic and alicyclic varieties of the functional group under consideration and a note is included in the text section indicating when omissions of this type exist in the chapter. Secondly, certain types of chromophores did not meet the criteria required for inclusion in the Sadtler Standard UV Collection from which the spectra in this volume were derived, i.e., a maximum above 215 mμ with a molar absorptivity of more than 100. For groups such as these, a few selected spectra were specially prepared for this text to indicate the appearance and general wavelength and intensity trends expected from the group. Thirdly, the production procedure at Sadtler Research is such that the infrared and NMR spectra of samples are prepared before the corresponding near UV spectra. In several cases, due to the small amount of material originally submitted there would not be sufficient material remaining to prepare the near UV scan or in the case of certain samples, the material may have decomposed before the spectrum could be prepared. When spectra are missing from this volume for reasons such as these, the note "Pure Sample Not Available" is printed in the position that would have been occupied by the spectrogram.

Frequently, the bottom (and occasionally the middle) spectrum position of a right hand page will be found to be blank. These spaces have been purposely inserted so that the corresponding neutral, base and acid scans for the next compound in the book sequence will all appear on the same or facing pages of the text. This was done to allow the user to more easily make visible comparisons of the spectra and note the differences brought about by the changes in pH of the solvent medium.

The comments and tables of data that are presented at the beginning of each functional group section have been derived principally from the spectra contained in the chapter itself. Occasional references to the near UV literature have been made to provide data on compounds that do not appear in this work or for compounds that have had their spectra determined in a different solvent.

The two primary references that have been used are -

Ultra-violet and Visible Spectroscopy, Chemical Applications, Rao, C. N. R., Butterworths, London, 1961 and

UV-Atlas of Organic Compounds, Photoelectric Spectrometry Group, London, and Institut fur Spektrochemie und Angewandte Spektroskopie, Dortmund, Butterworths, London.

In order to make this handbook readily understandable to the student or chemist utilizing near UV spectra as an analytical technique, an attempt has been made to limit the number of terms used to describe changes in the intensity and wavelength of absorption bands. These four terms are defined below.

Bathochromic Shifts -- Changes to longer wavelength (red shift).
Hypsochromic Shifts -- Changes to shorter wavelength (blue shift).
Hyperchromic Effect -- Increase in band intensity.
Hypochromic Effect -- Decrease in band intensity.

In addition to the book order index (functional group order) and the alphabetical index, this volume contains a Sadtler UV Locator system. The Locator will be found to be a useful, empirical method of matching an unknown spectrum with the most similar spectra included in this handbook, utilizing the wavelength and intensity of the maxima observed in the spectrum to be matched.

Note
The spectrum numbers listed in the indices apply ***only*** to the spectra in the Sadtler Handbooks of Reference Spectra (Infrared, Proton NMR, Ultraviolet) and do not correspond in any way to the spectrum numbers in the Sadtler Standard Spectra volume.

TABLE OF CONTENTS

TABLE OF CONTENTS

TABLE OF CONTENTS

TABLE OF CONTENTS

pH MODIFICATION

The ultraviolet spectra of many compounds, especially those containing an ionizable group directly attached to a chromophore, can be distinctly affected by the polarity of the solvent system in which they are determined.

Because these changes can be a reliable indication of the presence of certain functional groups, many of the compounds included in this handbook have been scanned in acidic and/or basic media to note the influence of pH on the spectrum.

The experimental procedure involves recording the UV spectrum of the sample in the neutral solvent, then adjusting the pH to 0.5 by the addition of aqueous 2N HCl or to 11.0 by the addition of aqueous 2N KOH. Minor changes in band intensity can be expected for all samples that are treated in this way since the addition of acid tends to lower band intensity due to dilution while the absorption of KOH in the far UV extends up into the near UV sufficiently to increase the intensity of maxima, an effect which decreases with increasing wavelength, i.e., a band at 220 mμ will show an increase in intensity much greater than a band at 300 mμ.

In order to keep the size of this volume within reasonable bounds, not every compound that would change with the addition of acid and/or base will have those spectra included and, conversely, there are included some selected pH modified spectra for certain functional groups that might be expected to change but do not.

The table provided below summarizes the groups of compounds which have been observed to show significant changes with these procedures. A "+" indicates that the spectrum is altered in the pH modified solution.

Compound Type	Acid	Base
Acid halides	–	+
Aldehydes	+	–
Anhydrides	–	+
Amidines	+	–
Aniline	+	–
Aniline salts	–	+
Barbituric acids	–	+
Carboxylic acids	–	+
Carboxylic acid salts	+	–
β-Diketones	–	+
Hydrazides	+	–
Hydrazines	+	–
Hydrazine salts	–	+
Hydrazones	+	–
Hydroxamic acids	–	+
Imides	–	+
Lactones	–	+
Oximes	–	+
Phenols	–	+

Compound Type	Acid	Base
Pyridines	+	–
Pyrroles	+	–
Semicarbazides	–	+
Sulfonamides	–	+
Sulfonic acids	–	+
Thioamides	–	+
Thiols	–	+
Thioureas	–	+
Triazenes	+	–
Uracils	–	+
Ylidene compounds	+	–

THE SATURATED HYDROCARBONS

The normal, branched and cyclic alkanes are transparent in the near UV region from 200 mμ to 380 mμ. As a result, their spectra have not been prepared for the Sadtler Standard UV collection and are not included in this volume.

Their characteristic lack of absorption in the near UV region makes them suitable choices as solvents for the preparation of the spectra of other compounds. N-Hexane, isooctane and cyclohexane are commonly used for this purpose.

THE ACYCLIC AND CYCLIC ALKENES

The alkenes, which contain the ethylenic chromophore, display intense absorption in the ***far*** UV region below 200 mμ. Substitution of the ethylenic linkage by heteroatoms containing a nonbonding electron pair may bring about a bathochromic shift to longer wavelengths but rarely result in maxima above the 210 mμ cut-off region required for inclusion in this volume.

Conjugated ethylenic groups however, do produce maxima above 210 mμ (spectra 73, 87, 95, 105 and 112).

A table of absorption data for several conjugated olefins is presented below.

Compound	λ_{max} (mμ)	ϵ_{max}	Solvent	Spectrum
1,3-Butadiene	217	21,000	Hexane	Lit.
2-Methyl-1,3-butadiene	223	10,800	Methanol	73
2,3-Dimethyl-1,3-Butadiene	226	21,400	Cyclohexane	Lit.
2,4-Hexadiene	227	14,200	Methanol	87
2,5-Dimethyl-2,4-Hexadiene	242	13,100	Methanol	95
1,3,5-Hexatriene	253	50,000	Isooctane	Lit.

THE ALKYNES

Aliphatic compounds containing an acetylenic chromophore do not display any absorption bands in the near UV region. Their absorption in the far UV region consists of a weak band near 174 mμ. The conjugated polyynes produce two bands in the near UV region of the spectrum which are often characterized with the appearance of fine structure. For example, 2,4,6-Octatriyne displays one band at 207 mμ (135,000) and one at 268 mμ (200).

Note: Because they do not produce maxima in the near UV region, there are no spectra in this volume for the following compounds: 1 - 72, 75 - 86, 88, 90 - 94, 96 - 104, 106 - 111, 113 - 131.

2-METHYL-1,3-BUTADIENE (ISOPRENE) 73

C_5H_8
Mol. Wt. 68.12
B.P. 33-34°C
Solvent: Methanol

λ Max. mμ	a_m	Cell mm	Conc. g/L
222.5	10800	0.5	0.100

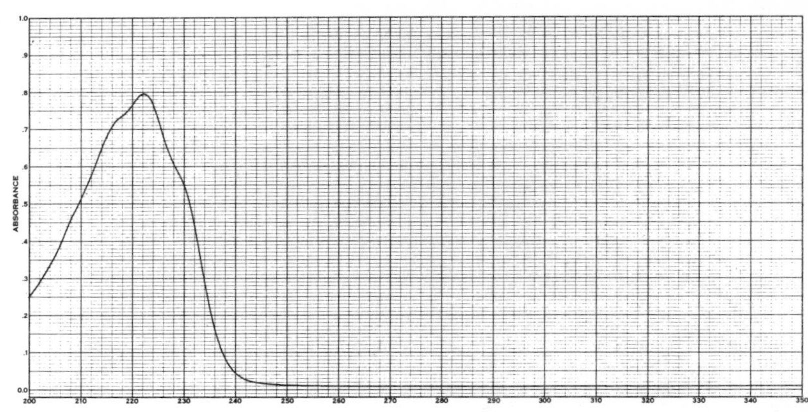

2,3-DIMETHYL-1,3-BUTADIENE (3-METHYLISOPRENE) 74

C_6H_{10}
Mol. Wt. 82.15
B.P. 68-69°C

λ Max. mμ	a_m	Cell mm	Conc. g/L

Pure sample not available.

2,4-HEXADIENE 87

C_6H_{10}
Mol. Wt. 82.15
B.P. 82-84°C
Solvent: Methanol

λ Max. mμ	a_m	Cell mm	Conc. g/L
227	14200	.5	0.100

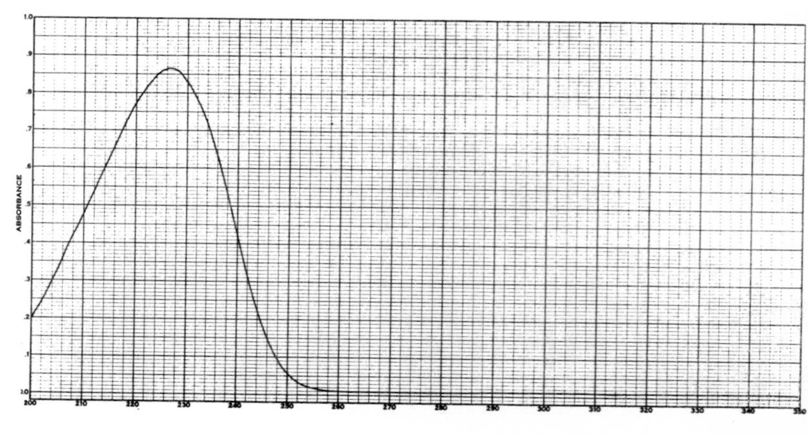

5-METHYL-1,3,6-HEPTATRIENE 89

C_8H_{12}
Mol. Wt. 108.18
B.P. 117°C

λ Max. mμ	a_m	Cell mm	Conc. g/L

Pure sample not available.

2,5-DIMETHYL-2,4-HEXADIENE 95

C_8H_{14}
Mol. Wt. 110.20
Solvent: Methanol

λ Max. mμ	a_m	Cell mm	Conc. g/L
241.5	13100	1	0.0656

Methanol
$CH_3-\overset{CH_3}{C}=CH-CH=\overset{CH_3}{C}-CH_3$
ABSORBANCE
1.0 .9 .8 .7 .6 .5 .4 .3 .2 .1 0.0
200 210 220 230 240 250 260 270 280 290 300 310 320 330 340 350

BI-1-CYCLOHEXEN-1-YL 105

$C_{12}H_{18}$
Mol. Wt. 162.28
Solvent: Methanol

λ Max. mμ	a_m	Cell mm	Conc. g/L
238.5	13800	1	0.1130

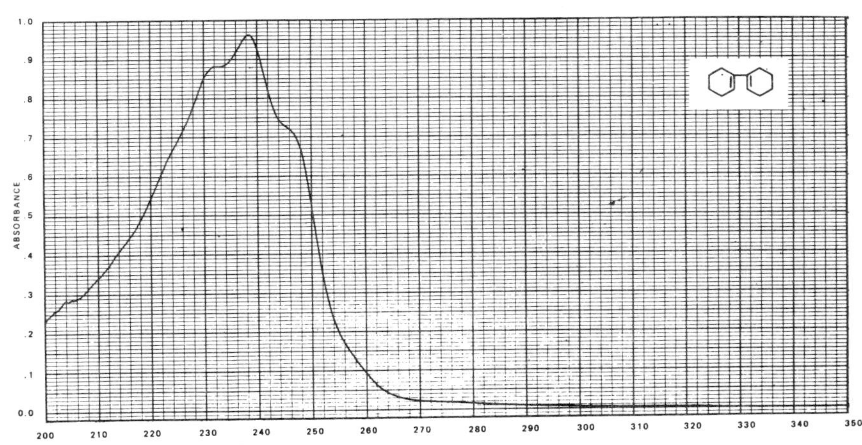

1,3-CYCLOHEXADIENE 112

C_6H_8

Mol. Wt. 80.13

Solvent: Methanol

λ Max. mμ	a_m	Cell mm	Conc. g/L
223.5	9810	0.5	0.100

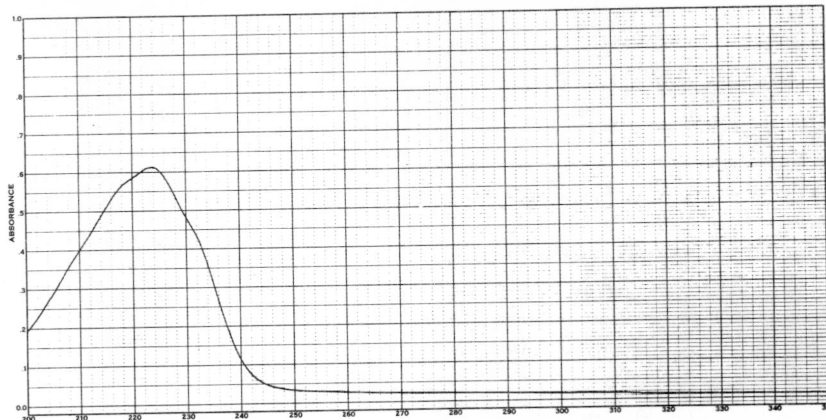

λ Max. mμ	a_m	Cell mm	Conc. g/L

λ Max. mμ	a_m	Cell mm	Conc. g/L

THE ARENES

Benzene and its alkyl substituted derivatives produce one major band in the near UV region with considerable fine structure arising from the superimposition of sub-levels of vibrational absorption upon the electronic absorption.

The most intense band in the spectrum of Benzene (spectrum 132) appears at 254 mμ (ϵ_{max} 212). Additional bands are seen at 268, 261, 249, 243, 239 and 234 mμ.

Substitution of the Benzene ring by alkyl groups produces a shift to longer wavelength (near 260 mμ) for the most intense band in the spectrum. The following table lists the wavelength and ϵ_{max} for the most intense peaks observed in the near UV for benzene and a series of monosubstituted benzenes.

Compound	λ_{max}(mμ)	ϵ_{max}	Solvent	Spectrum
Benzene	254	212	Cyclohexane	132
Toluene	261	238	Methanol	133
Hexyl Benzene	261	235	Methanol	142
Diphenyl methane	261	444	Methanol	148
Diphenyl ethane	259	489	Methanol	149
Triphenyl methane	262	770	Cyclohexane	150
Styrene	245	15,200	Cyclohexane	156
cis-Stilbene	223	20,600	Methanol	158
trans-Stilbene	294	33,200	Methanol	159
Phenylacetylene	234	19,900	Methanol	166
Diphenylacetylene	278	30,300	Methanol	169
Biphenyl	247	19,300	Methanol	171

Substitution of benzene by an unsaturated group as in the last six compounds listed in the table above results in the appearance of a very intense K-band in the region from 200 - 300 mμ region. The weaker B-bands undergo a strong bathochromic shift and no longer represent the most intense band in the spectrum.

Linear Polyenes

In the linear series of polyenes (Benzene, Naphthalene, Anthracene, etc.) as the number of rings increase, the absorption bands move to progressively longer wavelengths eventually appearing in the visible region.

Compound	$\lambda_{max}(\epsilon_{max})$	$\lambda_{max}(\epsilon_{max})$	$\lambda_{max}(\epsilon_{max})$	Spectrum
Benzene	----------	204 (7900)	254 (212)	132
Naphthalene	220 (10600)	275 (5530)	311 (239)	200
Anthracene	250 (20000)	376 (7590)	----------	213

BENZENE

132

C_6H_6
Mol. Wt. 78.11
B.P. 80.1°C (lit.)
Solvent: Cyclohexane

λ Max. mμ	^{a}m	Cell mm	Conc. g/L
268	13.6	10	4.152
260.5	149	10	0.519
254	212	10	0.519
248.5	169	10	0.519
243	99.3	10	0.519
239	52.7	10	0.519
233.5	31.5	10	0.519

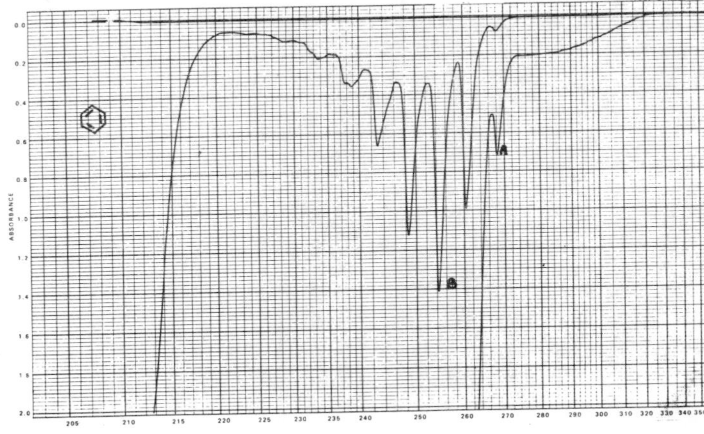

TOLUENE

133

C_7H_8
Mol. Wt. 92.14
B.P. 110.6°C
Solvent: Methanol

λ Max. mμ	^{a}m	Cell mm	Conc. g/L
268	222	2	1.00
264	167	2	1.00
261	238	2	1.00
259.5	198	2	1.00
255	175	2	1.00
253.5	163	2	1.00
207.5	8870	1	0.08

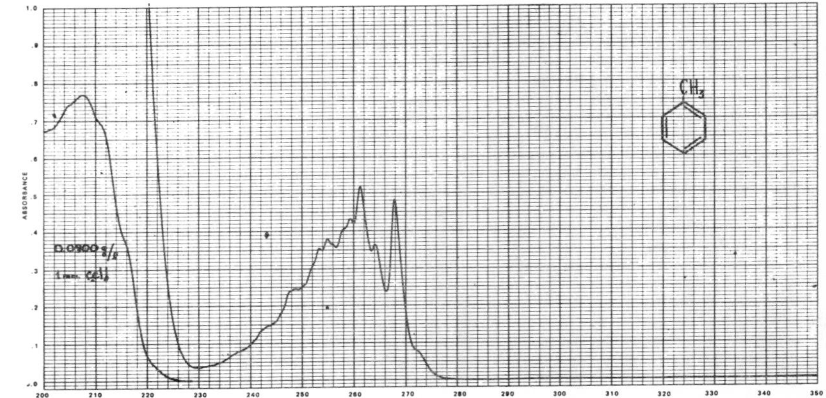

ETHYLBENZENE

134

C_8H_{10}
Mol. Wt. 106.17
B.P. 134-136°C
Solvent: Methanol

λ Max. mμ	^{a}m	Cell mm	Conc. g/L
268	142	5	0.850
260.5	200	5	0.850
254.5	168	5	0.850
208	7520	1	0.0850

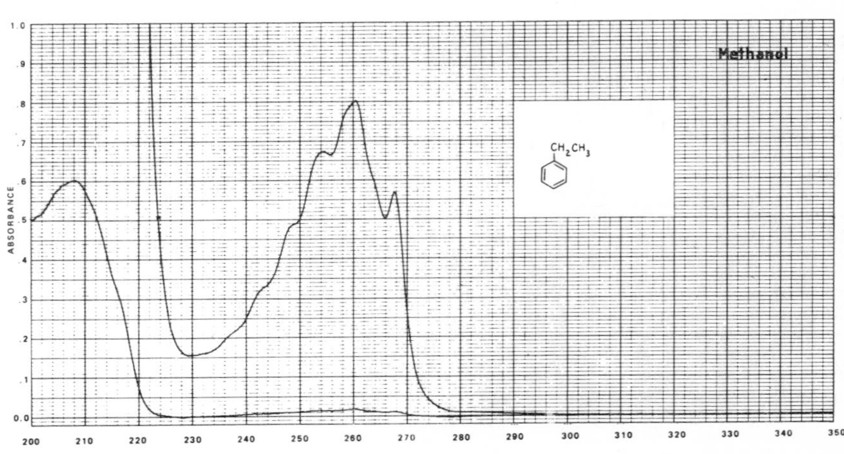

PROPYLBENZENE

C_9H_{12}
Mol. Wt. 120.20
B.P. 157-159°C
Solvent: Methanol

λ Max. mμ	a_m	Cell mm	Conc. g/L
268	173	10	0.3260
261	218	10	0.3260
259	214	10	0.3260
253	209	10	0.3260
248	194	10	0.3260

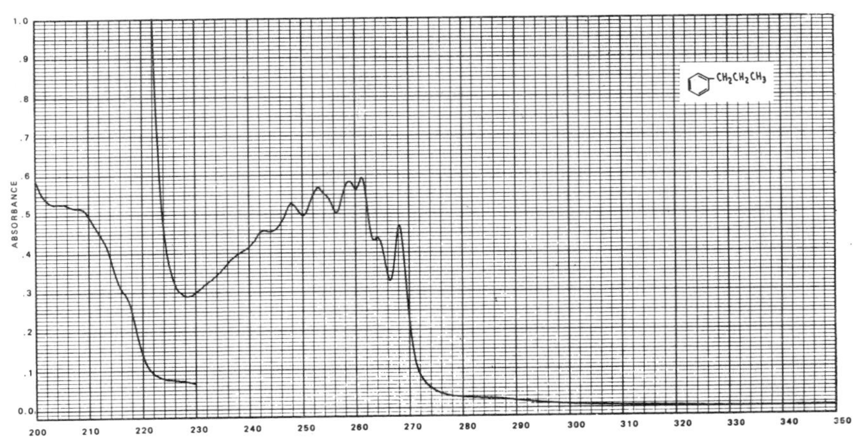

ISOPROPYL BENZENE (CUMENE)

C_9H_{12}
Mol. Wt. 120.19
Solvent: Cyclohexane

136

λ Max. mμ	a_m	Cell mm	Conc. g/L
x	x	10	1.76
267.5	157	10	0.527
264	164	10	0.527
260	240	10	0.527
258	240	10	0.527
252.5	228	10	0.527
248	197	10	0.527

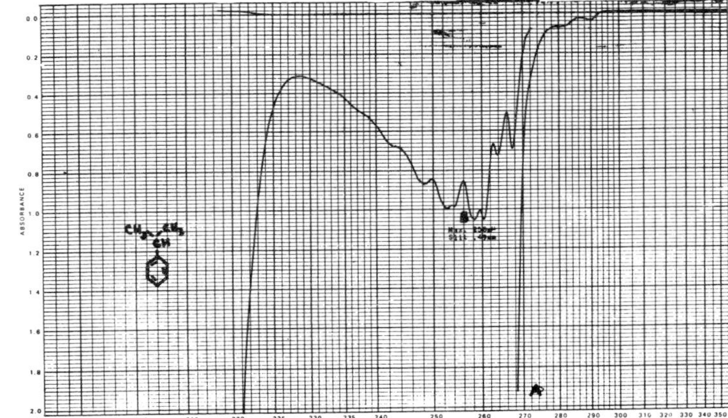

n-BUTYLBENZENE

$C_{10}H_{14}$
Mol. Wt. 134.21
B.P. 183.27°C (lit.)
Solvent: Cyclohexane

137

λ Max. mμ	a_m	Cell mm	Conc. g/L
x	x	10	1.61
268	200	10	0.805
264	180	10	0.805
261.5	247	10	0.805
258	233	10	0.805
254.5	200	10	0.805
253	200	10	0.805
248	150	10	0.805
x	x	10	0.081

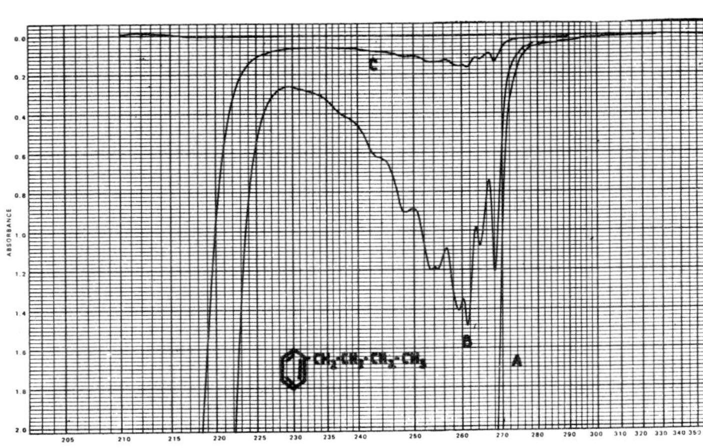

sec-BUTYLBENZENE **138**

$C_{10}H_{14}$
Mol. Wt. 134.22
B.P. 173-175°C
Solvent: Methanol

λ Max. mμ	a_m	Cell mm	Conc. g/L
267	151	20	0.350
263.5	146	20	0.350
260.5	183	20	0.350
252.5	153	20	0.350
x	x	2	0.0700

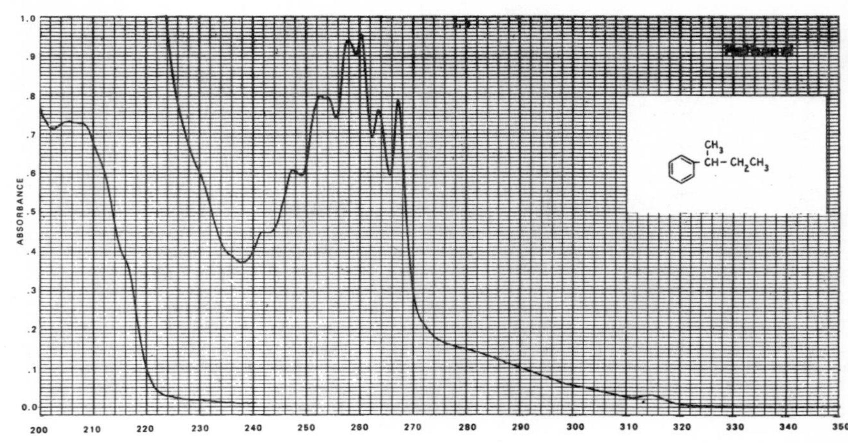

ISOBUTYLBENZENE **139**

$C_{10}H_{14}$
Mol. Wt. 134.22
B.P. 172°C
Solvent: Methanol

λ Max. mμ	a_m	Cell mm	Conc. g/L
267.5	174	10	0.485
264	170	10	0.485
260.5	216	10	0.485
258.5	221	10	0.485
x	x	1	0.0970

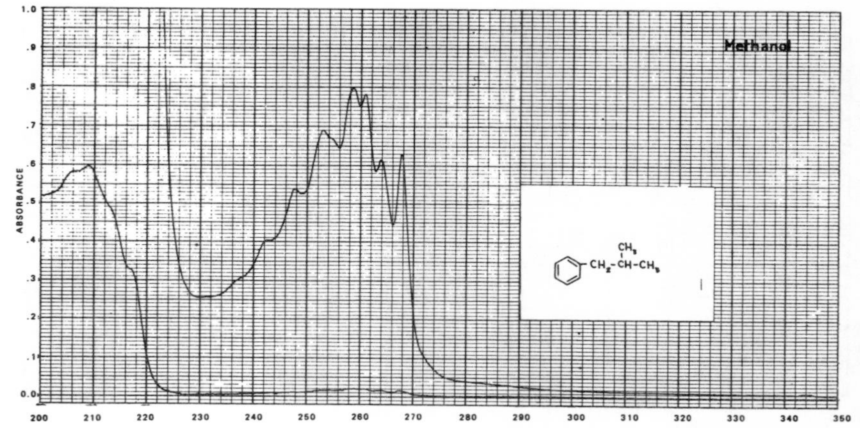

tert-BUTYLBENZENE **140**

$C_{10}H_{14}$
Mol. Wt. 134.11
Solvent: Cyclohexane

λ Max. mμ	a_m	Cell mm	Conc. g/L
266	117	10	1.940
263.5	147	10	0.970
257	203	10	0.970
252	161	10	0.970
247	120	10	0.970

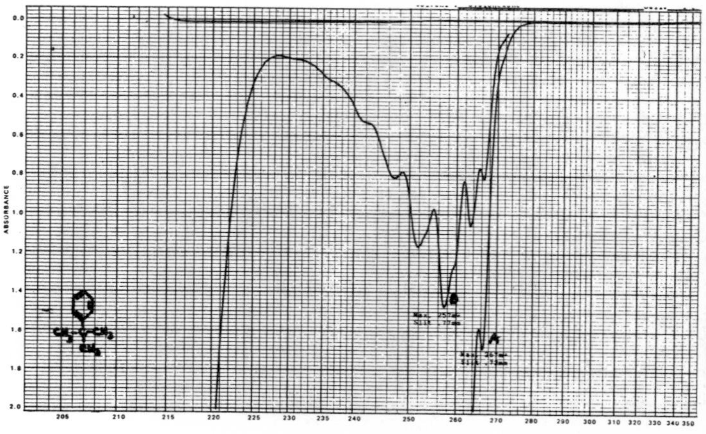

PENTYLBENZENE 141

$C_{11}H_{16}$

Mol. Wt. 148.25

Solvent: Methanol

λ Max. mμ	a_m	Cell mm	Conc. g/L
268	191	10	0.480
261	235	10	0.480
259	220	10	0.480
253.5	190	10	0.480
209	12500	1	0.0960

1-PHENYLHEXANE 142

$C_{12}H_{18}$

Mol. Wt. 162.28

B.P. 95-96°C/9mm

Solvent: Methanol

λ Max. mμ	a_m	Cell mm	Conc. g/L
268.5	194	10	0.300
264	173	10	0.300
261.5	235	10	0.300
259	222	10	0.300
209	7980	1	0.150

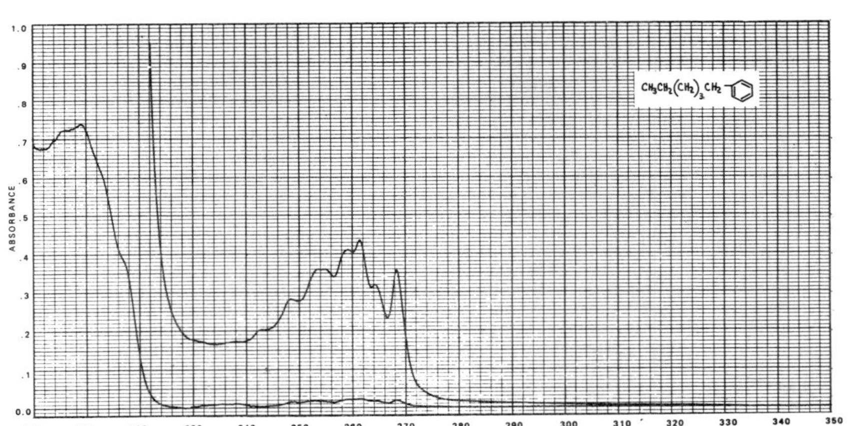

OCTYLBENZENE(1-PHENYL OCTANE) 143

$C_{14}H_{22}$

Mol. Wt. 190.33

Solvent: Methanol

λ Max. mμ	a_m	Cell mm	Conc. g/L
267.5	183	40	0.100
259.5	212	40	0.100
253.0	200	40	0.100
x	x	2	0.100

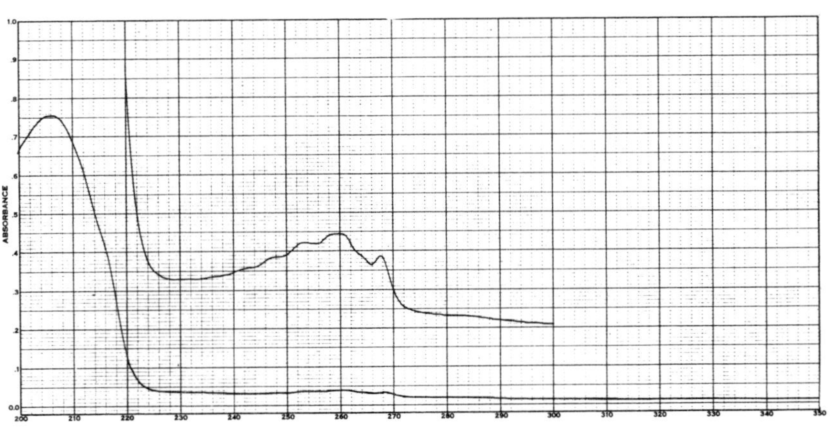

(CYCLOPROPYL)PHENYLMETHANE

144

$C_{10}H_{12}$
Mol. Wt. 132.21
Solvent: Methanol

λ Max. mμ	a_m	Cell mm	Conc. g/L
270	191	10	0.548
266.5	181	10	0.548
264	224	10	0.548
261	224	10	0.548
256	193	10	0.548
250.5	148	10	0.548
206	8290	10	0.011

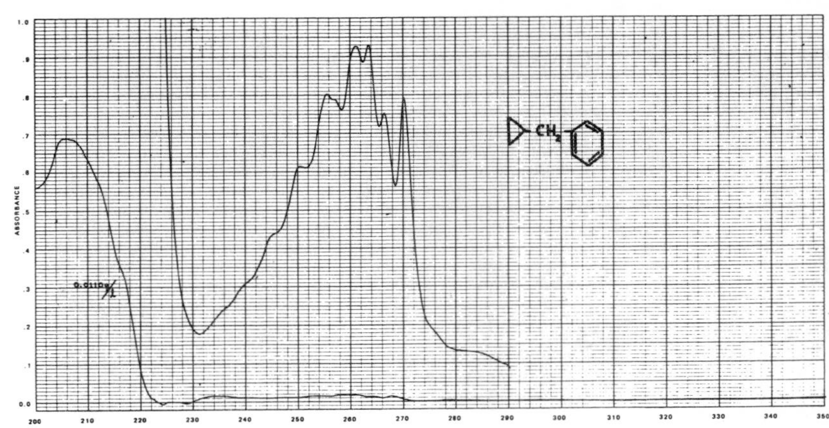

PHENYLCYCLOHEXANE

145

$C_{12}H_{16}$
Mol. Wt. 160.25
Solvent: Cyclohexane

λ Max. mμ	a_m	Cell mm	Conc. g/L
x	x	10	2.50
267.5	164	10	1.25
264	158	10	1.25
260	211	10	1.25
258	213	10	1.25
253	180	10	1.25
248	129	10	1.25

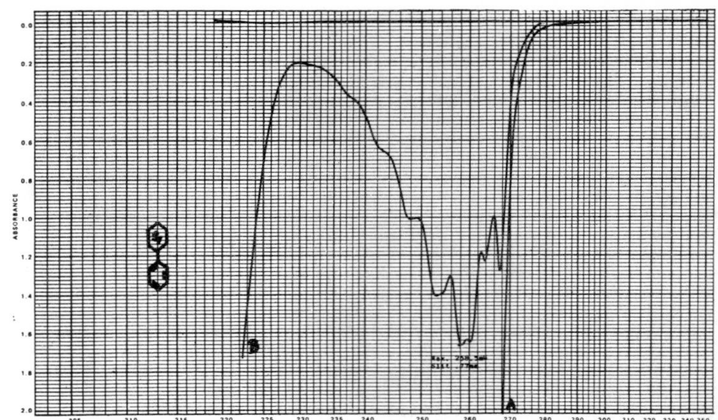

(1-CYCLOHEXEN-1-YL)BENZENE

146

$C_{12}H_{14}$
Mol. Wt. 158.25
M.P. -11°C B.P. 251-253°C
Solvent: Methanol

λ Max. mμ	a_m	Cell mm	Conc. g/L
244	10900	1	0.083

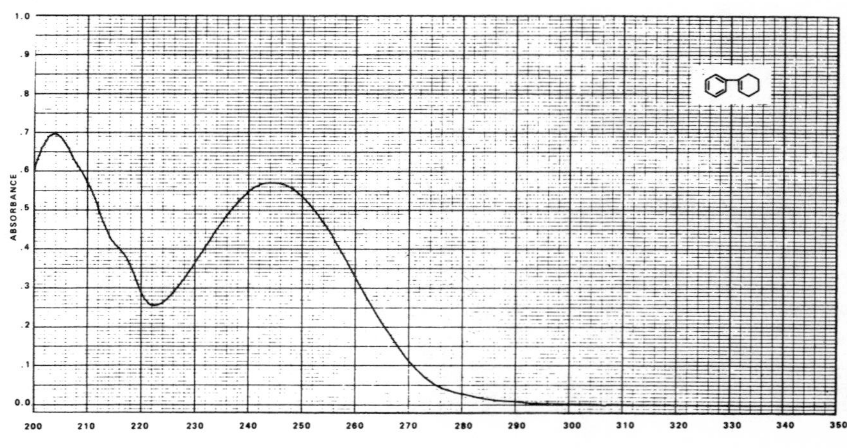

5-PHENYL-1-PENTYNE

147

$C_{11}H_{12}$
Mol. Wt. 144.22
Solvent: Methanol

λ Max. mμ	a_m	Cell mm	Conc. g/L
268	134	20	0.100
259	183	20	0.100
254	154	20	0.100
x	x	2	0.100

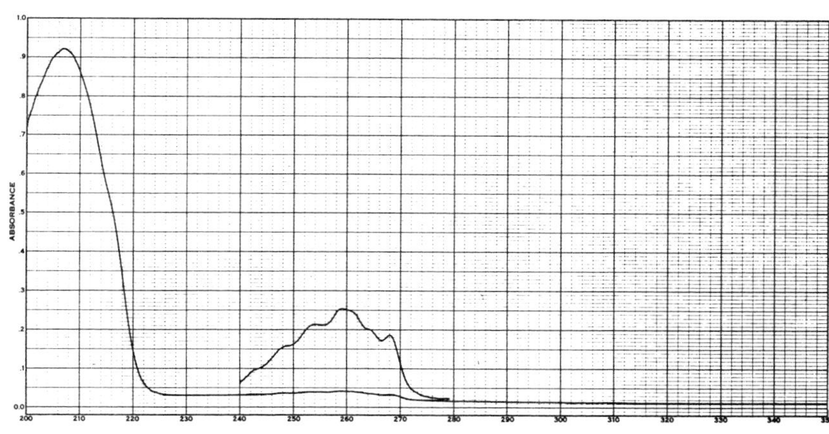

DIPHENYLMETHANE

148

$C_{13}H_{12}$
Mol. Wt. 168.24
M.P. 22-24°C
Solvent: Methanol

λ Max. mμ	a_m	Cell mm	Conc. g/L
269	346	20	0.100
260.5	444	20	0.100
x	x	1	0.100

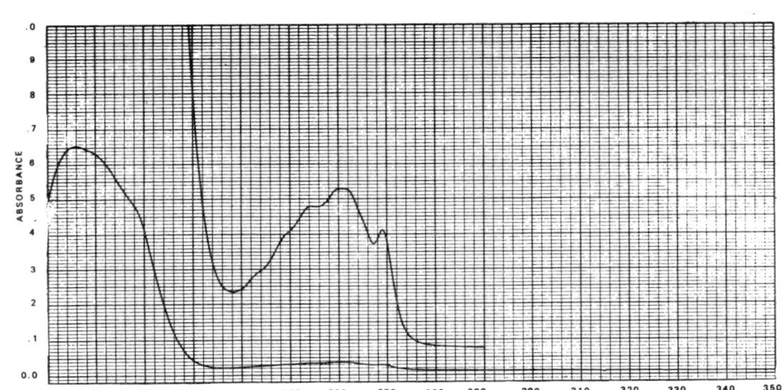
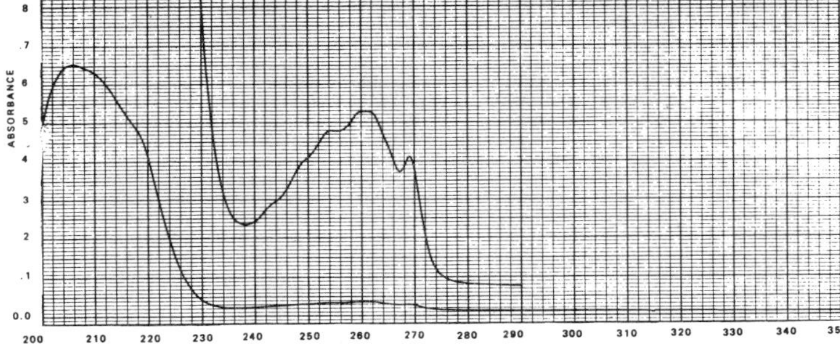

BIBENZYL

149

$C_{14}H_{14}$
Mol. Wt. 182.27
M.P. 50-51°C
Solvent: Methanol

λ Max. mμ	a_m	Cell mm	Conc. g/L
267.5	345	20	0.100
264	377	20	0.100
258.5	489	20	0.100
253	420	20	0.100
x	x	1	0.100

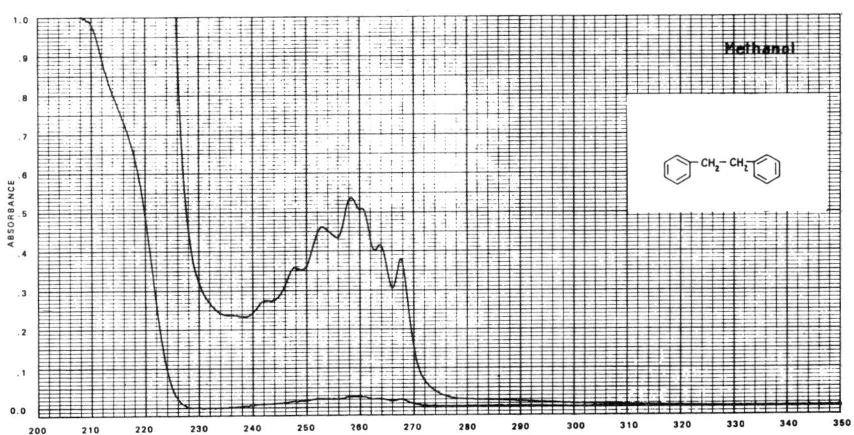

TRIPHENYLMETHANE

150

$C_{19}H_{16}$
Mol. Wt. 244.34
M.P. 92°C (lit.)
Solvent: Cyclohexane

λ Max. mμ	a_m	Cell mm	Conc. g/L
x	x	10	2.00
270	547	10	0.400
262	770	10	0.400
256	651	10	0.400
x	x	10	0.004

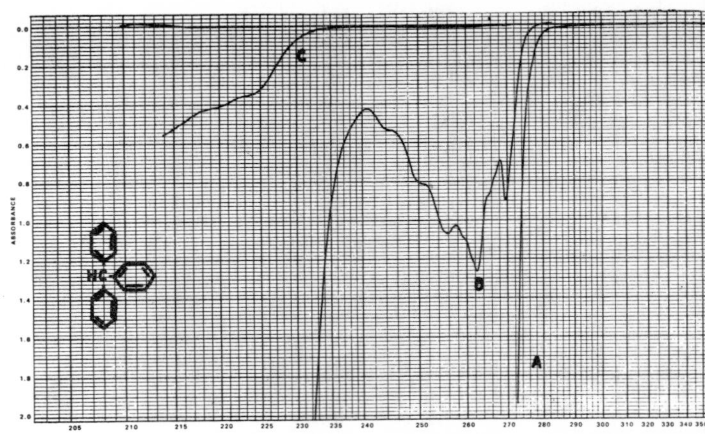

1,1,2-TRIPHENYLETHANE

151

$C_{20}H_{18}$
Mol. Wt. 258.37
M.P. 53-55°C
Solvent: Methanol

λ Max. mμ	a_m	Cell mm	Conc. g/L
298	904	2	0.500
269	951	2	0.500
261.5	1040	2	0.500
259	1060	2	0.500
253	992	2	0.500

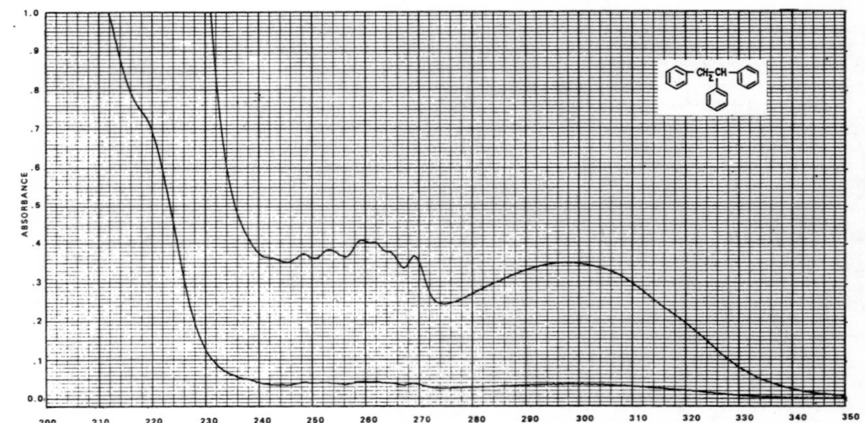

meso-1,2,3,4-TETRAPHENYLBUTANE

152

$C_{28}H_{26}$
Mol. Wt. 362.52
M.P. 188°C
Solvent: Methanol

λ Max. mμ	a_m	Cell mm	Conc. g/L
268.5	629	5	0.500
265	750	5	0.500
259.5	949	5	0.500
253.5	790	5	0.500
249	597	5	0.500

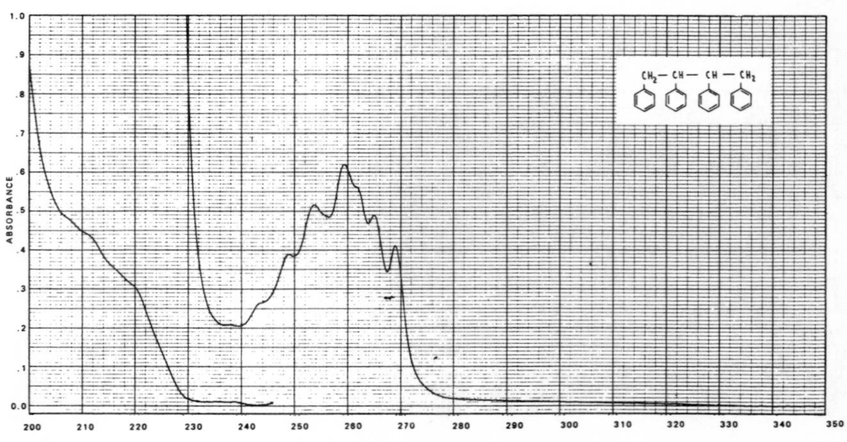

ALLYLBENZENE 153

C_9H_{10}

Mol. Wt. 118.18

B.P. 155-157°C

Solvent: Methanol

λ Max. mμ	a_m	Cell mm	Conc. g/L
267.5	205	10	0.386
261	274	10	0.386
258.5	283	10	0.386
253	263	10	0.386
x	x	1	0.386

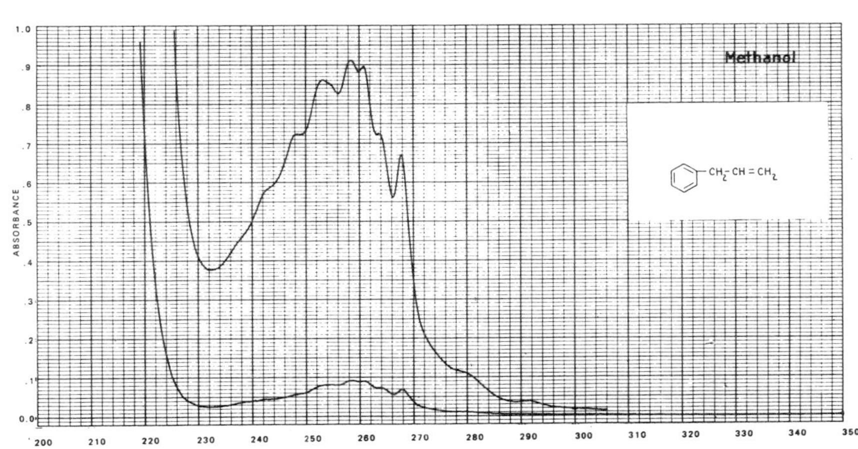

1-PHENYL-2-BUTENE 154

$C_{10}H_{12}$

Mol. Wt. 132.20

Solvent: Cyclohexane

λ Max. mμ	a_m	Cell mm	Conc. g/L
x	x	10	2.41
268	505	10	0.241
253.5	767	10	0.241

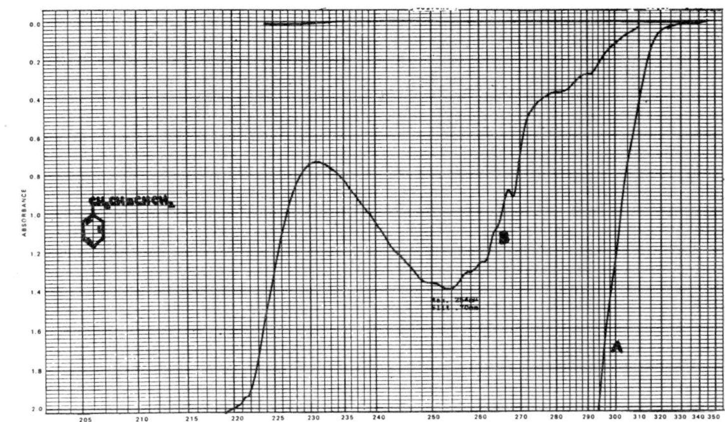

4-PHENYL-1-BUTENE 155

$C_{10}H_{12}$

Mol. Wt. 132.21

Solvent: Methanol

λ Max. mμ	a_m	Cell mm	Conc. g/L
267.5	173	40	0.100
258	235	40	0.100
252	242	40	0.100
247	231	40	0.100
212.5	2600	5	0.100

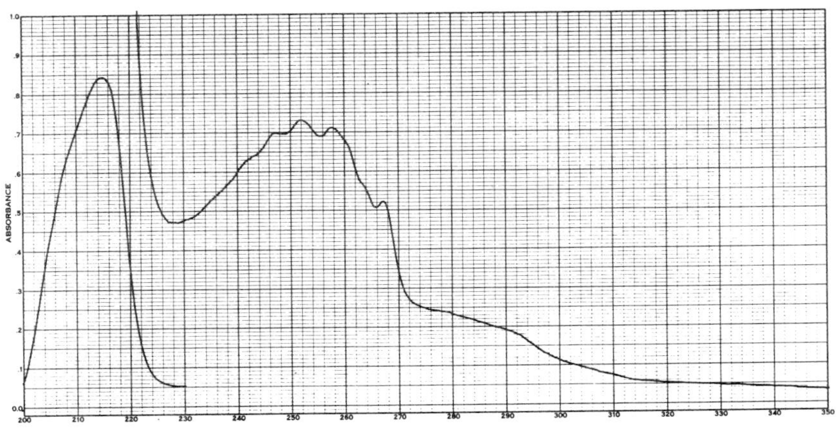

STYRENE

C_8H_8

Mol. Wt. 104.14

B.P. 146°C (lit.)

Solvent: Cyclohexane

156

λ Max. mμ	a_m	Cell mm	Conc. g/L
x	x	10	2.22
289	666	10	0.111
281	927	10	0.111
272	919	10	0.111
245	15200	10	0.0111

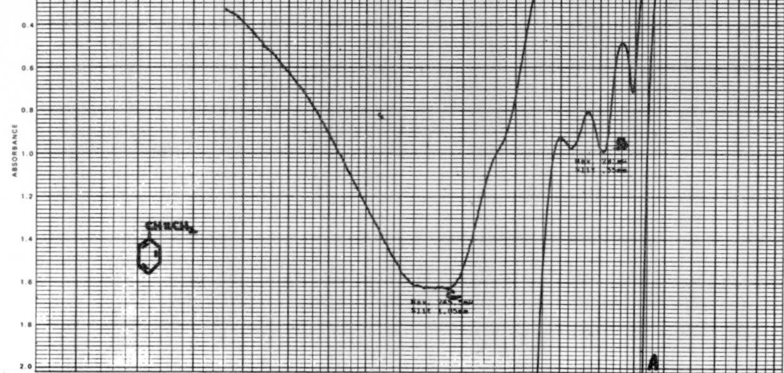

α-METHYLSTYRENE

C_9H_{10}

Mol. Wt. 118.18

Solvent: Cyclohexane

157

λ Max. mμ	a_m	Cell mm	Conc. g/L
x	x	10	1.9360
241.5	10200	10	0.0194

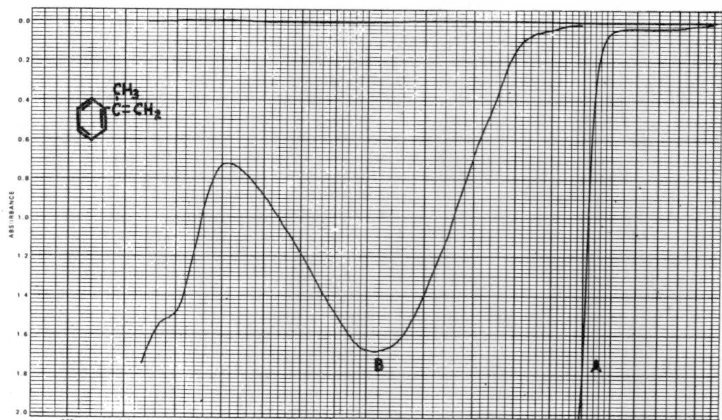

cis-STILBENE

$C_{14}H_{12}$

Mol. Wt. 180.25

Solvent: Methanol

158

λ Max. mμ	a_m	Cell mm	Conc. g/L
276	10900	1	0.100
223	20600	1	0.0500

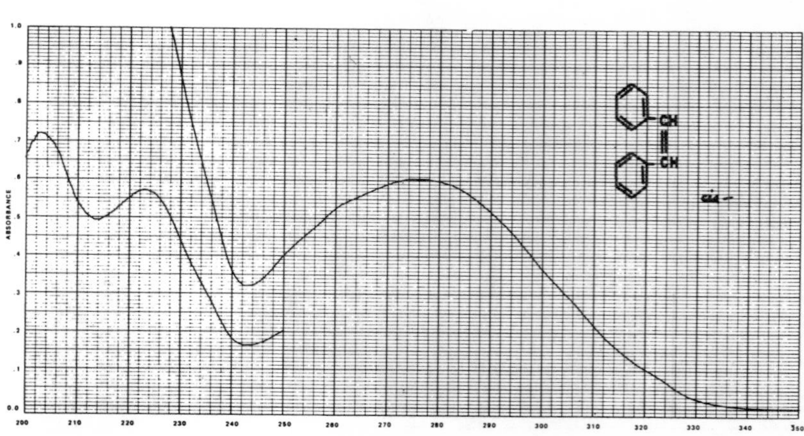

trans-STILBENE 159

$C_{14}H_2$
Mol. Wt. 180.25
M.P. 124°C
Solvent: Methanol

λ Max. mμ	a_m	Cell mm	Conc. g/L
307	32100	1	0.0500
294	33200	1	0.0500
227	21000	1	0.0500

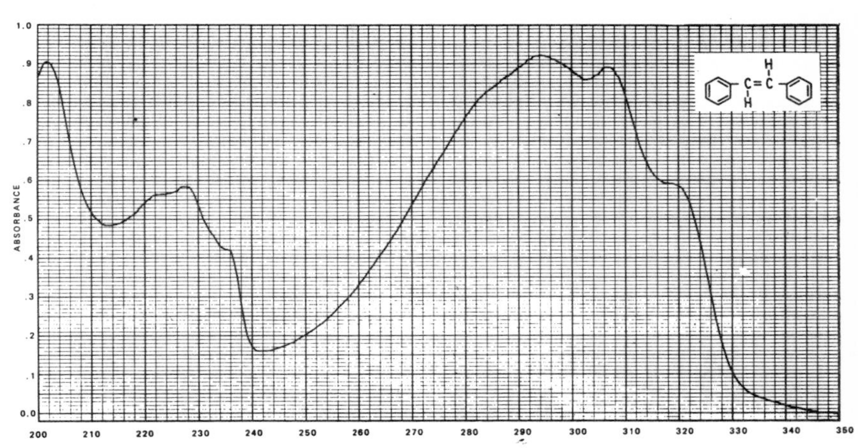

1,1-DIPHENYL-1-HEXENE 160

$C_{18}H_{20}$
Mol. Wt. 236.36
B.P. 188-192°C/15mm

λ Max. mμ	a_m	Cell mm	Conc. g/L

Pure sample not available.

1,1-DIPHENYL-1-NONENE 161

$C_{21}H_{26}$
Mol. Wt. 278.44
B.P. 176°C/1mm
Solvent: Methanol

λ Max. mμ	a_m	Cell mm	Conc. g/L
248	13400	2	0.100
x	x	1	0.100

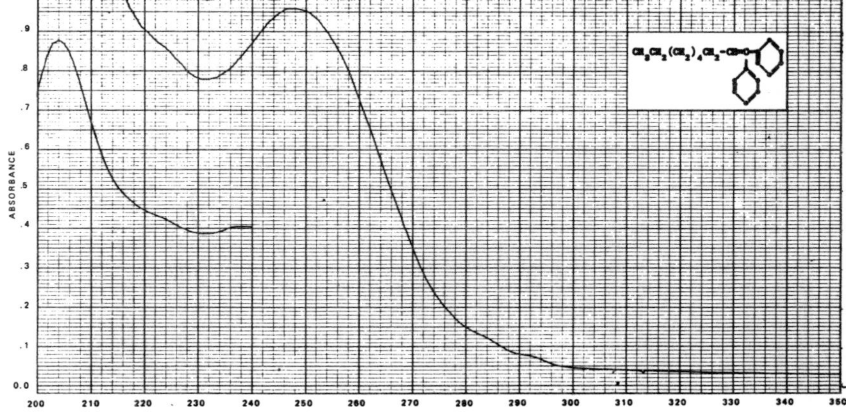

1,1-DIPHENYL-1-DODECENE

$C_{24}H_{32}$
Mol. Wt. 320.52
B.P. 210°C/0.6mm
Solvent: Methanol

λ Max. mμ	a_m	Cell mm	Conc. g/L
248.5	11200	2	0.100

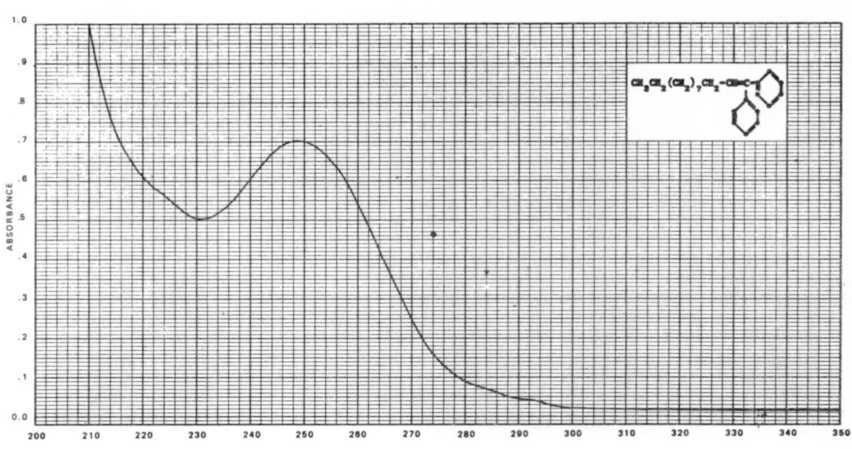

TRIPHENYLETHYLENE

$C_{20}H_{16}$
Mol. Wt. 256.35
M.P. 72-73°C (lit.) B.P. 220-221°C/14mm
Solvent: Methanol

λ Max. mμ	a_m	Cell mm	Conc. g/L
296	20000	1	0.100
227	18700	1	0.100

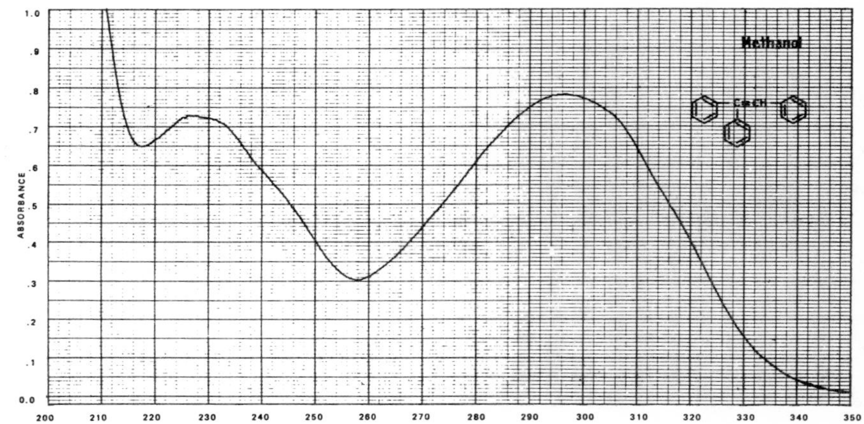

1,2,3,4-TETRAPHENYL-1,3-BUTADIENE

$C_{28}H_{22}$
Mol. Wt. 358.48
M.R. 104-106°C (lit.)
Solvent: Cyclohexane

λ Max. mμ	a_m	Cell mm	Conc. g/L
248.5	27300	10	0.020

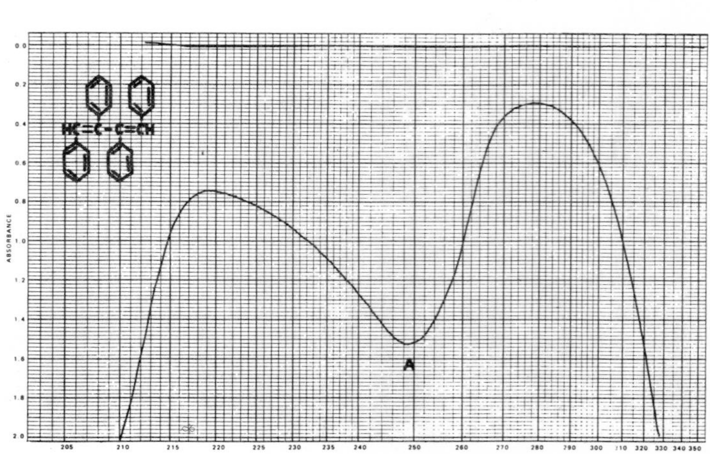

TETRAPHENYLALLENE

165

$C_{27}H_{20}$
Mol. Wt. 344.46
M.P. 164°C
Solvent: Methanol

λ Max. mμ	a_m	Cell mm	Conc. g/L
265	30400	1	0.100
x	x	1	0.100

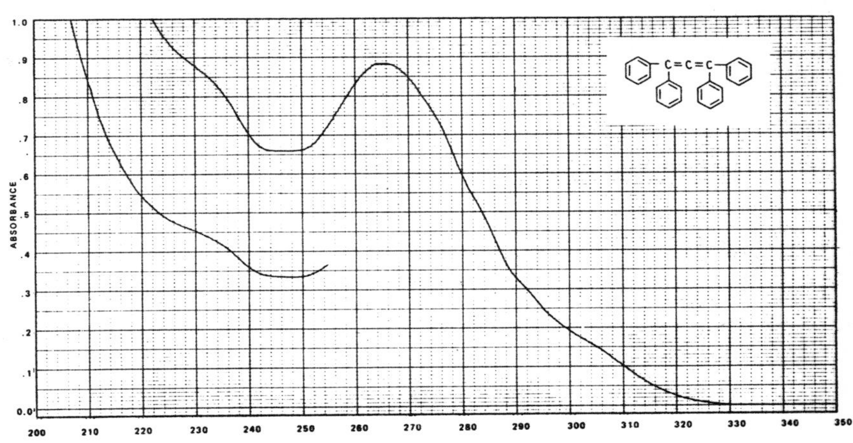

ETHYNYLBENZENE

166

C_8H_6
Mol. Wt. 102.14
B.P. 142-144°C
Solvent: Methanol

λ Max. mμ	a_m	Cell mm	Conc. g/L
276.5	367	10	0.150
269.5	463	10	0.150
261.5	502	10	0.150
244.5	18200	1	0.0300
234	19900	1	0.0300

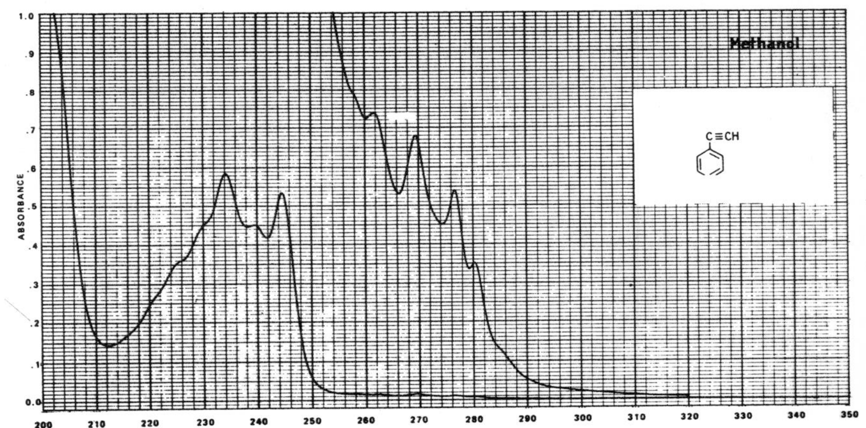

(1-PROPYNYL) BENZENE

167

C_9H_8
Mol. Wt. 116.16
B.P. 185°C
Solvent: Methanol

λ Max. mμ	a_m	Cell mm	Conc. g/L
278	272	20	0.100
271	401	20	0.100
263.5	398	20	0.100
247.5	15300	0.5	0.100
237	16000	0.5	0.100
x	x	0.5	0.100

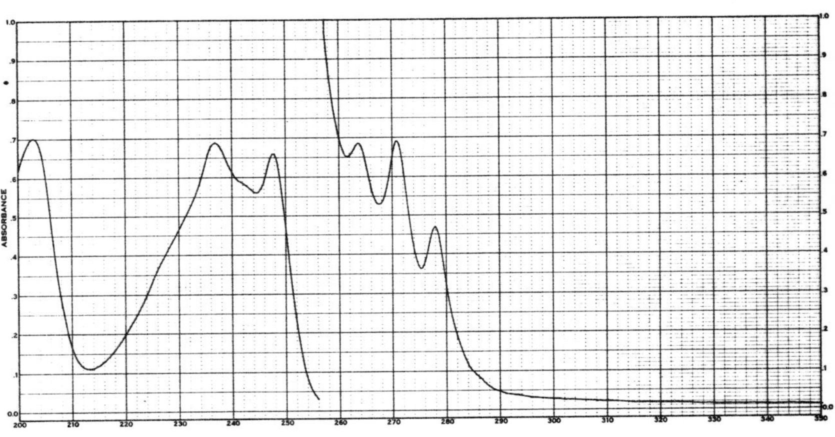

1-PHENYL-1-NONYNE

$C_{15}H_{20}$

Mol. Wt. 200.33

Solvent: Methanol

λ Max. mμ	a_m	Cell mm	Conc. g/L
279	1030	5	0.2020
272	1240	5	0.2020
265	1200	5	0.2020
250.5	17100	1	0.1010
239.5	17800	1	0.1010

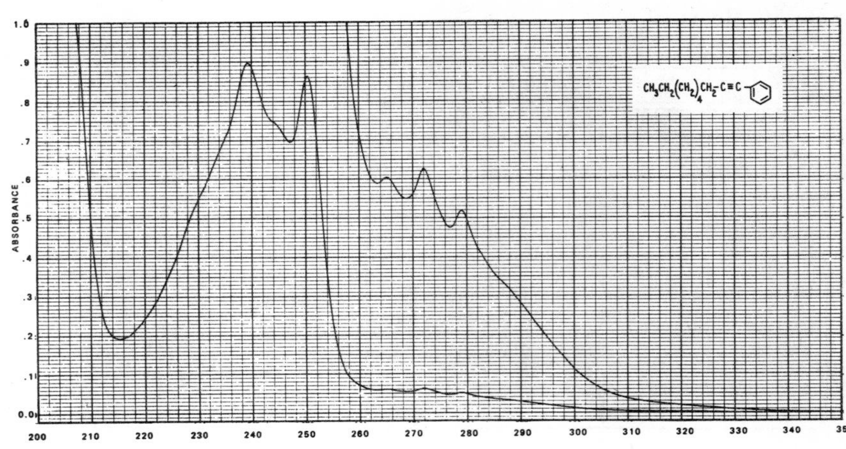

DIPHENYLACETYLENE

$C_{14}H_{10}$

Mol. Wt. 178.24

M.P. 59-60°C (lit.)

Solvent: Methanol

λ Max. mμ	a_m	Cell mm	Conc. g/L
295.5	26400	1	0.0500
286.5	21300	1	0.0500
278	30300	1	0.0500
271	22900	1	0.0500
263	20900	1	0.0500
236	8090	1	0.0500
230	7910	1	0.0500
220	16800	1	0.0500
216	18900	1	0.0500

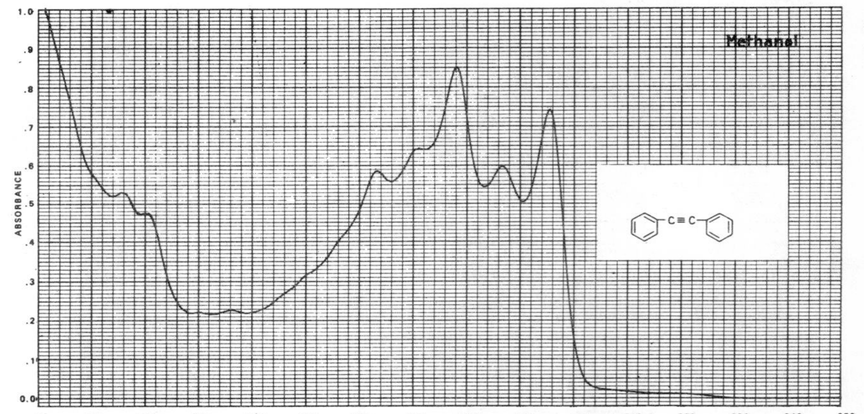

1,4-DIPHENYLBUTADIYNE

$C_{16}H_{10}$

Mol. Wt. 202.26

Solvent: Methanol

λ Max. mμ	a_m	Cell mm	Conc. g/L
325.5	29400	1	0.0500
305	32400	1	0.0500
259	30100	1	0.0500
246.5	30700	1	0.0500
227.5	30100	1	0.0500

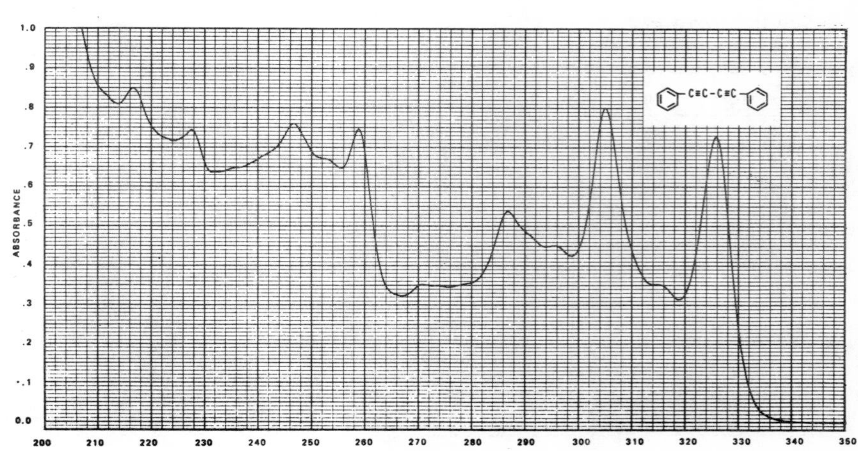

171

BIPHENYL

$C_{12}H_{10}$

Mol. Wt. 154.21

M.P. 70°C B.P. 255.9°C (lit.)

Solvent: Methanol

λ Max. mμ	a_m	Cell mm	Conc. g/L
246.5	19300	1	0.0500

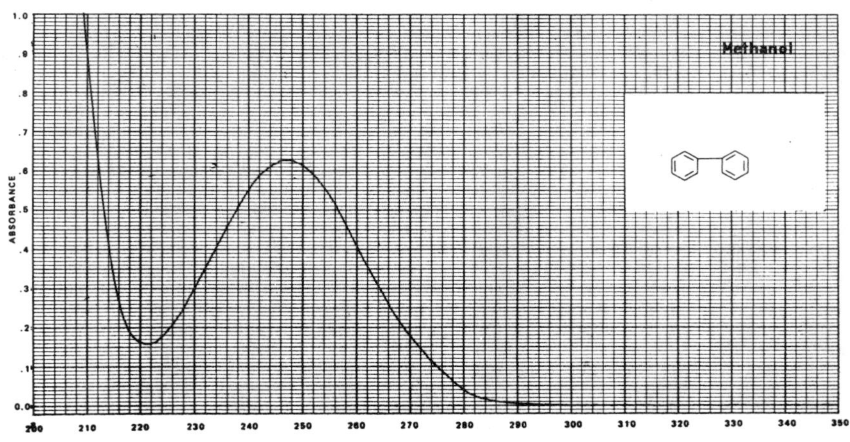

172

2-ETHYL-4′-METHYLBIPHENYL

$C_{15}H_{16}$

Mol. Wt. 196.29

Solvent: Methanol

λ Max. mμ	a_m	Cell mm	Conc. g/L
236	11600	1	0.1225
x	x	1	0.0245

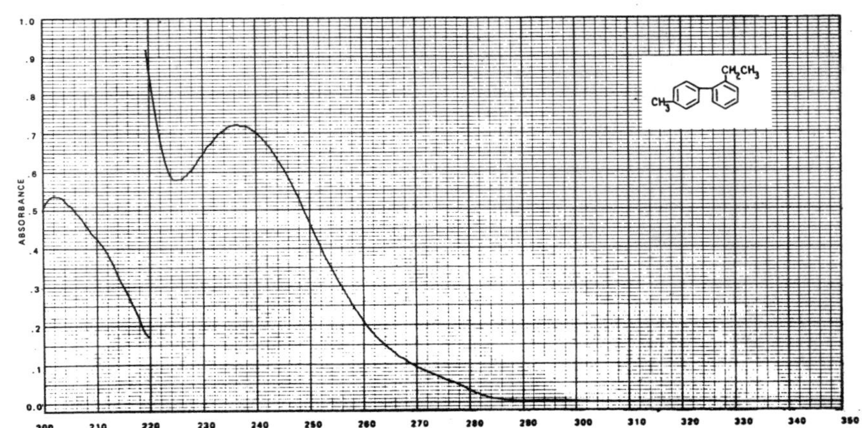

173

4-PHENYLBIBENZYL

$C_{20}H_{18}$

Mol. Wt. 258.37

M.P. 106-108°C

Solvent: Methanol

λ Max. mμ	a_m	Cell mm	Conc. g/L
320	4410	5	0.100
253	19000	1	0.100

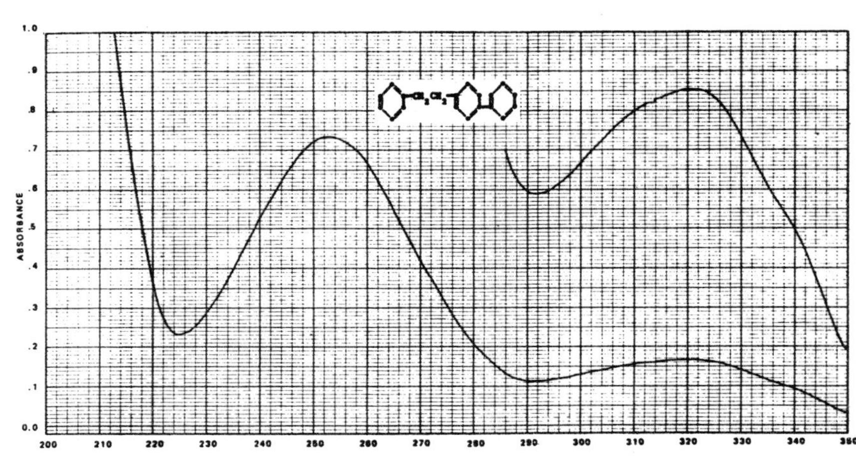

o-XYLENE

174

C_8H_{10}
Mol. Wt. 106.17
B.P. 143.5-144.5°C (lit.)
Solvent: Methanol

λ Max. mμ	a_m	Cell mm	Conc. g/L
269.5	211	20	0.145
262	254	20	0.145
x	x	1	0.145

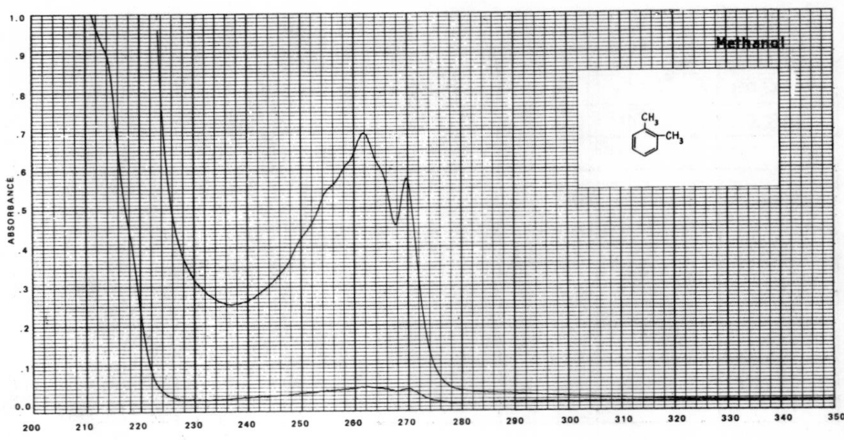

o-(1-CYCLOHEXEN-1-YL)TOLUENE

175

$C_{13}H_{16}$
Mol. Wt. 172.27
Solvent: Methanol

λ Max. mμ	a_m	Cell mm	Conc. g/L
x	x	0.5	0.100

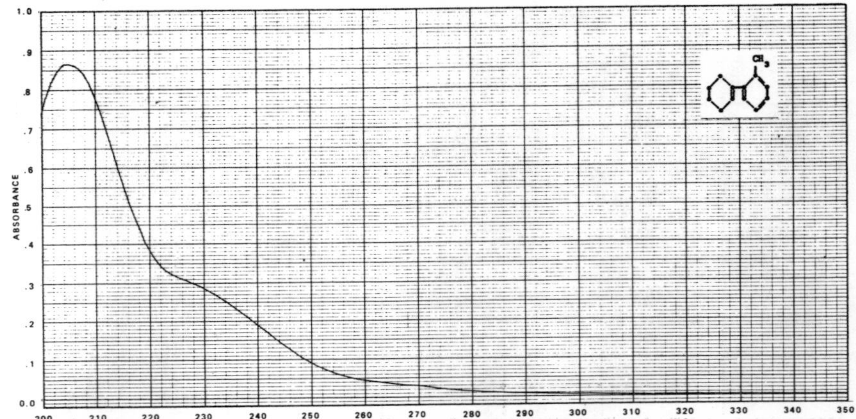

o-TERPHENYL

176

$C_{18}H_{14}$
Mol. Wt. 230.30
Solvent: Isooctane

λ Max. mμ	a_m	Cell mm	Conc. g/L
x	x	10	2.00
232	25200	10	0.010

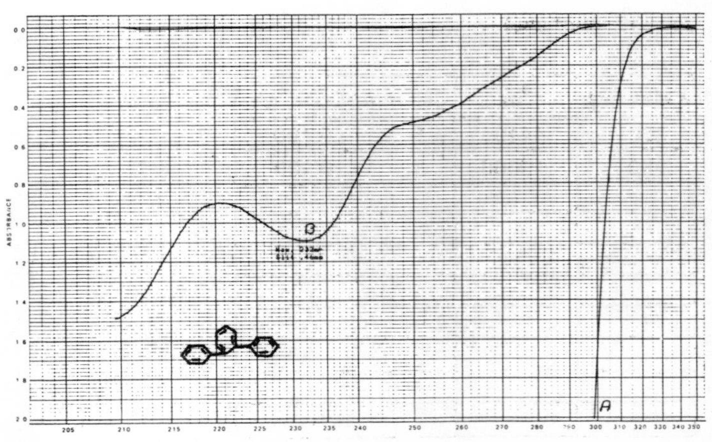

m-XYLENE

177

C_8H_{10}
Mol. Wt. 106.16
Solvent: Cyclohexane

λ Max. mμ	a_m	Cell mm	Conc. g/L
x	x	10	1.76
272	278	10	0.528
268	255	10	0.528
264.5	329	10	0.528
260	238	10	0.528
x	x	10	0.0528

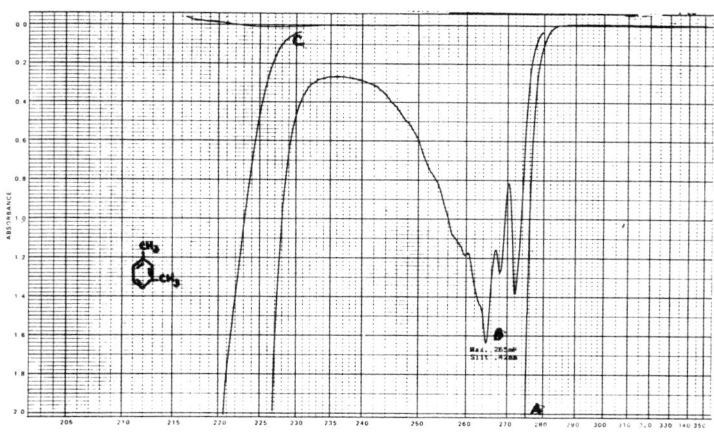

m-ETHYLTOLUENE

178

C_9H_{12}
Mol. Wt. 120.20
B.P. 158-159°C
Solvent: Methanol

λ Max. mμ	a_m	Cell mm	Conc. g/L
271.5	215	20	0.100
264	253	20	0.100
210	6600	1	0.100

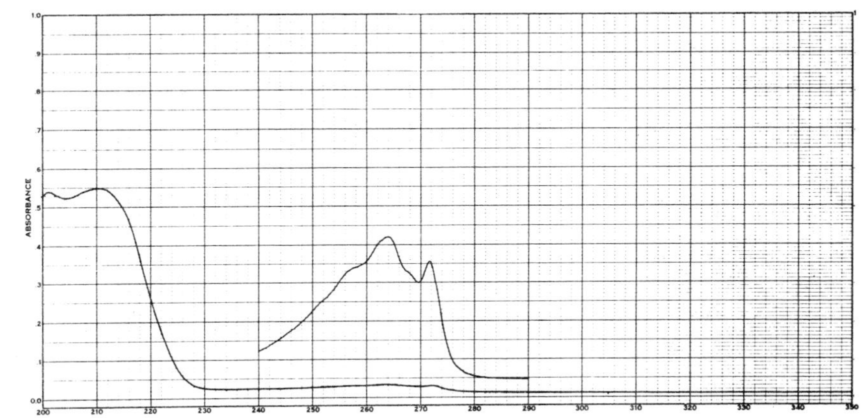

m-DIETHYLBENZENE

179

$C_{10}H_{14}$
Mol. Wt. 134.22
Solvent: Cyclohexane

λ Max. mμ	a_m	Cell mm	Conc. g/L
x	x	10	2.304
271	226	10	0.4608
768	197	10	0.4608
264	266	10	0.4608
258	204	10	0.4608
x	x	10	0.0461

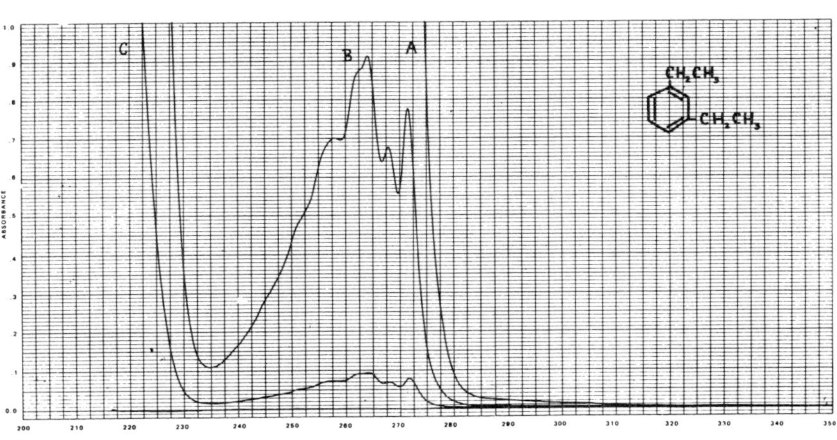

m-TERPHENYL

$C_{18}H_{14}$
Mol. Wt. 230.29
M.R. 86-87°C (lit.)
Solvent: Cyclohexane

λ Max. mμ	a_m	Cell mm	Conc. g/L
x	x	10	2.00
245.5	121000	10	0.002

180

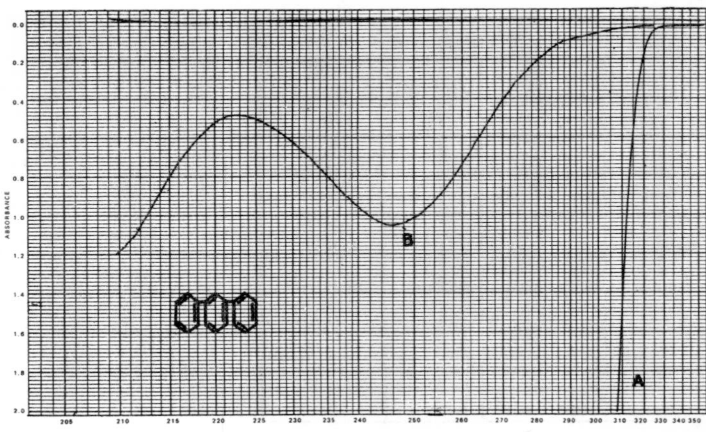

p-XYLENE

C_8H_{10}
Mol. Wt. 106.16
B.P. 138.5°C (lit.)
Solvent: Cyclohexane

λ Max. mμ	a_m	Cell mm	Conc. g/L
x	x	10	1.77
273.5	588	10	0.354
268	516	10	0.354
265	489	10	0.354
262	316	10	0.354
259.5	377	10	0.354
257	264	10	0.354
254	182	10	0.354
213	8160	10	0.0177

181

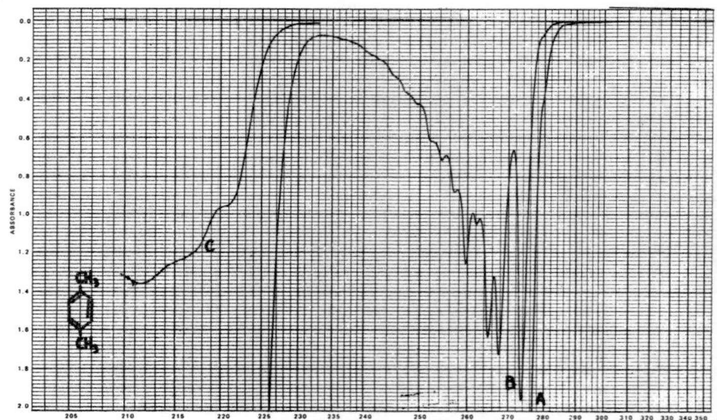

p-CYMENE

$C_{10}H_{14}$
Mol. Wt. 134.17
Solvent: Cyclohexane

λ Max. mμ	a_m	Cell mm	Conc. g/L
x	x	10	1.73
285	1460	10	0.0864
279	1680	10	0.0864
276	1540	10	0.0864
273	1430	10	0.0864
270	1400	10	0.0864
246.5	4090	10	0.0086

182

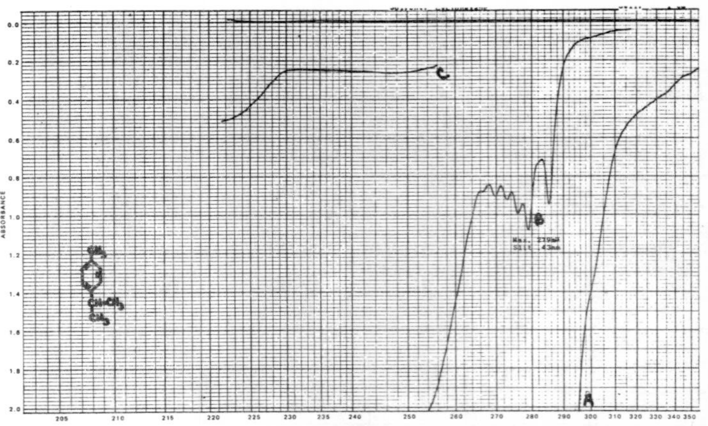

p-DICYCLOHEXYLBENZENE 183

$C_{18}H_{26}$
Mol. Wt. 242.39
M.P. 102-103.5°C
Solvent: Methanol

λ Max. mμ	a_m	Cell mm	Conc. g/L
211.5	487	10	0.30
265	435	10	0.30
263	454	10	0.30
257	355	10	0.30
222	9380	10	0.02
218.5	222	10	0.02
213	10500	10	0.02

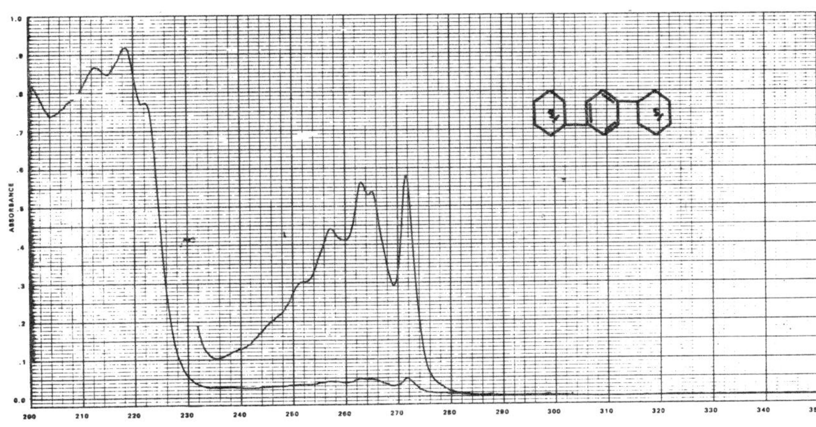

1-(p-TOLYL)-1-CYCLOHEXENE 184

$C_{13}H_{16}$
Mol. Wt. 172.27
Solvent: Methanol

λ Max. mμ	a_m	Cell mm	Conc. g/L
243.5	13000	1	0.100

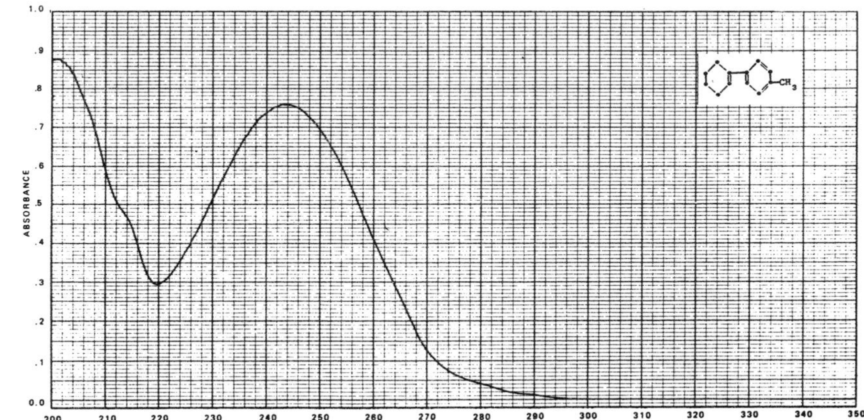

4,4'-DIMETHYLBIBENZYL 185

$C_{16}H_{18}$
Mol. Wt. 210.32

λ Max. mμ	a_m	Cell mm	Conc. g/L

Pure sample not available.

p-TERPHENYL

186

$C_{18}H_{14}$
Mol. Wt. 230.31
Solvent: Methanol

λ Max. mμ	a_m	Cell mm	Conc. g/L
278	33000	1	0.0300
204.5	58100	1	0.0300

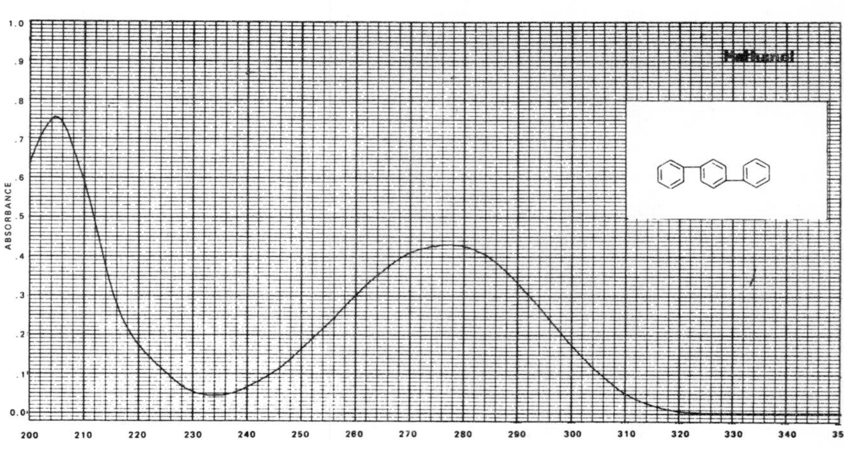

1,2,3-TRIMETHYLBENZENE

187

C_9H_{12}
Mol. Wt. 120.20
B.P. 175-175.5°C
Solvent: Methanol

λ Max. mμ	a_m	Cell mm	Conc. g/L
268.5	303	10	0.135
261	374	10	0.135
x	x	10	0.135

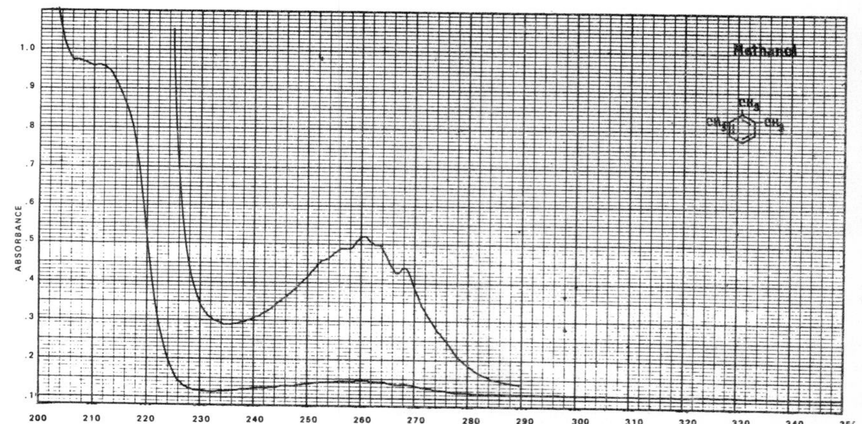

1,2,4-TRIMETHYLBENZENE

188

C_9H_{12}
Mol. Wt. 120.19
B.P. 168°C/760mm
Solvent: Methanol

λ Max. mμ	a_m	Cell mm	Conc. g/L
276.5	482	10	0.1672
267.5	477	10	0.1672

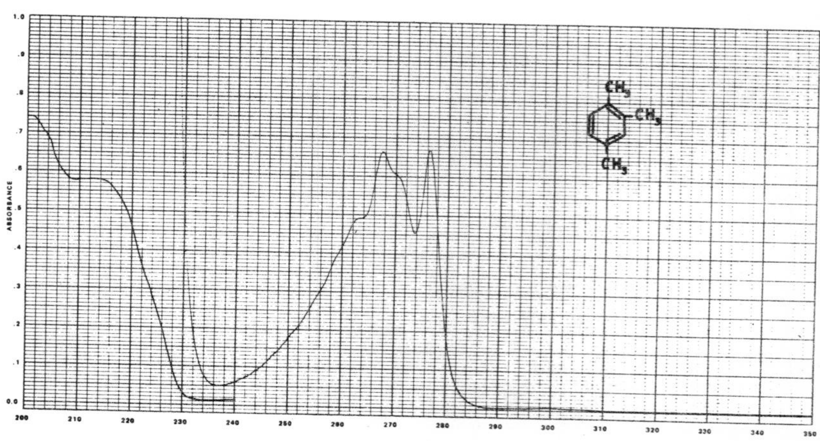

MESITYLENE 189

C_9H_{12}
Mol. Wt. 120.20
B.P. 163-166°C
Solvent: Methanol

λ Max. mμ	a_m	Cell mm	Conc. g/L
272.5	148	20	0.100
265.5	180	20	0.100
x	x	1	0.100

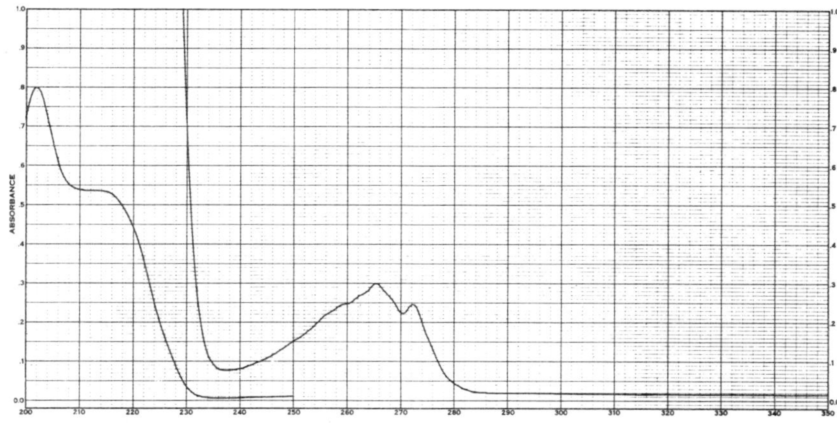

1,3,5-TRIETHYLBENZENE 190

$C_{12}H_{18}$
Mol. Wt. 162.28
B.P. 218°C
Solvent: Methanol

λ Max. mμ	a_m	Cell mm	Conc. g/L
270	182	10	0.411
264	224	10	0.411
258	182	10	0.411
x	x	1	0.0410

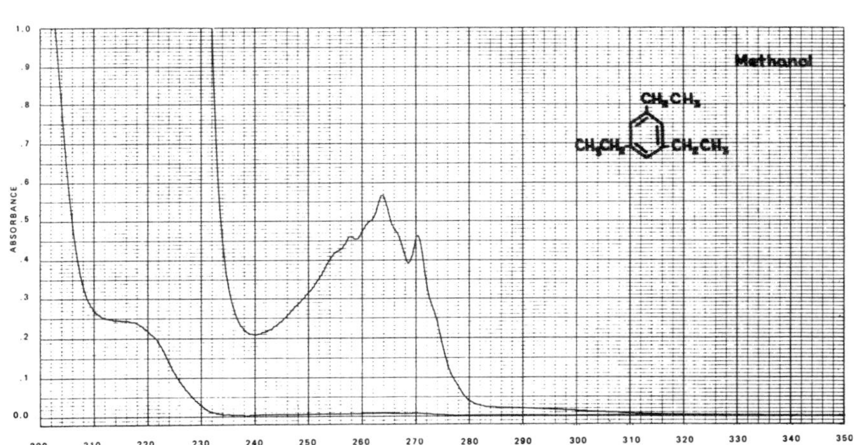

1,2,3,4-TETRAMETHYLBENZENE 191

$C_{10}H_{14}$
Mol. Wt. 134.22
B.P. 204°C/760mm
Solvent: Methanol

λ Max. mμ	a_m	Cell mm	Conc. g/L
277.5	726	10	0.10
272	636	10	0.10
268.5	701	10	0.10
x	x	10	0.01

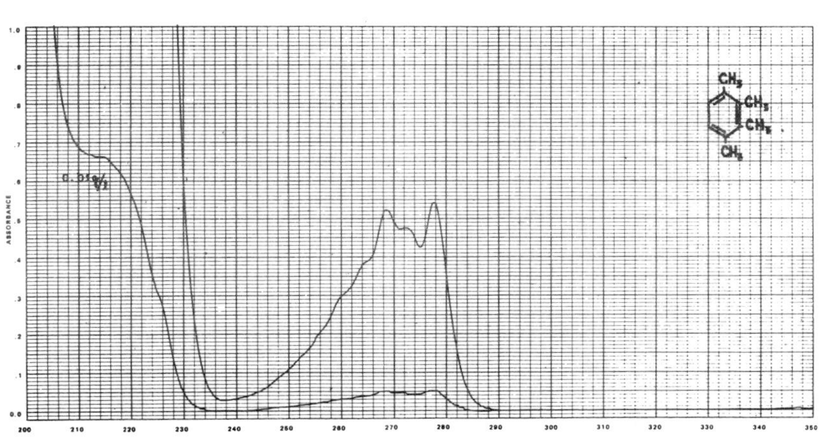

1,2,3,5-TETRAMETHYLBENZENE 192

$C_{10}H_{14}$
Mol. Wt. 134.22
Solvent: Methanol

λ Max. mμ	a_m	Cell mm	Conc. g/L
277	376	20	0.100
273	389	20	0.100
268.5	448	20	0.100
x	x	1	0.100

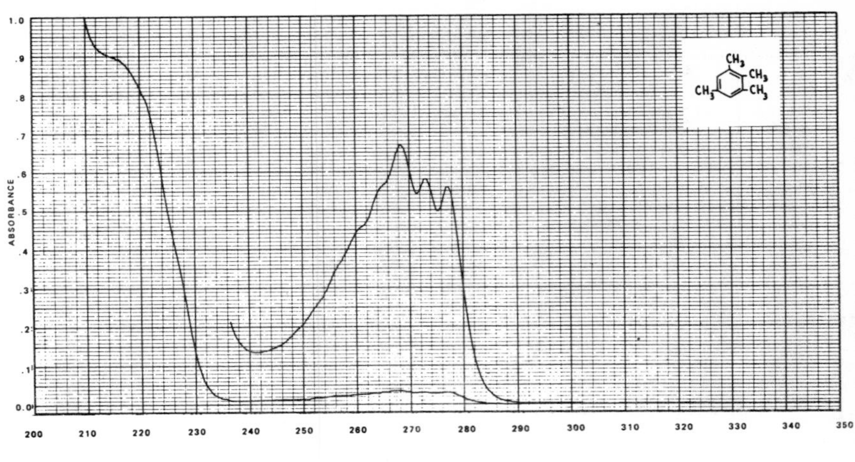

1,2,4,5-TETRAMETHYLBENZENE 193

$C_{10}H_{14}$
Mol. Wt. 134.18
M.P. 79°C (lit.)
Solvent: Cyclohexane

λ Max. mμ	a_m	Cell mm	Conc. g/L
x	x	10	1.94
278	692	10	0.194
269	652	10	0.194
x	x	10	0.0194

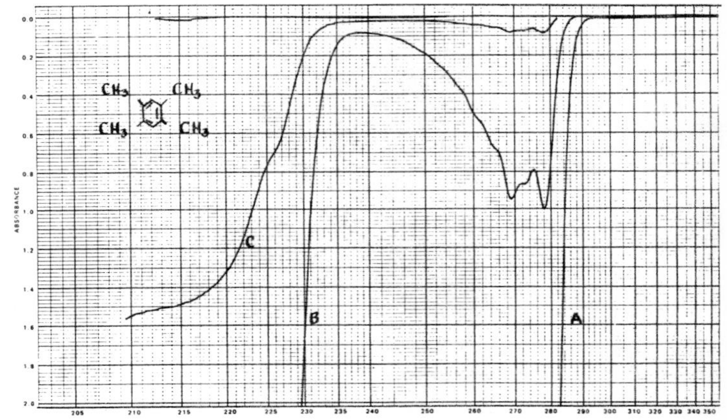

PENTAMETHYLBENZENE 194

$C_{11}H_{16}$
Mol. Wt. 148.25
M.P. 51-53°C
Solvent: Methanol

λ Max. mμ	a_m	Cell mm	Conc. g/L
279	252	20	0.100
275.5	273	20	0.100
270	314	20	0.100
x	x	1	0.0200

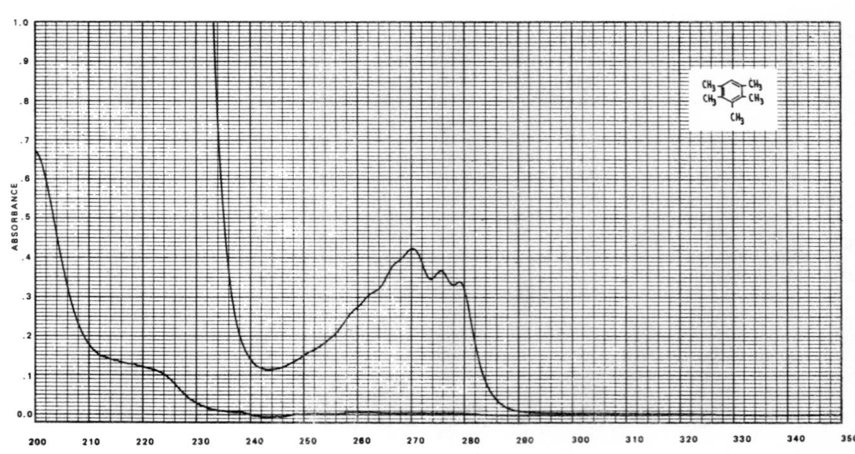

INDAN

C_9H_{10}
Mol. Wt. 118.18
Solvent: Methanol

λ Max. mμ	a_m	Cell mm	Conc. g/L
272.5	1230	2	0.438
266	1140	2	0.438
259.5	769	2	0.438

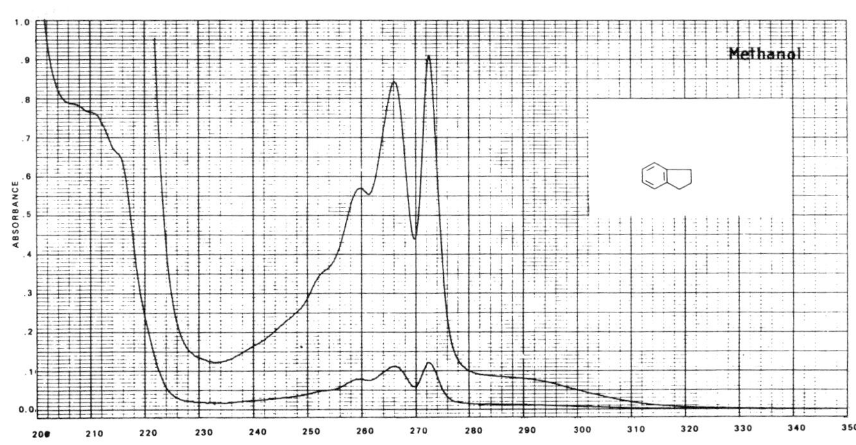

1,2,3,4-TETRAHYDRONAPHTHALENE

$C_{10}H_{12}$
Mol. Wt. 132.21
B.P. 204-207°C
Solvent: Methanol

λ Max. mμ	a_m	Cell mm	Conc. g/L
273.5	724	5	0.2090
266.5	669	5	0.2090
213	10200	1	0.1045

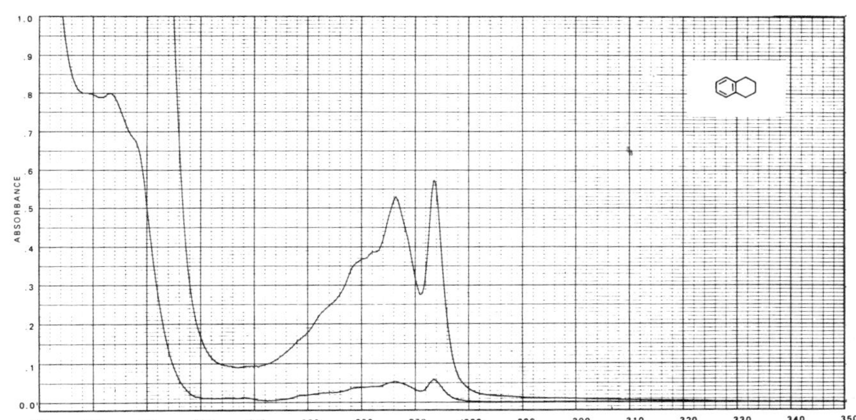

1-ETHYL-1,2,3,4-TETRAHYDRONAPHTHALENE

$C_{12}H_{16}$
Mol. Wt. 160.26
B.P. 239-246°C

λ Max. mμ	a_m	Cell mm	Conc. g/L

Pure sample not available.

2a,3,4,5-TETRAHYDROACENAPHTHENE

198

$C_{12}H_{14}$
Mol. Wt. 158.24
Solvent: Cyclohexane

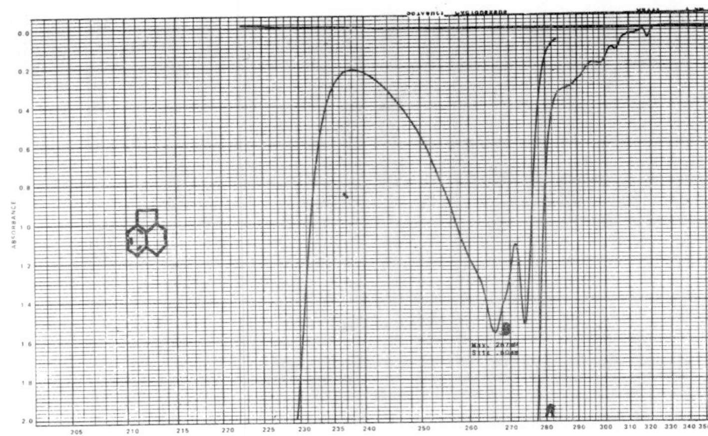

λ Max. mμ	a_m	Cell mm	Conc. g/L
318	2.94	10	2.15
304	8.83	10	2.15
298	13.4	10	2.15
274	559	10	0.430
266	575	10	0.430

INDENE

199

C_9H_8
Mol. Wt. 116.16
Solvent: Methanol

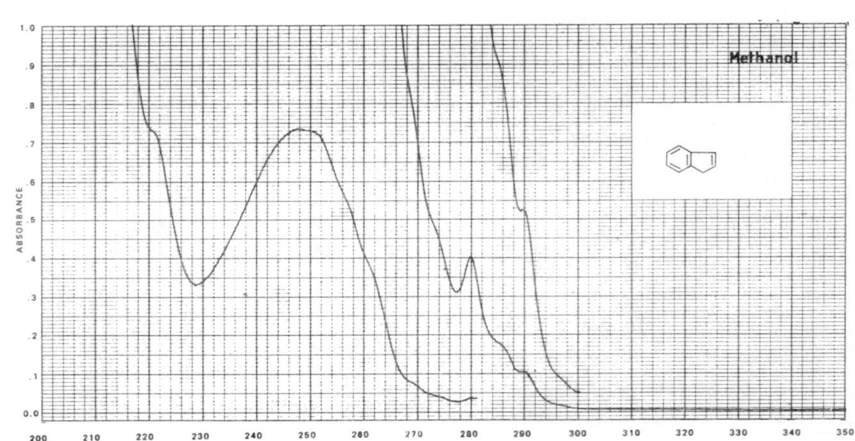

λ Max. mμ	a_m	Cell mm	Conc. g/L
289.5	211	10	0.247
280	944	2	0.247
247.5	17300	2	0.247

NAPHTHALENE

200

$C_{10}H_8$
Mol. Wt. 128.18
Solvent: Methanol

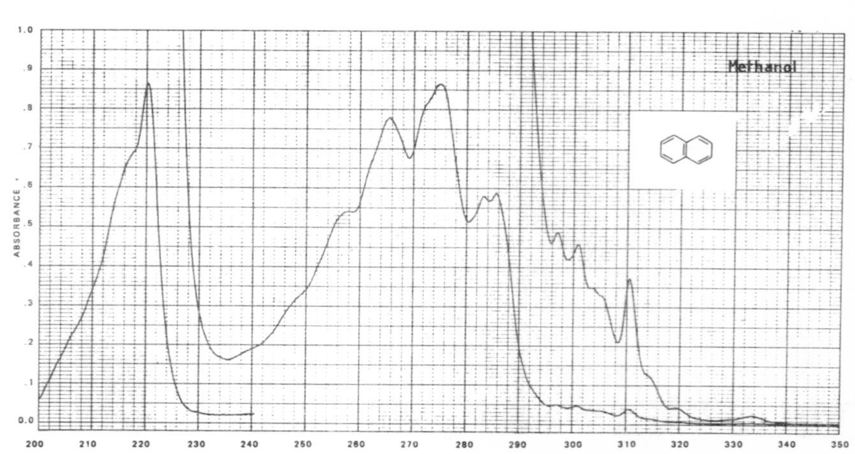

λ Max. mμ	a_m	Cell mm	Conc. g/L
310.5	239	20	0.100
303.5	224	20	0.100
301	294	20	0.100
297	313	20	0.100
285.5	3760	2	0.100
283	3710	2	0.100
275	5530	2	0.100
265.5	4990	2	0.100
258	3470	2	0.100
220.5	10600	1	0.0100

1-ETHYLNAPHTHALENE 201

$C_{12}H_{12}$
Mol. Wt. 156.23
Solvent: Methanol

λ Max. mμ	a_m	Cell mm	Conc. g/L
307.5	300	10	0.228
275.5	6240	1	0.228
265.5	5480	1	0.228
217.5	3690	1	0.0364

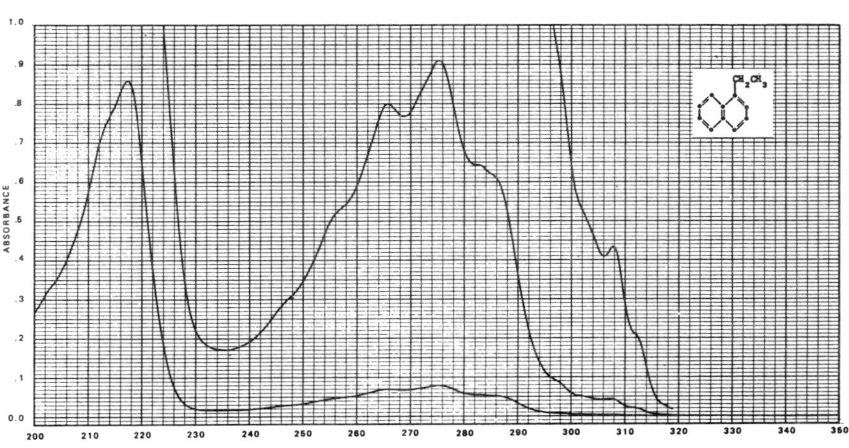

2-METHYLNAPHTHALENE 202

$C_{11}H_{10}$
Mol. Wt. 142.20
Solvent: Methanol

λ Max. mμ	a_m	Cell mm	Conc. g/L
318	515	20	0.100
310.5	314	20	0.100
304	495	20	0.100
274.5	5370	20	0.00900
223	16800	1	0.00900

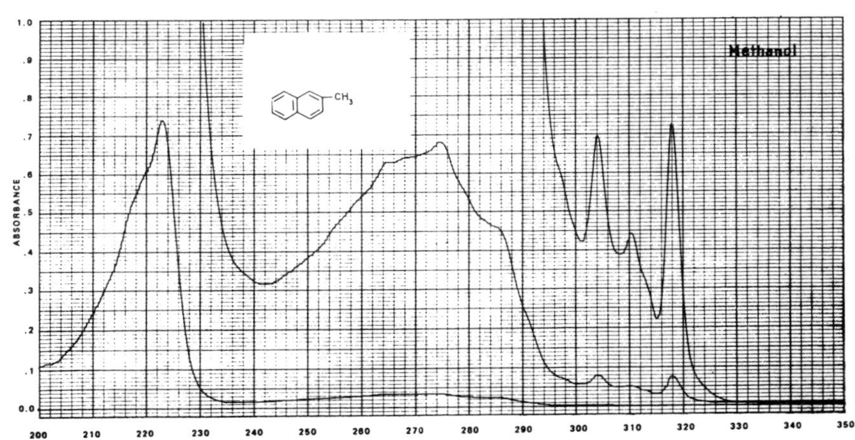

2,3-DIMETHYLNAPHTHALENE 203

$C_{12}H_{12}$
Mol. Wt. 156.23
M.P. 104°C B.P. 265°C
Solvent: Methanol

λ Max. mμ	a_m	Cell mm	Conc. g/L
319	313	2	1.00
315	259	2	1.00
305.5	443	2	1.00
278	4980	2	0.0800
268	4790	2	0.0800
225	99600	1	0.00800

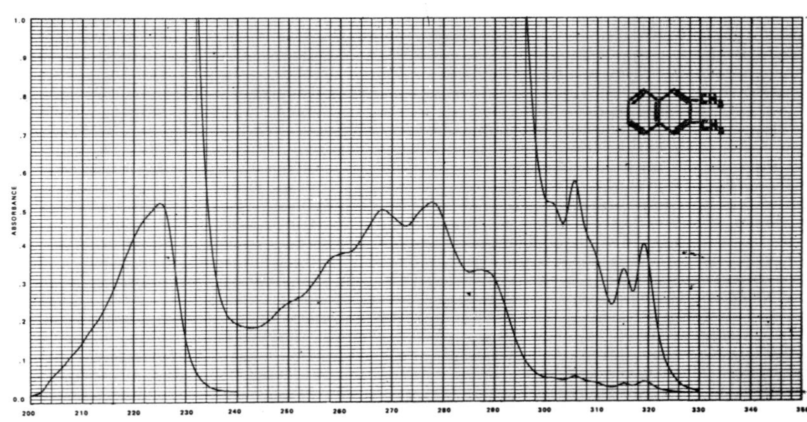

2,6-DIMETHYLNAPHTHALENE 204

$C_{12}H_{12}$
Mol. Wt. 156.23
M.P. 109-111°C
Solvent: Methanol

λ Max. mμ	a_m	Cell mm	Conc. g/L
323	1780	10	0.100
309	792	10	0.100
302	487	10	0.100
273	4620	2	0.100
226	10600	1	0.0100

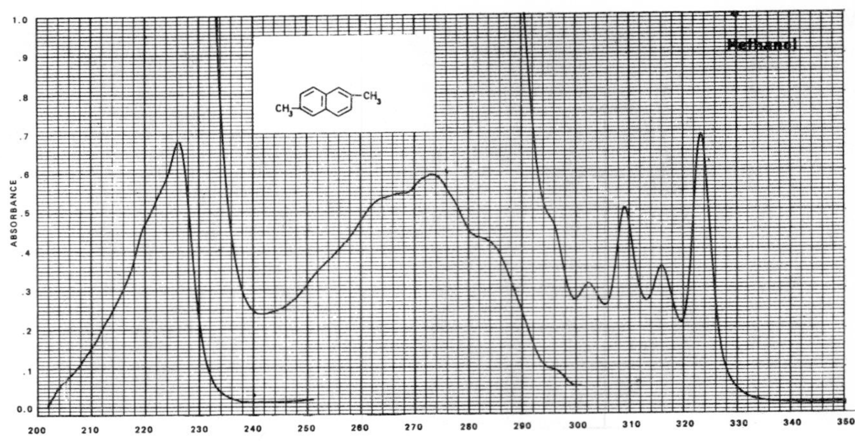

2,3,6-TRIMETHYLNAPHTHALENE 205

$C_{13}H_{14}$
Mol. Wt. 170.26
M.P. 102°C B.P. 286°C/762mm
Solvent: Methanol

λ Max. mμ	a_m	Cell mm	Conc. g/L
322.5	562	10	0.100
308.5	596	10	0.100
276	4800	1	0.100
270	4950	1	0.100
228	107000	1	0.0100

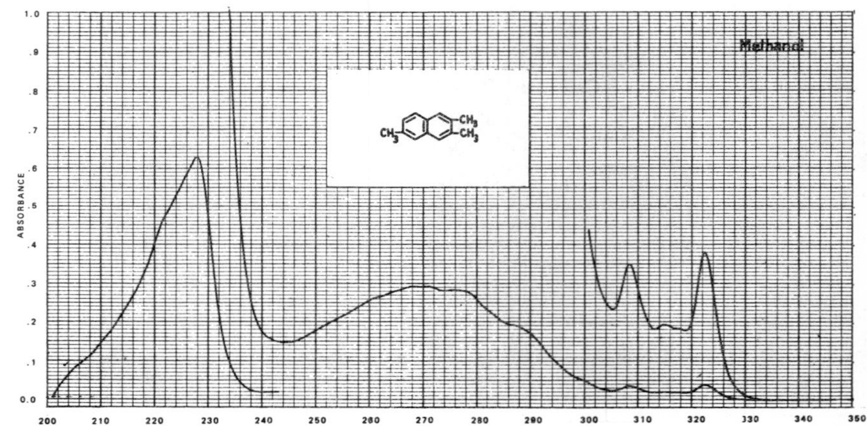

2,2'-BINAPHTHYL 206

$C_{20}H_{14}$
Mol. Wt. 254.33
Solvent: Methanol

λ Max. mμ	a_m	Cell mm	Conc. g/L
305	17900	1	0.100
253	98000	1	0.0200
212	42300	1	0.0200

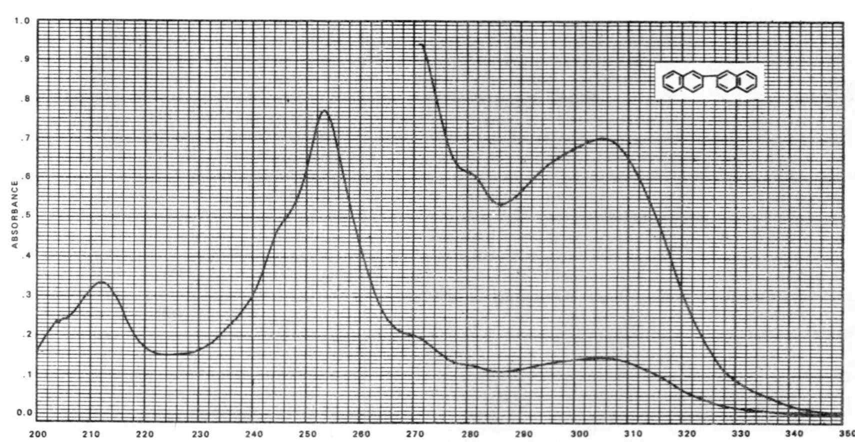

ACENAPHTHENE 207

$C_{12}H_{10}$
Mol. Wt. 154.21
Solvent: Methanol

λ Max. mμ	a_m	Cell mm	Conc. g/L
320	1430	2	0.100
313.5	856	2	0.100
306	2400	2	0.100
300	3470	2	0.100
288	5540	2	0.100
278.5	4930	2	0.100
243	1100	2	0.100
227	73100	2	0.0100

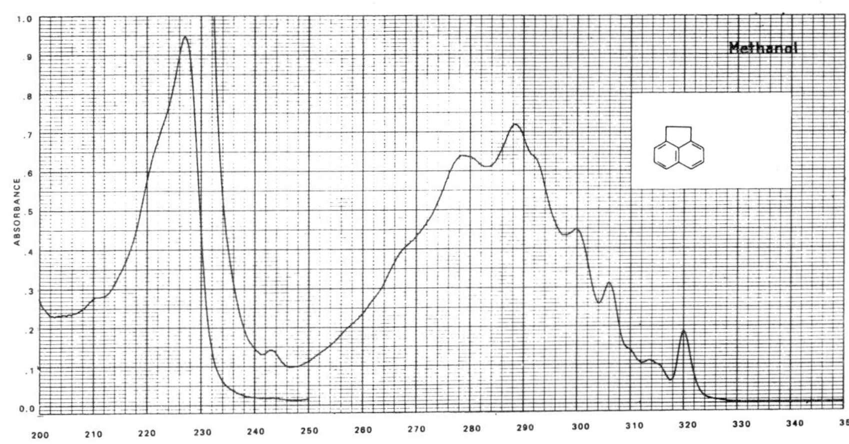

FLUORENE 208

$C_{13}H_{10}$
Mol. Wt. 166.22
Solvent: Methanol

λ Max. mμ	a_m	Cell mm	Conc. g/L
299	9680	5	0.0250
288	6380	5	0.0250
260	21200	1	0.0250
219	16600	1	0.0250

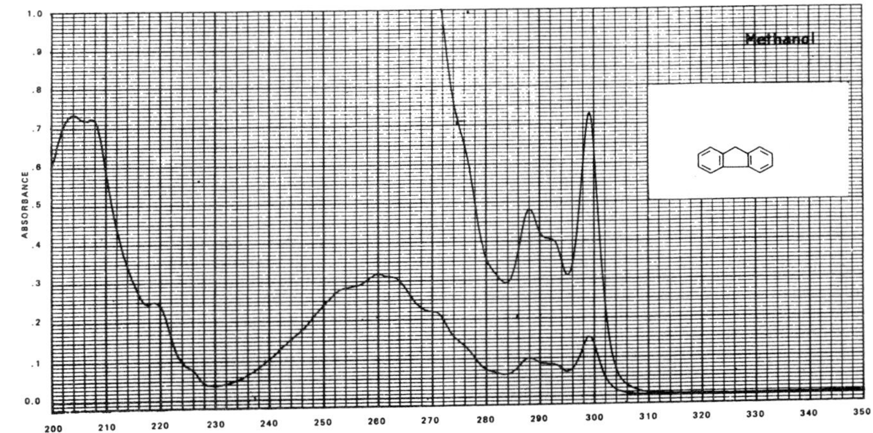

2-METHYLFLUORENE 209

$C_{14}H_{12}$
Mol. Wt. 180.25
Solvent: Methanol

λ Max. mμ	a_m	Cell mm	Conc. g/L
324	361	10	0.010
305	815	10	0.10
298	550	10	0.10
293.5	629	10	0.10
276	1400	10	0.10
276	14100	10	0.005
265.5	20400	10	0.005
221.5	19500	10	0.005

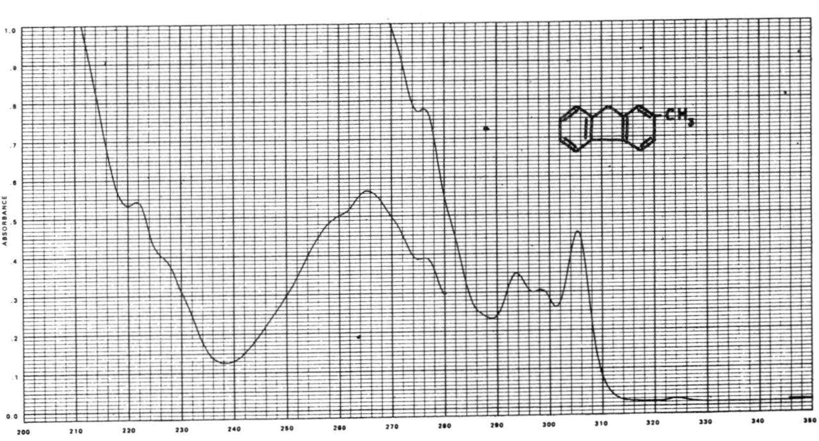

9-BENZYLIDENEFLUORENE 210

$C_{20}H_{14}$
Mol. Wt. 254.33
Solvent: Methanol

λ Max. mμ	a_m	Cell mm	Conc. g/L
322	19000	0.5	0.100
295	16800	0.5	0.100
255	46800	0.5	0.100
248	42600	0.5	0.100
226	50400	0.5	0.100

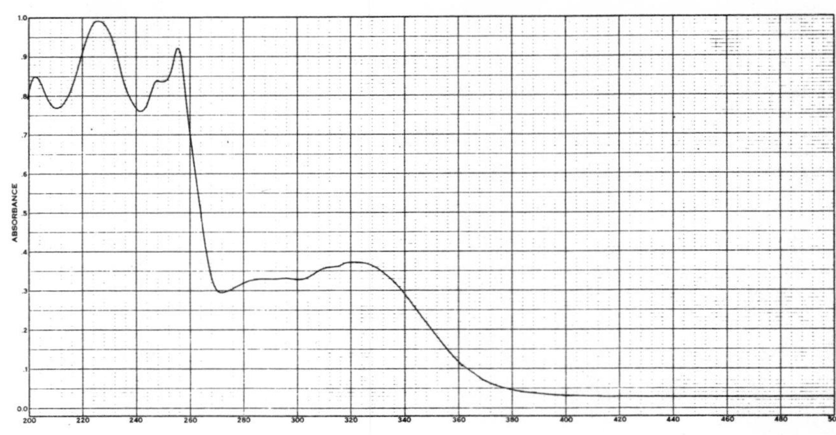

9,10-DIHYDROPHENANTHRENE 211

$C_{14}H_{12}$
Mol. Wt. 186.25
Solvent: Methanol

λ Max. mμ	a_m	Cell mm	Conc. g/L
293	8570	5	0.0268
259	17600	2	0.0268

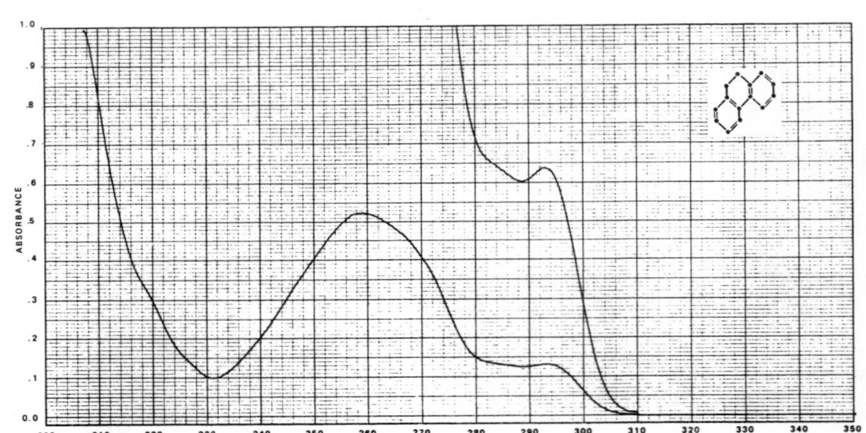

FLUORANTHENE 212

$C_{16}H_{10}$
Mol. Wt. 202.26
M.P. 110°C (lit.)
Solvent: Methanol

λ Max. mμ	a_m	Cell mm	Conc. g/L
357	8400	5	0.0350
339	8130	5	0.0350
286	45100	1	0.0350
274	24700	1	0.0350
234	52700	1	0.0350

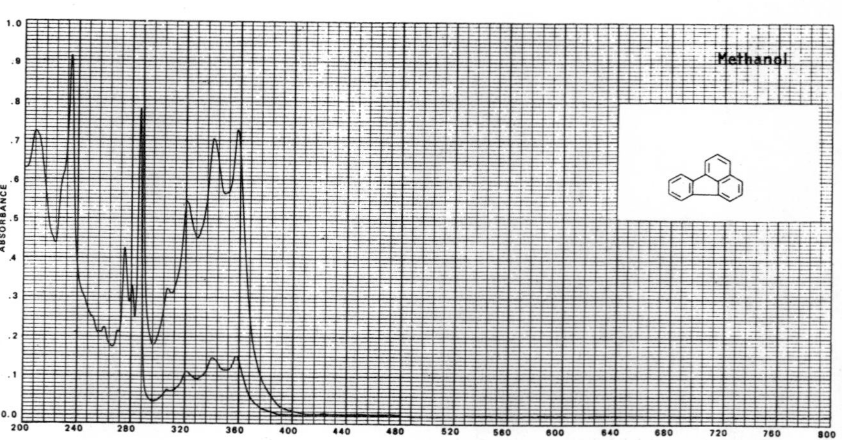

ANTHRACENE

$C_{14}H_{10}$
Mol. Wt. 178.24
Solvent: Methanol

213

λ Max. mμ	a_m	Cell mm	Conc. g/L
376	7590	2	0.100
355	7770	2	0.100
338	5290	2	0.100
322	2750	2	0.100
309	1230	10	0.100
296	531	10	0.100
250	20000	1	0.00800
220	11800	1	0.100
218	11700	1	0.100

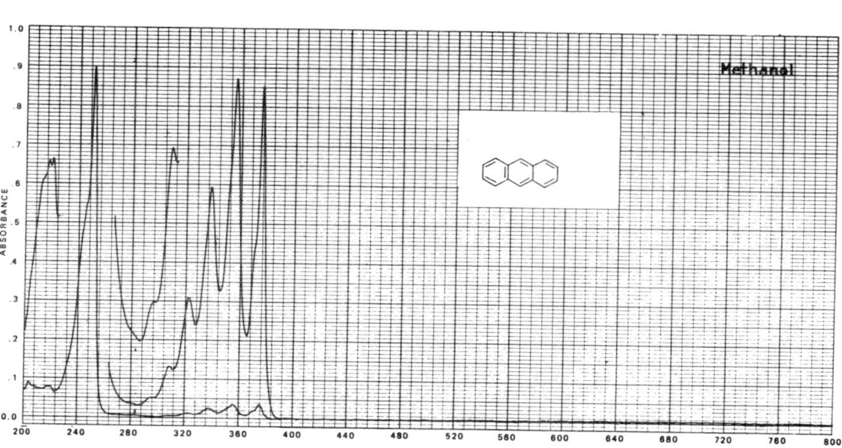

PHENANTHRENE

$C_{14}H_{10}$
Mol. Wt. 178.24
M.P. 97-99°C
Solvent: Methanol

214

λ Max. mμ	a_m	Cell mm	Conc. g/L
375	53.0	10	0.499
355	64.0	10	0.499
345	237	10	0.499
337	270	10	0.499
329	322	10	0.499
322	308	10	0.499
314	280	10	0.499
291	12800	1	0.111
273	13200	1	0.111
250	64600	1	0.0222

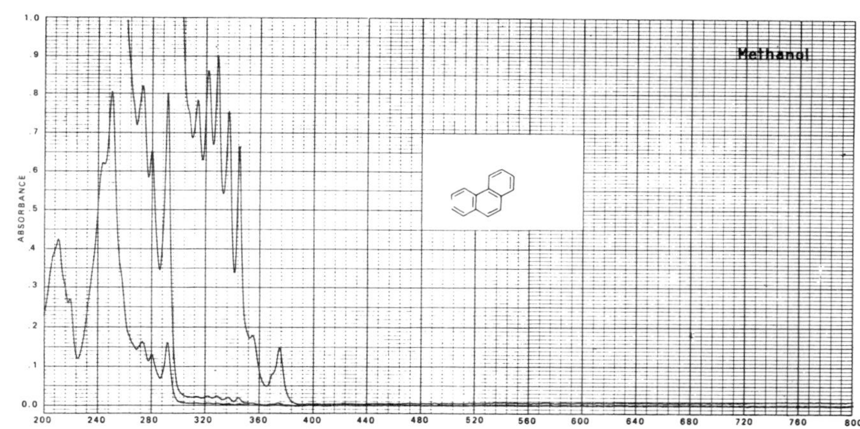

2-METHYLPHENANTHRENE

$C_{15}H_{12}$
Mol. Wt. 192.26
M.P. 56-57°C
Solvent: Methanol

215

λ Max. mμ	a_m	Cell mm	Conc. g/L
294	11500	1	0.0200
282	12000	1	0.0200
275.5	15400	1	0.0200
252	75000	1	0.0200
210	33000	1	0.0200

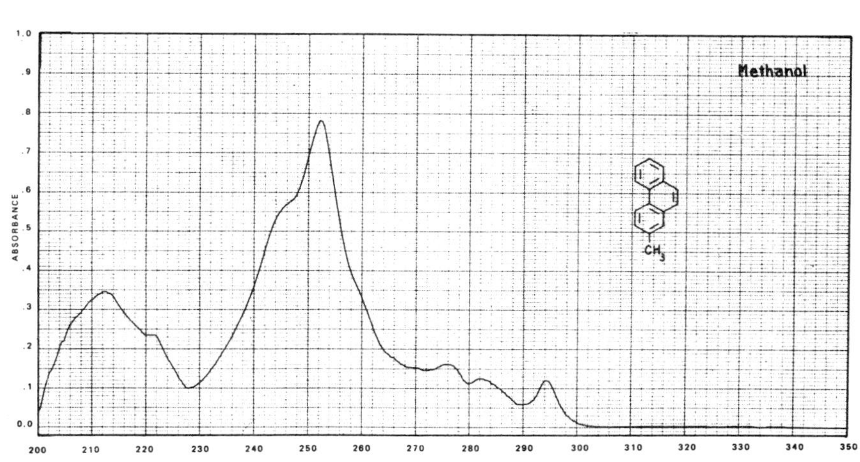

7-ISOPROPYL-1-METHYLPHENANTHRENE 216

$C_{18}H_{18}$
Mol. Wt. 234.34
Solvent: Methanol

λ Max. mμ	a_m	Cell mm	Conc. g/L
318	325	20	0.100
299.5	14800	5	0.0300
287.5	11600	5	0.0300
279	14700	5	0.0300
257.5	68700	1	0.0300

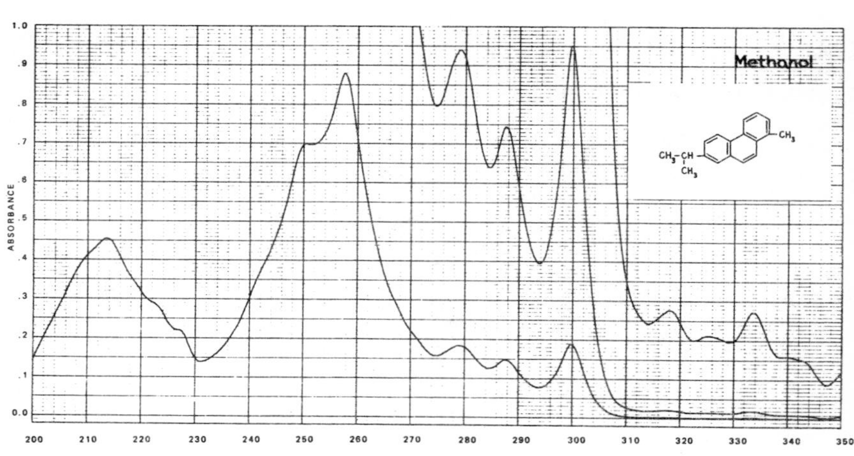

PYRENE 217

$C_{16}H_{10}$
Mol. Wt. 202.26
Solvent: Methanol

λ Max. mμ	a_m	Cell mm	Conc. g/L
333.5	29400	2	0.0100
318	17600	2	0.0100
305	6910	10	0.0100
294	2680	10	0.0100
271.5	49800	2	0.0100
261	24400	2	0.0100
251	11800	10	0.0100
239.5	85100	2	0.0100
230.5	43400	2	0.0100

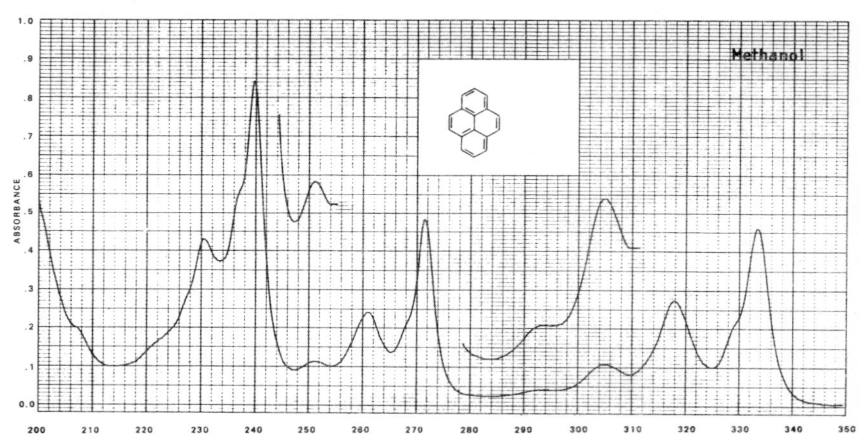

CHRYSENE 218

$C_{18}H_{12}$
Mol. Wt. 228.29
M.P. 254°C
Solvent: Methanol

λ Max. mμ	a_m	Cell mm	Conc. g/L
319	12200	1	0.100
306	12100	1	0.100
294	11400	1	0.100
266.5	164000	1	0.0100
257	92000	1	0.0100

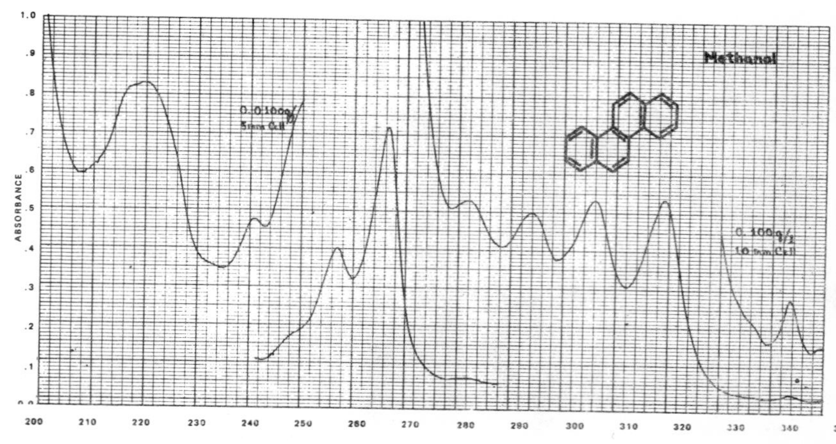

THE FLUORINATED HYDROCARBONS

Aliphatic Compounds

The fluorine containing aliphatic compounds display no significant absorption in the near UV region of the spectrum and as a consequence there are no spectra presented in this volume for compounds numbers 219 and 220.

Aromatic Compounds

The substitution of benzene by a fluorine group has only a negligible effect on the wavelength of the corresponding bands but does display a relatively strong hyperchromic effect resulting in an increase in the intensity of the bands by a factor of about 7, for fluorobenzene (spectrum 223) and p-difluorobenzene (spectrum 232).

A table of reference compounds and their fluorinated analogs is provided below.

Compound	$\lambda_{max}(\epsilon_{max})$	$\lambda_{max}(\epsilon_{max})$	$\lambda_{max}(\epsilon_{max})$	Spectrum
Benzene	268 (14)	261 (149)	254 (212)	132
Fluorobenzene	266 (1580)	260 (1770)	254 (1220)	223
o-Difluorobenzene	265 (550)	259 (685)	255 (560)	230
m-Difluorobenzene	265 (551)	259 (648)	254 (516)	231
p-Difluorobenzene	266 (2270)	260 (1560)	252 (780)	232
Toluene	268 (222)	261 (238)	255 (175)	133
α-Fluorotoluene	267 (176)	261 (238)	256 (258)	221
o-Fluorotoluene	269 (611)	262 (676)	----------	224
m-Difluorotoluene	270 (684)	262 (751)	257 (612)	225
p-Difluorotoluene	267 (1060)	261 (690)	259 (637)	226

221

α-FLUOROTOLUENE

C_7H_7F

Mol. Wt. 110.13

Solvent: Methanol

λ Max. mμ	a_m	Cell mm	Conc. g/L
267	176	20	0.100
261	238	20	0.100
256.5	258	20	0.100
250.5	214	20	0.100
x	x	1	0.100

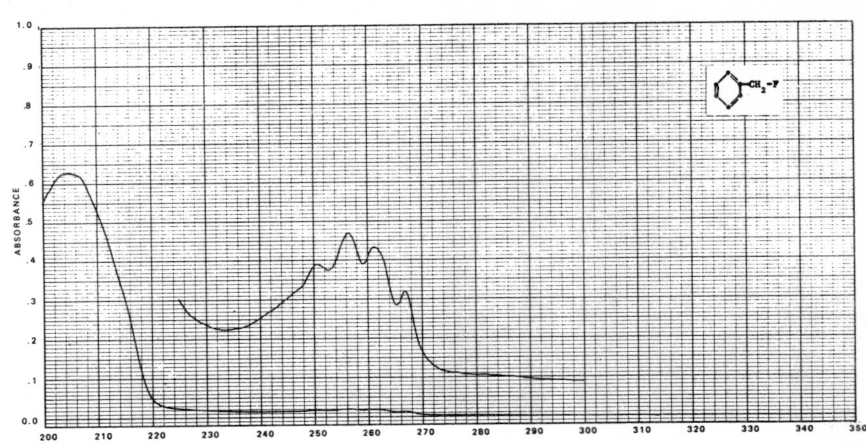

222

α,α,α-TRIFLUOROTOLUENE

$C_7H_5F_3$

Mol. Wt. 146.12

B.P. 101°C (lit.)

Solvent: Cyclohexane

λ Max. mμ	a_m	Cell mm	Conc. g/L
x	x	10	1.4120
265.5	448	10	0.4236
259	550	10	0.4236
253	390	10	0.4236
249	235	10	0.4236

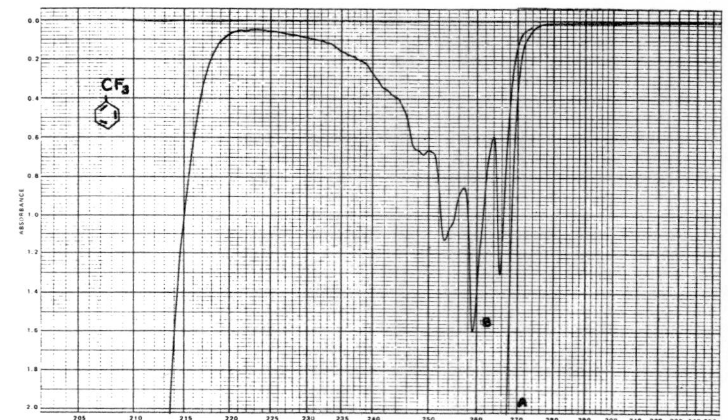

223

FLUOROBENZENE

C_6H_5F

Mol. Wt. 96.11

Solvent: Methanol

λ Max. mμ	a_m	Cell mm	Conc. g/L
265.5	1580	1	0.250
259.5	1770	1	0.250
253.5	1220	1	0.250
248	630	1	0.250

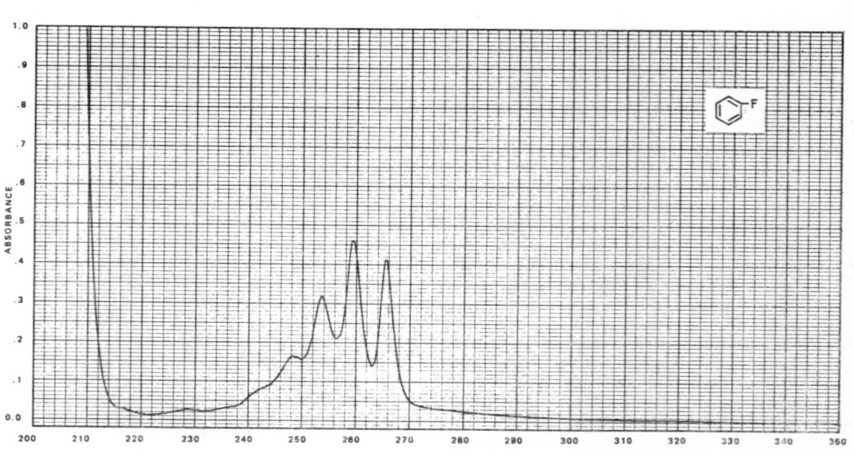

o-FLUOROTOLUENE

224

C_7H_7F

Mol. Wt. 110.13

Solvent: Methanol

λ Max. mμ	a_m	Cell mm	Conc. g/L
268.5	611	10	0.100
262	676	10	0.100
x	x	4	0.100

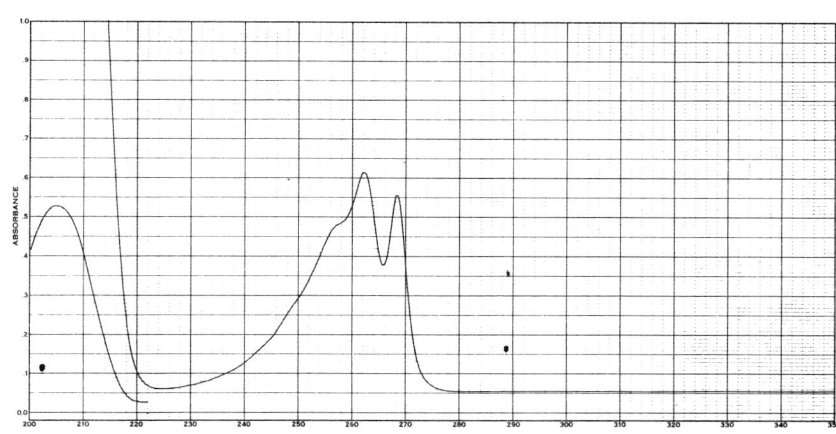

m-FLUOROTOLUENE

225

C_7H_7F

Mol. Wt. 110.13

B.P. 115°C

Solvent: Methanol

λ Max. mμ	a_m	Cell mm	Conc. g/L
269.5	684	10	0.100
262.5	151	10	0.100
257	612	10	0.100
x	x	1	0.100

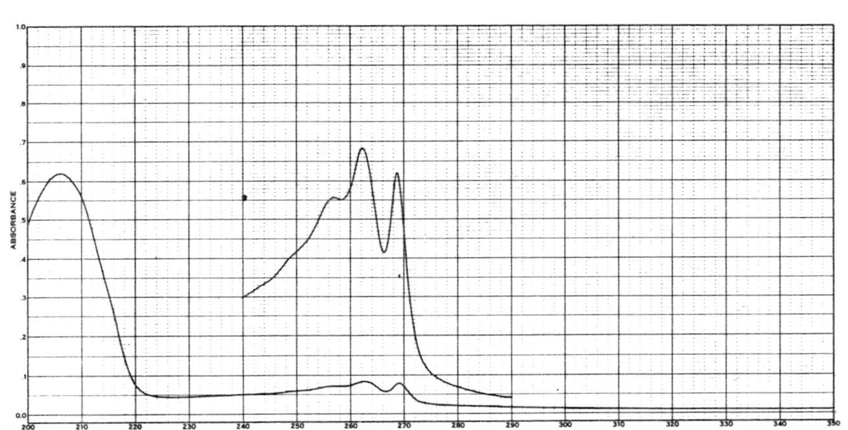

p-FLUOROTOLUENE

226

C_7H_7F

Mol. Wt. 110.13

B.P. 116-117°C

Solvent: Methanol

λ Max. mμ	a_m	Cell mm	Conc. g/L
273	1010	2	0.2410
267	1060	2	0.2410
261	690	2	0.2410
259	637	2	0.2410
253	388	2	0.2410

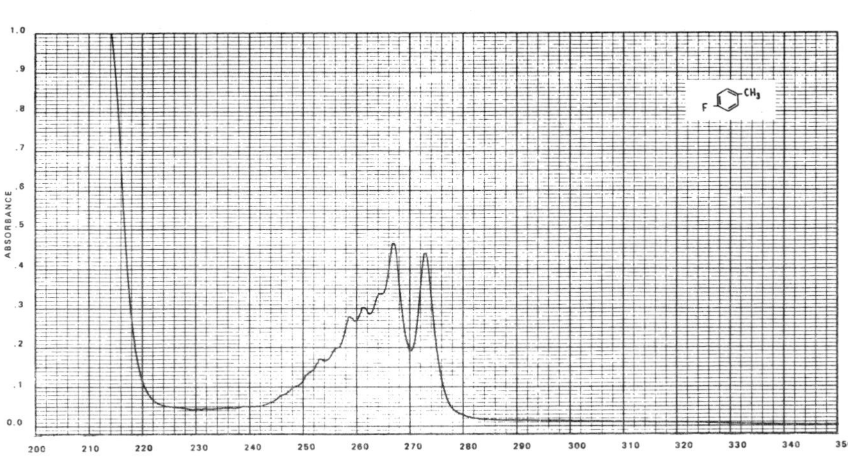

227

o,α,α,α-TETRAFLUOROTOLUENE

$C_7H_4F_4$

Mol. Wt. 164.10

B.P. 114.5°C/750mm

Solvent: Methanol

λ Max. mμ	a_m	Cell mm	Conc. g/L
268	527	5	0.300
261.5	569	5	0.300
x	x	1	0.300

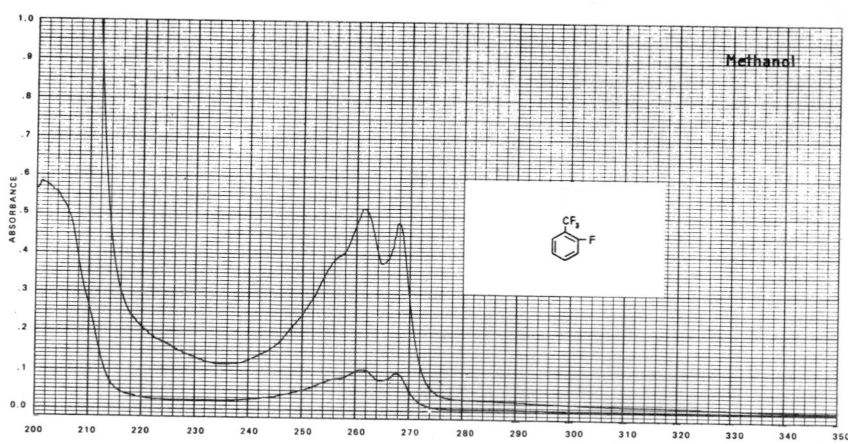

228

m,α,α,α-TETRAFLUOROTOLUENE

$C_7H_4F_4$

Mol. Wt. 164.10

Solvent: Methanol

λ Max. mμ	a_m	Cell mm	Conc. g/L
268.5	1020	2	0.400
262	1100	2	0.400

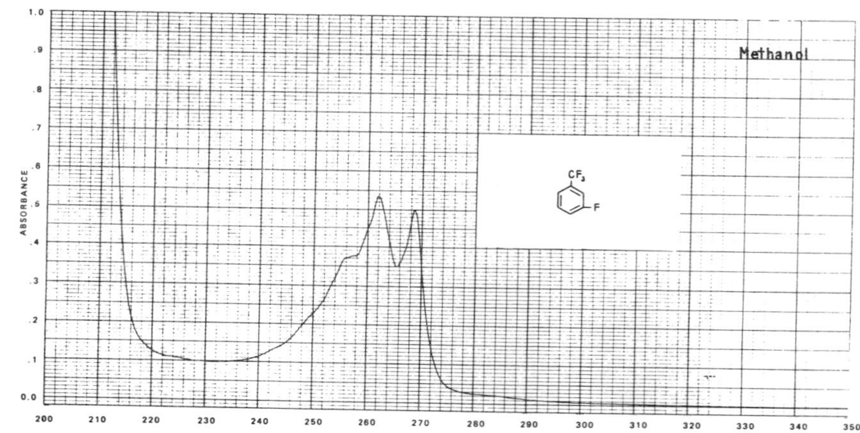

229

p-α,α,α-TETRAFLUOROTOLUENE

$C_7H_4F_4$

Mol. Wt. 164.10

B.P. 102-105°C (lit.)

Solvent: Methanol

λ Max. mμ	a_m	Cell mm	Conc. g/L
264	128	10	0.380
255.5	223	10	0.380
250	226	10	0.380
244	206	10	0.380
x	x	1	0.380

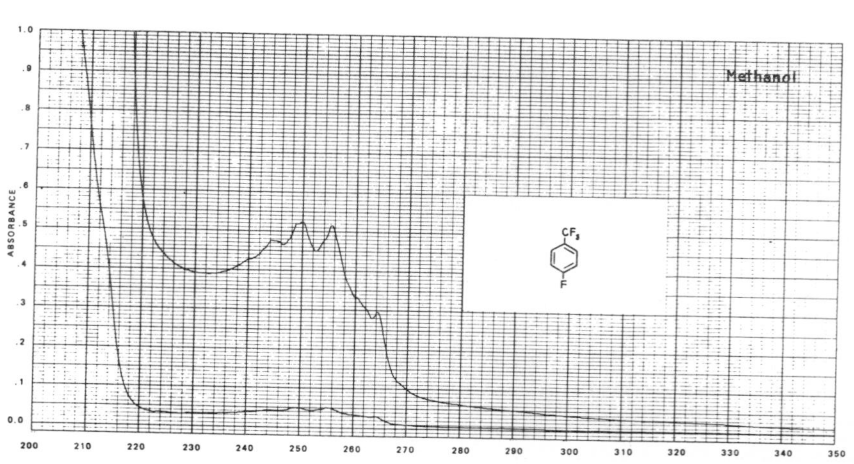

o-DIFLUOROBENZENE 230

$C_6H_4F_2$

Mol. Wt. 114.10

M.P. 39°C B.P. 91-92°C/751mm

Solvent: Methanol

λ Max. mμ	a_m	Cell mm	Conc. g/L
2645	550	10	0.100
259	685	10	0.100
254.5	560	10	0.100
x	x	2	0.100

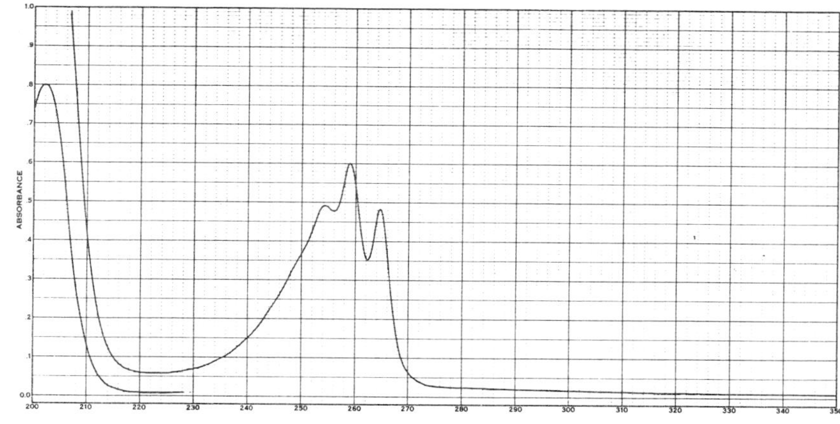

m-DIFLUOROBENZENE 231

$C_6H_4F_2$

Mol. Wt. 114.10

B.P. 81-83°C

Solvent: Methanol

λ Max. mμ	a_m	Cell mm	Conc. g/L
265.0	551	10	0.100
259.0	648	10	0.100
254.0	516	10	0.100
x	x	2	0.100

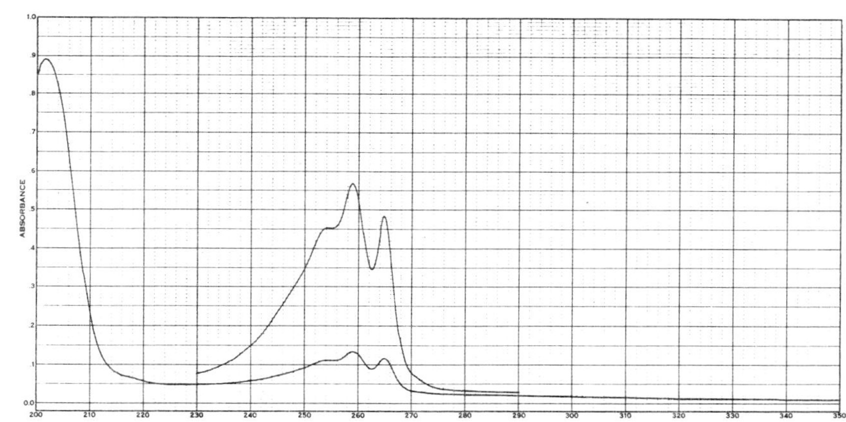

p-DIFLUOROBENZENE 232

$C_6H_4F_2$

Mol. Wt. 114.10

Solvent: Methanol

λ Max. mμ	a_m	Cell mm	Conc. g/L
x	x	10	3.248
271.5	1930	10	0.0455
266	2270	10	0.0455
262.5	1520	10	0.0455
260	1590	10	0.0455
257.5	1290	10	0.0455
252	780	10	0.0455

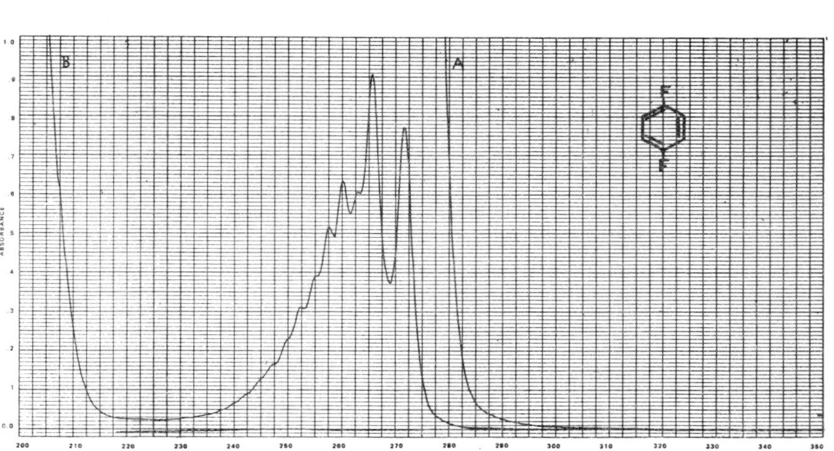

1-FLUORONAPHTHALENE 233

$C_{10}H_7F$

Mol. Wt. 146.17

B.P. 88.5-90°C/14mm

Solvent: Methanol

λ Max. mμ	a_m	Cell mm	Conc. g/L
286	3000	20	0.01430
278	4140	20	0.01430
276	4120	20	0.01430
269	3960	20	0.01430
219	64100	1	0.01430

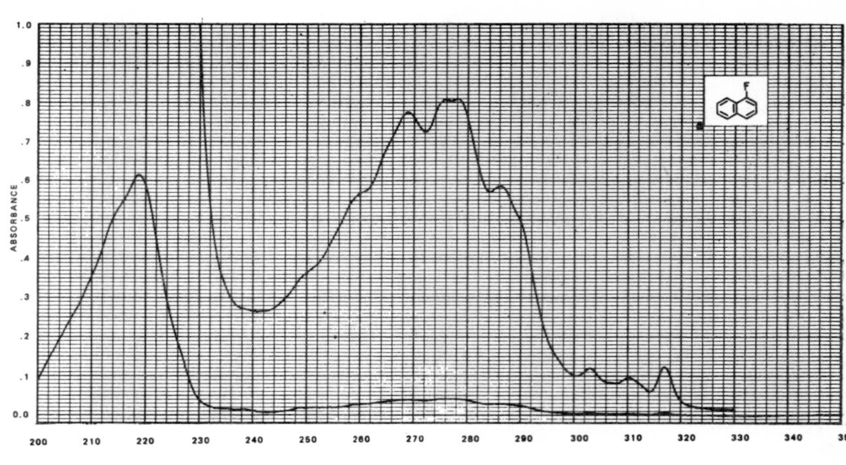

2-FLUORONAPHTHALENE 234

$C_{10}H_7F$

Mol. Wt. 146.16

M.P. 58°C (lit.)

Solvent: Methanol

λ Max. mμ	a_m	Cell mm	Conc. g/L
316.5	1160	10	0.109
309.5	713	10	0.109
303	842	10	0.109
272	4750	2	0.109
268	4780	2	0.109

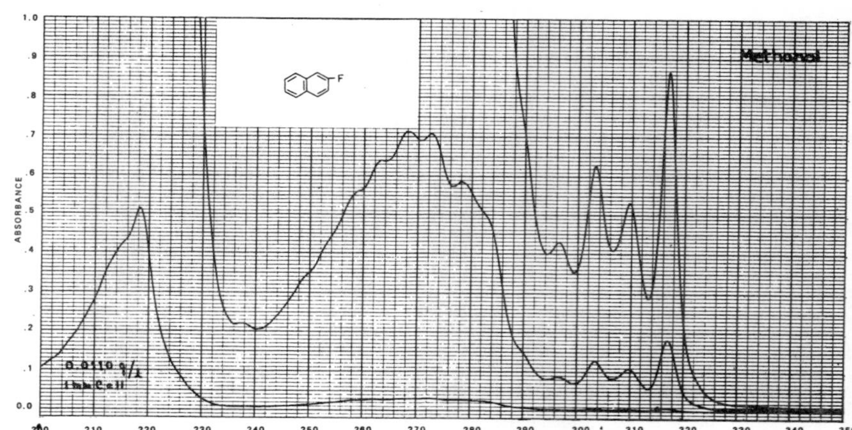

λ Max. mμ	a_m	Cell mm	Conc. g/L

THE CHLORINATED HYDROCARBONS

Aliphatic Compounds

The chlorine containing aliphatic, olefinic and acetylenic (non-conjugated) compounds display no significant absorption in the near UV region of the spectrum and thus there are no spectra included in this volume for compounds 235 through 283.

Aromatic Compounds

The substitution of aromatic hydrocarbons by chlorine results in both a slight bathochromic shift (5 - 10 mμ) and an increase in intensity (2X - 4X). These effects are noted for both ring substitution, and α- side chain substitution by two or three chlorine nuclei.

A table of parent compounds and their chlorine substituted derivatives is given below.

Compound	$\lambda_{max}(\epsilon_{max})$	$\lambda_{max}(\epsilon_{max})$	$\lambda_{max}(\epsilon_{max})$	Spectrum
Benzene	248 (169)	254 (212)	260 (149)	132
Chlorobenzene	257 (197)	264 (259)	271 (209)	291
o-Dichlorobenzene	262 (245)	269 (330)	276 (303)	305
m-Dichlorobenzene	262 (233)	270 (334)	278 (280)	306
p-Dichlorobenzene	264 (287)	272 (377)	280 (301)	307
α-Chlorotoluene	254 (190)	259 (231)	265 (211)	284
α,α-Dichlorotoluene	259 (401)	266 (447)	272 (443)	287
α,α,α-Trichlorotoluene	260 (499)	267 (558)	274 (450)	289
Toluene	255 (175)	261 (175)	268 (222)	133
o-Chlorotoluene	259 (276)	266 (288)	273 (250)	292
m-Chlorotoluene	260 (150)	267 (200)	274 (172)	293
p-Chlorotoluene	263 (388)	268 (527)	277 (507)	294

α-CHLOROTOLUENE

284

C_7H_7Cl

Mol. Wt. 126.59

B.P. 178-180°C

Solvent: Methanol

λ Max. mμ	a_m	Cell mm	Conc. g/L
265	211	10	0.442
259	231	10	0.442
253.5	190	10	0.442
216.5	6970	2	0.0884

α-CHLORO-p-XYLENE

285

C_8H_9Cl

Mol. Wt. 140.61

Solvent: Methanol

λ Max. mμ	a_m	Cell mm	Conc. g/L
264.5	342	10	0.304
258	334	10	0.304
224	9640	2	0.0304
x	x	1	0.0304

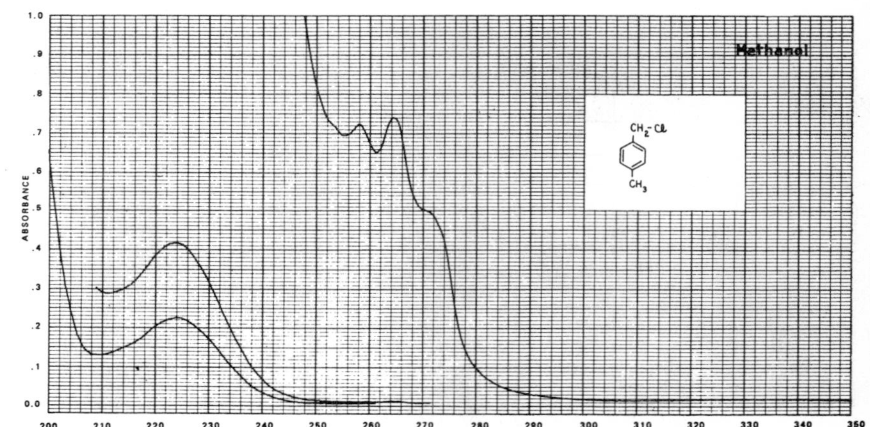

4,6-BIS(CHLOROMETHYL)-m-XYLENE

286

$C_{10}H_{12}Cl_2$

Mol. Wt. 203.12

Solvent: Dioxane

λ Max. mμ	a_m	Cell mm	Conc. g/L
x	x	10	1.9760
272.5	396	10	0.3952
x	x	10	0.0040

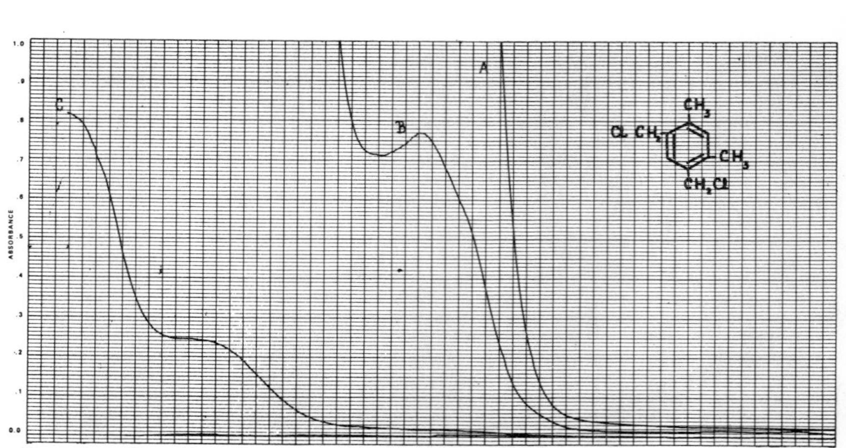

α,α-DICHLOROTOLUENE

287

$C_7H_6Cl_2$
Mol. Wt. 161.03
Solvent: Isooctane

λ Max. mμ	a_m	Cell mm	Conc. g/L
x	x	10	1.72
287.5	238	10	0.516
271.5	443	10	0.516
265.5	447	10	0.516
259.5	401	10	0.516
x	x	10	0.0516
220	27500	10	0.00152

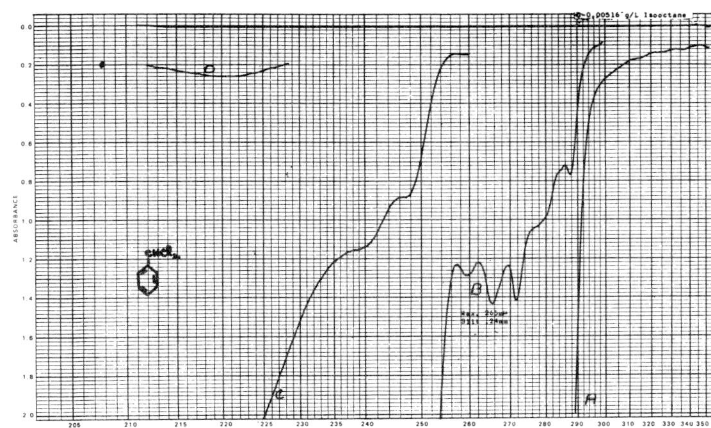

DICHLORODIPHENYLMETHANE

288

$C_{13}H_{10}Cl_2$
Mol. Wt. 237.13
Solvent: Methanol

λ Max. mμ	a_m	Cell mm	Conc. g/L
252	5120	2	0.206
x	x	1	0.103

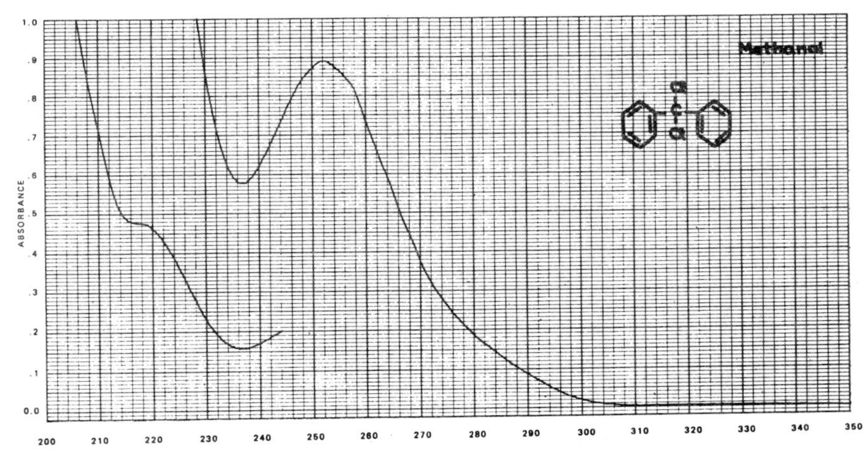

α,α,α-TRICHLOROTOLUENE

289

$C_7H_5Cl_3$
Mol. Wt. 195.48
Solvent: Methanol

λ Max. mμ	a_m	Cell mm	Conc. g/L
274	450	10	0.229
267	558	10	0.229
260.5	499	10	0.229
225	6910	1	0.229

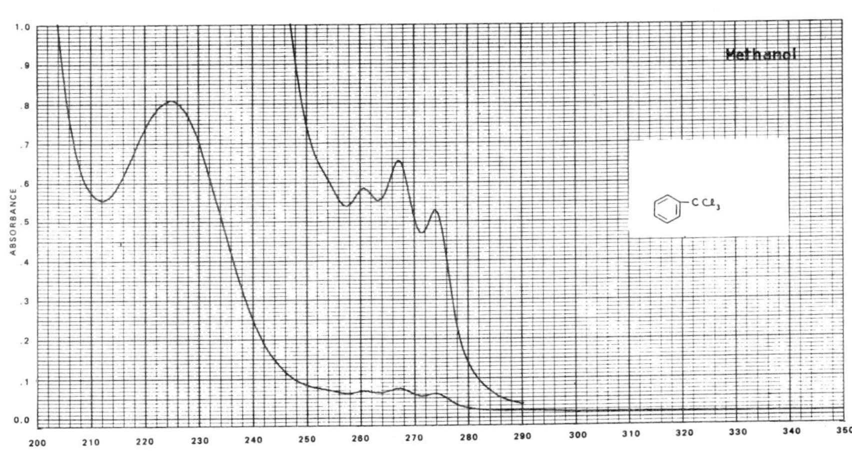

p-FLUORO-α,α,α-TRICHLOROTOLUENE 290

$C_7H_4Cl_3F$

Mol. Wt. 213.47

B.P. 98°C/16mm

Solvent: Methanol

λ Max. mμ	a_m	Cell mm	Conc. g/L
262	410	10	.1235
226	7160	2	.1235

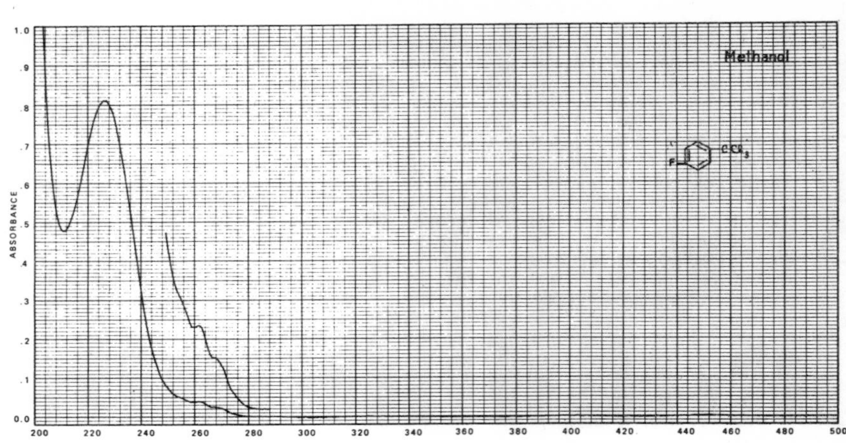

CHLOROBENZENE 291

C_6H_5Cl

Mol. Wt. 112.56

Solvent: Isooctane

λ Max. mμ	a_m	Cell mm	Conc. g/L
x	x	10	2.64
271	209	10	0.790
267	141	10	0.790
264	259	10	0.790
260.5	177	10	0.790
257	197	10	0.790
251	128	10	0.790
245	76.9	10	0.790
217.5	8740	10	0.0132
214.5	10900	10	0.0132

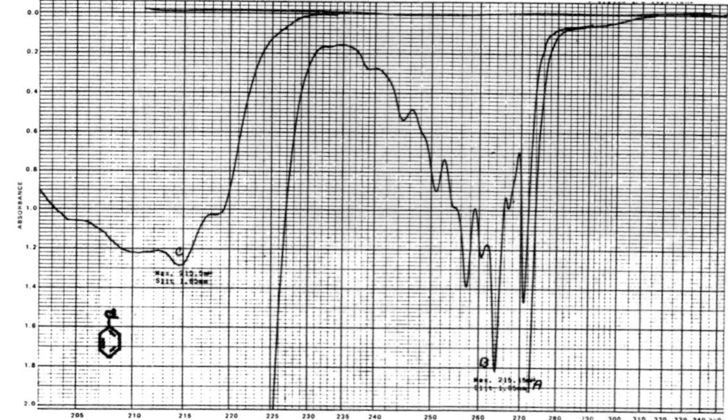

o-CHLOROTOLUENE 292

C_7H_7Cl

Mol. Wt. 126.59

B.P. 157-159°C

Solvent: Methanol

λ Max. mμ	a_m	Cell mm	Conc. g/L
272	250	5	0.440
265	288	5	0.440
211.5	9390	1	0.0880

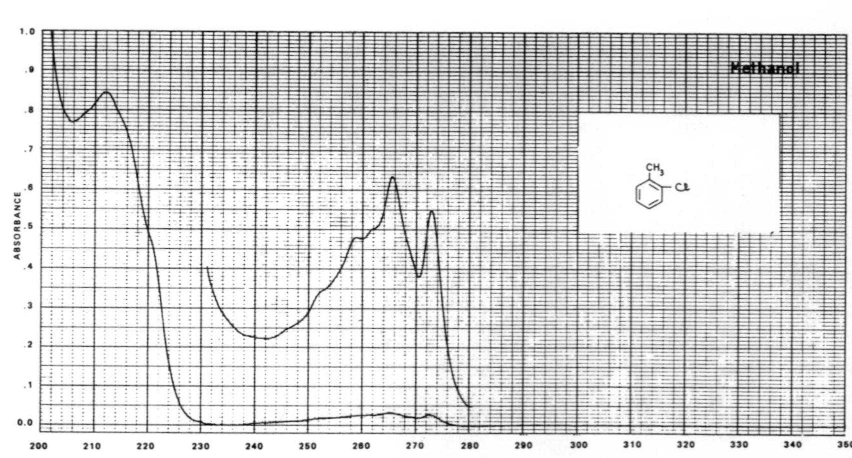

m-CHLOROTOLUENE 293

C_7H_7Cl
Mol. Wt. 126.59
B.P. 159-161°C
Solvent: Methanol

λ Max. mμ	a_m	Cell mm	Conc. g/L
274	172	10	0.378
265	200	10	0.378
260	150	10	0.378
212.5	5560	2	0.0756

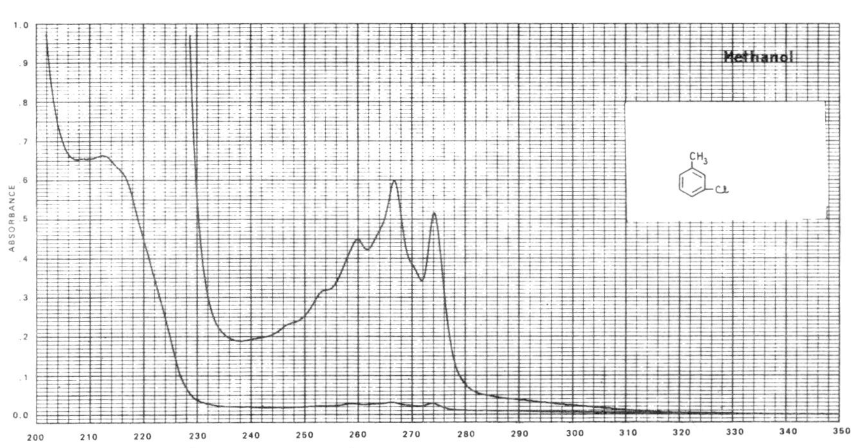

p-CHLOROTOLUENE 294

C_7H_7Cl
Mol. Wt. 126.59
M.P. 6-8°C B.P. 162°C (lit.)
Solvent: Methanol

λ Max. mμ	a_m	Cell mm	Conc. g/L
276.5	507	5	0.345
268.5	527	5	0.345
262.5	388	5	0.345
220	11000	2	0.0345

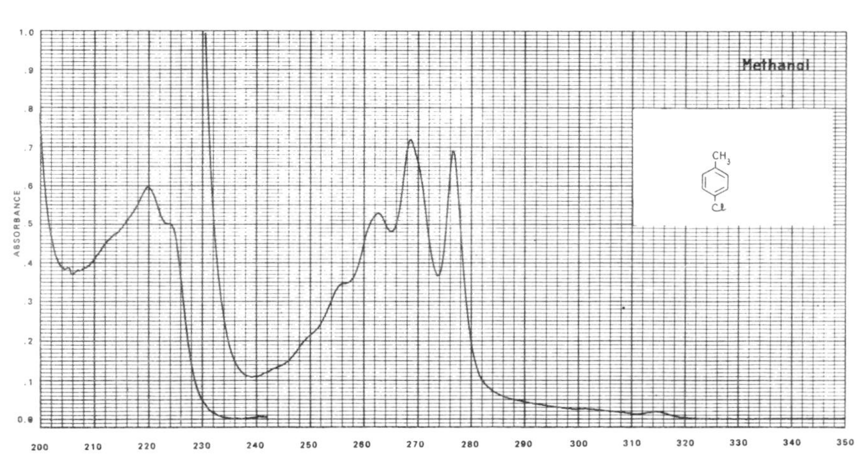

1-CHLORO-2-ETHYLBENZENE 295

C_8H_9Cl
Mol. Wt. 140.61
B.P. 178.4°C (lit.)
Solvent: Methanol

λ Max. mμ	a_m	Cell mm	Conc. g/L
272.5	222	10	0.500
265.5	267	10	0.500
258.5	203	10	0.500
212	9040	2	0.0500

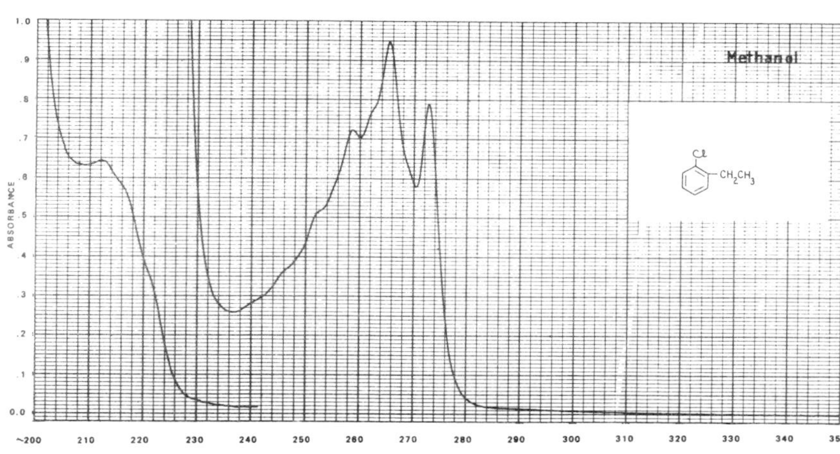

2-CHLOROSTYRENE

296

C_8H_7Cl

Mol. Wt. 138.60

B.P. 58-60°C/7mm (lit.)

Solvent: Cyclohexane

λ Max. mμ	a_m	Cell mm	Conc. g/L
x	x	10	1.5320
313	302	10	0.2298
300	642	10	0.2298
290	905	10	0.2298
280.5	991	10	0.2298
244	11100	10	0.0207
229.5	9240	10	0.0207
x	x	10	0.0021

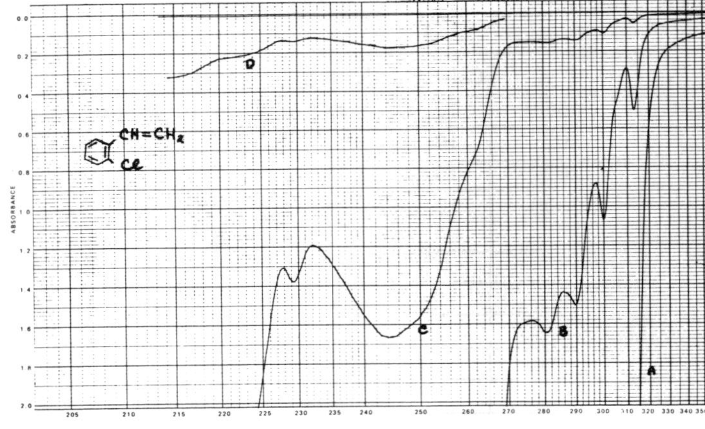

2-CHLOROBIPHENYL

297

$C_{12}H_9Cl$

Mol. Wt. 188.66

M.P. 31°C (lit.)

Solvent: Methanol

λ Max. mμ	a_m	Cell mm	Conc. g/L
x	x	10	2.00
241	11700	10	0.020

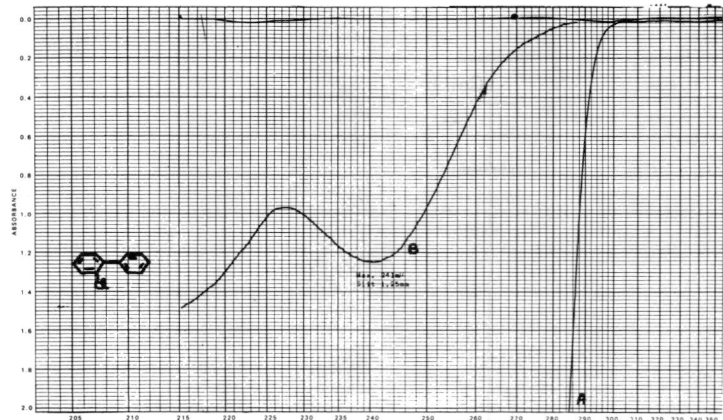

4-CHLOROBIPHENYL

298

$C_{12}H_9Cl$

Mol. Wt. 188.66

Solvent: Methanol

λ Max. mμ	a_m	Cell mm	Conc. g/L
251.5	47000	0.5	0.050
x	x	0.5	0.050

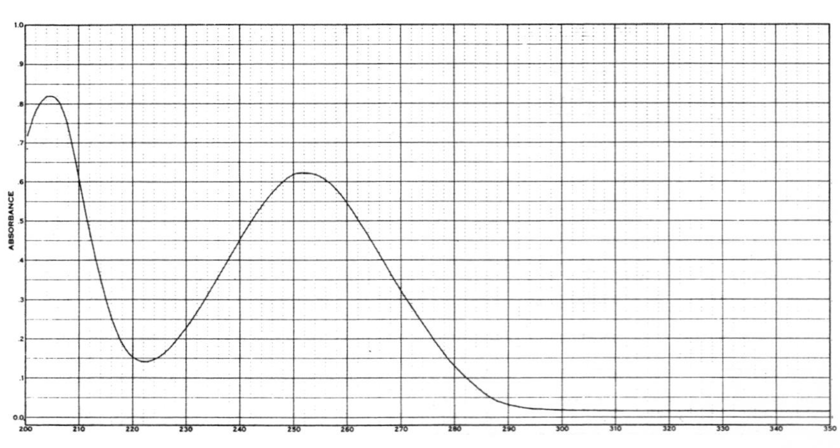

2-CHLORO-p-XYLENE **299**

C_8H_9Cl

Mol. Wt. 140.62

B.P. 186°C M.P. 2.0°C

Solvent: Methanol

λ Max. mμ	a_m	Cell mm	Conc. g/L
278	455	10	0.175
269	392	10	0.175
264	262	10	0.175
215	6000	10	0.0175

p-CHLORO-*a,a,a*-TRIFLUOROTOLUENE **300**

$C_7H_4ClF_3$

Mol. Wt. 180.56

Solvent: Methanol

λ Max. mμ	a_m	Cell mm	Conc. g/L
271.5	117	20	0.132
266.5	160	20	0.132
261	207	20	0.132
255	184	20	0.132
219.5	6680	1	0.132

1-CHLORO-2-FLUOROBENZENE **301**

C_6H_4ClF

Mol. Wt. 130.55

B.P. 137-138°C

Solvent: Methanol

λ Max. mμ	a_m	Cell mm	Conc. g/L
271	828	2	0.26650
264.5	856	2	0.26650
258.5	653	2	0.26650
208	7510	2	0.053300

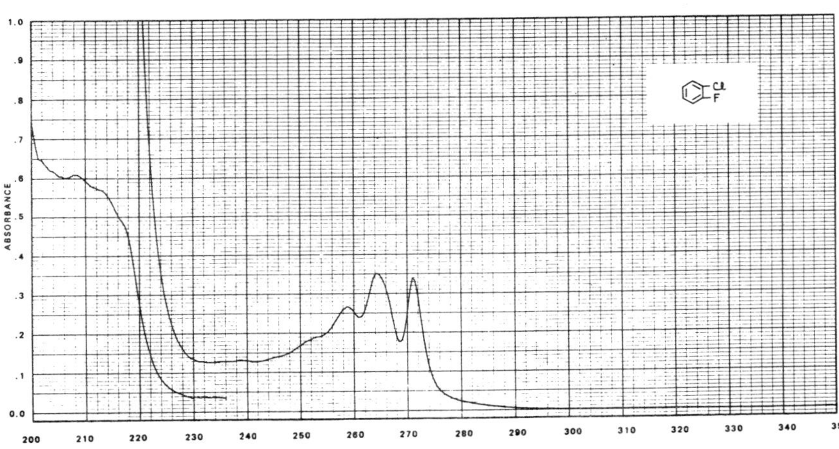

1-CHLORO-3-FLUOROBENZENE 302

C_6H_4ClF

Mol. Wt. 130.55

B.P. 126-128°C

Solvent: Methanol

λ Max. mμ	a_m	Cell mm	Conc. g/L
271	760	10	0.100
266.5	881	10	0.100
258.5	642	10	0.100
211	6800	1	0.100

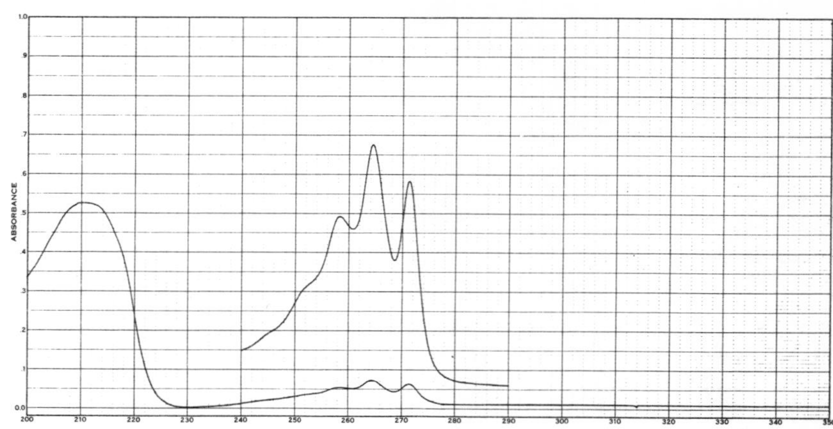

1-CHLORO-4-FLUOROBENZENE 303

C_6H_4ClF

Mol. Wt. 130.55

M.P. -21.5°C

λ Max. mμ	a_m	Cell mm	Conc. g/L

Pure sample not available.

2-CHLORO-4-FLUOROTOLUENE 304

C_7H_6ClF

Mol. Wt. 144.58

Solvent: Methanol

λ Max. mμ	a_m	Cell mm	Conc. g/L
276	1250	10	0.0800
269	1210	10	0.0800
210	7730	2	0.0800

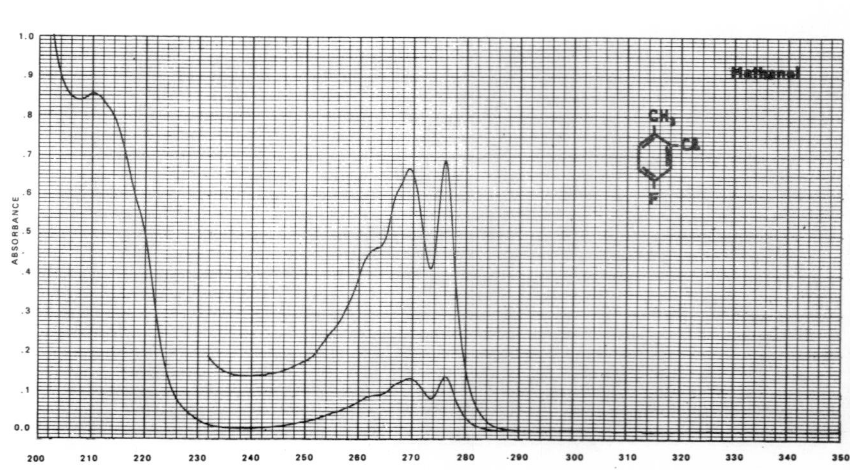

o-DICHLOROBENZENE **305**

$C_6H_4Cl_2$
Mol. Wt. 147.01
Solvent: Isooctane

λ Max. mμ	$^a m$	Cell mm	Conc. g/L
x	x	10	2.28
276.5	303	10	0.684
269	330	10	0.684
262	245	10	0.684
255	155	10	0.684
219	9250	10	0.0137

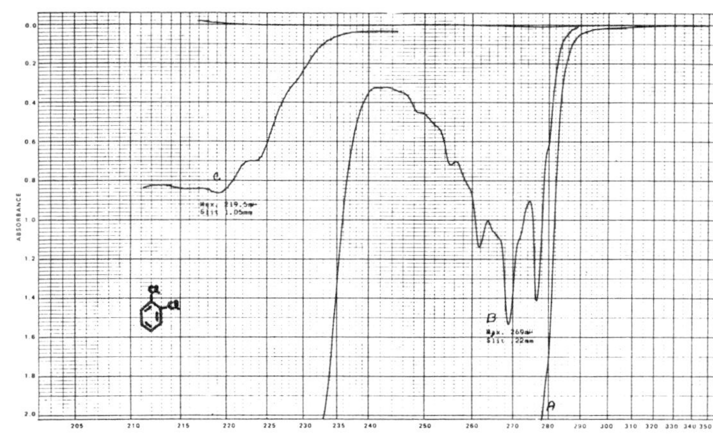

m-DICHLOROBENZENE **306**

$C_6H_4Cl_2$
Mol. Wt. 147.00
M.P. (-24.8°C) B.P. 172°C
Solvent: Methanol

λ Max. mμ	$^a m$	Cell mm	Conc. g/L
278.0	280	2	0.100
270.0	334	2	0.100
263.0	233	2	0.100
256.0	142	2	0.100
250.0	83	2	0.100
216	12800	1	0.0100

p-DICHLOROBENZENE **307**

$C_6H_4Cl_2$
Mol. Wt. 147.00
Solvent: Methanol

λ Max. mμ	$^a m$	Cell mm	Conc. g/L
280	301	5	0.500
271.5	377	5	0.500
264	287	5	0.500
223.5	12800	1	0.100

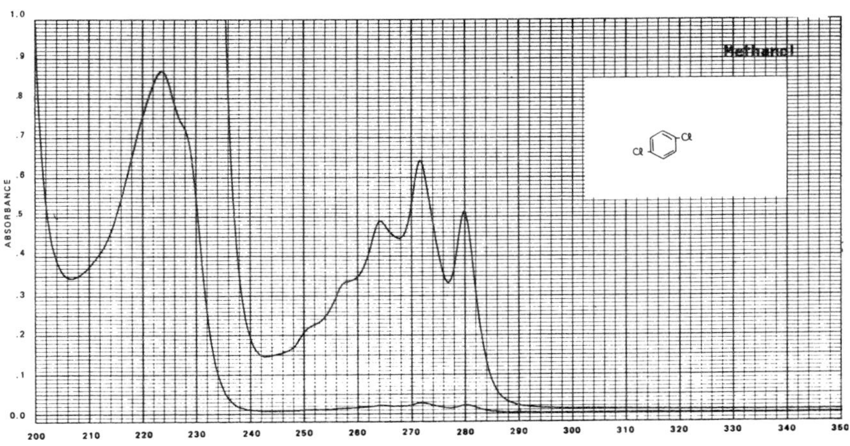

2,4-DICHLOROTOLUENE

$C_7H_6Cl_2$
Mol. Wt. 161.03
B.P. 200°C
Solvent: Methanol

λ Max. mμ	a_m	Cell mm	Conc. g/L
280.5	588	5	0.492
272.5	588	5	0.492
266	378	5	0.492
217.5	3740	2	0.0492

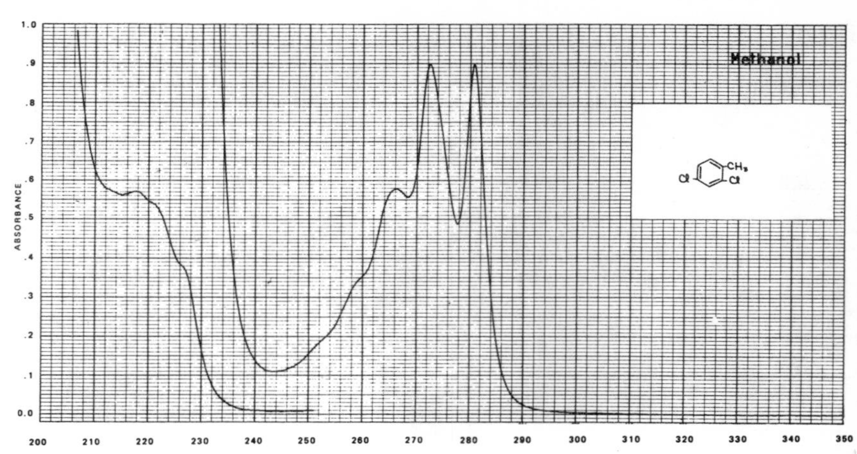

2,6-DICHLOROTOLUENE

309

$C_7H_6Cl_2$
Mol. Wt. 161.03
Solvent: Cyclohexane

λ Max. mμ	a_m	Cell mm	Conc. g/L
x	x	10	2.22
274	146	10	1.11
266	201	10	1.11
262	158	10	1.11
x	x	10	0.0278

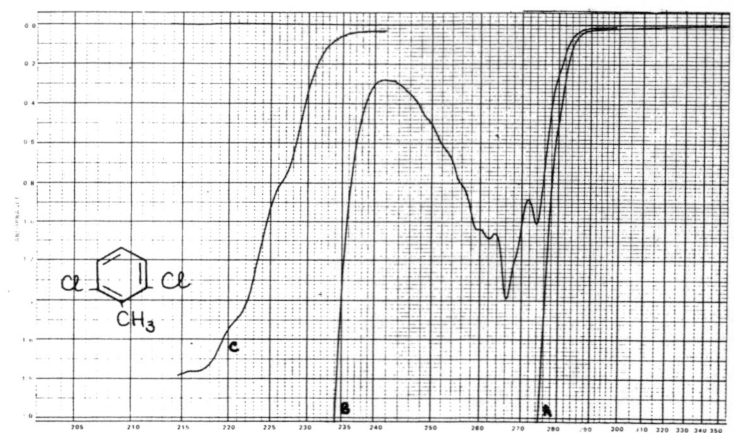

1,2-DICHLORO-4-FLUOROBENZENE

310

$C_6H_3Cl_2F$
Mol. Wt. 164.99
Solvent: Methanol

λ Max. mμ	a_m	Cell mm	Conc. g/L
280	1040	5	0.175
272	1080	5	0.175
x	x	1	0.175

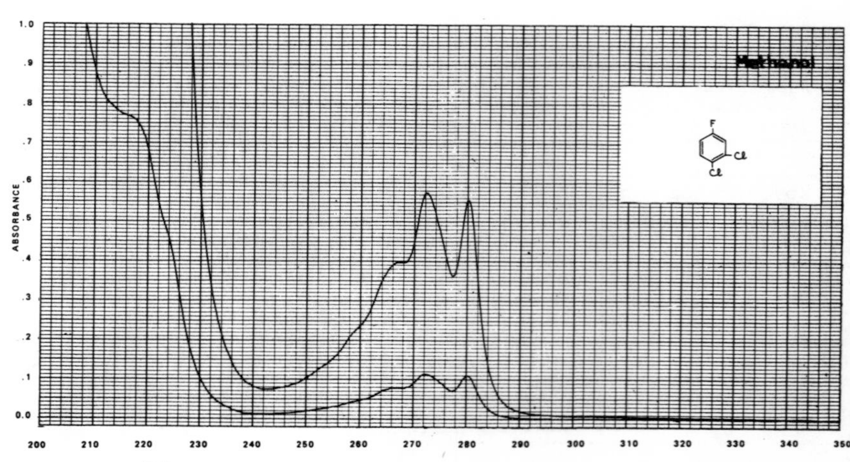

α,3,4-TRICHLOROTOLUENE

311

$C_7H_5Cl_3$
Mol. Wt. 195.48
B.P. 127-129°C/14mm
Solvent: Methanol

λ Max. mμ	a_m	Cell mm	Conc. g/L
283.5	307	10	0.2410
275	370	10	0.2410
268	287	10	0.2410
229	96300	1	0.0120

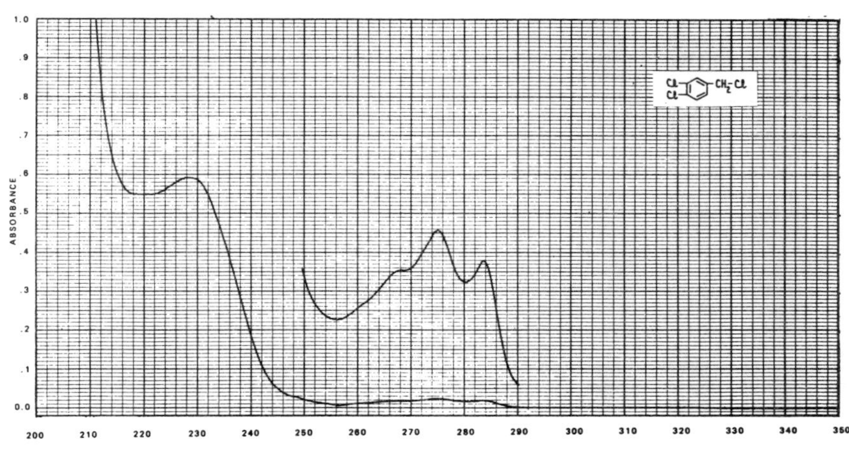

1,2,3-TRICHLOROBENZENE

312

$C_6H_3Cl_3$
Mol. Wt. 181.45
M.P. 50-52°C
Solvent: Methanol

λ Max. mμ	a_m	Cell mm	Conc. g/L
279	137	20	0.500
271	178	20	0.500
264	144	20	0.500
224	8080	2	0.500
x	x	1	0.100

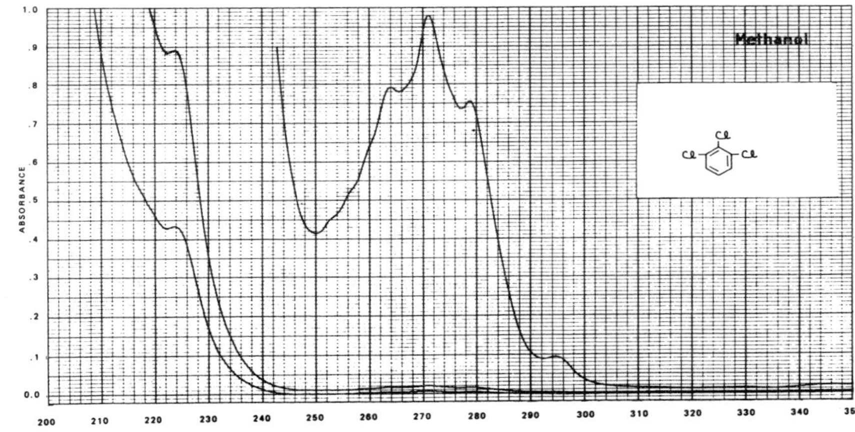

1,2,4-TRICHLOROBENZENE

313

$C_6H_3Cl_3$
Mol. Wt. 181.45
M.P. 15-17°C
Solvent: Methanol

λ Max. mμ	a_m	Cell mm	Conc. g/L
286	438	10	0.207
277	482	10	0.207
269	323	10	0.207
226.5	9200	1	0.104
219..5	9340	1	0.104

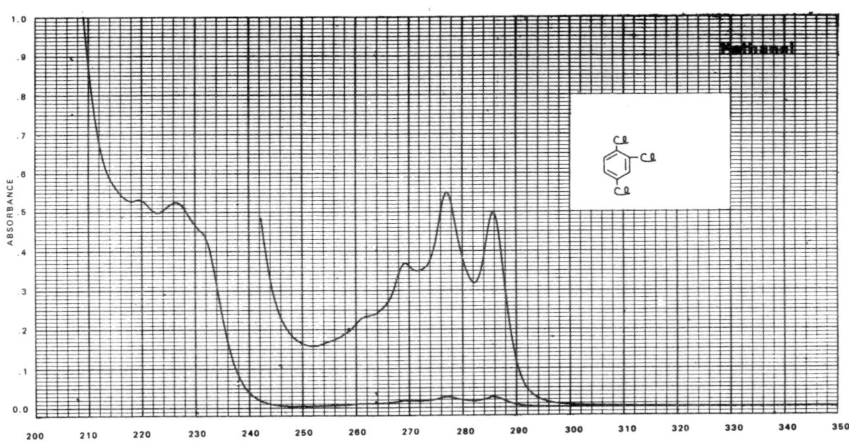

1,3,5-TRICHLOROBENZENE

314

$C_6H_3Cl_3$

Mol. Wt. 181.45

M.P. 63.5°C (lit.)

Solvent: Methanol

λ Max. mμ	a_m	Cell mm	Conc. g/L
280	198	20	0.100
272.5	240	20	0.100
265	196	20	0.100
225	9510	1	0.100
221	10700	1	0.100

1,2,4,5-TETRACHLOROBENZENE

315

$C_6H_2Cl_4$

Mol. Wt. 215.9

Solvent: Cyclohexane

λ Max. mμ	a_m	Cell mm	Conc. g/L
x	x	10	2.00
293.5	1320	10	0.200
284	1180	10	0.200
279	605	10	0.200
275.5	583	10	0.200
231.5	11700	10	0.020

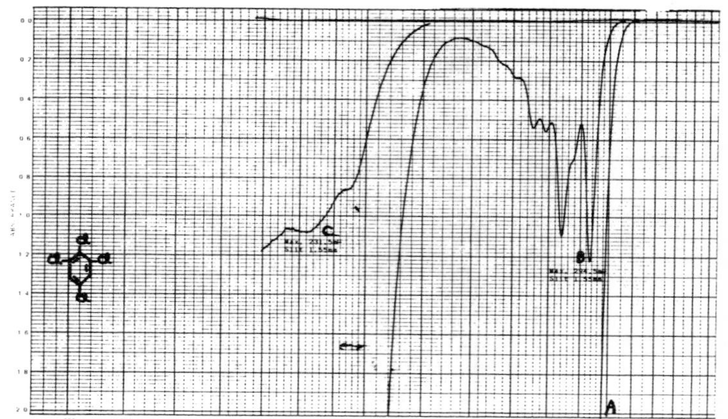

1-(CHLOROMETHYL)NAPHTHALENE

316

$C_{11}H_9Cl$

Mol. Wt. 176.65

Solvent: Methanol

λ Max. mμ	a_m	Cell mm	Conc. g/L
283.5	7350	2	0.100
222.5	55200	0.5	0.050

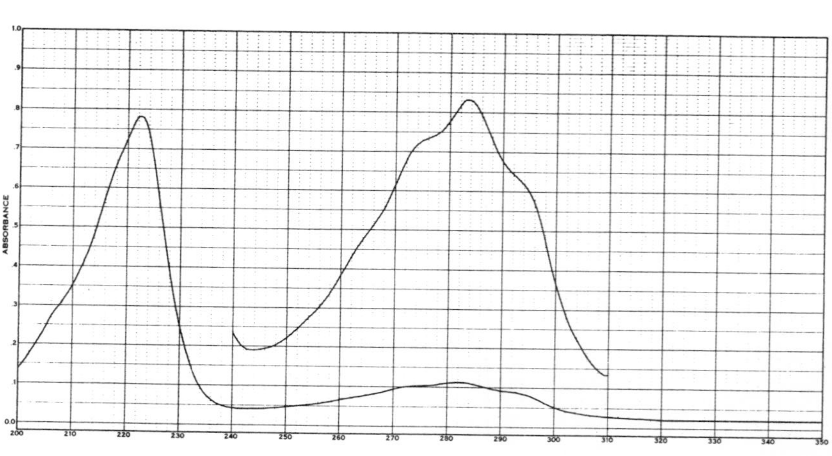

317

1-CHLORONAPHTHALENE

$C_{10}H_7Cl$

Mol. Wt. 162.62

B.P. 111-113°C/5mm

Solvent: Methanol

λ Max. mμ	a_m	Cell mm	Conc. g/L
319.5	249	2	1.00
315.0	372	2	1.00
309.5	443	2	1.00
290.5	5280	2	0.100
283.0	7490	2	0.100
273.0	6600	2	0.100

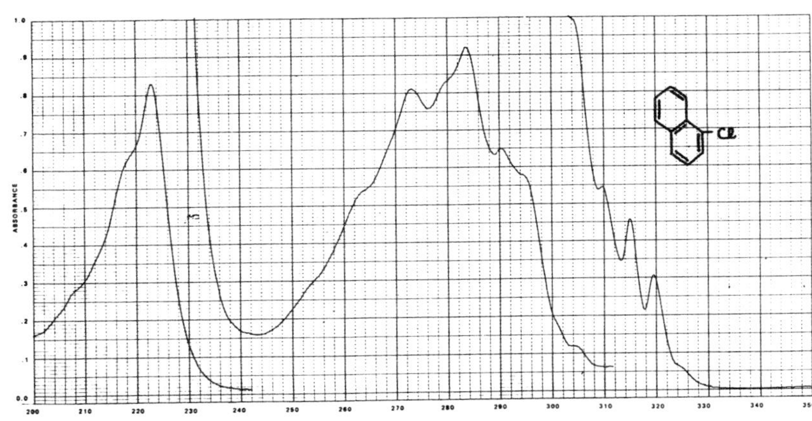

318

2-CHLORONAPHTHALENE

$C_{10}H_7Cl$

Mol. Wt. 162.62

M.P. 58°C

Solvent: Methanol

λ Max. mμ	a_m	Cell mm	Conc. g/L
320.5	338	10	0.100
306.5	387	10	0.100
276.5	5200	1	0.100
266.5	4720	1	0.100
225	10100	1	0.0100

λ Max. mμ	a_m	Cell mm	Conc. g/L

NOTES

THE BROMINATED HYDROCARBONS

Aliphatic and Olefinic Compounds

The brominated aliphatic and unconjugated olefinic compounds do not display any significant absorption in the near UV region of the spectrum and so there are no spectra in this volume for compounds 319 - 370.

Aromatic Compounds

The fine structure that has been observed in the region of 250 mμ to 270 mμ for benzene, fluorinated benzenes and chlorinated benzenes is often poorly resolved or unobserved in the UV spectra of many brominated aromatic compounds (spectra 371, 372, 377, 378).

Bromine is an auxochromic group which shifts the absorption wavelength of benzene and aliphatic substituted benzenes to longer wavelength by about 10 mμ.

A series of brominated hydrocarbons and their parent compounds is provided below.

Compound	$\lambda_{max}(\epsilon_{max})$	$\lambda_{max}(\epsilon_{max})$	$\lambda_{max}(\epsilon_{max})$	Spectrum
Benzene	248 (169)	254 (212)	260 (149)	132
Bromobenzene	260 (173)	264 (171)	271 (119)	381
o-Dibromobenzene	260 (255)	270 (255)	278 (183)	396
m-Dibromobenzene	264 (290)	272 (375)	279 (285)	397
p-Dibromobenzene	265 (326)	273 (333)	281 (210)	398

The auxochromic effect of bromine substitution is especially apparent when comparing the principal band absorption (E_2, $\pi \rightarrow \pi^*$ transition) of para substituted bromobenzenes.

Compound	$\lambda_{max}(\epsilon_{max})$	Spectrum
Benzene	204 (7900)	Lit.
Bromobenzene	221 (7280)	381
p-Bromotoluene	220 (10600)	384
p-Bromo-*a,a,a*-trifluorotoluene	223 (16200)	388
p-Bromochlorobenzene	224 (12600)	394
p-Dibromobenzene	227 (14000)	398

α-BROMOTOLUENE

371

C_7H_7Br

Mol. Wt. 171.04

Solvent: Methanol

λ Max. mμ	a_m	Cell mm	Conc. g/L
225	10400	1	0.100

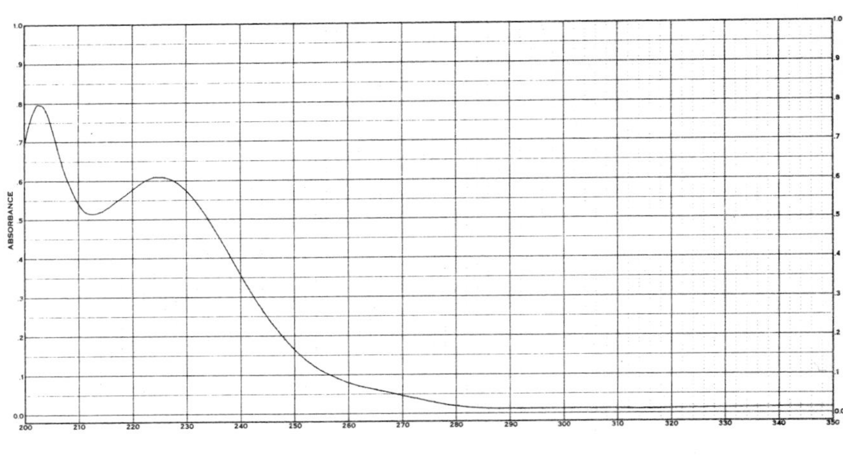

α-BROMO-o-XYLENE

372

C_8H_9Br

Mol. Wt. 185.07

B.P. 80-82°C/5mm

Solvent: Methanol

λ Max. mμ	a_m	Cell mm	Conc. g/L
231.5	7590	1	0.145

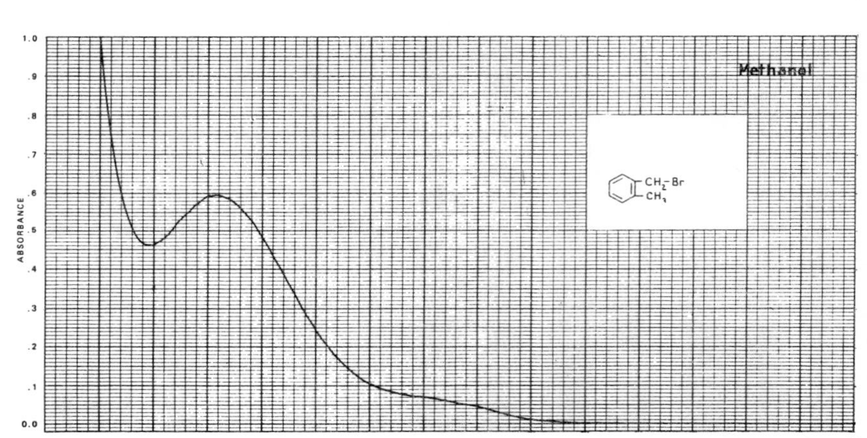

α-BROMO-p-XYLENE

373

C_8H_9Br

Mol. Wt. 185.07

Solvent: Dioxane

λ Max. mμ	a_m	Cell mm	Conc. g/L
x	x	10	2.00
245.5	15500	10	0.010

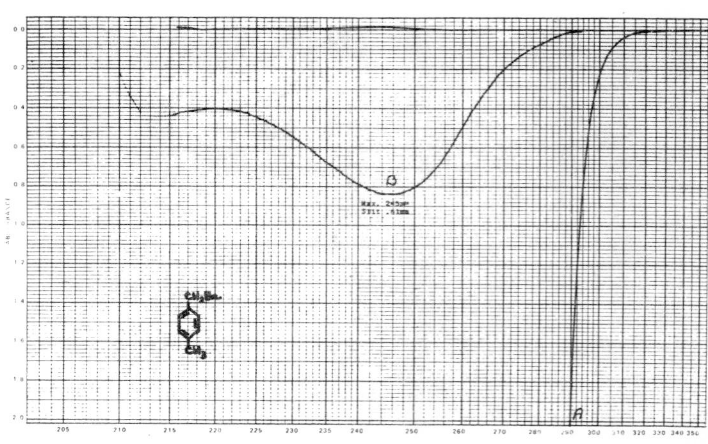

BROMODIPHENYLMETHANE 374

$C_{13}H_{11}Br$

Mol. Wt. 247.13

Solvent: Methanol

λ Max. mμ	a_m	Cell mm	Conc. g/L
264	484	10	0.3
258	634	10	0.3
252.5	593	10	0.3
x	x	10	0.01

0.01 g/l

Br
CH

(2-BROMOETHYL)BENZENE 375

C_8H_9Br

Mol. Wt. 185.07

B.P. 78-79°C/5mm

Solvent: Methanol

λ Max. mμ	a_m	Cell mm	Conc. g/L
263.5	281	10	0.378
257.5	378	10	0.378
252	385	10	0.378
247	366	10	0.378
x	x	1	0.189

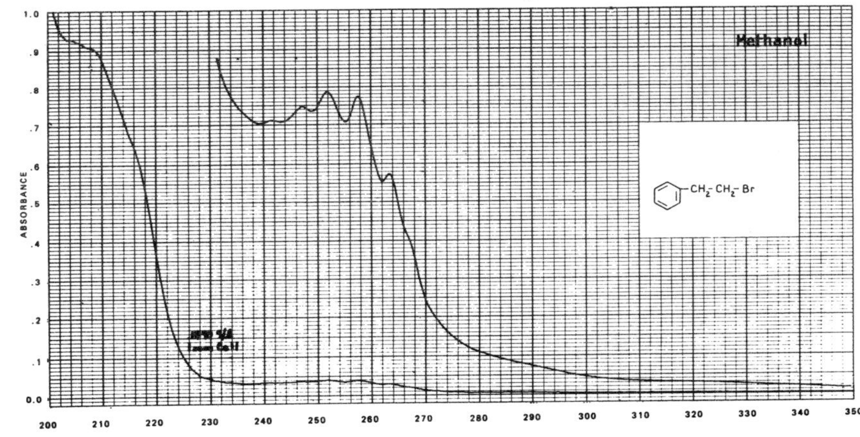

α,α-DIBROMOTOLUENE 376

$C_7H_6Br_2$

Mol. Wt. 249.94

B.P. 156°C/23mm

Solvent: Methanol

λ Max. mμ	a_m	Cell mm	Conc. g/L
226	15600	1	0.100
x	x	0.5	0.100

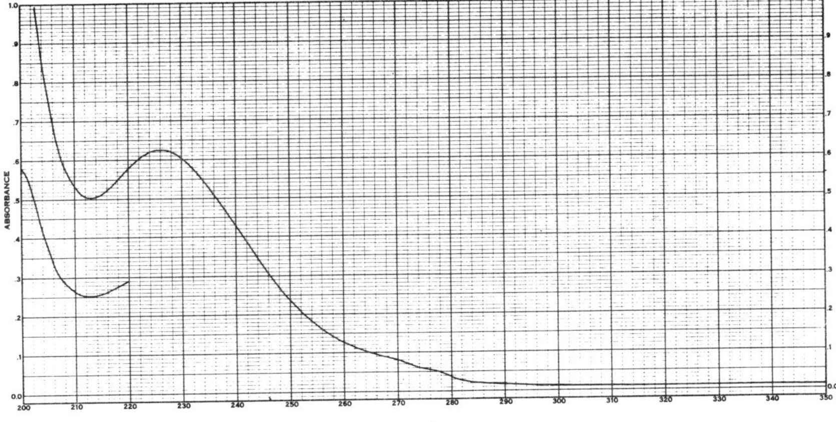

α,α-DIBROMO-m-XYLENE

377

$C_8H_8Br_2$

Mol. Wt. 263.97

B.P. 112-114°C/6mm

Solvent: Methanol

λ Max. mμ	a_m	Cell mm	Conc. g/L
x	x	5	0.283
227.5	7360	0.5	0.283

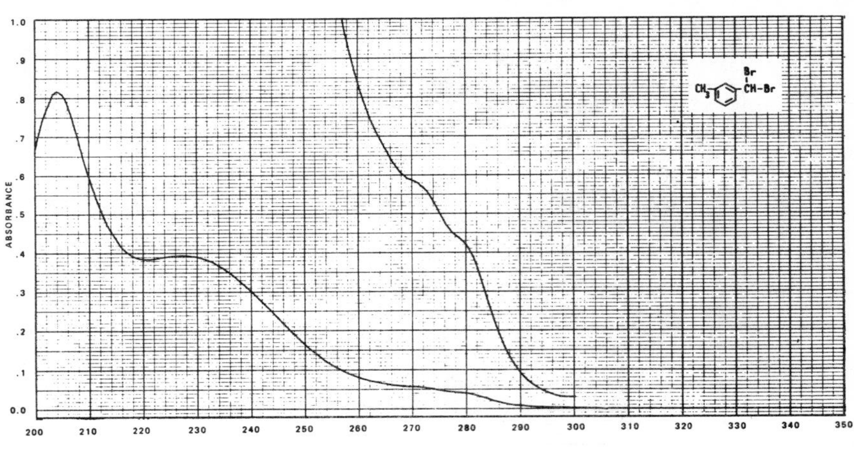

(1,2-DIBROMOETHYL)BENZENE

378

$C_8H_8Br_2$

Mol. Wt. 263.98

Solvent: Cyclohexane

λ Max. mμ	a_m	Cell mm	Conc. g/L
x	x	10	2.00
223	7130	10	0.060

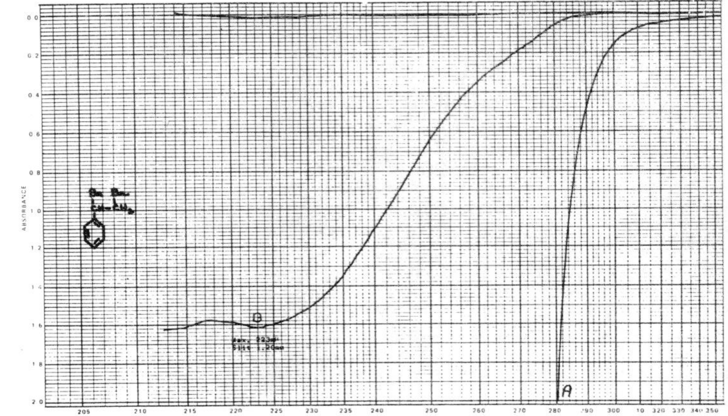

1,5-DIBROMO-3-PHENYLPENTANE

379

$C_{11}H_{14}Br_2$

Mol. Wt. 306.05

Solvent: Methanol

λ Max. mμ	a_m	Cell mm	Conc. g/L
264	347	40	0.100
258.5	438	40	0.100
253	396	40	0.100
247	344	40	0.100
212.5	5260	5	0.100

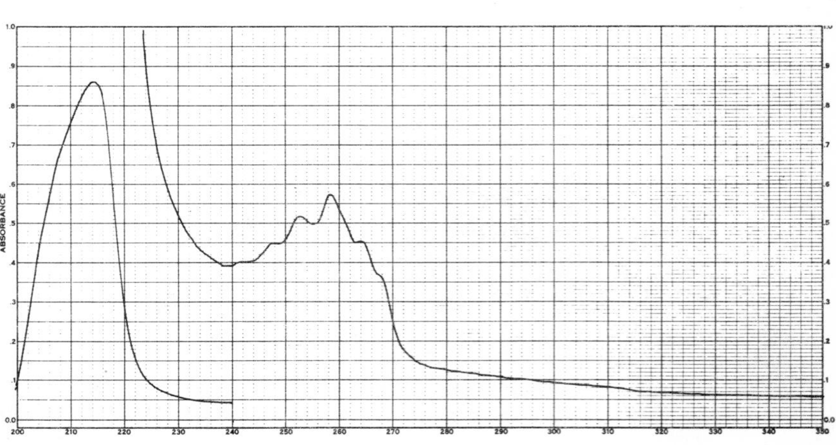

β-BROMOSTYRENE

380

C_8H_7Br

Mol. Wt. 183.05

B.P. 219°C (sl. dec.) M.P. 7°C

Solvent: Methanol

λ Max. mμ	a_m	Cell mm	Conc. g/L
295	1510	10	0.046
284.5	2420	10	0.046
257	18500	10	0.0046
207.5	20300	10	0.0046

BROMOBENZENE

381

C_6H_5Br

Mol. Wt. 157.02

B.P. 154-155°C

Solvent: Methanol

λ Max. mμ	a_m	Cell mm	Conc. g/L
270.5	119	20	0.164
264	171	20	0.164
260.5	173	20	0.164
257	159	20	0.164
250	139	20	0.164
211	7276	1	0.164

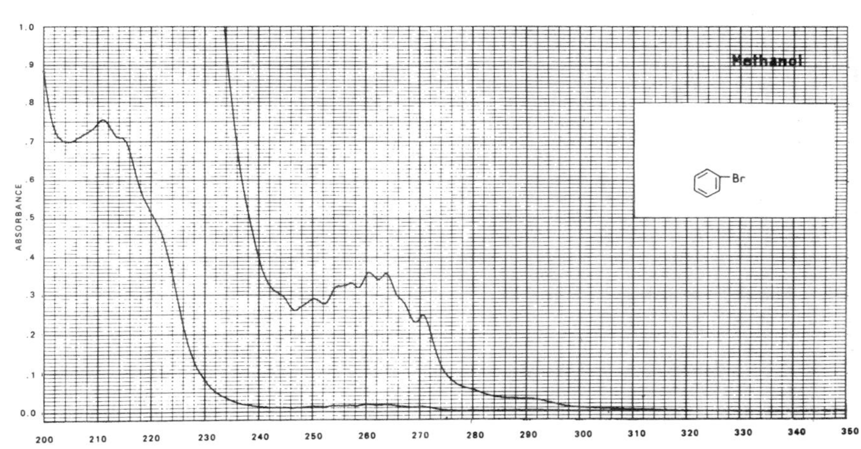

o-BROMOTOLUENE

382

C_7H_7Br

Mol. Wt. 171.04

B.P. 181.8°C (lit.)

Solvent: Methanol

λ Max. mμ	a_m	Cell mm	Conc. g/L
286.5	39.2	20	0.190
272.5	257	20	0.190
265.5	305	20	0.190
258.5	250	20	0.190
x	x	1	0.190

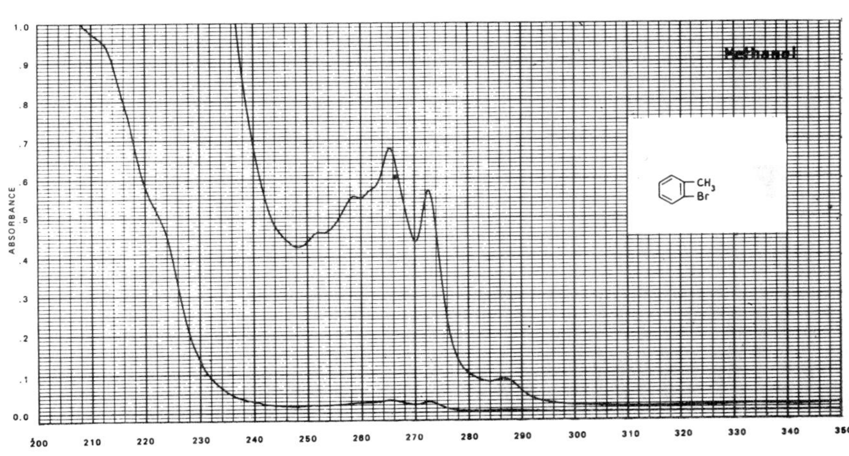

m-BROMOTOLUENE 383

C_7H_7Br

Mol. Wt. 171.04

B.P. 182-184°C

Solvent: Methanol

λ Max. mμ	a_m	Cell mm	Conc. g/L
274	248	10	0.472
267	303	10	0.472
260	237	10	0.472
x	x	2	0.0944

p-BROMOTOLUENE 384

C_7H_7Br

Mol. Wt. 171.04

B.P. 184-185°C (lit.)

Solvent: Methanol

λ Max. mμ	a_m	Cell mm	Conc. g/L
276.5	411	20	0.100
269	494	20	0.100
260.5	489	20	0.100
220	10600	1	0.100

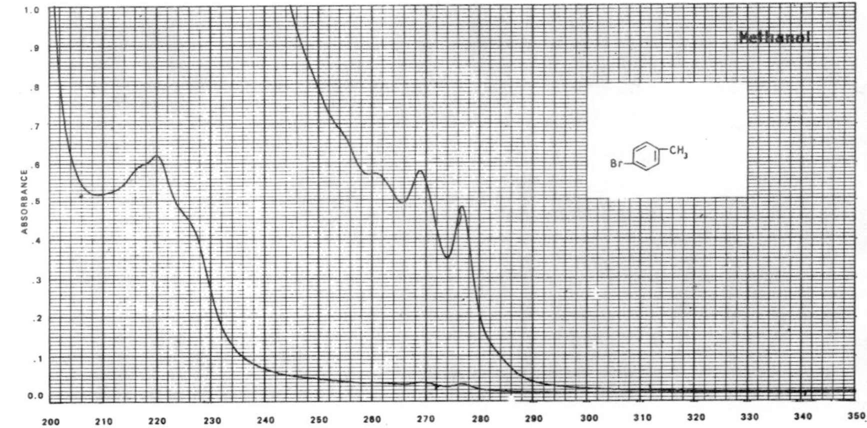

3-BROMO-p-CYMENE 385

$C_{10}H_{13}Br$

M.W. 213.12

B.P. 105-107°C/13mm

λ Max. mμ	a_m	Cell mm	Conc. g/L

No pure sample available.

1-BROMO-2,4,5-TRIMETHYLBENZENE

386

$C_9H_{11}Br$

Mol. Wt. 199.10

Solvent: Methanol

λ Max. mμ	a_m	Cell mm	Conc. g/L
x	x	10	2.036
280	714	10	0.2036
271.5	675	10	0.2036
x	x	10	0.0203

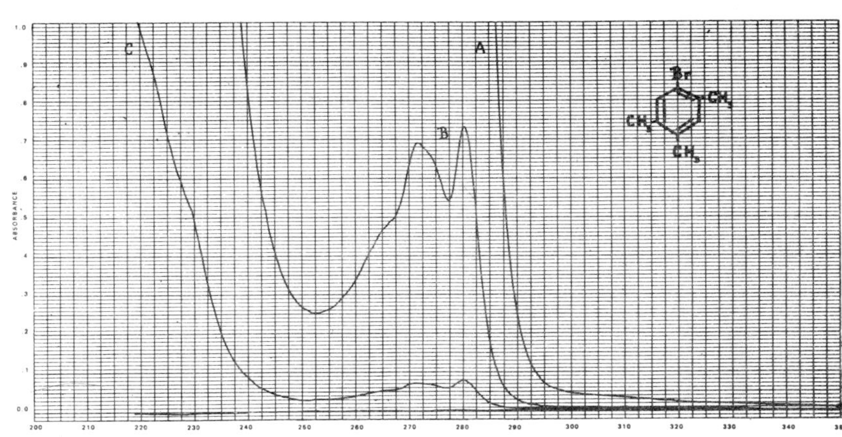

2-BROMOMESITYLENE

387

$C_9H_{11}Br$

Mol. Wt. 199.09

Solvent: Cyclohexane

λ Max. mμ	a_m	Cell mm	Conc. g/L
x	x	10	2.35
268	257	10	1.18
x	x	10	0.0235

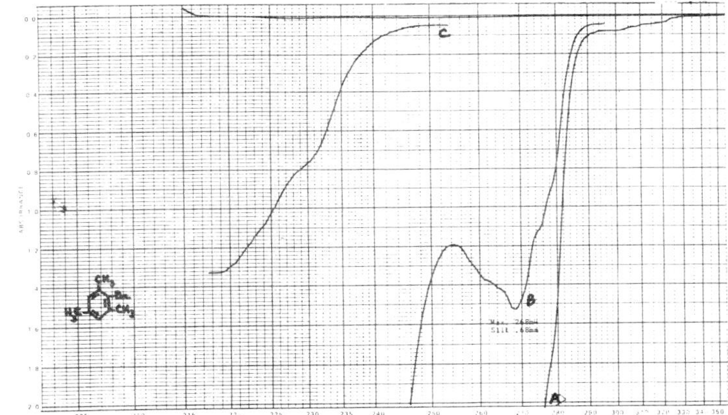

p-BROMO-α,α,α-TRIFLUOROTOLUENE

388

$C_7H_4BrF_3$

Mol. Wt. 225.01

B.P. 154-155°C

Solvent: Methanol

λ Max. mμ	a_m	Cell mm	Conc. g/L
271.5	334	20	0.100
261	567	20	0.100
255	507	20	0.100
223	16200	1	0.100

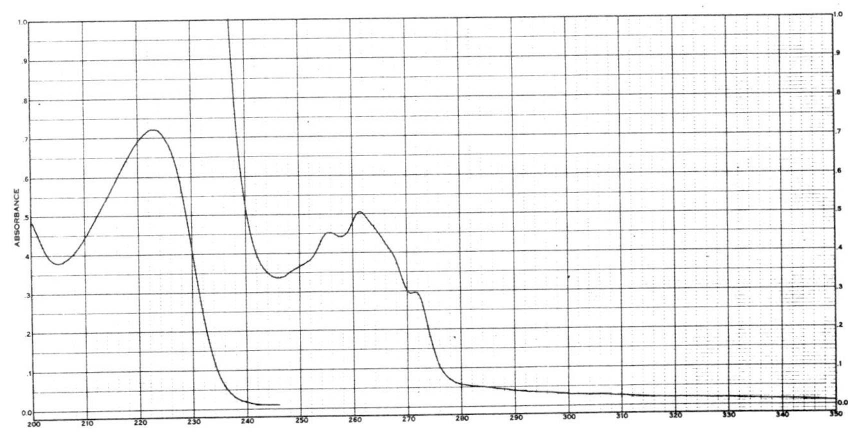

1-BROMO-2-FLUOROBENZENE 389

C_6H_4BrF

Mol. Wt. 199.04

Solvent: Methanol

λ Max. mμ	a_m	Cell mm	Conc. g/L
271	1130	10	0.106
264.5	1200	10	0.106
258	815	10	0.106
209.5	9200	10	0.0106

1-BROMO-3-FLUOROBENZENE 390

C_6H_4BrF

Mol. Wt. 175.01

Solvent: Cyclohexane

λ Max. mμ	a_m	Cell mm	Conc. g/L
x	x	10	2.216
272.5	1080	10	0.1330
266	1150	10	0.1330
258.5	730	10	0.1330
213	8070	10	0.0133

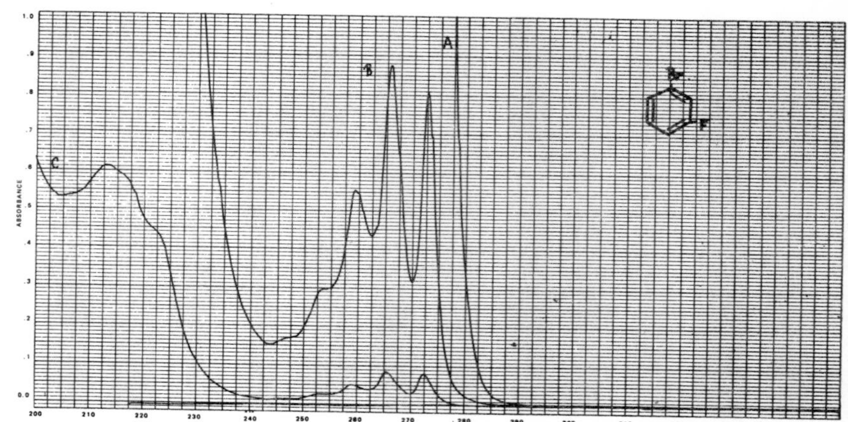

1-BROMO-4-FLUOROBENZENE 391

C_6H_4BrF

Mol. Wt. 175.00

B.P. 151-153°C

Solvent: Methanol

λ Max. mμ	a_m	Cell mm	Conc. g/L
277	718	5	0.1900
267	855	5	0.1900
263	628	5	0.1900
210	7040	1	0.1900

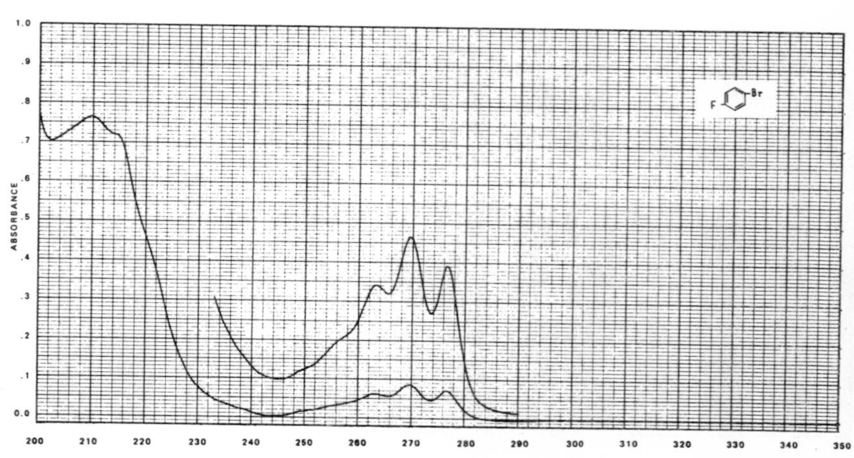

1-BROMO-2-CHLOROBENZENE

392

C_6H_4BrCl

Mol. Wt. 191.47

Solvent: Methanol

λ Max. mμ	a_m	Cell mm	Conc. g/L
277.5	191	10	0.480
269.5	241	10	0.480
262	192	10	0.480
256	151	10	0.480
x	x	10	0.012

1-BROMO-3-CHLOROBENZENE

393

C_6H_4BrCl

Mol. Wt. 191.46

B.P. 81-82°C/20mm

Solvent: Methanol

λ Max. mμ	a_m	Cell mm	Conc. g/L
278.5	293	5	0.572
271	398	5	0.572
263.5	272	5	0.572
257	179	5	0.572
249	146	5	0.572

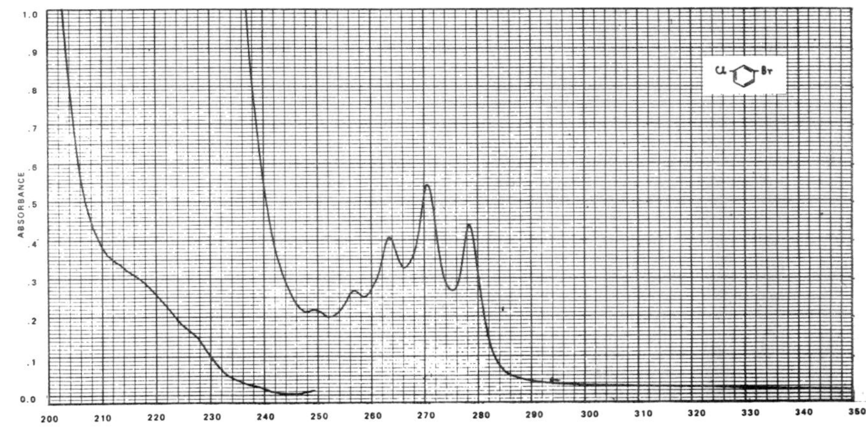

1-BROMO-4-CHLOROBENZENE

394

C_6H_4BrCl

Mol. Wt. 191.46

Solvent: Methanol

λ Max. mμ	a_m	Cell mm	Conc. g/L
280.5	251	20	0.100
272	348	20	0.100
264.5	305	20	0.100
258	249	20	0.100
224	12600	1	0.100

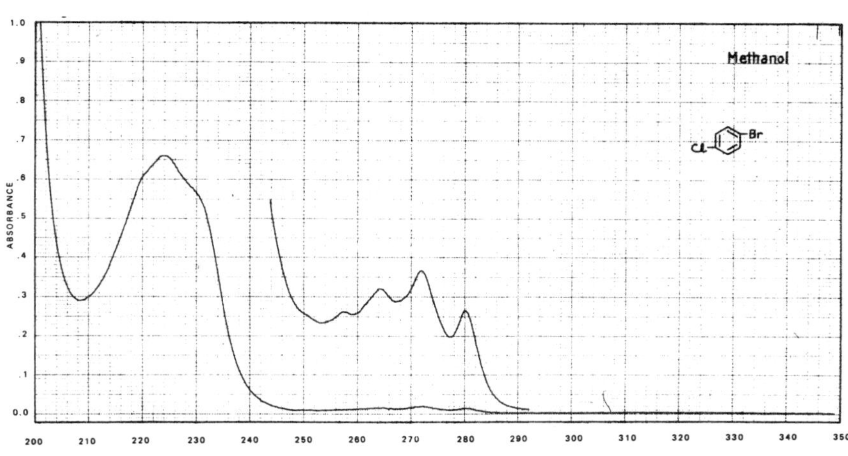

α,m-DIBROMOTOLUENE 395

$C_7H_6Br_2$

Mol. Wt. 249.93

M.P. 41-43°C

Solvent: Cyclohexane

λ Max. mμ	a_m	Cell mm	Conc. g/L
275	490	5	0.500
204	3685	1	0.0500

o-DIBROMOBENZENE 396

$C_6H_4Br_2$

Mol. Wt. 235.92

Solvent: Methanol

λ Max. mμ	a_m	Cell mm	Conc. g/L
278	183	10	0.315
270	255	10	0.315
x	x	1	0.0157

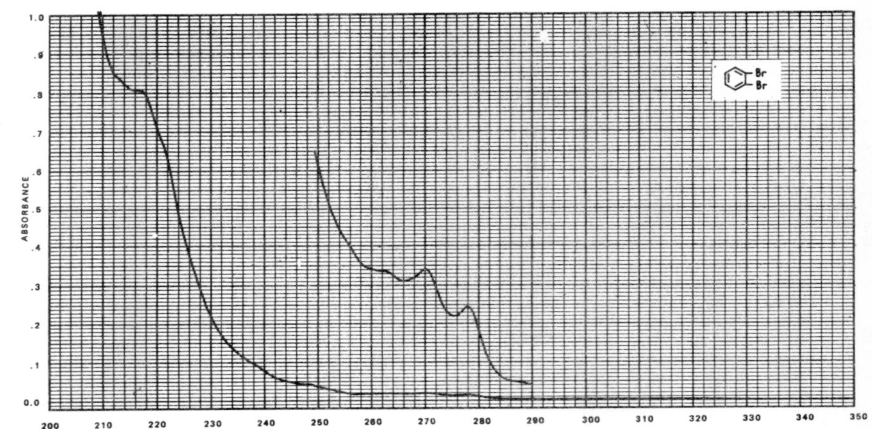

m-DIBROMOBENZENE 397

$C_6H_4Br_2$

Mol. Wt. 235.92

M.P. -7 to -5°C

Solvent: Methanol

λ Max. mμ	a_m	Cell mm	Conc. g/L
279	285	10	0.3620
271.5	375	10	0.3620
264	290	10	0.3620
257.5	209	10	0.3620
x	x	1	0.3620

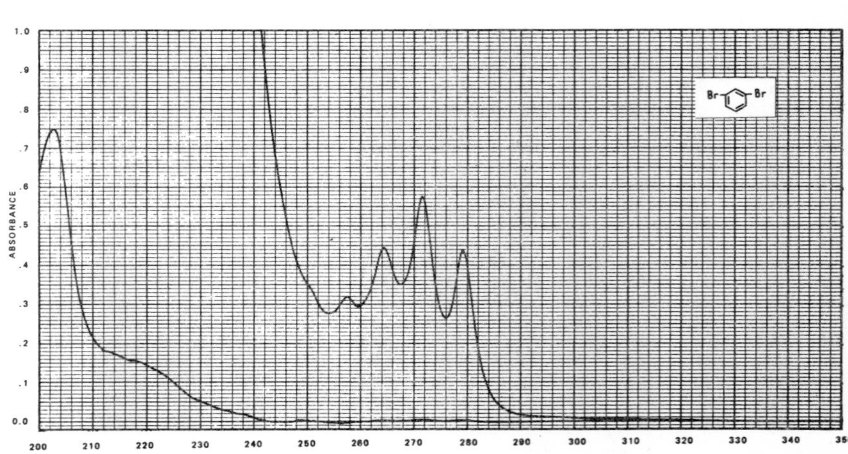

p-DIBROMOBENZENE 398

$C_6H_4Br_2$
Mol. Wt. 235.92
M.P. 86.9°C B.P. 218-219°C/760mm
Solvent: Methanol

λ Max. mμ	a_m	Cell mm	Conc. g/L
281	210	10	0.60
272.5	333	10	0.60
264.5	326	10	0.60
257.5	288	10	0.60
226.5	14000	10	0.01

4-BROMOBIPHENYL 399

$C_{12}H_9Br$
Mol. Wt. 233.12
Solvent: Cyclohexane

λ Max. mμ	a_m	Cell mm	Conc. g/L
x	x	10	2.00
255	26100	10	0.010

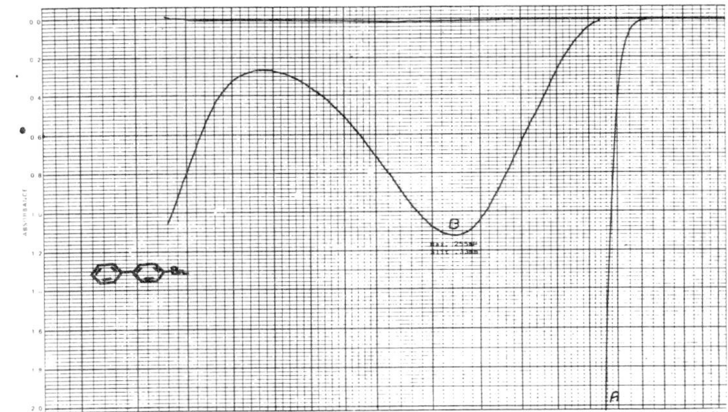

1-BROMONAPHTHALENE 400

$C_{10}H_7Br$
Mol. Wt. 207.08
B.P. 122-125°C/5mm
Solvent: Methanol

λ Max. mμ	a_m	Cell mm	Conc. g/L
319	262	10	0.435
314.5	447	10	0.435
284	8670	5	0.0435
274	7290	5	0.0435
223	96900	1	0.0174

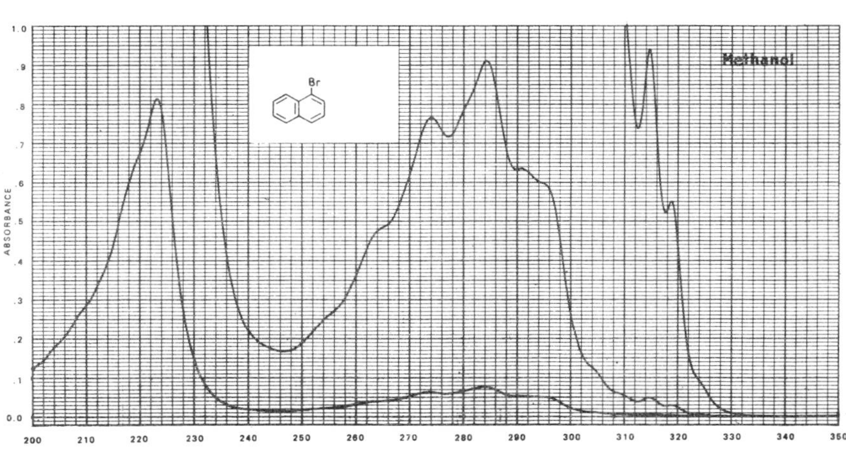

2-BROMONAPHTHALENE

401

$C_{10}H_7Br$

Mol. Wt. 207.08

M.P. 55-56°C

Solvent: Methanol

λ Max. mμ	a_m	Cell mm	Conc. g/L
320.5	229	10	0.500
306.5	347	10	0.500
288	3390	2	0.100
277	5220	2	0.100
226.5	7760	1	0.0200

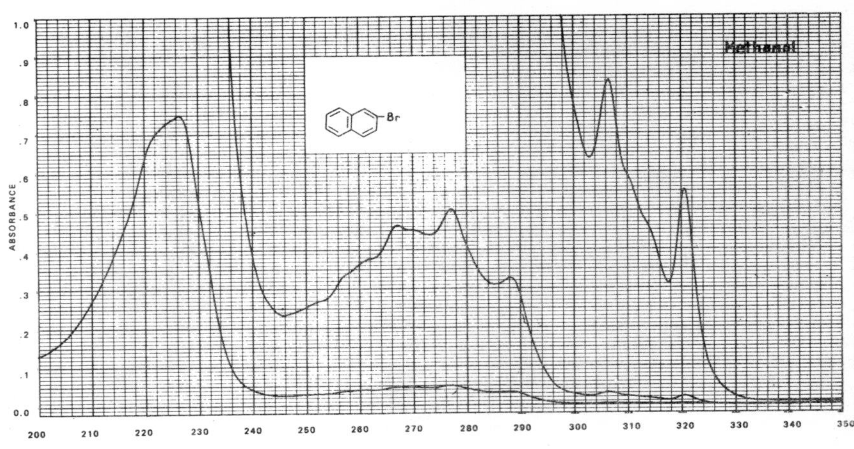

1,4-DIBROMONAPHTHALENE

402

$C_{10}H_6Br_2$

Mol. Wt. 285.98

Solvent: Methanol

λ Max. mμ	a_m	Cell mm	Conc. g/L
304	7350	5	0.0500
293.5	10400	5	0.0500
284	8350	5	0.0500
224.5	56200	1	0.0500

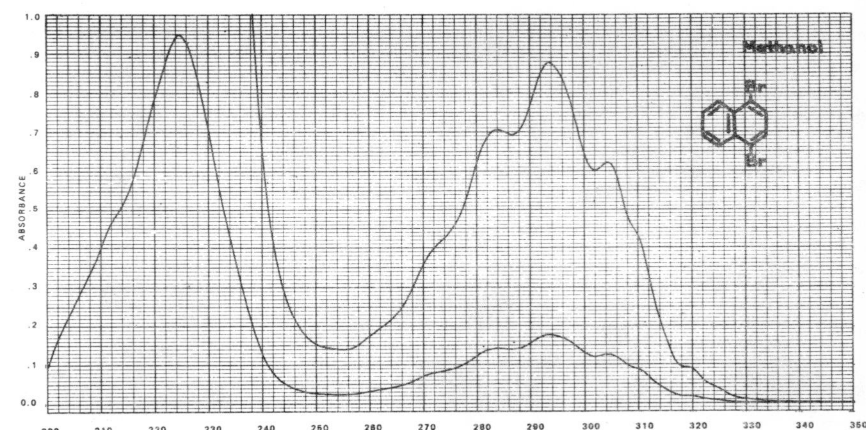

λ Max. mμ	a_m	Cell mm	Conc. g/L

THE IODINATED HYDROCARBONS

Aliphatic Compounds

Although there are no spectra in this volume for compounds 403 through 423, the iodinated aliphatic hydrocarbons do display an absorption maxima in the near UV region near 254 $m\mu$.

The table provided below lists six compounds that were recently determined at the Sadtler Laboratories and two references from the literature.

Compound	$\lambda_{max}(\epsilon_{max})$	Solvent	Spectrum
Iodomethane	253 (375)	Methanol	Sadtler
Iodomethane	259 (400)	Hexane	Lit.
Iodoethane	255 (400)	Methanol	Sadtler
Iodopropane	254 (733)	Methanol	Sadtler
1-Iodo-1-methylmethane	263 (525)	Heptane	Lit.
1-Iodo-2-methylethane	253 (754)	Methanol	Sadtler
Iodononane	254 (607)	Methanol	Sadtler
1,6-Diiodohexane	255 (1980)	Methanol	Sadtler

Aromatic Compounds

The iodine substituent has a strong auxochromic effect on the comparable bands of benzene, increasing their intensity by a factor of 2 - 3. The fine structure in the region from 250 $m\mu$ to 270 $m\mu$ displays the same loss of resolution that was noted in the spectrum of bromobenzene.

The following table lists the wavelength and ϵ_{max} for the two major bands of benzene and a series of iodinated aromatic compounds.

Compound	$\lambda_{max}(\epsilon_{max})$	$\lambda_{max}(\epsilon_{max})$	Solvent	Spectrum
Benzene	204 (7900)	256 (200)		Lit. (1)
Iodobenzene	226 (11700)	256* (734)	Methanol	426
m-Diiodobenzene	226 (24800)	260* (1363)	Methanol	436
p-Diiodobenzene	226* (13000)	----------	Methanol	437
2-Iodotoluene	228 (13000)	258 (786)	Cyclohexane	427
3-Iodotoluene	229 (13400)	260 (781)	Cyclohexane	428
4-Iodotoluene	228 (16100)	258 (774)	Methanol	429

* Shoulder

(2-IODOETHYL) BENZENE 424

C_8H_9I

Mol. Wt. 232.07

Solvent: Methanol

λ Max. mμ	a_m	Cell mm	Conc. g/L
257.5	1880	10	0.100
252.4	18700	10	0.100
x	x	0.5	0.100

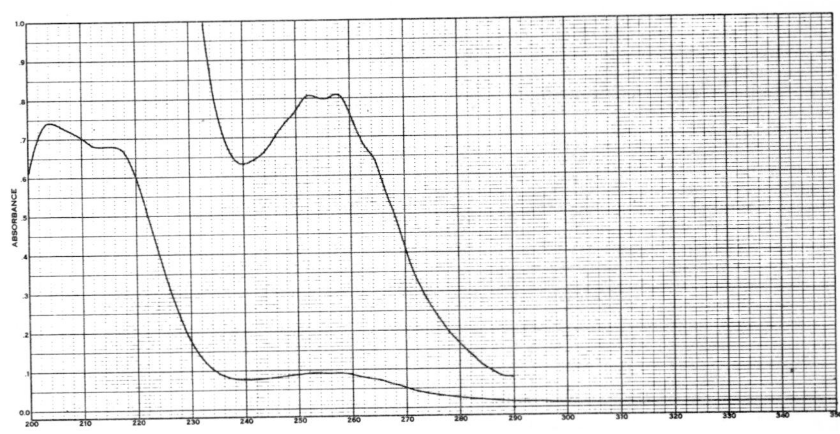

α-IODOTOLUENE 425

C_7H_7I

Mol. Wt. 218.04

M.P. 23-24°C

λ Max. mμ	a_m	Cell mm	Conc. g/L

No pure sample available.

IODOBENZENE 426

C_6H_5I

Mol. Wt. 204.01

B.P. 186-188°C

Solvent: Methanol

λ Max. mμ	a_m	Cell mm	Conc. g/L
250	732	10	0.139
225.5	11700	1	0.139

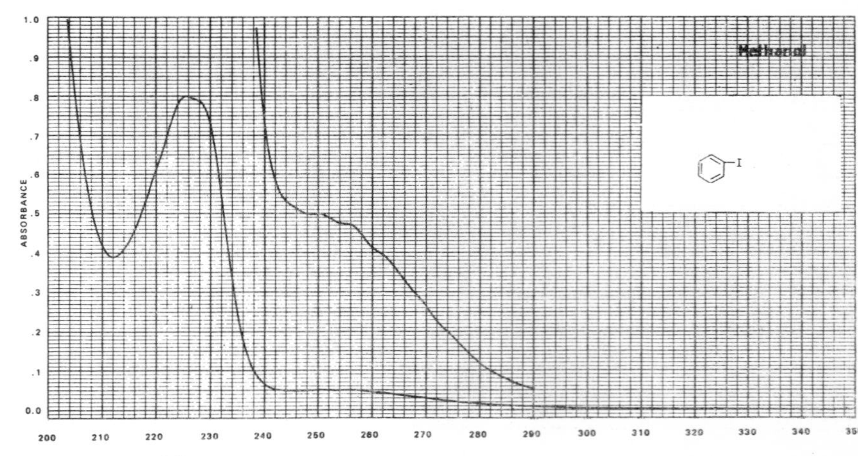

o-IODOTOLUENE

427

C_7H_7I

Mol. Wt. 218.05

Solvent: Cyclohexane

λ Max. mμ	a_m	Cell mm	Conc. g/L
x	x	10	2.16
276	496	10	0.432
258.5	786	10	0.432
233	12900	10	0.0216
228	13000	10	0.0216

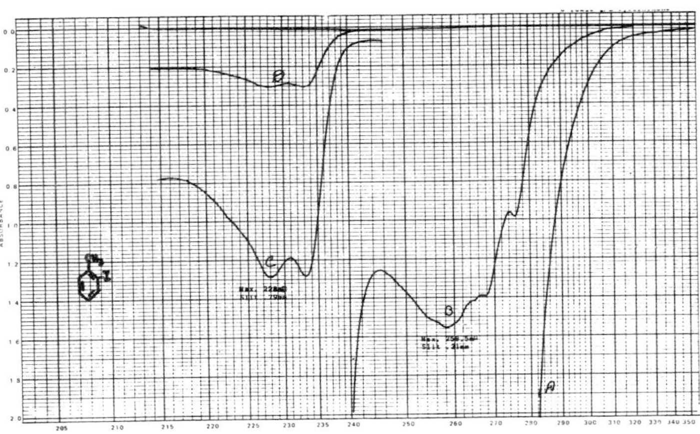

m-IODOTOLUENE

428

C_7H_7I

Mol. Wt. 218.05

Solvent: Cyclohexane

λ Max. mμ	a_m	Cell mm	Conc. g/L
x	x	10	2.86
277.5	496	10	0.286
269	701	10	0.286
260	781	10	0.286
229	13400	10	0.0148

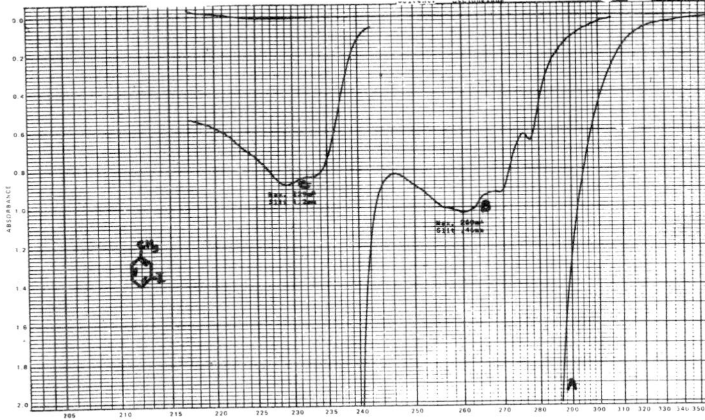

p-IODOTOLUENE

429

C_7H_7I

Mol. Wt. 218.04

Solvent: Methanol

λ Max. mμ	a_m	Cell mm	Conc. g/L
x	x	10	2.00
256	774	10	0.20
232	15100	10	0.020
227.5	16100	10	0.020

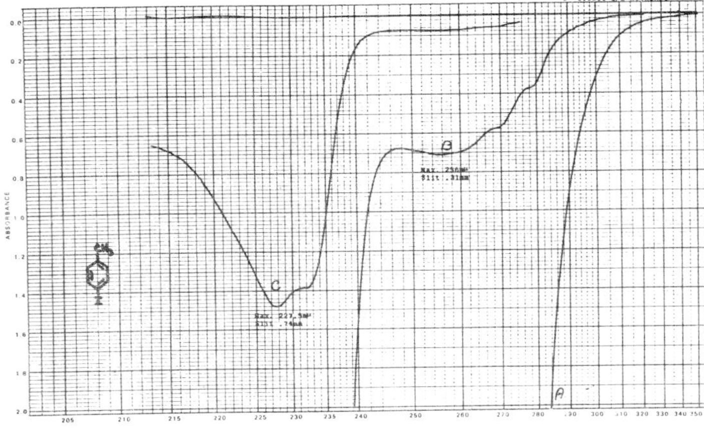

2-IODO-p-XYLENE

C_8H_9I

Mol. Wt. 232.07

B.P. 113-114°C/20mm

Solvent: Methanol

λ Max. mμ	a_m	Cell mm	Conc. g/L
280.5	1480	10	0.100
272.5	1590	10	0.100
265	1430	10	0.100
227	17400	1	0.100

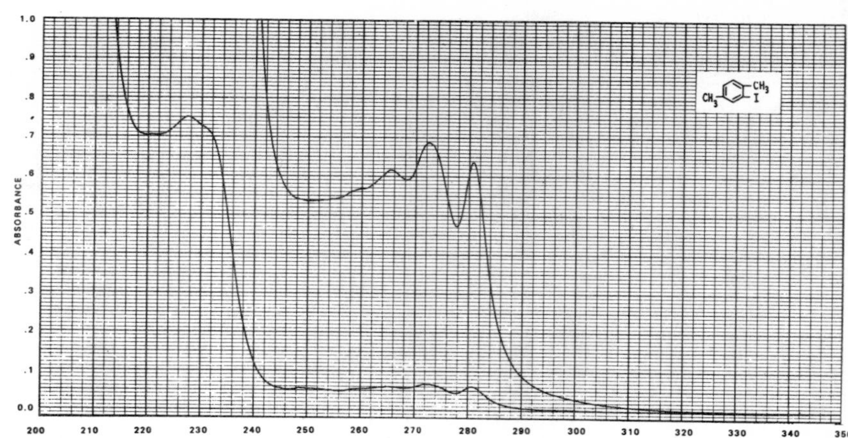

m-IODO-a,a,a-TRIFLUOROTOLUENE

431

$C_7H_4F_3I$

Mol. Wt. 272.01

Solvent: Methanol

λ Max. mμ	a_m	Cell mm	Conc. g/L
278	594	5	0.440
271	804	5	0.440
264	823	5	0.440
232	10600	2	0.088

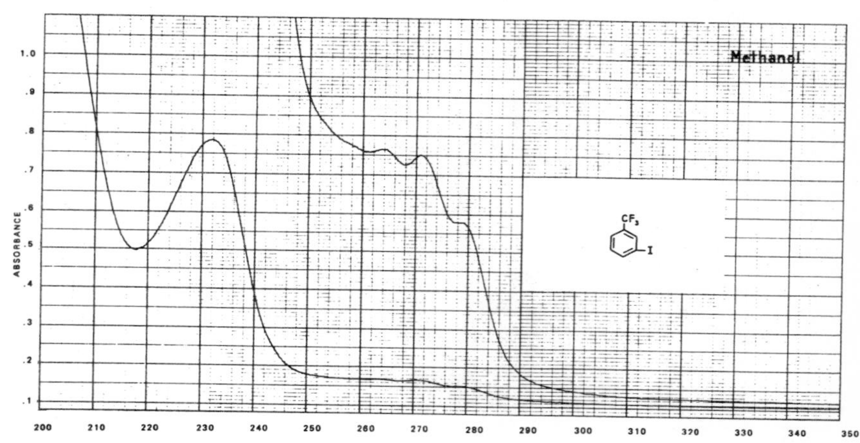

1-FLUORO-4-IODOBENZENE

432

C_6H_4FI

Mol. Wt. 222.00

Solvent: Methanol

λ Max. mμ	a_m	Cell mm	Conc. g/L
270	868	10	0.142
264.5	875	10	0.142
223	9540	1	0.142

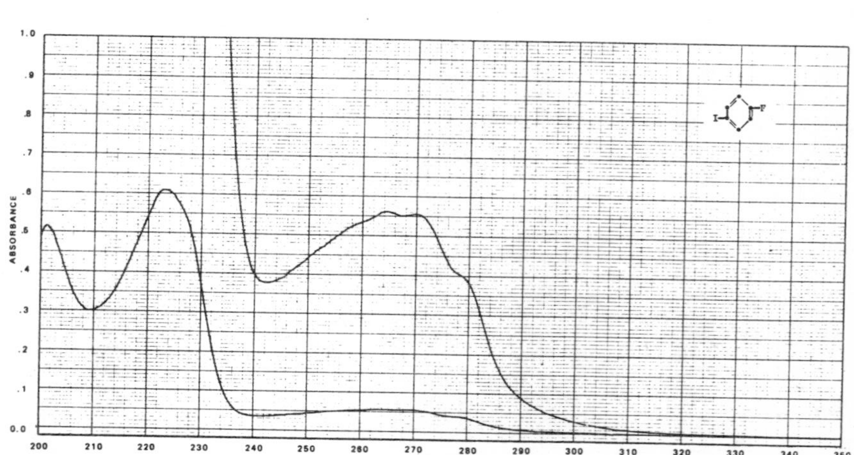

1-CHLORO-2-IODOBENZENE

433

C_6H_4ClI

Mol. Wt. 238.46

B.P. 119-120°C/27mm

Solvent: Methanol

λ Max. mμ	a_m	Cell mm	Conc. g/L
276	2970	1	0.227
224	8840	1	0.227

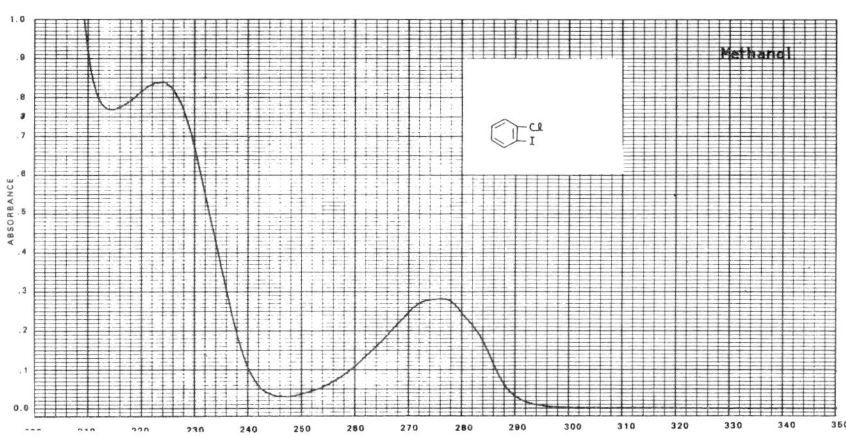

1-BROMO-2-IODOBENZENE

434

C_6H_4BrI

Mol. Wt. 282.92

Solvent: Cyclohexane

λ Max. mμ	a_m	Cell mm	Conc. g/L
x	x	10	2.46
270	612	10	0.492
263.5	667	10	0.492
239	1210	10	0.246
234	1160	10	0.246

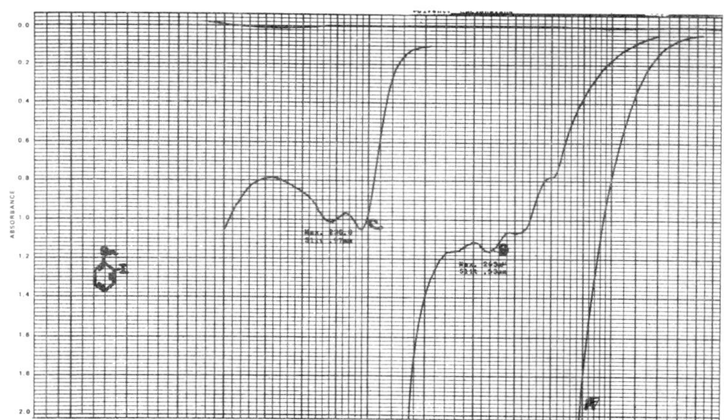

1-BROMO-4-IODOBENZENE

435

C_6H_4BrI

Mol. Wt. 282.91

M.P. 91-92°C

Solvent: Methanol

λ Max. mμ	a_m	Cell mm	Conc. g/L
238.5	18700	1	0.100

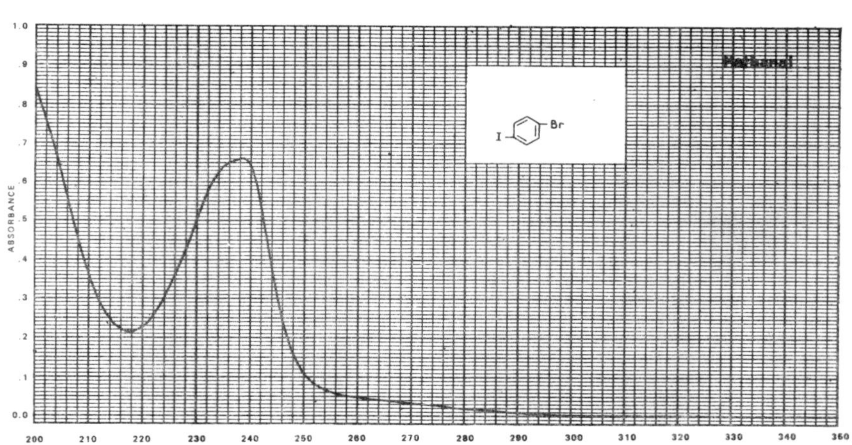

m-DIIODOBENZENE

436

$C_6H_4I_2$

Mol. Wt. 329.91

M.P. 35-37°C

Solvent: Methanol

λ Max. mμ	a_m	Cell mm	Conc. g/L
225.5	24800	1	0.121
204.5	16200	1	0.121

p-DIIODOBENZENE

437

$C_6H_4I_2$

Mol. Wt. 329.91

M.P. 127-129°C

Solvent: Methanol

λ Max. mμ	a_m	Cell mm	Conc. g/L
x	x	1	0.100

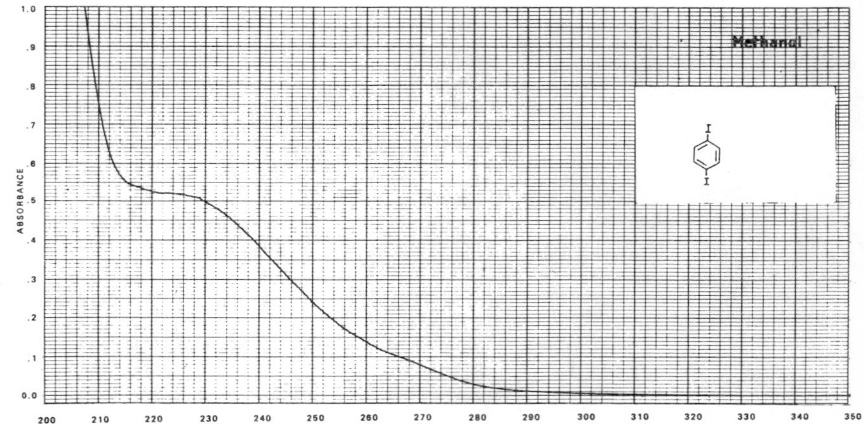

1-IODONAPHTHALENE

438

$C_{10}H_7I$

Mol. Wt. 254.07

B.P. 162-164°C/19mm

Solvent: Methanol

λ Max. mμ	a_m	Cell mm	Conc. g/L
316	642	10	0.219
299	5530	5	0.0430
287.5	7850	5	0.0430
278	6760	5	0.0430
224.5	58300	1	0.0430

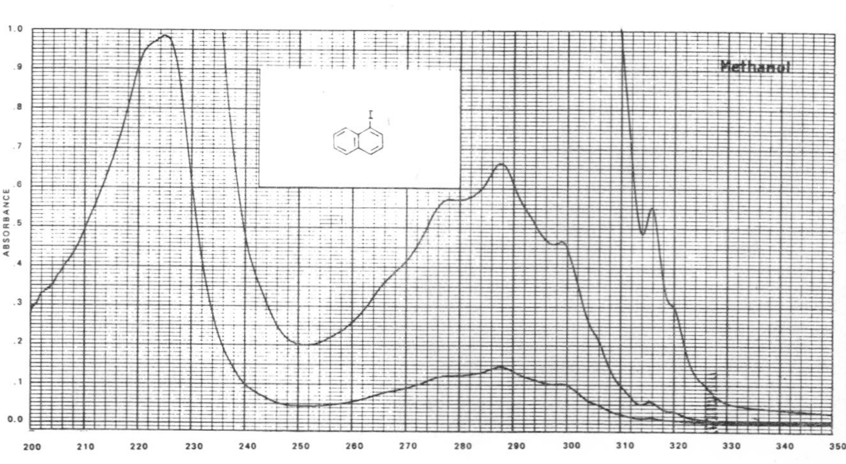

THE PRIMARY AMINES

Aliphatic Compounds

The aliphatic and non-conjugated olefinic primary amines do not display absorption in the near UV region above 200 mμ. As a consequence there are no spectra in this volume for compounds 439 through 475.

Aromatic Compounds

Substitution of benzene and the aromatic hydrocarbons by a primary amine group results in a red shift to longer wavelength by about 25 mμ. This bathochromic effect is almost exactly reversed upon the addition of acid to the solution, resulting in the formation of the anilinium cation with an attendant blue shift to lower wavelength by about 25 mμ for the major bands in the spectrum.

A table of reference compounds, their amino derivatives and the amino cationic forms is given below.

Compound	$\lambda_{max}(\epsilon_{max})$	$\lambda_{max}(\epsilon_{max})$	Solvent	Spectrum
Benzene	204 (7900)	256 (200)	Hexane	Lit.
Aniline	230 (8600)	280 (1430)	Water	Lit.
Anilinium cation	203 (7500)	254 (160)	Water/acid	Lit.
Toluene	208 (4434)	261 (238)	Methanol	133
3-Aminotoluene	236 (8900)	286 (1460)	Methanol	489
3-Aminotoluene (cation)	207 * (8050)	261 (283)	Methanol/HCl	489

* Shoulder or inflection

BENZYLAMINE 476

C_7H_9N

Mol. Wt. 107.15

B.P. 185°C (lit.)

Solvent: Methanol

λ Max. mμ	a_m	Cell mm	Conc. g/L
x	x	10	2.0520
248	1490	10	0.1231
x	x	10	0.0246

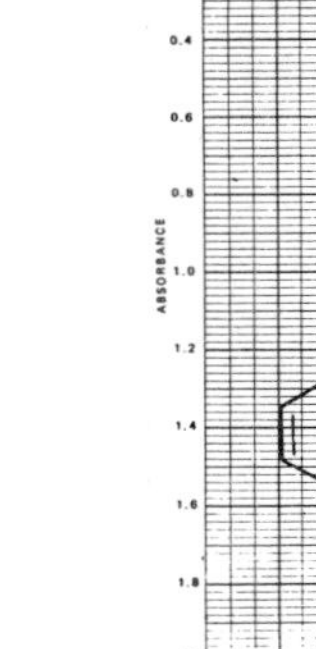

PHENETHYLAMINE 477

$C_8H_{11}N$

Mol. Wt. 121.18

B.P. 195 (198) (lit.)

Solvent: Cyclohexane

λ Max. mμ	a_m	Cell mm	Conc. g/L
x	x	10	1.56
268	169	10	0.780
264.5	174	10	0.780
261	221	10	0.780
258.5	228	10	0.780
253	196	10	0.780
248	152	10	0.780
x	x	10	0.078
x	x	10	0.039

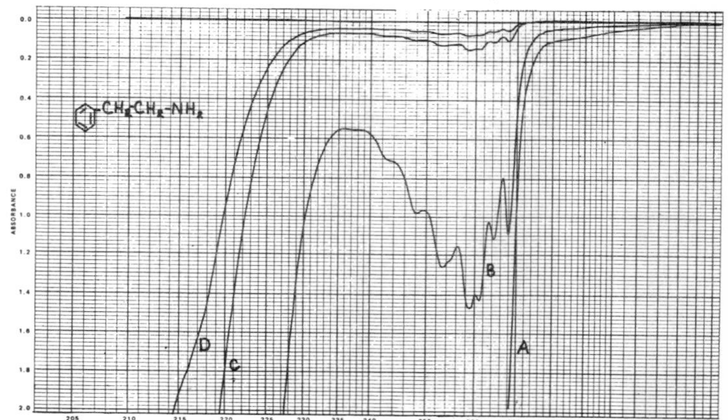

DL-α-METHYLBENZYLAMINE 478

$C_8H_{11}N$

Mol. Wt. 121.18

B.P. 69-70°C/10mm

Solvent: Methanol

λ Max. mμ	a_m	Cell mm	Conc. g/L
262.5	181	10	0.404
257	257	10	0.404
251	280	10	0.404
246.5	285	10	0.404
205	8430	1	0.0808

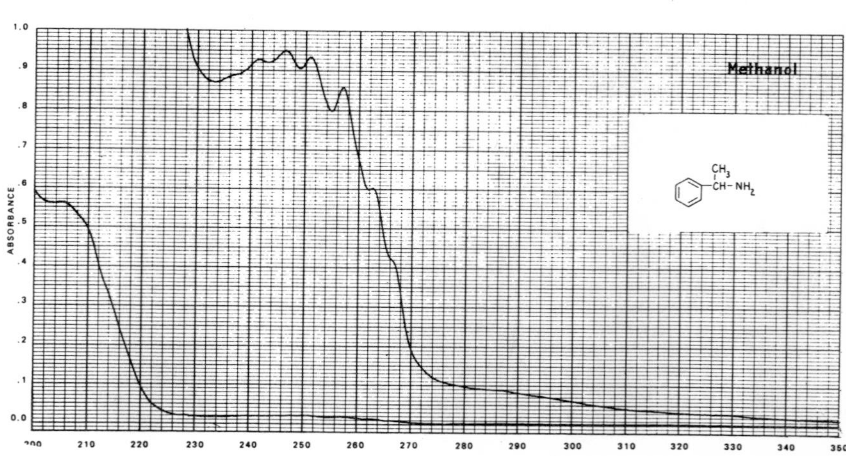

β-METHYLPHENETHYLAMINE

479

$C_9H_{13}N$

Mol. Wt. 135.21

Solvent: Methanol

λ Max. mμ	a_m	Cell mm	Conc. g/L
267	124	10	0.416
263.5	113	10	0.416
257.5	189	10	0.416
252	154	10	0.416
247	111	10	0.416

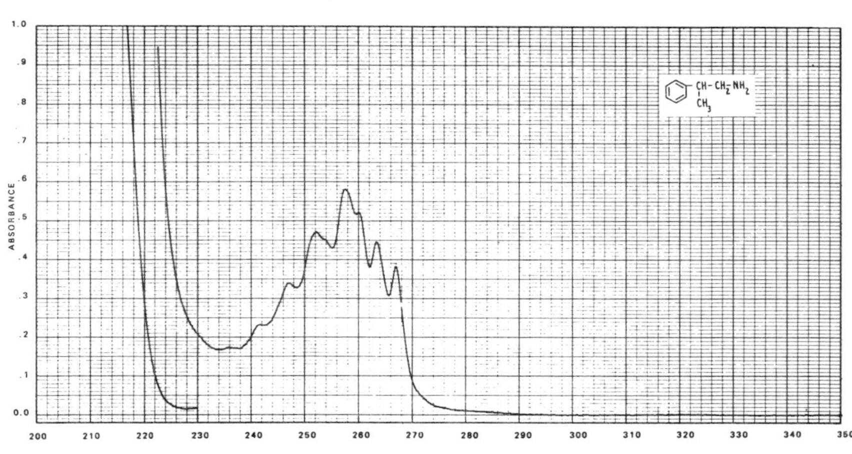

α,α-DIMETHYLBENZYLAMINE

480

$C_9H_{13}N$

Mol. Wt. 135.21

Solvent: Methanol

λ Max. mμ	a_m	Cell mm	Conc. g/L
x	x	10	2.460
267.5	121	10	0.4920
263.5	184	10	0.4920
257.5	243	10	0.4920
252	214	10	0.4920
247	182	10	0.4920
x	x	10	0.0984

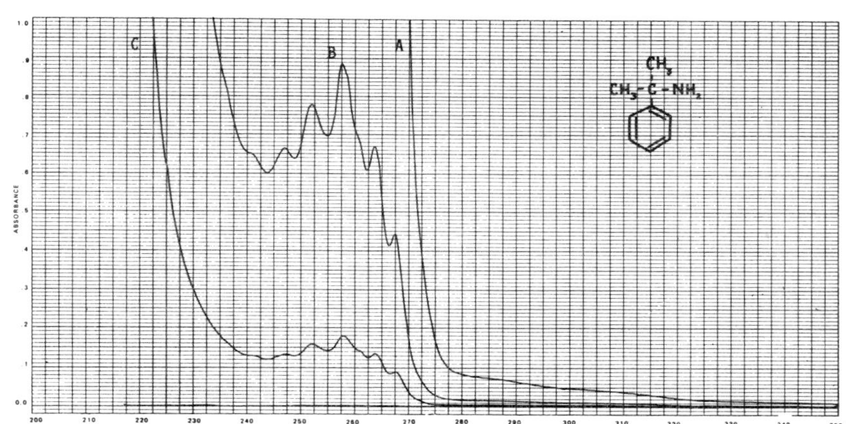

3-PHENYLPROPYLAMINE

481

$C_9H_{13}N$

Mol. Wt. 135.21

Solvent: Methanol

λ Max. mμ	a_m	Cell mm	Conc. g/L
268	284	20	0.100
259	366	20	0.100
253.5	329	20	0.100
x	x	1	0.100

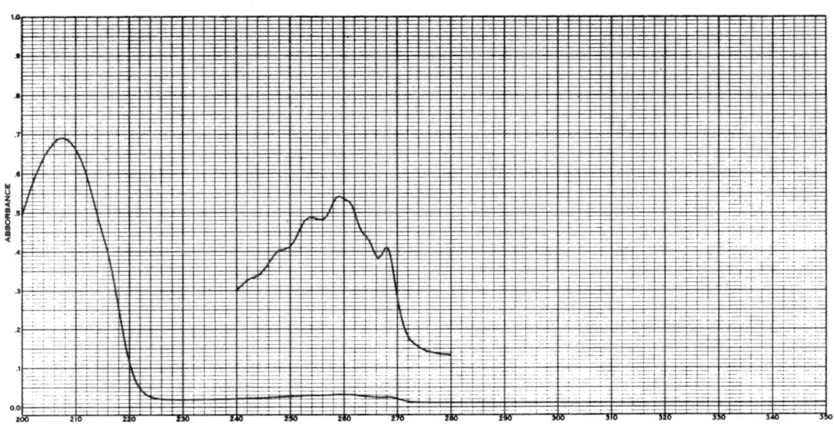

4-PHENYLBUTYLAMINE

482

$C_{10}H_{15}N$

Mol. Wt. 149.24

B.P. 114-115°C/14mm (lit.)

Solvent: Methanol

λ Max. mμ	a_m	Cell mm	Conc. g/L
268	152	10	0.468
264	147	10	0.468
261	194	10	0.468
258.5	192	10	0.468
253	169	10	0.468

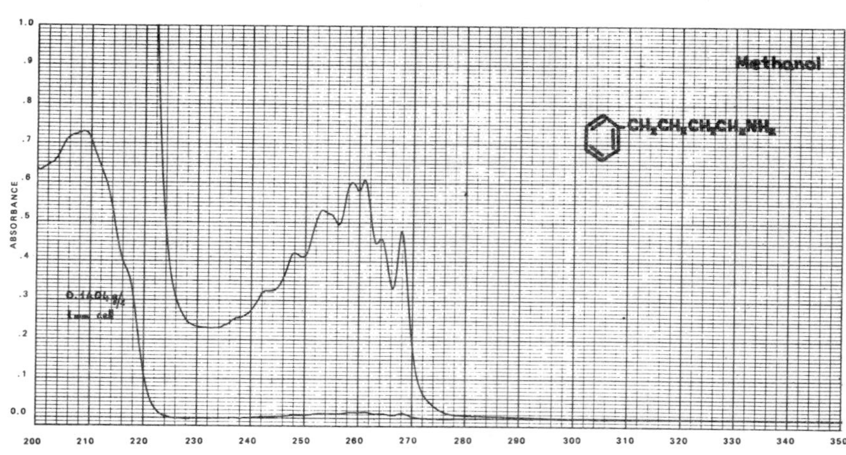

o-METHYLBENZYLAMINE

483

$C_8H_{11}N$

Mol. Wt. 121.18

Solvent: Cyclohexane

λ Max. mμ	a_m	Cell mm	Conc. g/L
x	x	10	2.132
270	101	10	1.066
255.5	164	10	1.066
x	x	10	0.1066
x	x	10	0.053

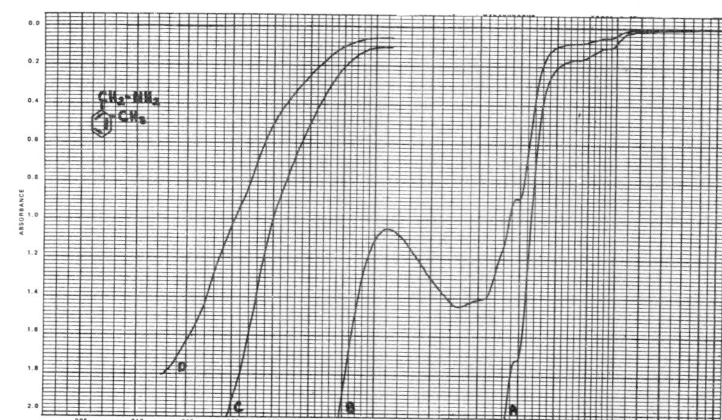

m-METHYLBENZYLAMINE

484

$C_8H_{11}N$

Mol. Wt. 121.18

Solvent: Cyclohexane

λ Max. mμ	a_m	Cell mm	Conc. g/L
297	18.7	10	1.812
274	254	10	0.362
264	378	10	0.362
259	395	10	0.362
254	383	10	0.362
x	x	10	0.036

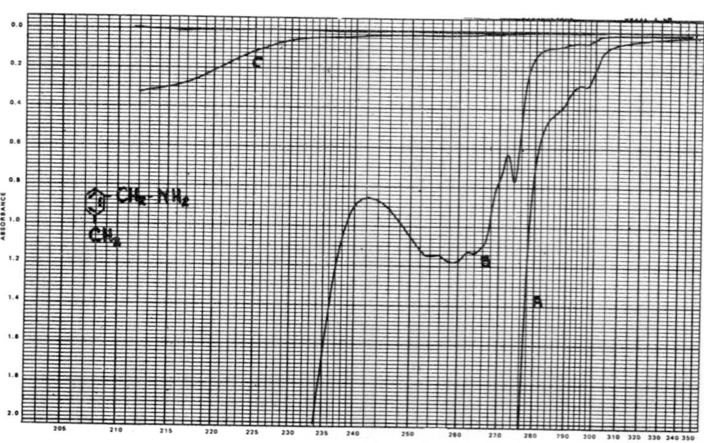

p-METHYLBENZYLAMINE

$C_8H_{11}N$

Mol. Wt. 121.18

Solvent: Methanol

λ Max. mμ	a_m	Cell mm	Conc. g/L
272.5	313	5	0.419
264	374	5	0.419
258.5	326	5	0.419
212	7880	1	0.0838

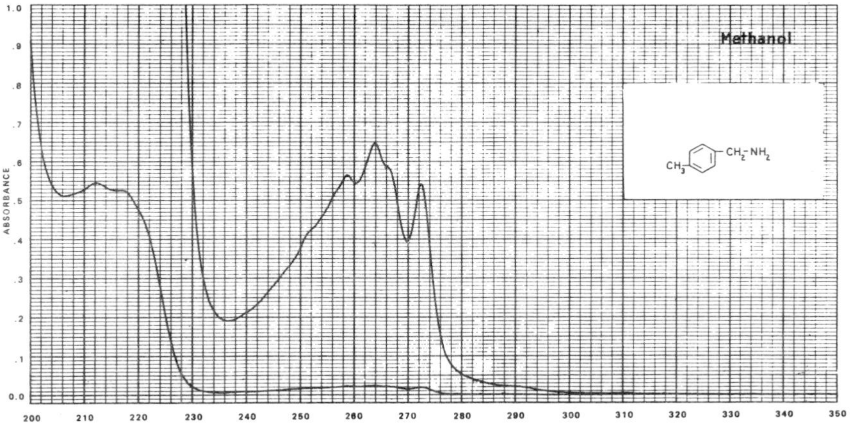

p-METHYLBENZYLAMINE

$C_8H_{11}N$

Mol. Wt. 121.18

Solvent: Methanol HCl

λ Max. mμ	a_m	Cell mm	Conc. g/L
291	78.0	10	0.419
270.5	184	10	0.419
266	210	10	0.419
262	264	10	0.419
255	223	10	0.419

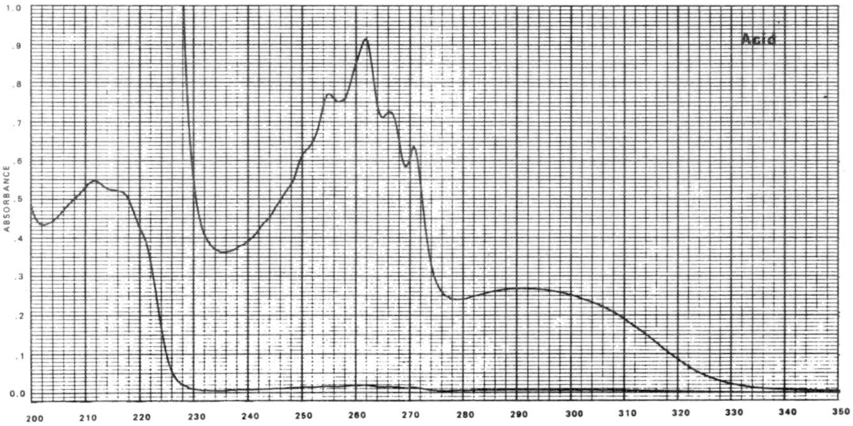

λ Max. mμ	a_m	Cell mm	Conc. g/L

p-ISOPROPYLBENZYLAMINE 486

$C_{10}H_{15}N$
Mol. Wt. 149.24
B.P. 45-46°C/1mm
Solvent: Methanol

λ Max. mμ	a_m	Cell mm	Conc. g/L
271	480	5	0.349
262	693	5	0.349
257.5	694	5	0.349

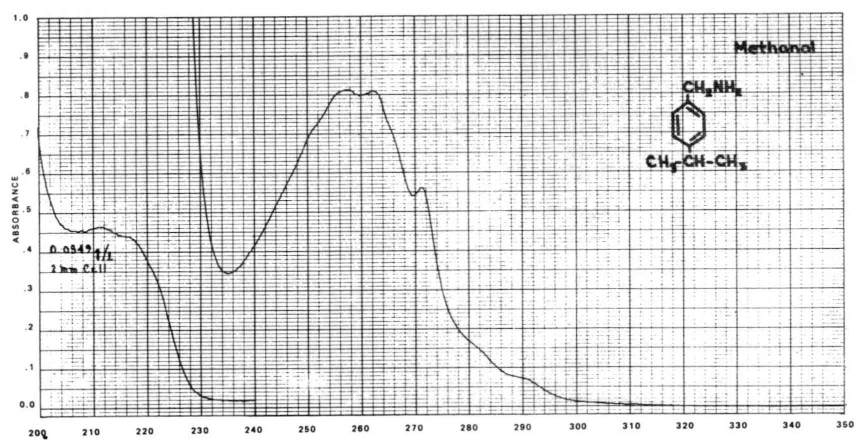

p-ISOPROPYLBENZYLAMINE

$C_{10}H_{15}N$
Mol. Wt. 149.24
B.P. 45-46°C/1mm
Solvent: Methanol HCl

λ Max. mμ	a_m	Cell mm	Conc. g/L
293.5	462	5	0.349
270.5	403	5	0.349
266	393	5	0.349
261	389	5	0.349

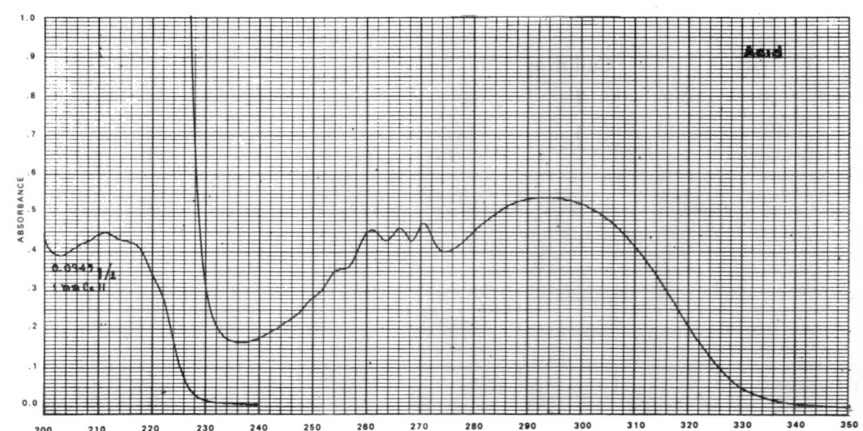

ANILINE 487

C_6H_7N
Mol. Wt. 93.12
Solvent: Cyclohexane

λ Max. mμ	a_m	Cell mm	Conc. g/L
x	x	10	2.31
289	1780	10	0.069
286	1970	10	0.069
282.5	1900	10	0.069
280	1750	10	0.069
233.5	9910	10	0.007

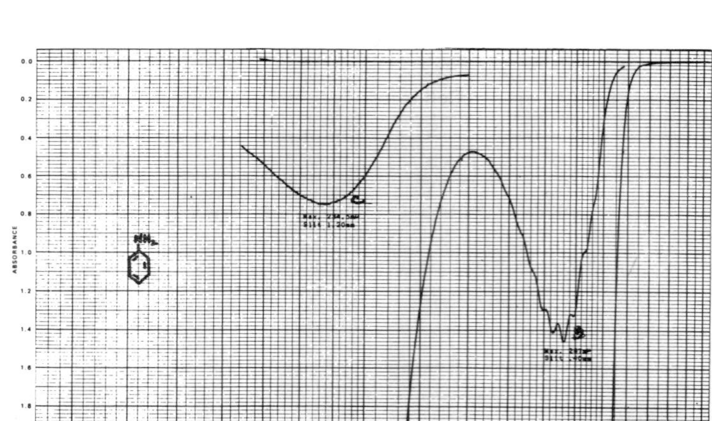

o-TOLUIDINE

C_7H_9N

Mol. Wt. 107.15

B.P. 199.84°C (lit.)

Solvent: Cyclohexane

488

λ Max. mμ	a_m	Cell mm	Conc. g/L
x	x	10	1.804
285	3150	10	0.054
233	11800	10	0.014

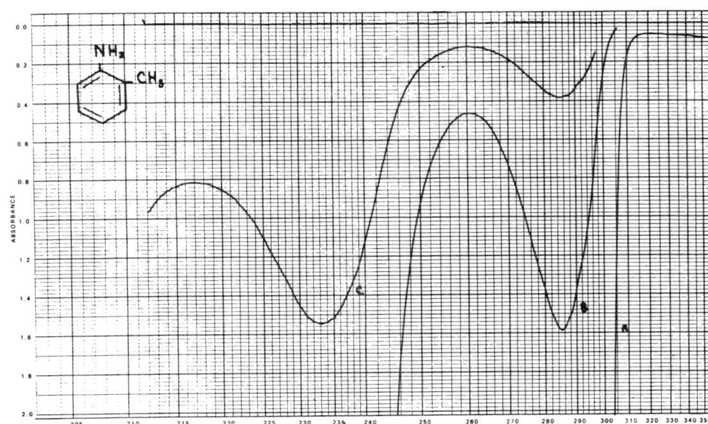

m-TOLUIDINE

C_7H_9N

Mol. Wt. 107.16

B.P. 83-84°C/10mm

Solvent: Methanol

489

λ Max. mμ	a_m	Cell mm	Conc. g/L
286	1460	1	0.446
236	8900	1	0.0892

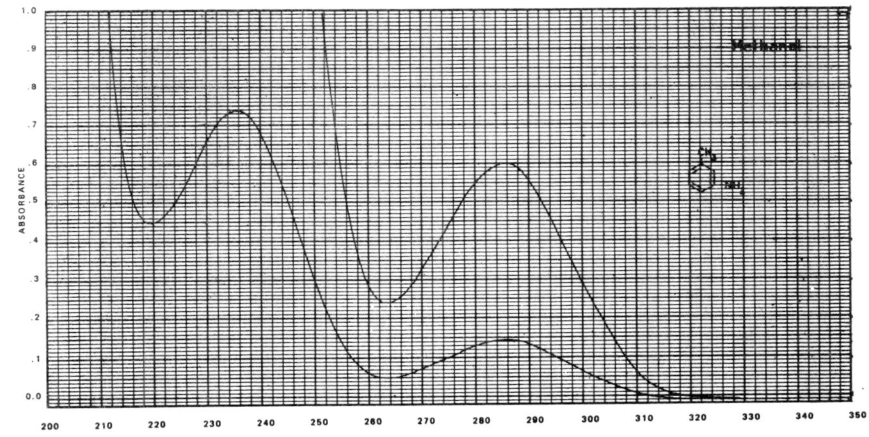

m-TOLUIDINE

C_7H_9N

Mol. Wt. 107.16

B.P. 83-84°C/10mm

Solvent: Methanol HCl

489

λ Max. mμ	a_m	Cell mm	Conc. g/L
267.5	256	5	0.446
260.5	283	5	0.446
x	x	1	0.0892

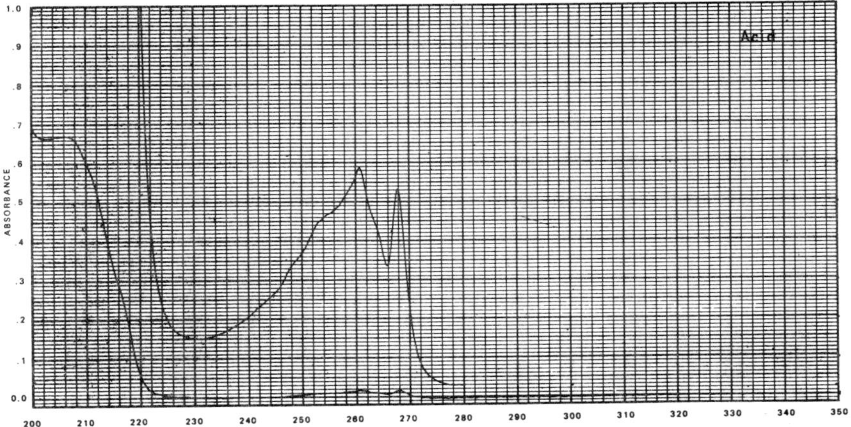

p-TOLUIDINE

490

C_7H_9N

Mol. Wt. 107.15

Solvent: Cyclohexane

λ Max. mμ	a_m	Cell mm	Conc. g/L
x	x	10	2.00
294	1900	10	0.080
291	1930	10	0.080
288	1850	10	0.080
237	9700	10	0.010

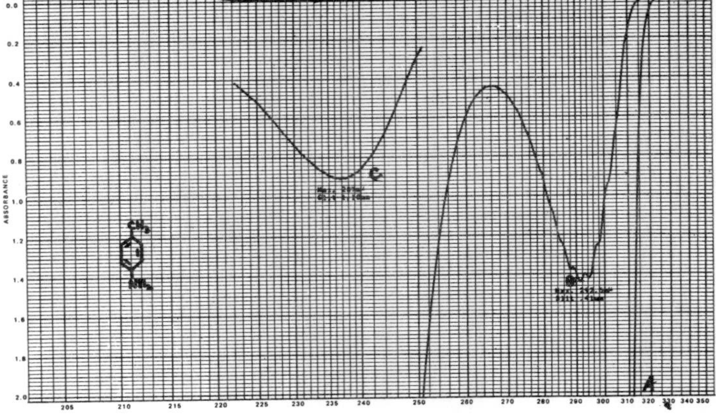

o-ETHYLANILINE

491

$C_8H_{11}N$

Mol. Wt. 121.18

Solvent: Cyclohexane

λ Max. mμ	a_m	Cell mm	Conc. g/L
x	x	10	2.78
284.5	2550	10	0.056
234.5	8340	10	0.017

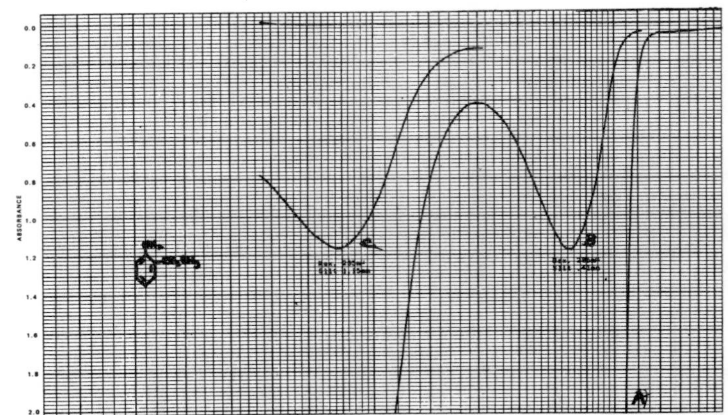

m-ETHYLANILINE

492

$C_8H_{11}N$

Mol. Wt. 121.18

Solvent: Methanol

λ Max. mμ	a_m	Cell mm	Conc. g/L
284	2840	4	0.100
234	12800	0.5	0.100
206.5	20600	0.5	0.100

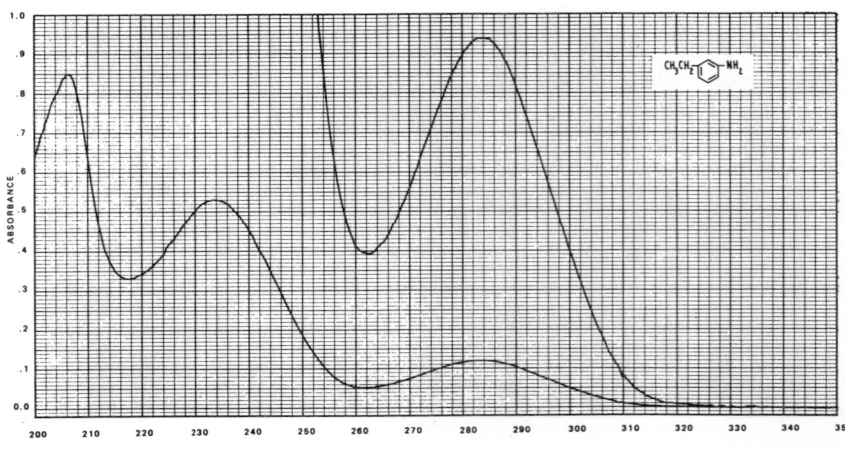

m-ETHYLANILINE

492

$C_8H_{11}N$

Mol. Wt. 121.18

Solvent: Methanol HCl

λ Max. mμ	a_m	Cell mm	Conc. g/L
265.5	443	20	0.100
258	545	20	0.100
250	535	20	0.100
246.5	519	20	0.100
206	6180	1	0.100

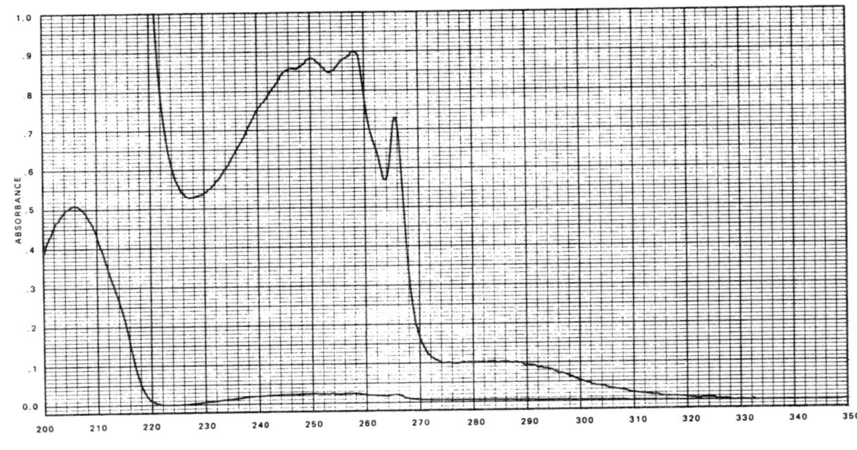

CUMIDINE

493

$C_9H_{13}N$

Mol. Wt. 135.21

Solvent: Methanol

λ Max. mμ	a_m	Cell mm	Conc. g/L
286	1530	5	0.105
232.5	9920	1	0.105

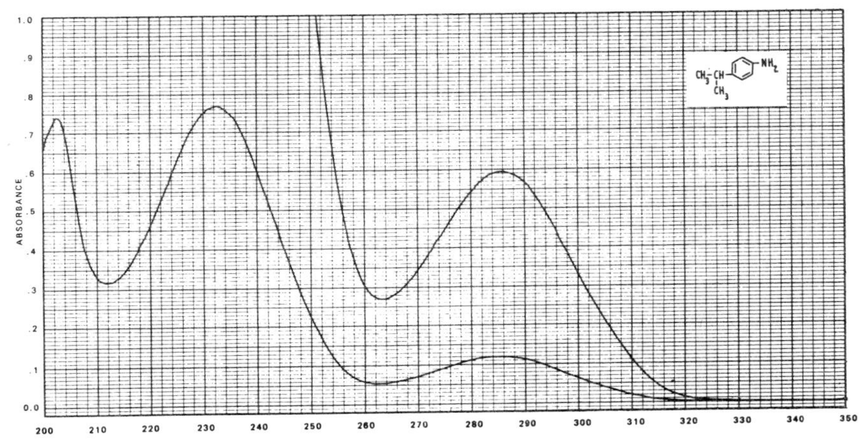

CUMIDINE

493

$C_9H_{13}N$

MOl. Wt. 135.21

Solvent: Methanol HCl

λ Max. mμ	a_m	Cell mm	Conc. g/L
266.5	235	20	0.105
257.5	309	20	0.105
249.5	314	20	0.105
245	315	20	0.105
206	7120	1	0.105

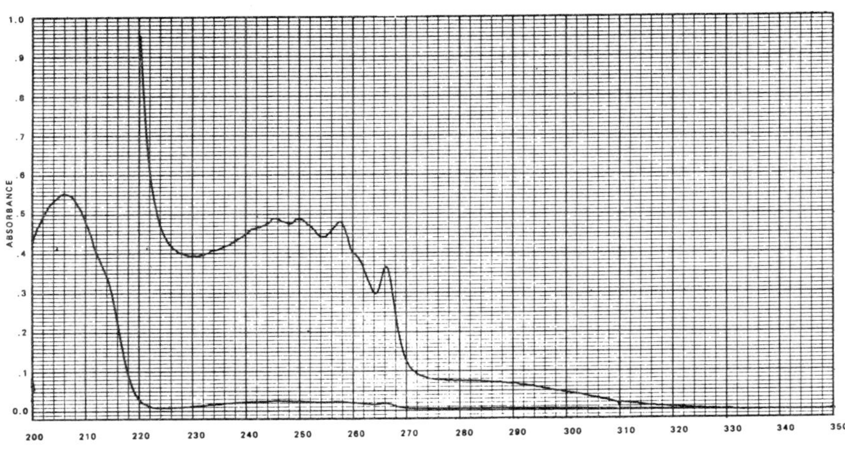

2-(sec-BUTYL)ANILINE

494

$C_{10}H_{15}N$
Mol. Wt. 149.24
Solvent: Cyclohexane

λ Max. mμ	a_m	Cell mm	Conc. g/L
x	x	10	2.660
285.5	2550	10	0.106
234.5	11100	10	0.011

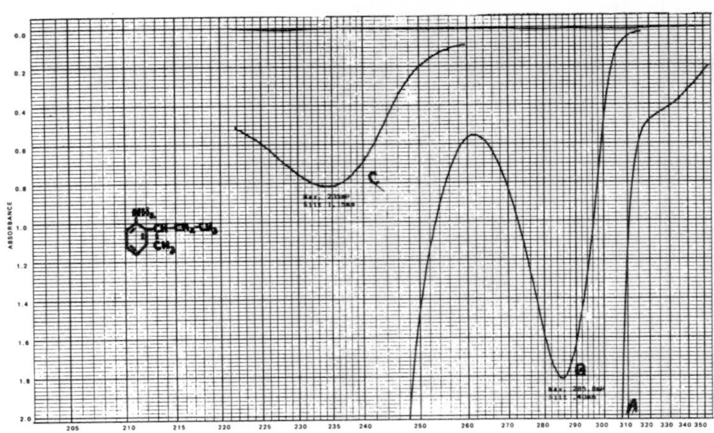

2,3-XYLIDINE

495

$C_8H_{11}N$
Mol. Wt. 121.19
Solvent: Cyclohexane

λ Max. mμ	a_m	Cell mm	Conc. g/L
x	x	10	1.89
286	1970	10	0.094
236.5	7230	10	0.019

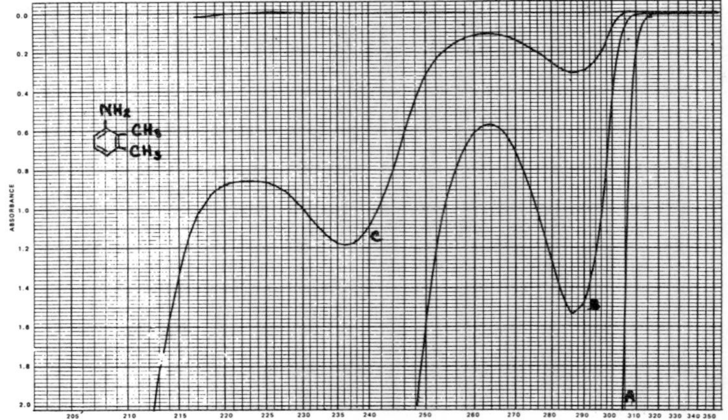

2,4-XYLIDINE

496

$C_8H_{11}N$
Mol. Wt. 121.18
Solvent: Methanol

λ Max. mμ	a_m	Cell mm	Conc. g/L
x	x	10	2.14
286.5	1850	10	0.086
234.5	7990	10	0.021

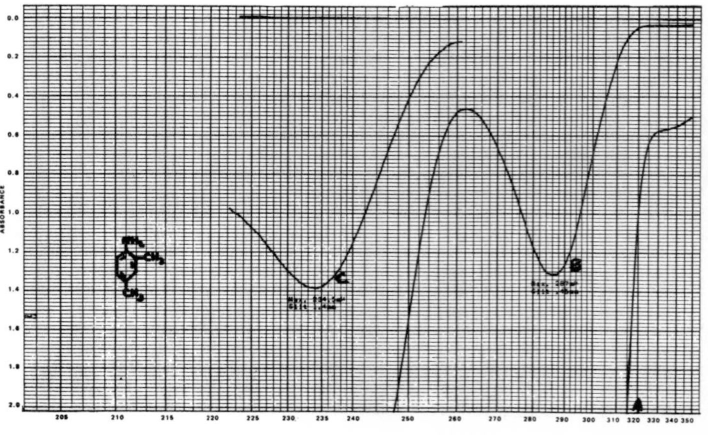

2,5-XYLIDINE

$C_8H_{11}N$

Mol. Wt. 121.18

Solvent: Cyclohexane

497

λ Max. mμ	a_m	Cell mm	Conc. g/L
x	x	10	1.868
287.5	2520	10	0.075
236.5	7810	10	0.019

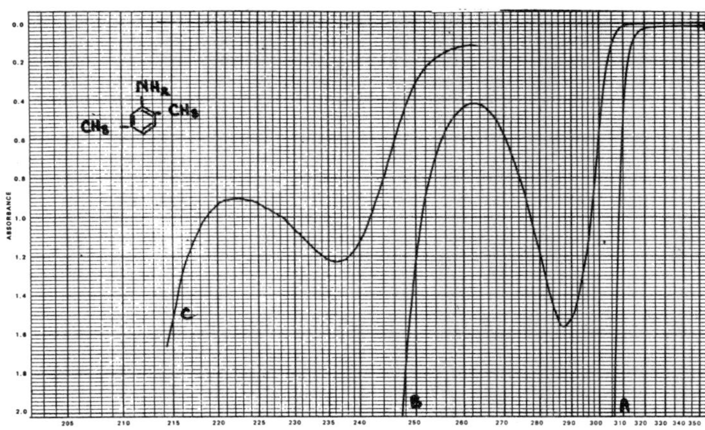

3,4-XYLIDINE

$C_8H_{11}N$

Mol. Wt. 121.18

M.P. 47-49°C (lit.)

Solvent: Cyclohexane

498

λ Max. mμ	a_m	Cell mm	Conc. g/L
x	x	10	1.876
292.5	1910	10	0.094
237.5	8320	10	0.019

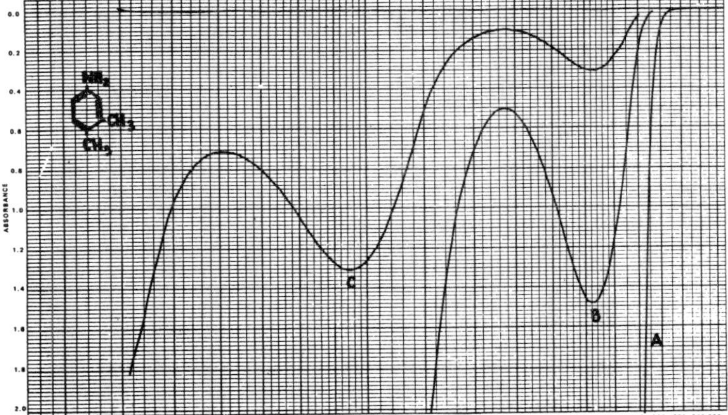

λ Max. mμ	a_m	Cell mm	Conc. g/L

3,5-XYLIDINE 499

$C_8H_{11}N$
Mol. Wt. 121.18
Solvent: Methanol

λ Max. mμ	a_m	Cell mm	Conc. g/L
288	2420	1	0.100
239	11000	1	0.100
207	35900	1	0.0326

3,5-XYLIDINE 499

$C_8H_{11}N$
Mol. Wt. 121.18
Solvent: Methanol HCl

λ Max. mμ	a_m	Cell mm	Conc. g/L
263	211	20	0.100
261	224	20	0.100
257	197	20	0.100
210	9510	1	0.0652
x	x	1	0.100

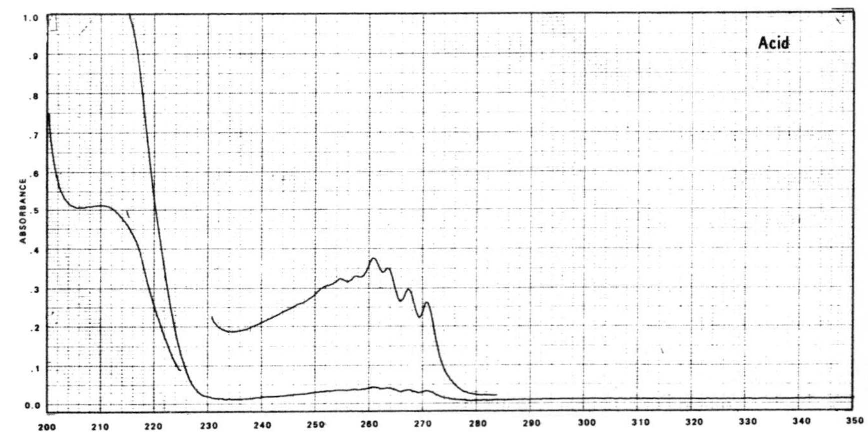

6-ETHYL-o-TOLUIDINE 500

$C_9H_{13}N$
Mol. Wt. 135.21
Solvent: Cyclohexane

λ Max. mμ	a_m	Cell mm	Conc. g/L
x	x	10	2.42
282.5	2350	10	0.097
234	7500	10	0.010

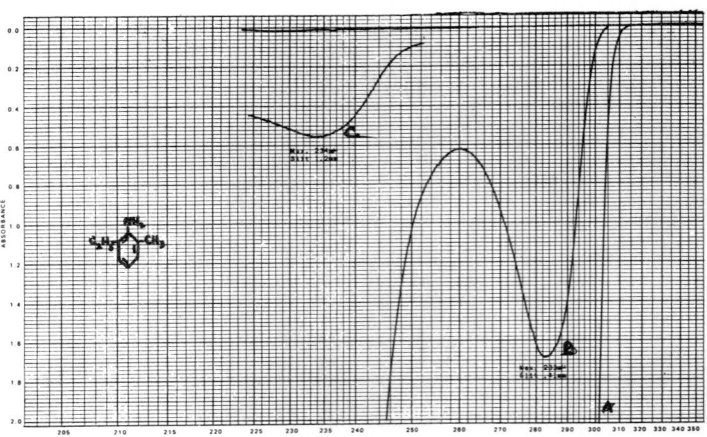

2,6-DIISOPROPYLANILINE

501

$C_{12}H_{19}N$

Mol. Wt. 177.29

Solvent: Cyclohexane

λ Max. mμ	a_m	Cell mm	Conc. g/L
x	x	10	2.27
283.5	2700	10	0.068
x	x	10	0.007

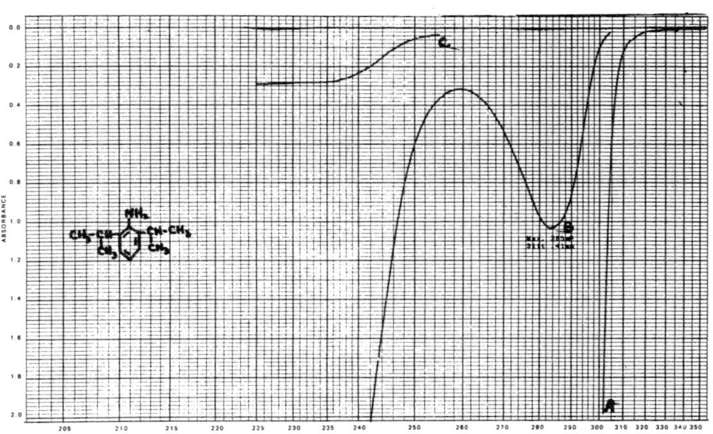

2,4,6-TRIMETHYLANILINE

502

$C_9H_{13}N$

Mol. Wt. 135.21

M.P. 233°C (lit.)

Solvent: Methanol

λ Max. mμ	a_m	Cell mm	Conc. g/L
288	2050	2	0.0800
234	7770	2	0.0800
x	x	1	0.0800

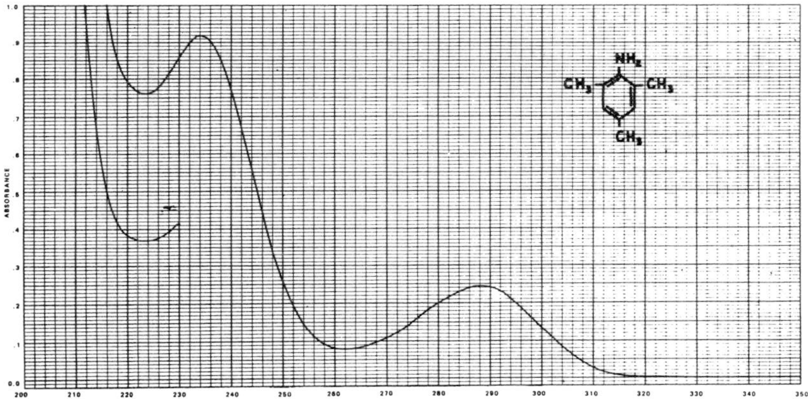

2,4,6-TRIMETHYLANILINE

502

$C_9H_{13}N$

Mol. Wt. 135.21

M.P. 233°C (lit.)

Solvent: Methanol HCl

λ Max. mμ	a_m	Cell mm	Conc. g/L
269	413	5	1.00
261.5	530	5	1.00
211	9900	1	0.0800

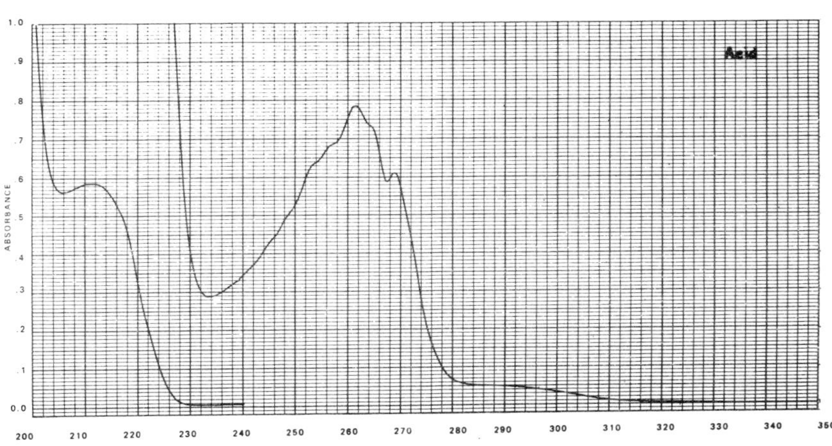

2,6-DIETHYL-p-TOLUIDINE

503

$C_{11}H_{12}N$
Mol. Wt. 163.26
Solvent: Cyclohexane

λ Max. mμ	a_m	Cell mm	Conc. g/L
321	40.6	10	2.250
290.5	2660	10	0.090
237.5	7570	10	0.018

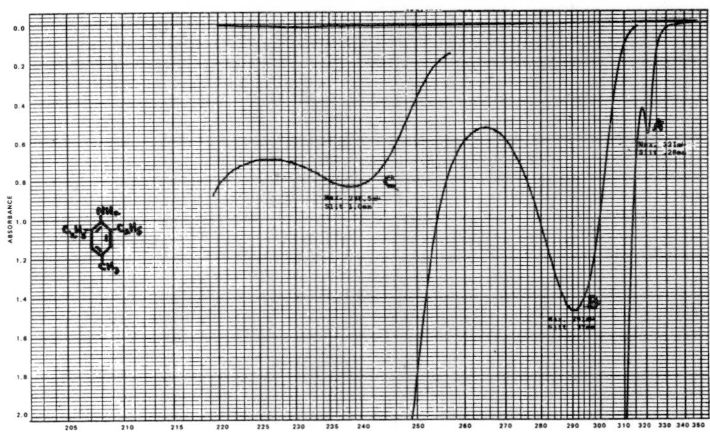

2-BIPHENYLAMINE

504

$C_{12}H_{11}N$
Mol. Wt. 169.23
Solvent: Methanol

λ Max. mμ	a_m	Cell mm	Conc. g/L
x	x	10	0.416
300	3190	10	0.083
x	x	10	0.025
223.5	22400	10	0.008

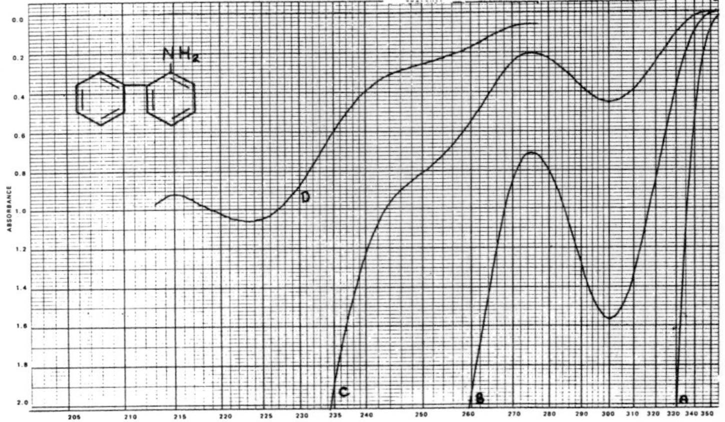

4-BIPHENYLAMINE

505

$C_{12}H_{11}N$
Mol. Wt. 169.23
M.P. 54-55°C
Solvent: Methanol

λ Max. mμ	a_m	Cell mm	Conc. g/L
278	20500	10	0.008

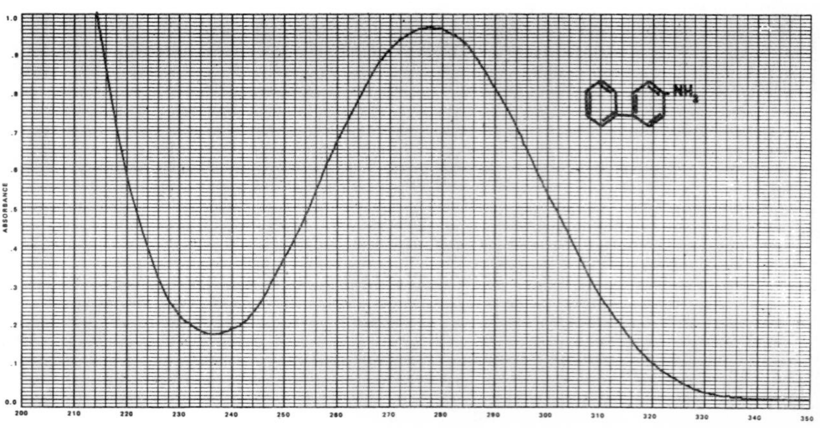

α,α,α-TRIFLUORO-m-TOLUIDINE

506

$C_7H_6NF_3$

Mol. Wt. 161.13

B.P. 189°C (lit.)

Solvent: Cyclohexane

λ Max. mμ	a_m	Cell mm	Conc. g/L
x	x	10	1.700
295	2780	10	0.068
237.5	12200	10	0.020

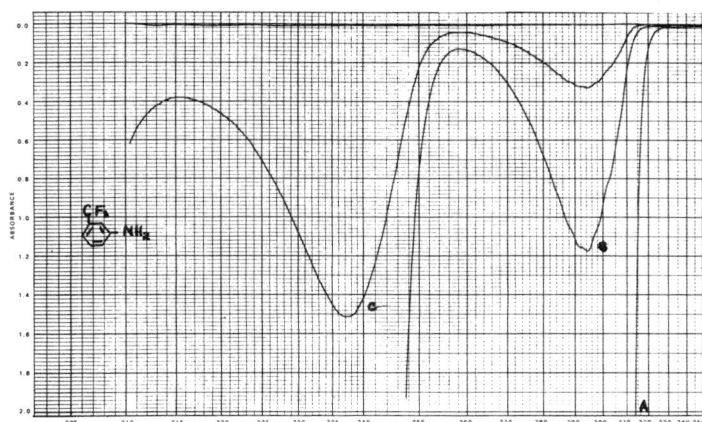

α,α,α-TRIFLUORO-p-TOLUIDINE

507

$C_7H_6F_3N$

Mol. Wt. 161.13

B.P. 90-91°C/20mm (lit.)

Solvent: Methanol

λ Max. mμ	a_m	Cell mm	Conc. g/L
289	1610	5	0.108
250.5	11800	1	0.108

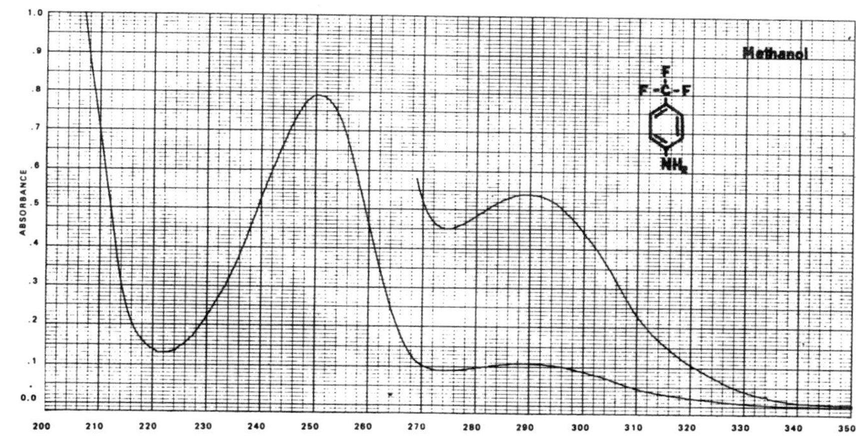

α,α,α-TRIFLUORO-p-TOLUIDINE

507

$C_7H_6F_3N$

Mol. Wt. 161.13

B.P. 90-91°C/20mm (lit.)

Solvent: Methanol HCl

λ Max. mμ	a_m	Cell mm	Conc. g/L
303	352	10	0.155
265	653	5	0.108
248.5	2010	5	0.108
205	8790	1	0.108

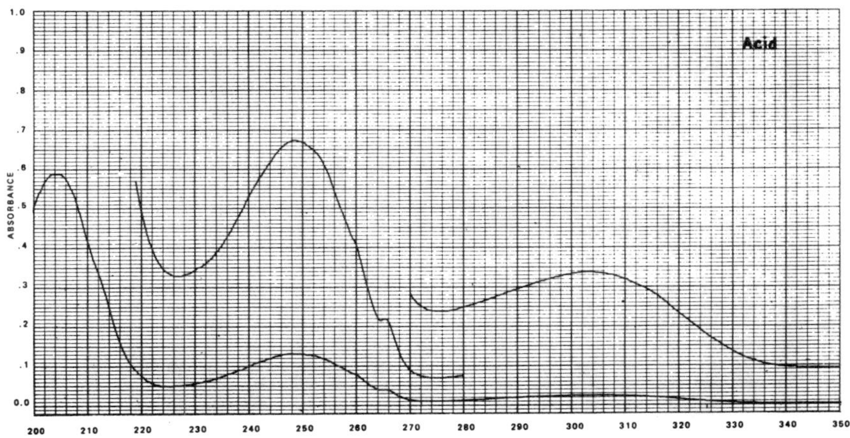

o-FLUOROANILINE 508

C_6H_6FN

Mol. Wt. 111.12

B.P. 67-69°C/13mm

Solvent: Methanol

λ Max. mμ	a_m	Cell mm	Conc. g/L
392	31	20	0.2480
282	1900	2	0.2480
232	9410	2	0.0496

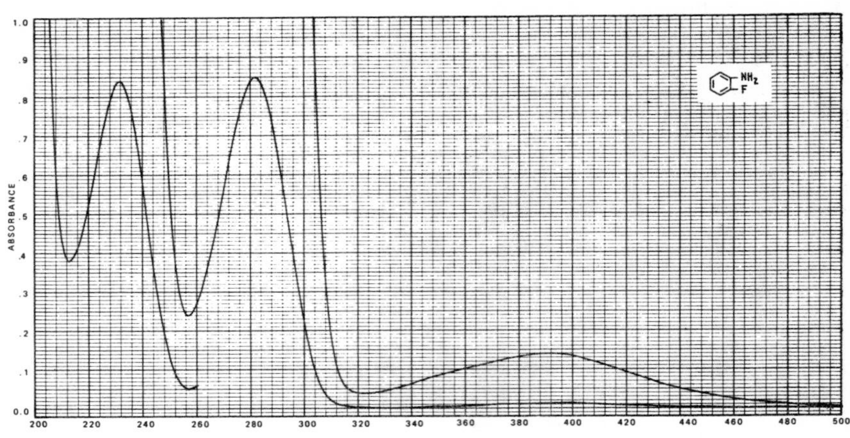

o-FLUOROANILINE 508

C_6H_6FN

Mol. Wt. 111.12

B.P. 67-69°C/13mm

Solvent: Methanol HCl

λ Max. mμ	a_m	Cell mm	Conc. g/L
392	1	5	0.2480
265	752	5	0.2480
259.5	829	5	0.2480
255	634	5	0.2480
x	x	2	0.0496

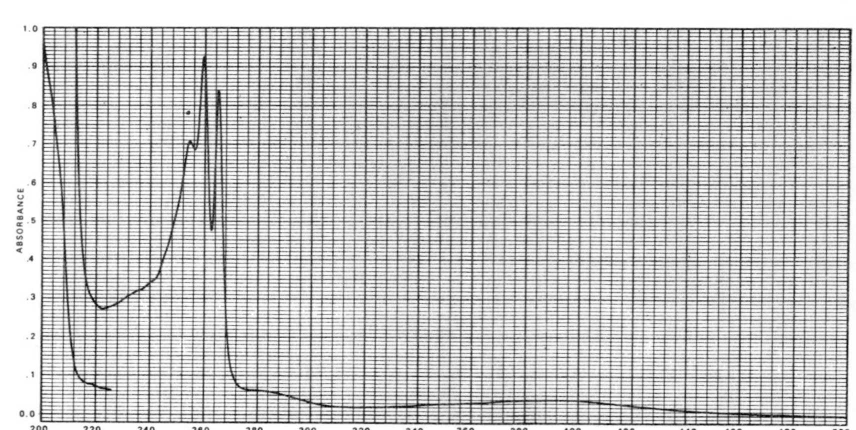

m-FLUOROANILINE 509

C_6H_6FN

Mol. Wt. 111.12

Solvent: Methanol

λ Max. mμ	a_m	Cell mm	Conc. g/L
283.5	1800	5	0.0950
236.5	10100	1	0.0950

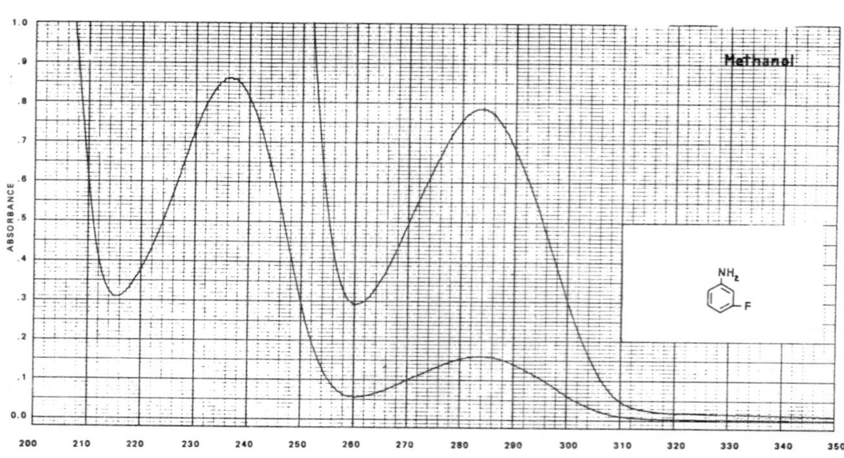

m-FLUOROANILINE 509

C_6H_6FN

Mol. Wt. 111.12

Solvent: Methanol HCl

λ Max. mμ	a_m	Cell mm	Conc. g/L
264.5	855	10	0.0950
258.5	862	10	0.0950
253.5	689	10	0.0950
204	6670	1	0.0950

p-FLUOROANILINE 510

C_6H_6FN

Mol. Wt. 111.12

Solvent: Methanol

λ Max. mμ	a_m	Cell mm	Conc. g/L
290	1730	2	0.0700
229.5	6100	2	0.0700

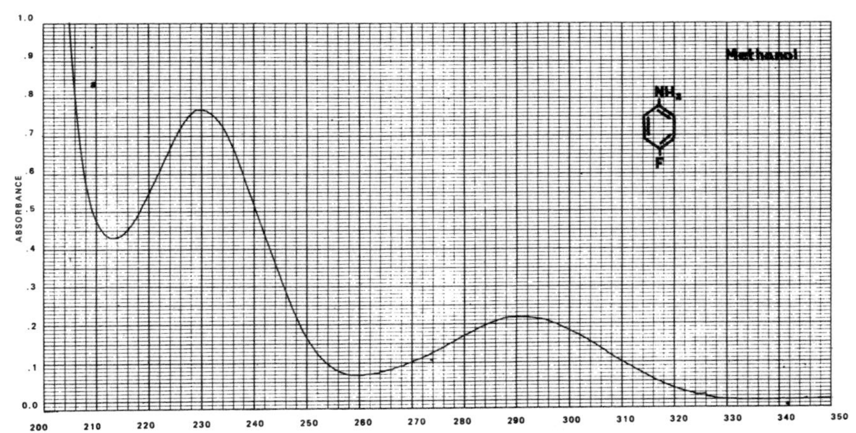

p-FLUOROANILINE 510

C_6H_6FN

Mol. Wt. 111.12

Solvent: Methanol HCl

λ Max. mμ	a_m	Cell mm	Conc. g/L
267	911	10	0.0700
261	1020	10	0.0700
256	819	10	0.0700
x	x	2	0.0700

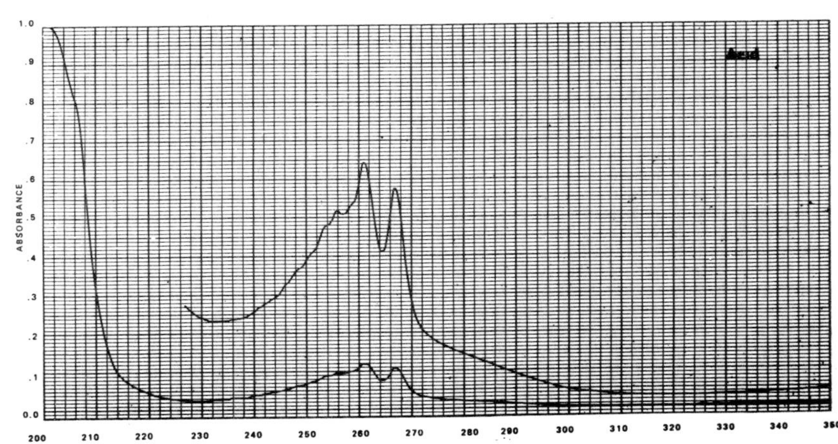

4-FLUORO-m-TOLUIDINE

511

C_7H_8FN

Mol. Wt. 125.15

M.P. 36-37°C (lit.)

Solvent: Methanol

λ Max. mμ	a_m	Cell mm	Conc. g/L
293	2070	2	0.2945
232	5650	1	0.14725

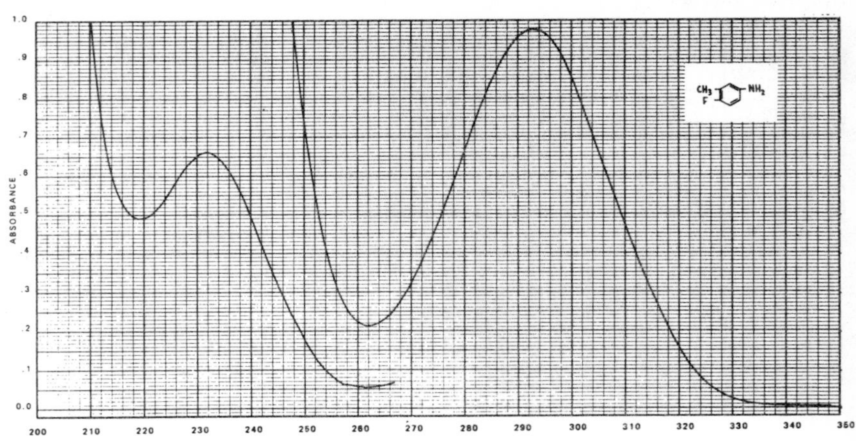

4-FLUORO-m-TOLUIDINE

511

C_7H_8FN

Mol. Wt. 125.15

M.P. 36-37°C (lit.)

Solvent: Methanol HCl

λ Max. mμ	a_m	Cell mm	Conc. g/L
269.5	763	2	0.2945
264	789	2	0.2945
260.5	717	2	0.2945

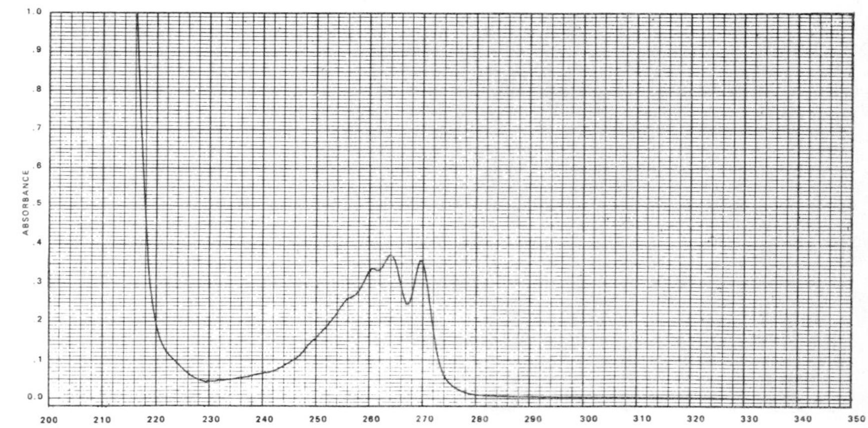

o-CHLOROANILINE

512

C_6H_6ClN

Mol. Wt. 127.57

Solvent: Cyclohexane

λ Max. mμ	a_m	Cell mm	Conc. g/L
x	x	10	1.940
290	3030	10	0.058
236.5	10900	10	0.019

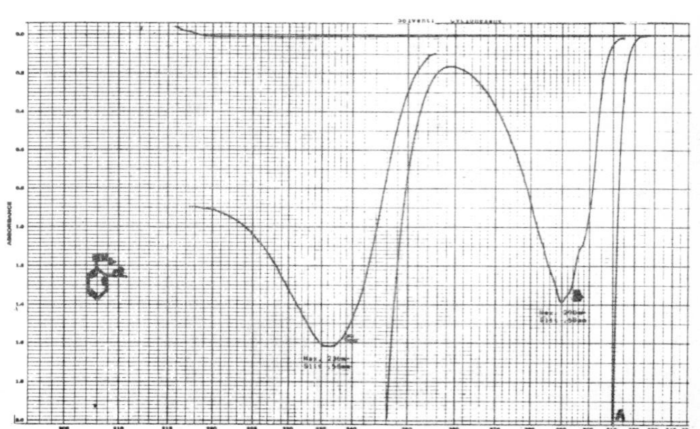

m-CHLOROANILINE

513

C_6H_6ClN

Mol. Wt. 127.57

B.P. 228-231°C

Solvent: Methanol

λ Max. mμ	a_m	Cell mm	Conc. g/L
294	1970	10	0.012
242	8700	10	0.012

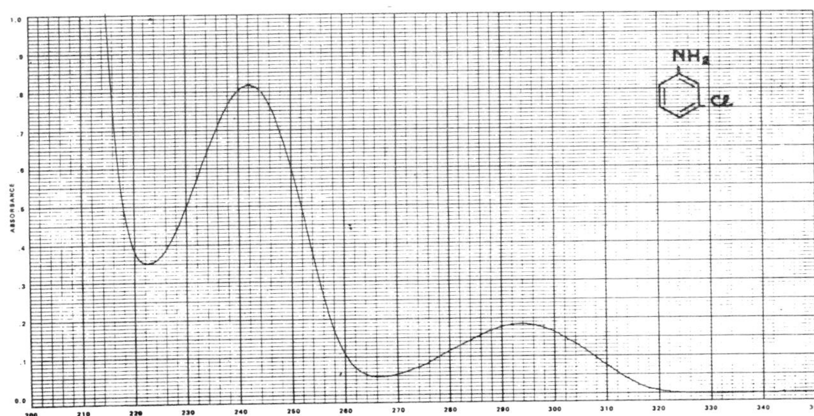

p-CHLOROANILINE

514

C_6H_6ClN

Mol. Wt. 127.57

B.R. 229-233°C (lit.)

Solvent: Methanol

λ Max. mμ	a_m	Cell mm	Conc. g/L
x	x	10	0.210
296	16300	10	0.010
243	12400	10	0.001

λ Max. mμ	a_m	Cell mm	Conc. g/L

4-CHLORO-o-TOLUIDINE

515

C_7H_8ClN

Mol. Wt. 141.60

M.P. 26-29°C

Solvent: Methanol

λ Max. mμ	a_m	Cell mm	Conc. g/L
296	2550	1	0.500
241.5	13300	1	0.100

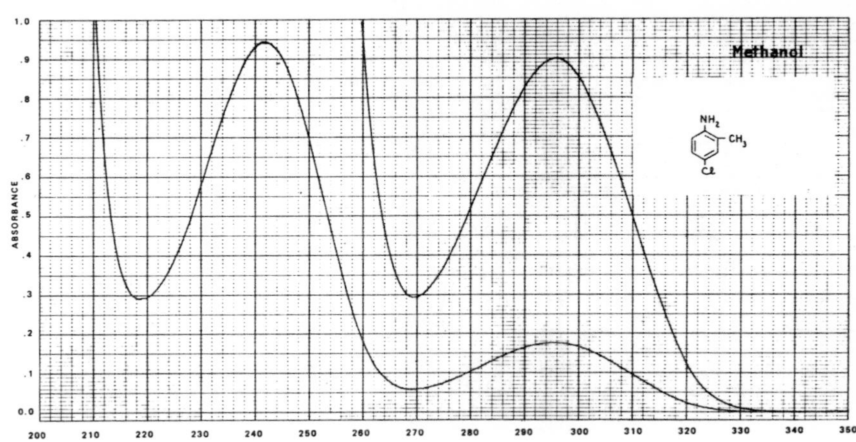

4-CHLORO-o-TOLUIDINE

515

C_7H_8ClN

Mol. Wt. 141.60

M.P. 26-29°C

Solvent: Methanol HCl

λ Max. mμ	a_m	Cell mm	Conc. g/L
274.5	274	5	0.500
266	340	5	0.500
213	11600	1	0.100

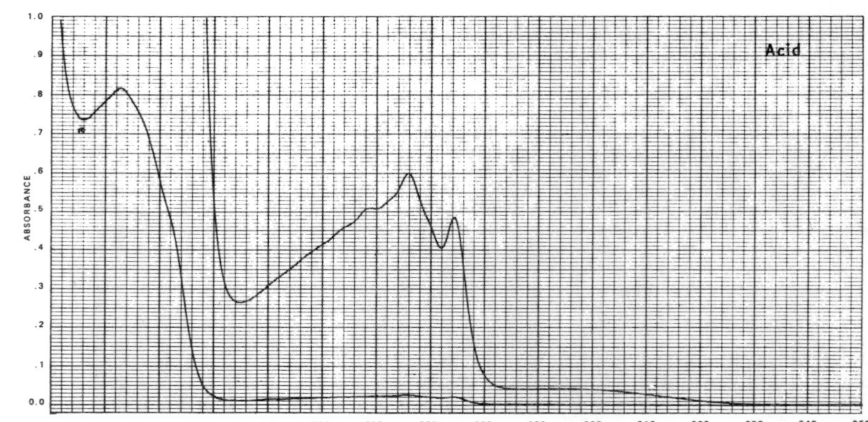

2,4-DICHLOROANILINE

516

$C_6H_5Cl_2N$

Mol. Wt. 162.02

Solvent: Methanol

λ Max. mμ	a_m	Cell mm	Conc. g/L
305	1540	5	0.100
244.5	10900	1	0.100

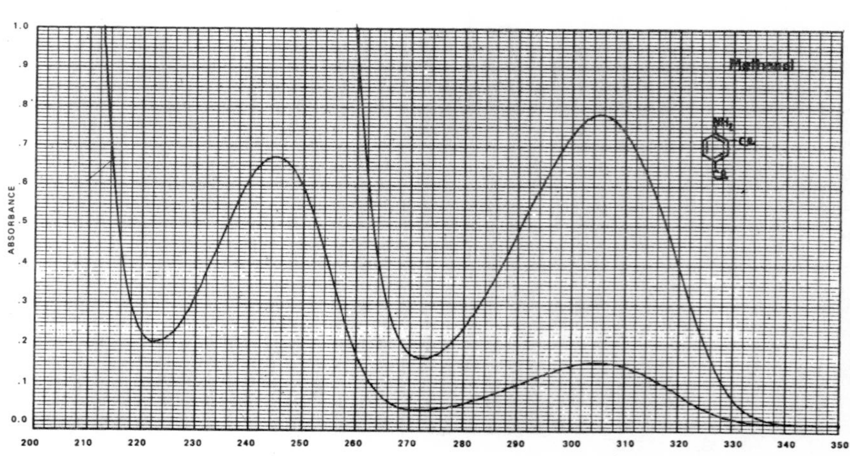

2,4-DICHLOROANILINE

516

$C_6H_5Cl_2N$

Mol. Wt. 162.02

Solvent: Methanol HCl

λ Max. mμ	a_m	Cell mm	Conc. g/L
305	698	20	0.100
279	411	20	0.100
269.5	410	20	0.100
245.5	3160	5	0.100
x	x	1	0.100

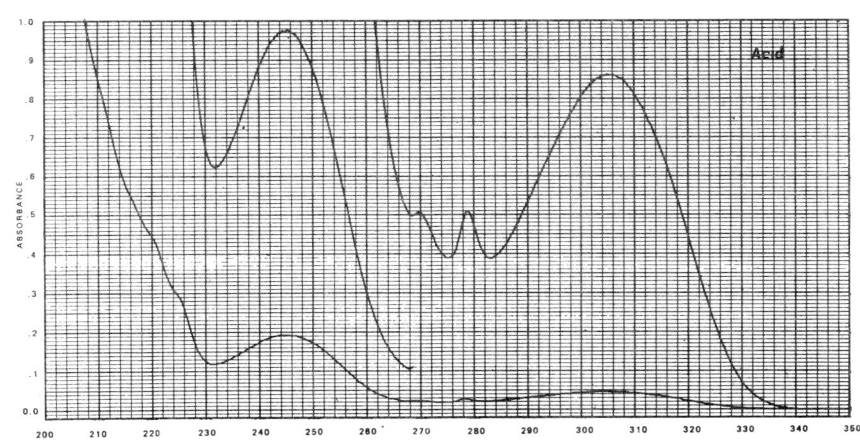

2,4,6-TRICHLOROANILINE

517

$C_6H_4Cl_3N$

Mol. Wt. 196.46

Solvent: Methanol

λ Max. mμ	a_m	Cell mm	Conc. g/L
309.5	3160	5	0.100
243.5	8900	1	0.100
209	31700	1	0.0500

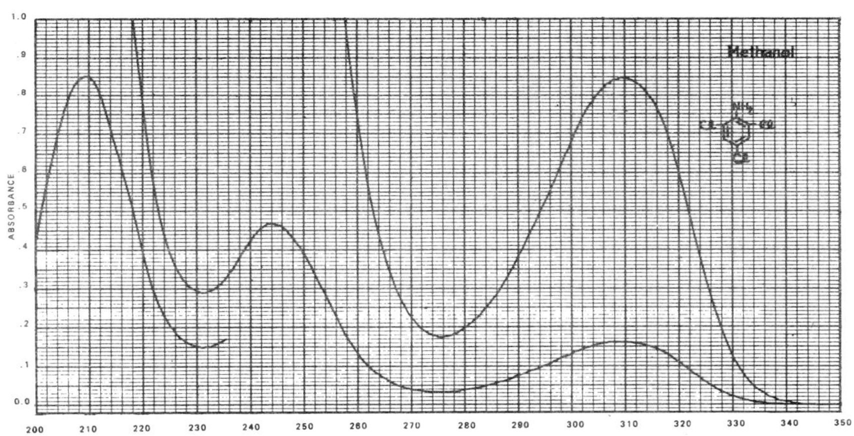

λ Max. mμ	a_m	Cell mm	Conc. g/L

o-BROMOANILINE

518

C_6H_6BrN

Mol. Wt. 172.03

M.P. 28-29°C

Solvent: Methanol

λ Max. mμ	a_m	Cell mm	Conc. g/L
293	2720	1	0.178
236.5	7750	1	0.178

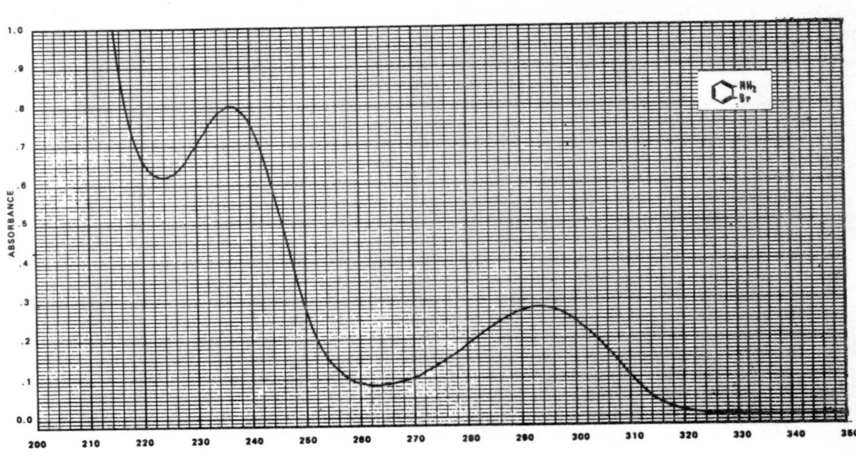

o-BROMOANILINE

518

C_6H_6BrN

Mol. Wt. 172.03

M.P. 28-29°C

Solvent: Methanol HCl

λ Max. mμ	a_m	Cell mm	Conc. g/L
292	135	10	0.178
270.5	175	10	0.178
260	234	10	0.178
x	x	1	0.178

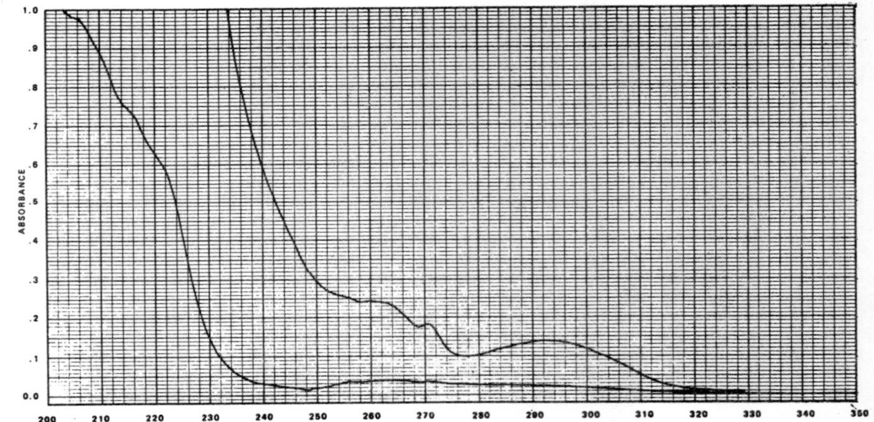

m-BROMOANILINE

519

C_6H_6BrN

Mol. Wt. 172.03

Solvent: Methanol

λ Max. mμ	a_m	Cell mm	Conc. g/L
292	4770	1	0.100
239.5	14900	1	0.100

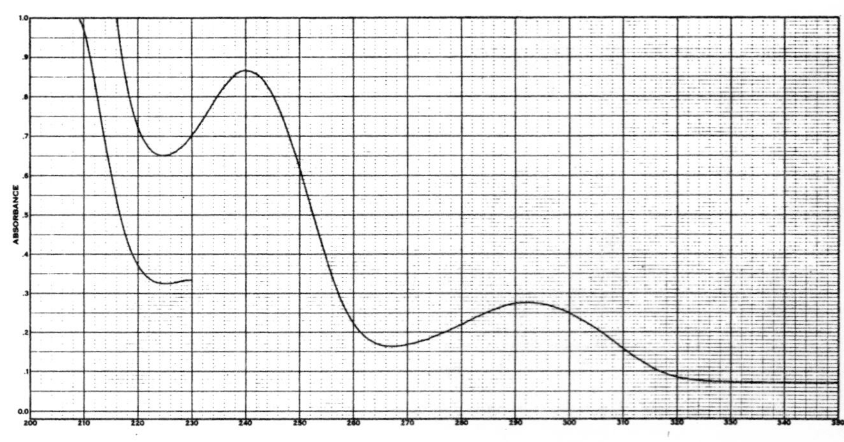

m-BROMOANILINE 519

C_6H_6ClN

Mol. Wt. 127.57

M.P. 71-73°C

Solvent: Methanol HCl

λ Max. mμ	a_m	Cell mm	Conc. g/L
272.5	256	20	0.100
265.5	276	20	0.100
256.0	248	20	0.100
250.5	262	20	0.100

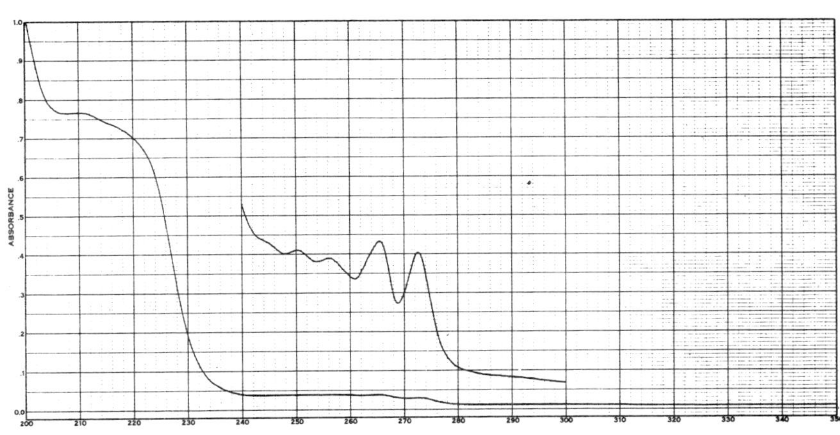

p-BROMOANILINE 520

C_6H_6BrN

Mol. Wt. 172.03

M.R. 62-64°C (lit.)

Solvent: Methanol

λ Max. mμ	a_m	Cell mm	Conc. g/L
x	x	10	2.00
296.5	1460	10	0.200
244.5	12600	10	0.020

λ Max. mμ	a_m	Cell mm	Conc. g/L

2-BROMO-p-TOLUIDINE 521

C_7H_8BrN

Mol. Wt. 186.06

M.P. 14-16°C

Solvent: Methanol

λ Max. mμ	$^a m$	Cell mm	Conc. g/L
299	2240	1	0.1820
238	7600	1	0.1820

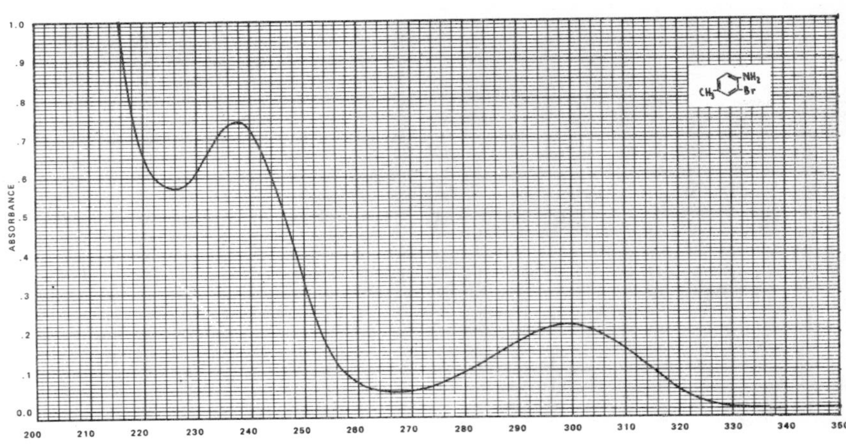

2-BROMO-p-TOLUIDINE 521

C_7H_8BrN

Mol. Wt. 186.06

M.P. 14-16°C

Solvent: Methanol HCl

λ Max. mμ	$^a m$	Cell mm	Conc. g/L
299	159	20	0.1820
275	325	20	0.1820
266	360	20	0.1820
257	335	20	0.1820
x	x	1	0.1820

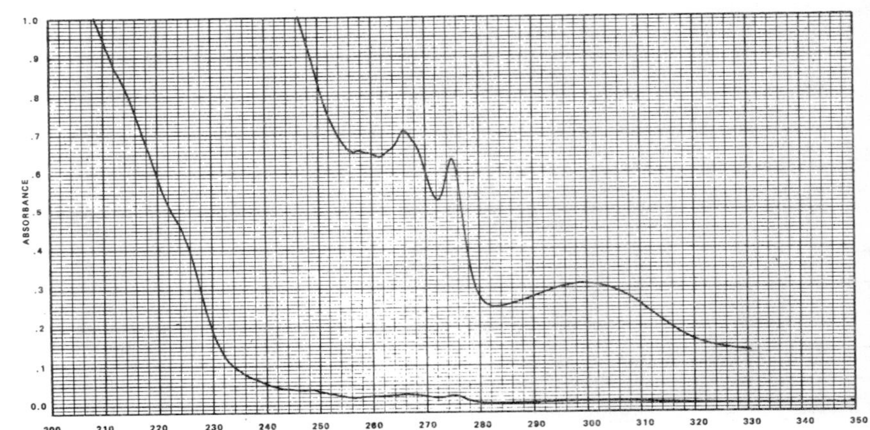

4-BROMO-3-CHLOROANILINE 522

C_6H_5BrClN

Mol. Wt. 206.48

M.P. 60°C

Solvent: Methanol

λ Max. mμ	$^a m$	Cell mm	Conc. g/L
306	2120	5	0.100
248	14500	1	0.0500
206	31000	1	0.0500

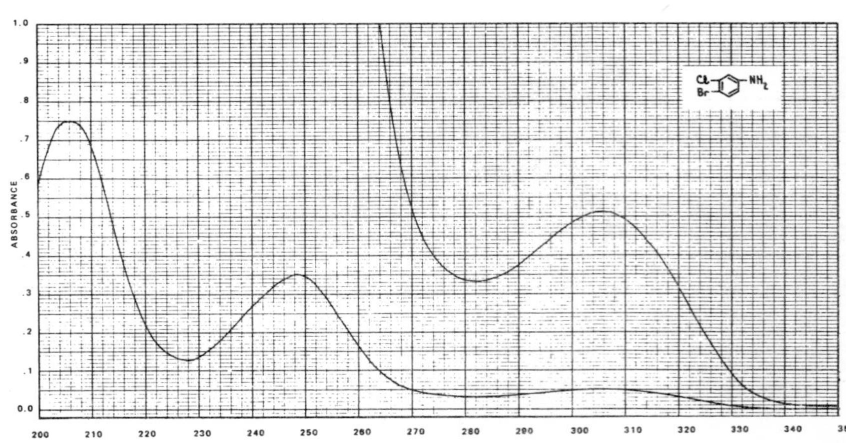

4-BROMO-3-CHLOROANILINE

C_6H_5BrClN

Mol. Wt. 206.48

M.P. 60°C

Solvent: Methanol HCl

522

λ Max. mμ	a_m	Cell mm	Conc. g/L
306	140	10	0.100
280.5	409	10	0.100
272	467	10	0.100
x	x	1	0.0200

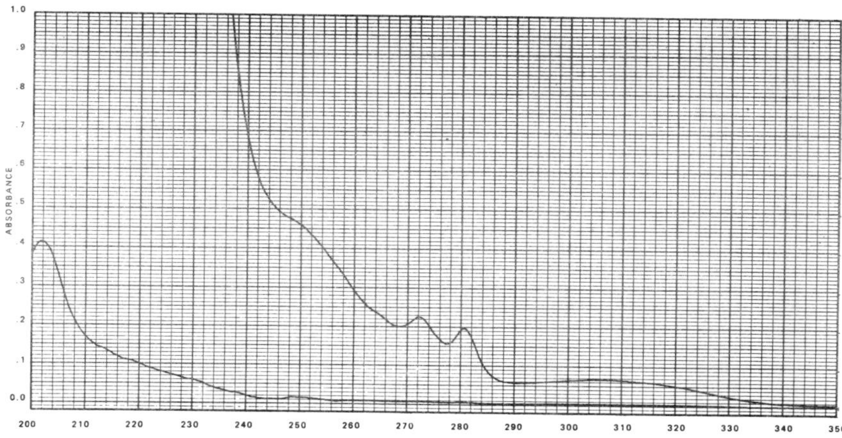

2,4-DIBROMOANILINE

$C_6H_5Br_2N$

Mol. Wt. 250.93

M.P. 78-79°C

Solvent: Methanol

523

λ Max. mμ	a_m	Cell mm	Conc. g/L
307	2820	5	0.100
247	13400	1	0.100
x	x	1	0.100

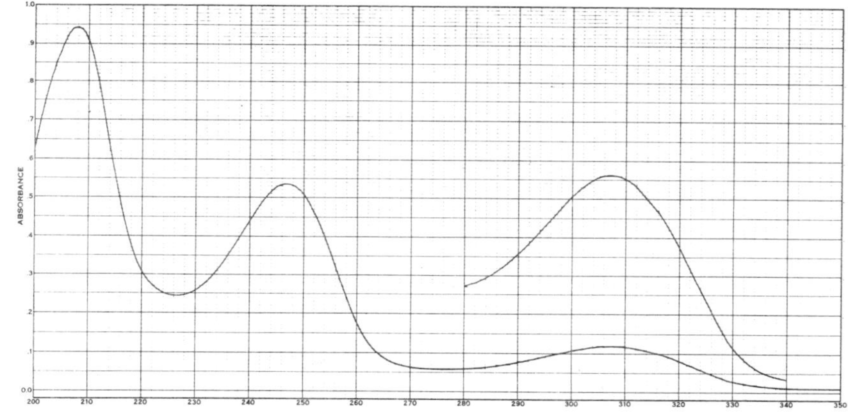

2,4-DIBROMOANILINE

$C_6H_5Br_2N$

Mol. Wt. 250.93

M.P. 78-79°C

Solvent: Methanol HCl

523

λ Max. mμ	a_m	Cell mm	Conc. g/L
306.5	1080	20	0.100
281	729	20	0.100
246	5270	1	0.100
x	x	1	0.100

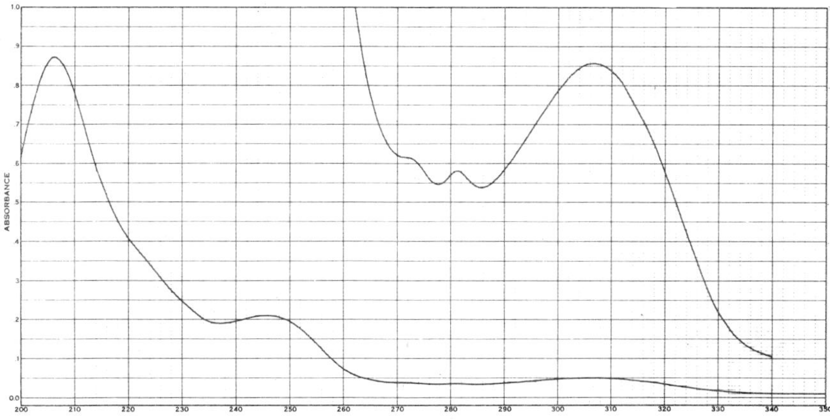

2,4,6-TRIBROMOANILINE

524

$C_6H_4Br_3N$

Mol. Wt. 329.85

Solvent: Dioxane

λ Max. mμ	a_m	Cell mm	Conc. g/L
x	x	10	0.200
313	3830	10	0.100
250	20600	10	0.010

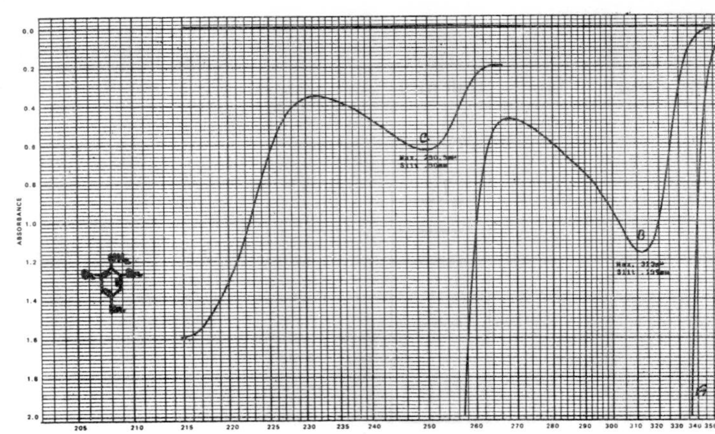

o-IODOANILINE

525

C_6H_6IN

Mol. Wt. 219.03

M.P. 56-58°C

Solvent: Methanol

λ Max. mμ	a_m	Cell mm	Conc. g/L
296	2770	2	0.100
238	7960	2	0.100
211	29700	1	0.0500

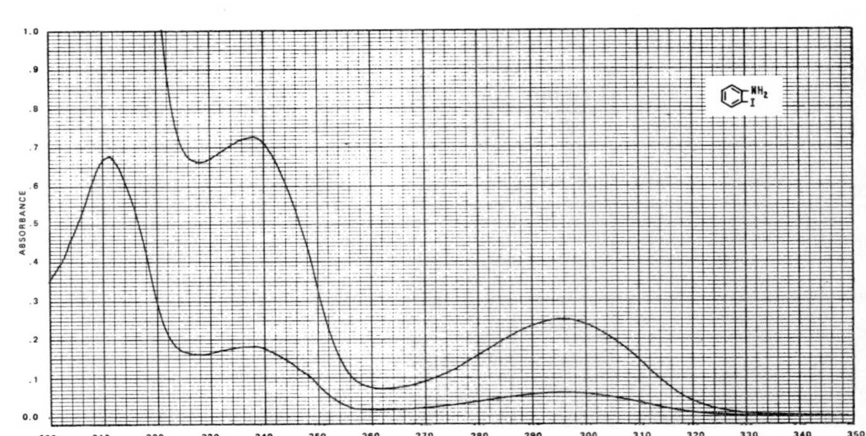

o-IODOANILINE

525

C_6H_6IN

Mol. Wt. 219.03

M.P. 56-58°C

Solvent: Methanol HCl

λ Max. mμ	a_m	Cell mm	Conc. g/L
230	10600	2	0.100

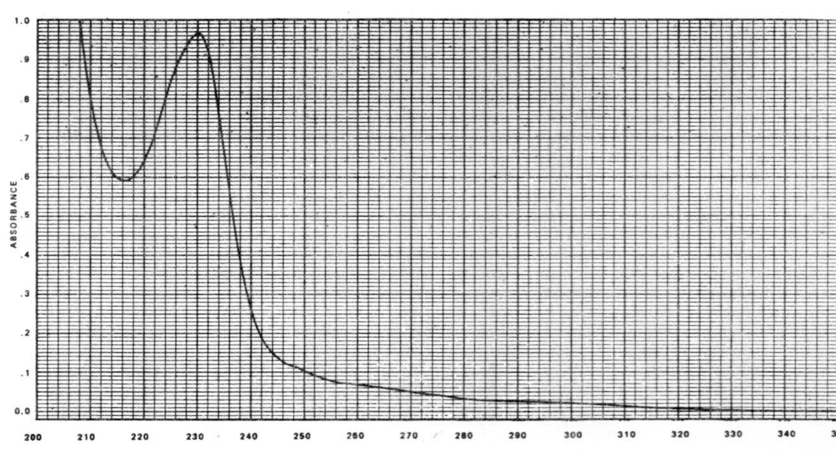

m-IODOANILINE 526

C_6H_6IN

Mol. Wt. 219.03

M.P. 27-29°C

Solvent: Methanol

λ Max. mμ	a_m	Cell mm	Conc. g/L
295	2210	1	0.238
243	8150	1	0.238
215	33700	1	0.0480

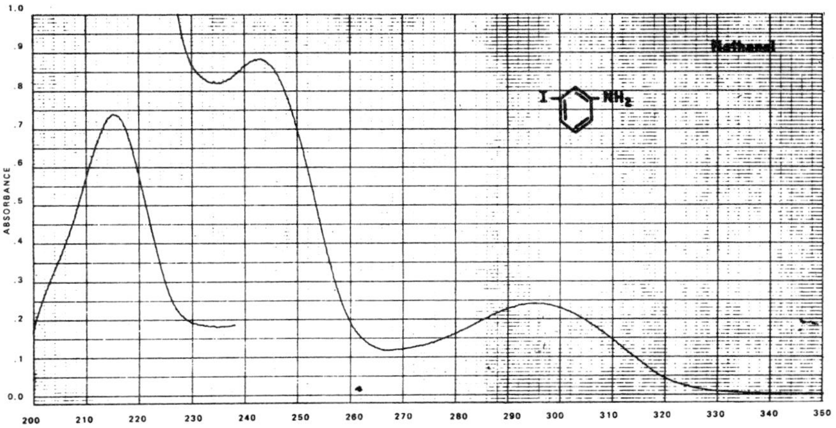

m-IODOANILINE 526

C_6H_6IN

Mol. Wt. 219.03

M.P. 27-29°C

Solvent: Methanol HCl

λ Max. mμ	a_m	Cell mm	Conc. g/L
232.5	11800	2	0.0480

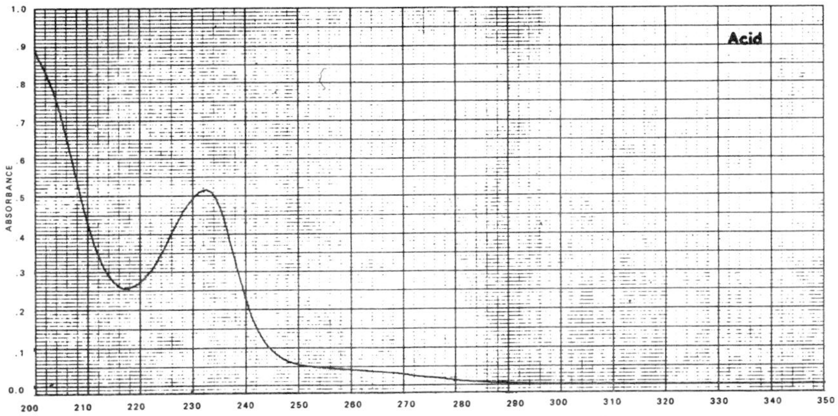

λ Max. mμ	a_m	Cell mm	Conc. g/L

p-IODOANILINE 527

C_6H_6IN

Mol. Wt. 219.03

Solvent: Methanol

λ Max. mμ	a_m	Cell mm	Conc. g/L
296	1790	4	0.100
249	14600	1	0.100
x	x	1	0.100

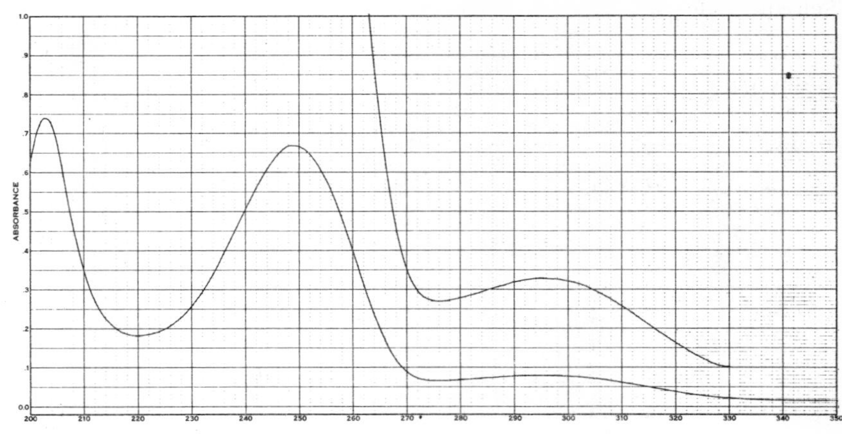

p-IODOANILINE 527

C_6H_6IN

Mol. Wt. 219.03

Solvent: Methanol HCl

λ Max. mμ	a_m	Cell mm	Conc. g/L
232	10300	2	0.100

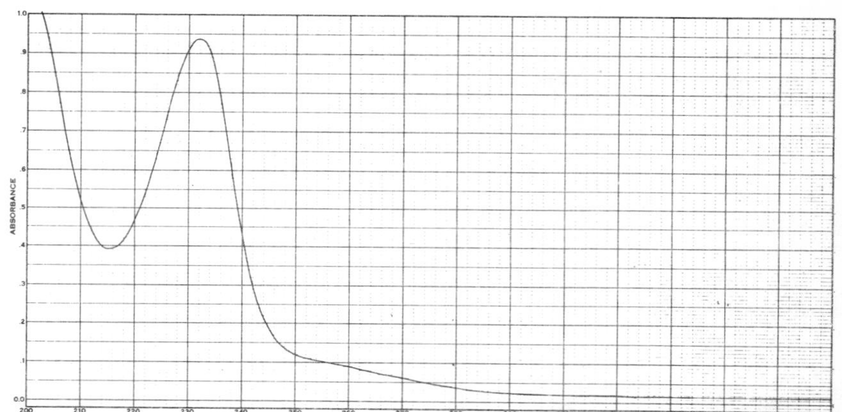

4-IODO-o-TOLUIDINE 528

C_7H_8IN

Mol. Wt. 233.05

M.P. 89.5°C

Solvent: Methanol

λ Max. mμ	a_m	Cell mm	Conc. g/L
296.0	2110	1	1.00
247.0	16200	1	0.100

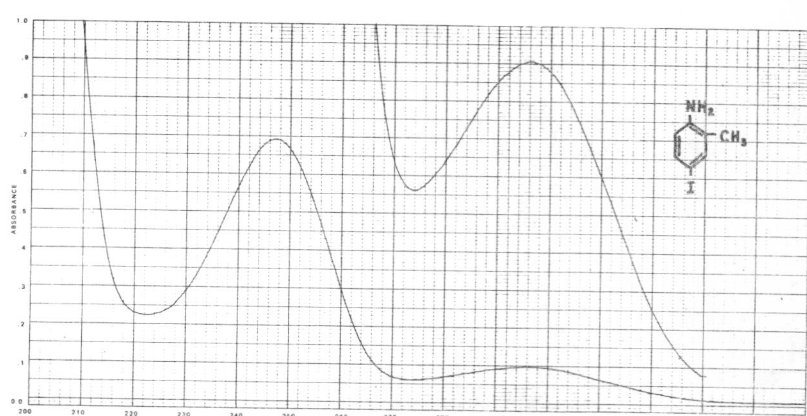

4-IODO-o-TOLUIDINE

528

C_7H_8IN

Mol. Wt. 233.05

M.P. 89.5°C

Solvent: Methanol HCl

λ Max. mμ	a_m	Cell mm	Conc. g/L
233	11800	1	0.100

p-AMINOPHENETHYLAMINE

529

$C_8H_{12}N_2$

Mol. Wt. 136.20

Solvent: Methanol

λ Max. mμ	a_m	Cell mm	Conc. g/L
x	x	10	0.286
290	1770	10	0.057
238.5	10100	10	0.011

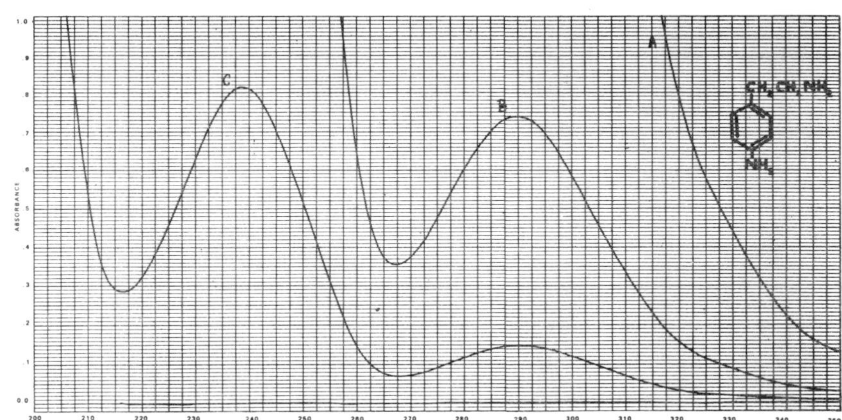

p-AMINOPHENETHYLAMINE

529

$C_8H_{12}N_2$

Mol. Wt. 136.20

Solvent: Methanol HCl

λ Max. mμ	a_m	Cell mm	Conc. g/L
303	66.8	10	0.257
287.5	90.1	10	0.257
258.5	426	10	0.257
253	421	10	0.257

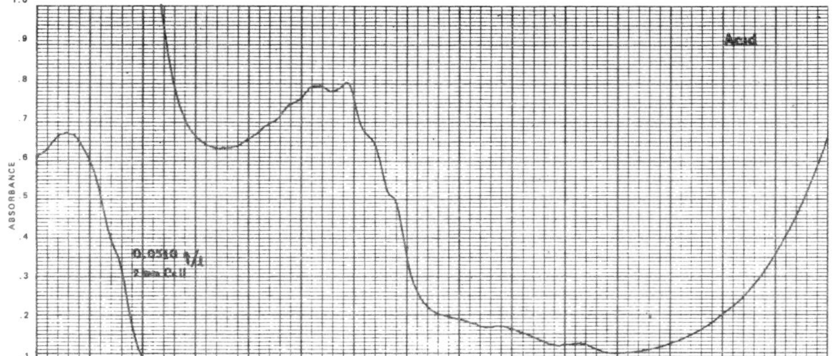

4,4'-METHYLENEDIANILINE 530

$C_{13}H_{14}N_2$

Mol. Wt. 198.27

M.P. 70°C

Solvent: Methanol

λ Max. mμ	a_m	Cell mm	Conc. g/L
289	3120	5	0.100
243	22000	1	0.0500

4,4'-METHYLENEDIANILINE 530

$C_{13}H_{14}N_2$

Mol. Wt. 198.27

M.P. 70°C

Solvent: Methanol HCl

λ Max. mμ	a_m	Cell mm	Conc. g/L
270	436	20	0.100
261	617	20	0.100
255	563	20	0.100
x	x	1	0.100

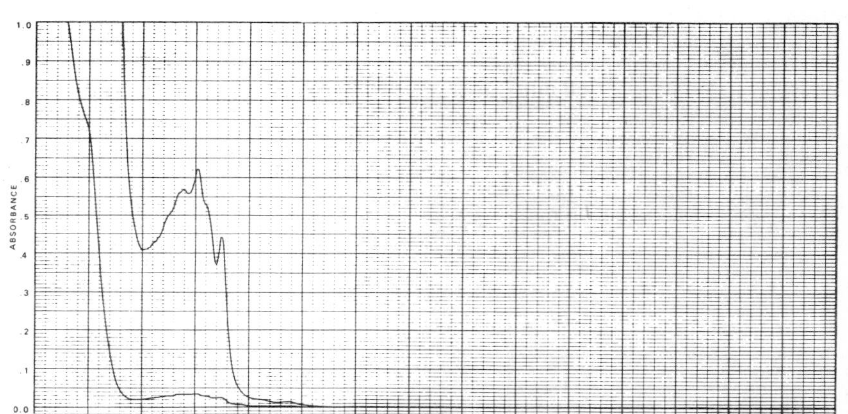

BENZIDINE 531

$C_{12}H_{12}N_2$

Mol. Wt. 184.23

M.P. 127-129°C (lit.)

Solvent: Methanol

λ Max. mμ	a_m	Cell mm	Conc. g/L
x	x	10	0.239
284	24300	10	0.012

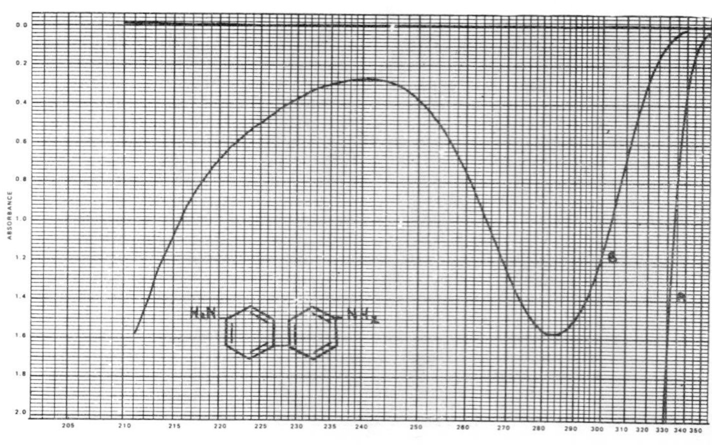

3,3'-DIMETHYLBENZIDINE 532

$C_{14}H_{16}N_2$
Mol. Wt. 212.28
Solvent: Methanol

λ Max. mμ	a_m	Cell mm	Conc. g/L
x	x	10	2.00
282	23400	10	0.010

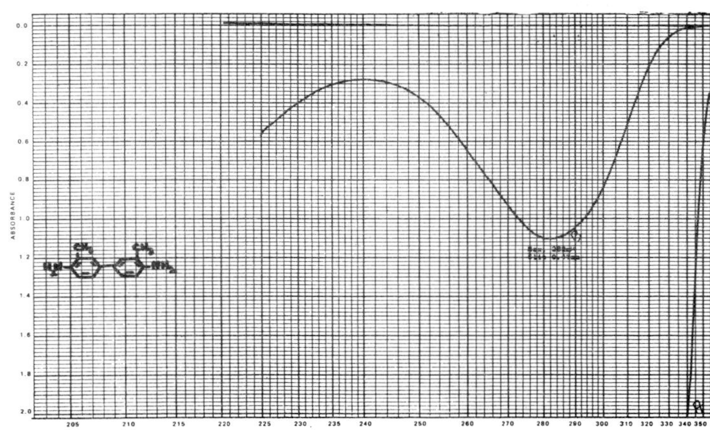

o-PHENYLENEDIAMINE 533

$C_6H_8N_2$
Mol. Wt. 108.14
M.P. 101-103°C
Solvent: Methanol

λ Max. mμ	a_m	Cell mm	Conc. g/L
293.5	3220	1	0.100
282	2730	1	0.100
238	6020	1	0.100
x	x	0.5	0.100

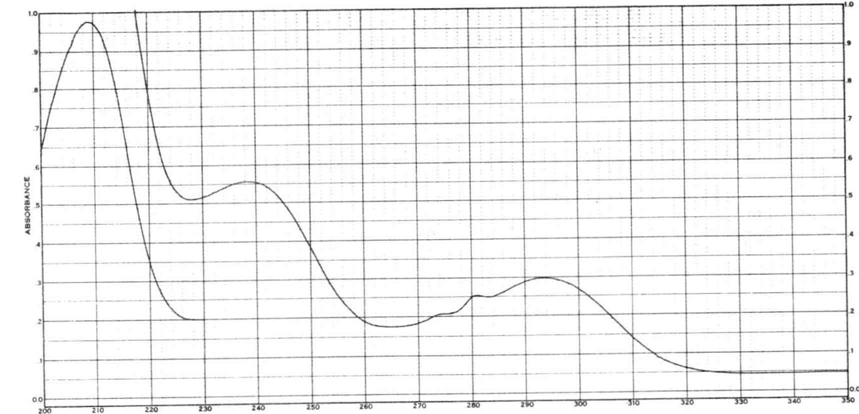

o-PHENYLENEDIAMINE 533

$C_6H_8N_2$
Mol. Wt. 108.14
M.P. 101-103°C
Solvent: Methanol HCl

λ Max. mμ	a_m	Cell mm	Conc. g/L
285.5	2510	1	0.100
275.5	2790	1	0.100
269	2400	1	0.100
235	7870	1	0.100

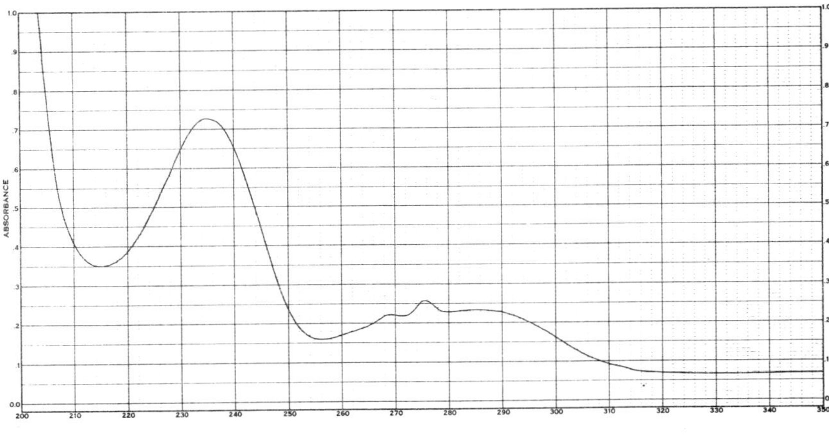

m-PHENYLENEDIAMINE

534

$C_6H_8N_2$
Mol. Wt. 108.14
F.P. 62.0°C
Solvent: Methanol

λ Max. mμ	a_m	Cell mm	Conc. g/L
x	x	10	0.476
293.5	2310	10	0.071
x	x	10	0.007

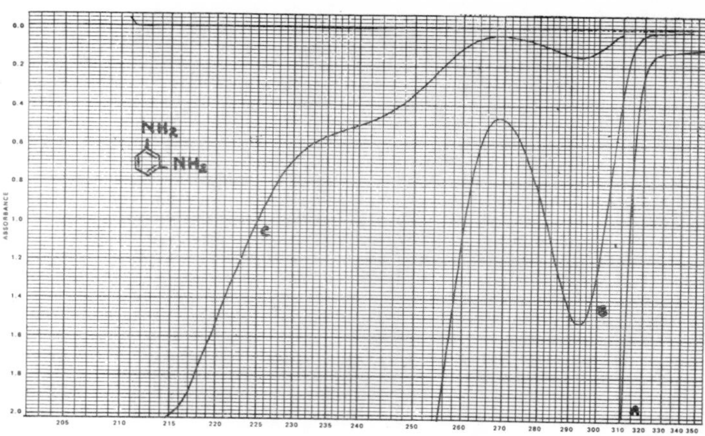

p-PHENYLENEDIAMINE

535

$C_6H_8N_2$
Mol. Wt. 108.14
M.P. 139°C (lit.)
Solvent: Methanol

λ Max. mμ	a_m	Cell mm	Conc. g/L
x	x	10	0.200
308	1830	10	0.100
243	11200	10	0.010

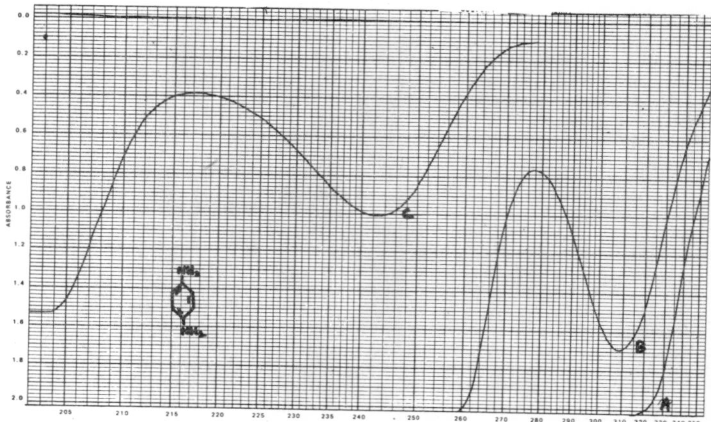

TOLUENE-2,4-DIAMINE

536

$C_7H_{10}N_2$
Mol. Wt. 122.17
M.R. 97-100°C (lit.)
Solvent: Methanol

λ Max. mμ	a_m	Cell mm	Conc. g/L
x	x	10	2.00
294	2890	10	0.060
x	x	10	0.006

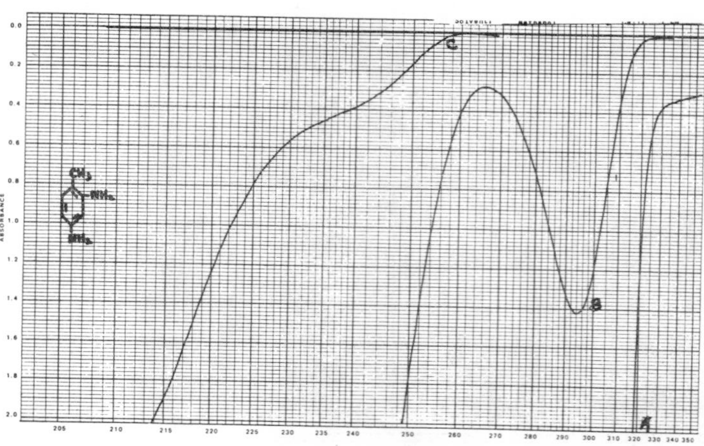

2,6-DIMETHYL-p-PHENYLENEDIAMINE 537

$C_8H_{12}N_2$
Mol. Wt. 136.20
M.P. 104°C
Solvent: Methanol

λ Max. mμ	a_m	Cell mm	Conc. g/L
301	3060	1	0.100
241	9300	1	0.100
x	x	1	0.0200

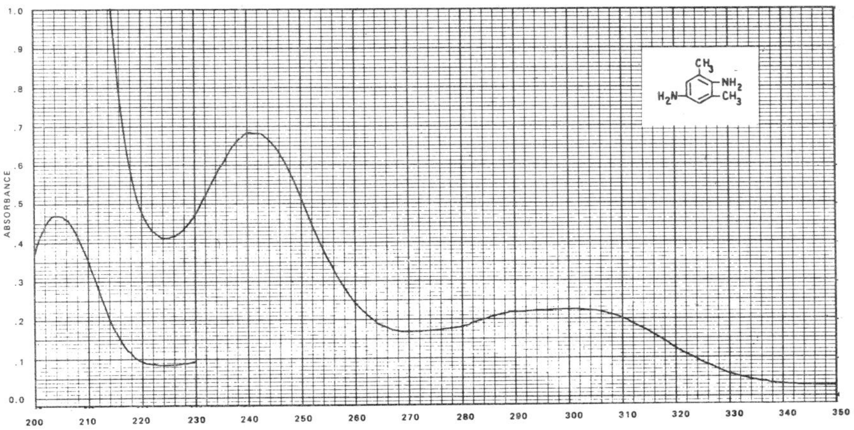

2,6-DIMETHYL-p-PHENYLENEDIAMINE 537

$C_8H_{12}N_2$
Mol. Wt. 136.20
M.P. 104°C
Solvent: Methanol HCl

λ Max. mμ	a_m	Cell mm	Conc. g/L
297	1110	5	0.100
269.5	732	5	0.100
242	2380	5	0.100
x	x	1	0.100

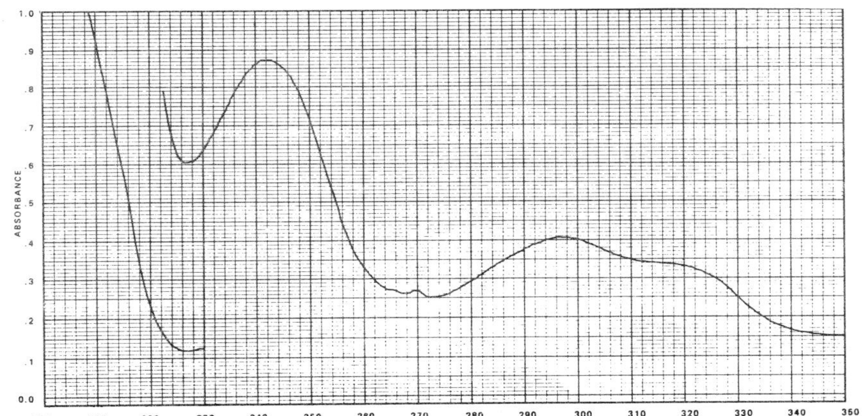

2,5-DIETHYL-p-PHENYLENEDIAMINE 538

$C_{10}H_{16}N_2$
Mol. Wt. 164.25
M.P. 80-81°C

λ Max. mμ	a_m	Cell mm	Conc. g/L

Pure sample not available.

1-NAPHTHYLAMINE

539

$C_{10}H_9N$
Mol. Wt. 143.18
M.P. 50°C (lit.)
Solvent: Cyclohexane

λ Max. mμ	a_m	Cell mm	Conc. g/L
x	x	10	0.120
318	5100	10	0.048
243	26600	10	0.005
212.5	43500	10	0.005

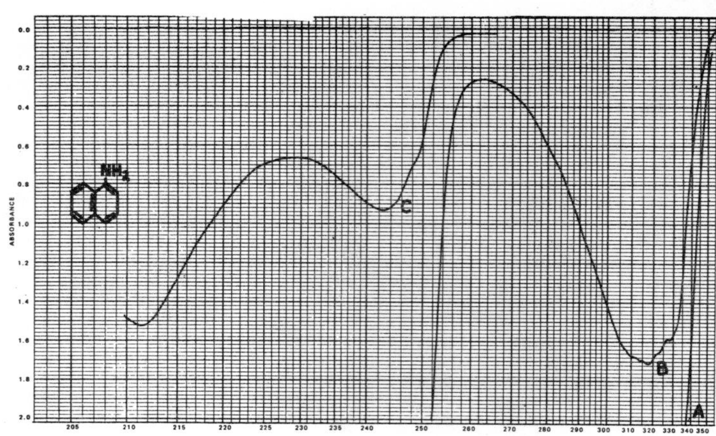

2,7-NAPHTHALENEDIAMINE

540

$C_{10}H_{10}N_2$
Mol. Wt. 158.20
M.P. 157-160°C
Solvent: Methanol

λ Max. mμ	a_m	Cell mm	Conc. g/L
340	2850	2	0.100
247.5	55000	1	0.0200

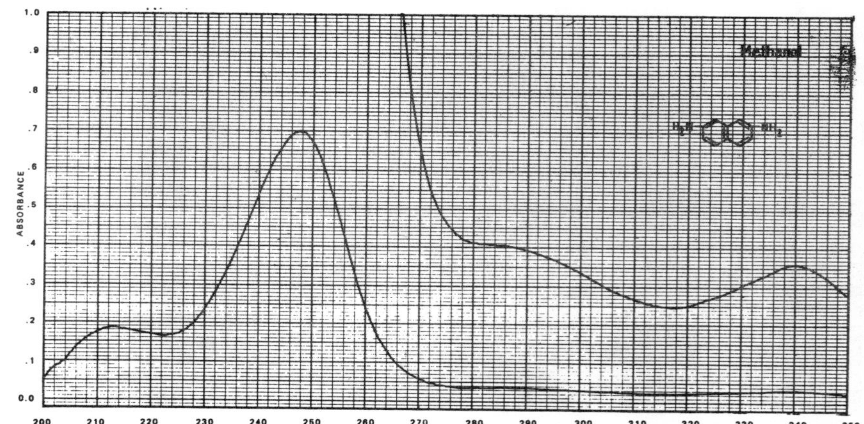

2,7-NAPHTHALENEDIAMINE

540

$C_{10}H_{10}N_2$
Mol. Wt. 158.20
M.P. 157-160°C
Solvent: Methanol HCl

λ Max. mμ	a_m	Cell mm	Conc. g/L
272	4750	10	0.0200
264.5	4600	10	0.0200
245.5	3500	10	0.0200
221	99700	1	0.0100

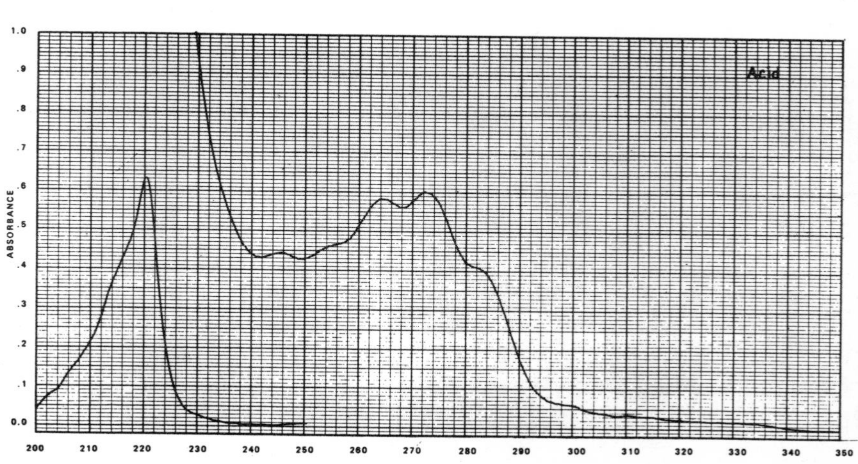

9-AMINOPHENANTHRENE 541

$C_{14}H_{11}N$
Mol. Wt. 193.25
M.P. 137-139°C
Solvent: Methanol

λ Max. mμ	a_m	Cell mm	Conc. g/L
312	7750	1	0.100
250	43100	2	0.0200
221	24700	2	0.0200
209	30900	2	0.0200

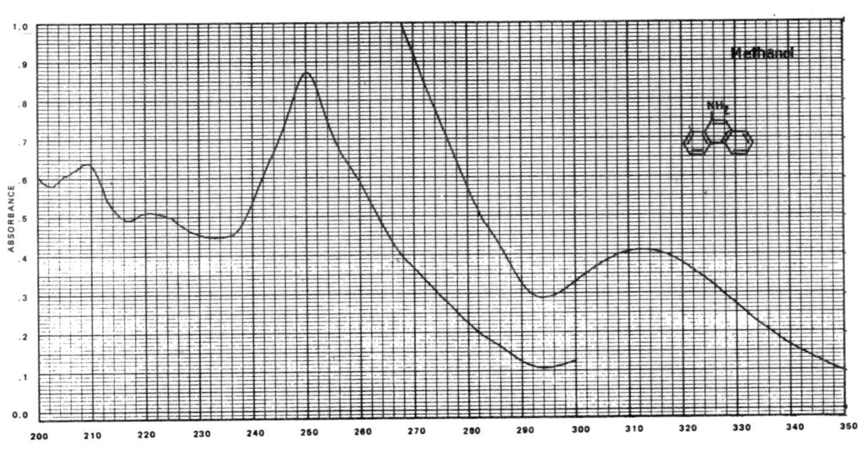

9-AMINOPHENANTHRENE 541

$C_{14}H_{11}N$
Mol. Wt. 193.25
M.P. 137-139°C
Solvent: Methanol HCl

λ Max. mμ	a_m	Cell mm	Conc. g/L
345	77	10	0.100
227.5	141	10	0.100
329	236	10	0.100
321	213	10	0.100
313.5	296	10	0.100

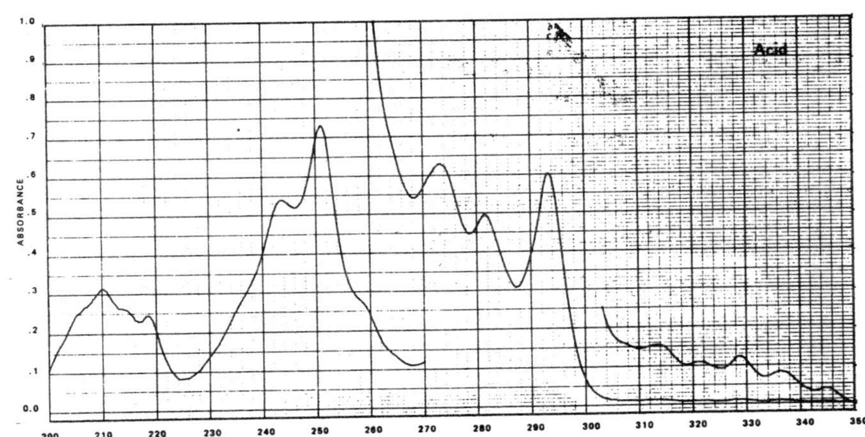

λ Max. mμ	a_m	Cell mm	Conc. g/L

NOTES

THE SECONDARY AMINES

Aliphatic and Olefinic Compounds

The aliphatic and unconjugated olefinic secondary amines do not produce any maxima in the near UV region and thus there are no spectra included in this volume for compounds 542 through 574 nor 576.

Aromatic Compounds

Substitution of the aniline NH_2 by an aliphatic group causes a bathochromic shift to longer wavelength by about 10 mμ in comparison to the parent compound, aniline.

The addition of acid to the solutions of secondary amines result in the formation of the anilinium cation with an attendant shift to shorter wavelengths, a decrease in band intensity and the appearance of benzenoid-like fine structure.

The table presented below lists the major bands of benzene, aniline and a series of secondary amine aromatic compounds.

Compound	$\lambda_{max}(\epsilon_{max})$	$\lambda_{max}(\epsilon_{max})$	Solvent	Spectrum
Benzene	204 (7900)	256 (200)	Hexane	Lit.
Aniline	234 (9910)	286 (1970)	Cyclohexane	487
N-Methylaniline	245 (11100)	294 (1890)	Methanol	582
N-Ethylaniline	246 (11000)	295 (2040)	Methanol	583
N-Methyl-o-toluidine	240 (9980)	291 (2300)	Methanol	589
N-Methyl-m-toluidine	247 (9670)	296 (1830)	Methanol	590
Diphenylamine	230 * (4430)	281 (8240)	Cyclohexane	597

*Shoulder

Pyrrole

The unsubstituted nitrogen cyclic compound, pyrrole, produces a maximum near 209 mμ with an ϵ_{max} of 6730 (spectrum 575).

Aliphatic substitution at position 2 results in a shift to longer wavelength and a slight increase in intensity (spectrum 677, λ_{max} = 215, ϵ_{max} = 8560).

PYRROLE 575

C_4H_5N

Mol. Wt. 67.09

B.P. 130.2°C

Solvent: Methanol

λ Max. mμ	a_m	Cell mm	Conc. g/L
x	x	2	1.00
209	6730	1	0.0800

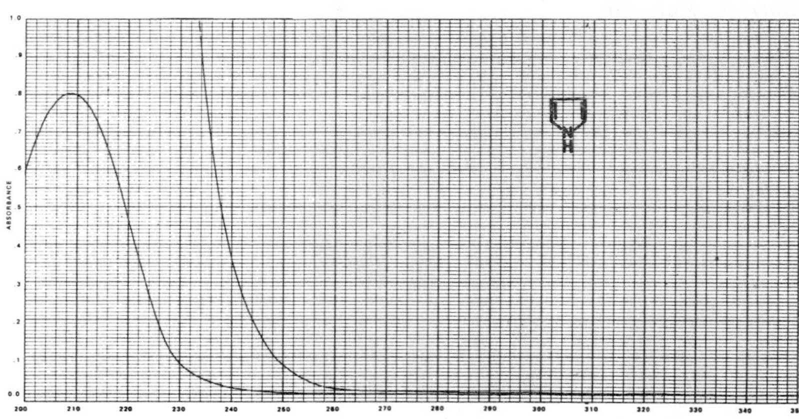

1,2,3,6-TETRAHYDROPYRIDINE 576

C_5H_9N

Mol. Wt. 83.13

M.P. 61°F

B.P. 108°C

λ Max. mμ	a_m	Cell mm	Conc. g/L

Compound does not absorb in near UV.

N-ETHYLBENZYLAMINE 577

$C_9H_{13}N$

Mol. Wt. 135.21

B.P. 79-83°C/12mm (lit.)

Solvent: Methanol

λ Max. mμ	a_m	Cell mm	Conc. g/L
263	174	10	0.398
257	249	10	0.398
251	247	10	0.398
246.5	228	10	0.398
205	9500	1	0.0800

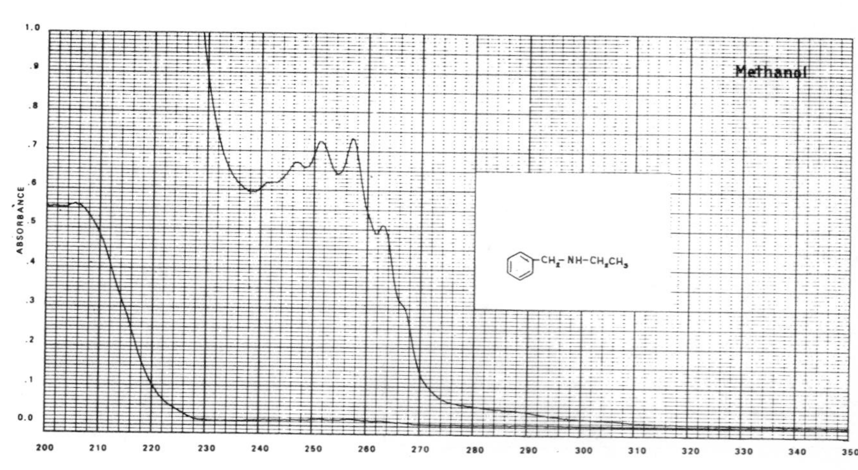

N-PROPYLBENZYLAMINE 578

$C_{10}H_{15}N$

Mol. Wt. 149.24

B.P. 102-108°C/12mm (lit.)

Solvent: Methanol

λ Max. mμ	a_m	Cell mm	Conc. g/L
263	182	10	0.400
257	265	10	0.400
251	269	10	0.400
246	256	10	0.400
x	x	1	0.0800

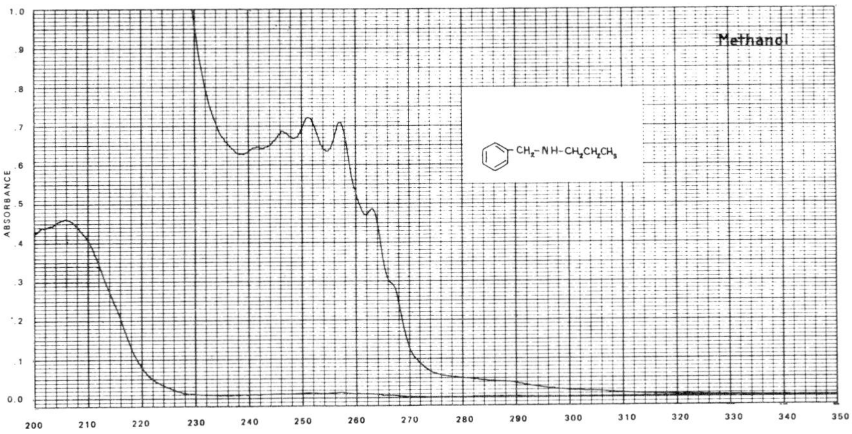

N-BUTYLBENZYLAMINE 579

$C_{11}H_{17}N$

Mol. Wt. 163.26

B.P. 120-127°C/16mm (lit.)

Solvent: Methanol

λ Max. mμ	a_m	Cell mm	Conc. g/L
263	182	10	0.439
257	260	10	0.439
251	257	10	0.439
246.5	241	10	0.439
x	x	1	0.0880

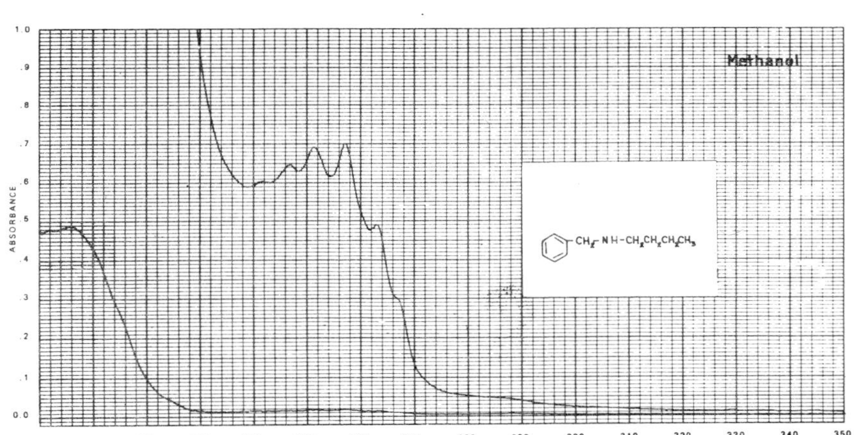

N-BUTYLBENZYLAMINE 579

$C_{11}H_{17}N$

Mol. Wt. 163.26

B.P. 120-127°C/16mm (lit.)

Solvent: Methanol HCl

λ Max. mμ	a_m	Cell mm	Conc. g/L
266.5	232	10	0.439
260.5	283	10	0.439
256.5	290	10	0.439
250.5	224	10	0.439
x	x	1	0.0880

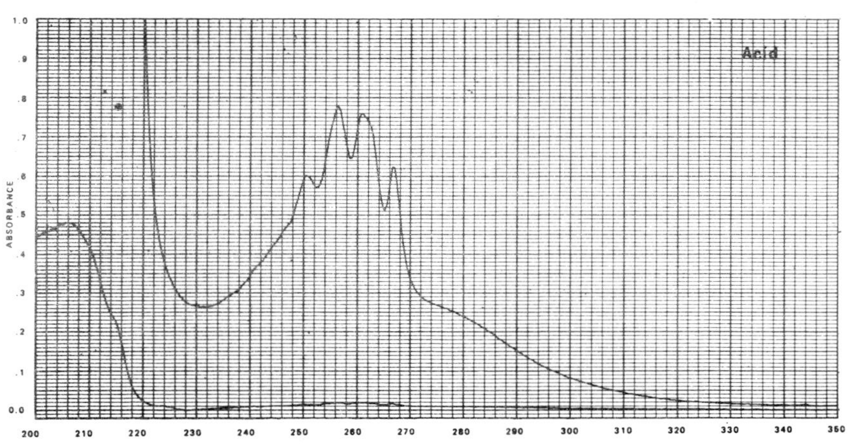

N-BENZYLETHYLENEDIAMINE

580

$C_9H_{14}N_2$
Mol. Wt. 150.23
B.P. 129-130°C/11mm
Solvent: Methanol

λ Max. mμ	a_m	Cell mm	Conc. g/L
262.5	364	5	0.467
256.5	547	5	0.467
251	564	5	0.467
246.5	540	5	0.467
241.5	508	5	0.467

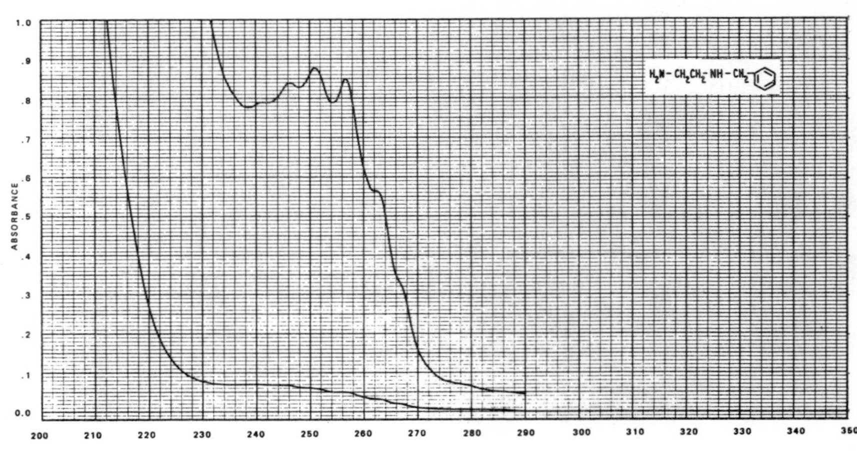

DIBENZYLAMINE

581

$C_{14}H_{15}N$
Mol. Wt. 197.27
Solvent: Methanol

λ Max. mμ	a_m	Cell mm	Conc. g/L
x	x	10	2.51
263	452	10	0.502
257	527	10	0.502
251.5	633	10	0.502
247	603	10	0.502

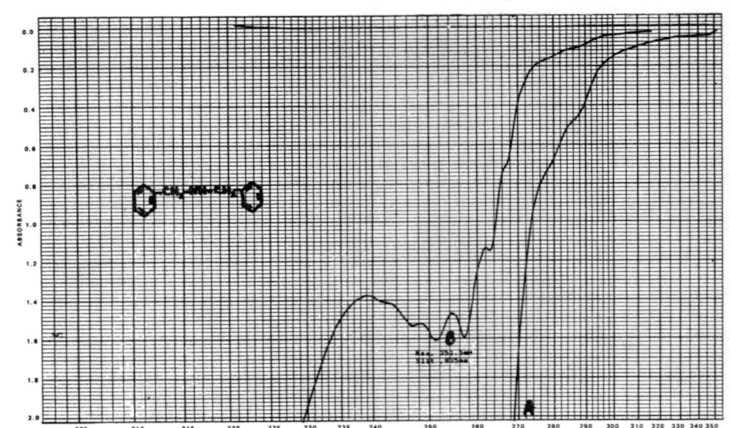

N-METHYLANILINE

582

C_7H_9N
Mol. Wt. 107.15
Solvent: Methanol

λ Max. mμ	a_m	Cell mm	Conc. g/L
294	1890	10	0.089
245	11100	10	0.009

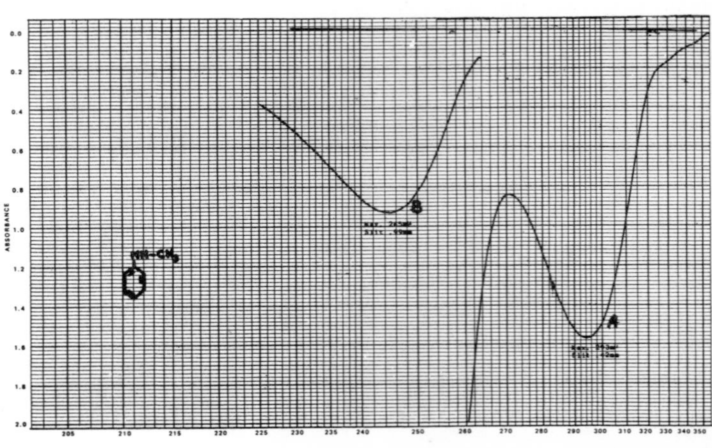

N-ETHYLANILINE

583

$C_8H_{11}N$

Mol. Wt. 121.17

M.P. -63.5°C B.P. 204.7°C/760mm

Solvent: Methanol

λ Max. mμ	a_m	Cell mm	Conc. g/L
295	2040	10	0.01
246	11000	10	0.01

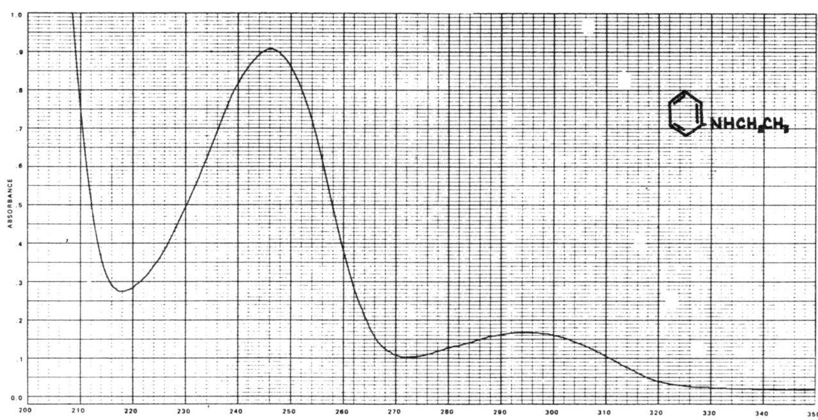

N-PROPYLANILINE

584

$C_9H_{13}N$

Mol. Wt. 135.21

B.P. 86-87°C/5mm

Solvent: Methanol

λ Max. mμ	a_m	Cell mm	Conc. g/L
297	1980	5	0.1020
248	11400	1	0.0510

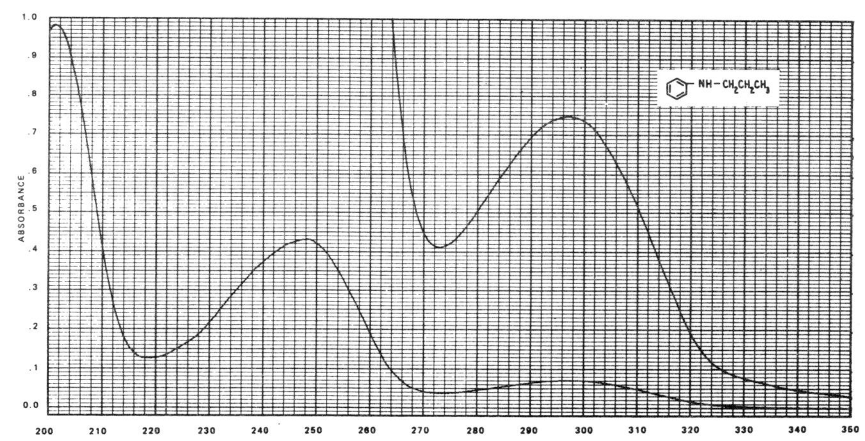

N-PROPYLANILINE

584

$C_9H_{13}N$

Mol. Wt. 135.21

B.P. 86-87°C/5mm

Solvent: Methanol HCl

λ Max. mμ	a_m	Cell mm	Conc. g/L
316	219	10	0.1020
260	291	10	0.1020
254	378	10	0.1020
248.5	403	10	0.1020
x	x	1	0.1020

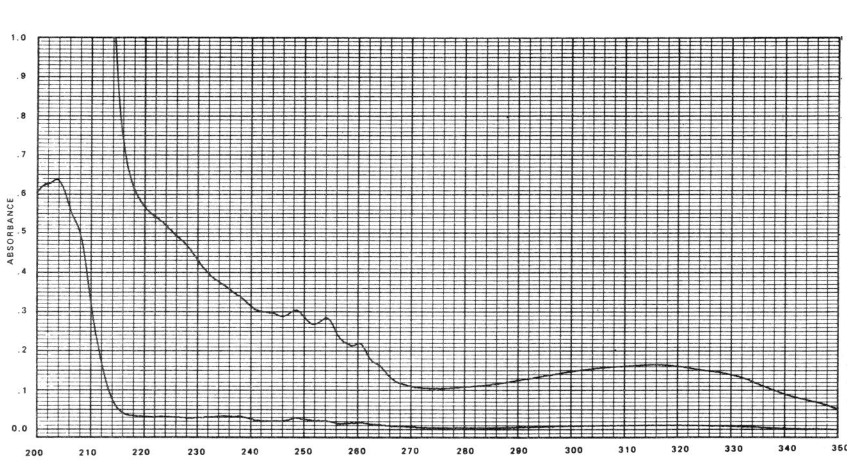

N-ISOPENTYLANILINE

585

$C_{11}H_{17}N$

Mol. Wt. 163.26

B.P. 117-119°C/10mm

Solvent: Methanol

λ Max. mμ	a_m	Cell mm	Conc. g/L
296	1840	2	0.2410
248	11600	1	0.0482
201	25500	1	0.0482

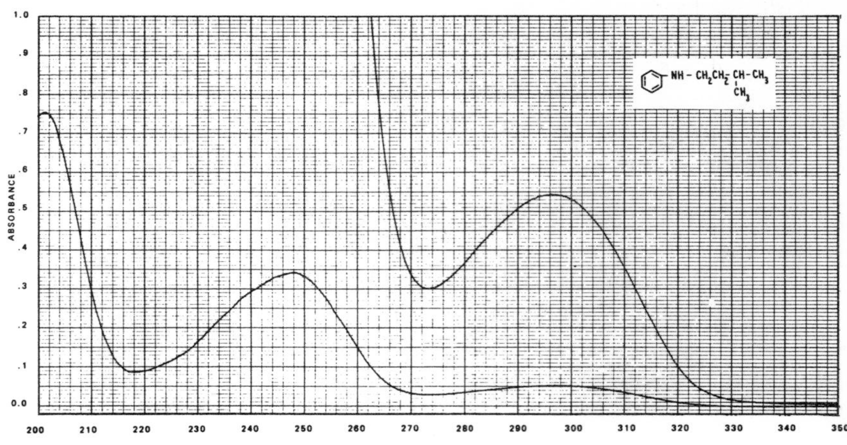

N-ISOPENTYLANILINE

585

$C_{11}H_{17}N$

Mol. Wt. 163.26

B.P. 117-119°C/10mm

Solvent: Methanol HCl

λ Max. mμ	a_m	Cell mm	Conc. g/L
260	161	10	0.241
254	217	10	0.241
248.5	204	10	0.241
244	176	10	0.241
238.5	171	10	0.241

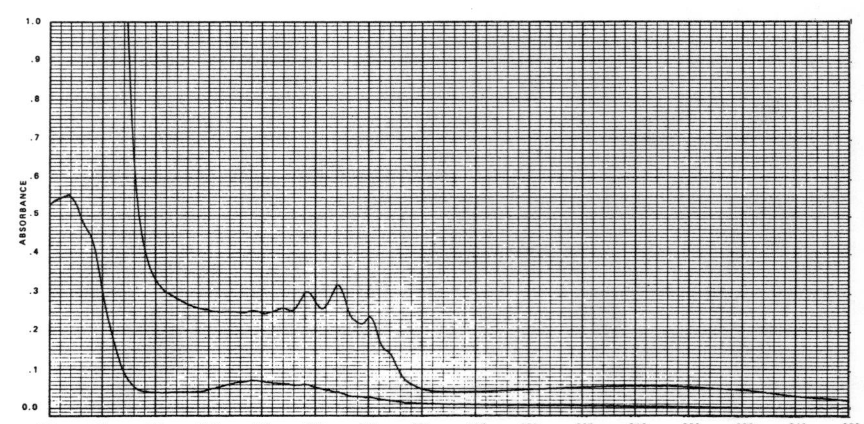

N-CYCLOHEXYLANILINE

586

$C_{12}H_{17}N$

Mol. Wt. 175.28

M.P. 7-8°C

Solvent: Methanol

λ Max. mμ	a_m	Cell mm	Conc. g/L
297	1680	2	0.2930
249	11300	1	0.1470

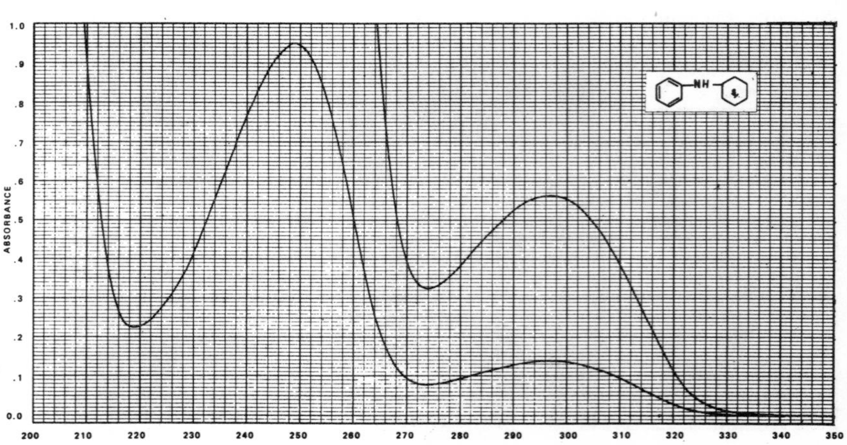

N-CYCLOHEXYLANILINE

586

$C_{12}H_{17}N$
Mol. Wt. 175.28
M.P. 7-8°C
Solvent: Methanol HCl

λ Max. mμ	a_m	Cell mm	Conc. g/L
260.5	177	10	0.2930
254.5	232	10	0.2930
249	212	10	0.2930
244.5	178	10	0.2930
239	162	10	0.2930

N-ALLYLANILINE

587

$C_9H_{11}N$
Mol. Wt. 133.19
B.P. 218-220°C
Solvent: Methanol

λ Max. mμ	a_m	Cell mm	Conc. g/L
294	1380	1	0.15260
246	8530	1	0.15260

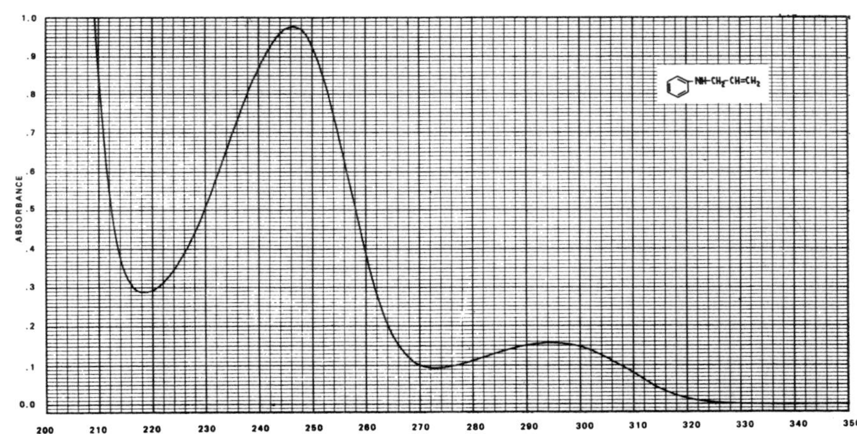

N-ALLYLANILINE

587

$C_9H_{11}N$
Mol. Wt. 133.19
B.P. 218-220°C
Solvent: Methanol HCl

λ Max. mμ	a_m	Cell mm	Conc. g/L
260	201	20	0.15260
254	251	20	0.15260
248.5	236	20	0.15260
238	206	20	0.15260
x	x	1	0.15260

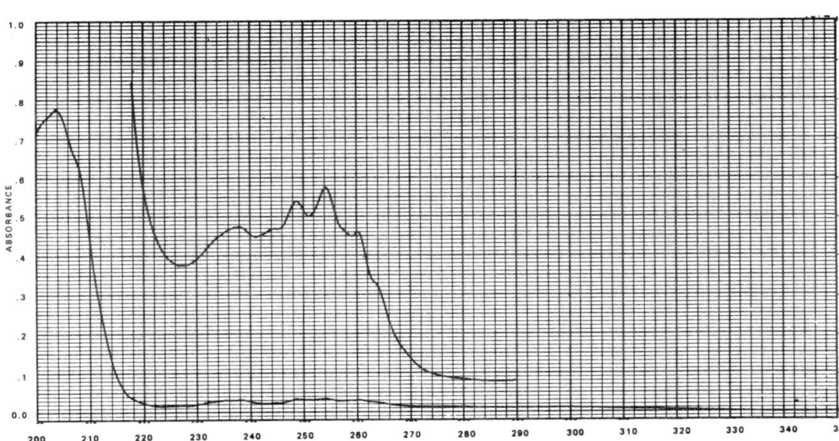

N-(1,1-DIMETHYL-2-PROPYNYL)ANILINE 588

$C_{11}H_{13}N$
Mol. Wt. 159.23
M.P. 49.5-51°C

λ Max. mμ	a_m	Cell mm	Conc. g/L

Pure sample not available.

N-METHYL-o-TOLUIDINE 589

$C_8H_{11}N$
Mol. Wt. 121.18
B.P. 98-100°C/12mm
Solvent: Methanol

λ Max. mμ	a_m	Cell mm	Conc. g/L
291	2300	1	0.117
240	9980	1	0.117

N-METHYL-o-TOLUIDINE 589

$C_8H_{11}N$
Mol. Wt. 121.18
B.P. 98-100°C/12mm
Solvent: Methanol HCl

λ Max. mμ	a_m	Cell mm	Conc. g/L
267.5	309	10	0.117
260.5	331	10	0.117
256	302	10	0.117
206.5	7900	1	0.117

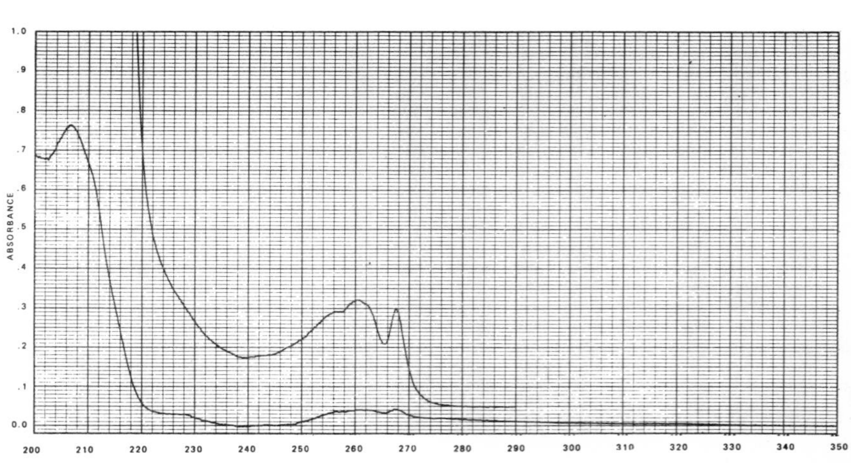

N-METHYL-m-TOLUIDINE

590

$C_8H_{11}N$

Mol. Wt. 121.18

B.P. 86-87°C/7mm

Solvent: Methanol

λ Max. mμ	a_m	Cell mm	Conc. g/L
295	1830	5	0.094
246.3	9670	1	0.094

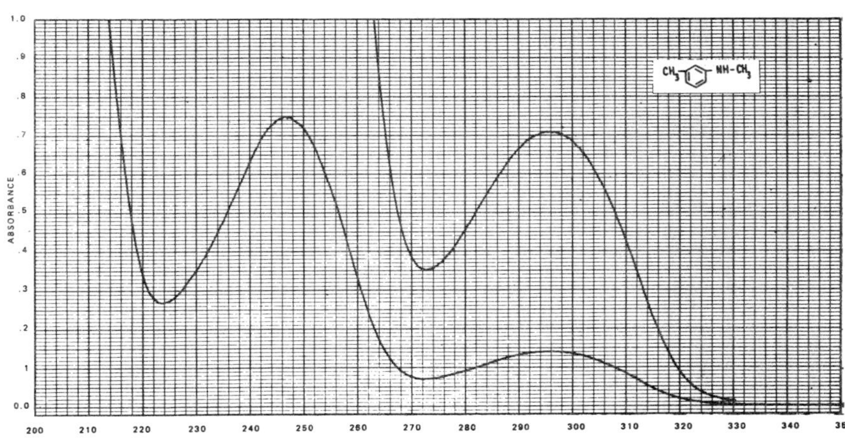

N-METHYL-m-TOLUIDINE

590

$C_8H_{11}N$

Mol. Wt. 121.18

B.P. 86-87°C/7mm

Solvent: Methanol HCl

λ Max. mμ	a_m	Cell mm	Conc. g/L
322	52	20	0.094
268.5	316	20	0.094
261.5	339	20	0.094
208	7750	1	0.094

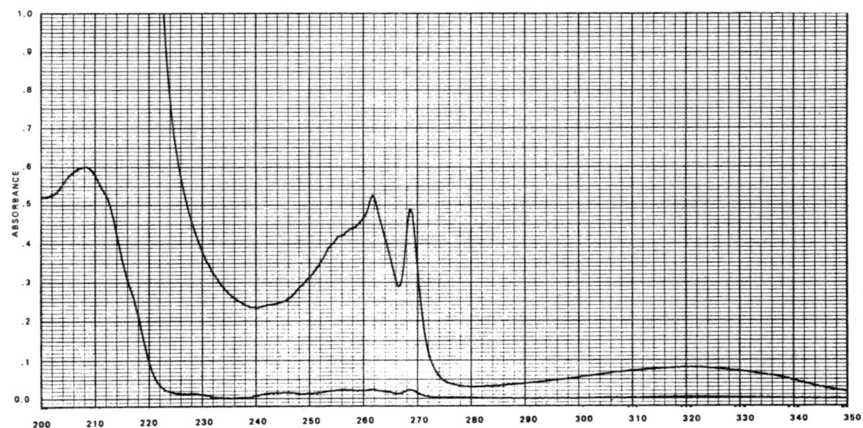

λ Max. mμ	a_m	Cell mm	Conc. g/L

591

N-METHYL-p-TOLUIDINE

C_6H_6ClN
Mol. Wt. 121.18
M.P. 88-90°C/10mm
Solvent: Methanol

λ Max. mμ	a_m	Cell mm	Conc. g/L
294.5	2690	1	0.100
241.5	10100	1	0.100
x	x	0.5	0.100

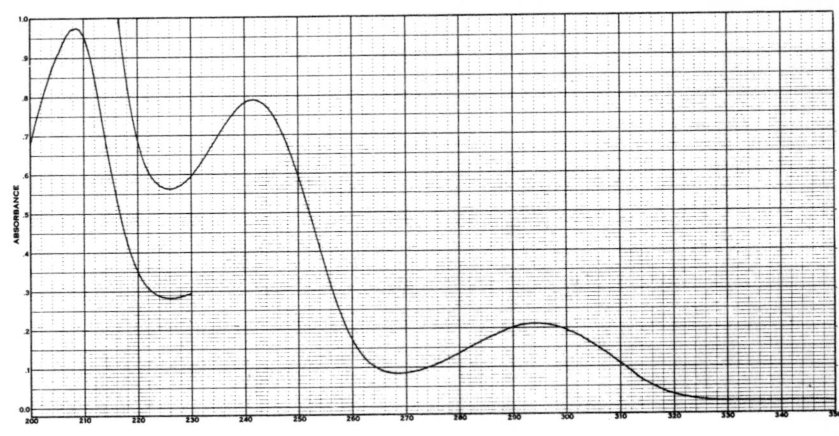

591

N-METHYL-p-TOLUIDINE

C_6H_6ClN
Mol. Wt. 121.18
M.P. 88-90°C/10mm
Solvent: Methanol HCl

λ Max. mμ	a_m	Cell mm	Conc. g/L
272.5	256	20	0.100
265.5	276	20	0.100
256	248	20	0.100
250.5	262	20	0.100

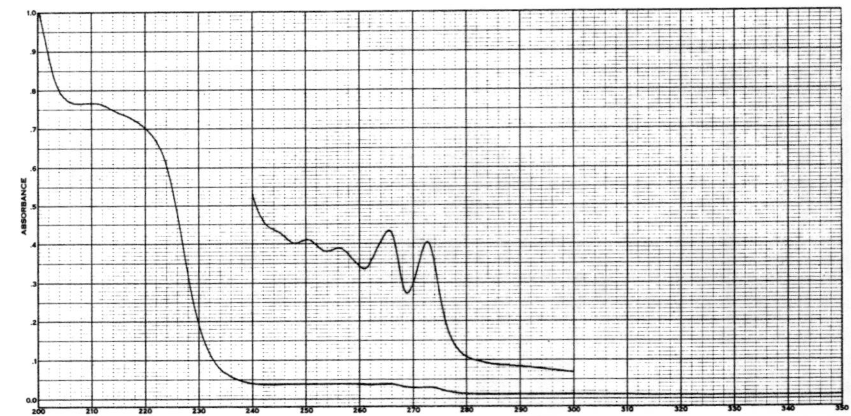

592

N-METHYLCUMIDINE

$C_{10}H_{15}N$
Mol. Wt. 149.24
Solvent: Methanol

λ Max. mμ	a_m	Cell mm	Conc. g/L
296.5	1800	10	0.077
243.5	11400	10	0.010

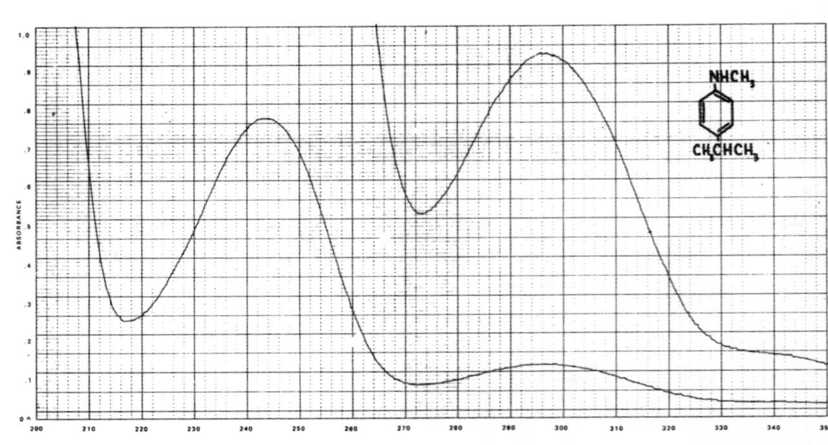

N-METHYLCUMIDINE 592

$C_{10}H_{15}N$
Mol. Wt. 149.24
Solvent: Methanol HCl

λ Max. mμ	a_m	Cell mm	Conc. g/L
330	394	10	0.155
267	250	10	0.155
257	404	10	0.155
234.5	598	10	0.155
208.5	8380	1	0.155

Acid

N-ETHYL-p-TOLUIDINE 593

$C_9H_{13}N$
Mol. Wt. 135.21
B.P. 101-102°C/10mm
Solvent: Methanol

λ Max. mμ	a_m	Cell mm	Conc. g/L
299	1560	2	0.3440
245	9870	1	0.03440

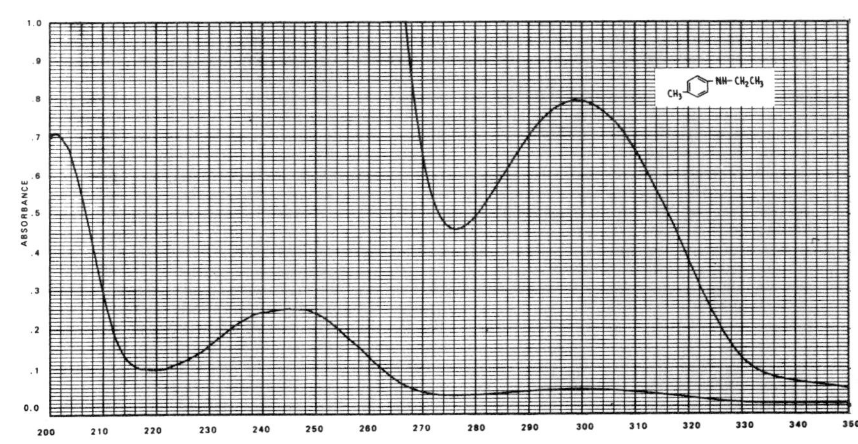

N-ETHYL-p-TOLUIDINE 593

$C_9H_{13}N$
Mol. Wt. 135.21
B.P. 101-102°C/10mm
Solvent: Methanol HCl

λ Max. mμ	a_m	Cell mm	Conc. g/L
328	134	10	0.3440
269	183	10	0.3440
260	268	10	0.3440
253	250	10	0.3440
244	251	10	0.3440

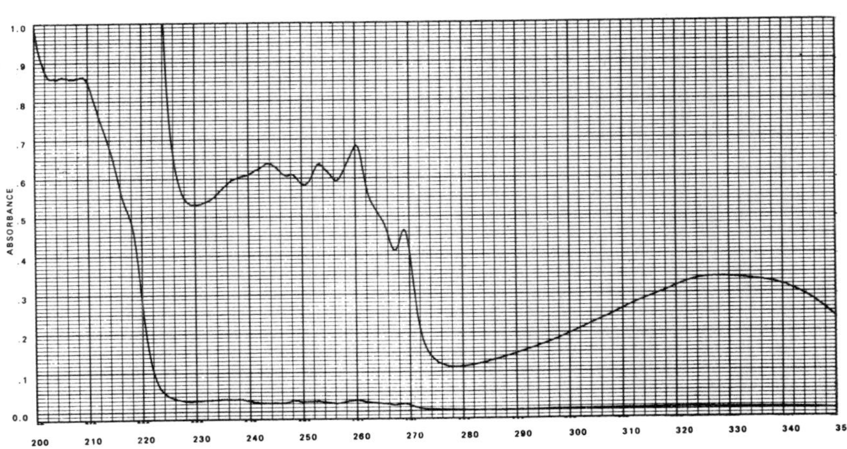

N-PHENYLBENZYLAMINE

594

$C_{13}H_{13}N$

Mol. Wt. 183.26

M.P. 37-39°C

Solvent: Methanol

λ Max. mμ	a_m	Cell mm	Conc. g/L
295	1940	5	0.100
246.5	12400	1	0.100

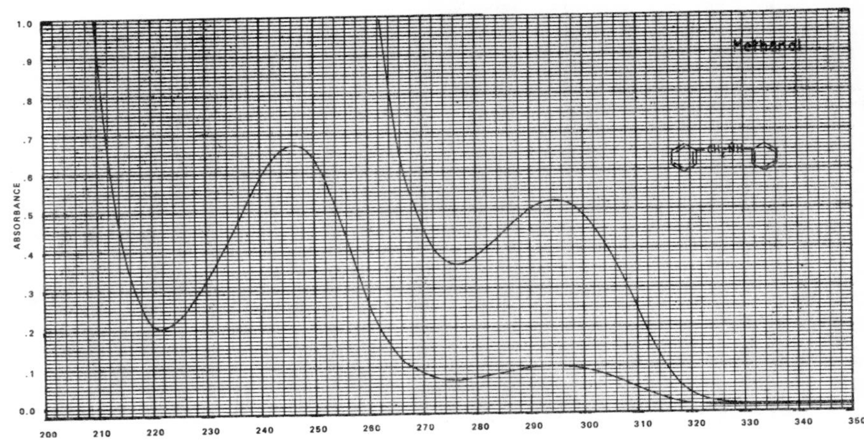

N-PHENYLBENZYLAMINE

594

$C_{13}H_{13}N$

Mol. Wt. 183.26

M.P. 37-39°C

Solvent: Methanol HCl

λ Max. mμ	a_m	Cell mm	Conc. g/L
267	215	20	0.100
260.5	386	20	0.100
255	431	20	0.100
250	376	20	0.100
x	x	1	0.100

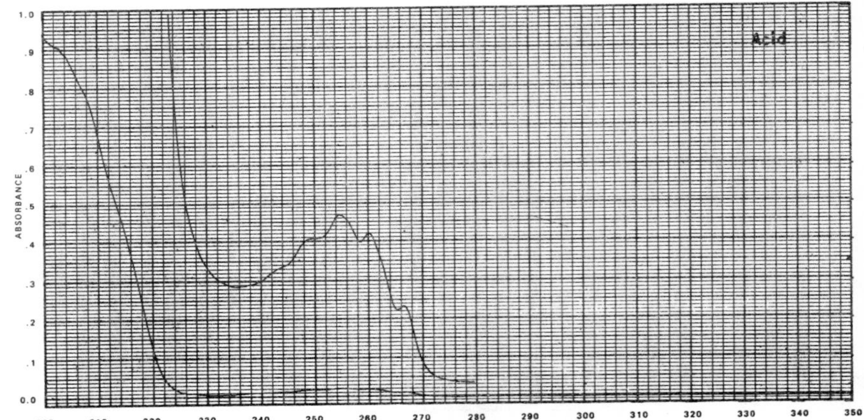

N-BENZYL-o-TOLUIDINE

595

$C_{14}H_{15}N$

Mol. Wt. 197.28

Solvent: Methanol

λ Max. mμ	a_m	Cell mm	Conc. g/L
292	3210	4	0.100
243	14600	1	0.100

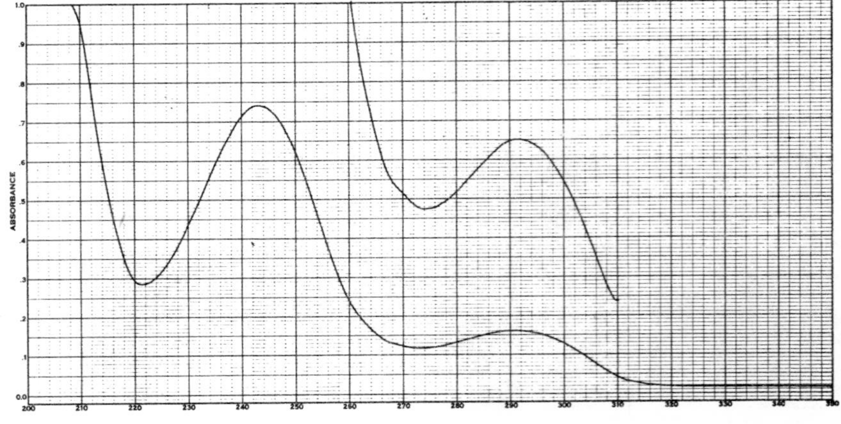

N-BENZYL-o-TOLUIDINE **595**

$C_{14}H_{15}N$
Mol. Wt. 197.28
Solvent: Methanol HCl

λ Max. mμ	a_m	Cell mm	Conc. g/L
267.5	612	20	0.100
261	779	20	0.100
256.5	730	20	0.100
x	x	1	0.100

N-BENZYL-p-TOLUIDINE **596**

$C_{14}H_{15}N$
Mol. Wt. 197.28
B.P. 178-180°C/10mm
Solvent: Methanol

λ Max. mμ	a_m	Cell mm	Conc. g/L
302	2010	2	0.200
248.5	12700	1	0.040

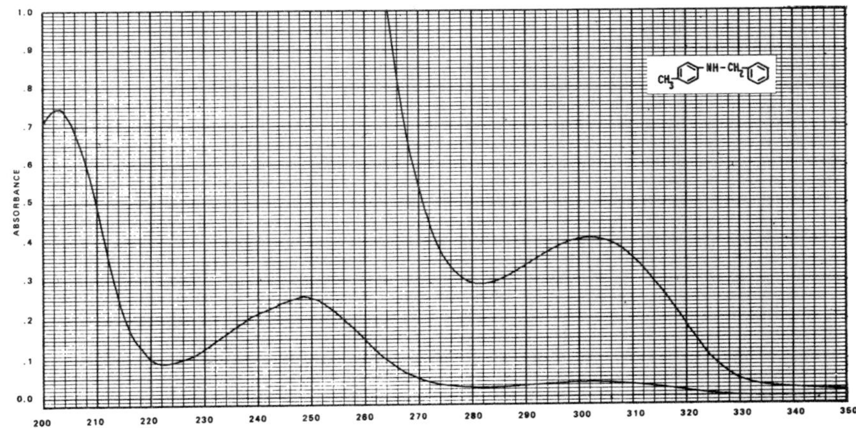

N-BENZYL-p-TOLUIDINE **596**

$C_{14}H_{15}N$
Mol. Wt. 197.28
B.P. 178-180°C/10mm
Solvent: Methanol HCl

λ Max. mμ	a_m	Cell mm	Conc. g/L
325	69	10	0.200
268	375	10	0.200
261	535	10	0.200
257.5	530	10	0.200
253	463	10	0.200

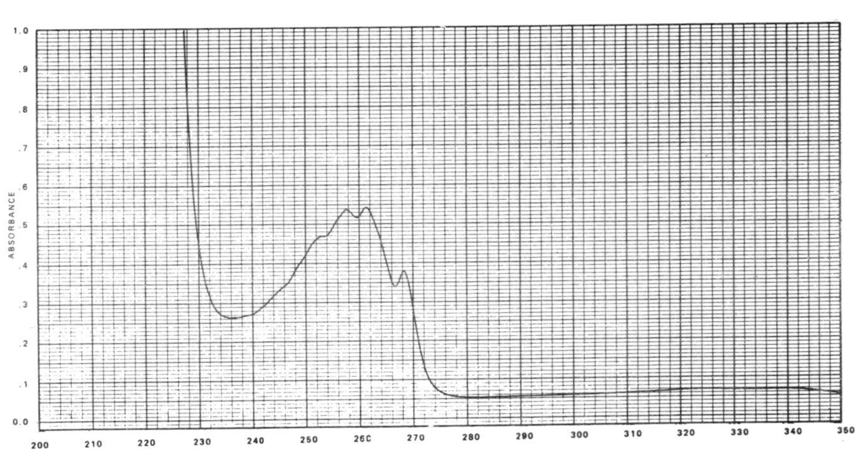

DIPHENYLAMINE 597

$C_{12}H_{11}N$
Mol. Wt. 69.22
Solvent: Cyclohexane

λ Max. mμ	a_m	Cell mm	Conc. g/L
x	x	10	2.00
281	8240	10	0.010

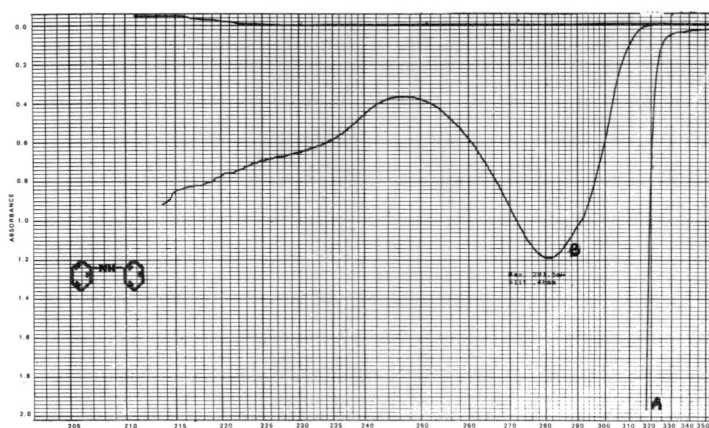

N,N'-DI-sec-BUTYL-p-PHENYLENEDIAMINE 598

$C_{14}H_{24}N_2$
Mol. Wt. 220.36
Solvent: Methanol

λ Max. mμ	a_m	Cell mm	Conc. g/L
x	x	20	0.1690
263	20900	1	0.100

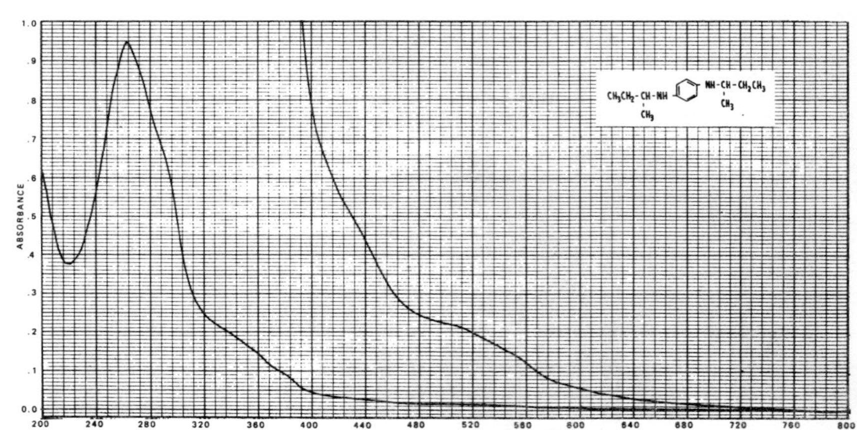

N,N'-DI-sec-BUTYL-p-PHENYLENEDIAMINE 598

$C_{14}H_{24}N_2$
Mol. Wt. 220.36
Solvent: Methanol HCl

λ Max. mμ	a_m	Cell mm	Conc. g/L
551	945	10	0.100
511	1260	10	0.100
261	10600	1	0.100

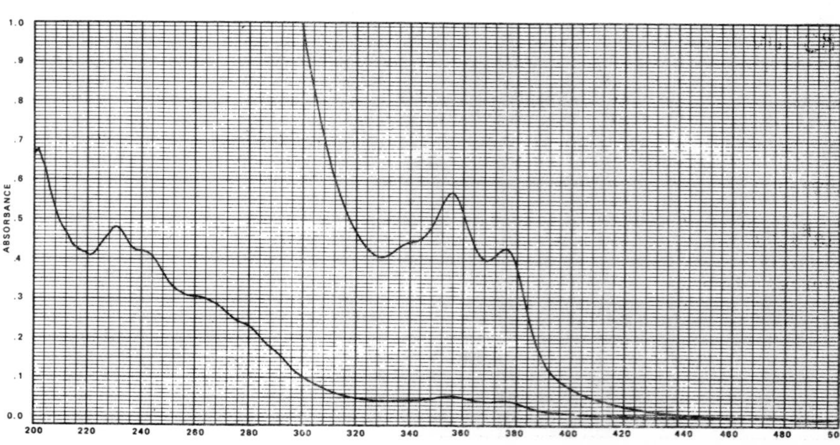

N-METHYL-1-NAPHTHYLAMINE

$C_{11}H_{11}N$
Mol. Wt. 157.22
B.P. 171-173°C/17mm
Solvent: Methanol

λ Max. mμ	a_m	Cell mm	Conc. g/L
416	102	20	0.260
332	6620	2	0.0520
248	16900	1	0.026
212	49000	1	0.026

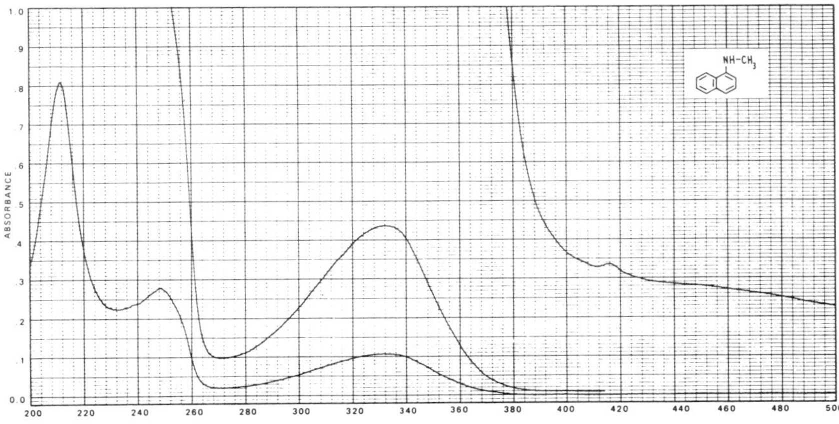

N-METHYL-1-NAPHTHYLAMINE

$C_{11}H_{11}N$
Mol. Wt. 157.22
B.P. 171-173°C/17mm
Solvent: Methanol HCl

λ Max. mμ	a_m	Cell mm	Conc. g/L
504	156	20	0.260
316	9580	2	0.052
311	11100	2	0.052
279	539	5	0.260
221	82100	1	0.013

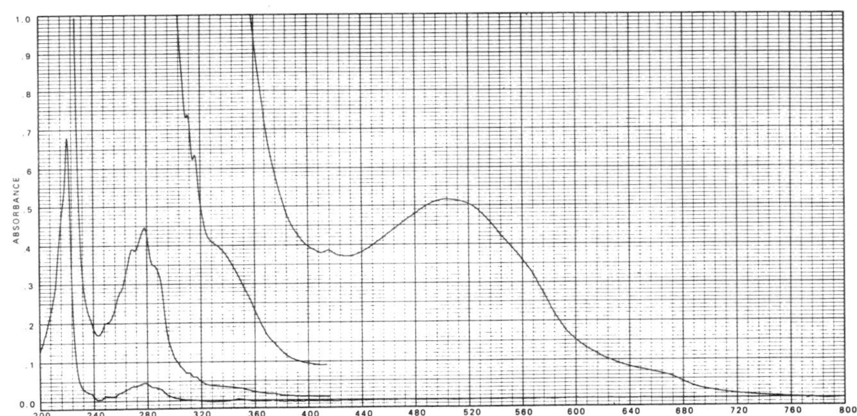

λ Max. mμ	a_m	Cell mm	Conc. g/L

N-ETHYL-1-NAPHTHYLAMINE 600

$C_{12}H_{13}N$

Mol. Wt. 171.24

Solvent: Methanol

λ Max. mμ	a_m	Cell mm	Conc. g/L
331	6450	10	0.0170
247.5	20500	1	0.0170
211.5	48400	1	0.0170

N-ETHYL-1-NAPHTHYLAMINE 600

$C_{12}H_{13}N$

Mol. Wt. 171.24

Solvent: Methanol HCl

λ Max. mμ	a_m	Cell mm	Conc. g/L
316	776	5	0.172
311	936	5	0.172
279	6270	1	0.172
270	5580	1	0.172
221	48600	1	0.0170

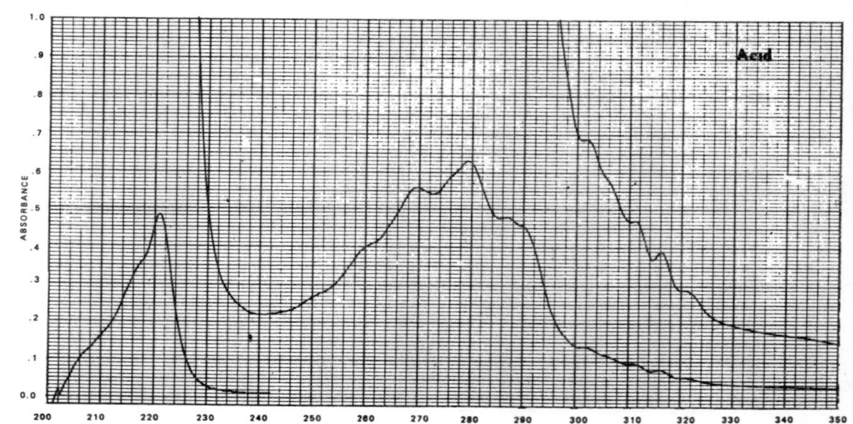

1,2,3,4-TETRAHYDROQUINOLINE 601

$C_9H_{11}N$

Mol. Wt. 133.19

M.P. 15-16°C

Solvent: Methanol

λ Max. mμ	a_m	Cell mm	Conc. g/L
300.5	1900	2	0.330
249	7200	2	0.0660
205	25800	1	0.0330

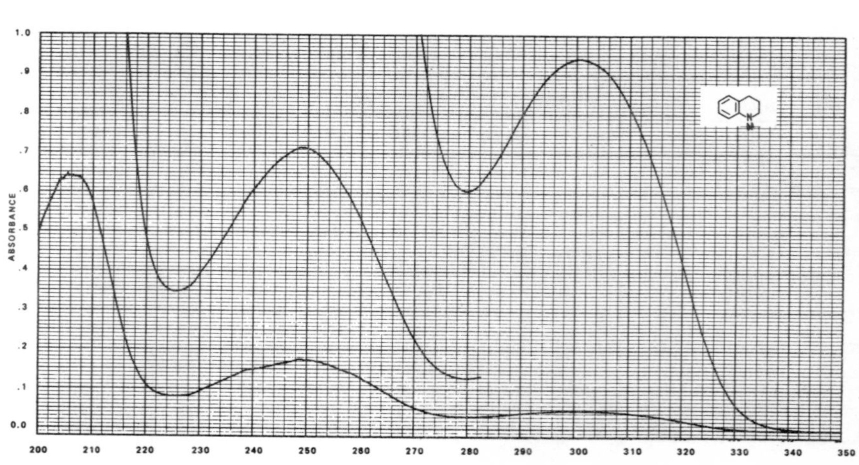

1,2,3,4-TETRAHYDROQUINOLINE

601

$C_9H_{11}N$
Mol. Wt. 133.19
M.P. 15-16°C
Solvent: Methanol HCl

λ Max. mμ	a_m	Cell mm	Conc. g/L
315	41	10	0.330
268.5	294	10	0.330
261	329	10	0.330
235	281	10	0.330
x	x	2	0.0660

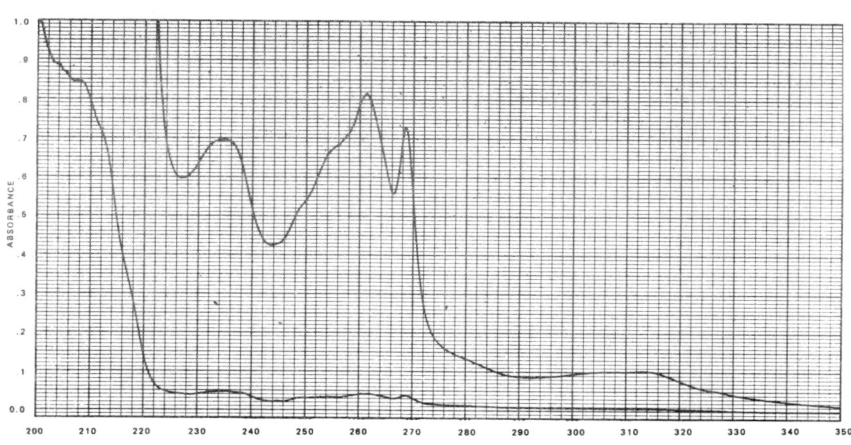

1,2,3,4-TETRAHYDROQUINALDINE

602

$C_{10}H_{13}N$
Mol. Wt. 147.22
Solvent: Methanol

λ Max. mμ	a_m	Cell mm	Conc. g/L
314.5	1990	5	0.100
301.0	2320	5	0.100
295.0	2150	5	0.100
248	6490	1	0.100
232.5	10300	1	0.100
228.5	9910	1	0.100

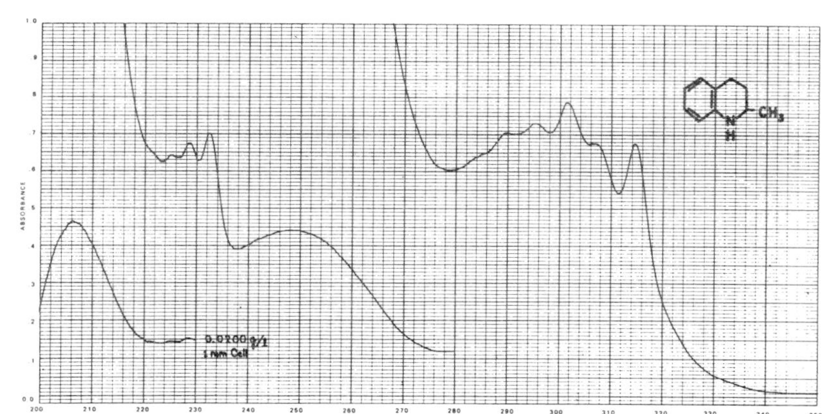

1,2,3,4-TETRAHYDROQUINALDINE

602

$C_{10}H_{13}N$
Mol. Wt. 147.22
Solvent: Methanol HCl

λ Max. mμ	a_m	Cell mm	Conc. g/L
316	1960	5	0.100
309	1760	5	0.100
268	950	1	1.00
261	816	1	1.00
238	40700	1	0.0200

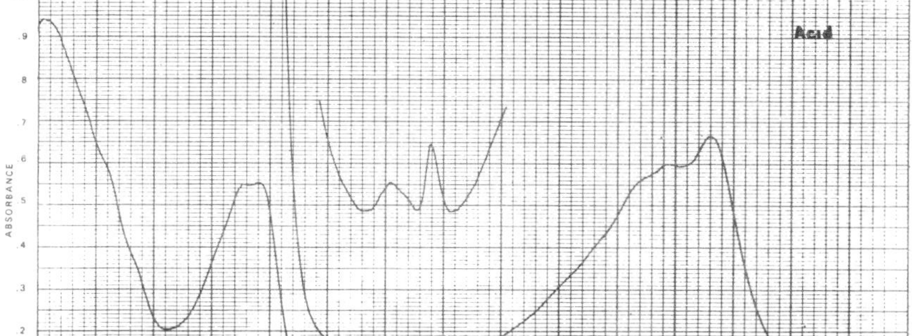

1,2,3,4-TETRAHYDROISOQUINOLINE

603

$C_9H_{11}N$

Mol. Wt. 133.20

Solvent: Cyclohexane

λ Max. mμ	a_m	Cell mm	Conc. g/L
x	x	10	2.600
316	174	10	1.300
310	116	10	1.300
302	136	10	1.300
296	109	10	1.300
289.5	117	10	1.300
272.5	676	10	0.260
265	740	10	0.260
258	712	10	0.260
x	x	10	0.026

N-PHENYL-1-NAPHTHYLAMINE

604

$C_{16}H_{13}N$

Mol. Wt. 219.29

M.P. 59.5-60.5°C

Solvent: Methanol

λ Max. mμ	a_m	Cell mm	Conc. g/L
338	8790	1	0.100
252	17500	1	0.100
217	65700	2	0.0100

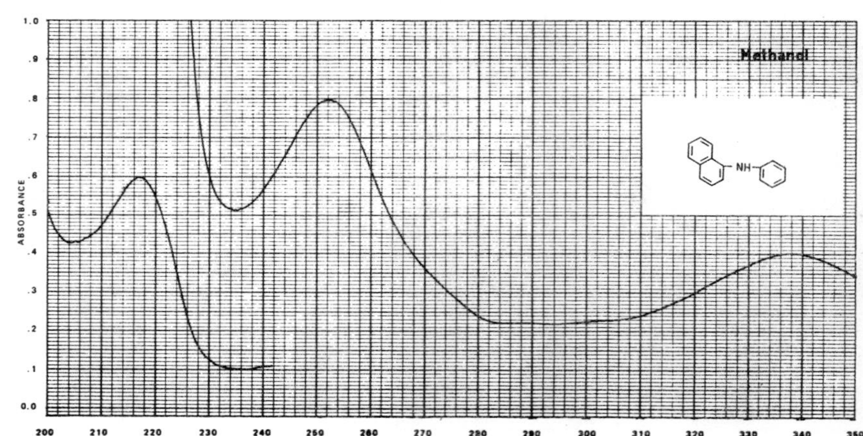

INDOLE

605

C_8H_7N

Mol. Wt. 117.14

M.P. 52.5°C (lit.)

Solvent: Cyclohexane

λ Max. mμ	a_m	Cell mm	Conc. g/L
x	x	10	1.890
287	4160	10	0.019
279	6460	10	0.019
266.5	6660	10	0.019
261	6410	10	0.019
214.5	36200	10	0.002

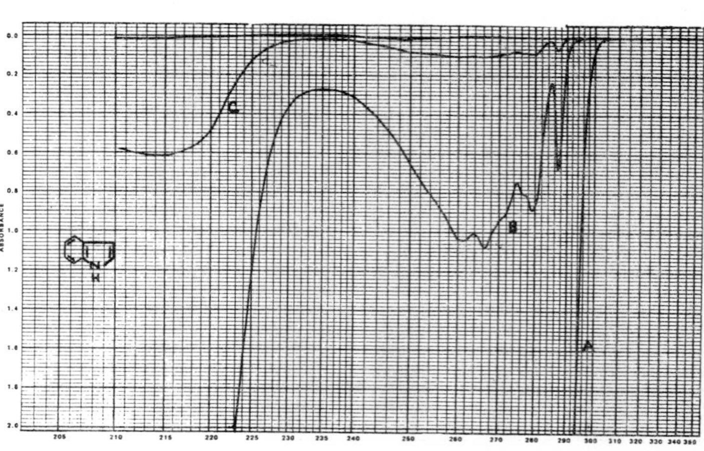

2-METHYLINDOLE

606

C_9H_9N

Mol. Wt. 131.17

M.P. 61°C B.P. 271°C/760mm

Solvent: Methanol

λ Max. mμ	a_m	Cell mm	Conc. g/L
290	3460	10	0.020
283	3910	10	0.020
260.5	5180	10	0.020
225	22600	10	0.005

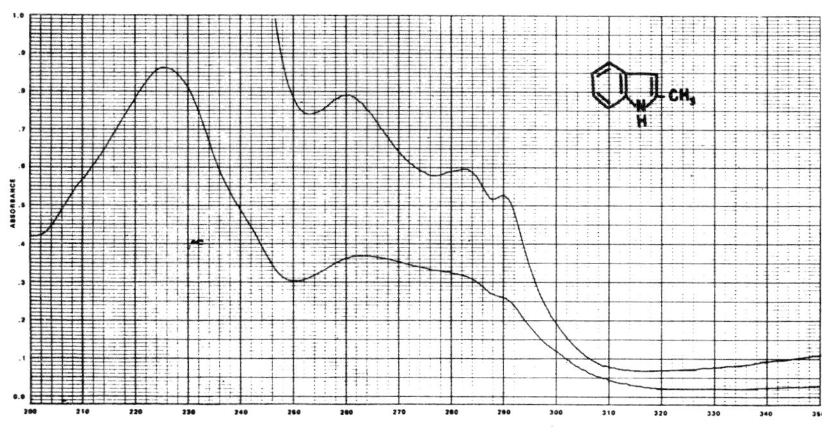

3-METHYLINDOLE

607

C_9H_9N

Mol. Wt. 131.18

Solvent: Methanol

λ Max. mμ	a_m	Cell mm	Conc. g/L
290	4700	2	0.100
282	5640	2	0.100
223	35500	1	0.0200

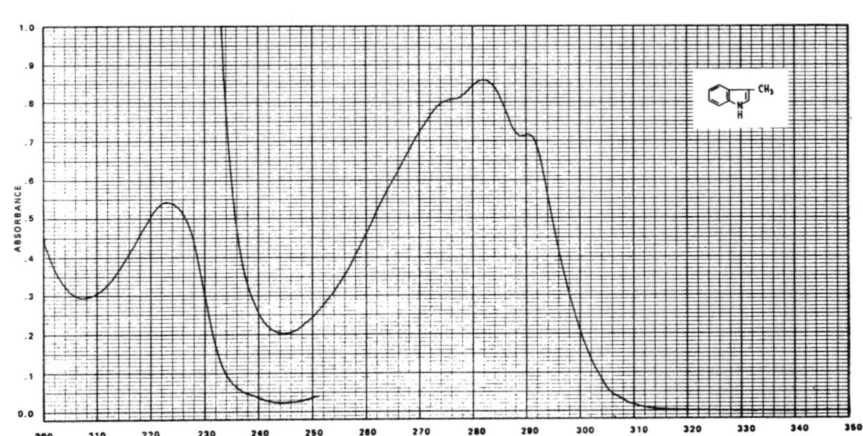

λ Max. mμ	a_m	Cell mm	Conc. g/L

4-METHYLINDOLE

608

C_9H_9N

Mol. Wt. 131.18

Solvent: Methanol

λ Max. mμ	a_m	Cell mm	Conc. g/L
288	2220	2	0.100
268	4260	2	0.100
218	21500	0.5	0.100

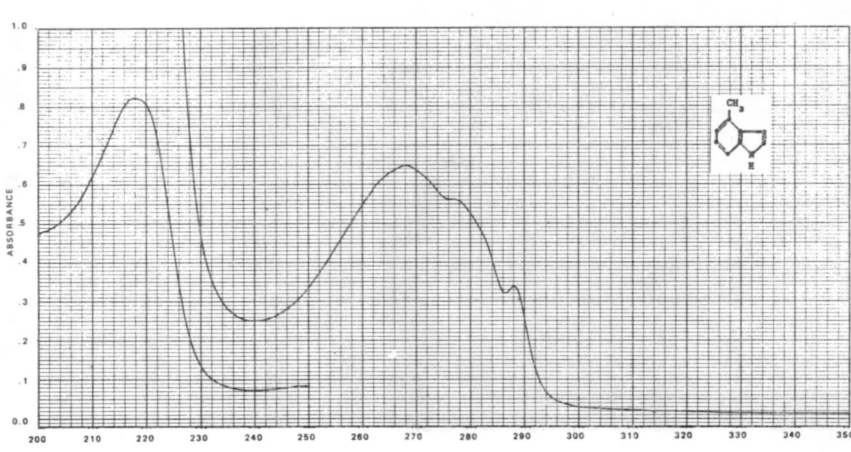

4-METHYLINDOLE

608

C_9H_9N

Mol. Wt. 131.18

Solvent: Methanol HCl

λ Max. mμ	a_m	Cell mm	Conc. g/L
286.5	2350	2	0.100
266.3	4360	2	0.100
217.5	20500	0.5	0.100

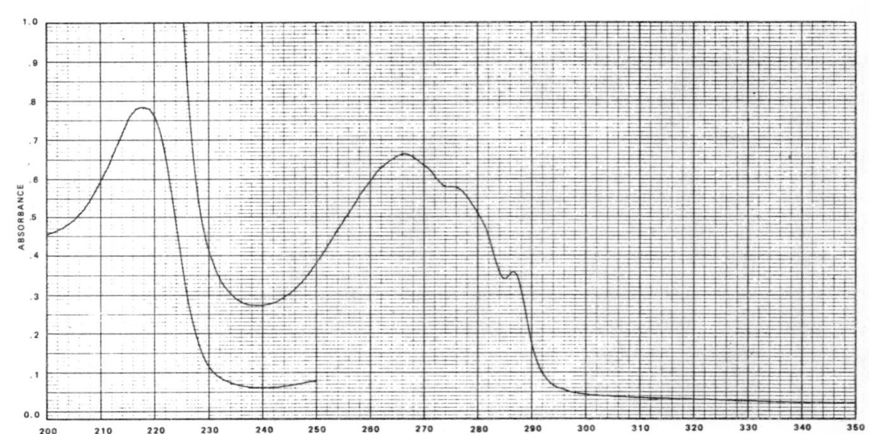

2,3-DIMETHYLINDOLE

609

$C_{10}H_{11}N$

Mol. Wt. 145.21

Solvent: Methanol

λ Max. mμ	a_m	Cell mm	Conc. g/L
292	5750	10	0.010
284	6680	10	0.010
227.5	33200	10	0.002

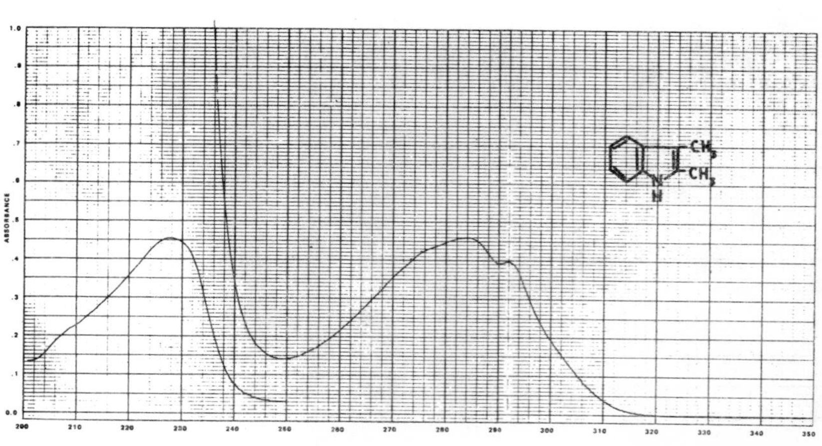

3-[(DIMETHYLAMINO)METHYL] INDOLE

610

$C_{11}H_{14}N_2$
Mol. Wt. 174.25
M.P. 134°C
Solvent: Methanol

λ Max. mμ	a_m	Cell mm	Conc. g/L
288	4870	2	0.0800
278.5	6110	2	0.0800
272	5910	2	0.0800
216.5	36800	1	0.0400

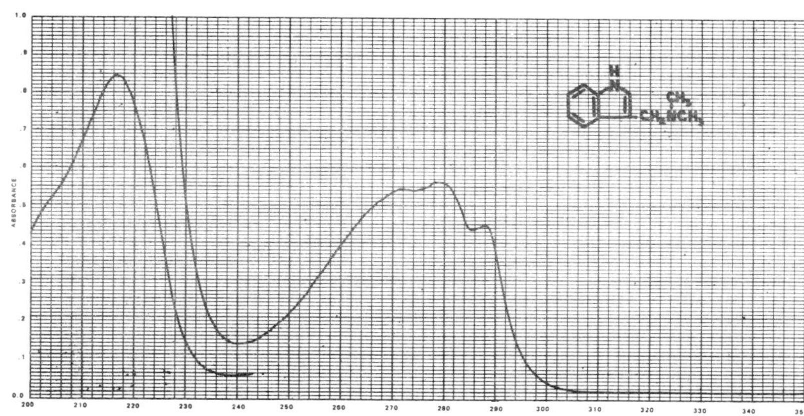

3-[(DIMETHYLAMINO)METHYL] INDOLE

610

$C_{11}H_{14}N_2$
Mol. Wt. 174.25
M.P. 134°C
Solvent: Methanol HCl

λ Max. mμ	a_m	Cell mm	Conc. g/L
286.5	5530	2	0.0800
278.5	6320	2	0.0800
275.5	6320	2	0.0800
269	6500	2	0.0800
214	42700	1	0.0400

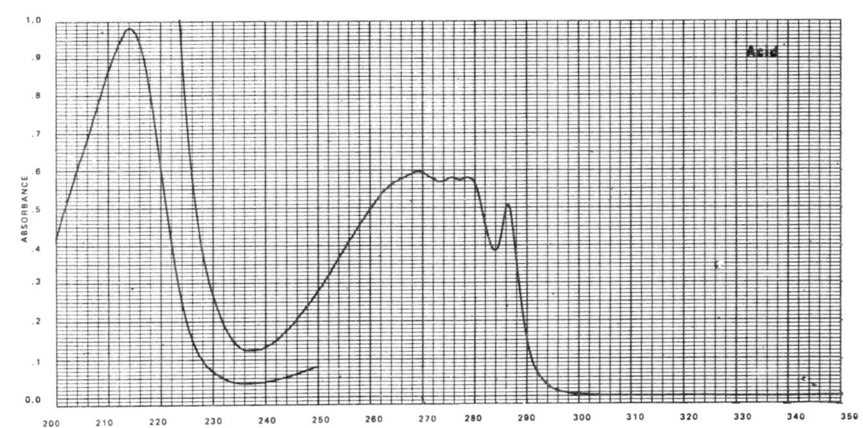

1,2,3,4-TETRAHYDROCARBAZOLE

611

$C_{12}H_{13}N$
Mol. Wt. 171.24
M.P. 113-116°C
Solvent: Methanol

λ Max. mμ	a_m	Cell mm	Conc. g/L
281	6850	1	0.100
226.5	32700	1	0.0500

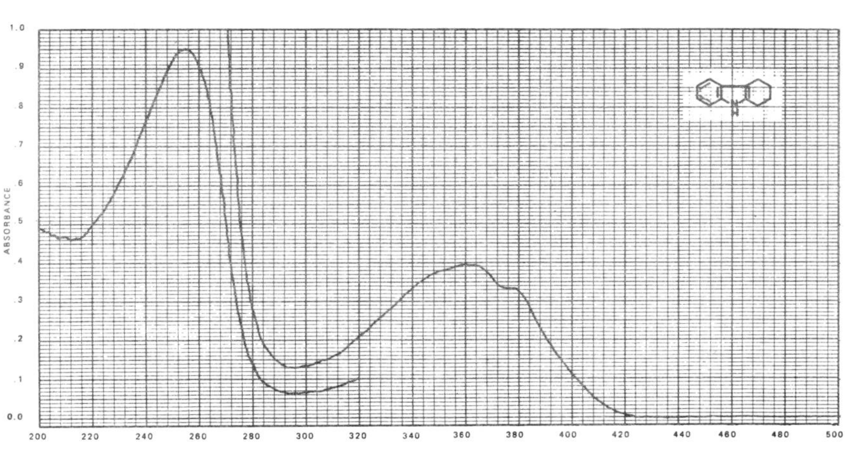

CARBAZOLE

$C_{12}H_9N$

Mol. Wt. 167.21

Solvent: Methanol

λ Max. mμ	a_m	Cell mm	Conc. g/L
334.5	3130	10	0.0300
322	3570	10	0.0300
291.5	18500	1	0.0300
255.5	19900	1	0.0300
233	45900	1	0.0300

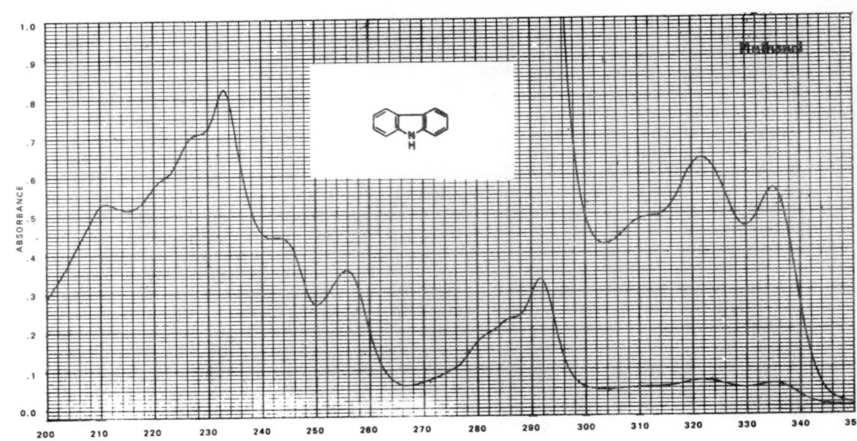

λ Max. mμ	a_m	Cell mm	Conc. g/L

λ Max. mμ	a_m	Cell mm	Conc. g/L

THE TERTIARY AMINES

Aliphatic Compounds

For all practical purposes, the aliphatic tertiary amines do not display maxima in the near UV region above 215 mμ. Several compounds do however absorb in the solvent cut-off region between 200 and 215 mμ, i.e. triethylamine at 203 mμ (3100), trimethylamine at 199 mμ (3950) and N-methylpiperidine at 213 mμ (1600).

Due to the questionable nature of maxima in the 200 - 215 mμ range, there are no spectra in this volume for compounds 613 through 638, 642 nor 643.

Aromatic Compounds

The N,N-disubstituted anilines undergo an additional bathochromic shift in comparison to the N-substituted secondary amines with little or no increase in band intensity.

The compounds react to the addition to acid in a manner analogous to that observed for the primary and secondary amines, i.e. a decrease in ϵ_{max}, a shift to shorter wavelength and the appearance of fine structure similar to that of benzene.

A table of reference compounds and tertiary amine aromatics is given below.

Compound	$\lambda_{max}(\epsilon_{max})$	$\lambda_{max}(\epsilon_{max})$	Solvent	Spectrum
Aniline	234 (9910)	286 (1970)	Cyclohexane	487
N-Methylaniline	245 (11100)	294 (1890)	Methanol	582
N,N-Dimethylaniline	251 (11600)	298 (2290)	Methanol	648
N,N-Diethylaniline	260 (13900)	304 (1940)	Methanol	649
Triphenylamine	227 * (9322)	297 (24800)	Methanol	657
N,N-Dimethyl-o-toluidine	242 (8020)	283 (1630)	Hexane	658
N,N-Dimethyl-m-toluidine	252 (12200)	299 (2000)	Methanol	659
N,N-Dimethyl-p-toluidine	252 (17000)	302 (2400)	Cyclohexane	660

* Shoulder

The Pyrroles

N-substitution of pyrrole results in a bathochromic shift of the most intense band and the appearance of a second much weaker maximum near 280 mμ.

Compound	$\lambda_{max}(\epsilon_{max})$	$\lambda_{max}(\epsilon_{max})$	Solvent	Spectrum
Pyrrole	208 (7700)	----------	Hexane	Lit.
Pyrrole	209 (6730)	----------	Methanol	575
N-Methylpyrrole	214 (6250)	280 (136)	Methanol	675

1-(DIPHENYLMETHYL)-4-METHYLPIPERAZINE 639

$C_{18}H_{22}N_2$
Mol. Wt. 266.39

Solvent: Methanol

λ Max. mμ	^{a}m	Cell mm	Conc. g/L
260.5	520	10	0.300
254.5	537	10	0.300
225.5	12200	10	0.010

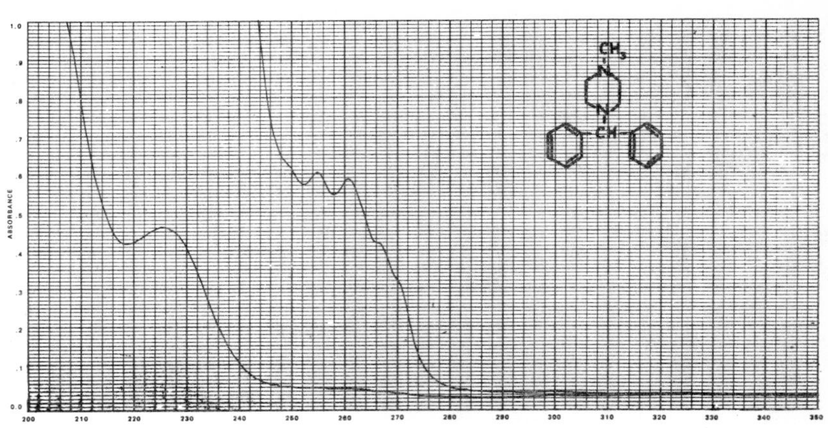

1-PHENYLPIPERAZINE 640

$C_{10}H_{14}N_2$
Mol. Wt. 162.24

Solvent: Cyclohexane

λ Max. mμ	^{a}m	Cell mm	Conc. g/L
x	x	10	2.056
285.5	1580	10	0.165
252	12300	10	0.016

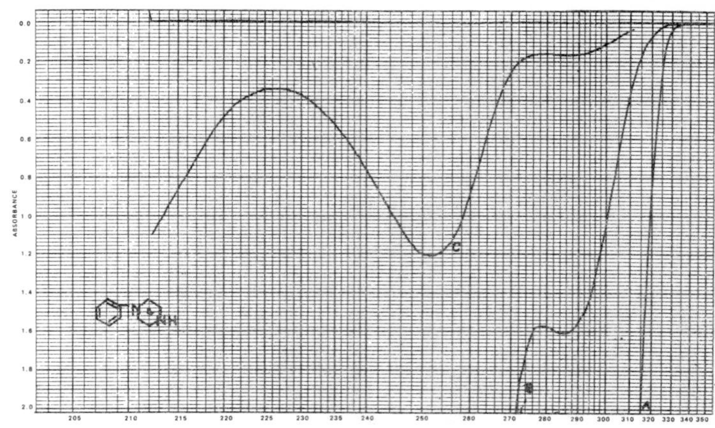

2-METHYL-1-PHENYLPIPERAZINE 641

$C_{11}H_{16}N_2$
Mol. Wt. 176.27

Solvent: Methanol

λ Max. mμ	^{a}m	Cell mm	Conc. g/L
285	939	10	0.114
249	7550	10	0.011

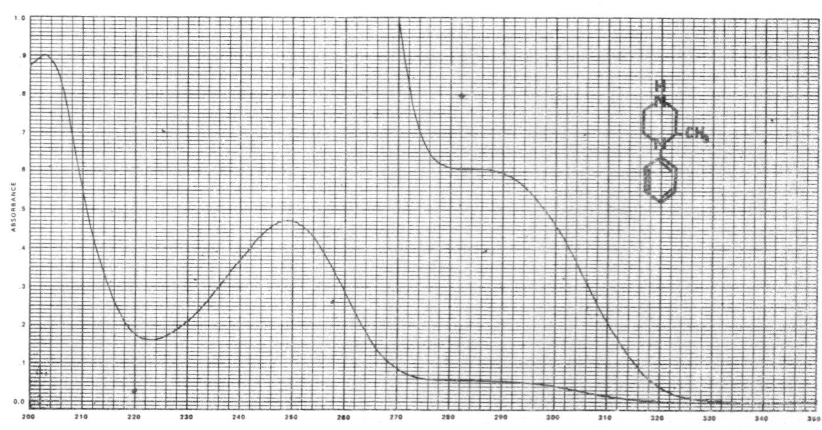

N,N-DIMETHYLALLYLAMINE

642

$C_5H_{11}N$
Mol. Wt. 85.15
B.P. 63-64°C

λ Max. mμ	a_m	Cell mm	Conc. g/L

Compound does not absorb in near UV.

N,N,2-TRIMETHYLPROPENYLAMINE

643

$C_6H_{13}N$
Mol. Wt. 99.18

λ Max. mμ	a_m	Cell mm	Conc. g/L

Compound does not absorb in near UV.

N,N-DIMETHYLBENZYLAMINE

644

$C_9H_{13}N$
Mol. Wt. 135.21
B.P. 73-74°C/15mm
Solvent: Cyclohexane

λ Max. mμ	a_m	Cell mm	Conc. g/L
x	x	10	1.712
264.5	171	10	0.856
258.5	250	10	0.856
252	271	10	0.856
x	x	10	0.034

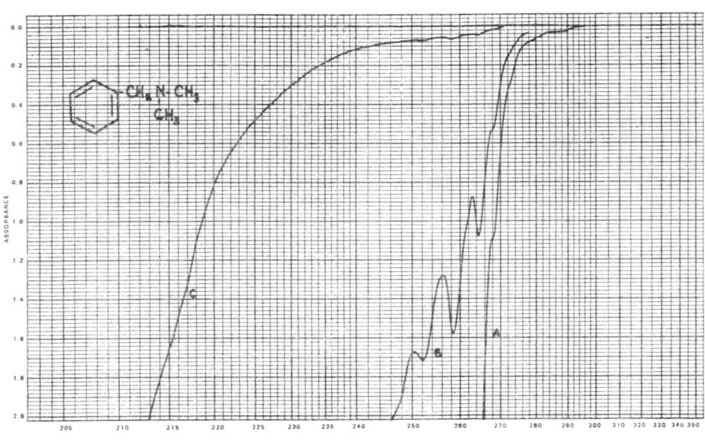

N,N-DIETHYLBENZYLAMINE

645

$C_{11}H_{17}N$

Mol. Wt. 163.25

B.R. 210-212°C (lit.)

Solvent: Cyclohexane

λ Max. mμ	^{a}m	Cell mm	Conc. g/L
286	80.8	10	2.08
x	x	10	0.208
x	x	10	0.021

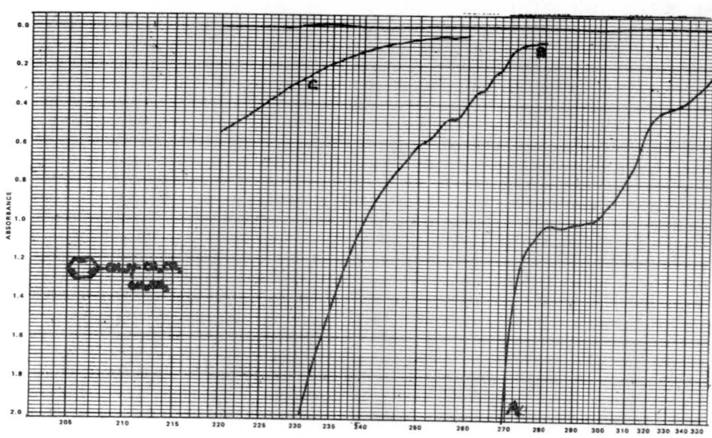

N-ETHYLDIBENZYLAMINE

646

$C_{16}H_{19}N$

Mol. Wt. 225.34

B.P. 155-156°C/9mm

Solvent: Methanol

λ Max. mμ	^{a}m	Cell mm	Conc. g/L
263.5	424	10	0.291
258.5	601	10	0.291
252	667	10	0.291
x	x	1	0.291

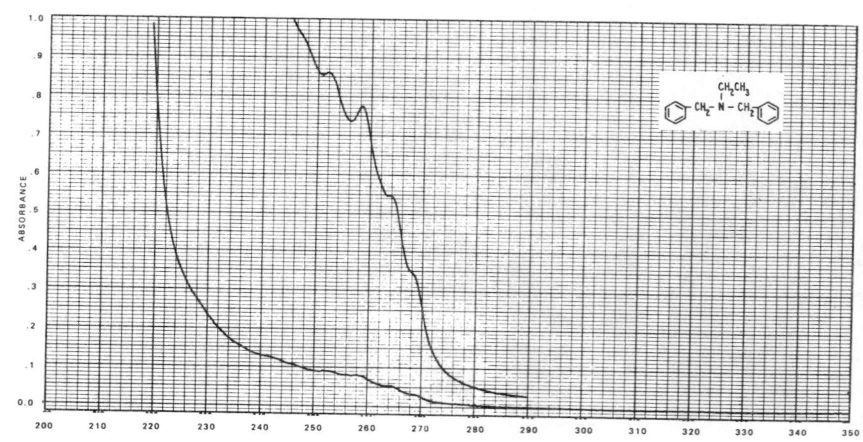

TRIBENZYLAMINE

647

$C_{21}H_{21}N$

Mol. Wt. 287.41

Solvent: Methanol

λ Max. mμ	^{a}m	Cell mm	Conc. g/L
x	x	10	2.004
268	378	10	0.200
264.5	606	10	0.200
258.5	833	10	0.200
252.5	848	10	0.200
x	x	10	0.020

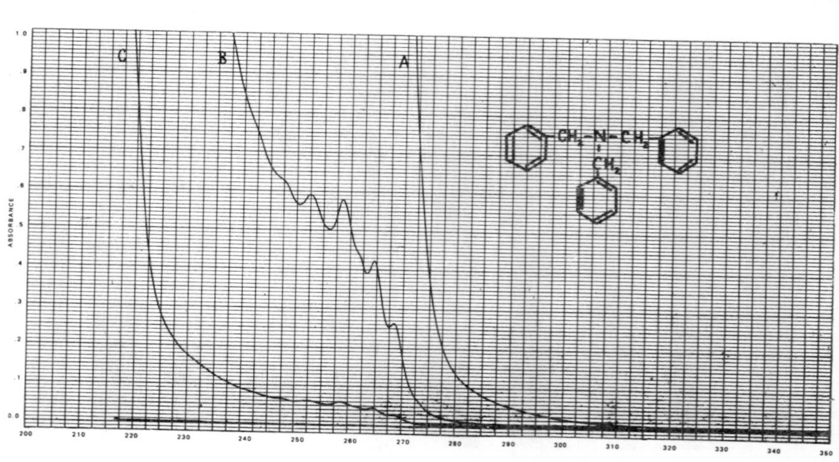

N,N-DIMETHYLANILINE 648

$C_8H_{11}N$

Mol. Wt. 121.18

B.P. 192.5-193.5°C (lit.)

Solvent: Methanol

λ Max. mμ	a_m	Cell mm	Conc. g/L
298	2290	2	0.185
251	11600	2	0.0370

N,N-DIMETHYLANILINE 648

$C_8H_{11}N$

Mol. Wt. 121.18

B.P. 192.5-193.5°C (lit.)

Solvent: Methanol HCl

λ Max. mμ	a_m	Cell mm	Conc. g/L
263	144	20	0.185
259.5	209	20	0.185
253.5	276	20	0.185
248	272	20	0.185
x	x	2	0.185

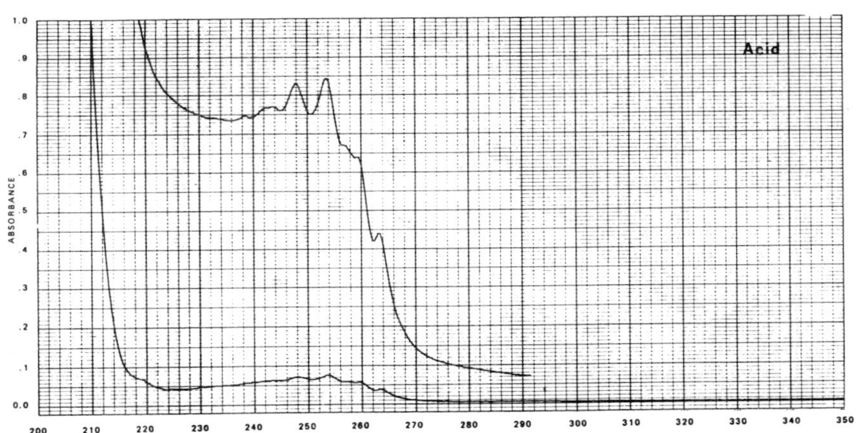

λ Max. mμ	a_m	Cell mm	Conc. g/L

N,N-DIETHYLANILINE 649

$C_{10}H_{15}N$

Mol. Wt. 149.24

Solvent: Methanol

λ Max. mμ	a_m	Cell mm	Conc. g/L
303.5	195	1	0.507
259.5	1390	1	0.101

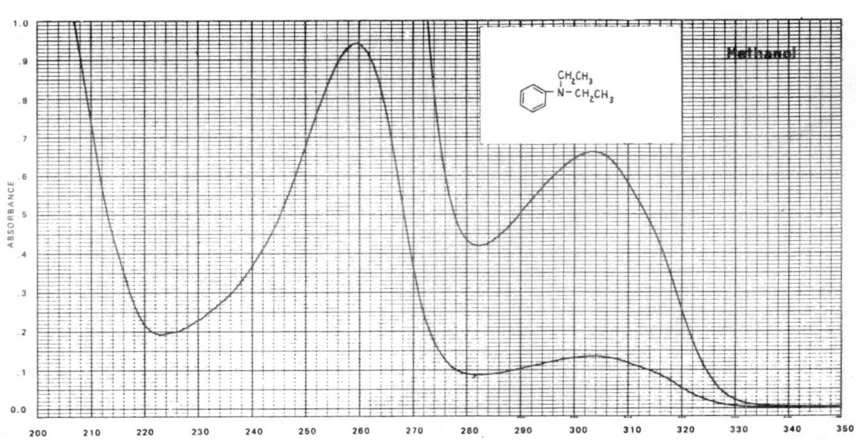

N,N-DIETHYLANILINE 649

$C_{10}H_{15}N$

Mol. Wt. 149.24

Solvent: Methanol HCl

λ Max. mμ	a_m	Cell mm	Conc. g/L
263.5	117	10	0.507
257.5	166	10	0.507
253.5	200	10	0.507
248	165	10	0.507
x	x	1	0.507

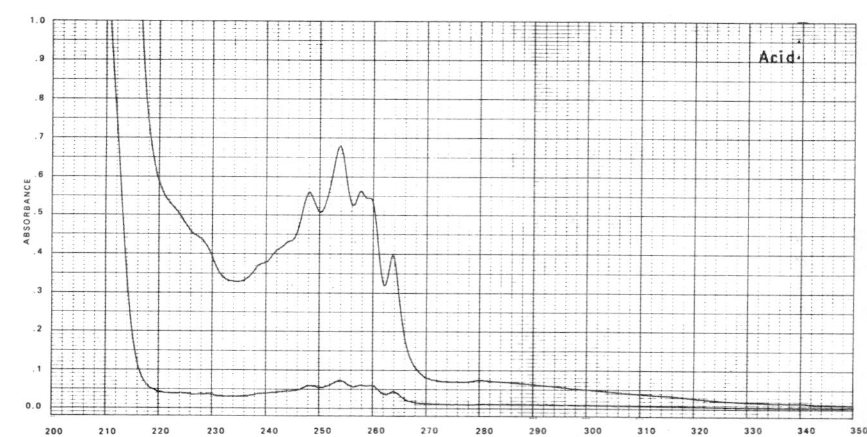

N,N-DIPROPYLANILINE 650

$C_{12}H_{19}N$

Mol. Wt. 177.29

B.P. 116-118°C/12mm

Solvent: Methanol

λ Max. mμ	a_m	Cell mm	Conc. g/L
304.5	2330	5	0.0850
258.5	16900	1	0.0850

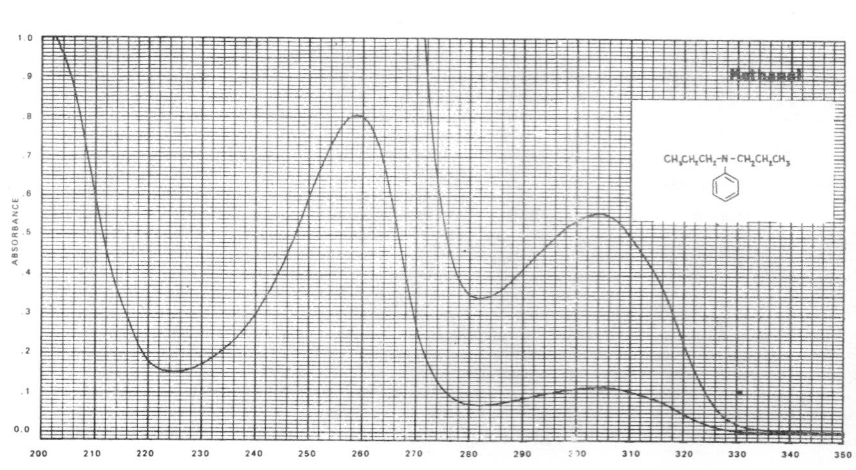

N,N-DIPROPYLANILINE

650

$C_{12}H_{19}N$
Mol. Wt. 177.29
B.P. 116-118°C/12mm
Solvent: Methanol HCl

λ Max. mμ	a_m	Cell mm	Conc. g/L
264	192	20	0.171
257.5	271	20	0.171
254	331	20	0.171
248	320	20	0.171
204	8200	1	0.171

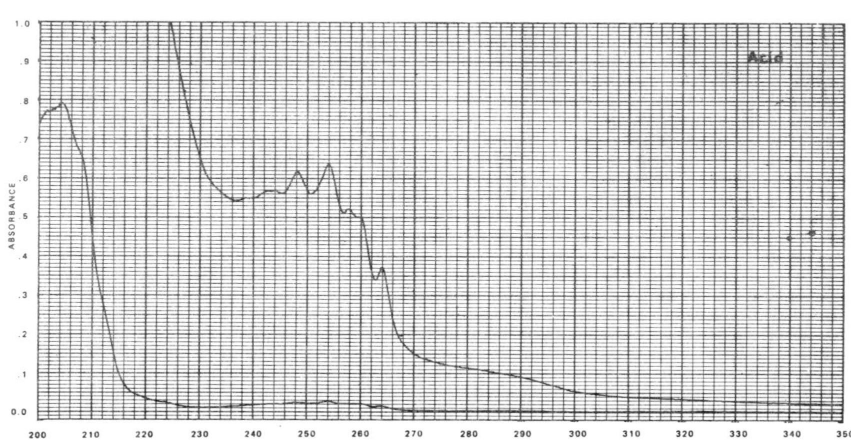

N,N-DIBUTYLANILINE

651

$C_{14}H_{23}N$
Mol. Wt. 205.35
B.P. 268-275°C
Solvent: Methanol

λ Max. mμ	a_m	Cell mm	Conc. g/L
305	1910	2	0.370
259	13300	2	0.0739

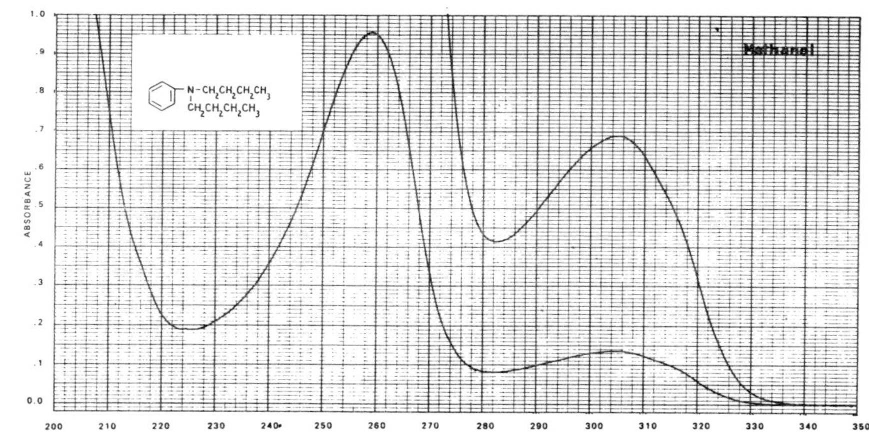

N-BENZYL-N-METHYLANILINE

652

$C_{14}H_{15}N$
Mol. Wt. 197.28
Solvent: Methanol

λ Max. mμ	a_m	Cell mm	Conc. g/L
300	2540	10	0.050
252.5	16400	10	0.010

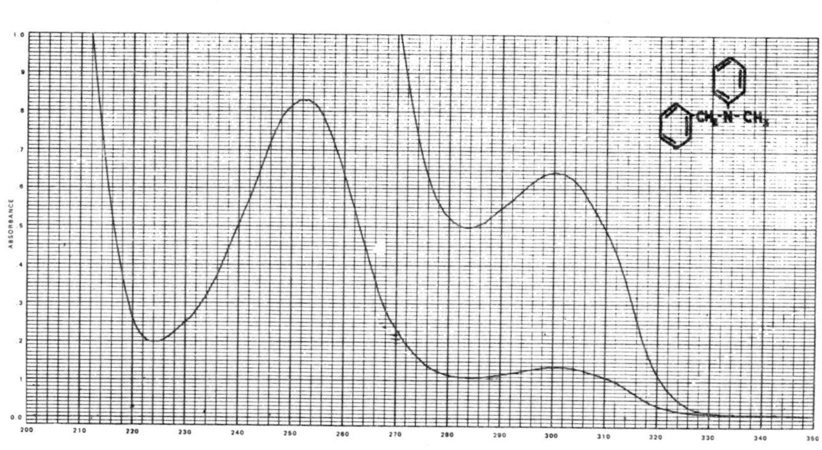

N-ETHYL-N-PHENYLBENZYLAMINE

653

$C_{15}H_{17}N$
Mol. Wt. 211.31
Solvent: Cyclohexane

λ Max. mμ	a_m	Cell mm	Conc. g/L
x	x	10	2.37
299	3010	10	0.119
253.5	17600	10	0.012

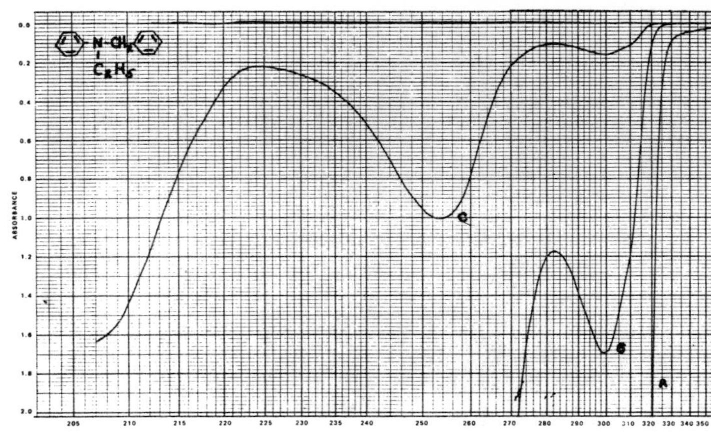

N,N-DIBENZYLANILINE

654

$C_{20}H_{19}N$
Mol. Wt. 273.38
Solvent: Cyclohexane

λ Max. mμ	a_m	Cell mm	Conc. g/L
x	x	10	2.27
297	2930	10	0.114
250	17400	10	0.023

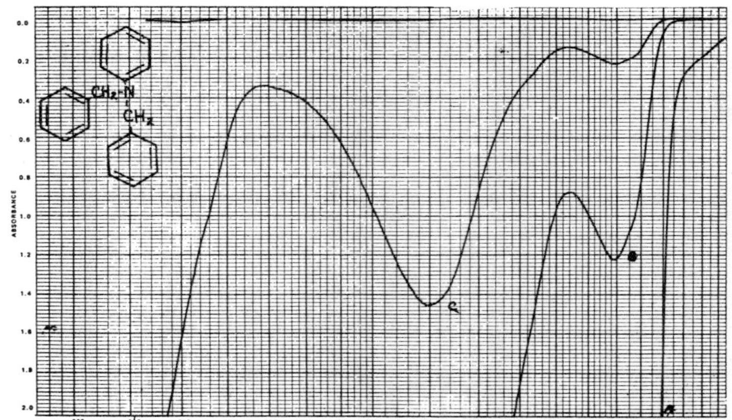

N,N-BIS(2-CHLOROETHYL)ANILINE

655

$C_{10}H_{13}Cl_2N$
Mol. Wt. 218.13
Solvent: Methanol

λ Max. mμ	a_m	Cell mm	Conc. g/L
296.5	2190	5	0.100
254.5	16900	1	0.100

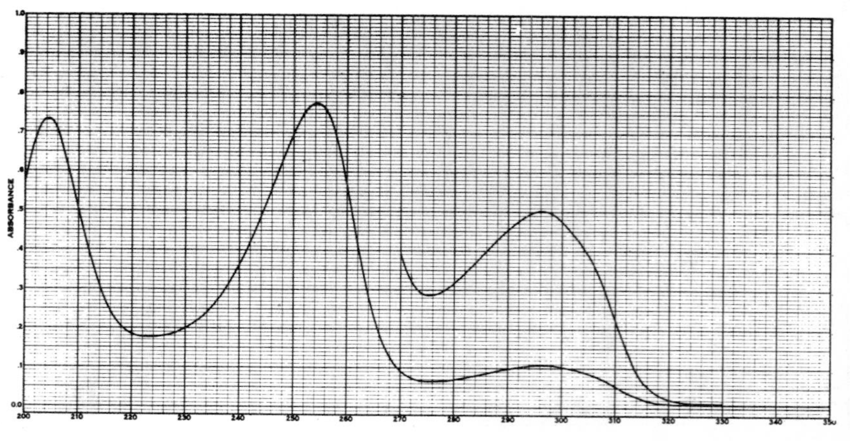

N,N-DIALLYLANILINE

$C_{12}H_{15}N$
Mol. Wt. 173.26
B.P. 102-103°C/8mm
Solvent: Methanol

λ Max. mμ	a_m	Cell mm	Conc. g/L
298.5	239	10	0.512
253.5	14400	10	0.010

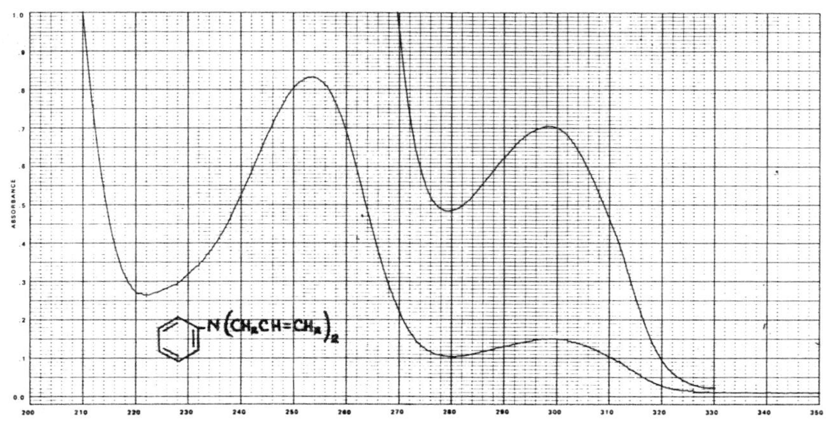

TRIPHENYLAMINE

$C_{18}H_{15}N$
Mol. Wt. 245.33
B.P. 365°C M.P. 126.5°C
Solvent: Methanol

λ Max. mμ	a_m	Cell mm	Conc. g/L
296.5	24800	1	0.0500

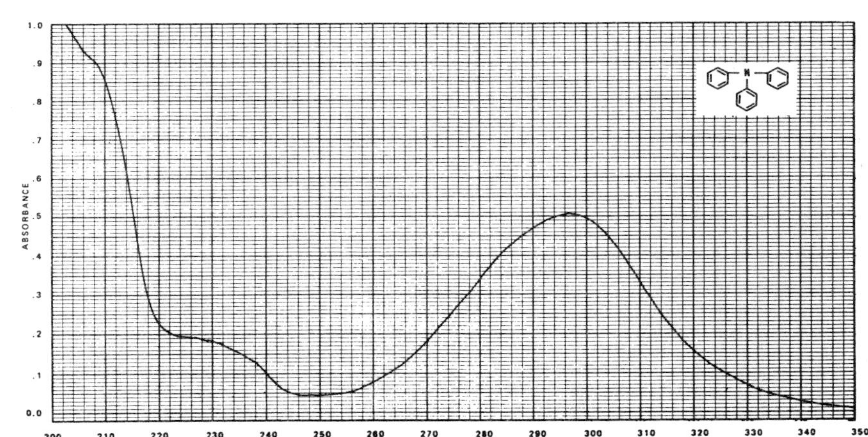

N,N-DIMETHYL-o-TOLUIDINE

$C_9H_{13}N$
Mol. Wt. 135.2
B.R. 65-66°C/8mm (lit.)
Solvent: Hexane

λ Max. mμ	a_m	Cell mm	Conc. g/L
x	x	10	2.160
282.5	1630	10	0.022
241.5	8020	10	0.022
220	5000	10	0.022

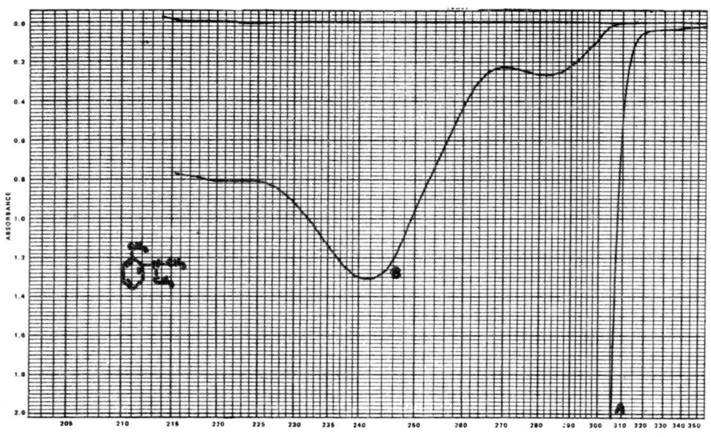

N,N-DIMETHYL-m-TOLUIDINE 659

$C_9H_{13}N$

Mol. Wt. 135.21

B.P. 97-100°C/20mm

Solvent: Methanol

λ Max. mμ	a_m	Cell mm	Conc. g/L
299	2000	1	0.1580
252	12200	1	0.0316

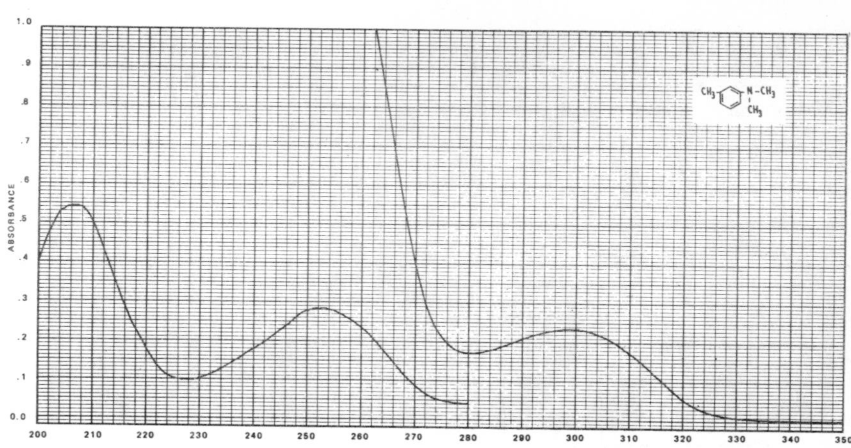

N,N-DIMETHYL-m-TOLUIDINE 659

$C_9H_{13}N$

Mol. Wt. 135.21

B.P. 97-100°C/20mm

Solvent: Methanol HCl

λ Max. mμ	a_m	Cell mm	Conc. g/L
268.5	385	5	0.3160
261	418	5	0.3160

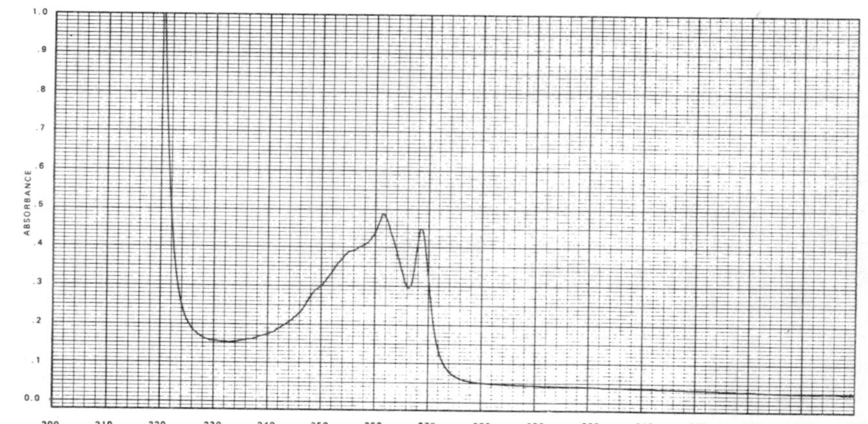

N,N-DIMETHYL-p-TOLUIDINE 660

$C_9H_{13}N$

Mol. Wt. 135.2

Solvent: Cyclohexane

λ Max. mμ	a_m	Cell mm	Conc. g/L
x	x	10	2.100
302	2400	10	0.084
252	17000	10	0.008

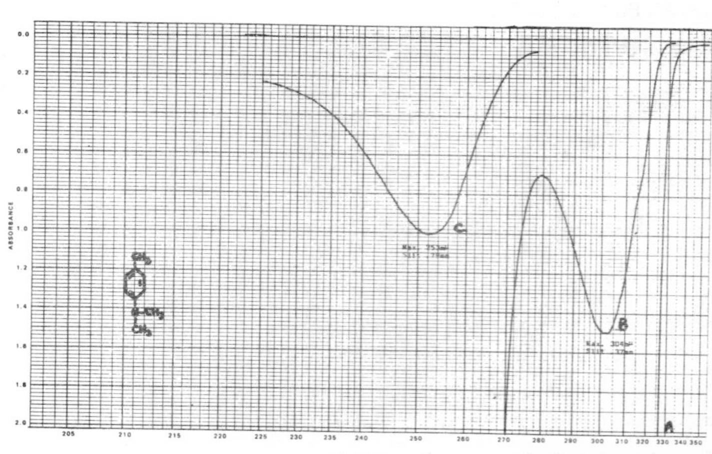

N,N-DIETHYL-o-TOLUIDINE 661

$C_{11}H_{17}N$

Mol. Wt. 163.26

Solvent: Methanol

λ Max. mμ	a_m	Cell mm	Conc. g/L
252	2870	4	0.100
x	x	1	0.100

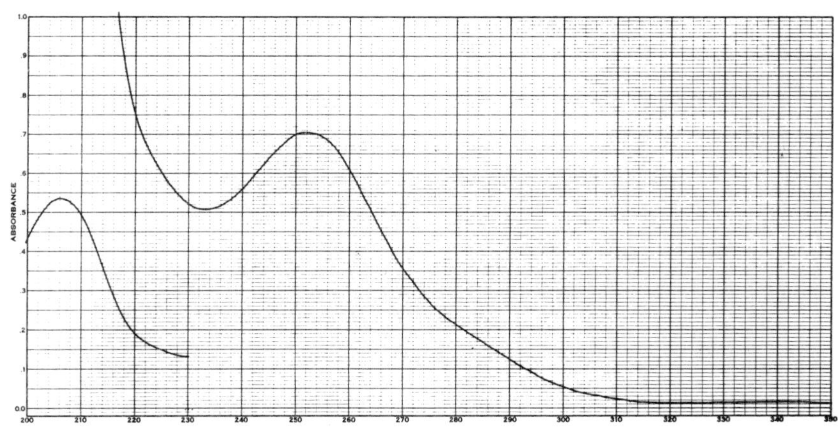

N,N-DIETHYL-o-TOLUIDINE 661

$C_{11}H_{17}N$

Mol. Wt. 163.26

Solvent: Methanol HCl

λ Max. mμ	a_m	Cell mm	Conc. g/L
269	390	20	0.100
261.5	423	20	0.100
x	x	2	0.100

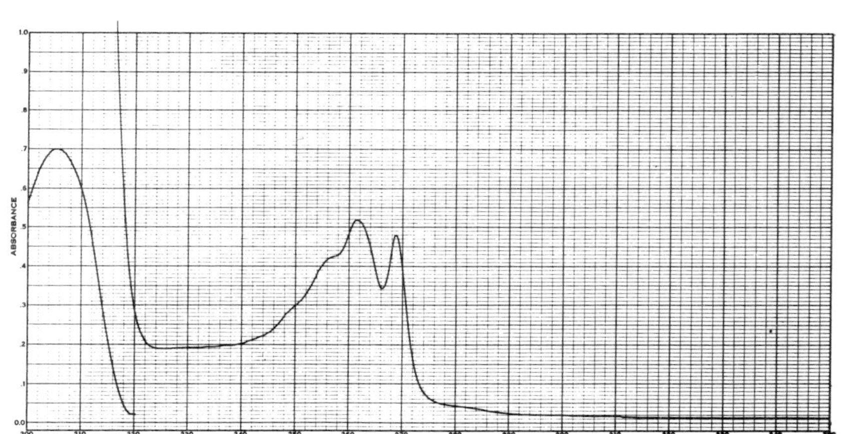

N,N-DIETHYL-m-TOLUIDINE 662

$C_{11}H_{17}N$

Mol. Wt. 163.25

Solvent: Methanol

λ Max. mμ	a_m	Cell mm	Conc. g/L
x	x	10	1.800
302	3710	10	0.072
260.5	25700	10	0.007

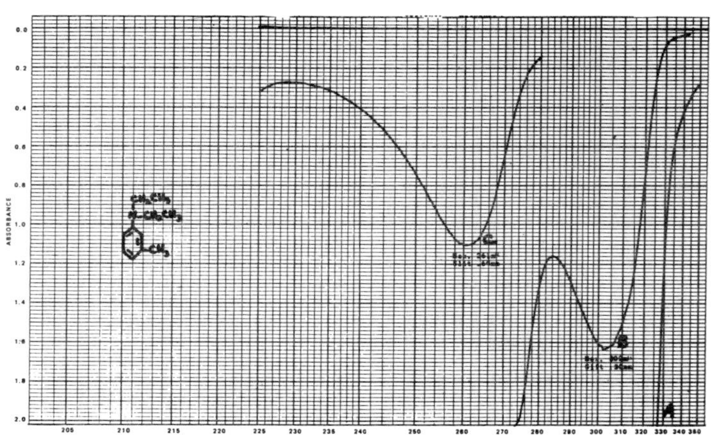

N,N-DIETHYL-p-TOLUIDINE

663

$C_{11}H_{17}N$

Mol. Wt. 163.26

B.P. 102-104°C/10mm

Solvent: Methanol

λ Max. mμ	a_m	Cell mm	Conc. g/L
312	1760	2	0.3420
262	12800	1	0.0684

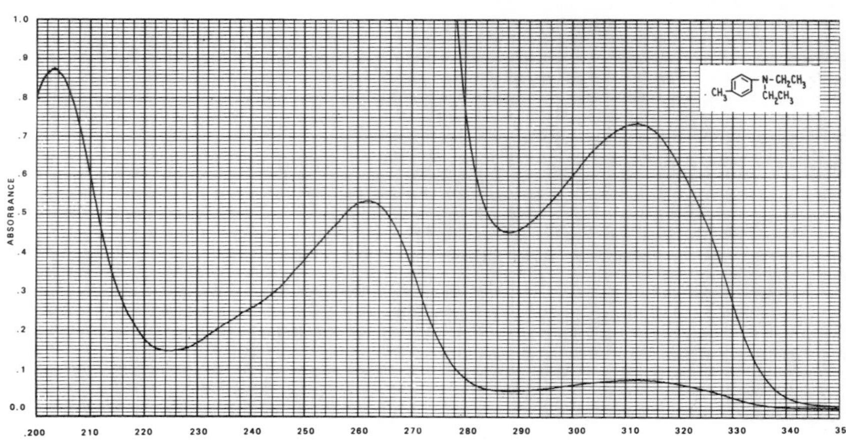

N,N-DIETHYL-p-TOLUIDINE

663

$C_{11}H_{17}N$

Mol. Wt. 163.26

B.P. 102-104°C/10mm

Solvent: Methanol HCl

λ Max. mμ	a_m	Cell mm	Conc. g/L
325	20	10	0.3420
269	147	10	0.3420
265	176	10	0.3420
260	257	10	0.3420
253.5	242	10	0.3420

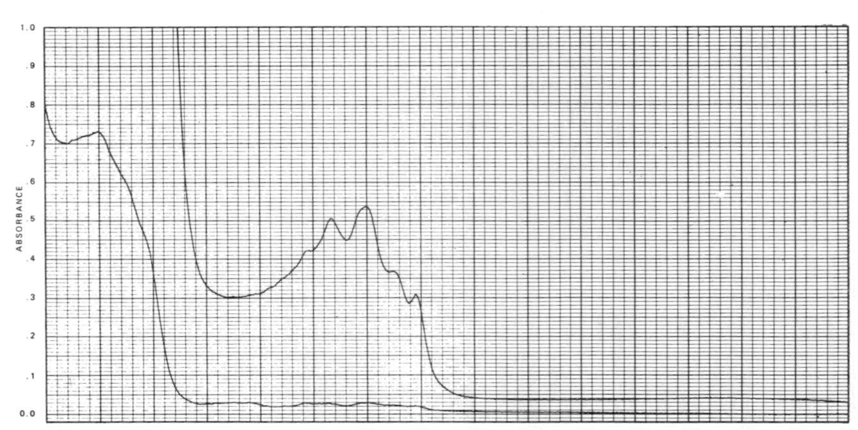

N,N-DIETHYL-2,5-XYLIDINE

664

$C_{12}H_{19}N$

Mol. Wt. 177.29

B.P. 95-96°C/11mm

Solvent: Methanol

λ Max. mμ	a_m	Cell mm	Conc. g/L
253.5	3670	2	0.146
212	13300	1	0.073

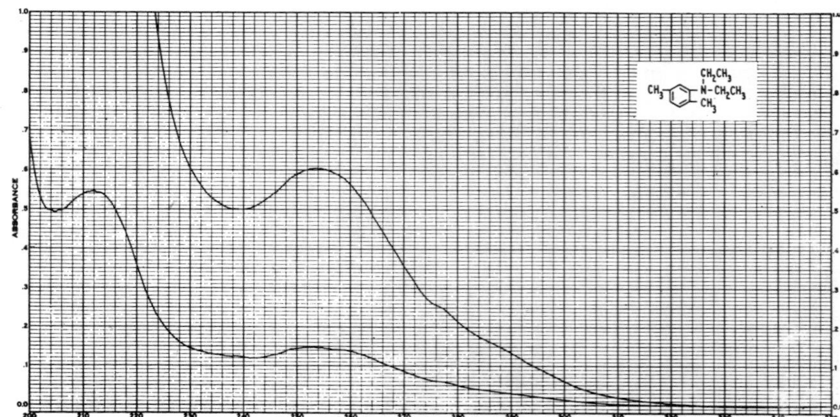

N,N-DIETHYL-2,5-XYLIDINE

$C_{12}H_{19}N$
Mol. Wt. 177.29
B.P. 95-96°C/11mm
Solvent: Methanol HCl

λ Max. mμ	a_m	Cell mm	Conc. g/L
275	879	10	0.146
268.5	783	10	0.146
266	844	10	0.146
262	614	10	0.146
211	8840	1	0.146

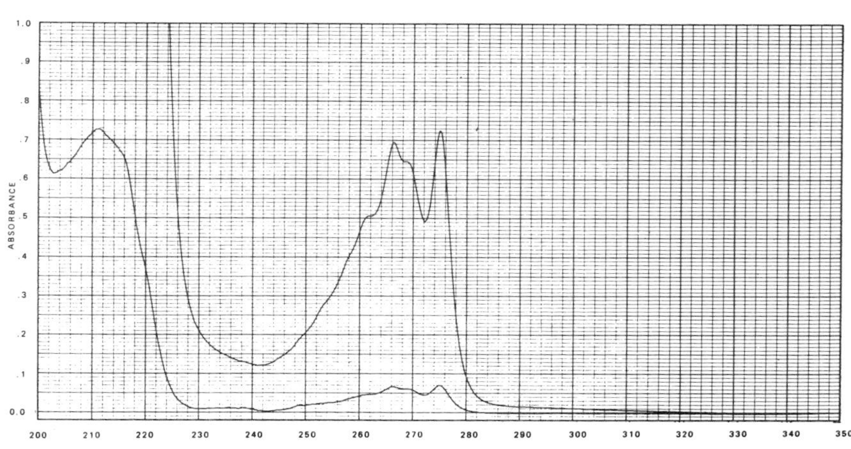

N,N-DIMETHYL-2,6-XYLIDINE

665

$C_{10}H_{15}N$
Mol. Wt. 149.24
B.P. 82-83°C/17mm
Solvent: Methanol

λ Max. mμ	a_m	Cell mm	Conc. g/L
261	3220	4	0.100
210	13300	1	0.100

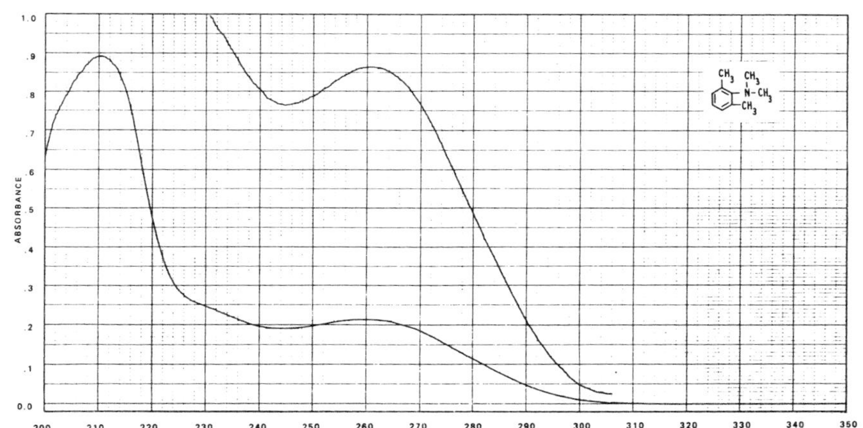

N,N-DIMETHYL-2,6-XYLIDINE

665

$C_{10}H_{15}N$
Mol. Wt. 149.24
B.P. 82-83°C/17mm
Solvent: Methanol HCl

λ Max. mμ	a_m	Cell mm	Conc. g/L
271.5	1110	10	0.100
263	1120	10	0.100
208	10600	1	0.100

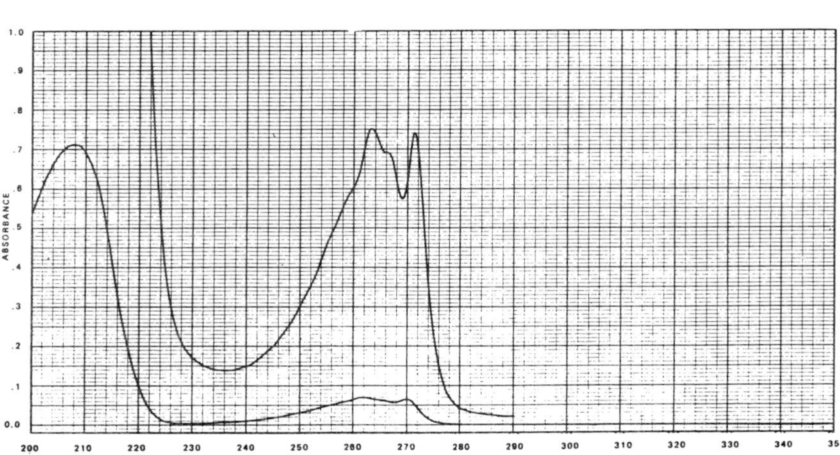

4,4'-METHYLENEBIS(N,N-DIMETHYLANILINE) 666

$C_{17}H_{22}N_2$
Mol. Wt. 254.36
M.P. 89-90°C (lit.)
Solvent: Methanol

λ Max. mμ	a_m	Cell mm	Conc. g/L
x	x	10	2.272
300	3690	10	0.091
261.5	28700	10	0.009

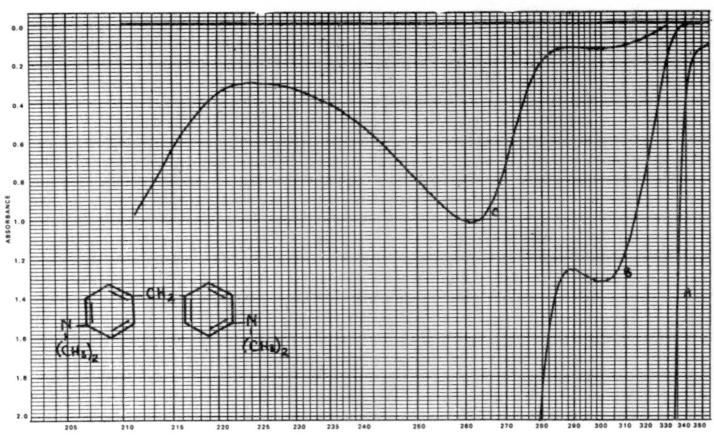

4,4',4''-METHYLIDYNETRIS[N,N-DIMETHYLANILINE] 667

$C_{25}H_{31}N_3$
Mol. Wt. 373.54
M.P. 178-180°C
Solvent: Methanol

λ Max. mμ	a_m	Cell mm	Conc. g/L
264.5	46800	1	0.0500
207	67600	1	0.0500

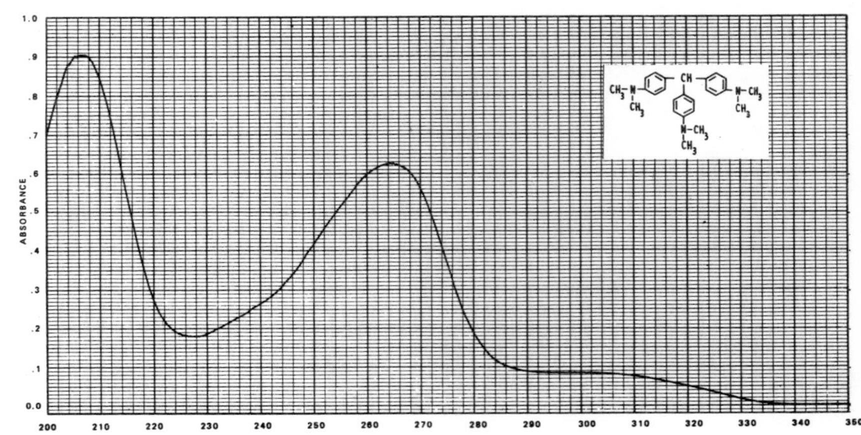

4,4',4''-METHYLIDYNETRIS[N,N-DIMETHYLANILINE] 667

$C_{25}H_{31}N_3$
Mol. Wt. 373.54
M.P. 178-180°C
Solvent: Methanol HCl

λ Max. mμ	a_m	Cell mm	Conc. g/L
260.5	1510	10	0.100
254	1380	10	0.100
x	x	1	0.0500

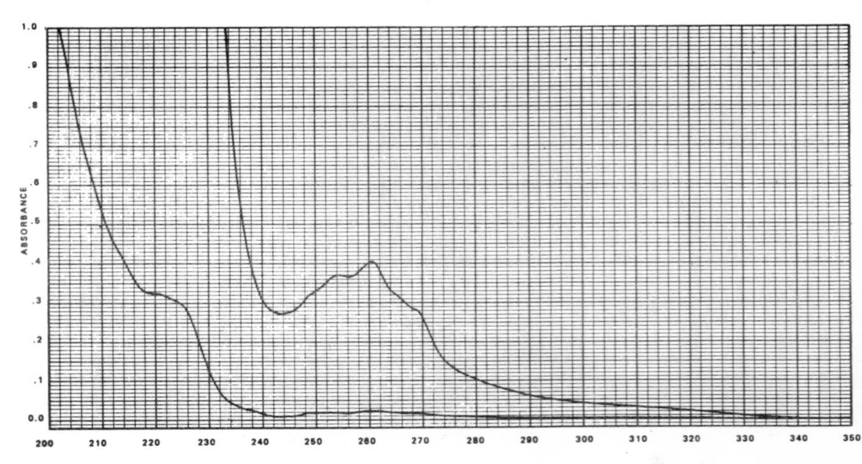

p-BROMO-N,N-DIMETHYLANILINE 668

$C_8H_{10}BrN$

Mol. Wt. 200.08

M.P. 51-54°C

Solvent: Methanol

λ Max. mμ	a_m	Cell mm	Conc. g/L
310	1990	5	0.100
261	18000	1	0.100

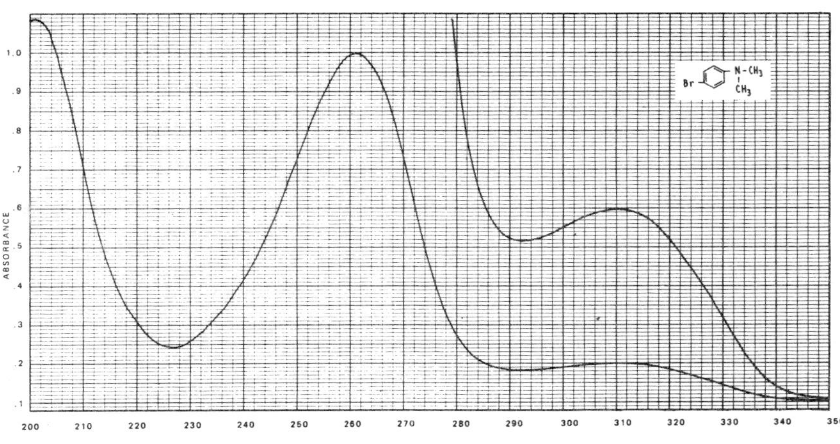

p-BROMO-N,N-DIMETHYLANILINE 668

$C_8H_{10}BrN$

Mol. Wt. 200.08

M.P. 51-54°C

Solvent: Methanol HCl

λ Max. mμ	a_m	Cell mm	Conc. g/L
262	920	10	0.100
257	933	10	0.100
222.5	9880	1	0.100

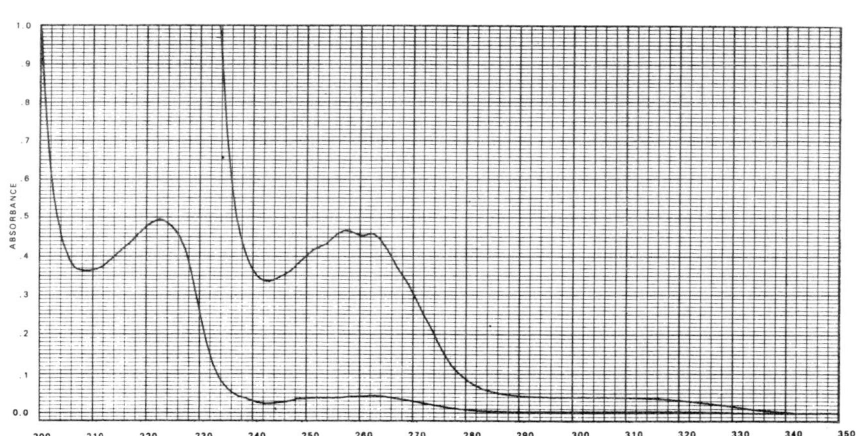

λ Max. mμ	a_m	Cell mm	Conc. g/L

N,N-DIMETHYL-p-PHENYLENEDIAMINE

669

$C_8H_{12}N_2$
Mol. Wt. 136.20
B.P. 157-158°C
Solvent: Methanol

λ Max. mμ	a_m	Cell mm	Conc. g/L
252.5	10700	1	0.0900

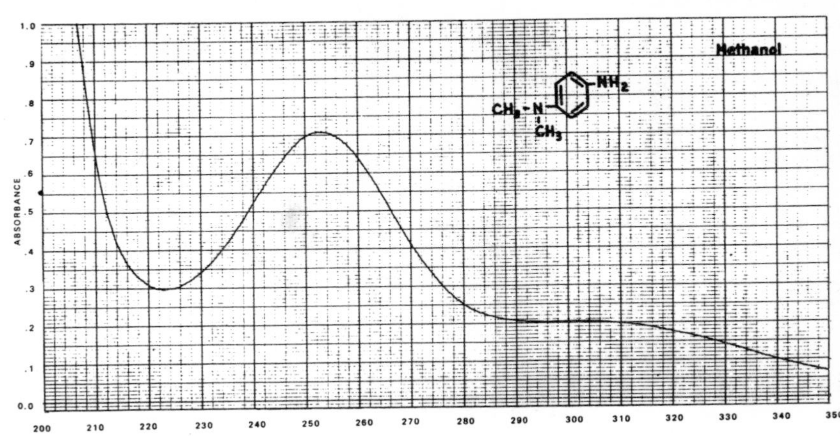

N,N-DIMETHYL-p-PHENYLENEDIAMINE

669

$C_8H_{12}N_2$
Mol. Wt. 136.20
B.P. 157-158°C
Solvent: Methanol HCl

λ Max. mμ	a_m	Cell mm	Conc. g/L
255	6030	2	0.0900

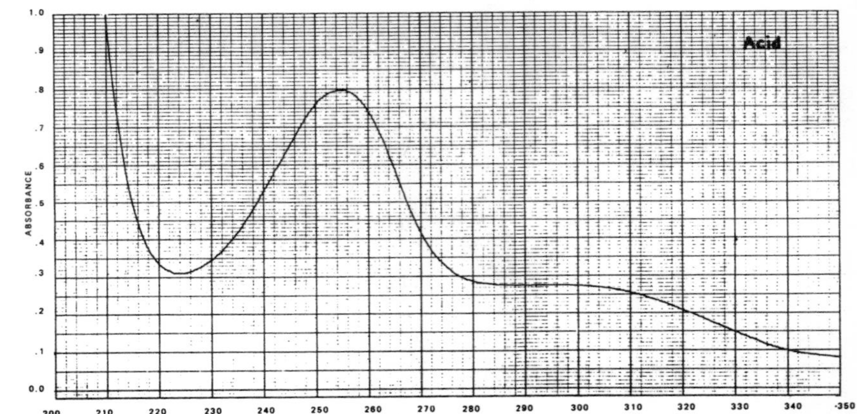

N,N-DIETHYL-p-PHENYLENEDIAMINE

670

$C_{10}H_{16}N_2$
Mol. Wt. 164.25
M.P. 22-24°C
Solvent: Methanol

λ Max. mμ	a_m	Cell mm	Conc. g/L
250	9170	1	0.1360

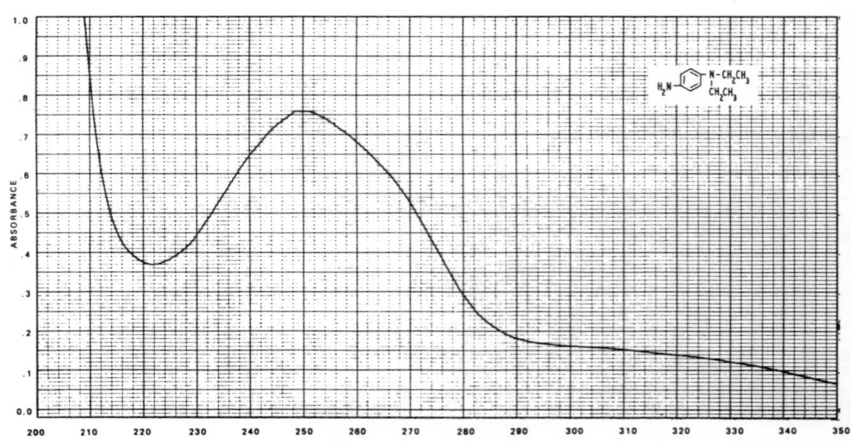

N,N-DIETHYL-p-PHENYLENEDIAMINE 670

$C_{10}H_{16}N_2$
Mol. Wt. 164.25
M.P. 22-24°C
Solvent: Methanol HCl

λ Max. mμ	a_m	Cell mm	Conc. g/L
x	x	10	0.1360
251	5040	1	0.1360

N,N-DIMETHYL-1-NAPHTHYLAMINE 671

$C_{12}H_{13}N$
Mol. Wt. 171.24
M.P. 52-53°C B.P. 305°C/780mm (lit.)
Solvent: Methanol

λ Max. mμ	a_m	Cell mm	Conc. g/L
302	4950	5	0.0207
215.5	54600	1	0.0207

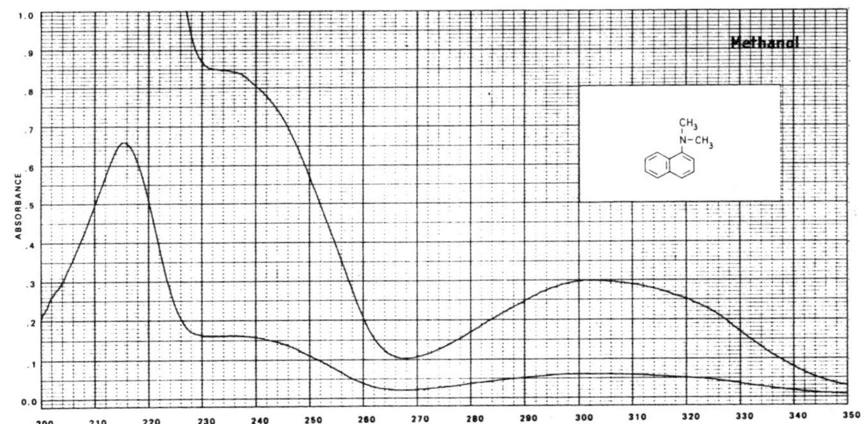

N,N-DIMETHYL-1-NAPHTHYLAMINE 671

$C_{12}H_{13}N$
Mol. Wt. 171.24
M.P. 52-53°C B.P. 305°C/780mm (lit.)
Solvent: Methanol HCl

λ Max. mμ	a_m	Cell mm	Conc. g/L
316.5	383	5	0.415
311	416	5	0.415
279.5	6350	10	0.0103
270.5	5700	10	0.0103
221	93600	1	0.0103

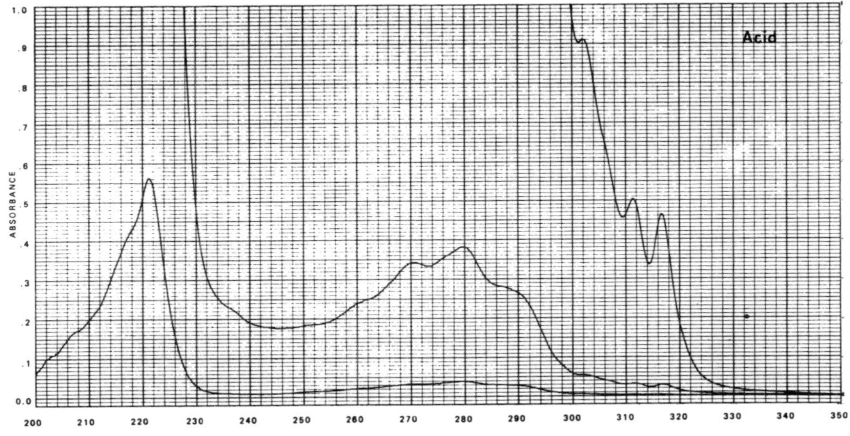

N,N-DIETHYL-1-NAPHTHYLAMINE 672

$C_{14}H_{17}N$

Mol. Wt. 199.30

B.P. 290°C (lit.)

Solvent: Methanol

λ Max. mμ	a_m	Cell mm	Conc. g/L
314	4170	10	0.071
241.5	10000	10	0.028
221.5	31100	10	0.011

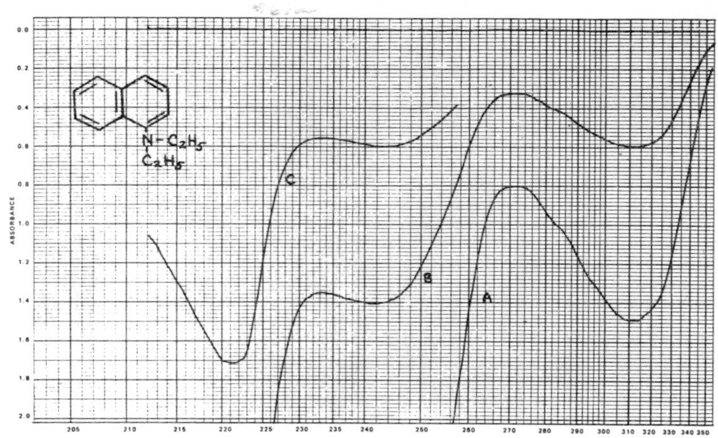

1-METHYL-1,2,3,6-TETRAHYDROPYRIDINE 673

$C_6H_{11}N$

Mol. Wt. 97.16

M.P. 113-114°C

λ Max. mμ	a_m	Cell mm	Conc. g/L

Compound does not absorb in near UV.

1,2-DIPHENYL-2-IMIDAZOLINE 674

$C_{15}H_{14}N_2$

Mol. Wt. 222.29

Solvent: Methanol

λ Max. mμ	a_m	Cell mm	Conc. g/L
276	6680	2	0.100

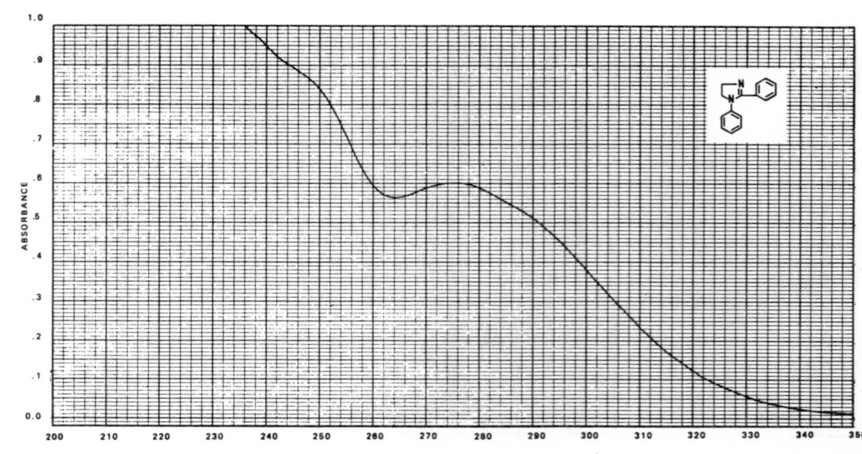

1,2-DIPHENYL-2-IMIDAZOLINE 674

$C_{15}H_{14}N_2$

Mol. Wt. 222.29

Solvent: Methanol HCl

λ Max. mμ	a_m	Cell mm	Conc. g/L
227.5	12000	1	0.100

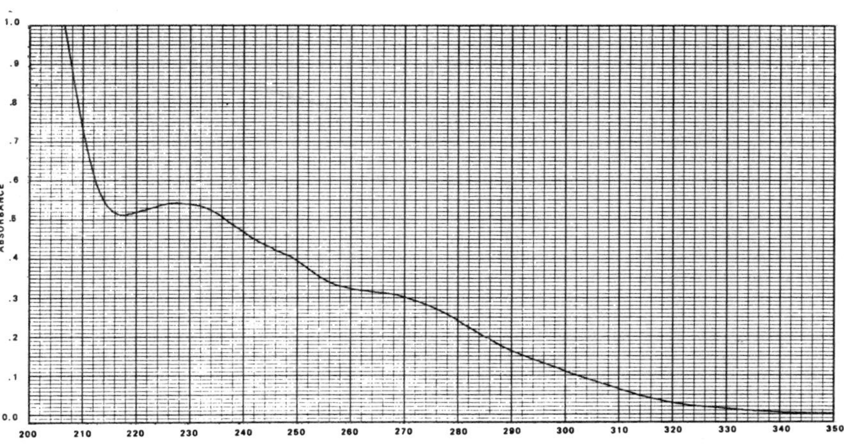

1-METHYLPYRROLE 675

C_5H_7N

Mol. Wt. 81.12

M.P. 114°C/748mm (lit.)

Solvent: Methanol

λ Max. mμ	a_m	Cell mm	Conc. g/L
280	136	10	0.239
214	6250	10	0.012

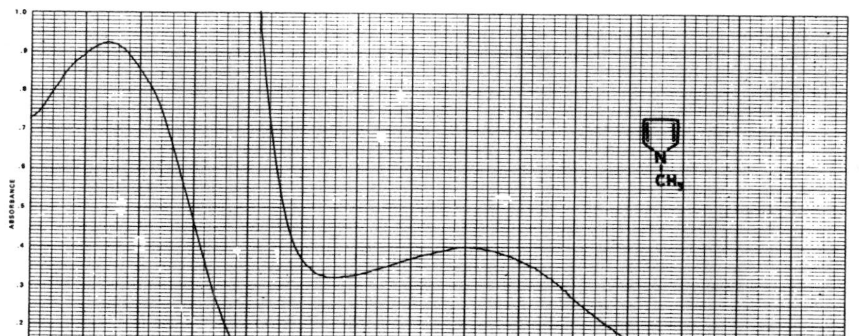

2,5-DIMETHYL-1-PHENYLPYRROLE 676

$C_{12}H_{13}N$

Mol. Wt. 171.24

M.P. 51-53°C

Solvent: Methanol

λ Max. mμ	a_m	Cell mm	Conc. g/L
x	x	1	0.100

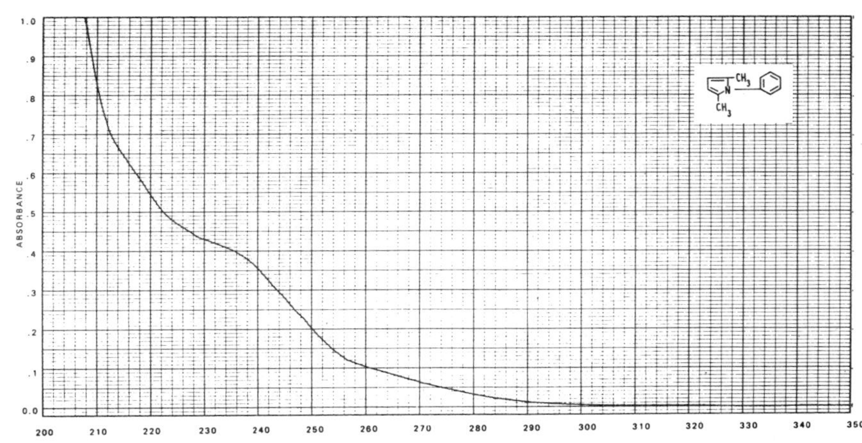

2-[(DIMETHYLAMINO)METHYL] PYRROLE

677

$C_7H_{12}N_2$
Mol. Wt. 124.19
M.P. 60-63°C
Solvent: Methanol

λ Max. mμ	a_m	Cell mm	Conc. g/L
215	8560	1	0.100

2-[(DIMETHYLAMINO)METHYL] PYRROLE

677

$C_7H_{12}N_2$
Mol. Wt. 124.19
M.P. 60-63°C
Solvent: Methanol HCl

λ Max. mμ	a_m	Cell mm	Conc. g/L
222.5	7740	1	0.100

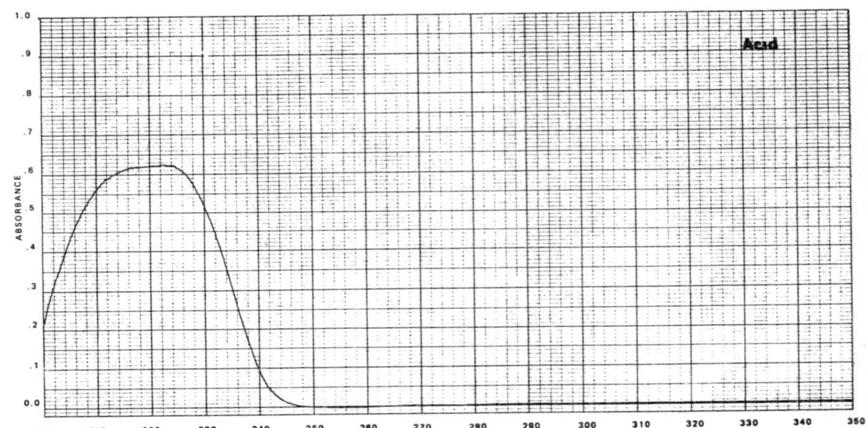

1-PHENYLPYRAZOLE

678

$C_9H_8N_2$
Mol. Wt. 144.18
B.P. 246.5°C/760mm
Solvent: Methanol

λ Max. mμ	a_m	Cell mm	Conc. g/L
252.5	13200	1	0.0900

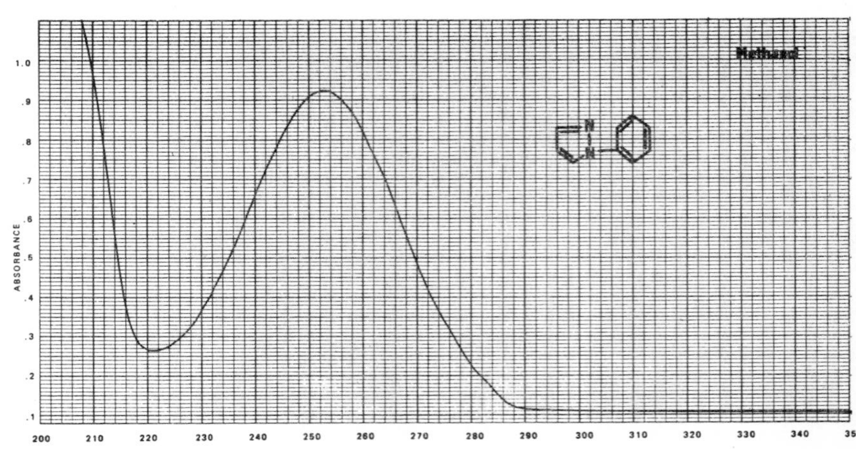

1-METHYL-5-PHENYLTETRAZOLE

679

$C_8H_8N_4$

Mol. Wt. 160.20

M.P. 103-104°C

Solvent: Methanol

λ Max. mμ	a_m	Cell mm	Conc. g/L
x	x	10	2.220
231	11600	10	0.011

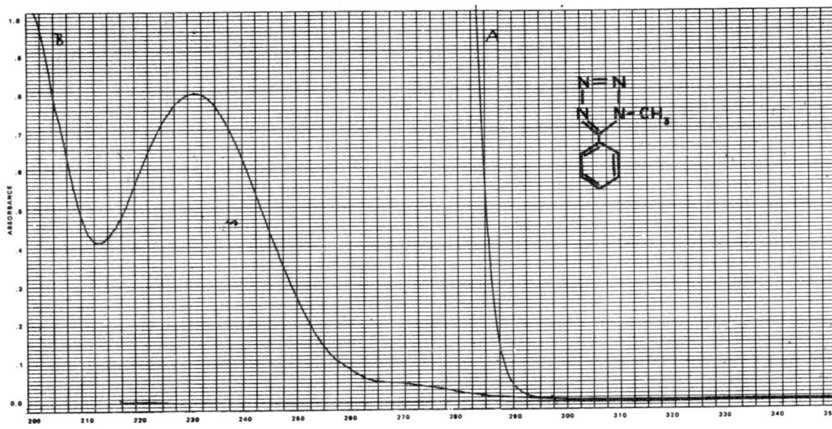

1,5-DIPHENYL-1H-TETRAZOLE

680

$C_{13}H_{10}N_4$

Mol. Wt. 222.20

M.P. 144.7-145.3°C

Solvent: Methanol

λ Max. mμ	a_m	Cell mm	Conc. g/L
x	x	10	2.344
238	12400	10	0.014

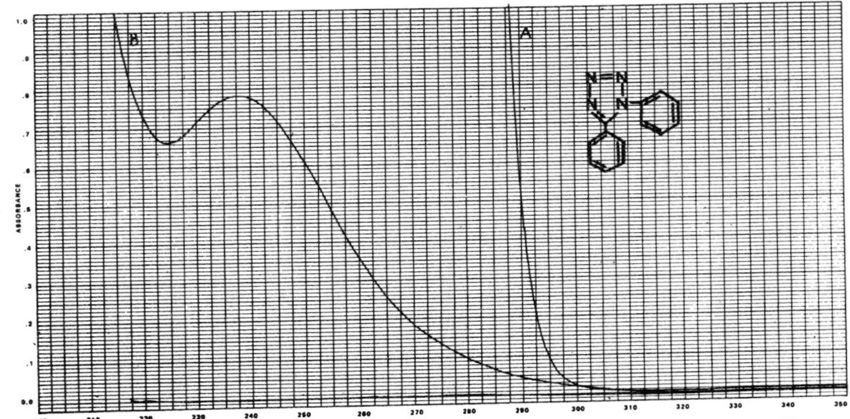

λ Max. mμ	a_m	Cell mm	Conc. g/L

THE PYRIDINES

The UV spectrum of pyridine is similar to that of benzene in that it contains a major band near 256 mμ with some superimposed fine structure. The intensity of this band is greater than that of benzene by a factor of about 10.

Methyl substitution of the pyridine ring at positions 2 or 3 has little effect upon the wavelengths of the corresponding bands but does exert a hyperchromic effect increasing the intensity of the bands by a factor of about 2.

Substitution at position 4, however, has both a hypsochromic and hypochromic effect as shown in the table below.

Compound	$\lambda_{max}(\epsilon_{max})$	$\lambda_{max}(\epsilon_{max})$	$\lambda_{max}(\epsilon_{max})$	Solvent	Spectrum
Pyridine	256 (2460)	262 (1880)	268 (1350)	Methanol	681
2-Methylpyridine	256 (3320)	262 (3890)	268 (2840)	Methanol	682
3-Methylpyridine	257 (2580)	263 (2970)	269 (2150)	Methanol	683
4-Methylpyridine	250 * (1730)	255 (2000)	262 (1590)	Methanol	684
2,4-Dimethylpyridine	260 (2620)	267 (2540)	275 * (745)	Methanol	690
2,5-Dimethylpyridine	262 * (2800)	268 (3250)	275 (2480)	Methanol	691
3,5-Dimethylpyridine	262 * (2650)	268 (3160)	275 (2610)	Methanol	692

* Shoulder

Upon the addition of acid to a pyridine sample, little change is noted in the wavelength of the major band but a two fold increase in its intensity is observed.

Compound	$\lambda_{max}(\epsilon_{max})$	$\lambda_{max}(\epsilon_{max})$	Solvent	Spectrum
Pyridine	195 (5400)	257 (3050)	H_2O	Lit.
Pyridinium cation	201 (3000)	256 (5500)	H_2O/H_2SO_4	Lit.
4-Ethylpyridine	----------	255 (1860)	Methanol	685
4-Ethylpyridinium cation	----------	253 (4040)	Methanol	685

The effect of halogen substitution on the spectrum of pyridine is analogous to that of benzene. Fluorine substitution has little effect on the wavelengths but increases the intensity of the bands, whereas chlorine or bromine substitution results in both a shift to longer wavelengths and an increase in the intensity of the major band (see spectra 699 - 704).

PYRIDINE

C_5H_5N

Mol. Wt. 79.10

M.P. -6.2°C B.P. 184.4°C (lit.)

Solvent: Methanol

λ Max. mμ	a_m	Cell mm	Conc. g/L
x	x	10	2.040
262	1880	10	0.041
256	2460	10	0.041
250	2140	10	0.041

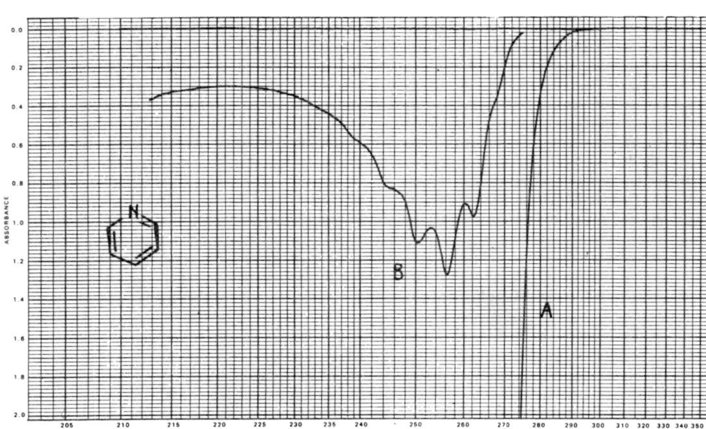

2-PICOLINE

682

C_6H_7N

Mol. Wt. 93.13

Solvent: Methanol

λ Max. mμ	a_m	Cell mm	Conc. g/L
x	x	10	2.300
268	2840	10	0.023
261.5	3890	10	0.023
256	3320	10	0.023

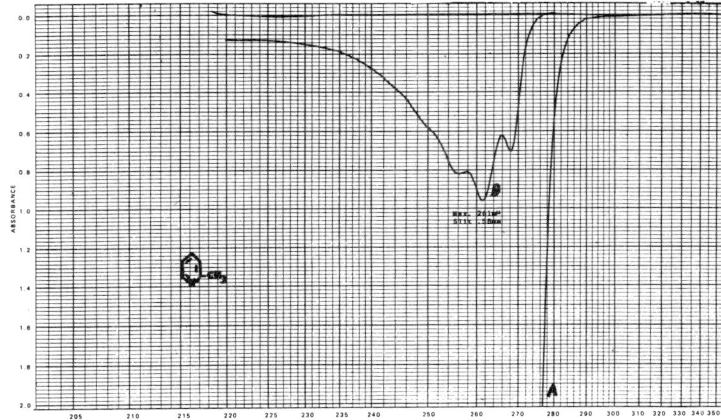

3-PICOLINE

683

C_6H_7N

Mol. Wt. 93.12

Solvent: Methanol

λ Max. mμ	a_m	Cell mm	Conc. g/L
x	x	10	2.190
269	2150	10	0.044
262.5	2970	10	0.044
256.5	2580	10	0.044

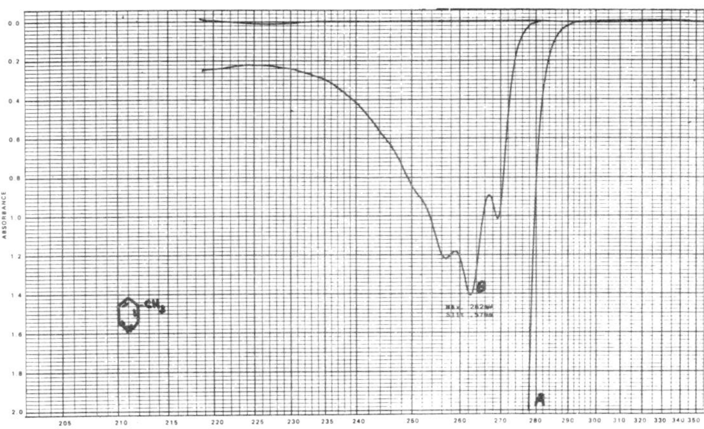

4-PICOLINE

684

C_6H_7N

Mol. Wt. 93.12

Solvent: Methanol

λ Max. mμ	$^a m$	Cell mm	Conc. g/L
x	x	10	2.280
262	1590	10	0.068
255.5	2000	10	0.068

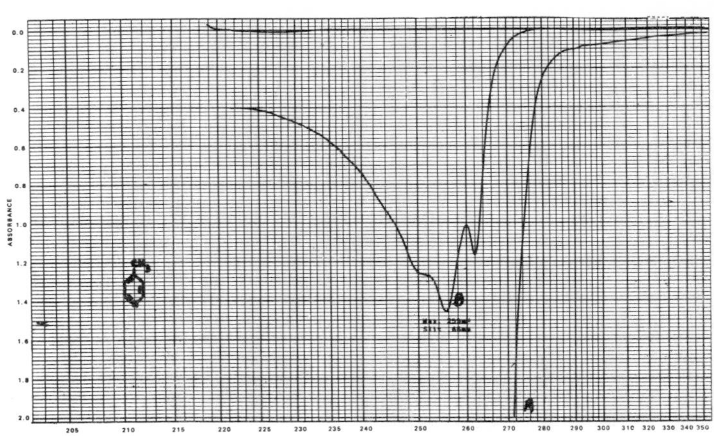

4-ETHYLPYRIDINE

685

C_7H_9N

Mol. Wt. 107.16

B.P. 165-167°C

Solvent: Methanol

λ Max. mμ	$^a m$	Cell mm	Conc. g/L
261.5	1430	1	0.1750
255	1860	1	0.1750

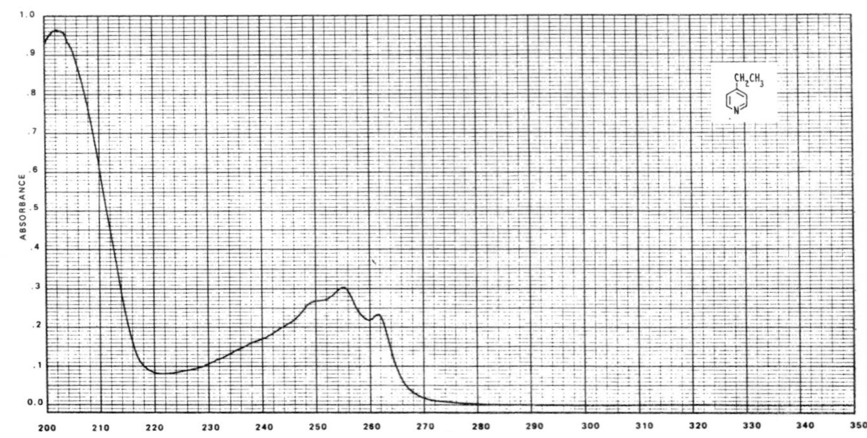

4-ETHYLPYRIDINE

685

C_7H_9N

Mol. Wt. 107.16

B.P. 165-167°C

Solvent: Methanol HCl

λ Max. mμ	$^a m$	Cell mm	Conc. g/L
253	4040	1	0.1750
220	5050	1	0.1750

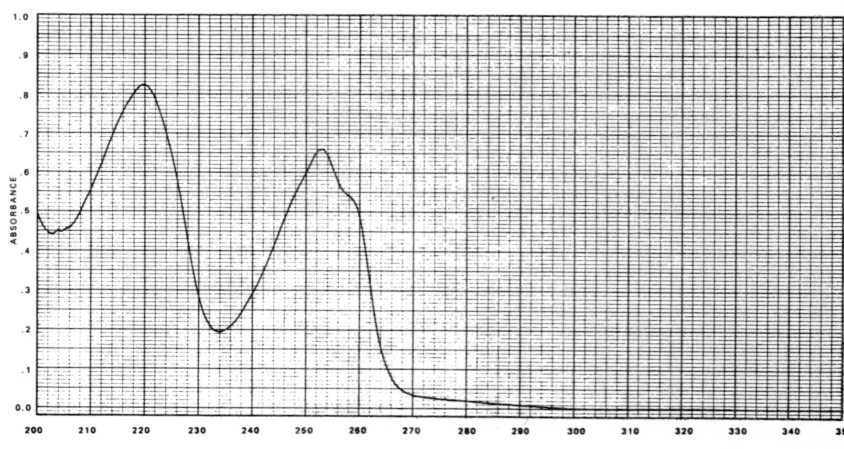

4-ISOPROPYLPYRIDINE 686

$C_8H_{11}N$

Mol. Wt. 121.18

Solvent: Methanol

λ Max. mμ	a_m	Cell mm	Conc. g/L
260	1430	2.5	0.205
253.5	1890	2.5	0.205
210	2230	2.5	0.205

4-ISOPROPYLPYRIDINE 686

$C_8H_{11}N$

Mol. Wt. 121.18

Solvent: Methanol HCl

λ Max. mμ	a_m	Cell mm	Conc. g/L
251	3980	1	0.205
218	4920	1	0.205

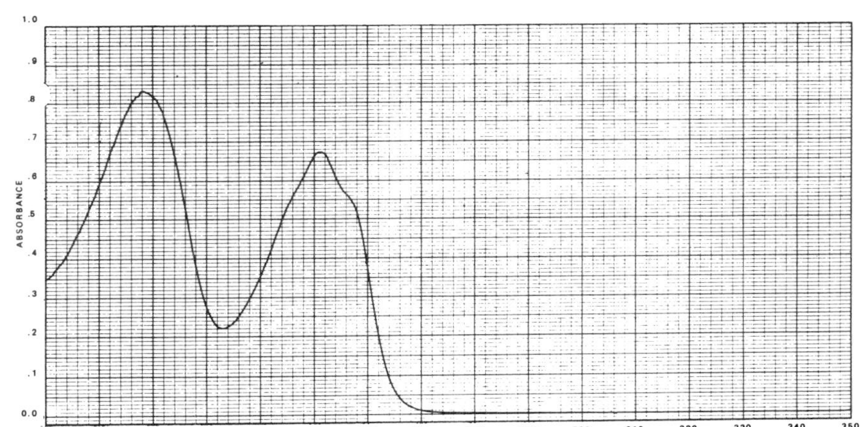

2-PENTYLPYRIDINE 687

$C_{10}H_{15}N$

Mol. Wt. 149.23

B.P. 81-84°C/10mm (lit.)

Solvent: Cyclohexane

λ Max. mμ	a_m	Cell mm	Conc. g/L
x	x	10	1.652
268	1980	10	0.083
261.5	2720	10	0.083
256	2710	10	0.083

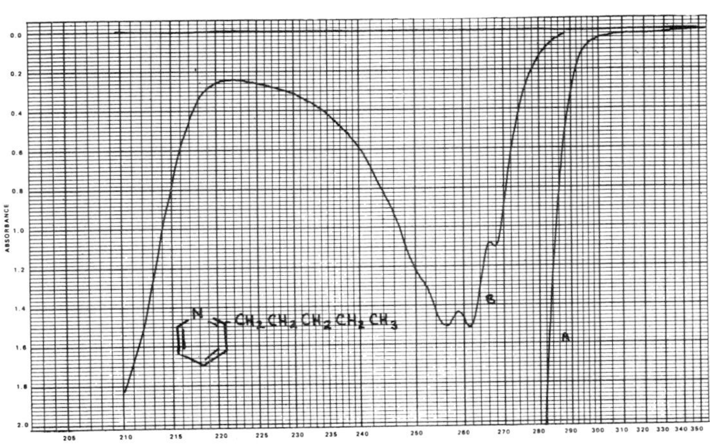

4-PENTYLPYRIDINE 688

$C_{10}H_{15}N$
Mol. Wt. 149.24
B.P. 103-106°C/11mm
Solvent: Methanol

λ Max. mμ	a_m	Cell mm	Conc. g/L
261	1570	1	0.639
255	2070	1	0.639

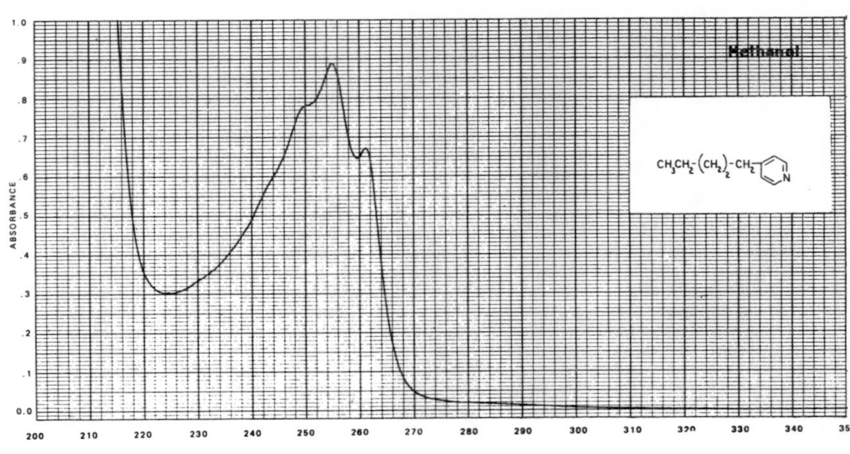

4-PENTYLPYRIDINE 688

$C_{10}H_{15}N$
Mol. Wt. 149.24
B.P. 103-106°C/11mm
Solvent: Methanol HCl

λ Max. mμ	a_m	Cell mm	Conc. g/L
252	4590	1	0.1280
221.5	6890	1	0.1280

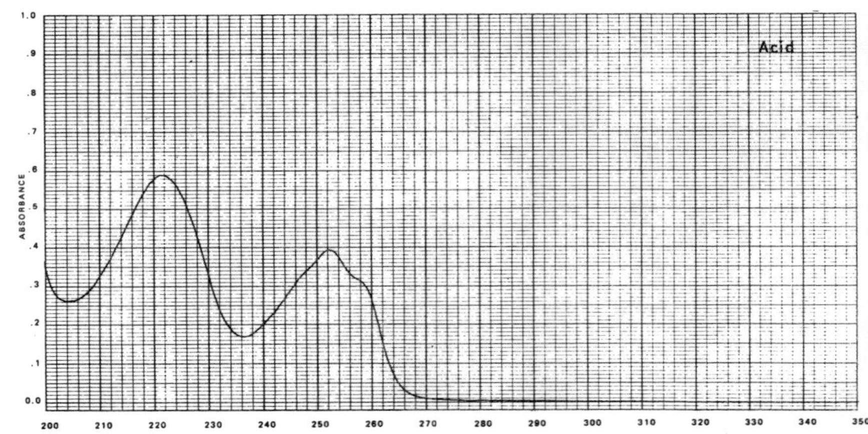

2-(1-BUTYLPENTYL)PYRIDINE 689

$C_{14}H_{23}N$
Mol. Wt. 205.35
Solvent: Cyclohexane

λ Max. mμ	a_m	Cell mm	Conc. g/L
x	x	10	1.576
261.5	2390	10	0.110
256	2460	10	0.110

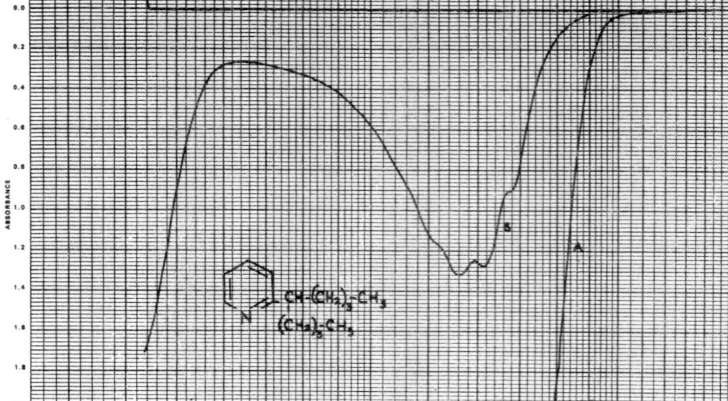

2,4-LUTIDINE 690

C_7H_9N

Mol. Wt. 107.16

Solvent: Methanol

λ Max. mμ	a_m	Cell mm	Conc. g/L
266.5	2540	1	0.2660
260	2620	1	0.2660
206	5370	1	0.1330

2,4-LUTIDINE 690

C_7H_9N

Mol. Wt. 107.16

Solvent: Methanol HCl

λ Max. mμ	a_m	Cell mm	Conc. g/L
261.5	5230	1	0.1330
213	3630	1	0.1330

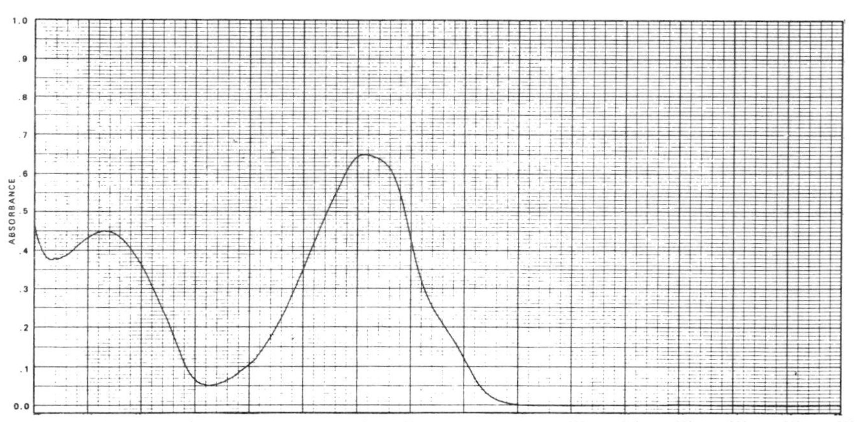

λ Max. mμ	a_m	Cell mm	Conc. g/L

2,5-LUTIDINE

691

C_7H_9N

Mol. Wt. 107.16

B.P. 157°C

Solvent: Methanol

λ Max. mμ	a_m	Cell mm	Conc. g/L
275	2480	2	0.1241
267.5	3250	2	0.1241
210.5	5630	1	0.1241

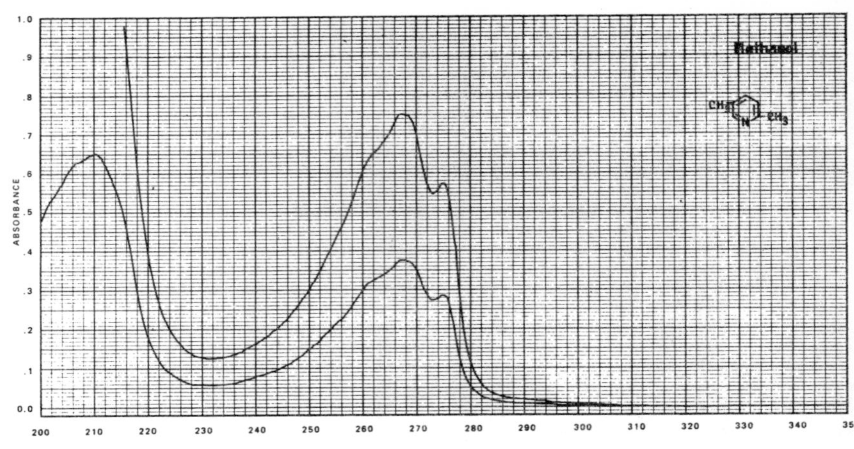

2,5-LUTIDINE

691

C_7H_9N

Mol. Wt. 107.16

B.P. 157°C

Solvent: Methanol HCl

λ Max. mμ	a_m	Cell mm	Conc. g/L
269	2960	1	0.1241
209	4090	1	0.1241

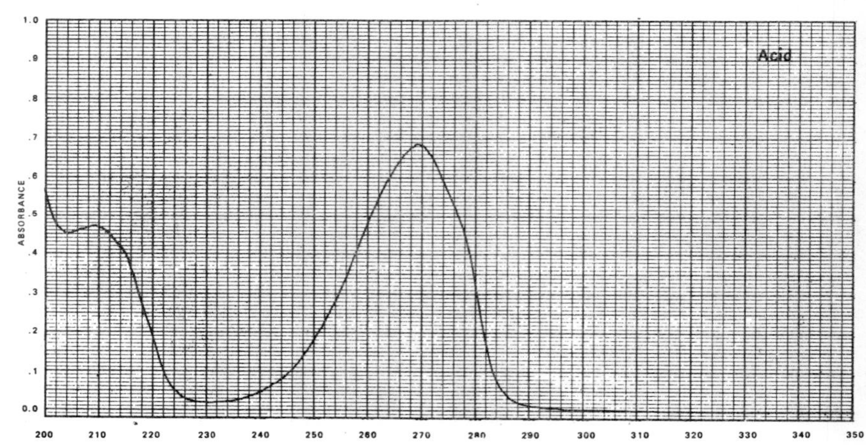

3,5-LUTIDINE

692

C_7H_9N

Mol. Wt. 107.16

B.P. 171°C M.P. -65°C

Solvent: Methanol

λ Max. mμ	a_m	Cell mm	Conc. g/L
275	2610	10	0.019
267.5	3160	10	0.019
207	5080	10	0.019

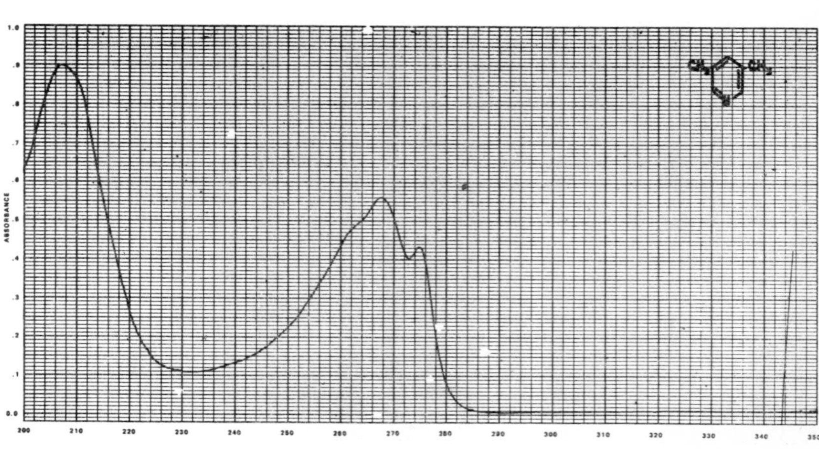

3,5-DIBUTYLPYRIDINE

$C_{13}H_{21}N$

Mol. Wt. 191.32

Solvent: Cyclohexane

λ Max. mμ	a_m	Cell mm	Conc. g/L
x	x	10	1.668
268	3010	10	0.083

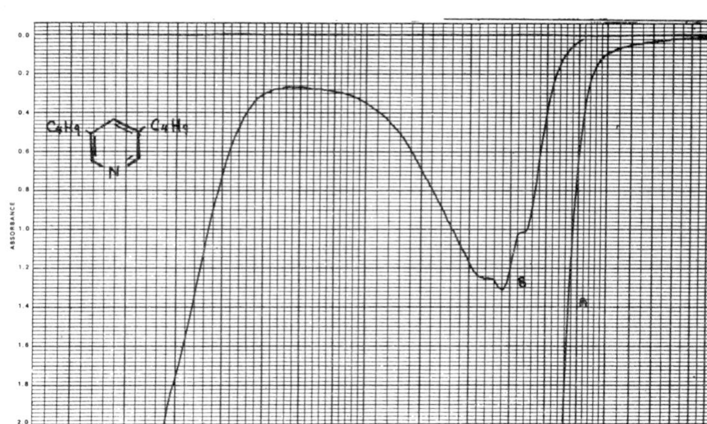

2,6-DI-tert-BUTYLPYRIDINE

$C_{13}H_{21}N$

Mol. Wt. 191.32

B.P. ∿205°C; 120-121°C/20mm

Solvent: Methanol

λ Max. mμ	a_m	Cell mm	Conc. g/L
261	3920	1	0.1385
257.5	3880	1	0.1385
207	7600	1	0.1385

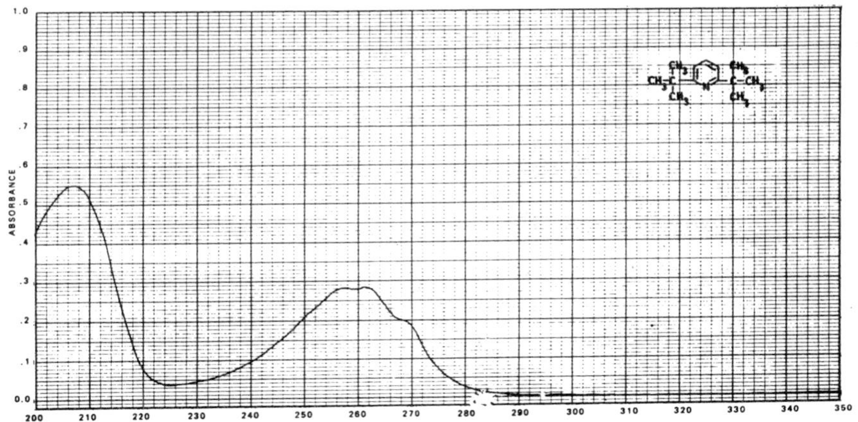

2,6-DI-tert-BUTYLPYRIDINE

$C_{13}H_{21}N$

Mol. Wt. 191.32

B.P. ∿205°C; 120-121°C/20mm

Solvent: Methanol HCl

λ Max. mμ	a_m	Cell mm	Conc. g/L
271.5	11200	1	0.1385

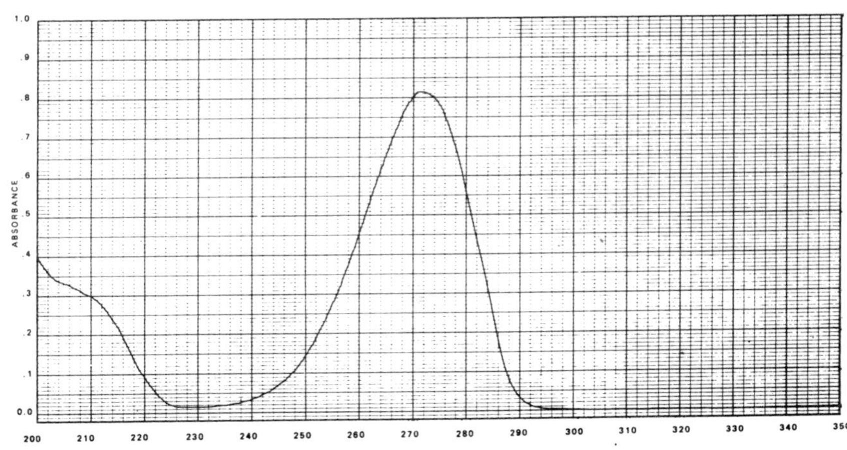

2,4,6-TRIMETHYLPYRIDINE 695

$C_8H_{11}N$
Mol. Wt. 121.18
B.P. 170.4°C
Solvent: Methanol

λ Max. mμ	a_m	Cell mm	Conc. g/L
264.5	3580	10	0.022
208	10200	10	0.006

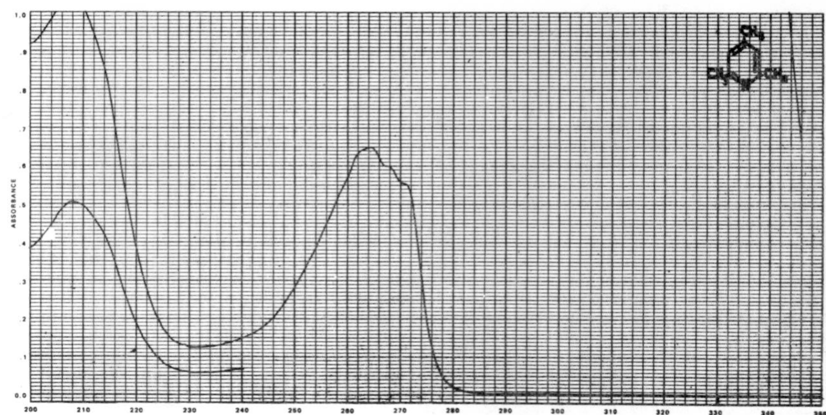

2,6-DI-tert-BUTYL-4-PICOLINE 696

$C_{14}H_{23}N$
Mol. Wt. 205.35
M.P. 33.5-33.8°C
Solvent: Methanol

λ Max. mμ	a_m	Cell mm	Conc. g/L
260.5	2940	1	0.484

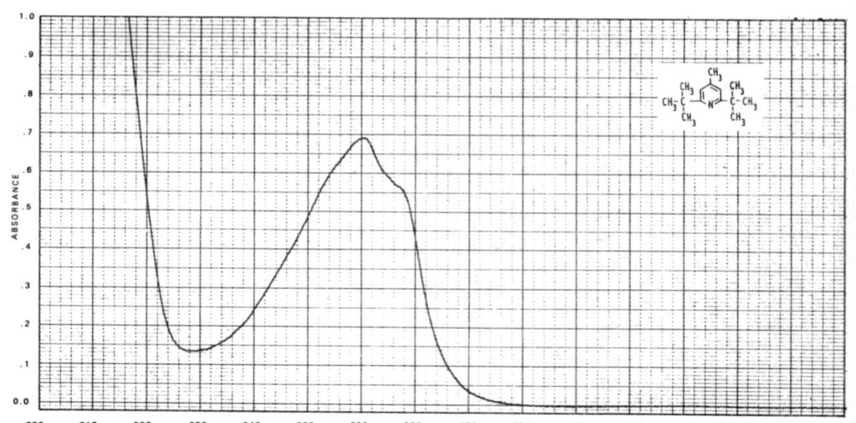

2,6-DI-tert-BUTYL-4-PICOLINE 696

$C_{14}H_{23}N$
Mol. Wt. 205.35
M.P. 22.5-33.8°C
Solvent: Methanol HCl

λ Max. mμ	a_m	Cell mm	Conc. g/L
268.5	9960	2	0.097
217	4050	2	0.097

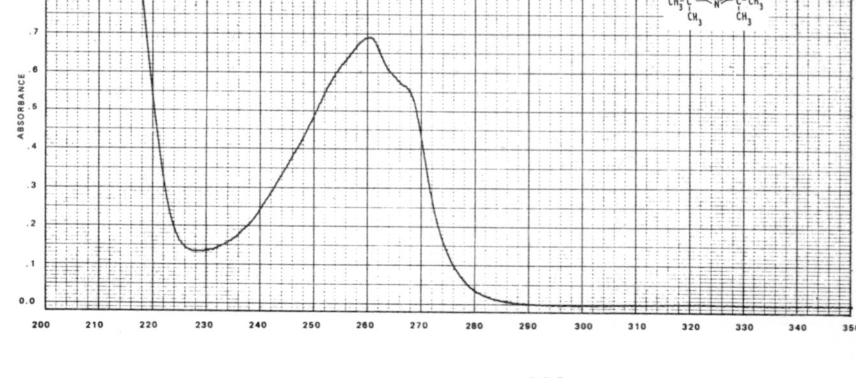

2-PHENYLPYRIDINE **697**

$C_{11}H_9N$

Mol. Wt. 155.20

Solvent: Methanol

λ Max. mμ	a_m	Cell mm	Conc. g/L
274	9170	1	0.100
242.5	11900	1	0.100
x	x	1	0.100

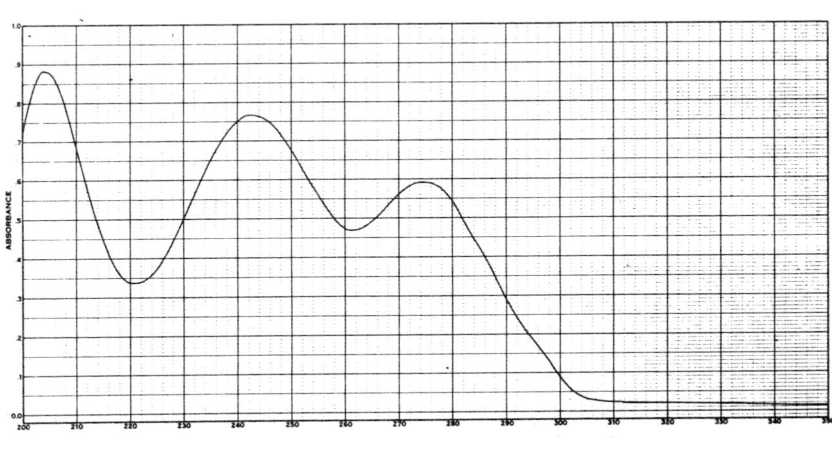

2-PHENYLPYRIDINE **697**

$C_{11}H_9N$

Mol. Wt. 155.20

Solvent: Methanol HCl

λ Max. mμ	a_m	Cell mm	Conc. g/L
295	11300	1	0.100
242.5	7570	1	0.100
x	x	1	0.100

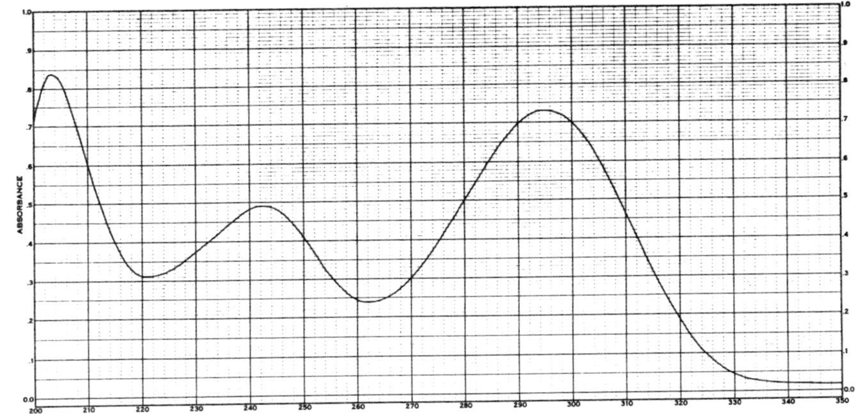

4-PHENYLPYRIDINE **698**

$C_{11}H_9N$

Mol. Wt. 155.20

M.P. 76-78°C (lit.)

Solvent: Methanol

λ Max. mμ	a_m	Cell mm	Conc. g/L
x	x	10	2.152
256	17600	10	0.011

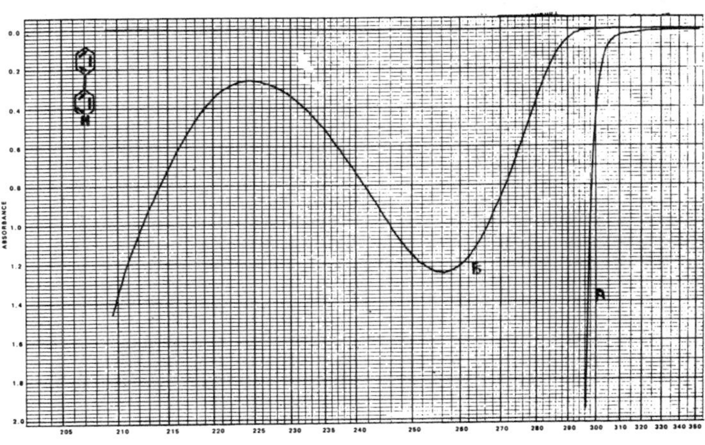

2-FLUOROPYRIDINE

C_5H_4FN

Mol. Wt. 97.09

B.P. 125°C/758mm

Solvent: Methanol

λ Max. mμ	a_m	Cell mm	Conc. g/L
264	2120	2	0.1088
257.5	3120	2	0.1088
252.5	2740	2	0.1088

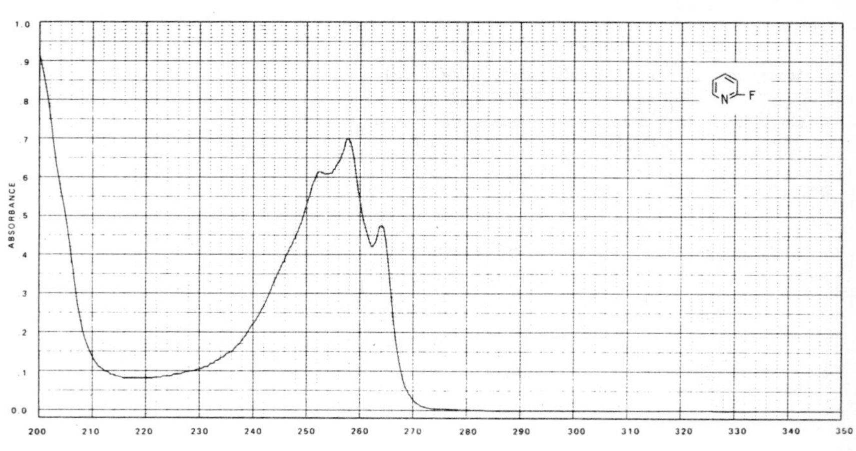

2-CHLOROPYRIDINE

700

C_5H_4ClN

Mol. Wt. 113.55

B.P. 62-63.5°C/37mm

Solvent: Methanol

λ Max. mμ	a_m	Cell mm	Conc. g/L
270	2380	10	0.010
263.5	3450	10	0.010
257	2840	10	0.010
207.5	6890	10	0.010

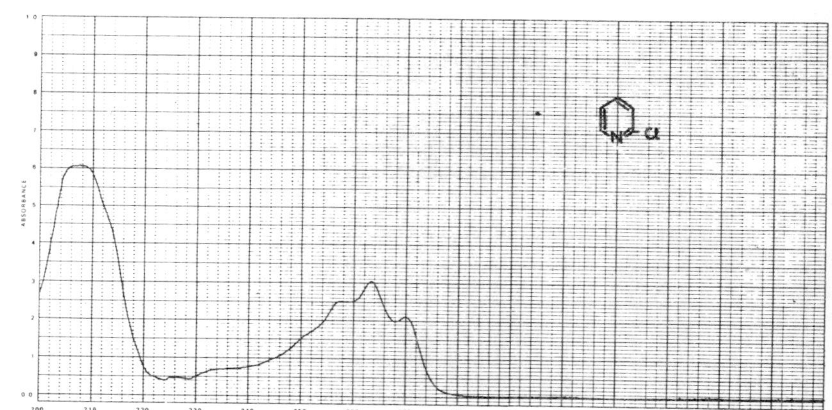

3-CHLOROPYRIDINE

701

C_5H_4ClN

Mol. Wt. 113.55

Solvent: Cyclohexane

λ Max. mμ	a_m	Cell mm	Conc. g/L
x	x	10	1.820
274	1660	10	0.073
267	2260	10	0.073
261	2160	10	0.073
x	x	10	0.036

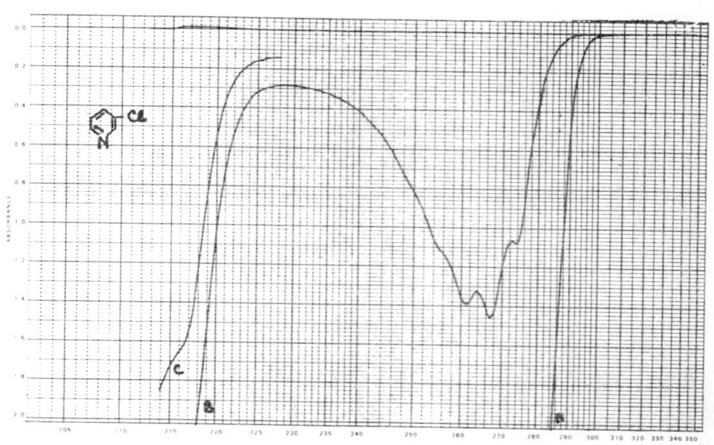

2,3-DICHLOROPYRIDINE 702

$C_5H_3Cl_2N$

Mol. Wt. 148.00

Solvent: Methanol

λ Max. mμ	a_m	Cell mm	Conc. g/L
271.5	4000	10	0.020
216	7330	10	0.020

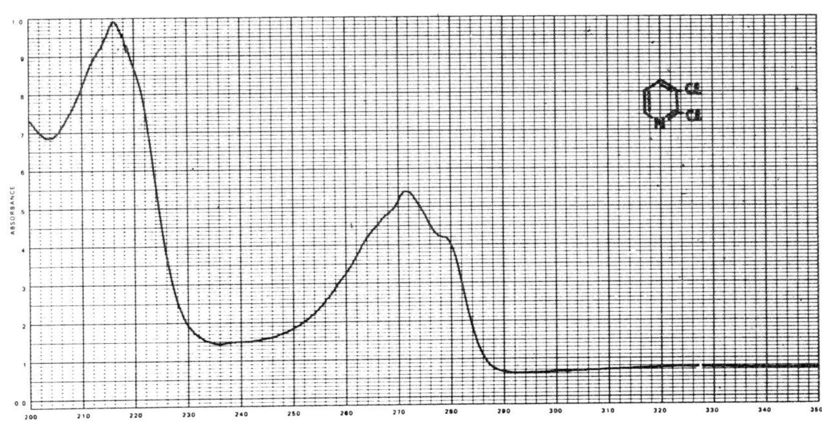

2-BROMOPYRIDINE 703

C_5H_4BrN

Mol. Wt. 158.00

B.P. 192-194°C

Solvent: Methanol

λ Max. mμ	a_m	Cell mm	Conc. g/L
270	2510	1	0.2522
264	3440	1	0.2522

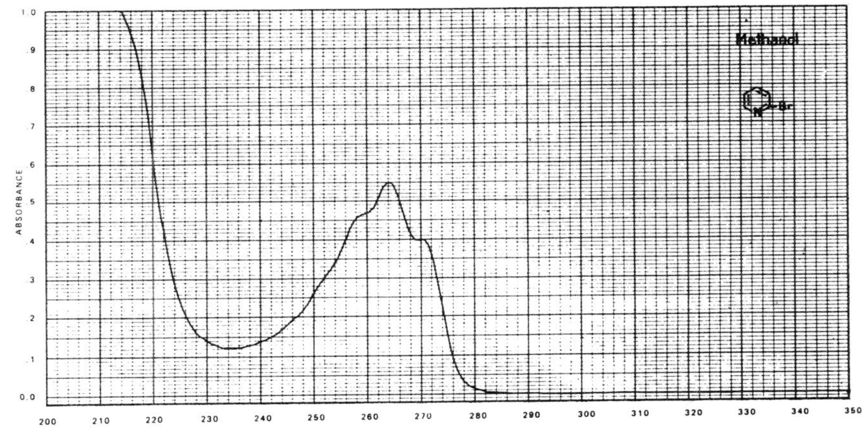

3-BROMOPYRIDINE 704

C_5H_4BrN

Mol. Wt. 158.00

Solvent: Methanol

λ Max. mμ	a_m	Cell mm	Conc. g/L
274.5	1970	10	0.020
268	2730	10	0.020
262	2350	10	0.020
213.5	6630	10	0.020

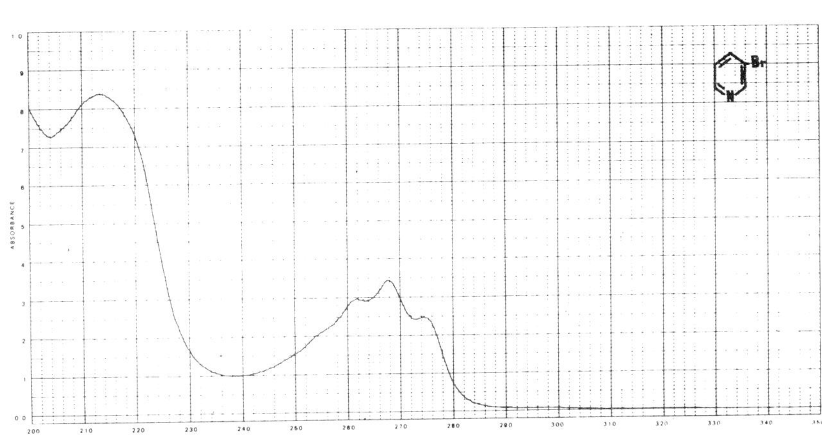

2-[(DIETHYLAMINO)METHYL] PYRIDINE

705

$C_{10}H_{16}N_2$
Mol. Wt. 164.25
Solvent: Methanol

λ Max. mμ	a_m	Cell mm	Conc. g/L
259.5	3290	2.5	0.100

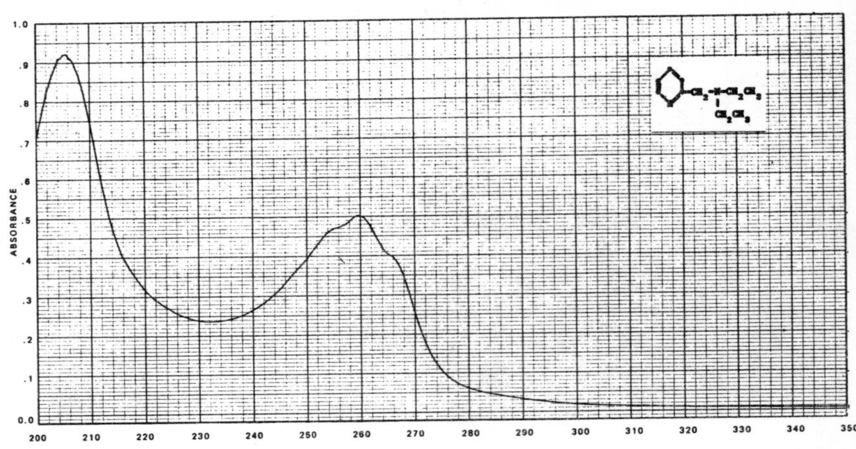

2-AMINOPYRIDINE

706

$C_5H_6N_2$
Mol. Wt. 94.11
M.P. 62.8-63.8°C
Solvent: Methanol

λ Max. mμ	a_m	Cell mm	Conc. g/L
x	x	10	1.348
296	3940	10	0.027
236	10700	10	0.014

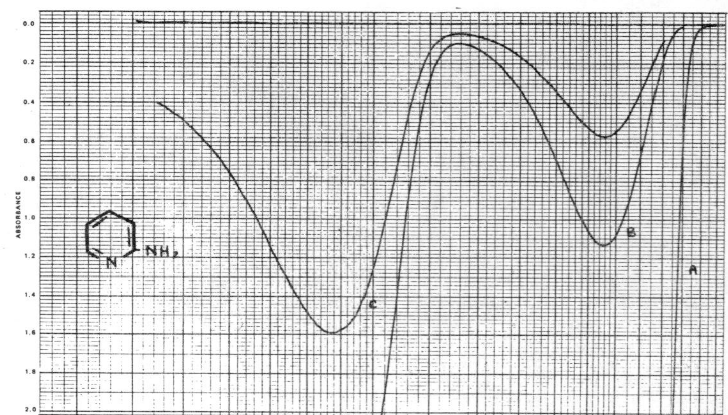

2-AMINO-5-CHLOROPYRIDINE

707

$C_5H_5ClN_2$
Mol. Wt. 128.57
Solvent: Dioxane

λ Max. mμ	a_m	Cell mm	Conc. g/L
x	x	10	2.292
307.5	3330	10	0.069
243.5	14900	10	0.012

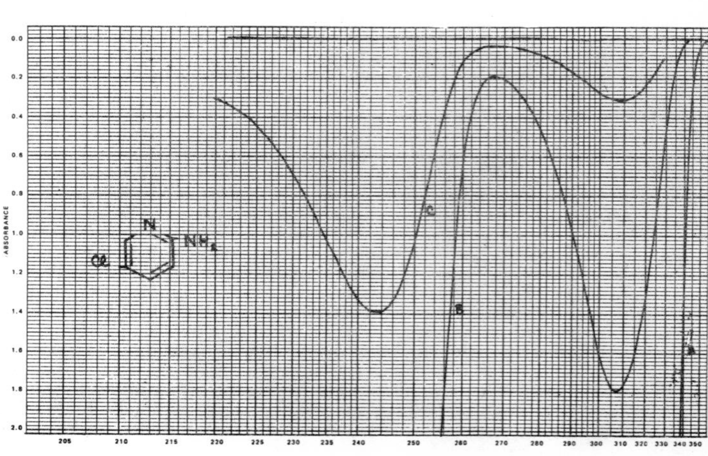

2- {[2-(DIMETHYLAMINO)ETHYL] AMINO} PYRIDINE

708

$C_9H_{15}N_3$
Mol. Wt. 165.24
B.P. 265°C (lit.)
Solvent: Cyclohexane

λ Max. mμ	a_m	Cell mm	Conc. g/L
301	3530	10	0.0808
243.5	15500	10	0.0162

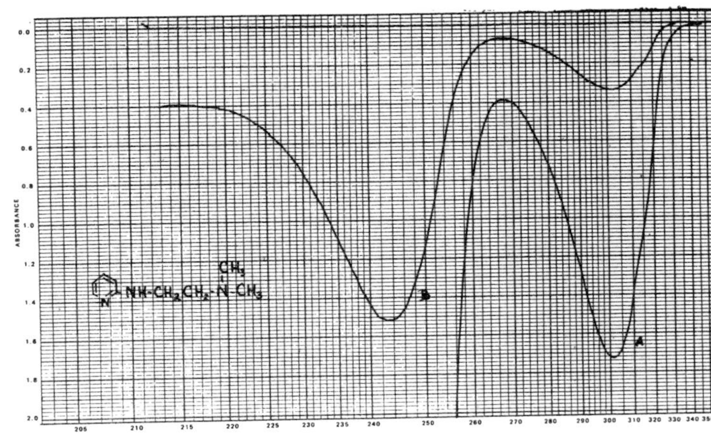

3-(BENZYLAMINO)PYRIDINE

709

$C_{12}H_{12}N_2$
Mol. Wt. 184.24
Solvent: Methanol

λ Max. mμ	a_m	Cell mm	Conc. g/L
310.5	3150	5	0.100
250.5	13300	1	0.100

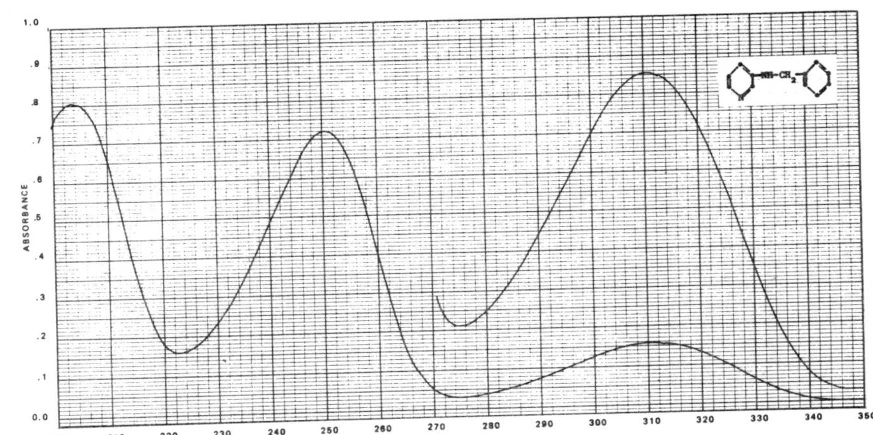

3-(BENZYLAMINO)PYRIDINE

709

$C_{12}H_{12}N_2$
Mol. Wt. 184.24
Solvent: Methanol HCl

λ Max. mμ	a_m	Cell mm	Conc. g/L
339	3450	5	0.100
259.5	12300	1	0.100
218	14600	1	0.100

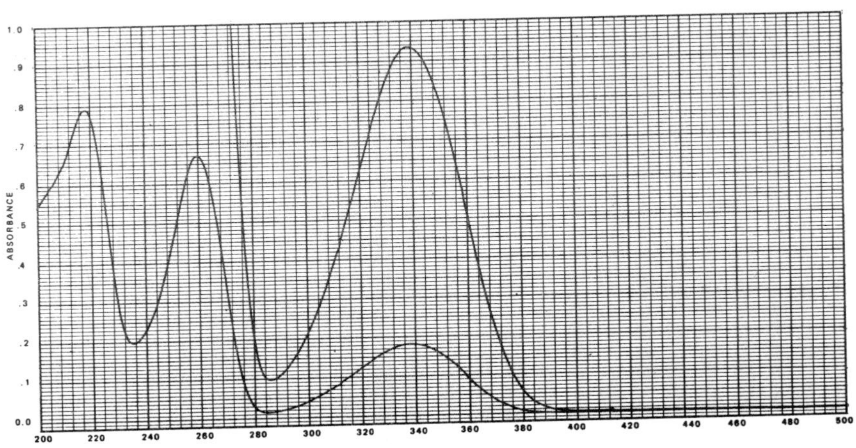

4-(DIMETHYLAMINO)PYRIDINE

710

$C_7H_{10}N_2$

Mol. Wt. 122.17

Solvent: Methanol

λ Max. mμ	a_m	Cell mm	Conc. g/L
257.5	16700	0.5	0.100

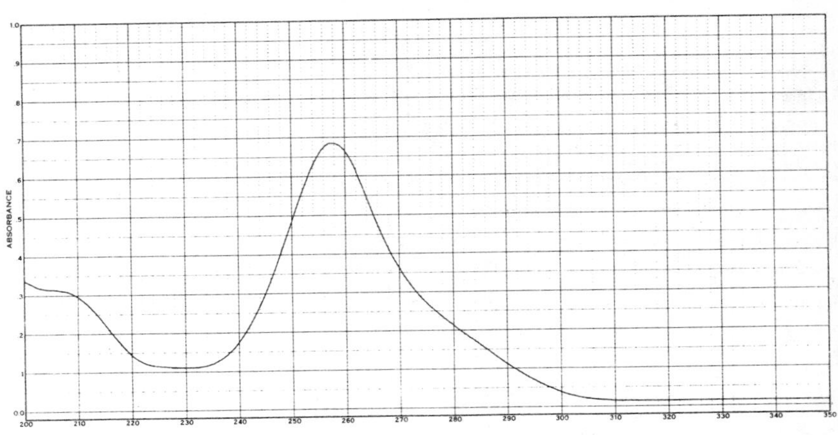

4-(DIMETHYLAMINO)PYRIDINE

710

$C_7H_{10}N_2$

Mol. Wt. 122.17

Solvent: Methanol HCl

λ Max. mμ	a_m	Cell mm	Conc. g/L
279	16600	0.5	0.100
x	x	0.5	0.100

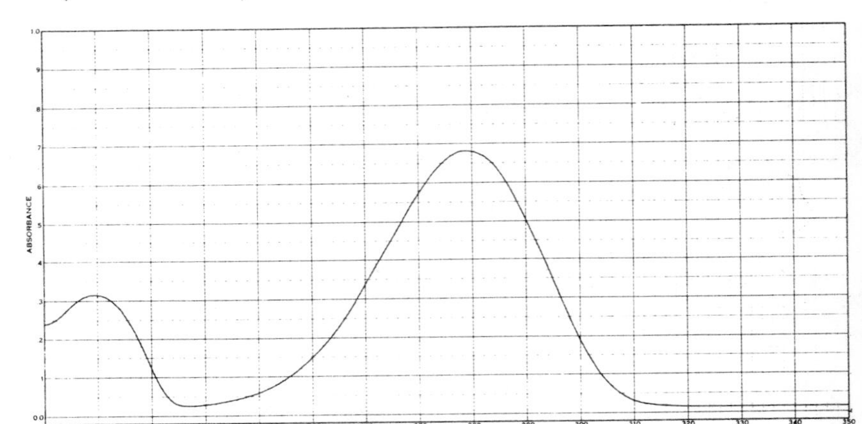

NICOTINE

711

$C_{10}H_{14}N_2$

Mol. Wt. 162.13

B.P. 247°C (lit.)

Solvent: Cyclohexane

λ Max. mμ	a_m	Cell mm	Conc. g/L
x	x	10	2.100
256	2440	10	0.084

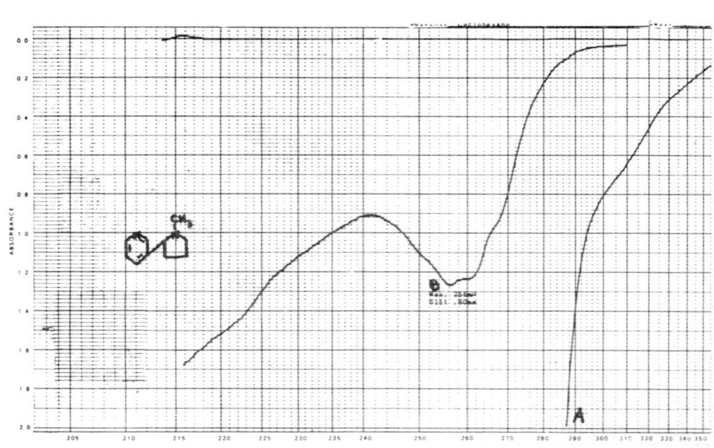

2-(PIPERIDINOMETHYL)PYRIDINE 712

$C_{11}H_{16}N_2$
Mol. Wt. 176.26

Solvent: Methanol

λ Max. mμ	a_m	Cell mm	Conc. g/L
288	2040	5	0.100
240	10600	1	0.100

3,4′-ETHYLENEDIPYRIDINE 713

$C_{12}H_{12}N_2$
Mol. Wt. 184.24

Solvent: Methanol

λ Max. mμ	a_m	Cell mm	Conc. g/L
268	2530	2	0.0920
262	4650	2	0.0920
256	4720	2	0.0920

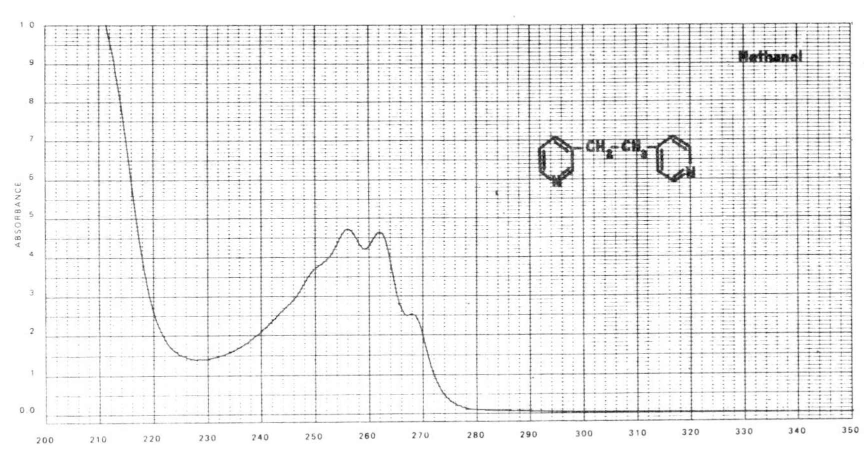

3,4′-ETHYLENEDIPYRIDINE 713

$C_{12}H_{12}N_2$
Mol. Wt. 184.24

Solvent: Methanol HCl

λ Max. mμ	a_m	Cell mm	Conc. g/L
256.5	8990	2	0.0920
256	8880	2	0.0920
216.5	8860	2	0.0920

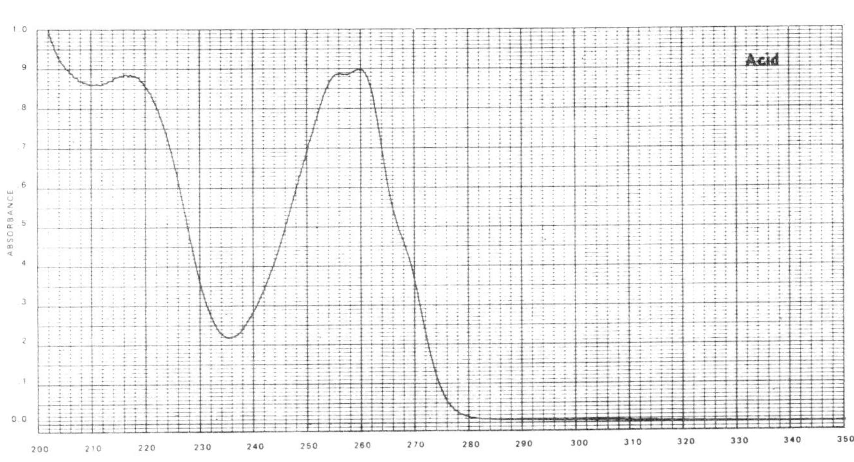

2,3'-VINYLENEDIPYRIDINE **714**

$C_{12}H_{10}N_2$
Mol. Wt. 182.23

λ Max. mμ	a_m	Cell mm	Conc. g/L

Pure sample not available.

2,4'-VINYLENEDIPYRIDINE **715**

$C_{12}H_{10}N_2$
Mol. Wt. 182.23
Solvent: Methanol

λ Max. mμ	a_m	Cell mm	Conc. g/L
304.5	26500	1	0.0500
218	11000	1	0.0500

Methanol

CH=CH

ABSORBANCE

2,4'-VINYLENEDIPYRIDINE **715**

$C_{12}H_{10}N_2$
Mol. Wt. 182.23
Solvent: Methanol HCl

λ Max. mμ	a_m	Cell mm	Conc. g/L
319	29500	1	0.0500
218	9110	1	0.0500

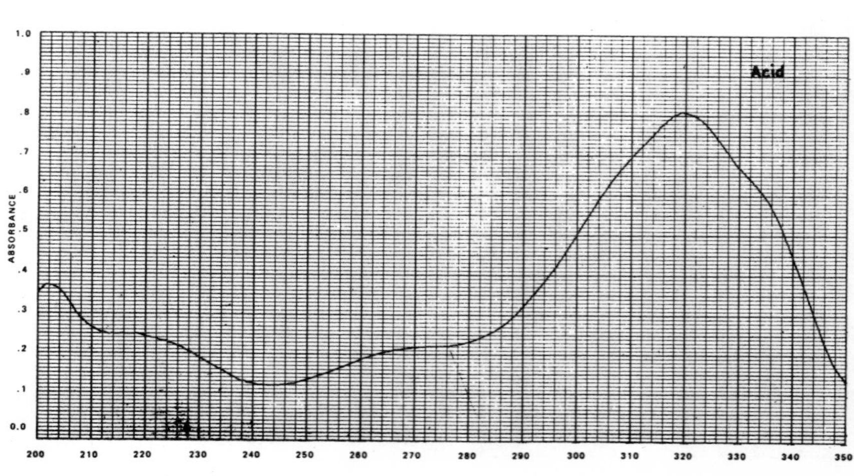

2,2′-BIPYRIDINE **716**

$C_{10}H_8N_2$

Mol. Wt. 156.19

M.P. 69-70°C

Solvent: Methanol

λ Max. mμ	a_m	Cell mm	Conc. g/L
281.5	13800	1	0.100
234.5	10700	1	0.100

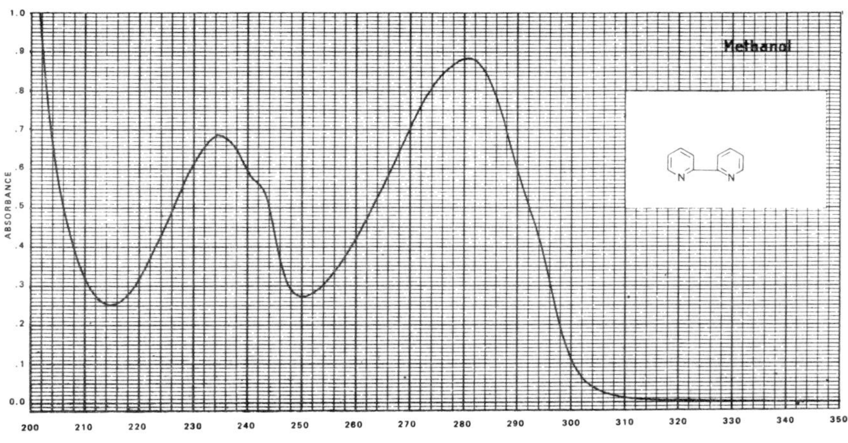

2,2′-BIPYRIDINE **716**

$C_{10}H_8N_2$

Mol. Wt. 156.19

M.P. 69-70°C

Solvent: Methanol HCl

λ Max. mμ	a_m	Cell mm	Conc. g/L
302.5	16600	1	0.0500
243	8280	1	0.0500

λ Max. mμ	a_m	Cell mm	Conc. g/L

4,4'-BIPYRIDINE

717

$C_{10}H_8N_2$

Mol. Wt. 156.19

M.P. 114°C (lit.)

Solvent: Methanol

λ Max. mμ	a_m	Cell mm	Conc. g/L
238.5	14500	1	0.100

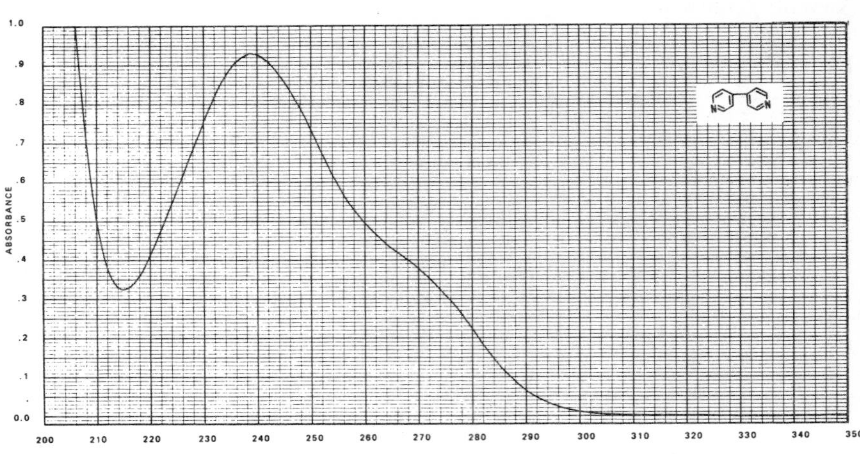

4,4'-BIPYRIDINE

717

$C_{10}H_8N_2$

Mol. Wt. 156.19

M.P. 114°C (lit.)

Solvent: Methanol HCl

λ Max. mμ	a_m	Cell mm	Conc. g/L
252	14000	1	0.100

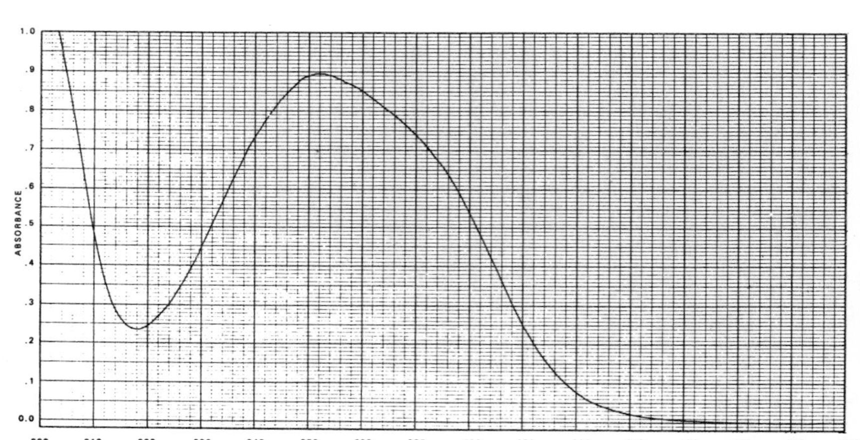

QUINOLINE

718

C_9H_7N

Mol. Wt. 129.1

B.P. 237.7°C/760mm F.P. -14.7°C

Solvent: Methanol

λ Max. mμ	a_m	Cell mm	Conc. g/L
313.5	3500	10	0.0224
300	3110	10	0.0224
287.5	3330	10	0.0224
277	3550	10	0.0224
231	29100	10	0.0022
226.5	33500	10	0.0022

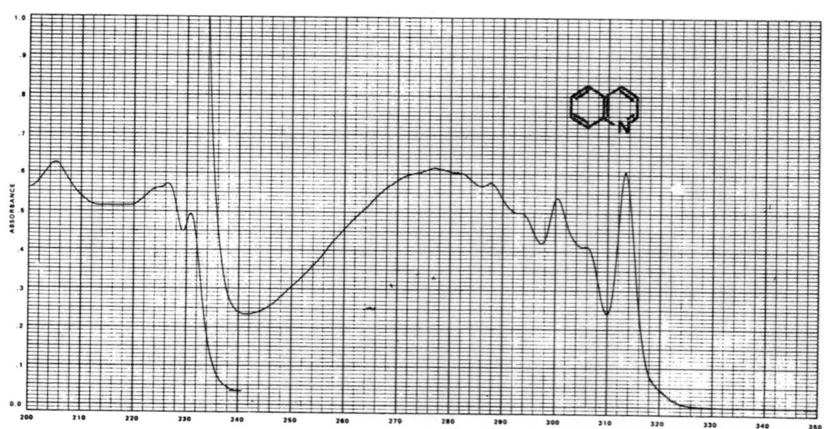

QUINALDINE 719

$C_{10}H_9N$

Mol. Wt. 143.18

F.P. -2°C B.P. 235.8°C/760mm

Solvent: Methanol

λ Max. mμ	a_m	Cell mm	Conc. g/L
316	4870	10	0.021
309	3020	10	0.021
303	3110	10	0.021
296	3100	10	0.021
290	3510	10	0.021
273.5	3950	10	0.021
233.5	36900	10	0.002
229	38700	10	0.002
226	37600	10	0.002
206.5	53000	10	0.002

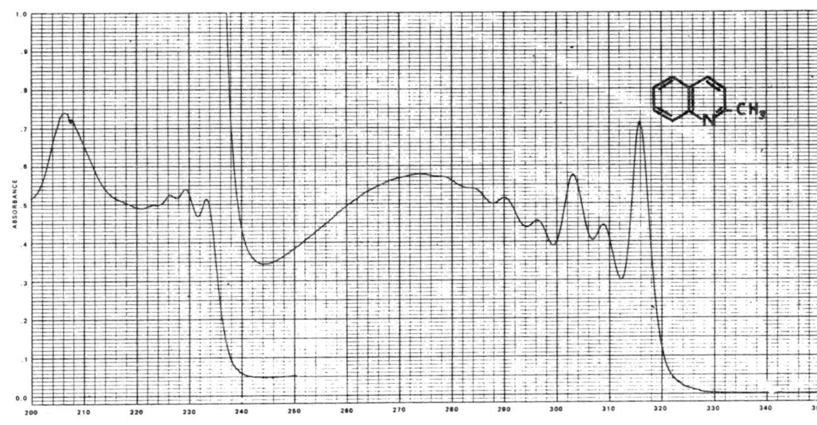

LEPIDINE 720

$C_{10}H_9N$

Mol. Wt. 143.18

M.P. 9-10°C (lit.) B.P. 261-263°C (lit.)

Solvent: Cyclohexane

λ Max. mμ	a_m	Cell mm	Conc. g/L
x	x	10	3.132
313	2400	10	0.031
300	2220	10	0.031
276	4990	10	0.031
268.5	5010	10	0.031
222	56300	10	0.003

λ Max. mμ	a_m	Cell mm	Conc. g/L

6-METHYLQUINOLINE

$C_{10}H_9N$

Mol. Wt. 143.19

Solvent: Methanol

λ Max. mμ	a_m	Cell mm	Conc. g/L
316	4080	10	0.020
302.5	3570	10	0.020
278	3870	10	0.020
228	41700	1	0.020
205	46300	1	0.020

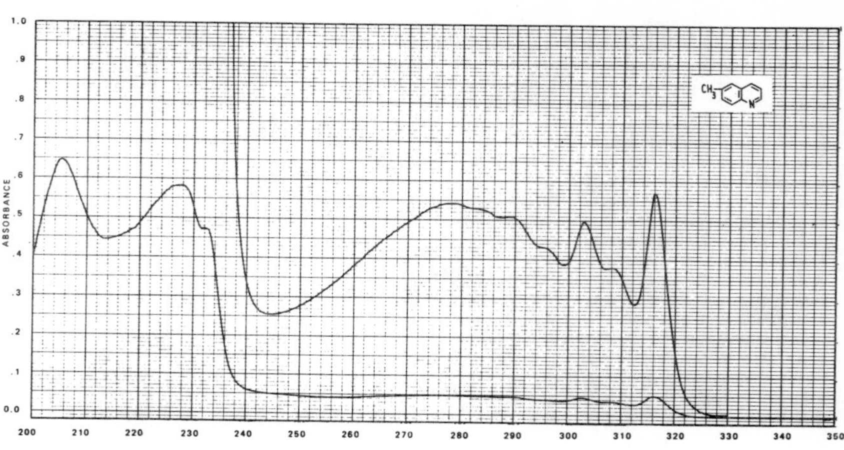

6-METHYLQUINOLINE

721

$C_{10}H_9N$

Mol. Wt. 143.19

Solvent: Methanol HCl

λ Max. mμ	a_m	Cell mm	Conc. g/L
315.5	7890	5	0.020
238.5	47100	1	0.020

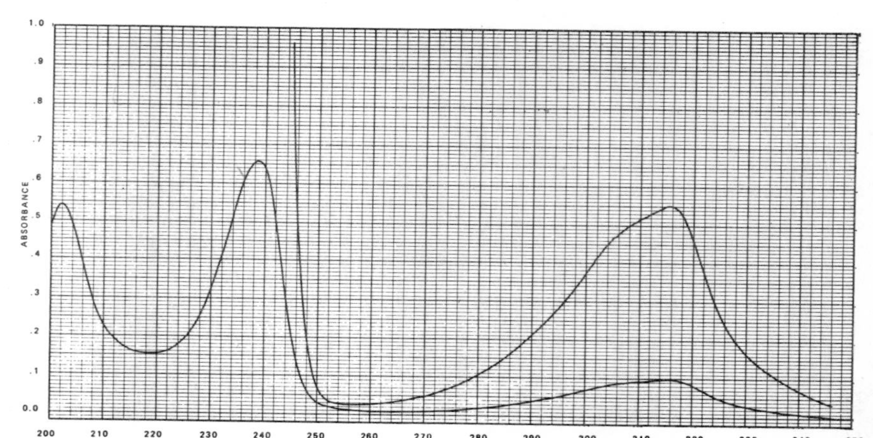

7-METHYLQUINOLINE

722

$C_{10}H_9N$

Mol. Wt. 143.19

B.P. 252.5°C M.P. <-20°C (lit.)

Solvent: Methanol

λ Max. mμ	a_m	Cell mm	Conc. g/L
317.5	4030	10	0.0320
304	3480	10	0.0320
278.5	3310	10	0.0320
229	36200	1	0.0320
205	42000	1	0.0320

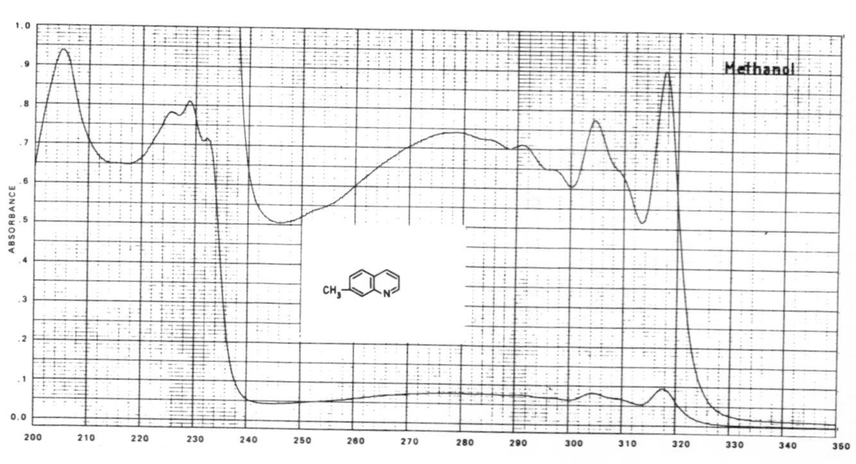

7-METHYLQUINOLINE 722

$C_{10}H_9N$

Mol. Wt. 143.19

B.P. 252.5°C M.P. <-20°C (lit.)

Solvent: Methanol HCl

λ Max. mμ	a_m	Cell mm	Conc. g/L
316.5	6950	5	0.0320
239	37500	1	0.0320

8-METHYLQUINOLINE 723

$C_{10}H_9N$

Mol. Wt. 143.19

B.P. 112-114°C/8mm

Solvent: Methanol

λ Max. mμ	a_m	Cell mm	Conc. g/L
315.5	2350	1	0.300
303	3150	1	0.300
291	3530	1	0.300
231	42500	1	0.0300

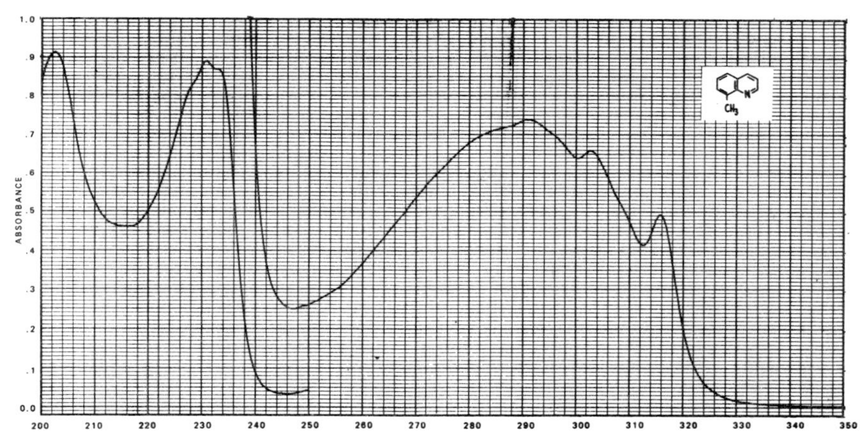

8-METHYLQUINOLINE 723

$C_{10}H_9N$

Mol. Wt. 143.19

B.P. 112-114°C/8mm

Solvent: Methanol HCl

λ Max. mμ	a_m	Cell mm	Conc. g/L
315	6300	1	0.0300
241	43100	1	0.0300

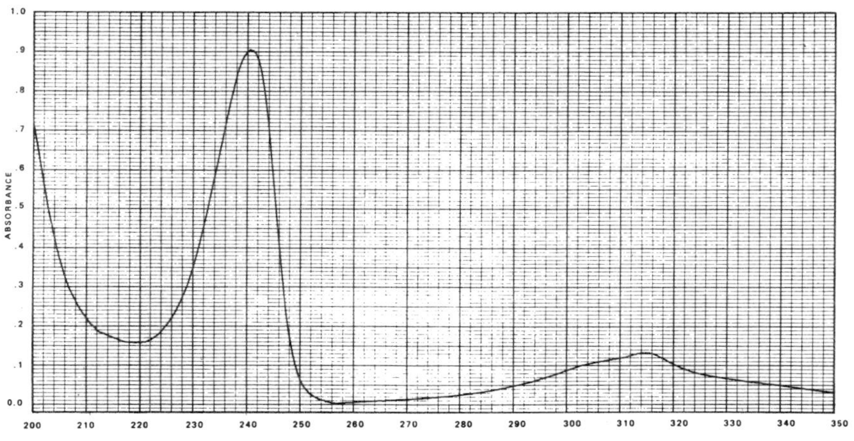

2-CHLOROQUINOLINE

724

C_9H_6ClN

Mol. Wt. 163.61

M.P. 35.2-36.7°C

Solvent: Methanol

λ Max. mμ	a_m	Cell mm	Conc. g/L
317	4580	10	0.0200
310	2800	10	0.0200
304	3450	10	0.0200
297	2680	10	0.0200
233	41000	1	0.0200

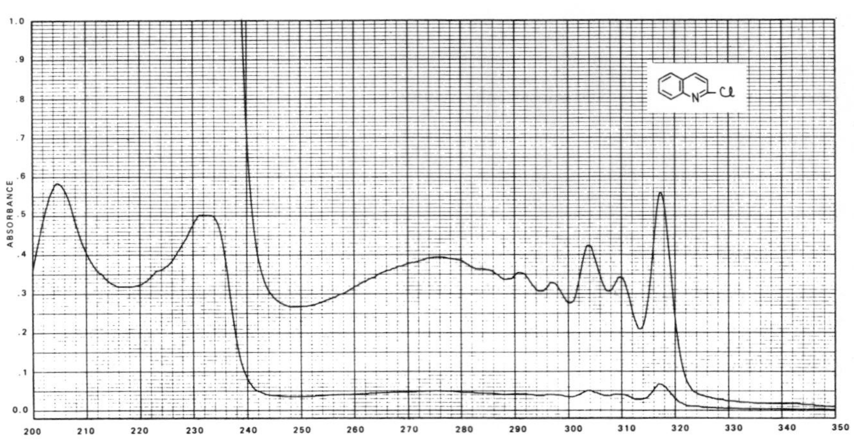

6-BROMOQUINOLINE

725

C_9H_6BrN

Mol. Wt. 208.06

M.P. 17-19°C

Solvent: Methanol

λ Max. mμ	a_m	Cell mm	Conc. g/L
320	3000	2	0.3020
307	2480	2	0.3020
274	3170	2	0.3020
228	41100	1	0.03020
210	27400	1	0.03020

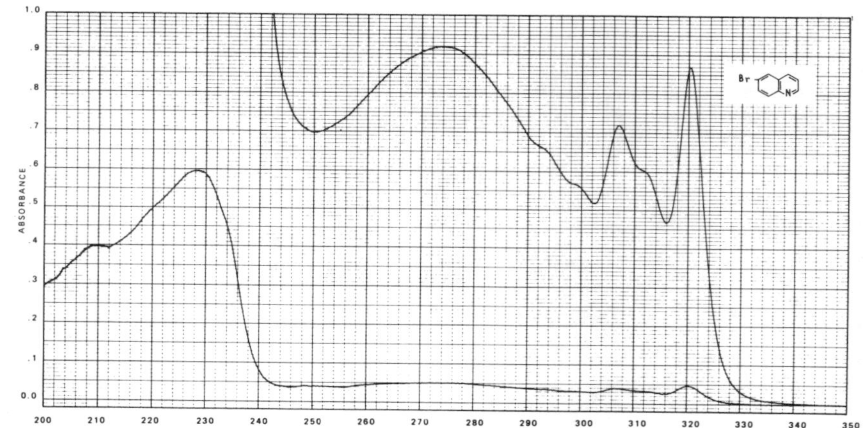

6-BROMOQUINOLINE

725

C_9H_6BrN

Mol. Wt. 208.06

M.P. 17-19°C

Solvent: Methanol HCl

λ Max. mμ	a_m	Cell mm	Conc. g/L
319	5430	1	0.3020
242	37100	1	0.03020
205	24800	1	0.03020

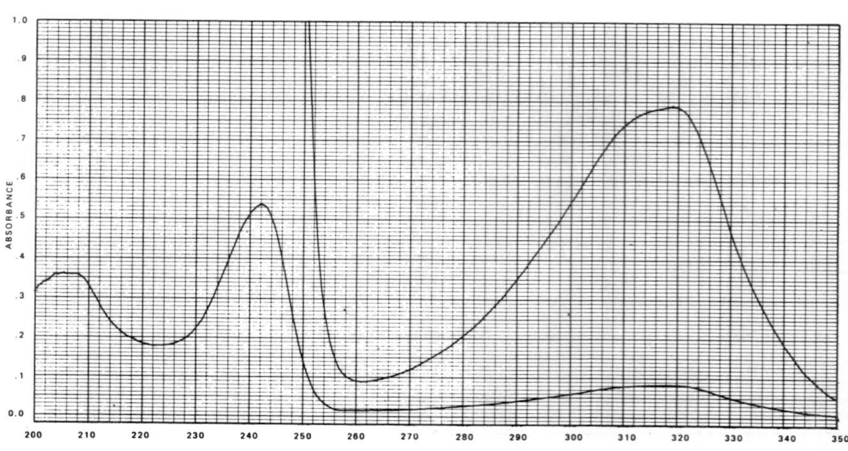

2-IODOQUINOLINE

C_9H_6IN

Mol. Wt. 255.06

M.P. 54-56°C

Solvent: Methanol

λ Max. mμ	$^a m$	Cell mm	Conc. g/L
323	4430	5	0.100
310	3500	5	0.100
302.5	2600	5	0.100
297	2640	5	0.100
208	34700	1	0.050

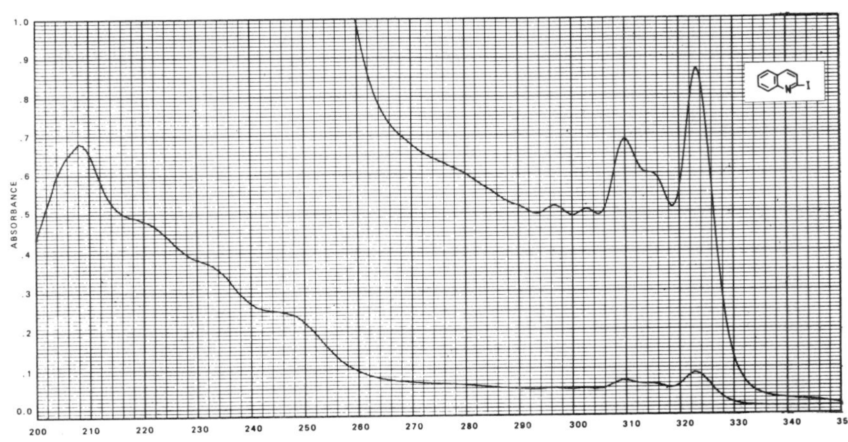

2-IODOQUINOLINE

726

C_9H_6IN

Mol. Wt. 255.06

M.P. 54-56°C

Solvent: Methanol HCl

λ Max. mμ	$^a m$	Cell mm	Conc. g/L
337	4500	2	0.100
324	6130	2	0.100
311	3930	2	0.100
232	18200	1	0.050
208	31600	1	0.050

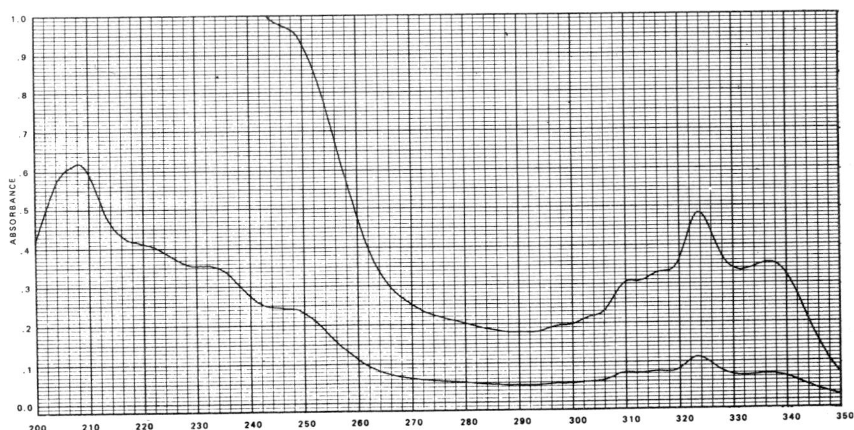

λ Max. mμ	$^a m$	Cell mm	Conc. g/L

3-AMINOQUINOLINE

727

$C_9H_8N_2$

Mol. Wt. 144.18

M.P. 92-94°C

Solvent: Methanol

λ Max. mμ	a_m	Cell mm	Conc. g/L
350	4100	10	0.0200
243	30300	1	0.0200
212	32700	1	0.0200

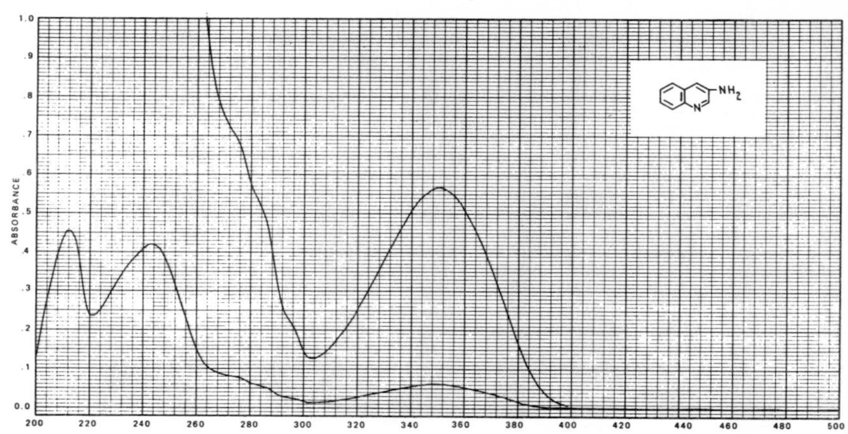

3-AMINOQUINOLINE

727

$C_9H_8N_2$

Mol. Wt. 144.18

M.P. 92-94°C

Solvent: Methanol HCl

λ Max. mμ	a_m	Cell mm	Conc. g/L
391	5050	5	0.0200
262	13100	5	0.0200
242	34800	1	0.0200
214	20500	1	0.0200

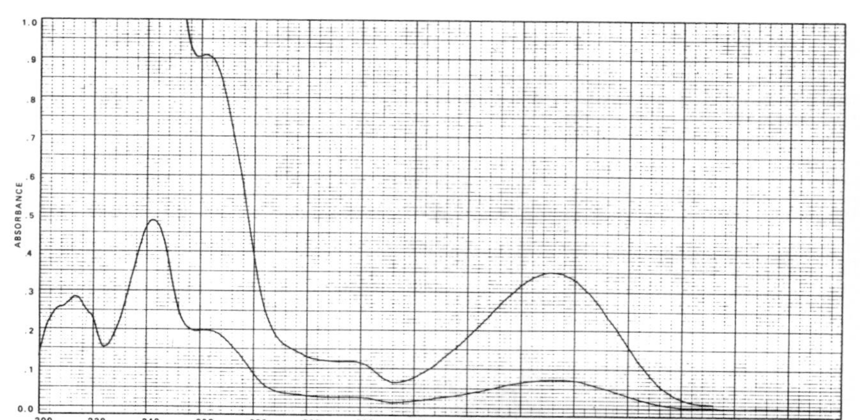

ISOQUINOLINE

728

C_9H_7N

Mol. Wt. 129.16

M.P. 25.5-27°C

Solvent: Methanol

λ Max. mμ	a_m	Cell mm	Conc. g/L
319.5	3130	2	0.1670
314	2320	2	0.1670
306	2480	2	0.1670
268	3720	2	0.1670
216.5	70100	1	0.01670

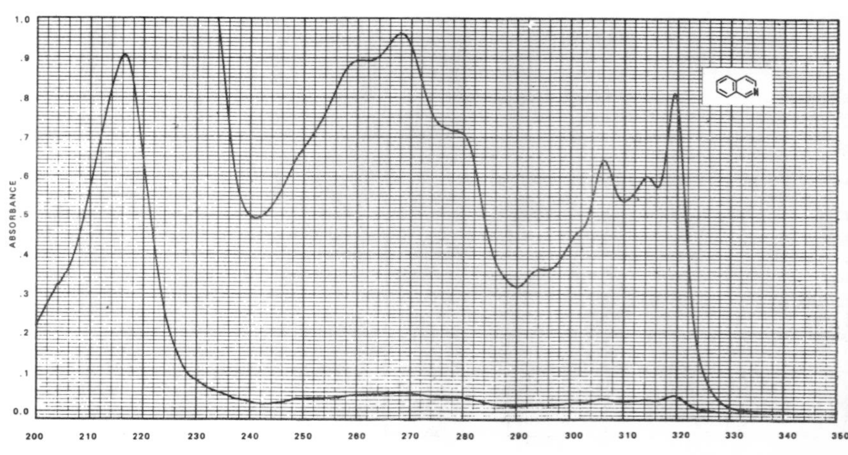

ISOQUINOLINE 728

C_9H_7N

Mol. Wt. 129.16

M.P. 25.5-27°C

Solvent: Methanol HCl

λ Max. mμ	a_m	Cell mm	Conc. g/L
332	4400	1	0.1670
274	2170	1	0.1670
266	2070	1	0.1670
227	44100	1	0.01670

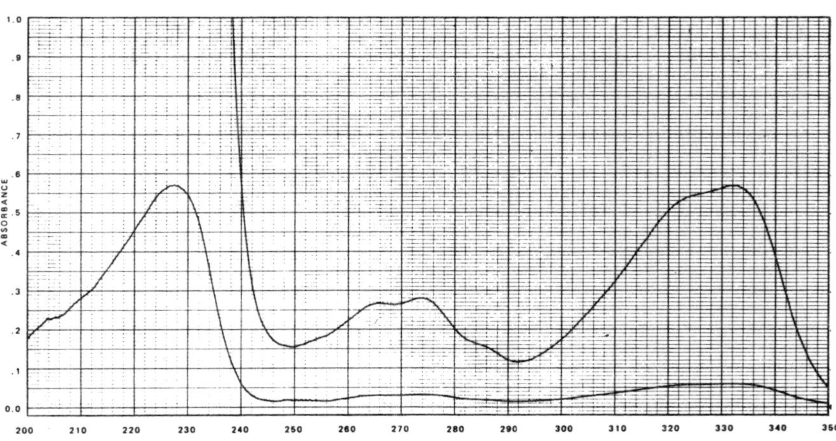

1-CHLOROISOQUINOLINE 729

C_9H_6ClN

Mol. Wt. 163.61

M.P. 35-37°C

Solvent: Methanol

λ Max. mμ	a_m	Cell mm	Conc. g/L
321	3400	2	0.100
310	3080	2	0.100
283	3800	2	0.100
271.5	4510	2	0.100
217.5	52000	1	0.0200

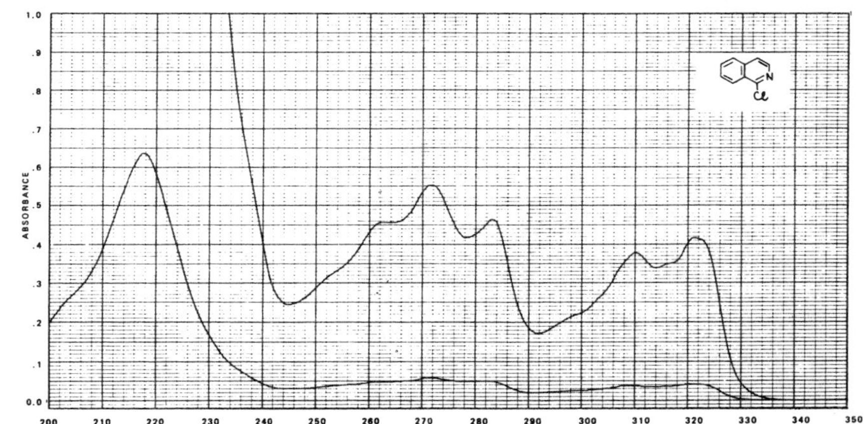

1-CHLORO-3-METHYLISOQUINOLINE 730

$C_{10}H_8ClN$

Mol. Wt. 177.63

Solvent: Methanol

λ Max. mμ	a_m	Cell mm	Conc. g/L
330.0	4000	2.0	0.100
317.0	3770	2.0	0.100
284.5	3970	2.0	0.100
273.5	5140	2.0	0.100
220.0	64200	0.5	0.050

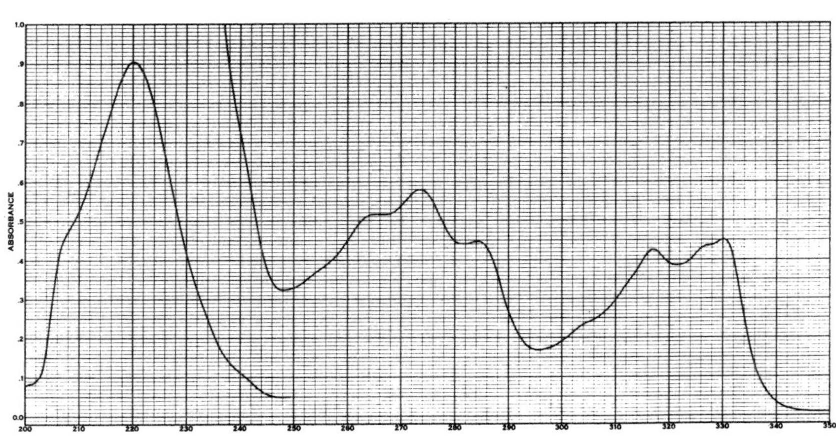

4-BROMOISOQUINOLINE 731

C_9H_6BrN
Mol. Wt. 208.07
Solvent: Methanol

λ Max. mμ	a_m	Cell mm	Conc. g/L
x	x	10	0.242
324	4150	10	0.034
311	3240	10	0.034
288	4260	10	0.034
276	4900	10	0.034
219	66200	10	0.003

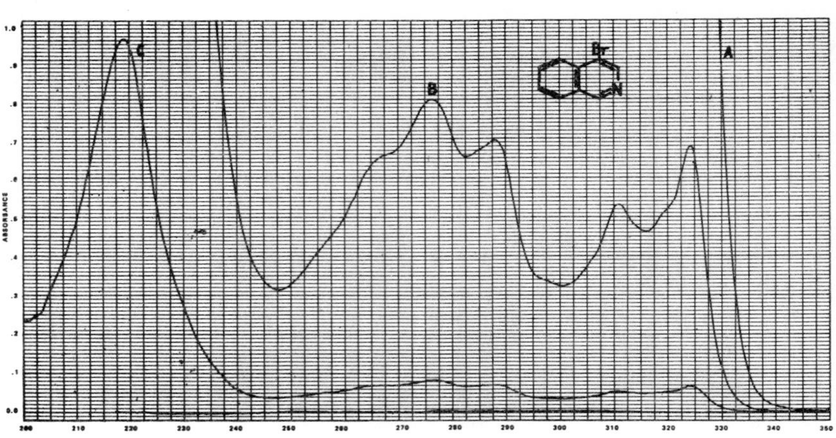

4-PHENYLPYRIMIDINE 732

$C_{10}H_8N_2$
Mol. Wt. 156.19
M.P. 60-63°C
Solvent: Methanol

λ Max. mμ	a_m	Cell mm	Conc. g/L
273.5	13500	1	0.100
x	x	1	0.0500

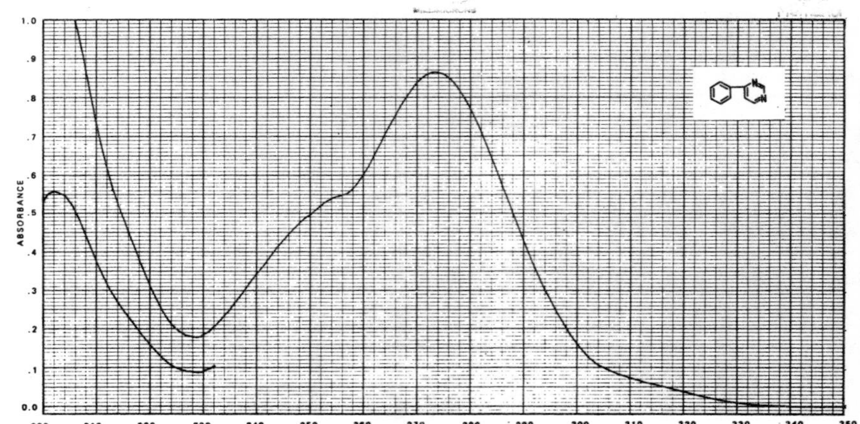

4-PHENYLPYRIMIDINE 732

$C_{10}H_8N_2$
Mol. Wt. 156.19
M.P. 60-63°C
Solvent: Methanol HCl

λ Max. mμ	a_m	Cell mm	Conc. g/L
301.5	13300	1	0.100

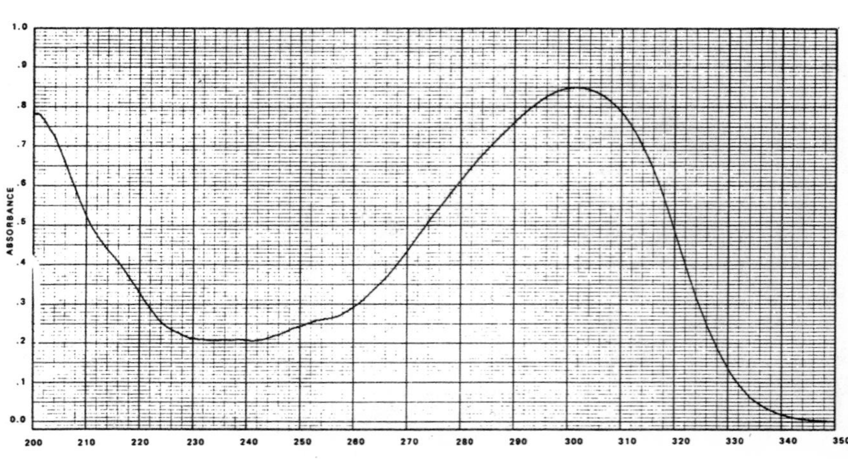

4,6-DICHLOROPYRIMIDINE

$C_4H_2Cl_2N_2$
Mol. Wt. 148.98
M.P. 61.5-63.5°C

λ Max. mμ	a_m	Cell mm	Conc. g/L

Pure sample not available.

2-AMINOPYRIMIDINE

734

$C_4H_5N_2$
Mol. Wt. 95.10
M.P. 124.6-126.0°C (lit.)
Solvent: Methanol

λ Max. mμ	a_m	Cell mm	Conc. g/L
x	x	10	1.952
296	3340	10	0.039
226.5	31300	10	0.004

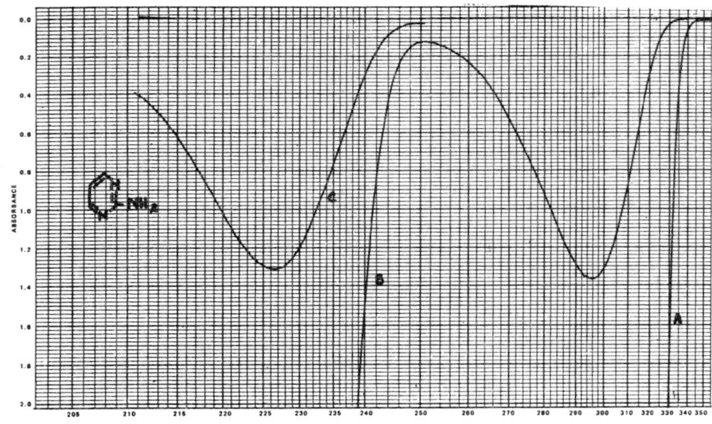

TETRAMETHYLPYRAZINE

735

$C_8H_{12}N_2$
Mol. Wt. 136.20
Solvent: Methanol

λ Max. mμ	a_m	Cell mm	Conc. g/L
x	x	10	2.108
278.5	8560	10	0.021
211.5	8560	10	0.021

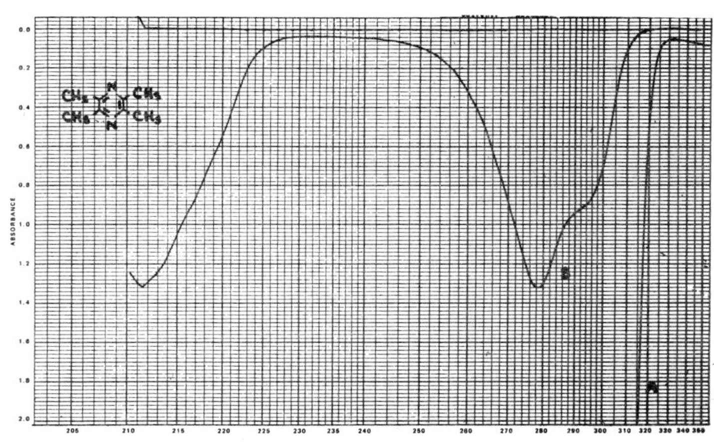

2,4,6-TRIPHENYL-s-TRIAZINE 736

$C_{21}H_{15}N_3$
Mol. Wt. 309.37
Solvent: Methanol

λ Max. mμ	a_m	Cell mm	Conc. g/L
269	7330	4	0.100

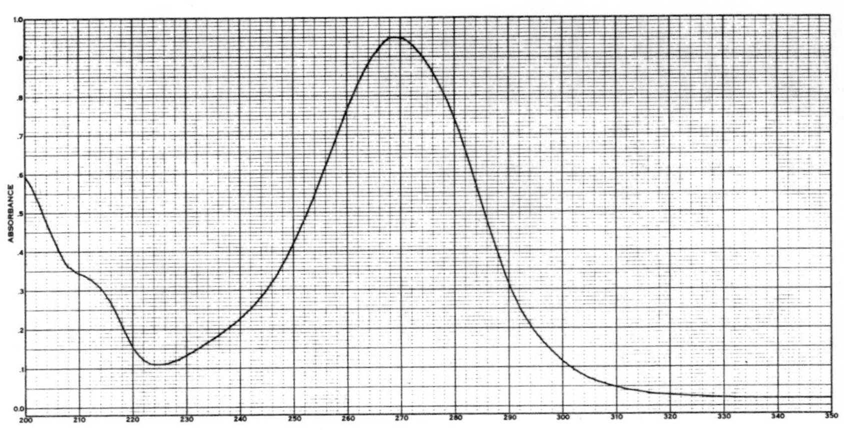

2,4,6-TRIS[DI(2-ETHYLHEXYL)AMINO]-s-TRIAZINE 737

$C_{51}H_{102}N_6$
Mol. Wt. 799.42
M.P. 245-247°C

λ Max. mμ	a_m	Cell mm	Conc. g/L

Pure sample not available.

BENZIMIDAZOLE 738

$C_7H_6N_2$
Mol. Wt. 118.14
M.P. 172°C
Solvent: Methanol

λ Max. mμ	a_m	Cell mm	Conc. g/L
278	6710	10	0.01
271	5750	10	0.01
265	4020	10	0.01
242.5	5820	10	0.01

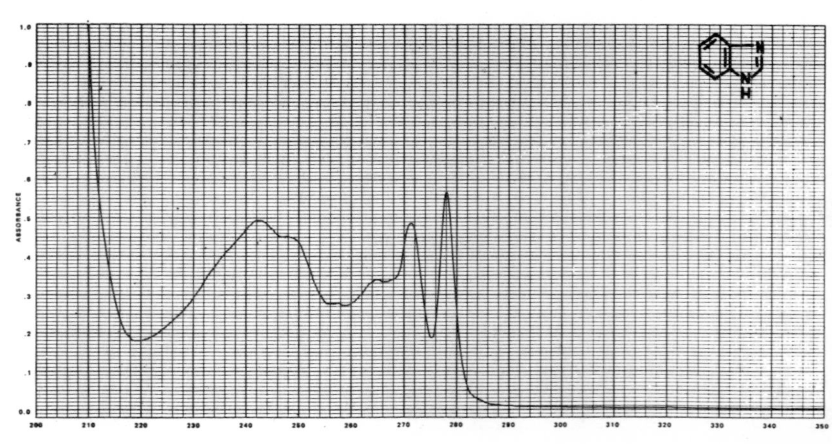

2-PROPYLBENZIMIDAZOLE 739

$C_{10}H_{12}N_2$

Mol. Wt. 160.22

M.P. 152.5-153^oC

Solvent: Dioxane

λ Max. mμ	a_m	Cell mm	Conc. g/L
282	6270	5	0.0500
275.5	5630	5	0.0500
246	6160	5	0.0500

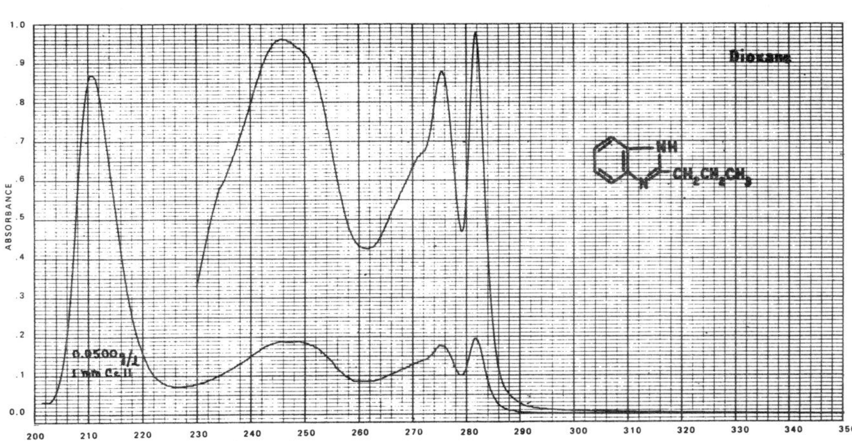

2-PROPYLBENZIMIDAZOLE 739

$C_{10}H_{12}N_2$

Mol. Wt. 160.22

M.P. 152.5-153^oC

Solvent: Dioxane HCl

λ Max. mμ	a_m	Cell mm	Conc. g/L
276	8990	2	0.0500
269	7760	2	0.0500
239	4200	2	0.0500

λ Max. mμ	a_m	Cell mm	Conc. g/L

5(or 6)-METHYLBENZIMIDAZOLE

740

$C_8H_8N_2$

Mol. Wt. 132.17

M.P. 116-118°C

Solvent: Methanol

λ Max. mμ	a_m	Cell mm	Conc. g/L
282.5	4970	2	0.100
276.5	5140	2	0.100
245	5130	2	0.100
204	43600	1	0.0300

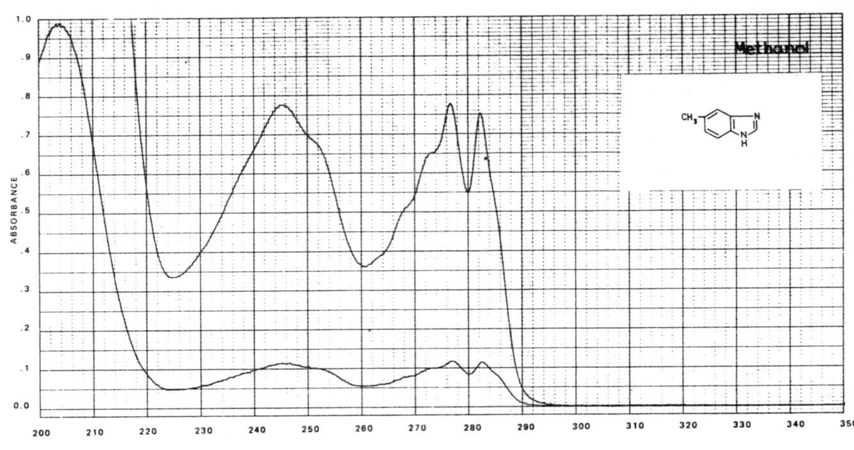

5(or 6)-METHYLBENZIMIDAZOLE

740

$C_8H_8N_2$

Mol. Wt. 132.17

M.P. 116-118°C

Solvent: Methanol HCl

λ Max. mμ	a_m	Cell mm	Conc. g/L
280	6780	5	0.0300
273.5	6500	5	0.0300
265.5	4990	5	0.0300
243	3700	5	0.0300
x	x	1	0.0300

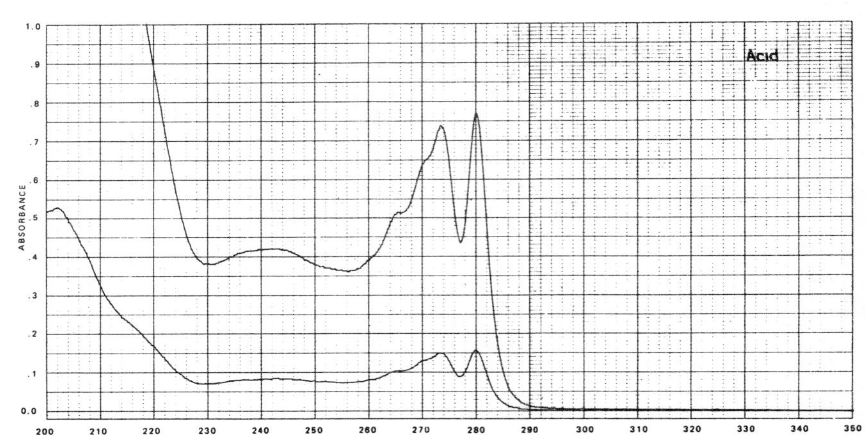

1H-BENZOTRIAZOLE

741

$C_6H_5N_3$

Mol. Wt. 119.12

M.P. 96.8-98.8°C

Solvent: Methanol

λ Max. mμ	a_m	Cell mm	Conc. g/L
275	4590	10	0.01
258	5660	10	0.01
253	5720	10	0.01

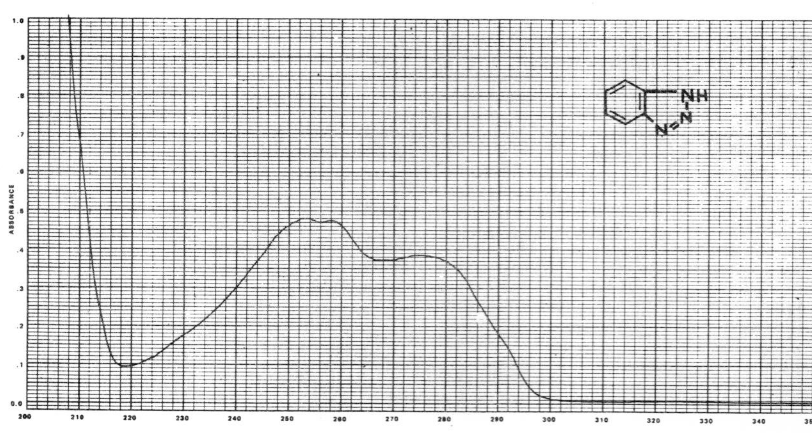

742

4-CHLOROQUINAZOLINE

$C_8H_5ClN_2$
Mol. Wt. 164.60
Solvent: Methanol

λ Max. mμ	a_m	Cell mm	Conc. g/L
312	1650	2	0.100
302	3030	2	0.100
291.5	3090	2	0.100
265	5020	2	0.100
225.5	18700	1	0.0500

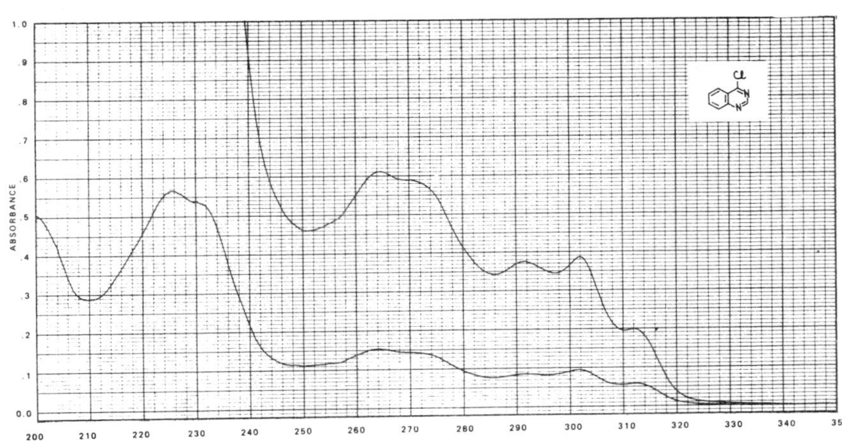

743

PURINE

$C_5H_4N_4$
Mol. Wt. 120.12
M.P. 216-217°C
Solvent: Methanol

λ Max. mμ	a_m	Cell mm	Conc. g/L
265	7600	10	0.010
x	x	10	0.003

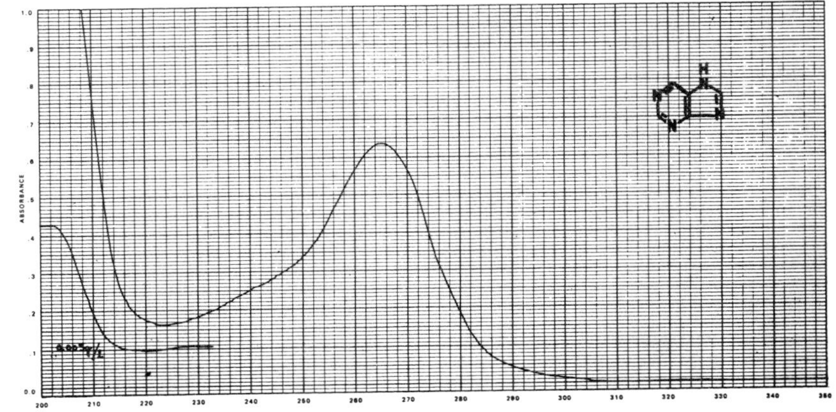

744

9-ETHYLCARBAZOLE

$C_{14}H_{13}N$
Mol. Wt. 195.27
Solvent: Methanol

λ Max. mμ	a_m	Cell mm	Conc. g/L
345	4040	10	0.03
329.5	3510	10	0.03
293.5	17200	10	0.003
287.5	10700	10	0.003
261.5	21600	10	0.003
235.5	44300	10	0.003
229	38400	10	0.003
212	24100	10	0.003

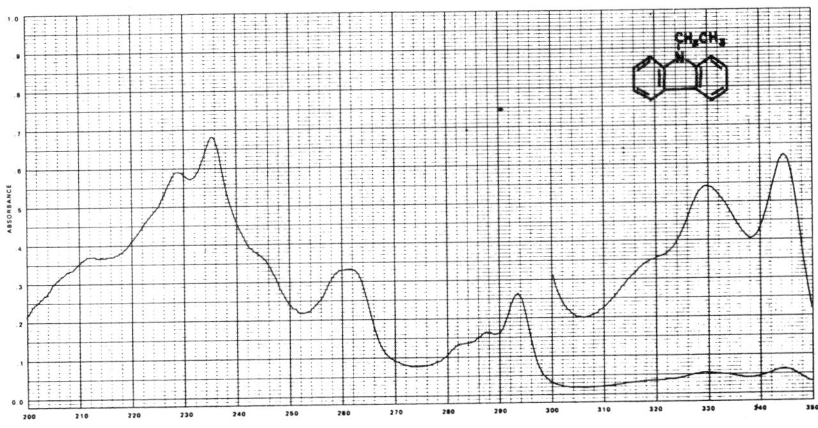

9-PHENYLCARBAZOLE

745

$C_{18}H_{13}N$
Mol. Wt. 243.30
Solvent: Methanol

λ Max. mμ	a_m	Cell mm	Conc. g/L
338.2	6780	4	0.050
325.4	6420	4	0.050
291.2	23600	0.5	0.050
284.8	19900	0.5	0.050
237.5	59100	0.5	0.050
x	x	0.5	0.050

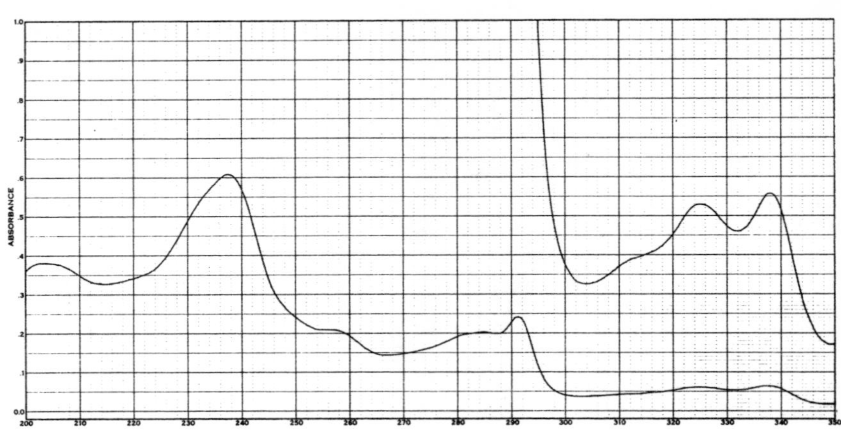

9-PHENYLCARBAZOLE

745

$C_{18}H_{13}N$
Mol. Wt. 243.30
Solvent: Methanol HCl

λ Max. mμ	a_m	Cell mm	Conc. g/L
338	6620	4	0.050
325.5	6290	4	0.050
290.8	24500	0.5	0.050
284.6	20900	0.5	0.050
237.2	59100	0.5	0.050
x	x	0.5	0.050

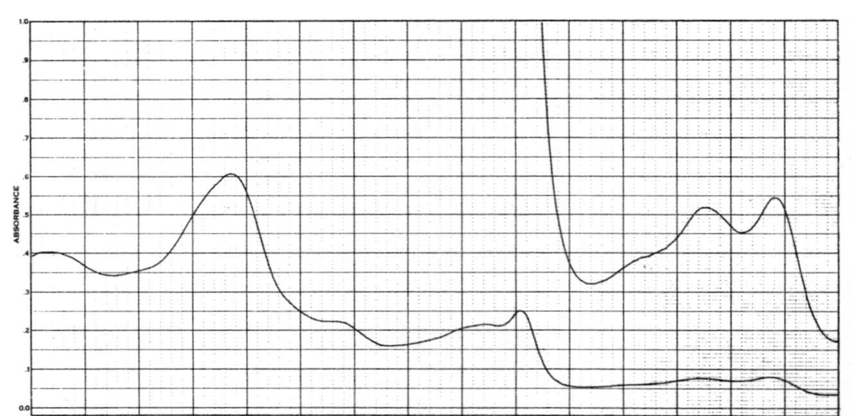

ACRIDINE

746

$C_{13}H_{9}N$
Mol. Wt. 179.21
M.P. 110°C B.P. 346°C
Solvent: Methanol

λ Max. mμ	a_m	Cell mm	Conc. g/L
348	7390	10	0.020
339.5	6850	10	0.020
250	11600	10	0.010
211.5	165000	10	0.001

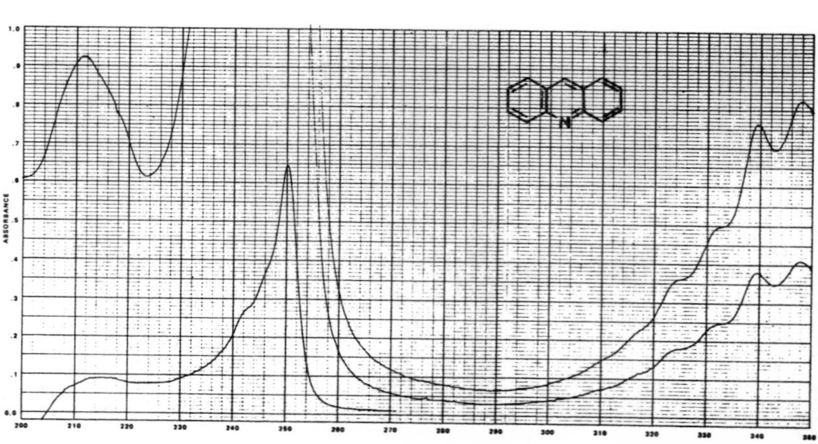

9-AMINOACRIDINE

747

$C_{13}H_{10}N_2$

Mol. Wt. 194.24

M.P. 234.5-235°C

Solvent: Methanol

λ Max. mμ	a_m	Cell mm	Conc. g/L
332	1050	1	1.00
315	641	1	1.00
260	59800	1	0.0300
218	19400	1	0.0300

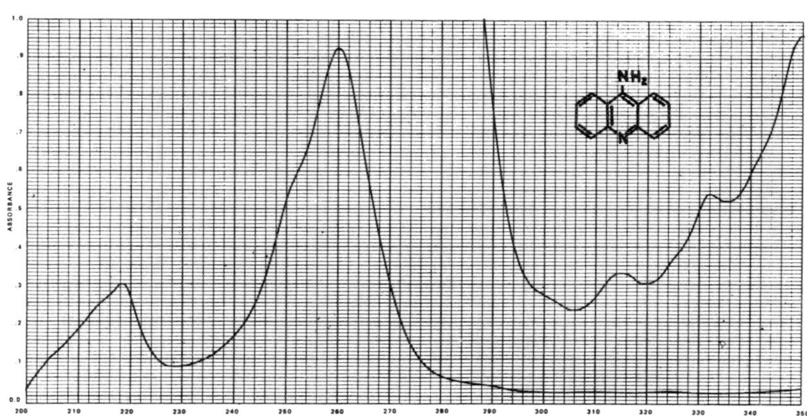

9-AMINOACRIDINE

747

$C_{13}H_{10}N_2$

Mol. Wt. 194.24

M.P. 234.5-235°C

Solvent: Methanol HCl

λ Max. mμ	a_m	Cell mm	Conc. g/L
324.5	1380	1	1.00
310.5	1460	1	1.00
260	63500	1	0.0300
218	19400	1	0.0300

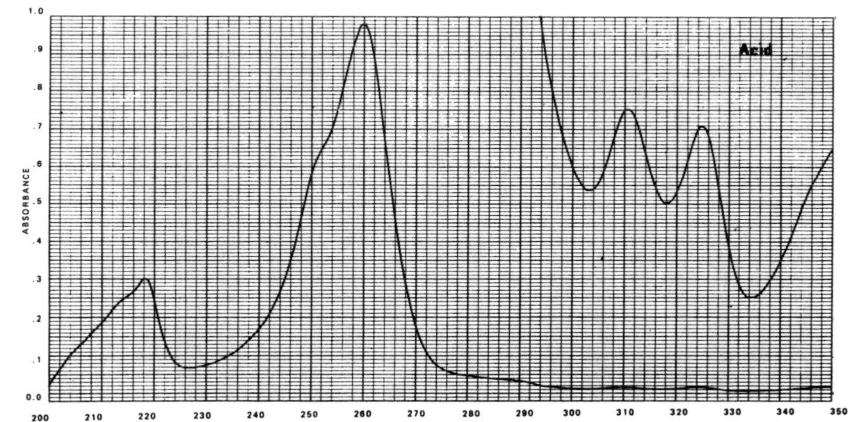

PHENANTHRIDINE

748

$C_{13}H_9N$

Mol. Wt. 179.22

M.P. 107°C (lit.) B.P. 349.5°C (lit.)

Solvent: Cyclohexane

λ Max. mμ	a_m	Cell mm	Conc. g/L
x	x	10	1.756
341	1970	10	0.141
335	635	10	0.141
327	1980	10	0.141
320	826	10	0.141
312	1420	10	0.141
246.5	44500	10	0.007
212.5	27700	10	0.007

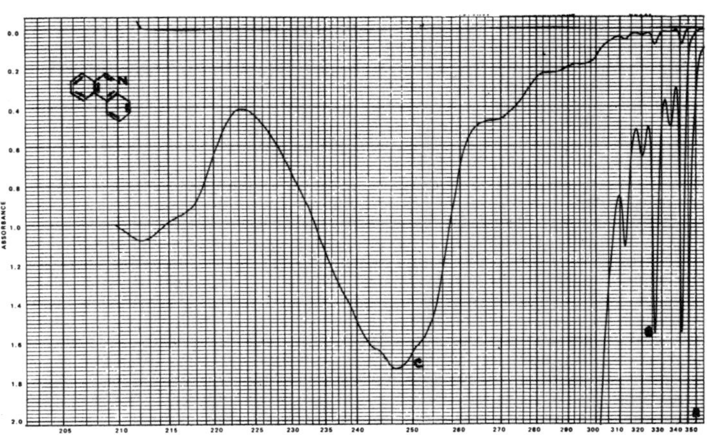

BENZO(f)QUINOLINE 749

$C_{13}H_9N$

Mol. Wt. 179.22

M.P. 90-93°C

Solvent: Methanol

λ Max. mμ	a_m	Cell mm	Conc. g/L
345	3180	4	0.100
330	2810	4	0.100
315	1590	4	0.100
267	35800	0.5	0.100
232	33800	0.5	0.100
216	30000	0.5	0.100

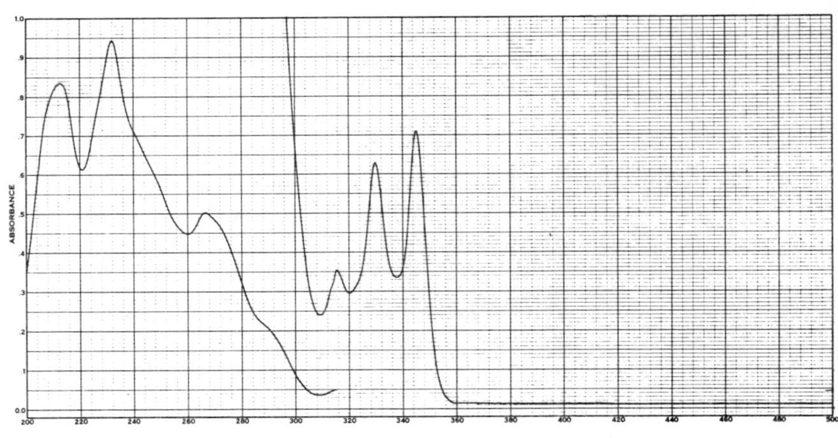

1,10-PHENANTHROLINE, HYDRATE 750

$C_{12}H_8N_2 \cdot H_2O$

Mol. Wt. 198.23

Solvent: Methanol

λ Max. mμ	a_m	Cell mm	Conc. g/L
263	30500	2	0.010
229	48100	2	0.010

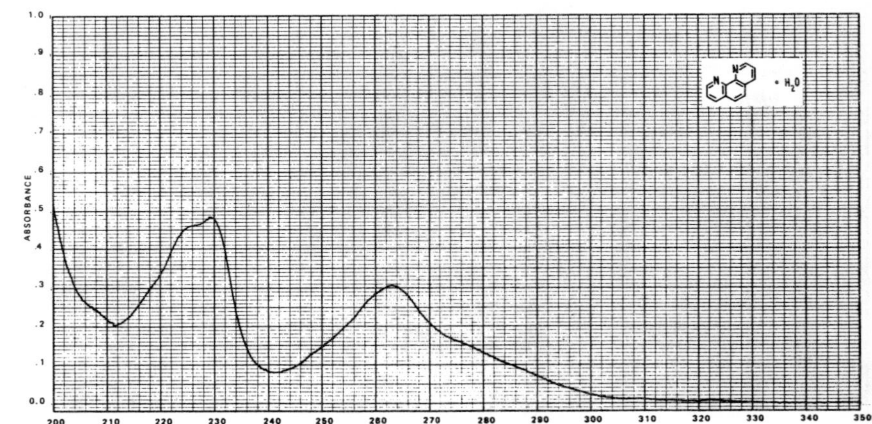

1,10-PHENANTHROLINE, HYDRATE 750

$C_{12}H_8N_2 \cdot H_2O$

Mol. Wt. 198.23

Solvent: Methanol HCl

λ Max. mμ	a_m	Cell mm	Conc. g/L
275	28300	5	0.010
271	28400	5	0.010
218	34500	5	0.010

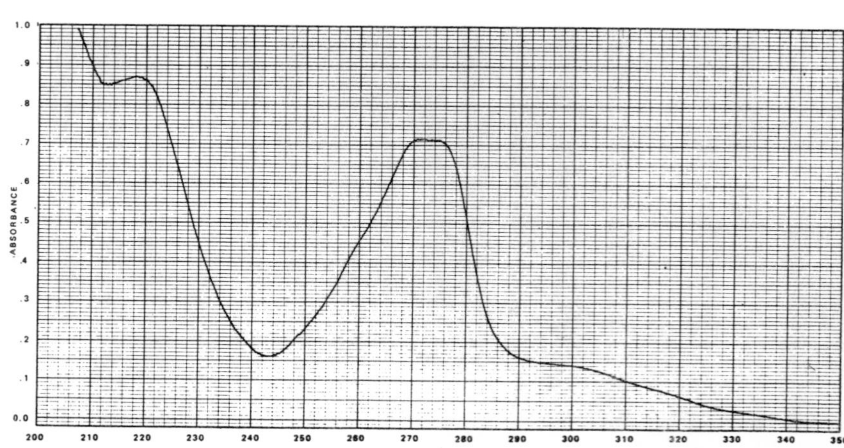

2,9-DIMETHYL-1,10-PHENANTHROLINE

$C_{14}H_{12}N_2$

Mol. Wt. 208.27

Solvent: Methanol

λ Max. mμ	a_m	Cell mm	Conc. g/L
325.5	652	20	0.065
311	1030	20	0.065
266	27600	0.5	0.065
228	46000	0.5	0.065

2,9-DIMETHYL-1,10-PHENANTHROLINE

751

$C_{14}H_{12}N_2$

Mol. Wt. 208.27

Solvent: Methanol HCl

λ Max. mμ	a_m	Cell mm	Conc. g/L
279	30400	0.5	0.065
219	36300	0.5	0.065

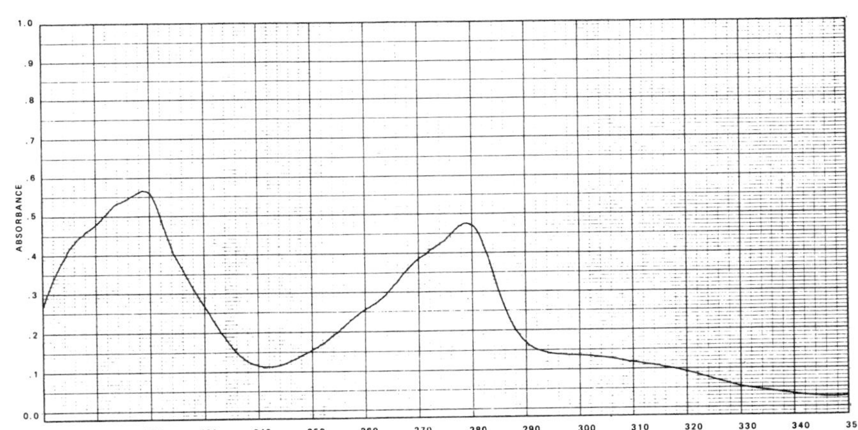

λ Max. mμ	a_m	Cell mm	Conc. g/L

NAPHTHO(1,8-de)TRIAZINE

$C_{10}H_7N_3$
Mol. Wt. 169.19
Solvent: Methanol

λ Max. mμ	a_m	Cell mm	Conc. g/L
442	795	10	0.100
338	9200	1	0.0500
276	3680	2	0.100
232	32300	1	0.0500

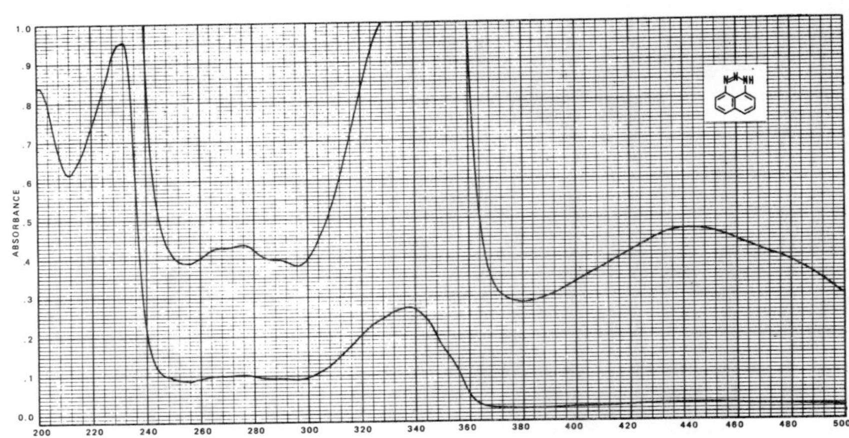

NAPHTHO(1,8-de)TRIAZINE

752

$C_{10}H_7N_3$
Mol. Wt. 169.19
Solvent: Methanol KOH

λ Max. mμ	a_m	Cell mm	Conc. g/L
476	1350	1	0.0500
362	13200	1	0.0500
232	25600	1	0.0500

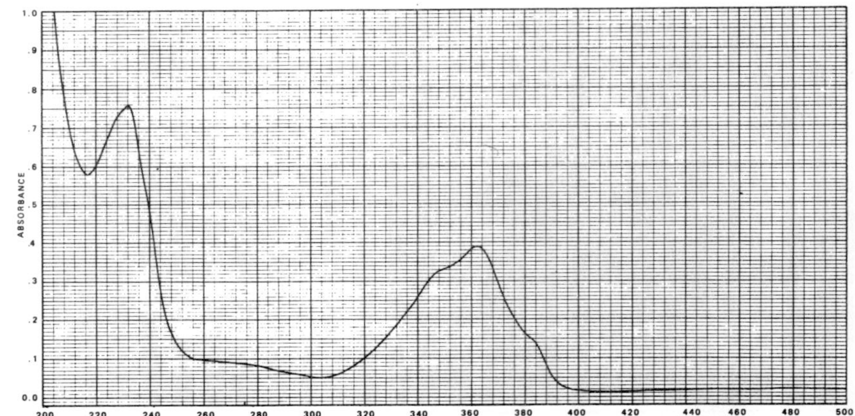

NAPHTHO(1,8-de)TRIAZINE

752

$C_{10}H_7N_3$
Mol. Wt. 169.19
Solvent: Methanol HCl

λ Max. mμ	a_m	Cell mm	Conc. g/L
480	355	1	0.100
333	6890	1	0.100
225	40800	2	0.0170

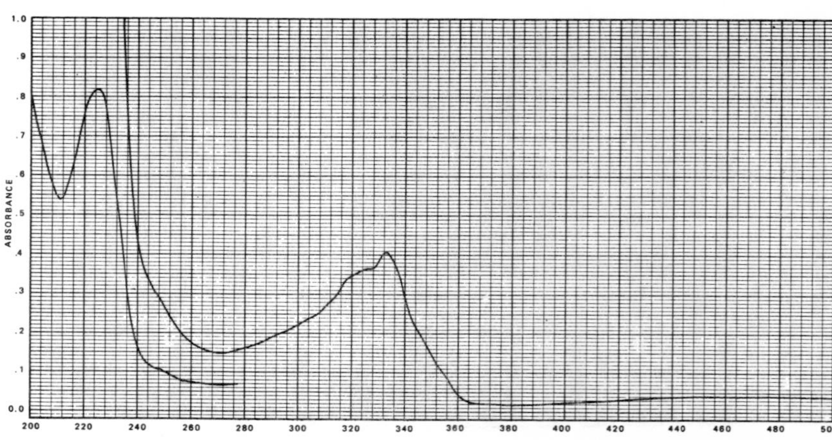

PHENYLHYDRAZINE **756**

$C_6H_8N_2$

Mol. Wt. 108.14

Solvent: Methanol

λ Max. mμ	a_m	Cell mm	Conc. g/L
272.5	5050	2	0.100
x	x	1	0.100

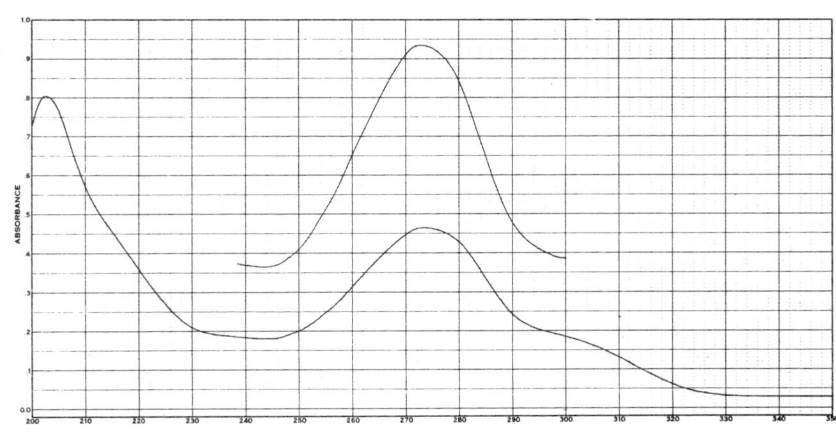

PHENYLHYDRAZINE **756**

$C_6H_8N_2$

Mol. Wt. 108.14

Solvent: Methanol HCl

λ Max. mμ	a_m	Cell mm	Conc. g/L
273	3690	2	0.100

λ Max. mμ	a_m	Cell mm	Conc. g/L

(2,5-DICHLOROPHENYL)HYDRAZINE

757

$C_6H_6Cl_2N_2$
Mol. Wt. 177.03
M.P. 102-103°C
Solvent: Methanol

λ Max. mμ	a_m	Cell mm	Conc. g/L
300	2850	5	0.100
279.5	1920	5	0.100
246.5	9770	1	0.050

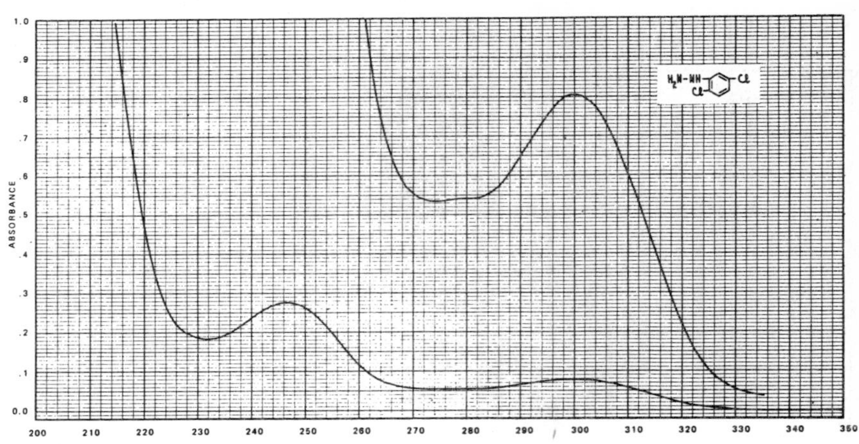

(2,5-DICHLOROPHENYL)HYDRAZINE

757

$C_6H_6Cl_2N_2$
Mol. Wt. 177.03
M.P. 102-103°C
Solvent: Methanol HCl

λ Max. mμ	a_m	Cell mm	Conc. g/L
281	2110	5	0.100
x	x	1	0.100
x	x	1	0.050

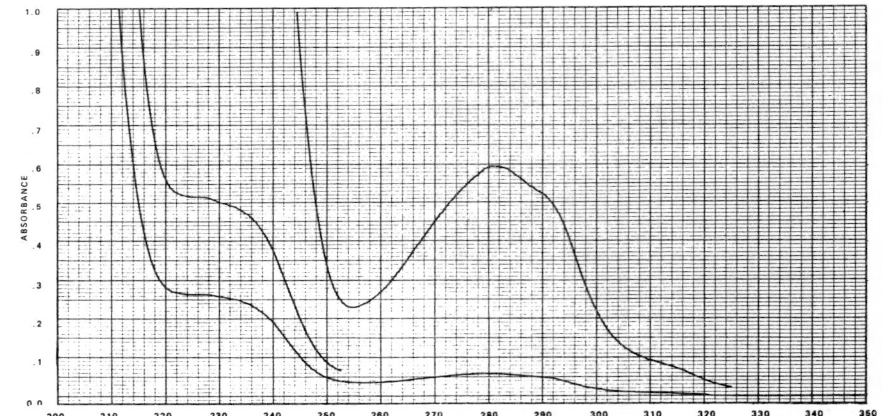

(2,4,6-TRICHLOROPHENYL)HYDRAZINE

758

$C_6H_5Cl_3N_2$
Mol. Wt. 211.48
M.P. 142-143°C
Solvent: Methanol

λ Max. mμ	a_m	Cell mm	Conc. g/L
256.5	7770	1	0.0800
217	22600	1	0.0800

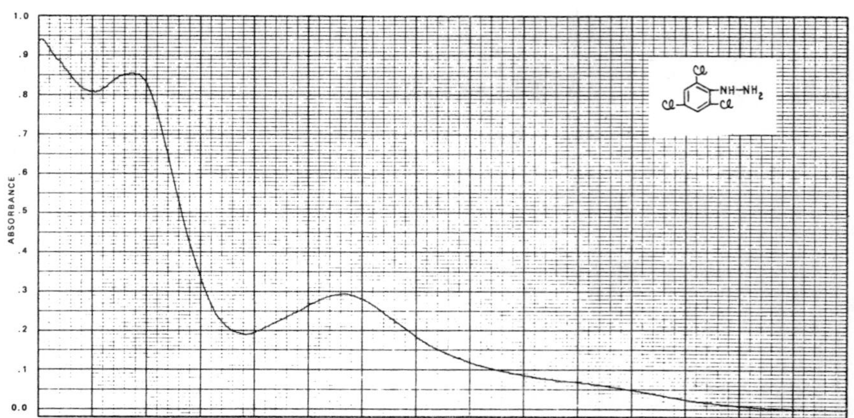

(2,4,6-TRICHLOROPHENYL)HYDRAZINE

758

$C_6H_5Cl_3N_2$
Mol. Wt. 211.48
M.P. 142-143°C
Solvent: Methanol HCl

λ Max. mμ	a_m	Cell mm	Conc. g/L
272	2680	10	0.04800
242	6610	1	0.04800
211	29500	1	0.04800

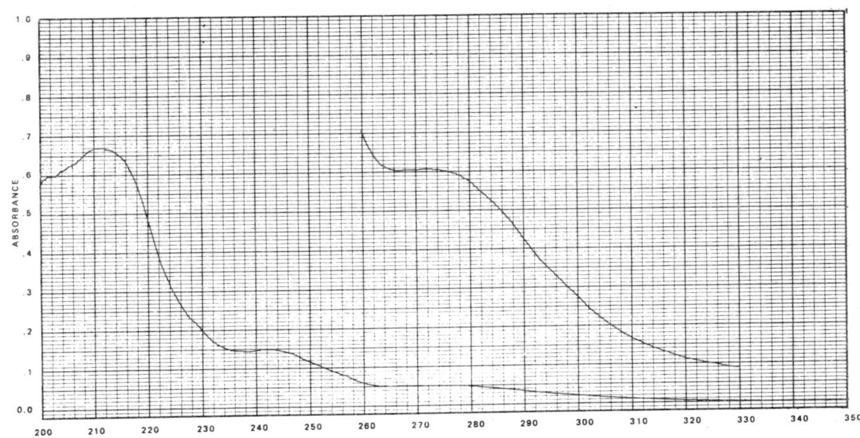

1,1-DIPHENYLHYDRAZINE

759

$C_{12}H_{12}N_2$
Mol. Wt. 184.24
M.P. 30-32°C
Solvent: Methanol

λ Max. mμ	a_m	Cell mm	Conc. g/L
315.5	16400	1	0.100
228.5	11800	1	0.100

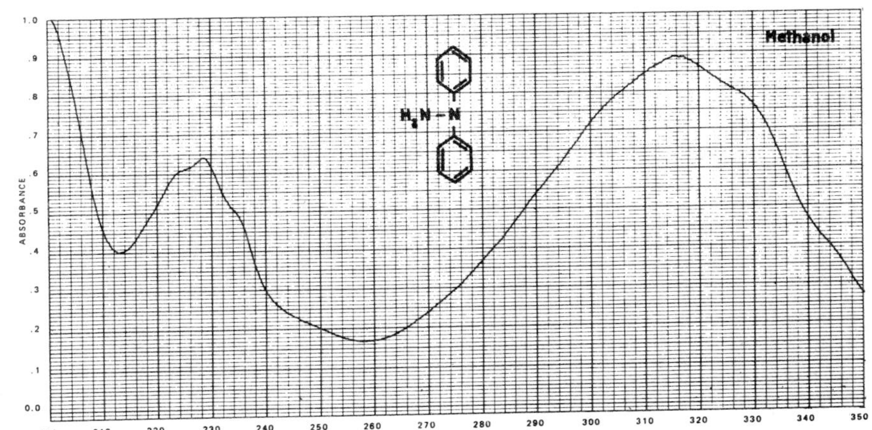

λ Max. mμ	a_m	Cell mm	Conc. g/L

HYDRAZOBENZENE

760

$C_{12}H_{12}N_2$
Mol. Wt. 184.24
M.P. 125-127°C
Solvent: Methanol

λ Max. mμ	a_m	Cell mm	Conc. g/L
435	446	20	0.100
315	11700	1	0.100
244	11600	1	0.100
235	12500	1	0.100
229	13000	1	0.100

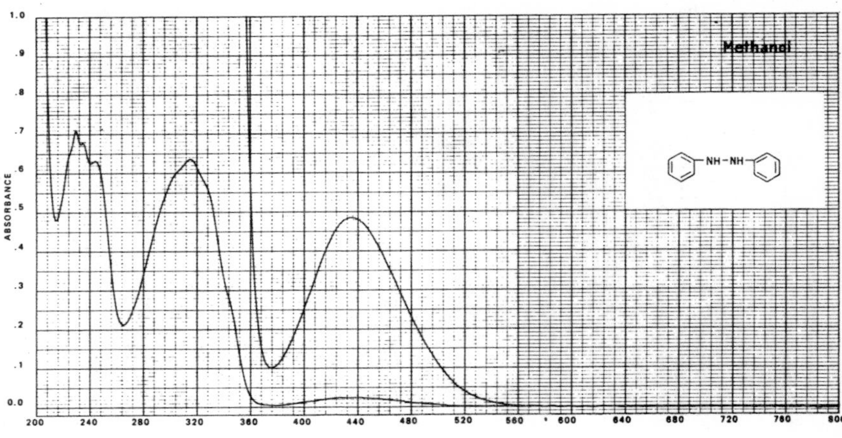

HYDRAZOBENZENE

760

$C_{12}H_{12}N_2$
Mol. Wt. 184.24
M.P. 125-127°C
Solvent: Methanol HCl

λ Max. mμ	a_m	Cell mm	Conc. g/L
435	426	20	0.100
315	13300	1	0.100
229	12600	1	0.100

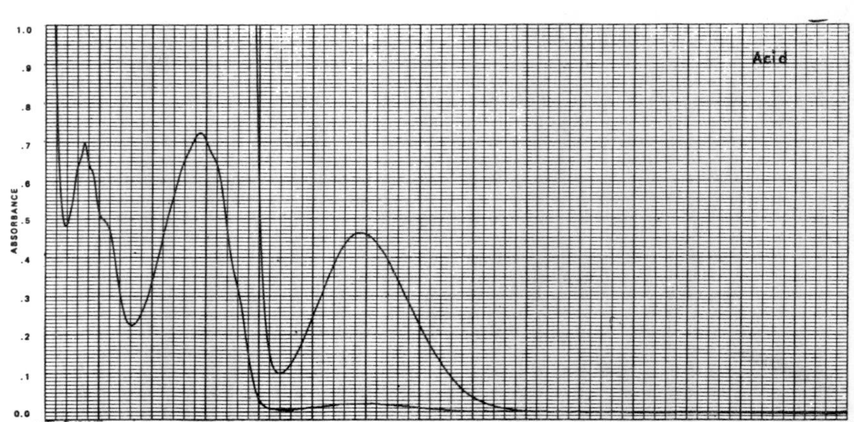

1,2-DIMETHYL-1,2-DI-p-TOLYLHYDRAZINE

761

$C_{16}H_{20}N_2$
Mol. Wt. 240.35
Solvent: Methanol

λ Max. mμ	a_m	Cell mm	Conc. g/L
298	2090	4	0.100
253	11200	2	0.100
x	x	1	0.100

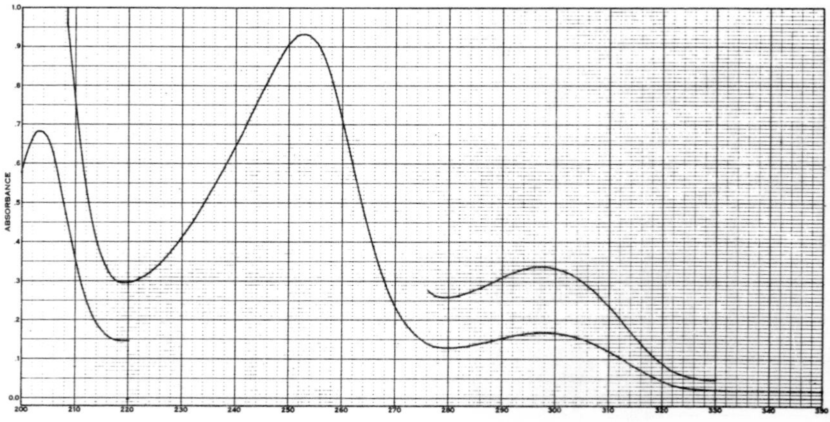

1,2-DIMETHYL-1,2-DI-p-TOLYLHYDRAZINE 761

$C_{16}H_{20}N_2$
Mol. Wt. 240.35
Solvent: Methanol HCl

λ Max. mμ	a_m	Cell mm	Conc. g/L
482	510	20	0.100
450	397	20	0.100
394	798	20	0.100
376	665	20	0.100
261	7500	2	0.100
x	x	1	0.100

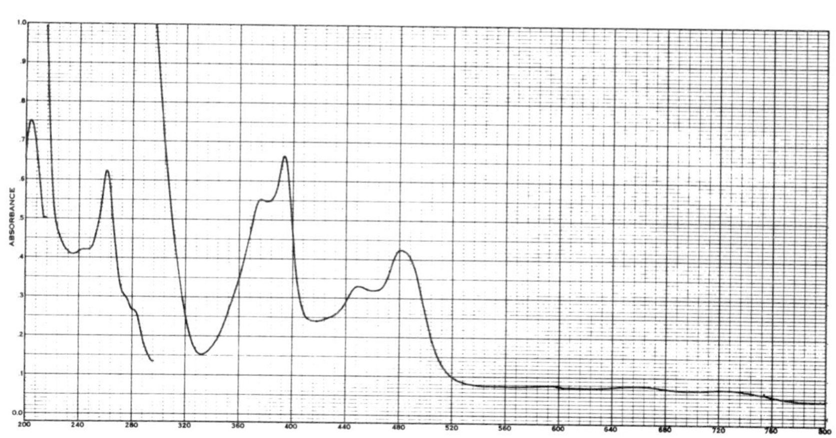

1,2-BIS(4-BIPHENYL)-1,2-DIMETHYLHYDRAZINE 762

$C_{26}H_{24}N_2$
Mol. Wt. 364.49
M.P. 173-174°C
Solvent: Methanol

λ Max. mμ	a_m	Cell mm	Conc. g/L
299.5	46200	1	0.0500

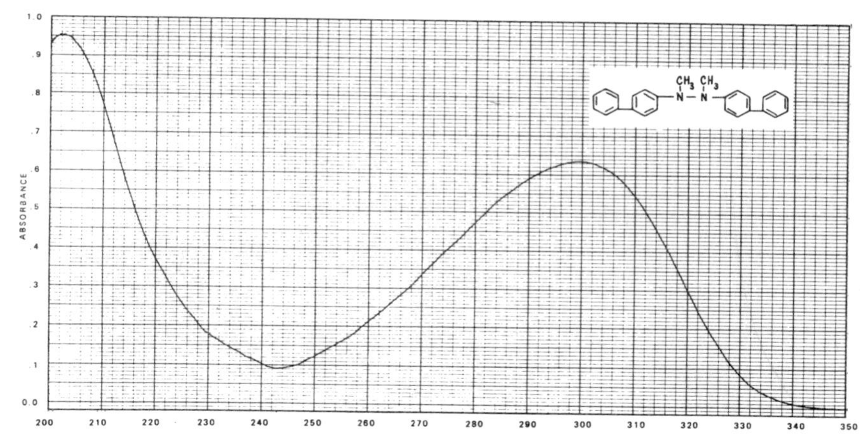

1,2-BIS(4-BIPHENYL)-1,2-DIMETHYLHYDRAZINE 762

$C_{26}H_{24}N_2$
Mol. Wt. 364.49
M.P. 173-174°C
Solvent: Methanol HCl

λ Max. mμ	a_m	Cell mm	Conc. g/L
250	32100	1	0.0500

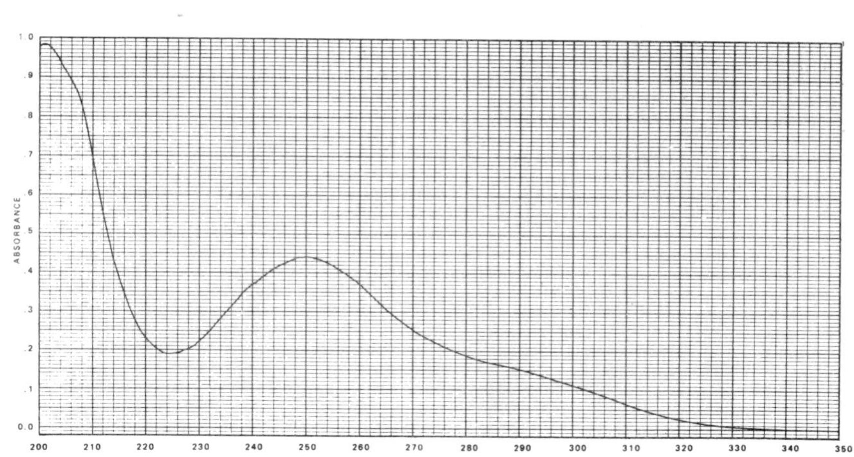

1,2-DIMESITYL-1,2-DIMETHYLHYDRAZINE

763

$C_{20}H_{28}N_2$
Mol. Wt. 296.46
M.P. 118-119°C
Solvent: Methanol

λ Max. mμ	a_m	Cell mm	Conc. g/L
284.5	2370	5	0.100
235.5	13500	2	0.100
x	x	2	0.0200

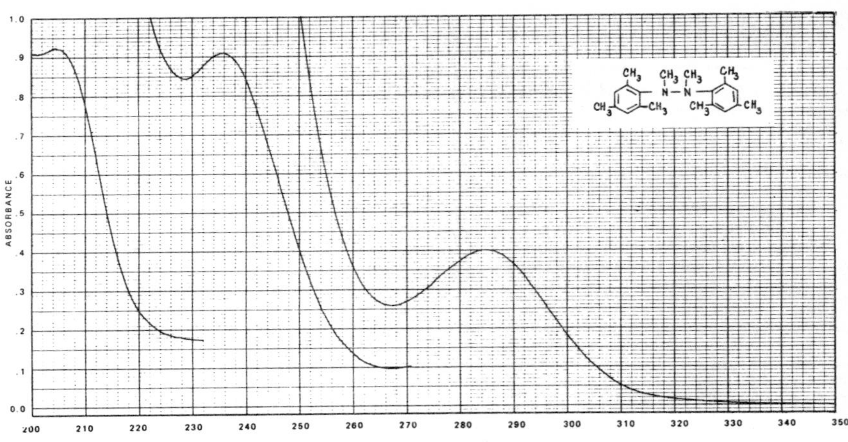

1,2-DIMESITYL-1,2-DIMETHYLHYDRAZINE

763

$C_{20}H_{28}N_2$
Mol. Wt. 296.46
M.P. 118-119°C
Solvent: Methanol HCl

λ Max. mμ	a_m	Cell mm	Conc. g/L
263	1140	10	0.100
212	17800	1	0.100

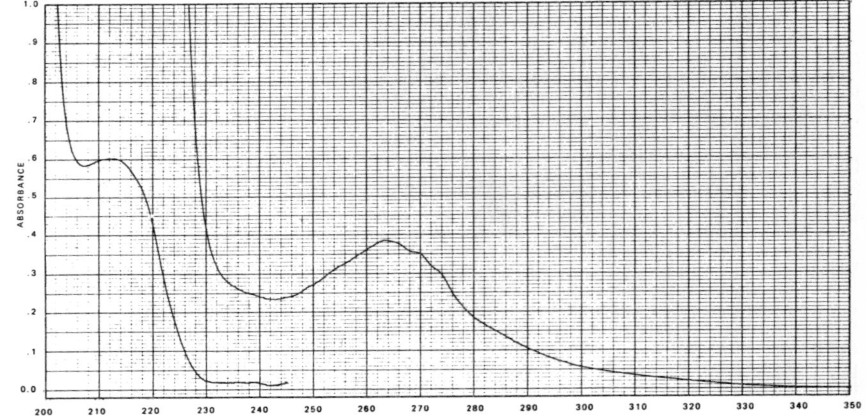

2-HYDRAZINOQUINOLINE

764

$C_9H_9N_3$
Mol. Wt. 159.19
M.P. 141.5-142.5°C
Solvent: Methanol

λ Max. mμ	a_m	Cell mm	Conc. g/L
339	4820	2	0.100
314	3360	2	0.100
240.5	25500	1	0.050
231	22400	1	0.050
207	30800	1	0.050

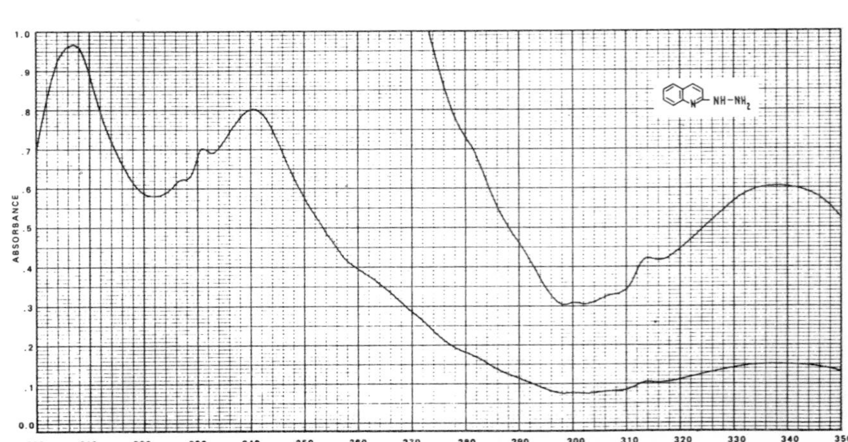

2-HYDRAZINOQUINOLINE

$C_9H_9N_3$

Mol. Wt. 159.19

M.P. 141.5-142.5°C

Solvent: Methanol HCl

λ Max. mμ	a_m	Cell mm	Conc. g/L
334	3740	1	0.050
268	7800	1	0.050
236	23200	1	0.050

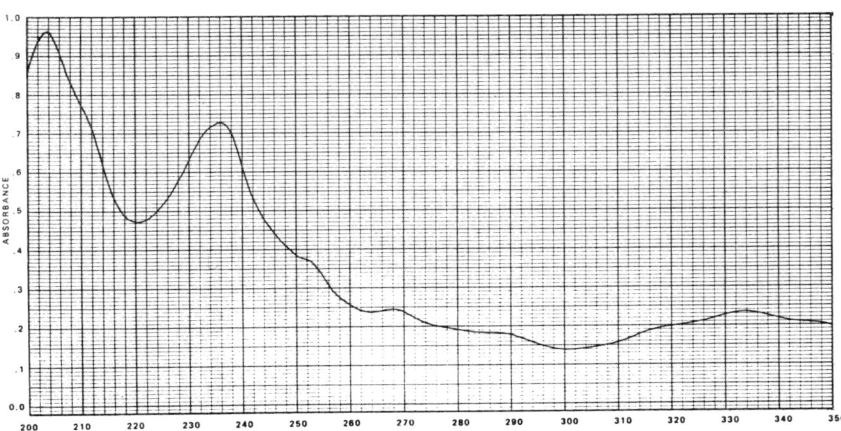

λ Max. mμ	a_m	Cell mm	Conc. g/L

λ Max. mμ	a_m	Cell mm	Conc. g/L

NOTES

THE PRIMARY AMINE SALTS

Aliphatic Compounds

The salts of the primary amine aliphatic compounds do not display any maxima in the near UV region and thus there are no spectra in this text for compounds 765 through 781.

Aromatic Compounds

The UV spectra of the primary amine salts display similar wavelengths and intensities as the fine structure that is observed for benzene. Upon the addition of base to the sample, the free base (aniline) is formed. This reaction is the opposite to that discussed on page 75 for the addition of acid to samples of aniline.

The table presented below lists the data obtained from these reversible reactions.

Compound	$\lambda_{max}(\epsilon_{max})$	$\lambda_{max}(\epsilon_{max})$	Solvent	Spectrum
Aniline	234 (9910)	286 (1970)	Cyclohexane	487
Aniline (acid added)	203 (7500)	254 (160)	H_2O	Lit.
Aniline hydrochloride	- - - - - - - - - -	254 (730)	Methanol	787
Aniline hydrochloride (base added)	232 (30500)	285 (7350)	Methanol	787

The differences observed in band intensity probably result from both the solvent employed and the amount of acid or base added to the sample to induce the desired change.

BENZYLAMINE, HYDROCHLORIDE 782

$C_7H_9N{\cdot}HCl$

Mol. Wt. 143.72

Solvent: Methanol

λ Max. mμ	a_m	Cell mm	Conc. g/L
263	172	10	0.500
261.5	176	10	0.500
257	213	10	0.500
251	172	10	0.500
x	x	1	0.500

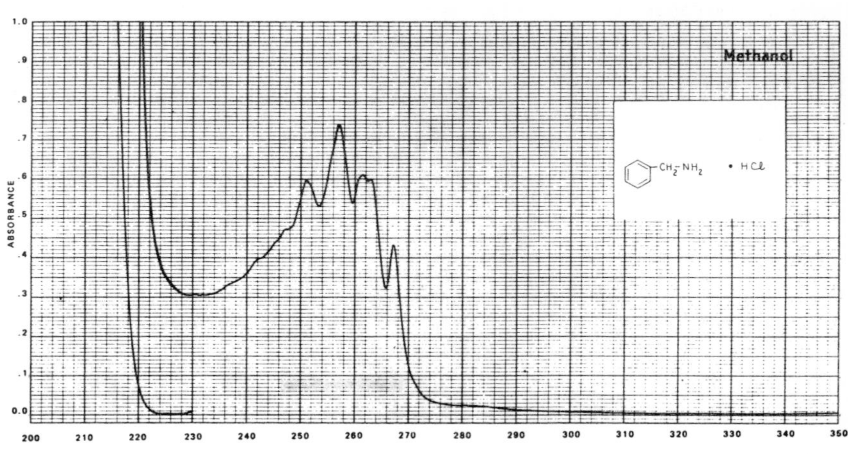

BENZYLAMINE, HYDROCHLORIDE 782

$C_7H_9N{\cdot}HCl$

Mol. Wt. 143.72

Solvent: Methanol KOH

λ Max. mμ	a_m	Cell mm	Conc. g/L
268	101	10	0.500
264.5	148	10	0.500
258.5	195	10	0.500
253	170	10	0.500
x	x	1	0.100

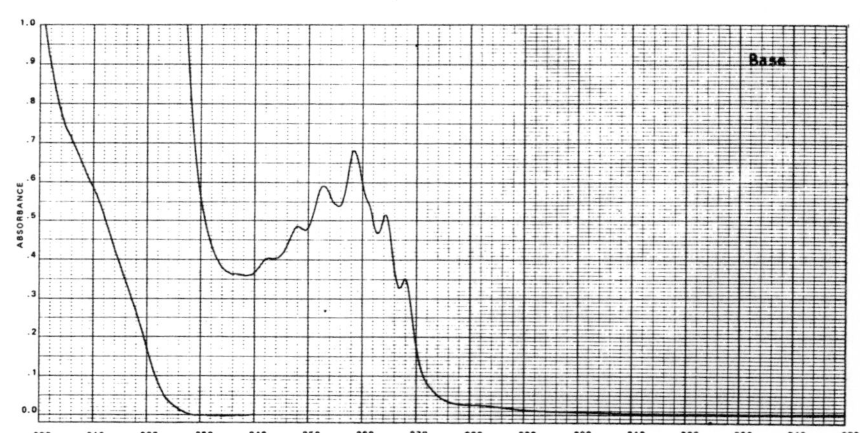
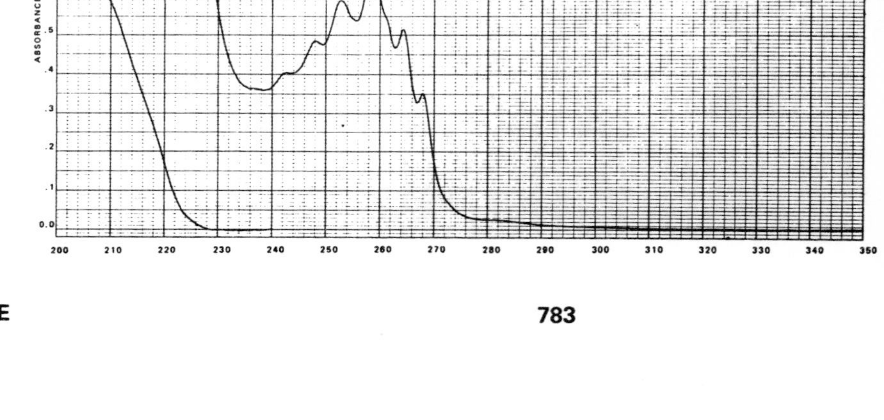

m-BROMOBENZYLAMINE, HYDROCHLORIDE 783

$C_7H_8BrN{\cdot}HCl$

Mol. Wt. 222.52

M.P. 226-227°C

Solvent: Methanol

λ Max. mμ	a_m	Cell mm	Conc. g/L
275.5	237	10	0.500
268	311	10	0.500
262	259	10	0.500
248	159	10	0.500
x	x	1	0.100

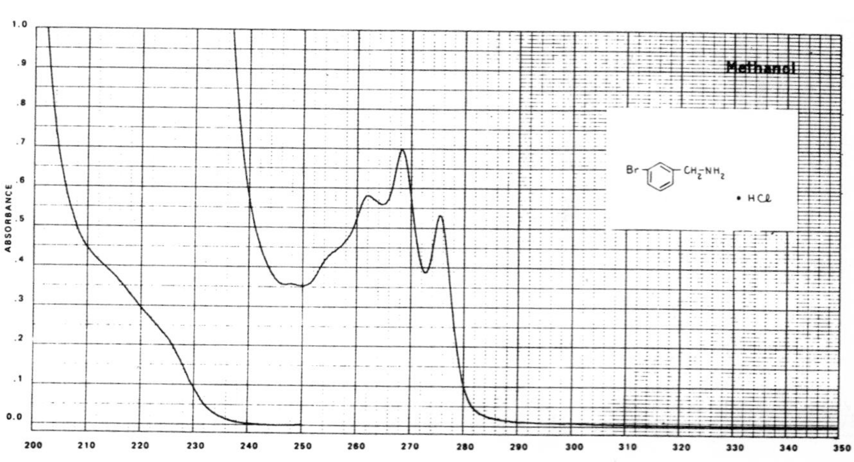

m-BROMOBENZYLAMINE, HYDROCHLORIDE

$C_7H_8BrN \cdot HCl$

Mol. Wt. 222.52

M.P. 226-227°C

Solvent: Methanol KOH

λ Max. mμ	a_m	Cell mm	Conc. g/L
274.5	187	10	0.500
267.5	260	10	0.500
261	225	10	0.500
x	x	1	0.100

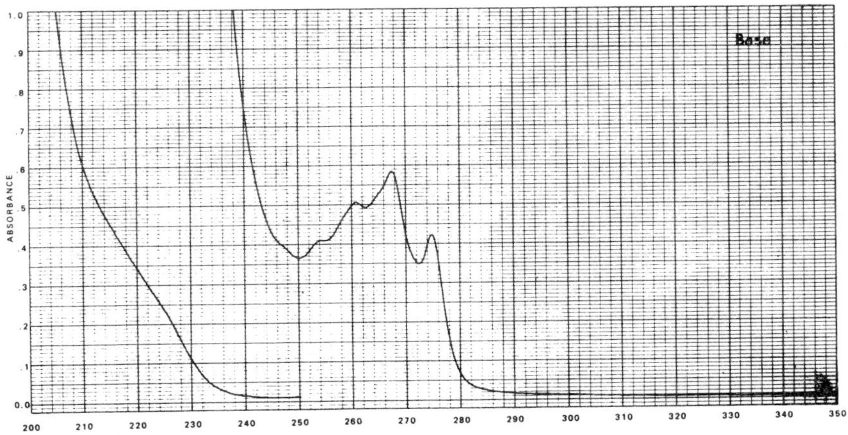

784

α-METHYLBENZYLAMINE, HYDROCHLORIDE

$C_8H_{11}N \cdot HCl$

Mol. Wt. 157.64

M.P. 158°C

Solvent: Methanol

λ Max. mμ	a_m	Cell mm	Conc. g/L
266.5	514	10	0.100
262.5	826	10	0.100
256.5	1040	10	0.100
250.5	853	10	0.100
x	x	1	0.100

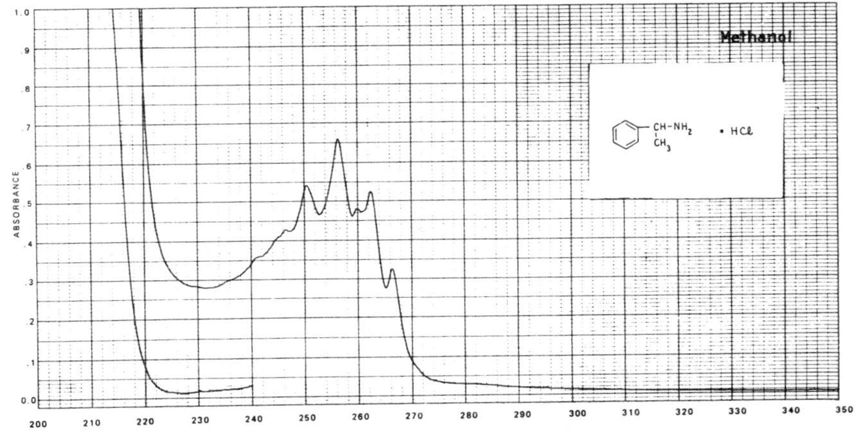

784

α-METHYLBENZYLAMINE, HYDROCHLORIDE

$C_8H_{11}N \cdot HCl$

Mol. Wt. 157.64

M.P. 158°C

Solvent: Methanol KOH

λ Max. mμ	a_m	Cell mm	Conc. g/L
263.5	713	10	0.100
257.5	960	10	0.100
251.5	837	10	0.100
247	691	10	0.100
x	x	1	0.100

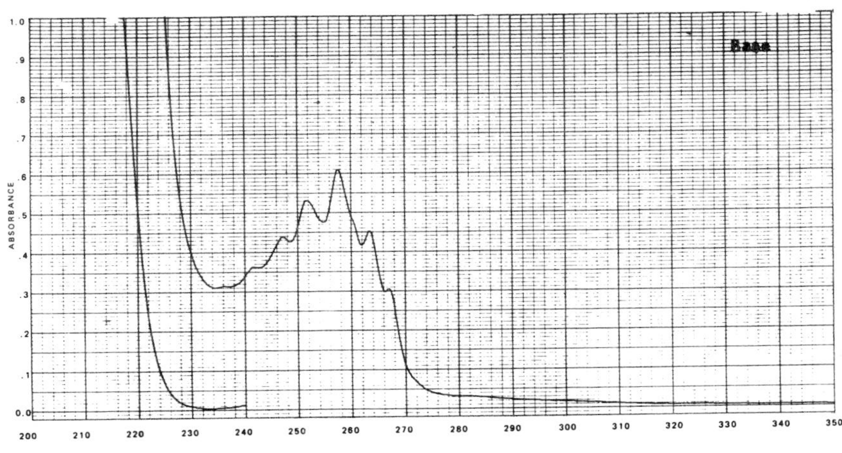

1-METHYL-3-PHENYLPROPYLAMINE, HYDROCHLORIDE 785

$C_{10}H_{15}N \cdot HCl$

Mol. Wt. 185.70

M.P. 146-149°C

Solvent: Methanol

λ Max. mμ	a_m	Cell mm	Conc. g/L
267.5	142	10	0.500
264	159	10	0.500
260.5	187	10	0.500
258.5	205	10	0.500
252.5	181	10	0.500

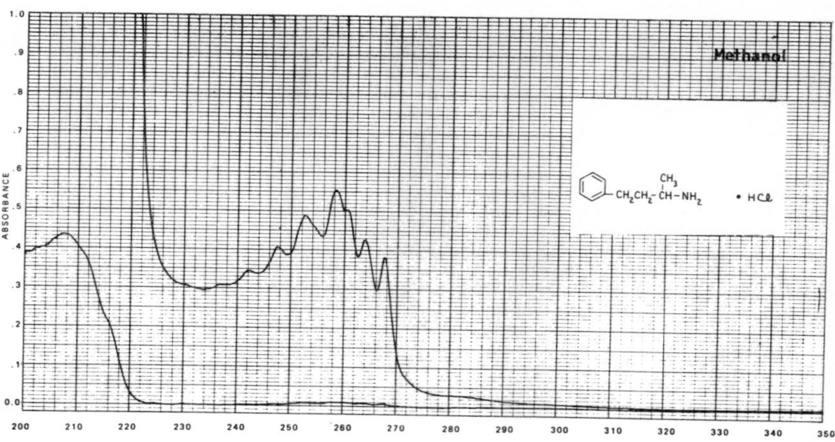

p-CHLORO-α,α-DIMETHYLPHENETHYLAMINE, HYDROCHLORIDE 786

$C_{10}H_{14}ClN \cdot HCl$

Mol. Wt. 220.14

Solvent: Methanol

λ Max. mμ	a_m	Cell mm	Conc. g/L
275	329	40	0.100
266	463	40	0.100
259.5	394	40	0.100
219	19400	1	0.100

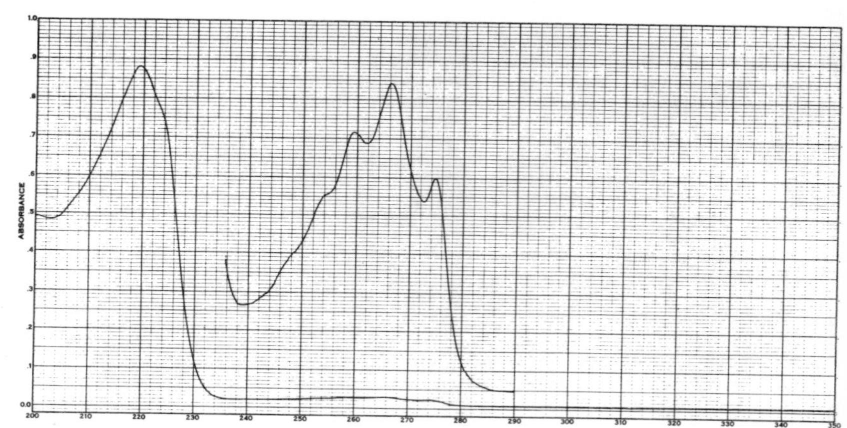

ANILINE, HYDROCHLORIDE 787

$C_6H_7N \cdot HCl$

Mol. Wt. 129.59

M.P. 198-199°C

Solvent: Methanol

λ Max. mμ	a_m	Cell mm	Conc. g/L
284	210	20	0.100
260.5	477	10	0.100
254	730	10	0.100
236	1250	10	0.100
x	x	5	0.100

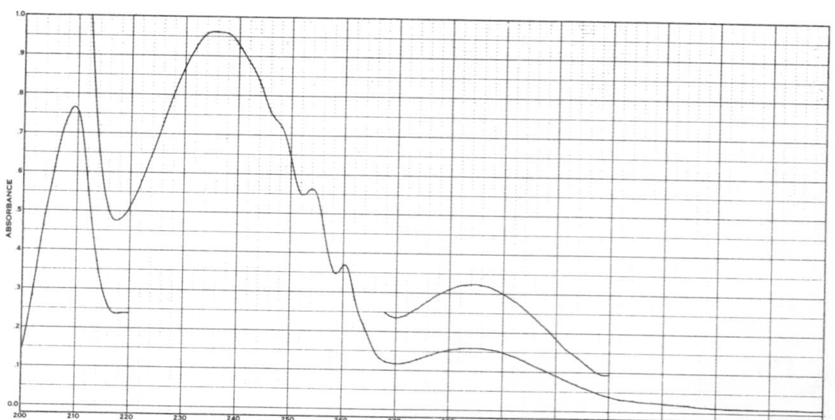

787

ANILINE, HYDROCHLORIDE

$C_6H_7N \cdot HCl$

Mol. Wt. 129.59

M.P. 198-199°C

Solvent: Methanol KOH

λ Max. mμ	a_m	Cell mm	Conc. g/L
284.5	7350	2	0.050
232	30500	0.5	0.050
x	x	0.5	0.050

788

ANILINE, SULFATE

$C_{12}H_{14}N_2 \cdot H_2SO_4$

Mol. Wt. 284.34

Solvent: Methanol

λ Max. mμ	a_m	Cell mm	Conc. g/L
285	1570	10	0.100
234	8570	2	0.100

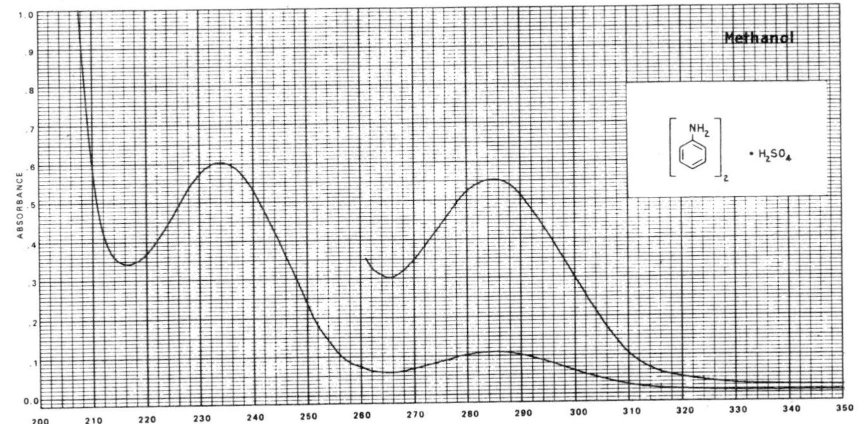

788

ANILINE, SULFATE

$C_{12}H_{14}N_2 \cdot H_2SO_4$

Mol. Wt. 284.34

Solvent: Methanol KOH

λ Max. mμ	a_m	Cell mm	Conc. g/L
284	3740	5	0.100
234	16800	1	0.100

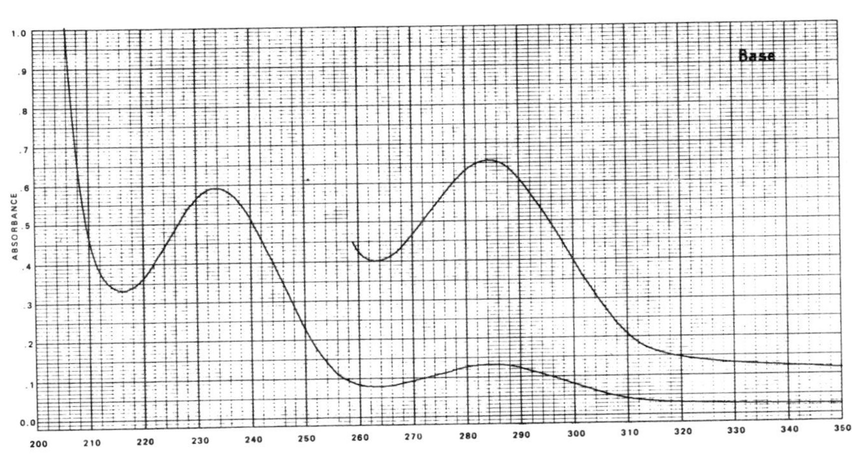

o-TOLUIDINE HYDROCHLORIDE

789

$C_7H_9N{\cdot}HCl$

Mol. Wt. 143.62

Solvent: Methanol

λ Max. mμ	a_m	Cell mm	Conc. g/L
284	22.3	10	2.00
266.5	200	10	1.00
258.5	229	10	1.00
242	181	10	1.00

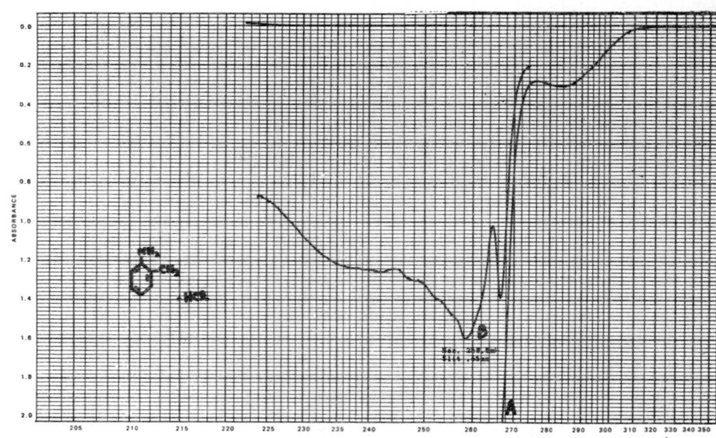

m-TOLUIDINE, HYDROCHLORIDE

790

$C_7H_9N{\cdot}HCl$

Mol. Wt. 143.62

Solvent: Methanol

λ Max. mμ	a_m	Cell mm	Conc. g/L
286	79.7	20	0.100
268.5	267	20	0.100
261	309	20	0.100
238	470	20	0.100
x	x	1	0.100

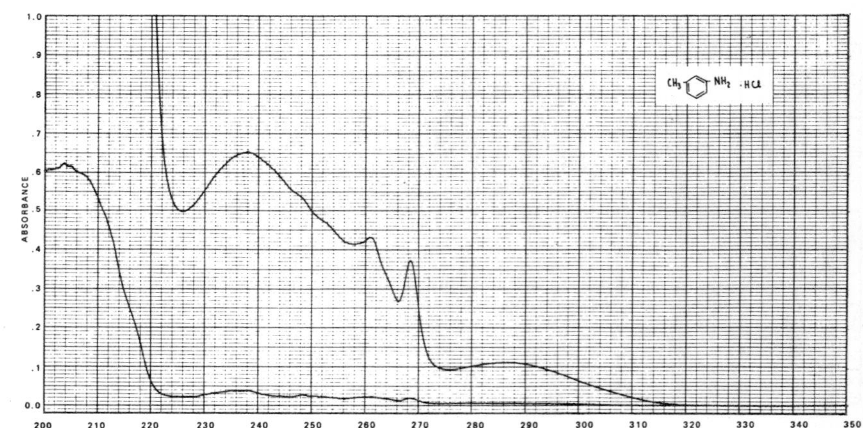

m-TOLUIDINE, HYDROCHLORIDE

790

$C_7H_9N{\cdot}HCl$

Mol. Wt. 143.62

Solvent: Methanol KOH

λ Max. mμ	a_m	Cell mm	Conc. g/L
287	1500	5	0.100
236	7180	1	0.100

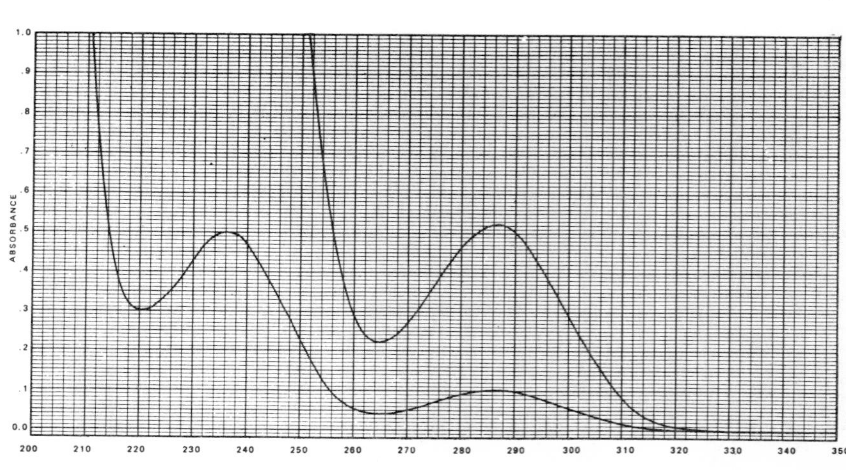

p-ANISIDINE, HYDROCHLORIDE

$C_7H_9NO{\cdot}HCl$

Mol. Wt. 159.62

M.P. 216-218°C

Solvent: Methanol

λ Max. mμ	a_m	Cell mm	Conc. g/L
281	1390	5	0.100
274.5	1630	5	0.100
222.5	9640	1	0.100

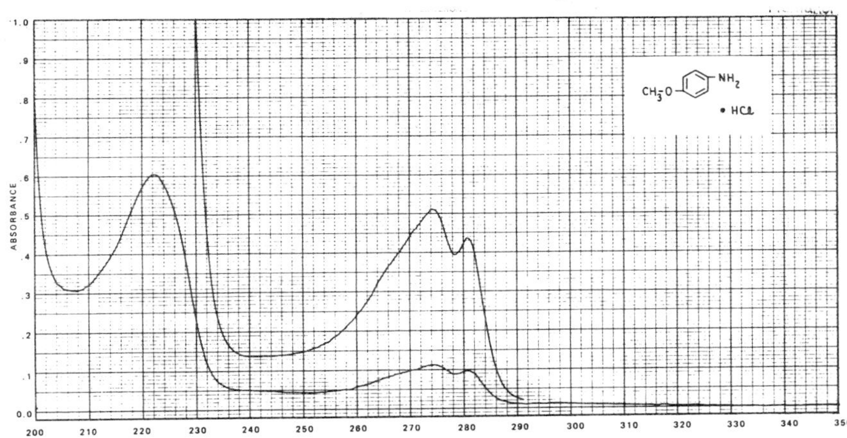

p-ANISIDINE, HYDROCHLORIDE

$C_7H_9NO{\cdot}HCl$

Mol. Wt. 159.62

M.P. 216-218°C

Solvent: Methanol KOH

λ Max. mμ	a_m	Cell mm	Conc. g/L
299	2210	5	0.100
234	10200	1	0.100

λ Max. mμ	a_m	Cell mm	Conc. g/L

2,5-XYLIDINE, HYDROCHLORIDE

792

$C_8H_{11}N{\cdot}HCl$

Mol. Wt. 157.64

M.P. 227-229°C

Solvent: Methanol

λ Max. mμ	a_m	Cell mm	Conc. g/L
272.5	6090	20	0.100
267	5210	20	0.100
263.5	5440	20	0.100
259	4180	20	0.100
236	4710	20	0.100

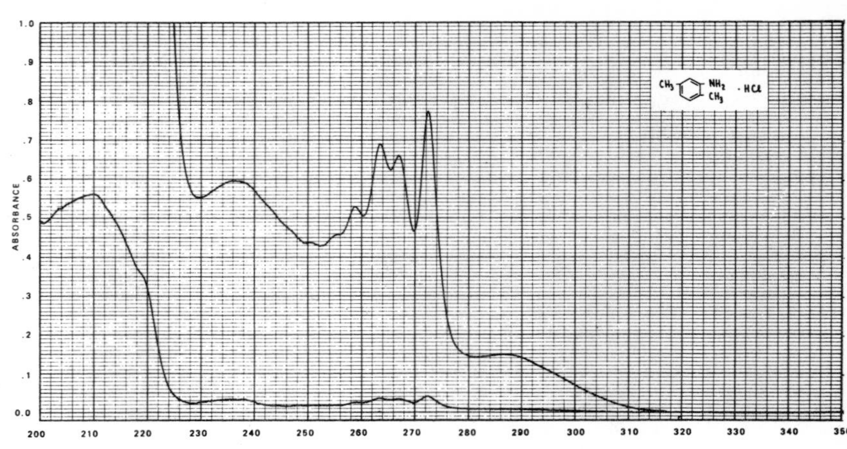

2,5-XYLIDINE, HYDROCHLORIDE

792

$C_8H_{11}N{\cdot}HCl$

Mol. Wt. 157.64

M.P. 227-229°C

Solvent: Methanol KOH

λ Max. mμ	a_m	Cell mm	Conc. g/L
287	2080	2	0.100
235	6850	2	0.100

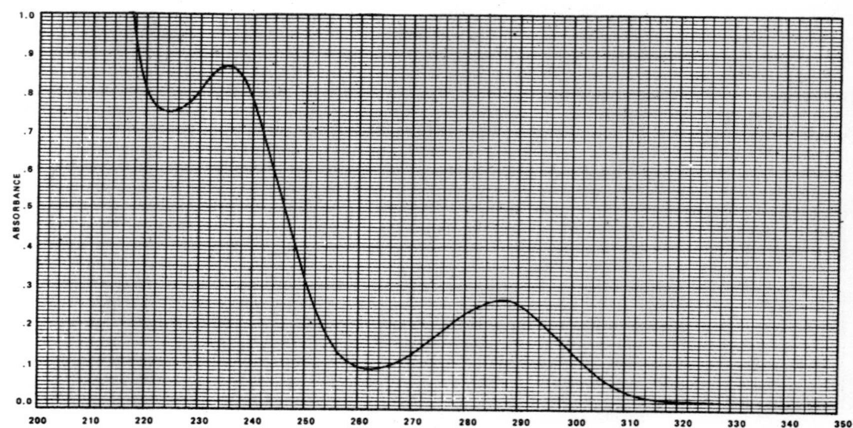

o-PHENYLENEDIAMINE, DIHYDROCHLORIDE

793

$C_6H_8N_22HCl$

Mol. Wt. 181.07

Solvent: Methanol

λ Max. mμ	a_m	Cell mm	Conc. g/L
287.5	2280	5	0.100
235.5	11900	1	0.100

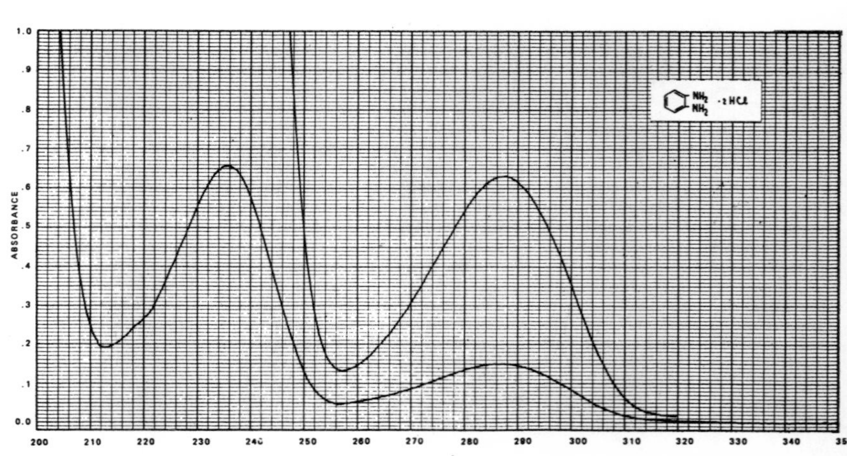

m-PHENYLENEDIAMINE, DIHYDROCHLORIDE

$C_6H_8N_2 \cdot 2HCl$
Mol. Wt. 181.07
Solvent: Methanol

λ Max. mμ	a_m	Cell mm	Conc. g/L
293	1880	5	0.100
243	9380	1	0.100

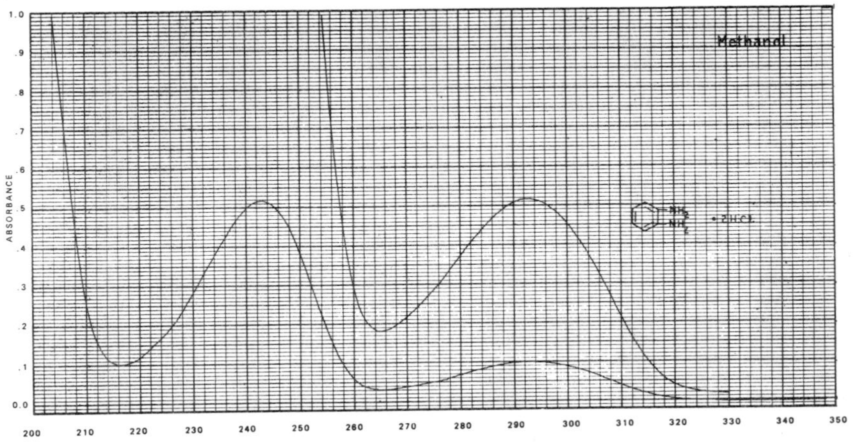

m-PHENYLENEDIAMINE, DIHYROCHLORIDE

$C_6H_8N_2 \cdot 2HCl$
Mol. Wt. 181.07
Solvent: Methanol KOH

λ Max. mμ	a_m	Cell mm	Conc. g/L
293	2070	5	0.100
211.5	32600	1	0.0500

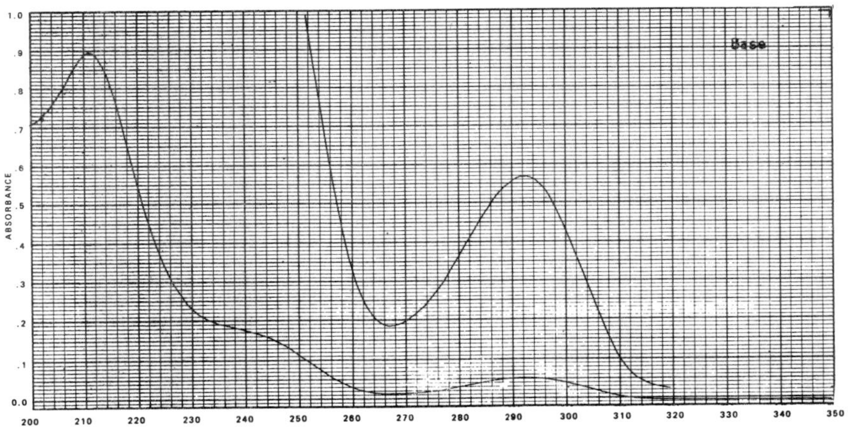

λ Max. mμ	a_m	Cell mm	Conc. g/L

p-PHENYLENEDIAMINE, DIHYDROCHLORIDE

795

$C_6H_8N_2 \cdot 2HCl$

Mol. Wt. 181.07

Solvent: Methanol

λ Max. mμ	a_m	Cell mm	Conc. g/L
295.5	1580	2.0	0.100
242.6	8670	2.0	0.100

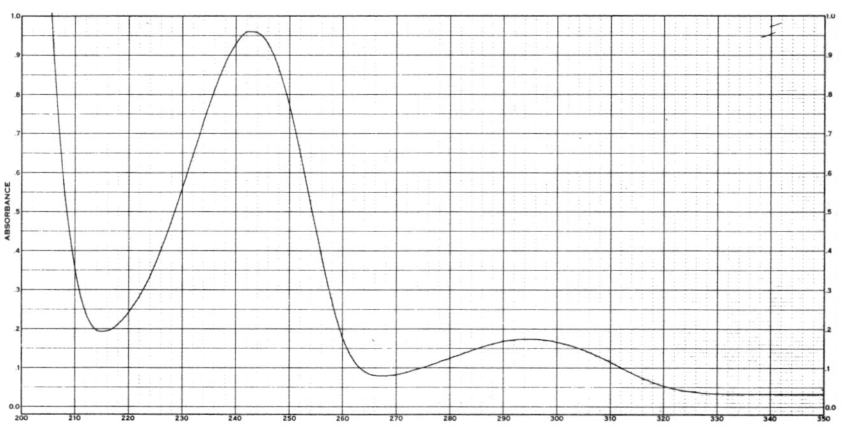

p-PHENYLENEDIAMINE, DIHYDROCHLORIDE

795

$C_6H_8N_2 \cdot 2HCl$

Mol. Wt. 181.07

Solvent: Methanol KOH

λ Max. mμ	a_m	Cell mm	Conc. g/L
307	2190	1.0	0.100
241.5	10500	1.0	0.100
x	x	1.0	0.100

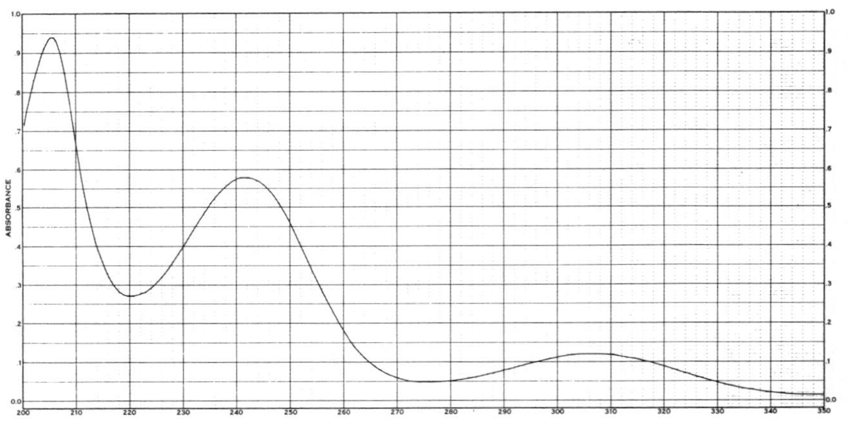

2-CHLORO-p-PHENYLENEDIAMINE, DIHYDROCHLORIDE

796

$C_6H_7ClN_2 \cdot 2HCl$

Mol. Wt. 215.51

Solvent: Methanol

λ Max. mμ	a_m	Cell mm	Conc. g/L
302	2430	5	0.100
246	9830	1	0.050
206	30300	1	0.050

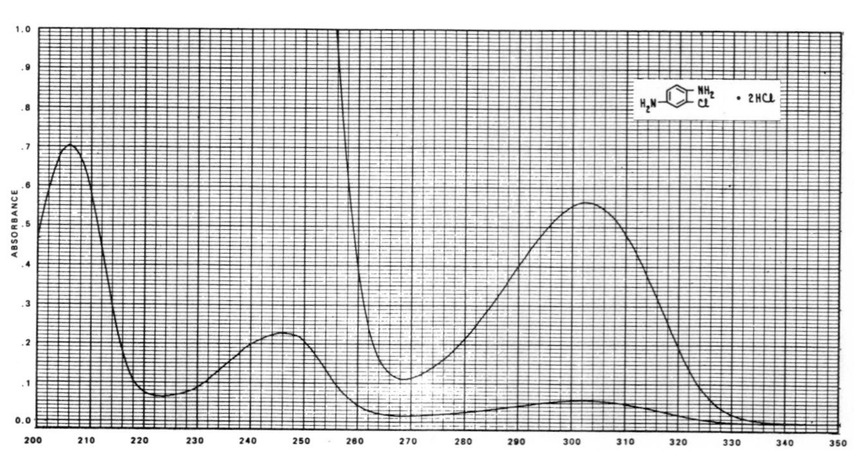

2-CHLORO-p-PHENYLENEDIAMINE, DIHYDROCHLORIDE

$C_6H_7ClN_2 \cdot 2HCl$

Mol. Wt. 215.51

Solvent: Methanol KOH

λ Max. mμ	a_m	Cell mm	Conc. g/L
317	2420	5	0.100
245	9120	1	0.100

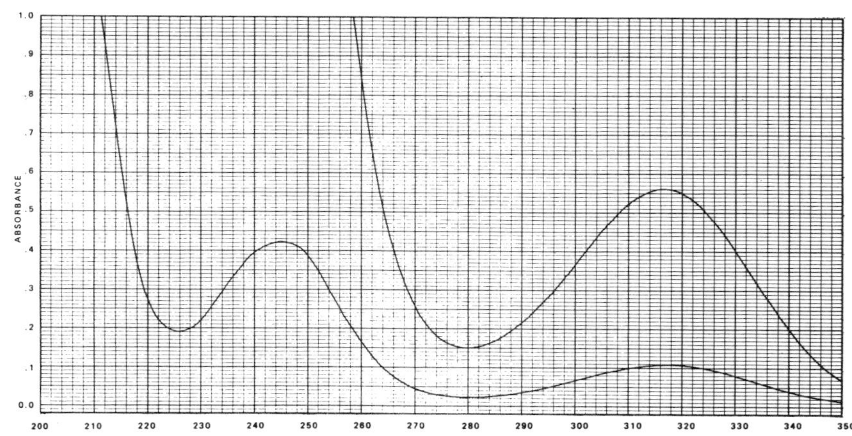

λ Max. mμ	a_m	Cell mm	Conc. g/L

λ Max. mμ	a_m	Cell mm	Conc. g/L

NOTES

THE SECONDARY AMINE SALTS

Aliphatic Compounds

The aliphatic secondary amine salts do not display maxima in the near UV region and thus there are no spectra in this text for compounds 797 through 803.

Aromatic Compounds

The presence of a secondary amine group on the side chain of an aromatic ring has little or no effect on the spectrum in comparison to that of the corresponding free base compound. Both dibenzylamine and dibenzylamine hydrochloride display a maximum with fine structure near 257 mμ.

Compound	$\lambda_{max}(\epsilon_{max})$	Solvent	Spectrum
Dibenzylamine	257 (527)	Methanol	581
Dibenzylamine, hydrochloride	256 (498)	Methanol	805
Dibenzylamine, hydrochloride	257 (431)	Methanol/KOH	805

Because of the insulating methylene group, there is no significant change in the spectra upon the addition of acid to the free amine nor of base to the spectrum of the amine hydrochloride.

As noted on page 111, formation of the salts of secondary anilines should result in a shift of the major band to shorter wavelengths, a decrease in band intensity and the appearance of fine structure. In actual practice, the appearance of spectra of the salts of secondary amines is complicated by the presence of small amounts of free amine in commercially available samples. Due to the greater intensity of the bands of the free amine, the relatively small amounts of the base mask the features expected for the salt. In spectrum 806 for example, the weak band at 295 mμ and the lack of resolved fine structure of the band near 248 mμ probably result from the presence of free n-ethylaniline.

DL-N, α-DIMETHYLPHENETHYLAMINE, HYDROCHLORIDE 804

$C_{10}H_{15}N \cdot HCl$
Mol. Wt. 185.70
M.P. 135-138°C
Solvent: Methanol

λ Max. mμ	a_m	Cell mm	Conc. g/L
267	81.7	10	0.500
263	147	10	0.500
257.5	190	10	0.500
251.5	158	10	0.500
247	125	10	0.500

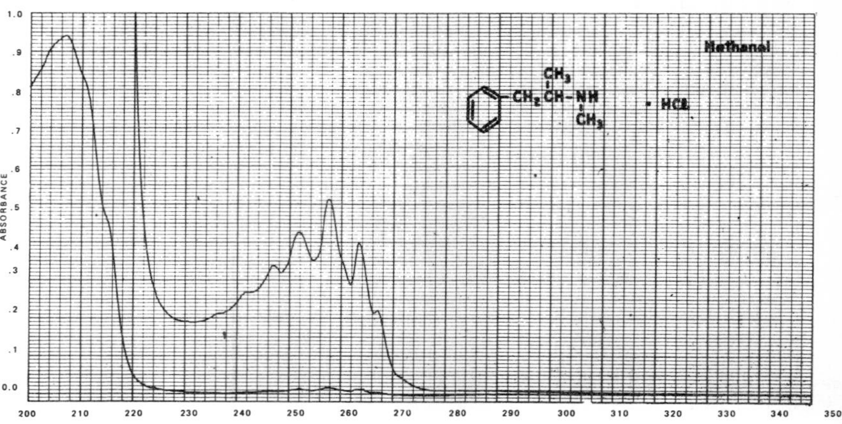

DL-N, α-DIMETHYLPHENETHYLAMINE, HYDROCHLORIDE 804

$C_{10}H_{15}N \cdot HCl$
Mol. Wt. 185.70
M.P. 135-138°C
Solvent: Methanol KOH

λ Max. mμ	a_m	Cell mm	Conc. g/L
268	144	10	0.500
264	167	10	0.500
258.5	214	10	0.500
252.5	185	10	0.500
147.5	147	10	0.500

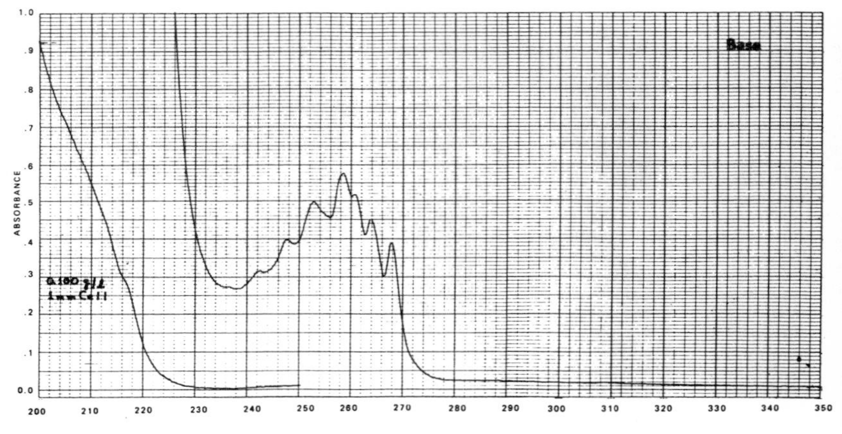

DIBENZYLAMINE, HYDROCHLORIDE 805

$C_{14}H_{15}N \cdot HCl$
Mol. Wt. 233.74
M.P. 260-262°C
Solvent: Methanol

λ Max. mμ	a_m	Cell mm	Conc. g/L
266.5	327	5	0.500
260.5	458	5	0.500
256	498	5	0.500
250.5	382	5	0.500
x	x	1	0.100

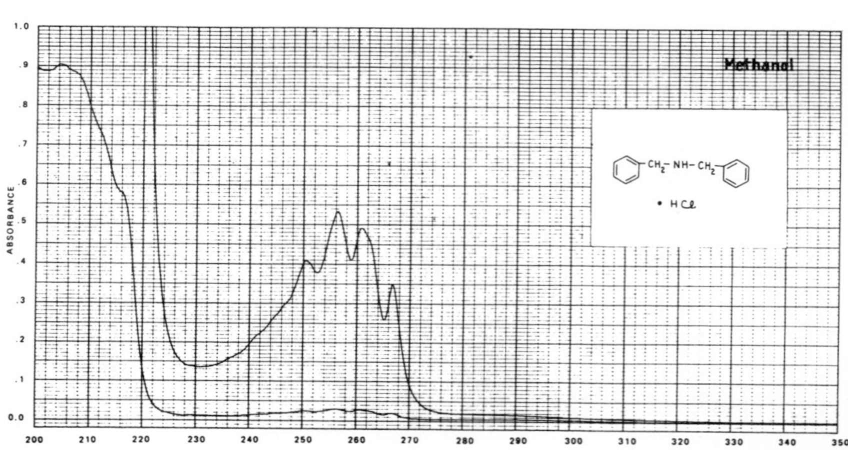

DIBENZYLAMINE, HYDROCHLORIDE

805

$C_{14}H_{15}N{\cdot}HCl$

Mol. Wt. 233.75

M.P. 260-262°C

Solvent: Methanol KOH

λ Max. mμ	a_m	Cell mm	Conc. g/L
263	324	10	0.500
257.5	431	10	0.500
251.5	373	10	0.500
247	313	10	0.500
x	x	1	0.100

N-ETHYLANILINE, HYDROCHLORIDE

806

$C_8H_{11}N{\cdot}HCl$

Mol. Wt. 157.64

M.P. 177-180°C

Solvent: Methanol

λ Max. mμ	a_m	Cell mm	Conc. g/L
293	142	10	0.100
248	962	10	0.100
x	x	1	0.100

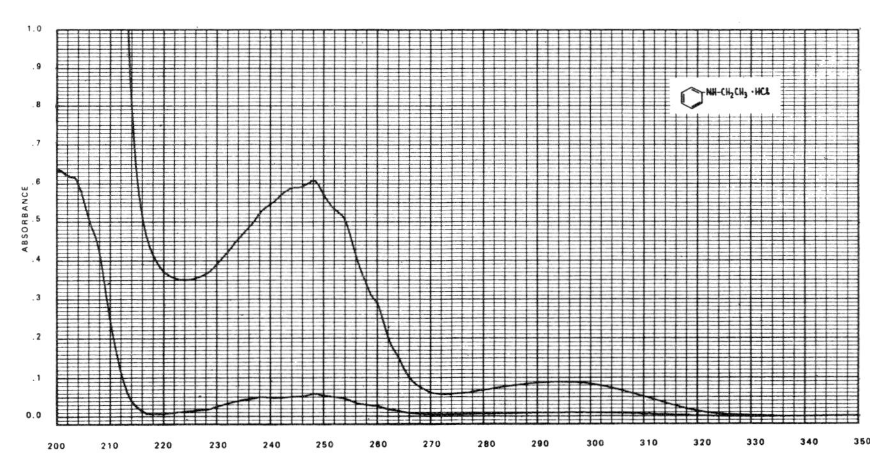

N-ETHYLANILINE, HYDROCHLORIDE

806

$C_8H_{11}N{\cdot}HCl$

Mol. Wt. 157.64

M.P. 177-180°C

Solvent: Methanol KOH

λ Max. mμ	a_m	Cell mm	Conc. g/L
294.5	1810	5	0.100
246.5	2210	1	0.100

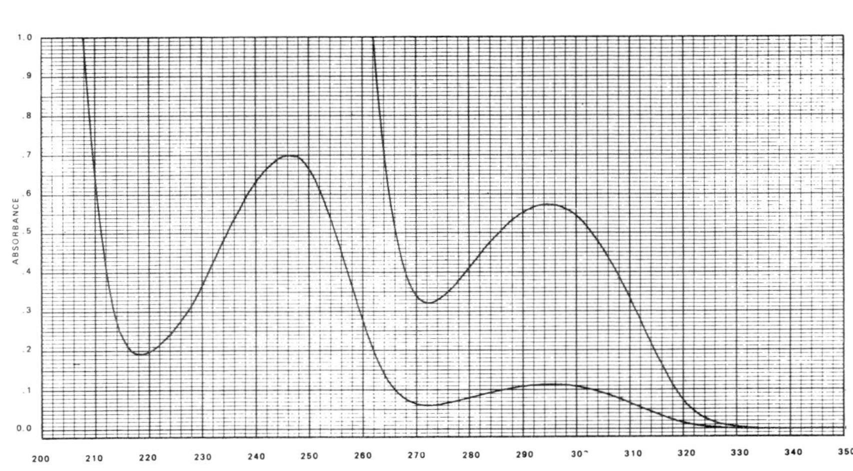

DIPHENYLAMINE, HYDROCHLORIDE

807

$C_{12}H_{11}N \cdot HCl$

Mol. Wt. 205.69

Solvent: Methanol

λ Max. mμ	a_m	Cell mm	Conc. g/L
284	21100	1	0.900

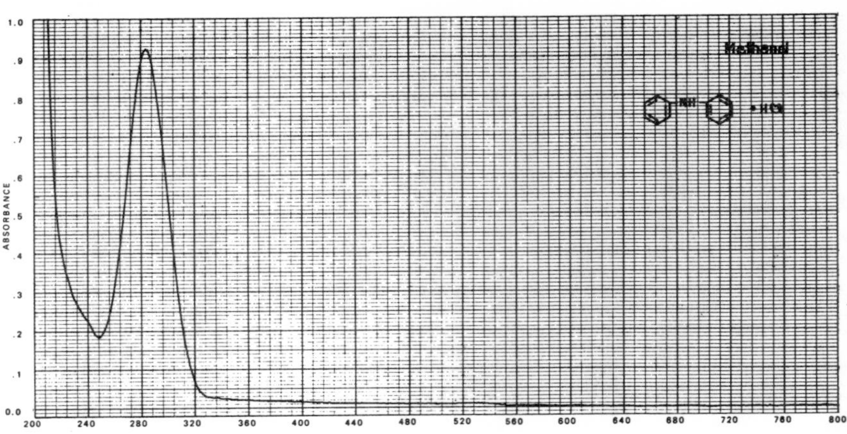

λ Max. mμ	a_m	Cell mm	Conc. g/L

λ Max. mμ	a_m	Cell mm	Conc. g/L

THE TERTIARY AMINE SALTS

Aliphatic Compounds

The aliphatic tertiary amine salts do not produce any maxima in the near UV region of the spectrum and thus there are no spectra in this volume for compounds 808 through 815.

Aromatic Compounds

Due to the relatively small number of aromatic tertiary amine salts included in this text, it is difficult to make any firm conclusions or define trends of wavelength/intensity in comparison to the aromatic free base tertiary amines. The spectral data for N,N-diethyl-p-phenylenediamine and its mono- and di-hydrochlorides that are given below point up this problem.

Compound	$\lambda_{max}(\epsilon_{max})$	$\lambda_{max}(\epsilon_{max})$	Spectrum
N,N-diethyl-p-phenylenediamine	253 (10700)	304 (3102)	670
N,N-diethyl-p-phenylenediamine (HCl)	251 (15300)	297 (1950)	817
N,N-diethyl-p-phenylenediamine (2 HCl)	257 (14100)	306 (1840)	818

As expected, the UV spectra of the tertiary amine salts of aromatic compounds do undergo changes upon the addition of base to the samples, however, the change in wavelength and intensity is not always clear cut nor as predictable as one might expect (compare spectra 806, 816, 817, 818, 819).

N,N-DIMETHYL-m-PHENYLENEDIAMINE, DIHYDROCHLORIDE

816

$C_8H_{12}N_2 \cdot 2HCl$
Mol. Wt. 209.12
M.P. 217°C (dec.)
Solvent: Methanol

λ Max. mμ	a_m	Cell mm	Conc. g/L
304	2670	5	0.100
257	16600	1	0.100

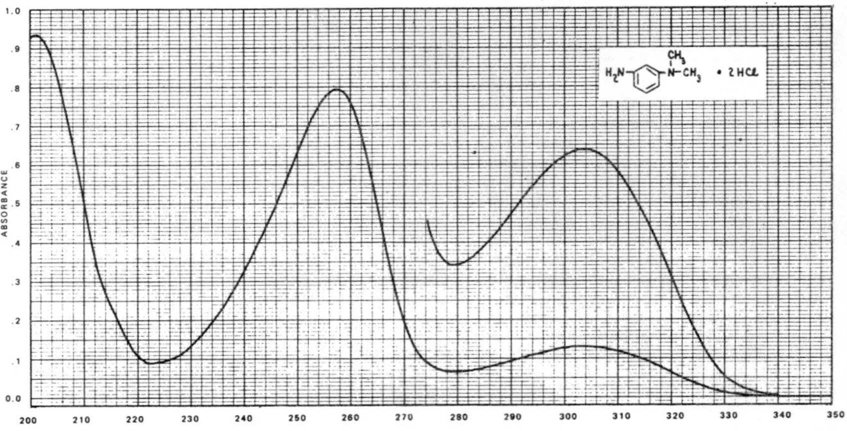

N,N-DIMETHYL-m-PHENYLENEDIAMINE, DIHYDROCHLORIDE

816

$C_8H_{12}N_2 \cdot 2HCl$
Mol. Wt. 209.12
M.P. 217°C (dec.)
Solvent: Methanol KOH

λ Max. mμ	a_m	Cell mm	Conc. g/L
300	3090	5	0.0500
253	9120	1	0.0500
222	28000	1	0.0500

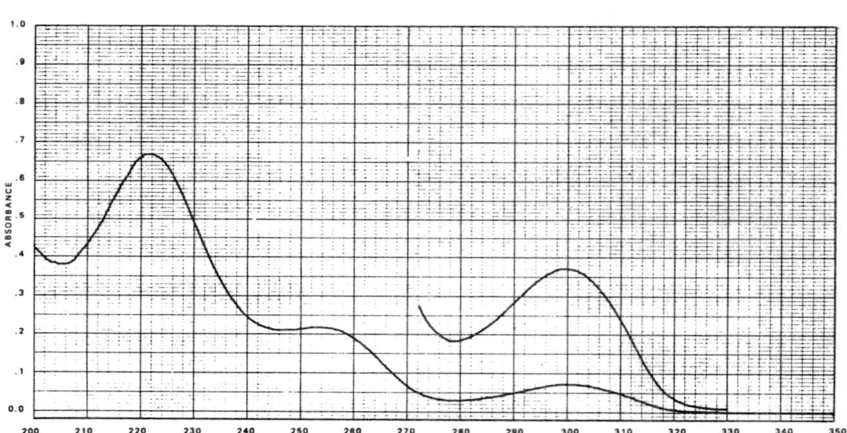

N,N-DIETHYL-p-PHENYLENEDIAMINE, MONOHYDROCHLORIDE

817

$C_{10}H_{16}N_2 \cdot HCl$
Mol. Wt. 200.71
Solvent: Methanol

λ Max. mμ	a_m	Cell mm	Conc. g/L
297	1950	5	0.114
251	15300	1	0.114

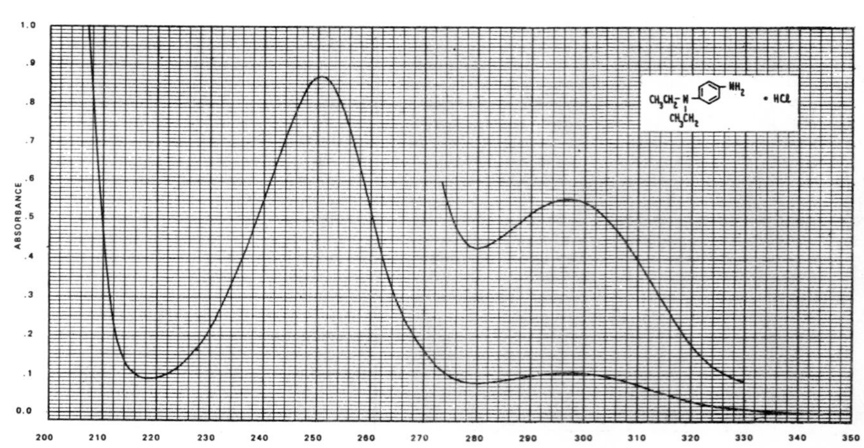

N,N-DIETHYL-p-PHENYLENEDIAMINE, MONOHYDROCHLORIDE 817

$C_{10}H_{16}N_2 \cdot HCl$
Mol. Wt. 200.71
Solvent: Methanol KOH

λ Max. mμ	a_m	Cell mm	Conc. g/L
249	10300	1	0.114

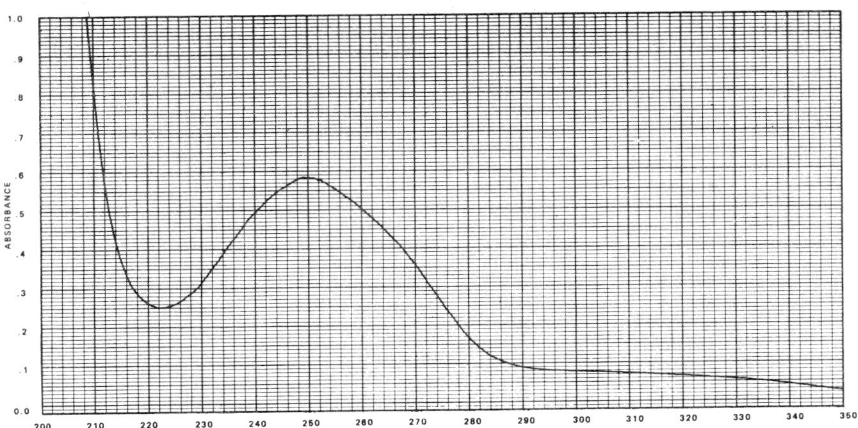

N,N-DIMETHYL-p-PHENYLENEDIAMINE, DIHYDROCHLORIDE 818

$C_8H_{12}N_2 \cdot 2HCl$
Mol. Wt. 209.12
Solvent: Methanol

λ Max. mμ	a_m	Cell mm	Conc. g/L
306	1840	10	0.100
257	14100	1	0.100

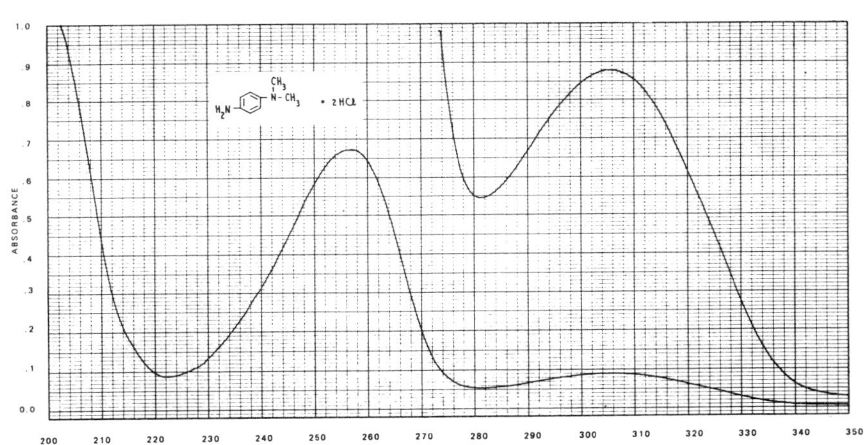

N,N-DIMETHYL-p-PHENYLENEDIAMINE, DIHYDROCHLORIDE 818

$C_8H_{12}N_2 \cdot 2HCl$
Mol. Wt. 209.12
Solvent: Methanol KOH

λ Max. mμ	a_m	Cell mm	Conc. g/L
311	1730	10	0.100
251	11900	1	0.100

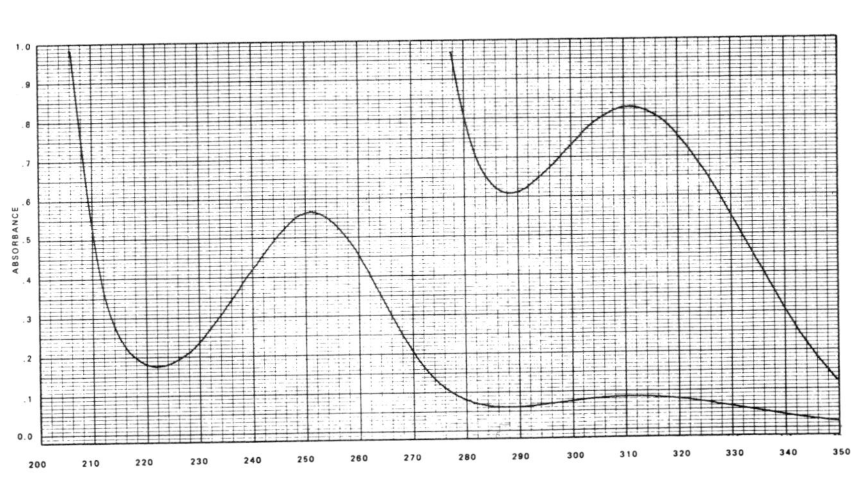

N,N,N',N'-TETRAMETHYL-p-PHENYLENEDIAMINE, HYDROCHLORIDE 819

$C_{10}H_{16}N_2 \cdot 2HCl$

Mol. Wt. 237.17

Solvent: Methanol

λ Max. mμ	a_m	Cell mm	Conc. g/L
612	372	20	0.100
566	393	20	0.100
309	2470	5	0.100
263	19900	1	0.100

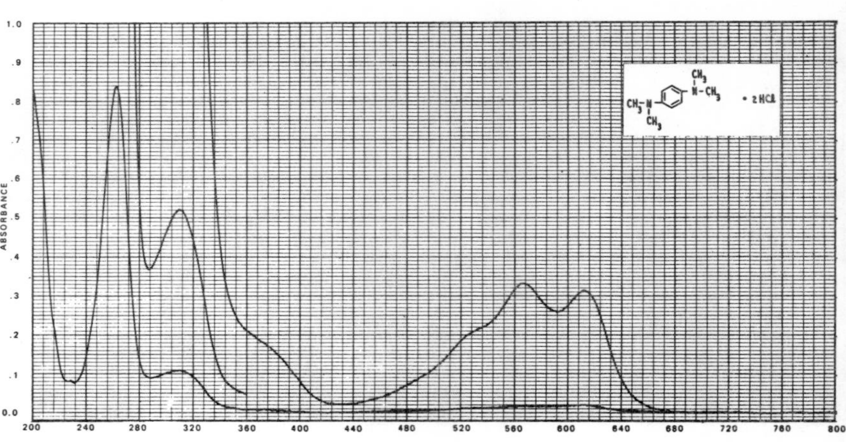

N,N,N',N'-TETRAMETHYL-p-PHENYLENEDIAMINE, HYDROCHLORIDE 819

$C_{10}H_{16}N_2 \cdot 2HCl$

Mol. Wt. 237.17

Solvent: Methanol KOH

λ Max. mμ	a_m	Cell mm	Conc. g/L
316	1990	10	0.100
260	15800	1	0.100

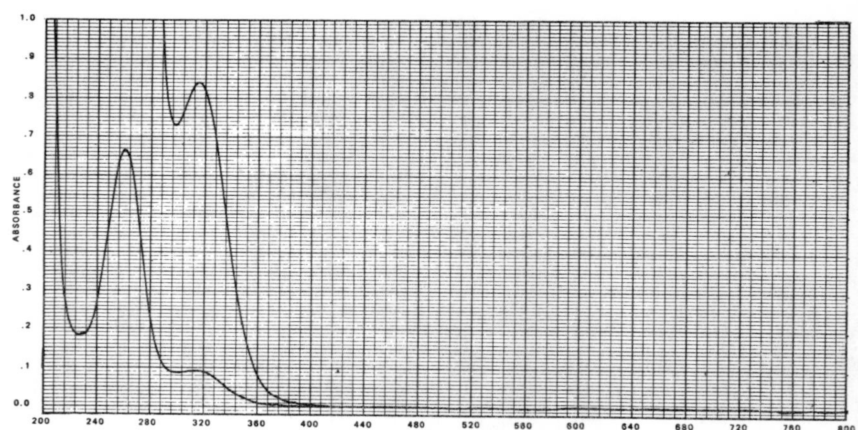
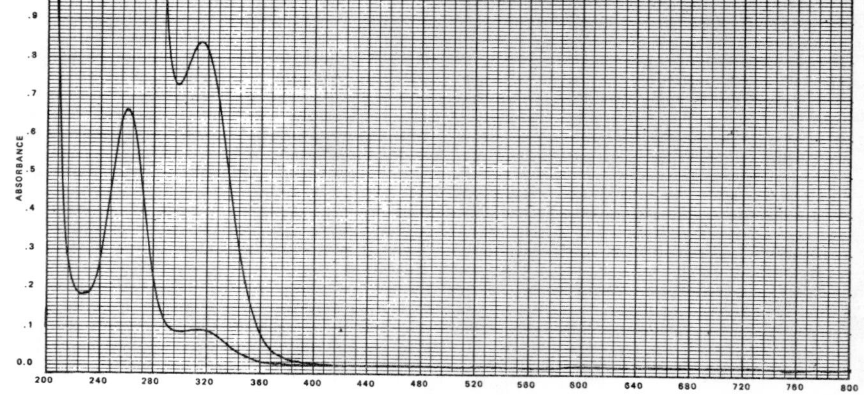

HISTAMINE, MONOHYDROCHLORIDE 820

$C_5H_9N_3 \cdot HCl$

Mol. Wt. 147.61

Solvent: Methanol

λ Max. mμ	a_m	Cell mm	Conc. g/L
211.5	4980	2	0.100

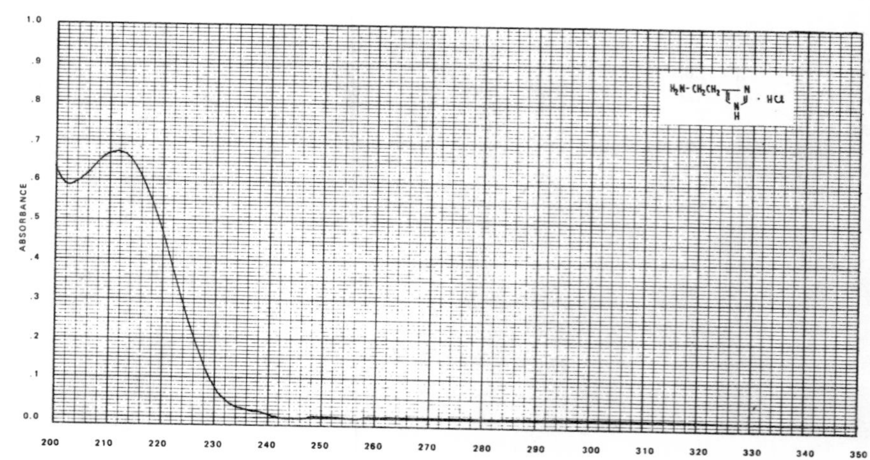

4-BROMOPYRIDINE, HYDROBROMIDE 821

$C_5H_4BrN \cdot HBr$

Mol. Wt. 238.94

Solvent: Methanol

λ Max. mμ	a_m	Cell mm	Conc. g/L
264	3000	2	0.100
257	4520	2	0.100
240.5	6320	2	0.100
219	5380	2	0.100

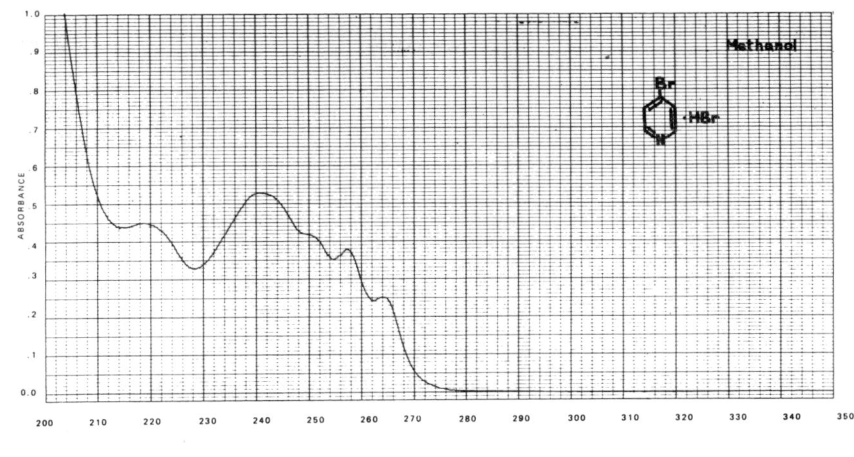

4-BROMOPYRIDINE, HYDROBROMIDE 821

$C_5H_4BrN \cdot HBr$

Mol. Wt. 238.94

Solvent: Methanol KOH

λ Max. mμ	a_m	Cell mm	Conc. g/L
265.5	1700	10	0.100
258	2280	10	0.100
252	1990	10	0.100
246	1600	10	0.100
216	9210	2	0.100

METHYLHYDRAZINE, SULFATE (1:1) 822

$CH_6N_2 \cdot H_2SO_4$

Mol. Wt. 144.15

M.P. 141-142°C

λ Max. mμ	a_m	Cell mm	Conc. g/L

This compound does not absorb in the near U.V.

(3-CHLORO-p-TOLYL)HYDRAZINE, MONOHYDROCHLORIDE 823

$C_7H_9ClN_2 \cdot HCl$
Mol. Wt. 193.08
M.P. 247°C (dec.)
Solvent: Methanol

λ Max. mμ	a_m	Cell mm	Conc. g/L
281	2120	2	0.100
232	6840	2	0.100
x	x	1	0.100

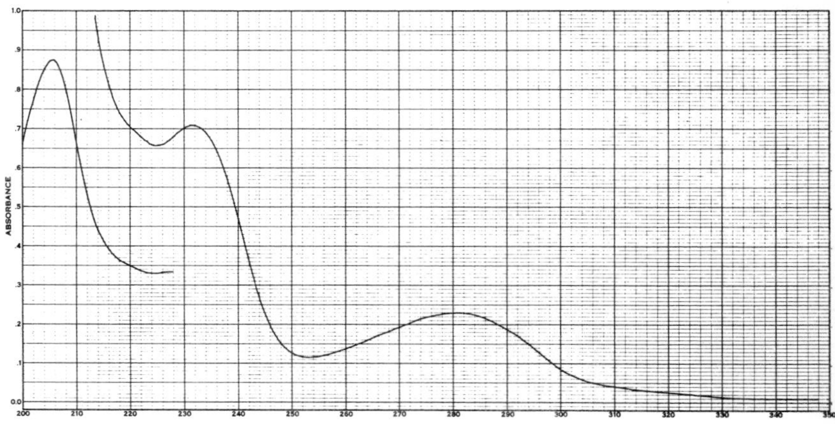

(3-CHLORO-p-TOLYL)HYDRAZINE, MONOHYDROCHLORIDE 823

$C_7H_9ClN_2 \cdot HCl$
Mol. Wt. 193.08
M.P. 247°C (dec.)
Solvent: Methanol KOH

λ Max. mμ	a_m	Cell mm	Conc. g/L
282	1930	2	0.100
242	6780	2	0.100
x	x	0.5	0.100

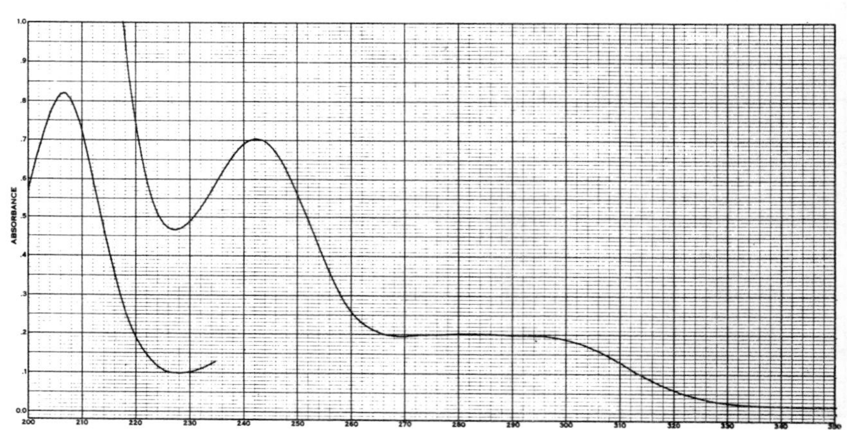

(p-METHOXYPHENYL)HYDRAZINE, MONOHYDROCHLORIDE 824

$C_7H_{10}N_2O \cdot HCl$
Mol. Wt. 174.63
Solvent: Methanol

λ Max. mμ	a_m	Cell mm	Conc. g/L
283	2100	2	0.100
231	5510	2	0.100

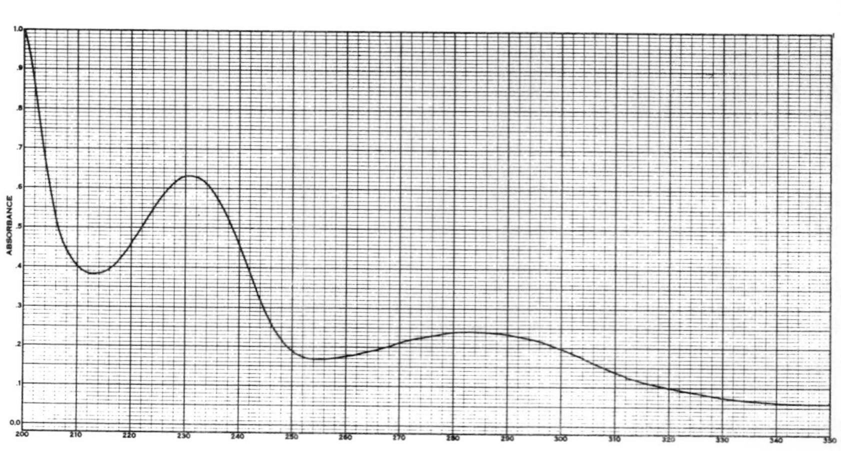

(p-METHOXYPHENYL)HYDRAZINE, MONOHYDROCHLORIDE 824

$C_7H_{10}N_2O \cdot HCl$

Mol. Wt. 174.63

Solvent: Methanol KOH

λ Max. mμ	a_m	Cell mm	Conc. g/L
277	1450	10	0.100
270.5	1530	10	0.100
x	x	1	0.100

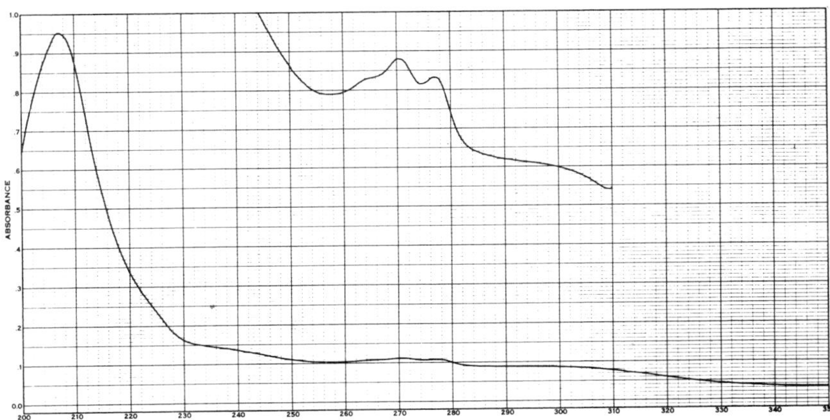

(2-NAPHTHYL)HYDRAZINE, MONOHYDROCHLORIDE 825

$C_{10}H_{10}N_2 \cdot HCl$

Mol. Wt. 194.67

M.P. 236-238°C (dec.)

Solvent: Methanol

λ Max. mμ	a_m	Cell mm	Conc. g/L
329.5	1150	10	0.100
273	5050	2	0.100
264.5	4690	2	0.100
232.5	47400	1	0.0200
213	23600	1	0.0200

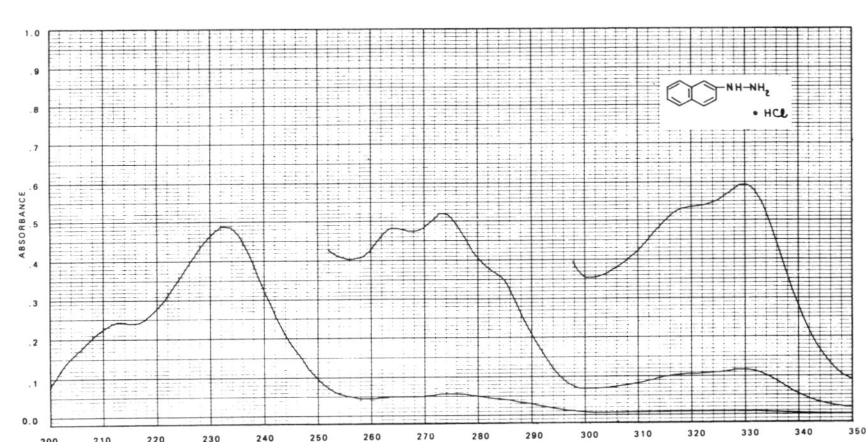

λ Max. mμ	a_m	Cell mm	Conc. g/L

3-HYDRAZINOQUINOLINE, DIHYDROCHLORIDE

$C_9H_9N_3 \cdot 2HCl$
Mol. Wt. 232.11
Solvent: Methanol

λ Max. mμ	a_m	Cell mm	Conc. g/L
399	1230	10	0.070
326	2750	10	0.070
241	26300	1	0.070
211.5	26600	1	0.070

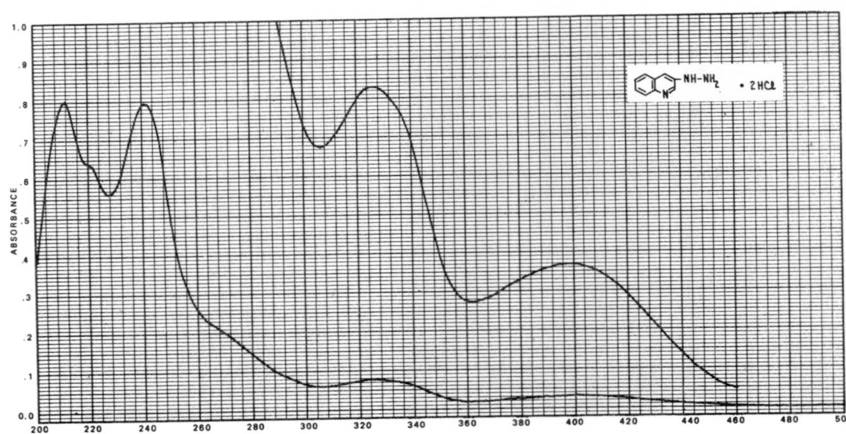

3-HYDRAZINOQUINOLINE, DIHYDROCHLORIDE

$C_9H_9N_3 \cdot 2HCl$
Mol. Wt. 232.11
Solvent: Methanol KOH

λ Max. mμ	a_m	Cell mm	Conc. g/L
352	2130	10	0.070
313	2390	10	0.070
300	2650	10	0.070
246	18700	1	0.070
230	19300	1	0.070

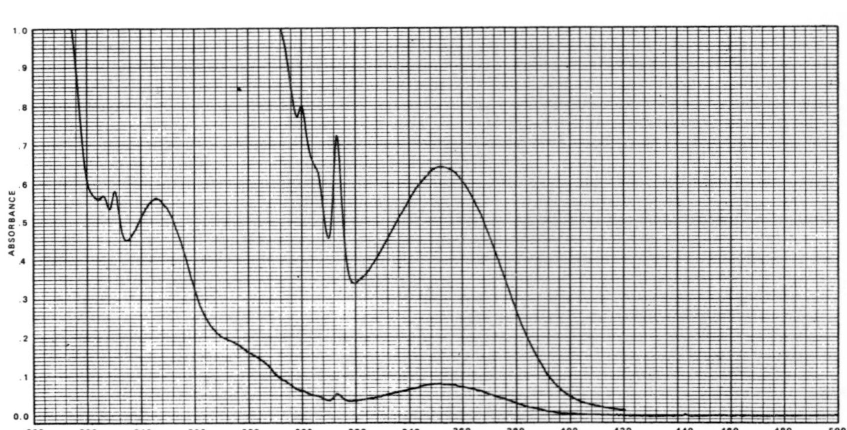

λ Max. mμ	a_m	Cell mm	Conc. g/L

THE QUATERNARY AMMONIUM COMPOUNDS

Aliphatic Compounds

As a group, the aliphatic quaternary ammonium compounds do not produce any maxima in the near UV region and as a consequence there are no spectra in this volume for compounds 827 through 834.

Certain of the anions associated with the quaternary ammonium compounds, however, may produce a maximum. For example, the I^- anion of spectra 837 and 841 produces an absorption band near 218 mμ (ϵ_{max} = 13000 - 18000). Other anions which produce maxima in the near UV region include Br_3^-, I_3^-, ClO^-, ClO_2^-, BrO^-, NO_2^- and NO_3^-.

Aromatic Compounds

The UV spectra of the benzyl and phenyl ammonium compounds resemble those of benzene and toluene in that they display relatively weak fine structure in the region from 240 mμ to 270 mμ.

Compound	$\lambda_{max}(\epsilon_{max})$		$\lambda_{max}(\epsilon_{max})$		$\lambda_{max}(\epsilon_{max})$		Solvent	Spectrum
Toluene	255	(175)	261	(175)	268	(222)	Methanol	133
Benzyltrimethyl - ammonium Iodide	257	(355)	263	(418)	269	(337)	Methanol	837
hexafluoroantimonate	256	(363)	262	(432)	268	(340)	Methanol	838

The N-Substituted Pyridinium Compounds

These compounds are characterized by two bands, a relatively strong band near 218 mμ and a weaker band near 258 mμ.

Pyridinium Halides	$\lambda_{max}(\epsilon_{max})$		$\lambda_{max}(\epsilon_{max})$		$\lambda_{max}(\epsilon_{max})$		Solvent	Spectrum
1-Methyl	218	(15100)	259	(4920)	----------		Methanol	842
1-Hexadecyl	215	(17600)	258	(4400)	289	(445)	Methanol	843
1-Methyl-3-amino	219	(2520)	258	(13500)	337	(5850)	Methanol	844
1,1-Ethylenebis	216 *	(9170)	259	(5750)	----------		Methanol	845

*Shoulder

BENZYLTRIMETHYLAMMONIUM CHLORIDE

836

$C_{10}H_{16}ClN$

Mol. Wt. 185.70

Solvent: Methanol

λ Max. mμ	a_m	Cell mm	Conc. g/L
268	839	10	0.100
261.5	1080	10	0.100
256	934	10	0.100
x	x	1	0.100

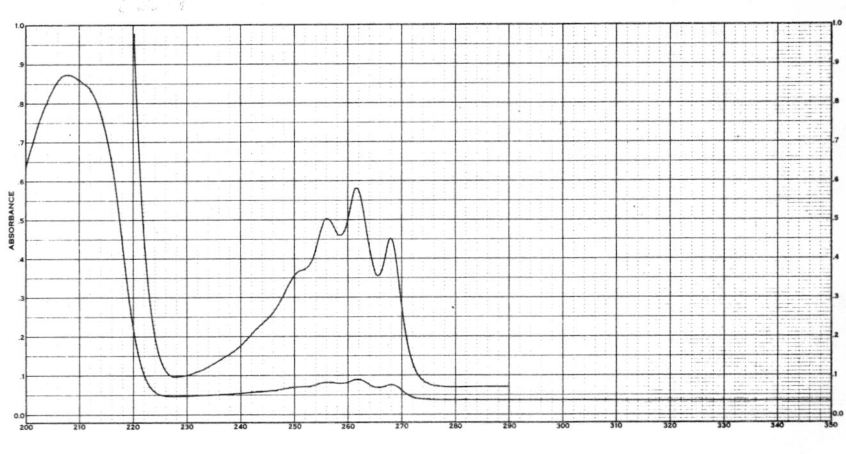

BENZYLTRIMETHYLAMMONIUM IODIDE

837

$C_{10}H_{16}IN$

Mol. Wt. 277.15

M.P. 181-182°C

Solvent: Methanol

λ Max. mμ	a_m	Cell mm	Conc. g/L
269	337	20	0.100
262.5	418	20	0.100
257	355	20	0.100
218	17300	1	0.100

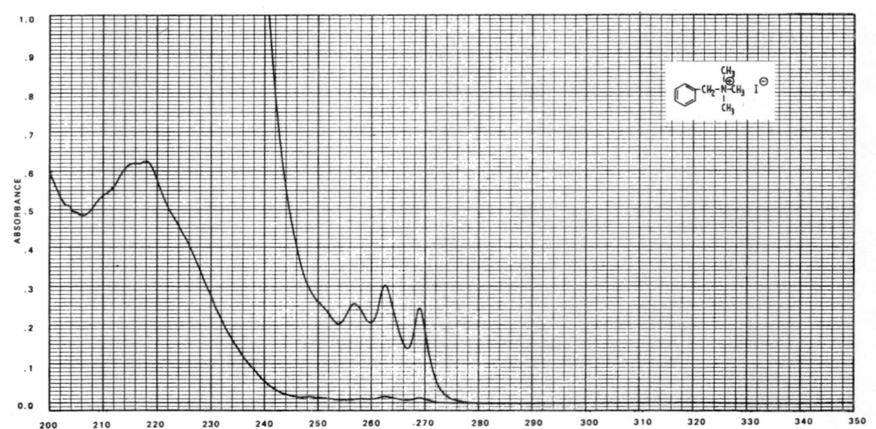

BENZYLTRIMETHYLAMMONIUM HEXAFLUOROANTIMONATE (1-)

838

$C_{10}H_{16}F_6NSb$

Mol. Wt. 385.99

Solvent: Methanol

λ Max. mμ	a_m	Cell mm	Conc. g/L
267.5	340	10	0.500
261.5	432	10	0.500
256	363	10	0.500
251	256	10	0.500
x	x	1	0.500

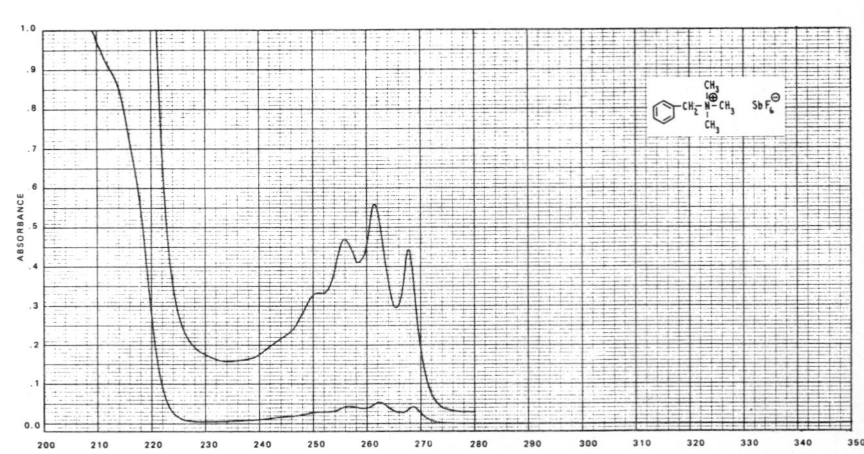

BENZYLDIMETHYLHEXADECYLAMMONIUM CHLORIDE, HYDRATE 839

$C_{25}H_{46}ClN \cdot H_2O$
Mol. Wt. 414.12
M.P. 55-56°C (anhyd.) (lit.)
Solvent: Methanol

λ Max. mμ	a_m	Cell mm	Conc. g/L
268.5	325	20	0.500
262	405	20	0.500
257	336	20	0.500
251.5	235	20	0.500
209	7610	1	0.500

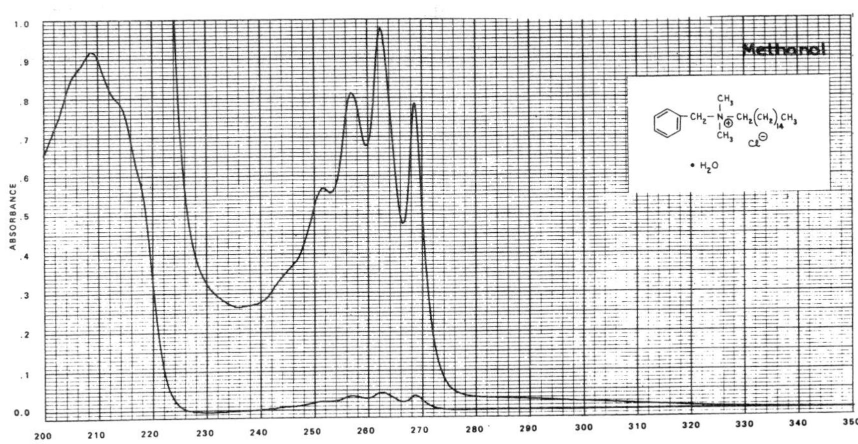

PHENYLTRIMETHYLAMMONIUM CHLORIDE 840

$C_9H_{14}ClN$
Mol. Wt. 171.67
Solvent: Methanol

λ Max. mμ	a_m	Cell mm	Conc. g/L
263.5	221	40	0.100
257.5	330	40	0.100
253	340	40	0.100
247	276	40	0.100
x	x	5	0.100

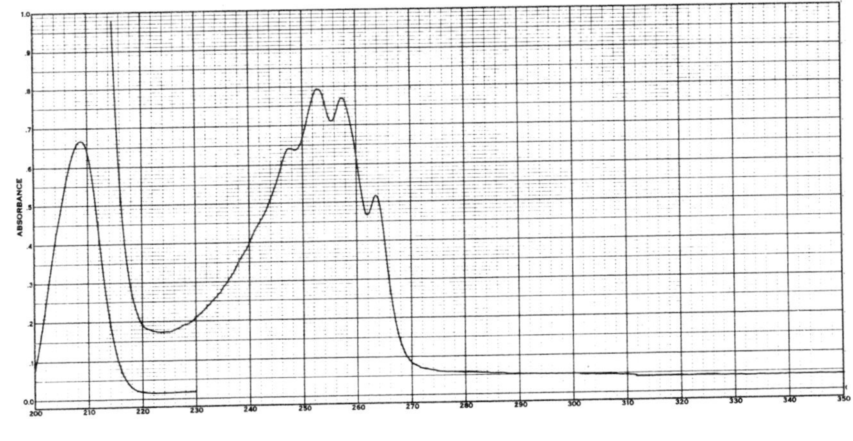

PHENYLTRIETHYLAMMONIUM IODIDE 841

$C_{12}H_{20}IN$
Mol. Wt. 305.20
Solvent: Methanol

λ Max. mμ	a_m	Cell mm	Conc. g/L
264.5	513	20	0.100
258.5	645	20	0.100
252.5	658	20	0.100
218	13400	2	0.100

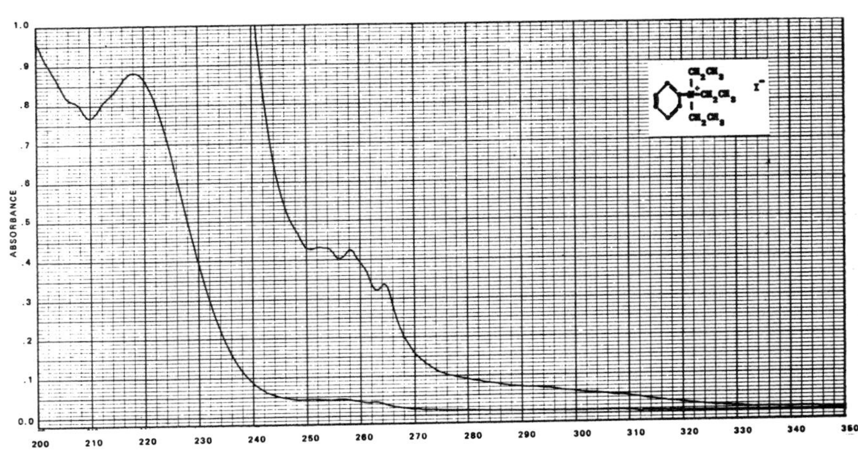

1-METHYLPYRIDINIUM IODIDE

C_6H_8IN

Mol. Wt. 221.04

M.P. 118-120°C

Solvent: Methanol

λ Max. mμ	a_m	Cell mm	Conc. g/L
259	4920	4	0.100
217.5	15100	1	0.100

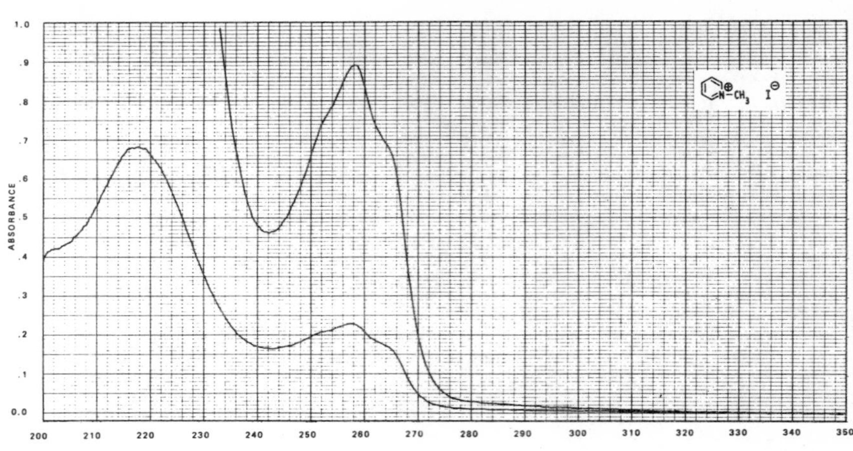

1-HEXADECYLPYRIDINIUM IODIDE

843

$C_{21}H_{38}IN$

Mol. Wt. 431.45

Solvent: Methanol

λ Max. mμ	a_m	Cell mm	Conc. g/L
289	445	10	1.222
258	4400	10	0.163
215	17600	10	0.033

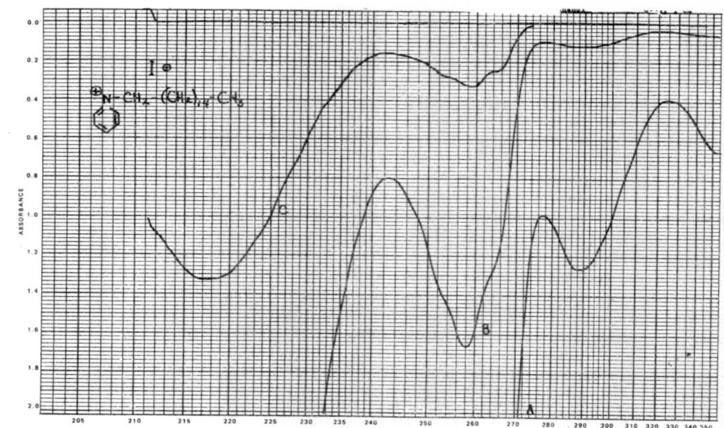

3-AMINO-1-METHYLPYRIDINIUM BROMIDE

844

$C_6H_9BrN_2$

Mol. Wt. 189.06

M.P. 178-180°C

Solvent: Methanol

λ Max. mμ	a_m	Cell mm	Conc. g/L
337	5850	2	0.100
258	13500	0.5	0.100
219	25200	0.5	0.100

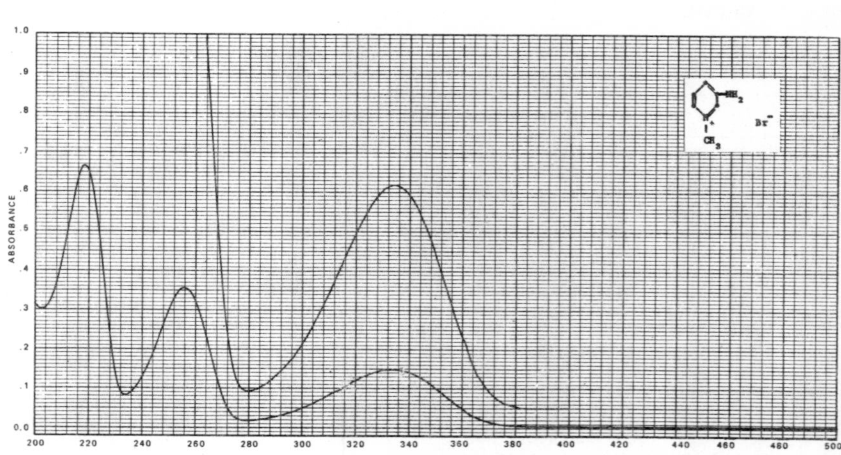

1,1'-ETHYLENEBIS[PYRIDINIUM BROMIDE] 845

$C_{12}H_{14}Br_2N_2$

Mol. Wt. 346.07

M.P. 290°C (dec.)

Solvent: Methanol

λ Max. mμ	a_m	Cell mm	Conc. g/L
259	5750	2	0.100

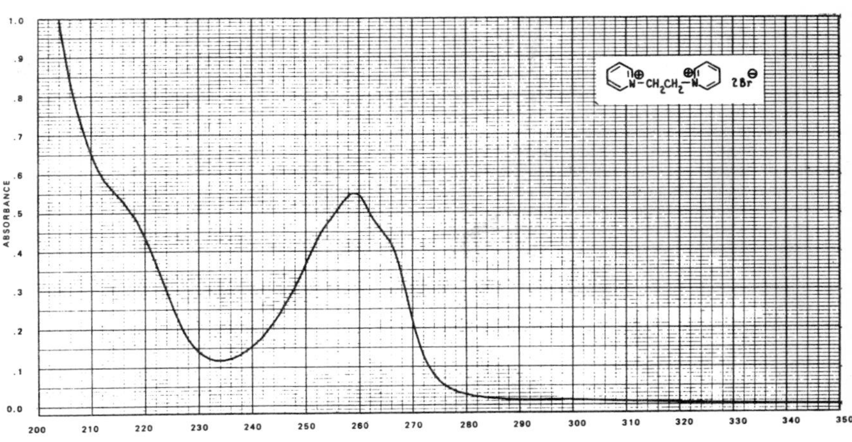

o-METHYLHYDROXYLAMINE, HYDROCHLORIDE 846

$CH_5NO \cdot HCl$

Mol. Wt. 83.52

λ Max. mμ	a_m	Cell mm	Conc. g/L

This compound does not produce maxima in the near UV.

λ Max. mμ	a_m	Cell mm	Conc. g/L

PYRIDINE, 1-OXIDE, HYDROCHLORIDE

847

$C_5H_5NO \cdot HCl$

Mol. Wt. 131.57

M.P. 175.8-179.1°C

Solvent: Methanol

λ Max. mμ	a_m	Cell mm	Conc. g/L
262	10400	1	0.100

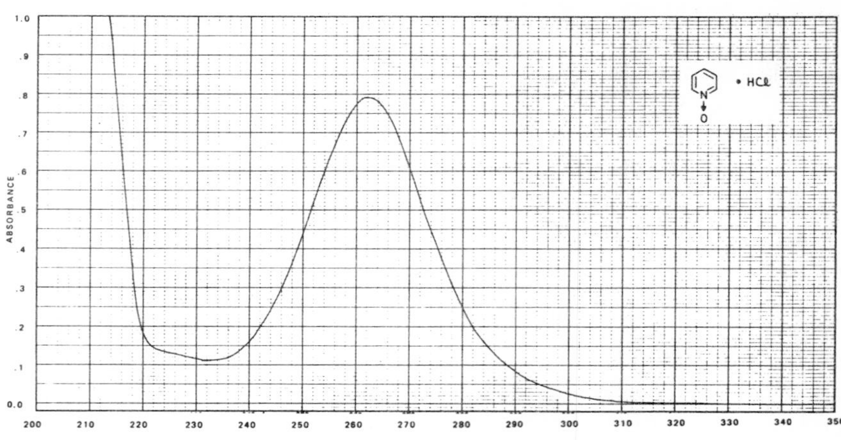

PYRIDINE, 1-OXIDE, HYDROCHLORIDE

847

$C_5H_5NO \cdot HCl$

Mol. Wt. 131.57

M.P. 175.8-179.1°C

Solvent: Methanol KOH

λ Max. mμ	a_m	Cell mm	Conc. g/L
262.5	13100	1	0.100

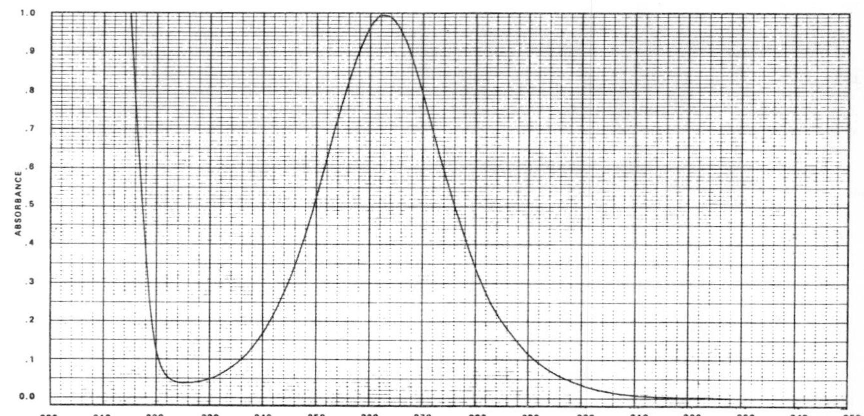

λ Max. mμ	a_m	Cell mm	Conc. g/L

THE OXIMES

Aliphatic Compounds

The aliphatic mono-oximes do not display any absorption bands above 220 mμ and thus there are no spectra in this volume for compounds 848, 849 nor 853 through 858.

The 1,2-dioximes due to conjugation exhibit a relatively strong maximum in the region from 225 - 240 mμ; glyoxime -- 232 mμ (15400), dimethyl glyoxime -- 227 mμ (15400) and 1,2-cyclohexane-dione, dioxime -- 237 mμ (6400).

Aromatic Compounds

The UV spectra of the aromatic oximes display a maximum in the region from 240 - 250 mμ as indicated in the table below.

Compound	$\lambda_{max}(\epsilon_{max})$	Solvent	Spectrum
Acetophenone, oxime	242 (11500)	Methanol	859
Benzaldehyde, oxime	252 (13200)	Methanol	852
4'-Chloroacetophenone, oxime	251 (12200)	Methanol	860
Benzophenone, oxime	252 (1830)	Methanol	861

THE IMINES

The spectra of the aromatic imines are very similar to those of the structurally similar styrenes. The UV spectra of the imines usually change markedly upon the addition of acid to the sample. The table given below lists the major absorption of styrene and several simple imine compounds.

Compound	$\lambda_{max}(\epsilon_{max})$	Solvent	Spectrum
Styrene	245 (15400)	Cyclohexane	156
N-Benzylidenemethylamine	244 (14800)	Methanol	866
N,N'-Dibenzylideneethylenediamine	247 (30200)	Methanol	868
N-Benzylideneaniline	260 (15200)	Methanol	871
N-(p-methylbenzylidine)aniline	268 (26700)	Methanol	872

GLYOXIME 850

$C_2H_4N_2O_2$
Mol. Wt. 88.07
M.P. 178°C (lit.)
Solvent: Methanol

λ Max. mμ	a_m	Cell mm	Conc. g/L
232	15400	1	0.0500

HON=CH−CH=NOH

CINNAMALDEHYDE, OXIME 851

C_9H_9NO
Mol. Wt. 147.18
Solvent: Methanol

λ Max. mμ	a_m	Cell mm	Conc. g/L
288	22600	1	0.0470
232.5	7920	1	0.0470
226	12500	1	0.0470
220.5	11900	1	0.0470
210	9710	1	0.0470

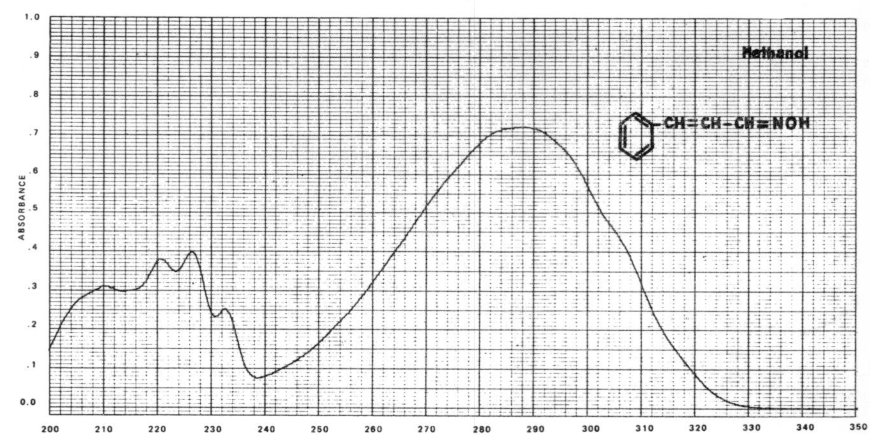

CINNAMALDEHYDE, OXIME 851

C_9H_9NO
Mol. Wt. 147.18
Solvent: Methanol KOH

λ Max. mμ	a_m	Cell mm	Conc. g/L
292	18400	1	0.0470
242	5320	1	0.0470
233	9080	1	0.0470
226.5	11500	1	0.0470
220.5	11200	1	0.0470

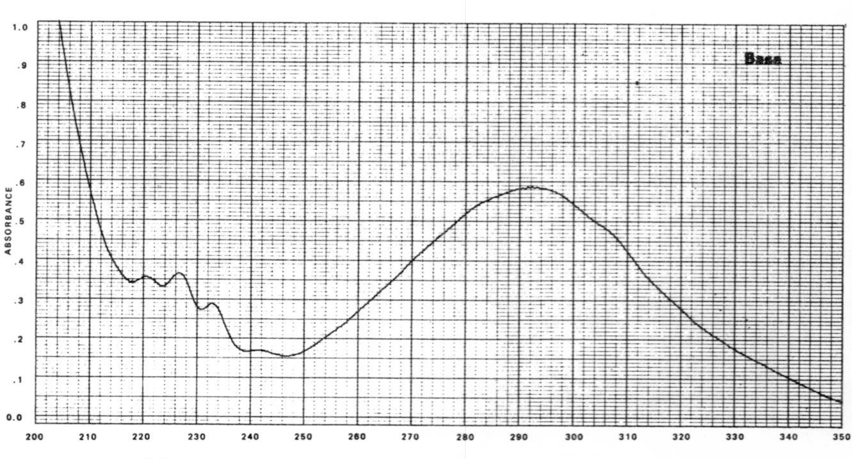

852

BENZALDEHYDE, OXIME

C_7H_7NO

Mol. Wt. 121.14

M.P. 33-35°C

Solvent: Methanol

λ Max. mμ	a_m	Cell mm	Conc. g/L
292	944	2	0.412
252	13200	1	0.0490
205	18700	1	0.0490

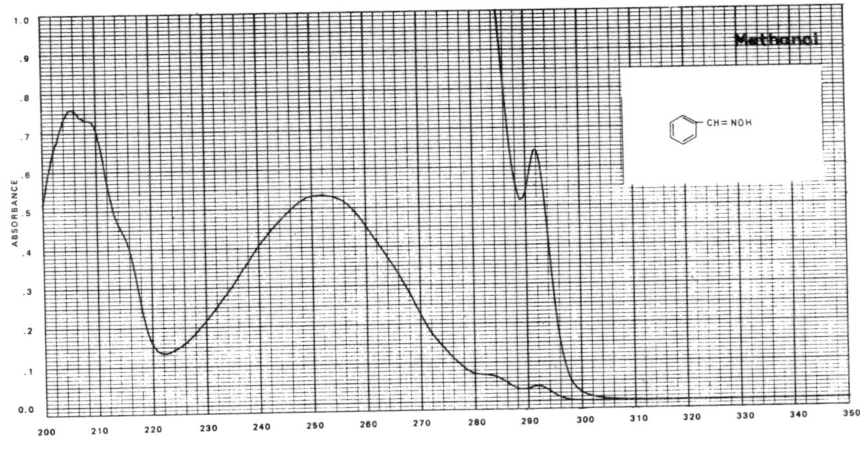

852

BENZALDEHYDE, OXIME

C_7H_7NO

Mol. Wt. 121.14

M.P. 33-35°C

Solvent: Methanol KOH

λ Max. mμ	a_m	Cell mm	Conc. g/L
256	11200	1	0.0490

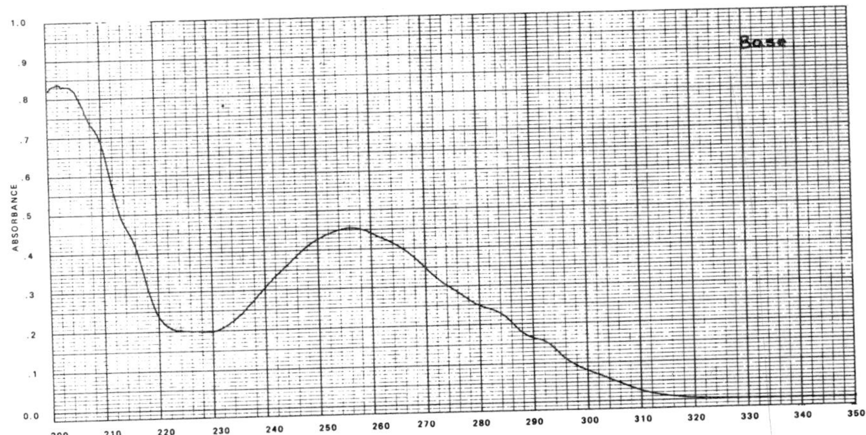

λ Max. mμ	a_m	Cell mm	Conc. g/L

Compounds 853 - 858 do not absorb in the near U.V.

ACETOPHENONE, OXIME

859

C_8H_9NO

Mol. Wt. 135.16

M.P. 56-58°C

Solvent: Methanol

λ Max. mμ	a_m	Cell mm	Conc. g/L
242	11500	10	0.010

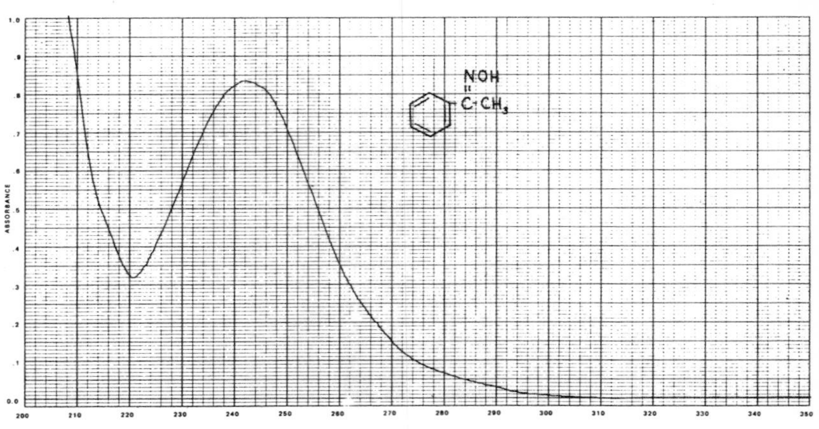

4'-CHLOROACETOPHENONE, OXIME

860

C_8H_8ClNO

Mol. Wt. 169.61

M.P. 95°C

Solvent: Methanol

λ Max. mμ	a_m	Cell mm	Conc. g/L
251	1220	1	0.100

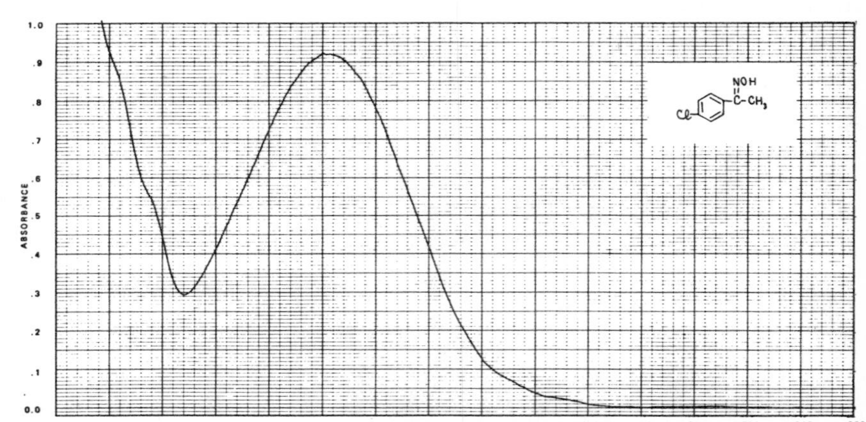

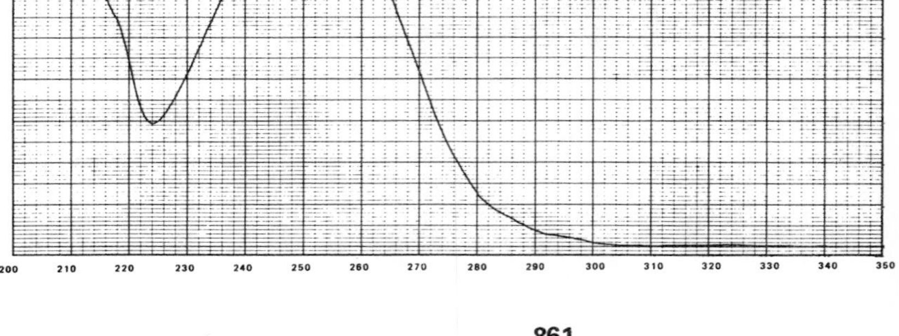

BENZOPHENONE, OXIME

861

$C_{13}H_{11}NO$

Mol. Wt. 197.23

M.P. 143-145°C

Solvent: Methanol

λ Max. mμ	a_m	Cell mm	Conc. g/L
252	1830	10	0.10

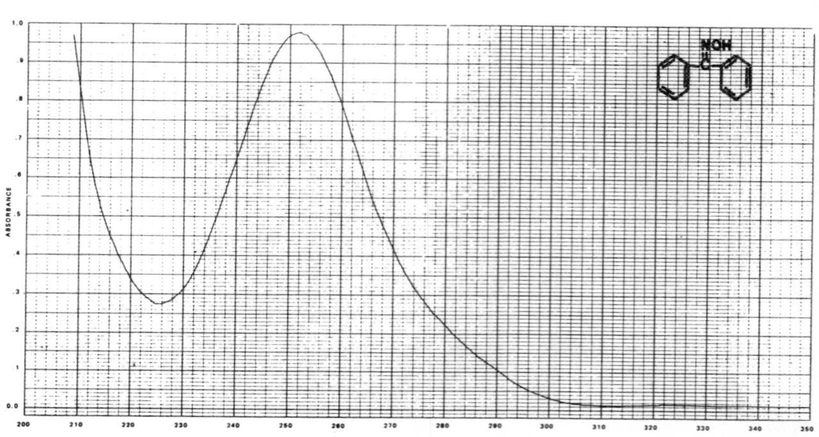

2-AMINOBENZOPHENONE, OXIME

862

$C_{13}H_{12}N_2O$
Mol. Wt. 212.25
M.P. 151-153°C
Solvent: Methanol

λ Max. mμ	a_m	Cell mm	Conc. g/L
292.5	3040	5	0.100
x	x	2	0.100
x	x	1	0.050

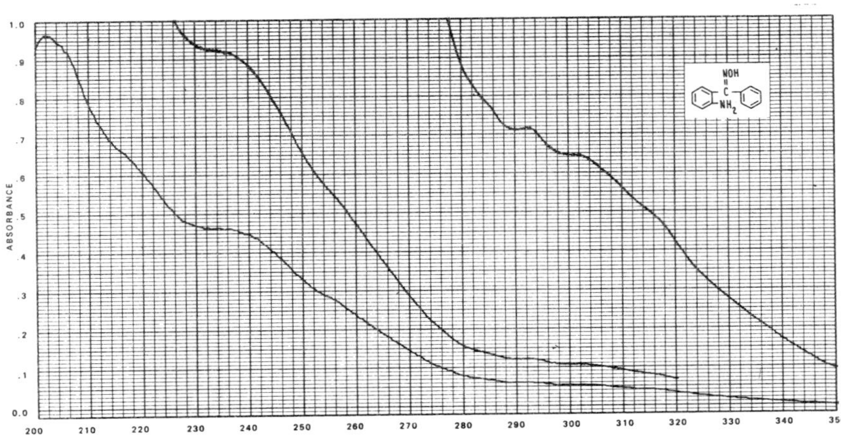

2-AMINOBENZOPHENONE, OXIME

862

$C_{13}H_{12}N_2O$
Mol. Wt. 212.25
M.P. 151-153°C
Solvent: Methanol KOH

λ Max. mμ	a_m	Cell mm	Conc. g/L
x	x	1	0.100

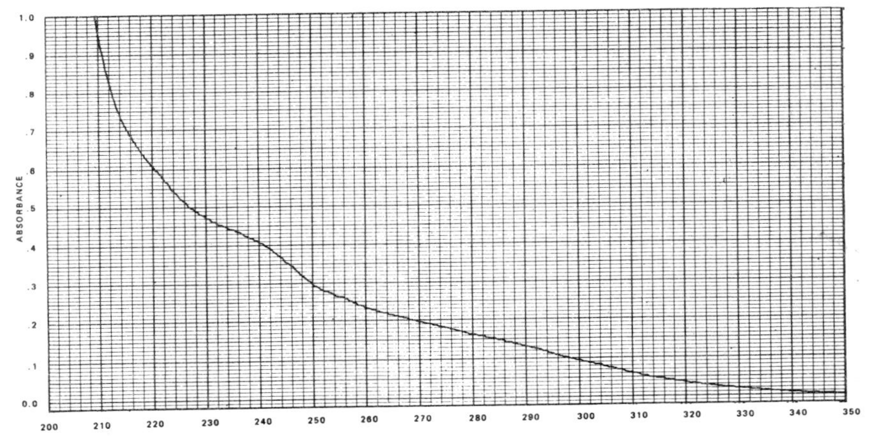

2-AMINOBENZOPHENONE, OXIME

862

$C_{13}H_{12}N_2O$
Mol. Wt. 212.25
M.P. 151-153°C
Solvent: Methanol HCl

λ Max. mμ	a_m	Cell mm	Conc. g/L
255	5700	2	0.100
x	x	1	0.100

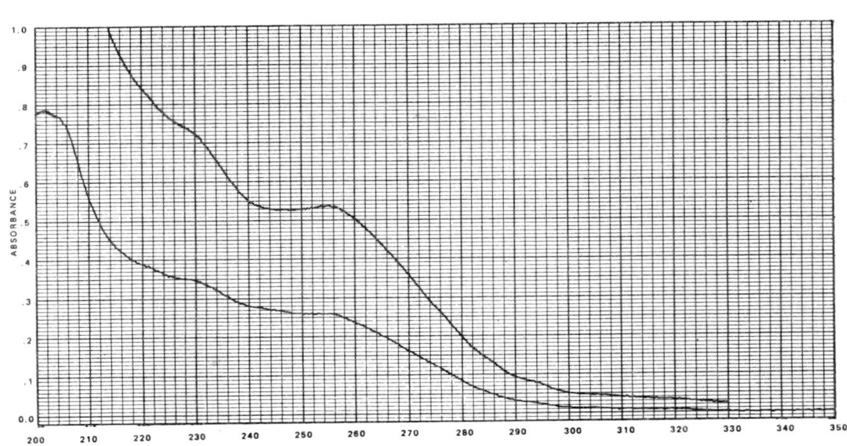

2-INDANONE, OXIME 863

C_9H_9NO

Mol. Wt. 147.18

Solvent: Methanol

λ Max. mμ	a_m	Cell mm	Conc. g/L
268.5	1280	10	0.100
261.5	1030	10	0.100
255	639	10	0.100
x	x	2	0.100

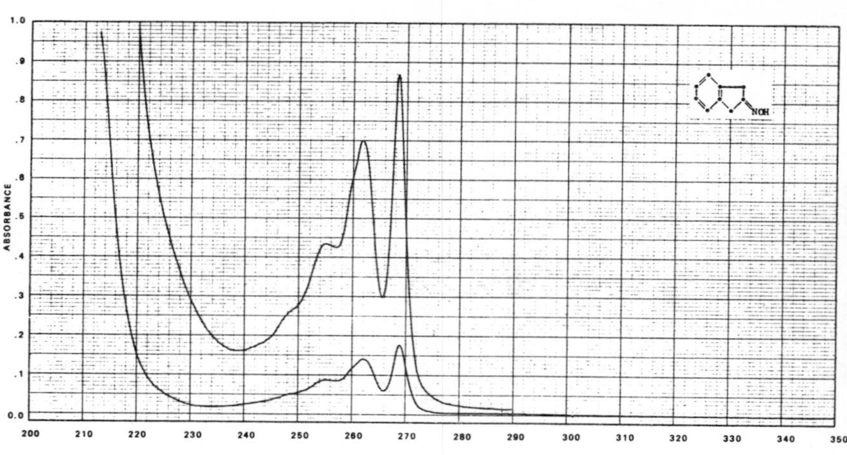

2-INDANONE, OXIME 863

C_9H_9NO

Mol. Wt. 147.18

Solvent: Methanol KOH

λ Max. mμ	a_m	Cell mm	Conc. g/L
269	1110	10	0.100
262	952	10	0.100
253.5	767	10	0.100
x	x	2	0.100

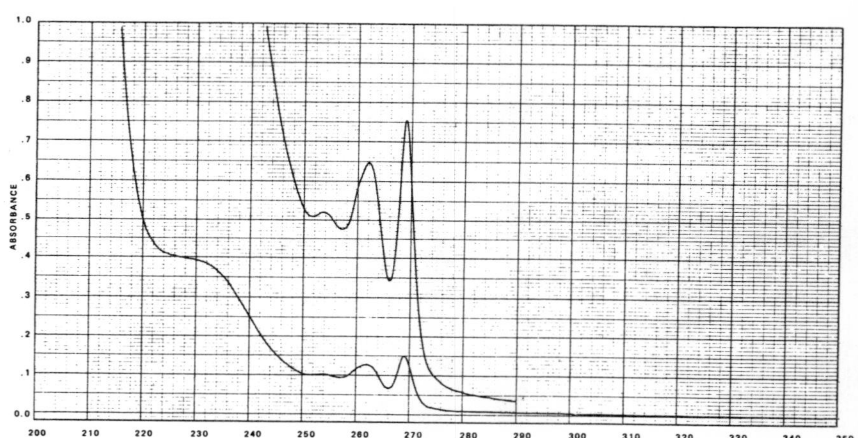

2,3-BUTANEDIONE, DIOXIME 864

$C_4H_8N_2O$

Mol. Wt. 116.12

M.P. 239°C (dec.)

Solvent: Methanol

λ Max. mμ	a_m	Cell mm	Conc. g/L
227	15400	10	0.005

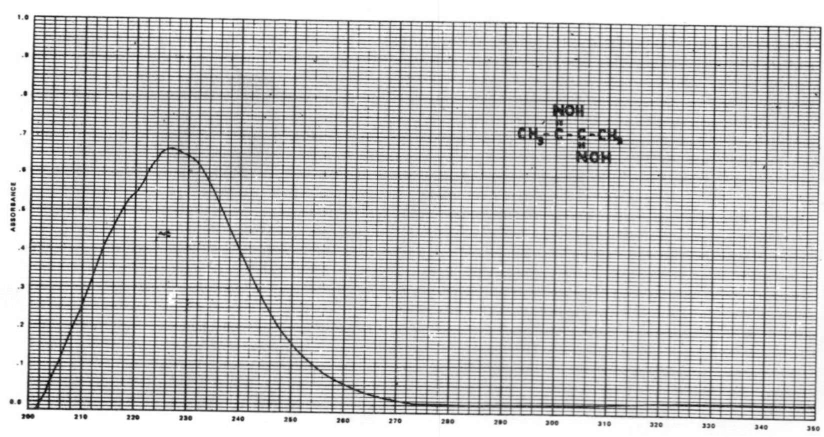

1,2-CYCLOHEXANEDIONE DIOXIME 865

$C_6H_{10}N_2O_2$
Mol. Wt. 142.16
Solvent: Methanol

λ Max. mμ	a_m	Cell mm	Conc. g/L
x	x	10	1.744
236.5	6390	10	0.035

N-BENZYLIDENEMETHYLAMINE 866

C_8H_9N
Mol. Wt. 119.17
Solvent: Methanol

λ Max. mμ	a_m	Cell mm	Conc. g/L
244	14800	0.5	0.100
x	x	0.5	0.100

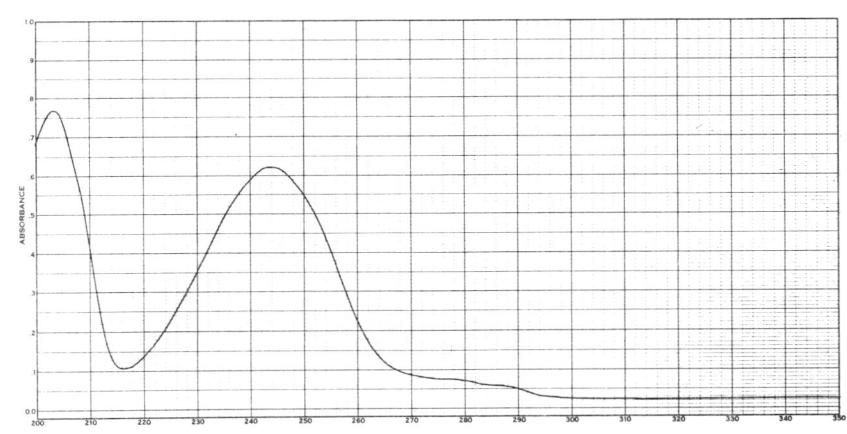

N-BENZYLIDENEMETHYLAMINE 866

C_8H_9N
Mol. Wt. 119.17
Solvent: Methanol HCl

λ Max. mμ	a_m	Cell mm	Conc. g/L
270.5	10500	1.0	0.100

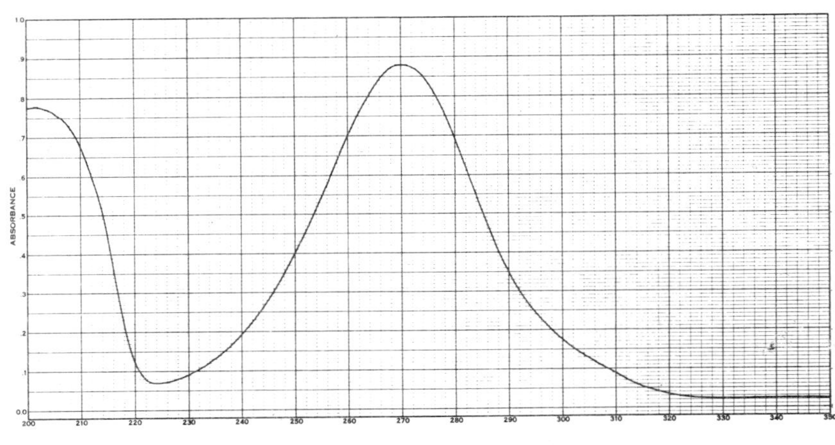

N,N′-DICINNAMYLIDENEETHYLENEDIAMINE

867

$C_{20}H_{20}N$
Mol. Wt. 288.40
M.P. 105-110°C
Solvent: Methanol

λ Max. mμ	a_m	Cell mm	Conc. g/L
283.5	43500	0.5	0.100
228	19300	0.5	0.100
222	24900	0.5	0.100
216.5	22100	0.5	0.100

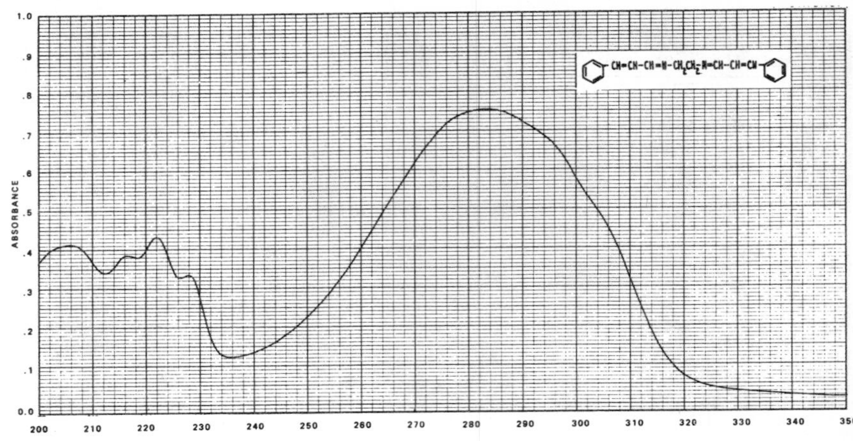

N,N′-DICINNAMYLIDENEETHYLENEDIAMINE

867

$C_{20}H_{20}N_2$
Mol. Wt. 288.40
M.P. 105-110°C
Solvent: Methanol HCl

λ Max. mμ	a_m	Cell mm	Conc. g/L
334	26700	1	0.100
232	8160	1	0.100

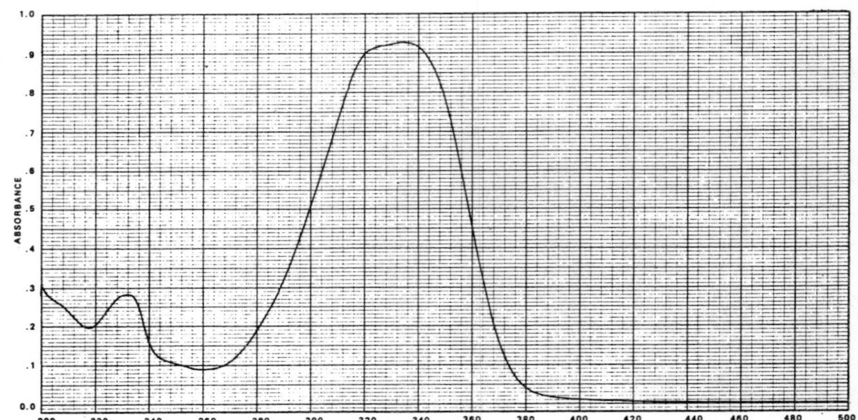

N,N′-DIBENZYLIDENEETHYLENEDIAMINE

868

$C_{16}H_{16}N_2$
Mol. Wt. 236.32
Solvent: Methanol

λ Max. mμ	a_m	Cell mm	Conc. g/L
246.5	30200	1	0.0500

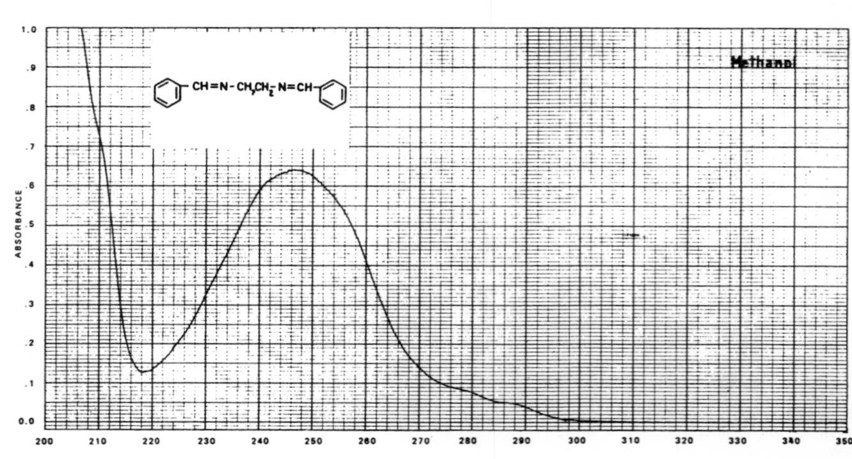

868

N,N′-DIBENZYLIDENEETHYLENEDIAMINE

$C_{16}H_{16}N_2$
Mol. Wt. 236.32
Solvent: Methanol HCl

λ Max. mμ	a_m	Cell mm	Conc. g/L
278	329	10	0.500
266	515	2	0.500
262	721	2	0.500
248.5	1500	2	0.500
245.5	1500	2	0.500

869

N-CINNAMYLIDENEANILINE

$C_{15}H_{13}N$
Mol. Wt. 207.28
Solvent: Methanol

λ Max. mμ	a_m	Cell mm	Conc. g/L
305.5	13500	1	0.100
228	6030	1	0.100

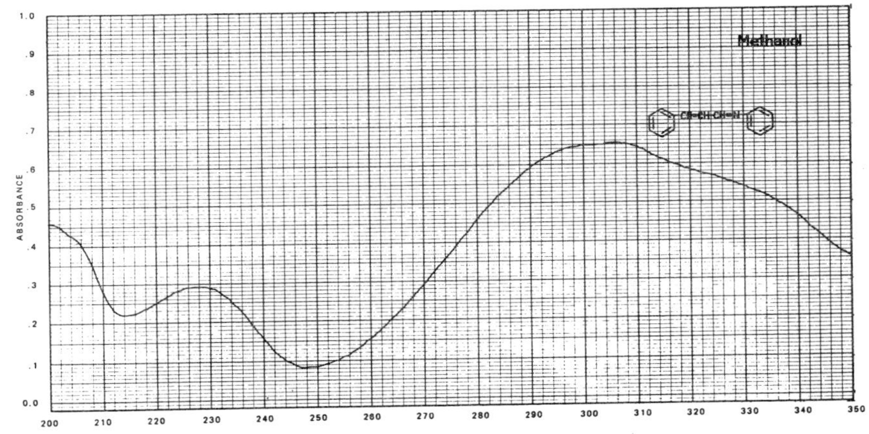

869

N-CINNAMYLIDENEANILINE

$C_{15}H_{13}N$
Mol. Wt. 207.28
Solvent: Methanol HCl

λ Max. mμ	a_m	Cell mm	Conc. g/L
282	956	2	0.0500
251	12000	2	0.0500
224	8500	2	0.0500

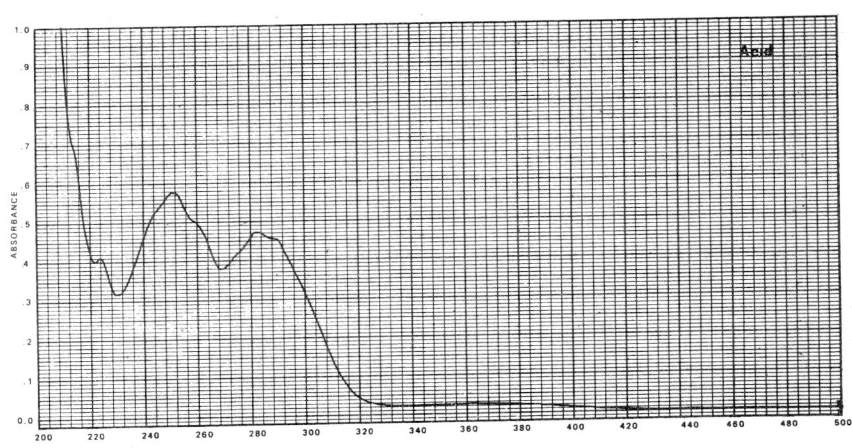

N-CINNAMYLIDENE-p-TOLUIDINE

870

$C_{16}H_{15}N$

Mol. Wt. 221.30

Solvent: Methanol

λ Max. mμ	a_m	Cell mm	Conc. g/L
326.5	23000	1	0.0500
297	24400	1	0.0500
229	11500	1	0.5000

N-CINNAMYLIDENE-p-TOLUIDINE

870

$C_{16}H_{15}N$

Mol. Wt. 221.30

Solvent: Methanol HCl

λ Max. mμ	a_m	Cell mm	Conc. g/L
372	586	20	0.0500
282	9290	2	0.0500
250	12800	2	0.0500
224	7920	2	0.500

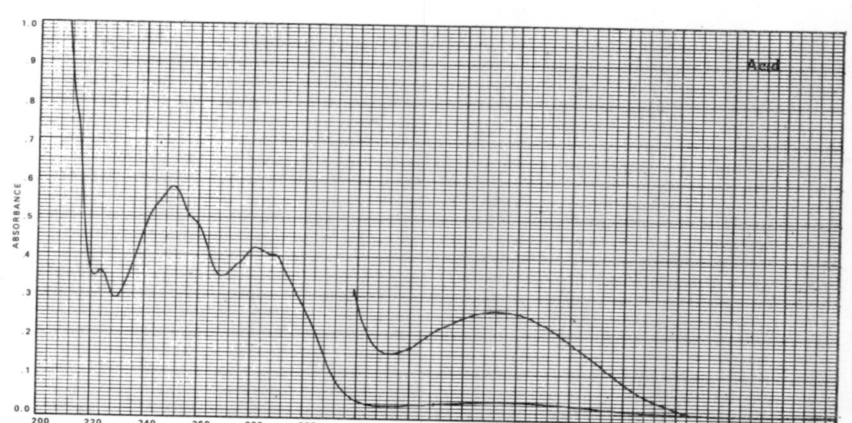

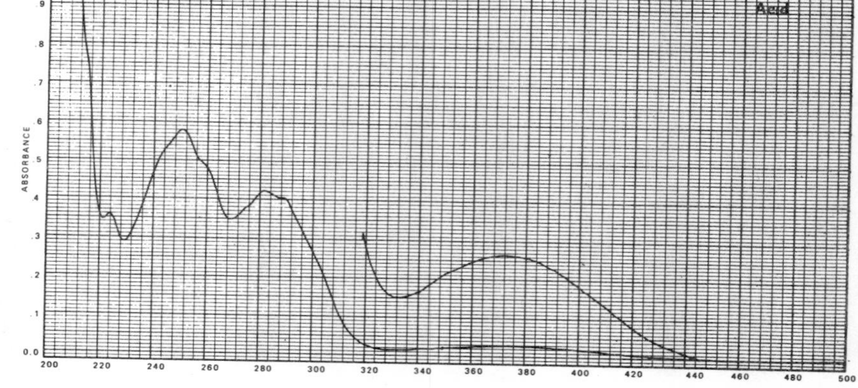

N-BENZYLIDENEANILINE

871

$C_{13}H_{11}N$

Mol. Wt. 181.24

M.P. 56°C

Solvent: Methanol

λ Max. mμ	a_m	Cell mm	Conc. g/L
260.5	15200	1	0.100
236	9230	1	0.100

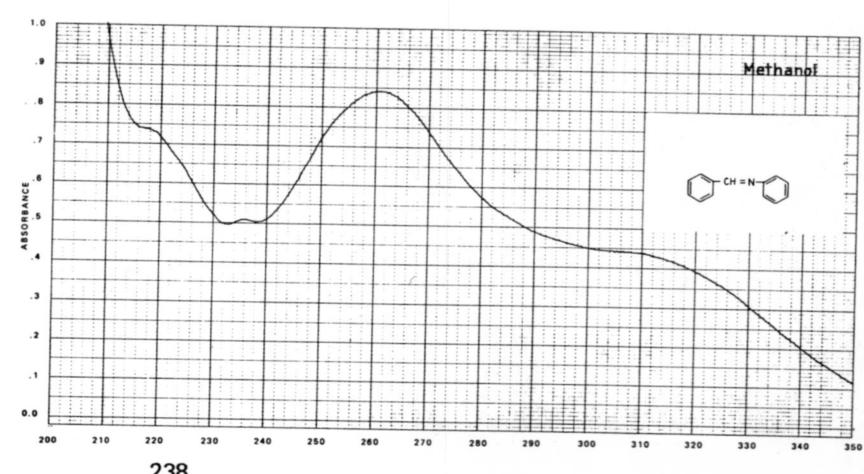

N-BENZYLIDENEANILINE

871

$C_{13}H_{11}N$

Mol. Wt. 181.24

M.P. 56°C

Solvent: Methanol HCl

λ Max. mμ	a_m	Cell mm	Conc. g/L
260	434	20	0.100
254	616	20	0.100
248.5	714	20	0.100
244	713	20	0.100
x	x	1	0.100

N-(p-METHYLBENZYLIDENE)ANILINE

872

$C_{14}H_{13}N$

Mol. Wt. 195.27

Solvent: Methanol

λ Max. mμ	a_m	Cell mm	Conc. g/L
267.5	26700	0.5	0.100
218	22900	0.5	0.100
x	x	0.5	0.100

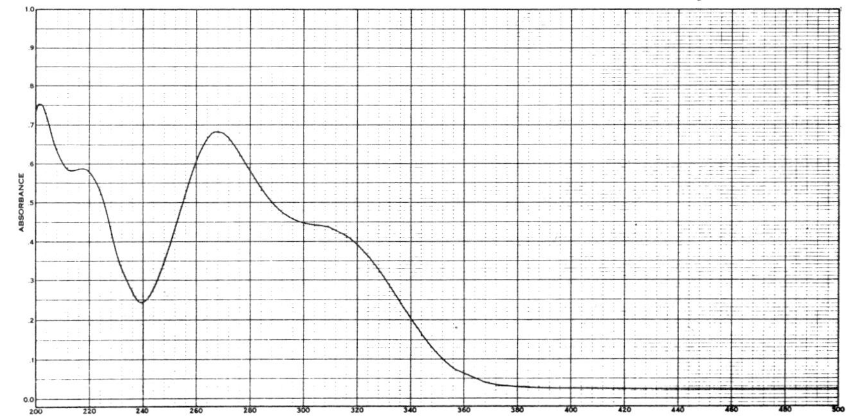

N-(p-METHYLBENZYLIDENE)ANILINE

872

$C_{14}H_{13}N$

Mol. Wt. 195.27

Solvent: Methanol HCl

λ Max. mμ	a_m	Cell mm	Conc. g/L
253	7550	2	0.100

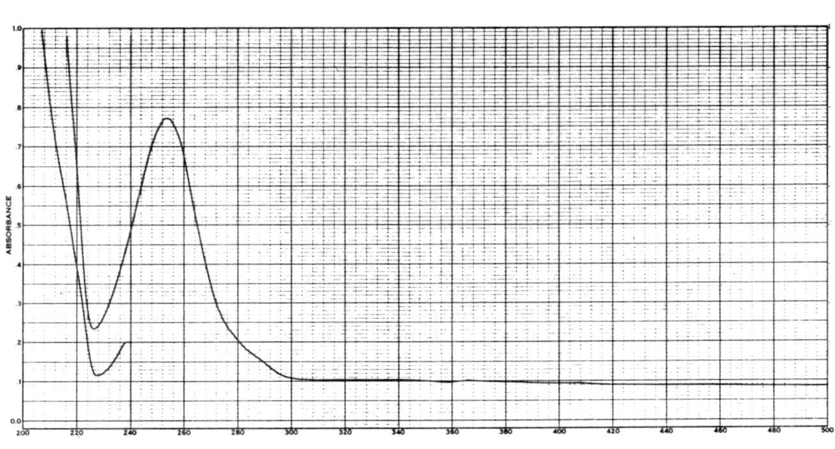

1-NAPHTHALDEHYDE, HYDRAZONE

873

$C_{11}H_{10}N_2$
Mol. Wt. 170.21
M.P. 93°C
Solvent: Methanol

λ Max. mμ	a_m	Cell mm	Conc. g/L
312.5	12900	0.5	0.100
228.5	34800	0.5	0.100
205	22600	0.5	0.100

1-NAPHTHALDEHYDE, HYDRAZONE

873

$C_{11}H_{10}N_2$
Mol. Wt. 170.21
M.P. 93°C
Solvent: Methanol HCl

λ Max. mμ	a_m	Cell mm	Conc. g/L
329	8590	0.5	0.100
317	8630	0.5	0.100
216.5	33900	0.5	0.100

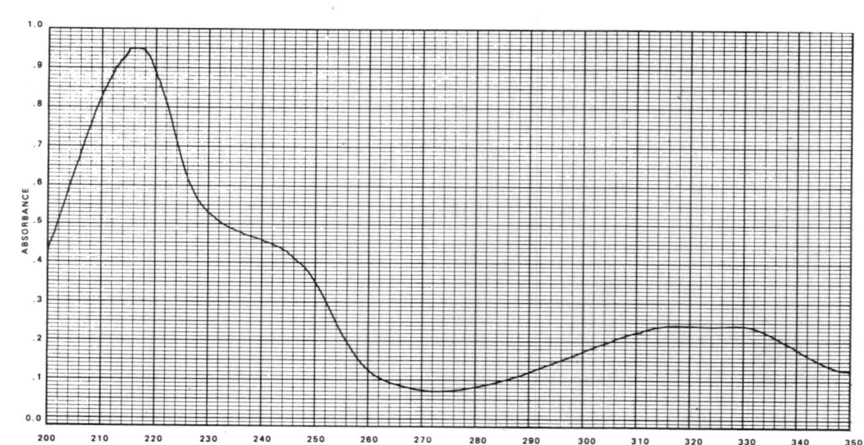

BUTYRALDEHYDE, PHENYLHYDRAZONE

874

$C_{10}H_{14}N_2$
Mol. Wt. 162.24
B.P. 152-155°C/18mm
Solvent: Methanol

λ Max. mμ	a_m	Cell mm	Conc. g/L
274	15900	1	0.09975

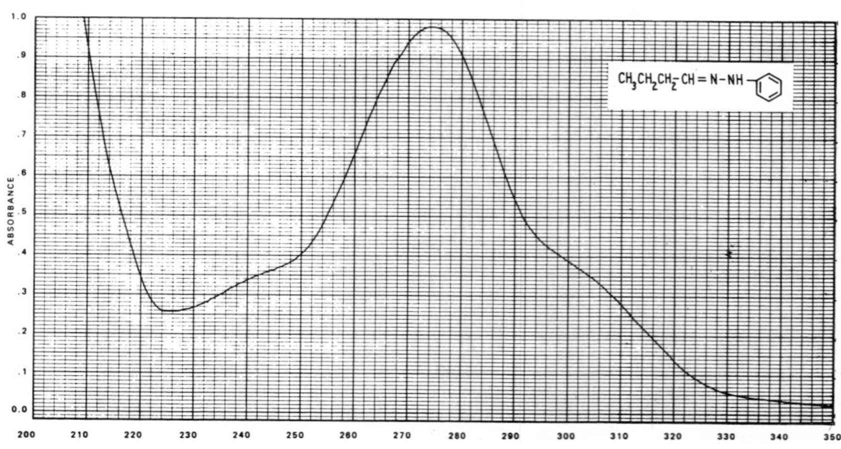

BUTYRALDEHYDE, PHENYLHYDRAZONE

874

$C_{10}H_{14}N_2$
Mol. Wt. 162.24
B.P. 152-155°C/18mm
Solvent: Methanol HCl

λ Max. mμ	a_m	Cell mm	Conc. g/L
275	1660	5	0.09975
224	6900	2	0.09975

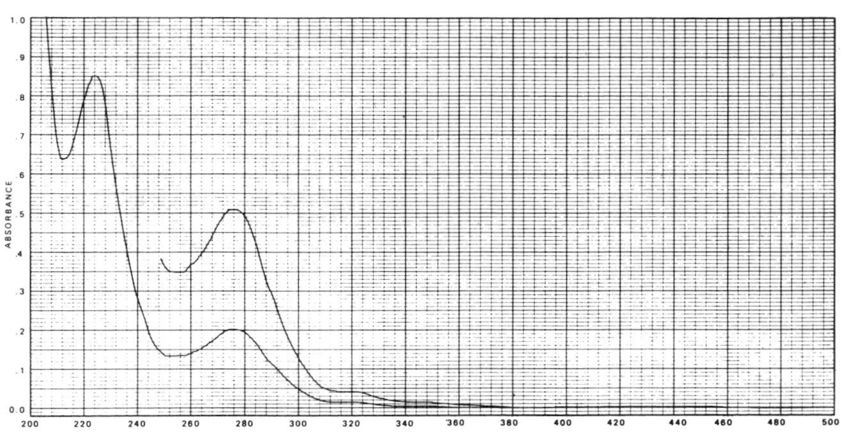

CINNAMALDEHYDE, PHENYL HYDRAZONE

875

$C_{15}H_{14}N_2$
Mol. Wt. 222.29
M.P. 170-171°C
Solvent: Methanol

λ Max. mμ	a_m	Cell mm	Conc. g/L
364	41000	1	0.0500
288	11600	1	0.0500
255	13300	1	0.0500

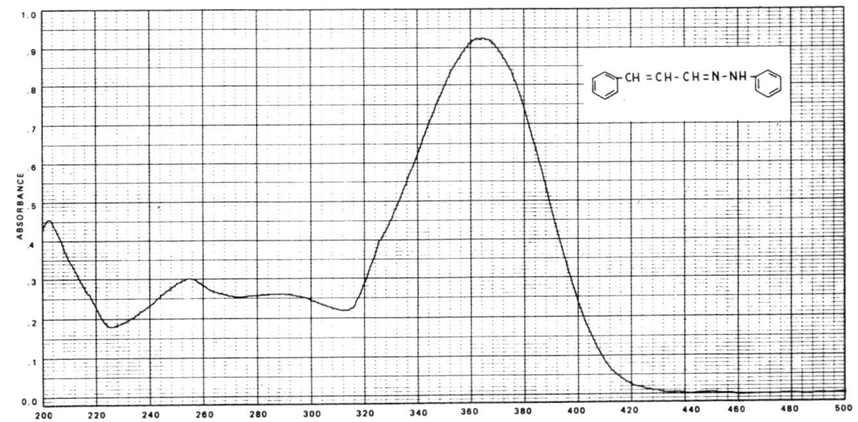

CINNAMALDEHYDE, PHENYL HYDRAZONE

875

$C_{15}H_{14}N_2$
Mol. Wt. 222.29
M.P. 170-171°C
Solvent: Methanol HCl

λ Max. mμ	a_m	Cell mm	Conc. g/L
364	38300	1	0.0500
290	11600	1	0.0500
254	12800	1	0.0500

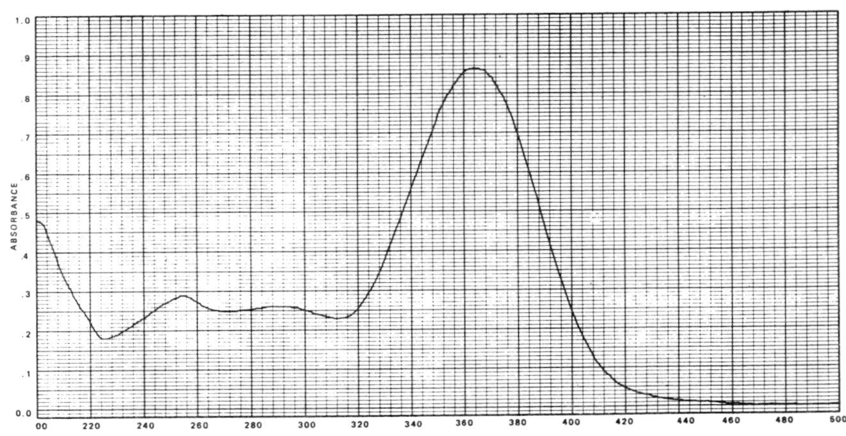

BENZALDEHYDE, PHENYLHYDRAZONE

876

$C_{13}H_{12}N_2$
Mol. Wt. 196.25
M.P. 157°C
Solvent: Methanol

λ Max. mμ	a_m	Cell mm	Conc. g/L
343	17200	1	0.100
299.5	8990	1	0.100
235.5	12900	1	0.100

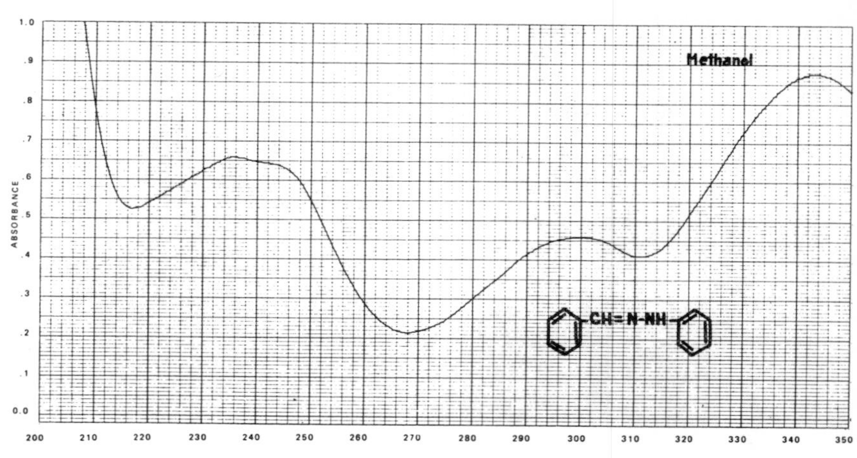

BENZALDEHYDE, PHENYLHYDRAZONE

876

$C_{13}H_{12}N_2$
Mol. Wt. 196.25
M.P. 157°C
Solvent: Methanol HCl

λ Max. mμ	a_m	Cell mm	Conc. g/L
343	17000	1	0.100
301	8380	1	0.100
235.5	12200	1	0.100

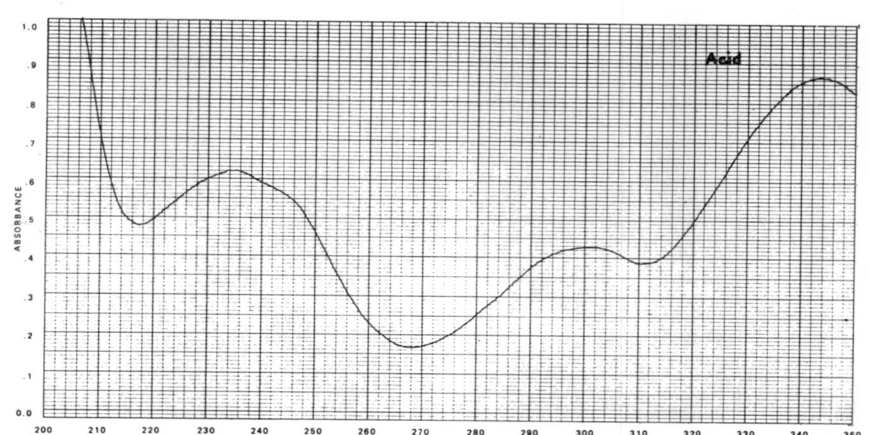

o-CHLOROBENZALDEHYDE, PHENYLHYDRAZONE

877

$C_{13}H_{11}ClN_2$
Mol. Wt. 230.70
M.P. 84°C
Solvent: Methanol

λ Max. mμ	a_m	Cell mm	Conc. g/L
352	17200	1	0.100
299	7310	1	0.100
249	12900	1	0.100

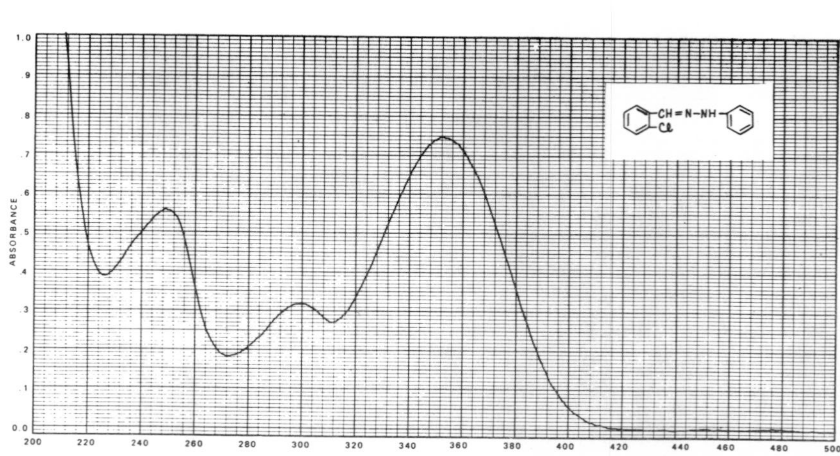

METHYL 2-PYRIDYL KETONE, PHENYL HYDRAZONE

878

$C_{13}H_{13}N_3$
Mol. Wt. 211.27
M.P. 155°C
Solvent: Methanol

λ Max. mμ	a_m	Cell mm	Conc. g/L
341	22800	1	0.0500
226	11200	1	0.0500

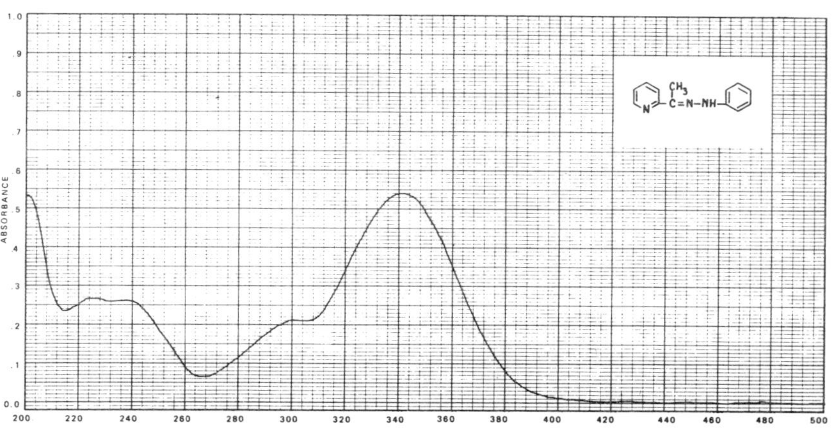

METHYL 2-PYRIDYL KETONE, PHENYL HYDRAZONE

878

$C_{13}H_{13}N_3$
Mol. Wt. 211.27
M.P. 155°C
Solvent: Methanol HCl

λ Max. mμ	a_m	Cell mm	Conc. g/L
418	17700	2	0.0500
317	7710	2	0.0500
264	6910	2	0.0500
243	9930	2	0.0500

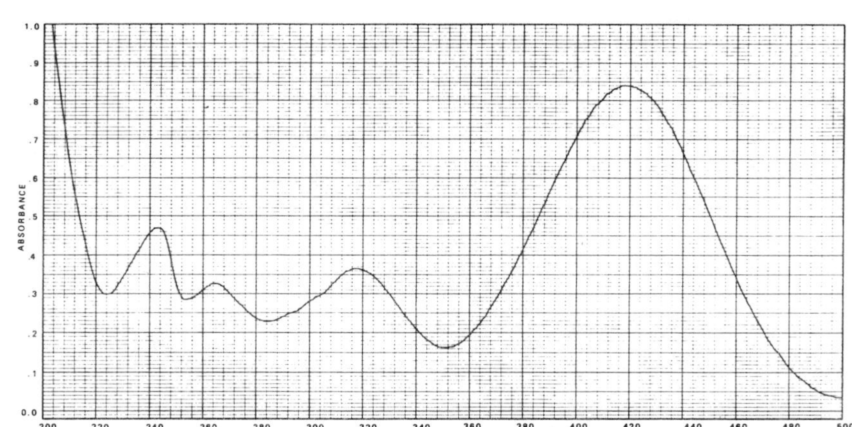

BENZIL, DIHYDRAZONE

879

$C_{14}H_{14}N_4$
Mol. Wt. 238.30
Solvent: Methanol

λ Max. mμ	a_m	Cell mm	Conc. g/L
x	x	10	0.191
272	24700	10	0.008

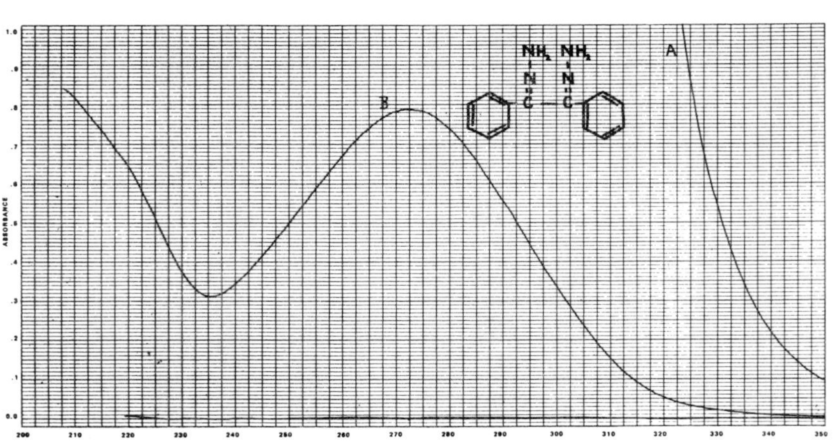

CINNAMALDEHYDE, AZINE

880

$C_{18}H_{16}N_2$
Mol. Wt. 260.34
M.P. 162°C
Solvent: Methanol

λ Max. mμ	$^a m$	Cell mm	Conc. g/L
343	63500	1	0.0200
229	12500	2	0.100

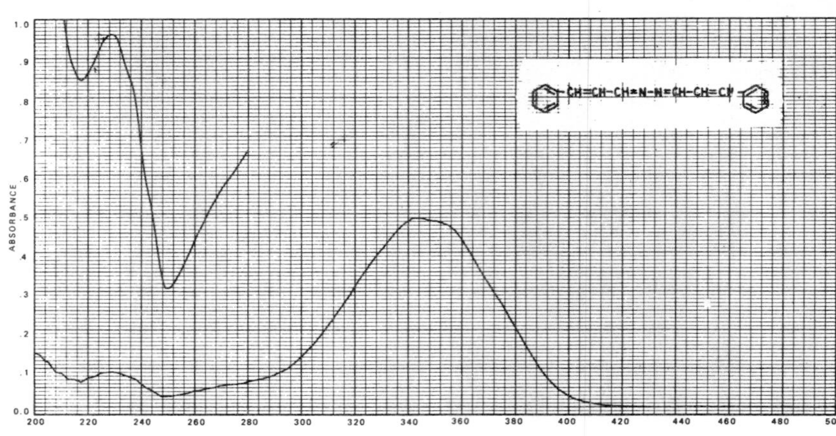

p-TOLUALDEHYDE, AZINE

881

$C_{16}H_{16}N_2$
Mol. Wt. 236.32
M.P. 158°C
Solvent: Methanol

λ Max. mμ	$^a m$	Cell mm	Conc. g/L
309	3500	1	0.0500
222	13900	1	0.0500

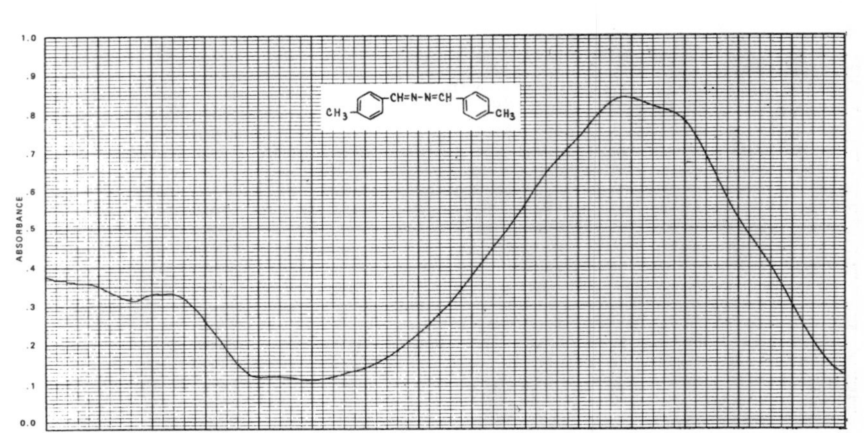

PICOLINALDEHYDE, AZINE

882

$C_{12}H_{10}N_4$
Mol. Wt. 210.23
M.P. 151-152°C
Solvent: Methanol

λ Max. mμ	$^a m$	Cell mm	Conc. g/L
299	31200	1	0.0500
206.5	16400	1	0.0500

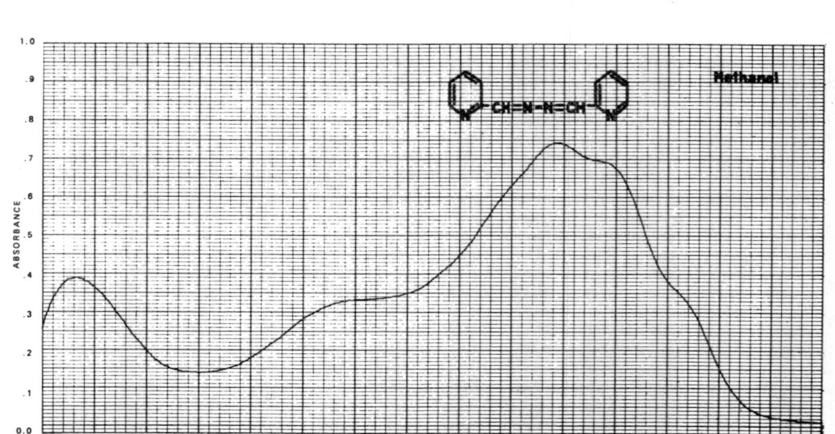

PICOLINALDEHYDE, AZINE

882

$C_{12}H_{10}N_4$
Mol. Wt. 210.23
M.P. 151-152°C
Solvent: Methanol HCl

λ Max. mμ	a_m	Cell mm	Conc. g/L
339	18500	2	0.0500
262	10700	2	0.0500

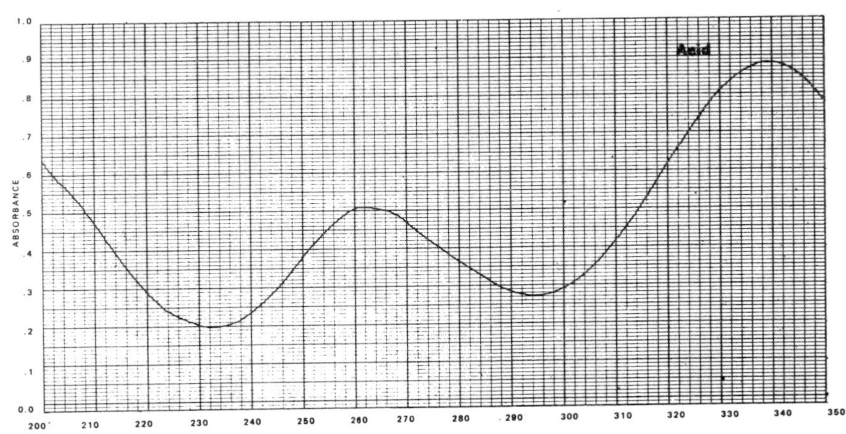

N'-CYCLOHEXYL-N,N-DIMETHYLFORMAMIDINE

883

$C_9H_{18}N_2$
Mol. Wt. 154.26
M.P. 41-43°C
B.P. 51-52°C/0.2mm

λ Max. mμ	a_m	Cell mm	Conc. g/L

Pure sample not available.

λ Max. mμ	a_m	Cell mm	Conc. g/L

N,N-DIMETHYL-N'-PHENYLFORMAMIDINE **884**

$C_9H_{12}N_2$
Mol. Wt. 148.21
B.P. 127-128.5°C/11mm
Solvent: Methanol

λ Max. mμ	a_m	Cell mm	Conc. g/L
263.5	14100	1	0.0810

N,N-DIMETHYL-N'-PHENYLFORMAMIDINE **884**

$C_9H_{12}N_2$
Mol. Wt. 148.21
B.P. 127-128.5°C/11mm
Solvent: Methanol HCl

λ Max. mμ	a_m	Cell mm	Conc. g/L
250	13300	1	0.0810
205.5	15900	1	0.0810

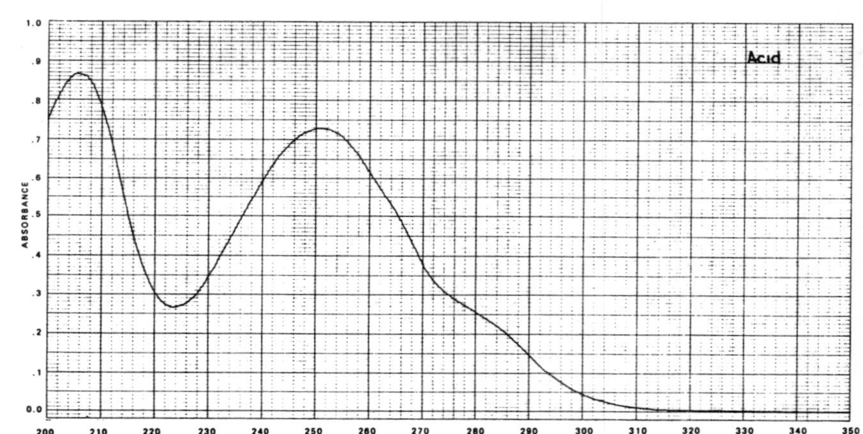

N,N-DIMETHYL-N'-p-TOLYLFORMAMIDINE **885**

$C_{10}H_{14}N_2$
Mol. Wt. 162.24
B.P. 103-105°C/0.5mm
Solvent: Methanol

λ Max. mμ	a_m	Cell mm	Conc. g/L
264	14000	1	0.103

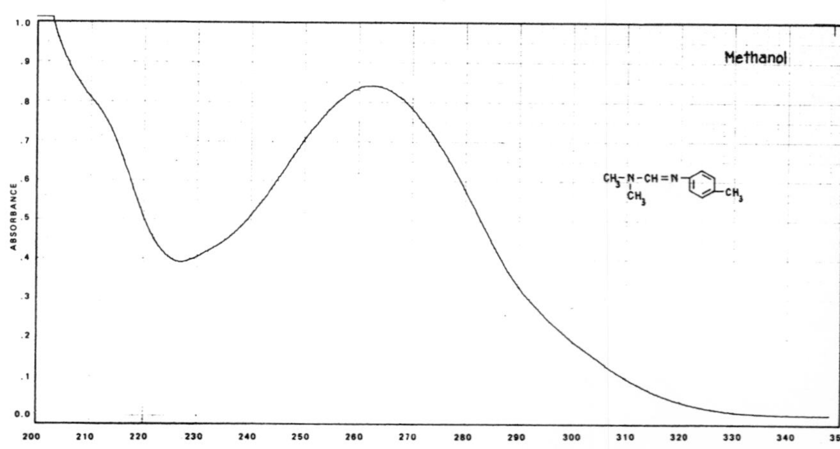

N,N-DIMETHYL-N'-p-TOLYLFORMAMIDINE

885

$C_{10}H_{14}N_2$
Mol. Wt. 162.24
B.P. 103-105°C/0.5mm
Solvent: Methanol HCl

λ Max. mμ	a_m	Cell mm	Conc. g/L
255	12900	1	0.103

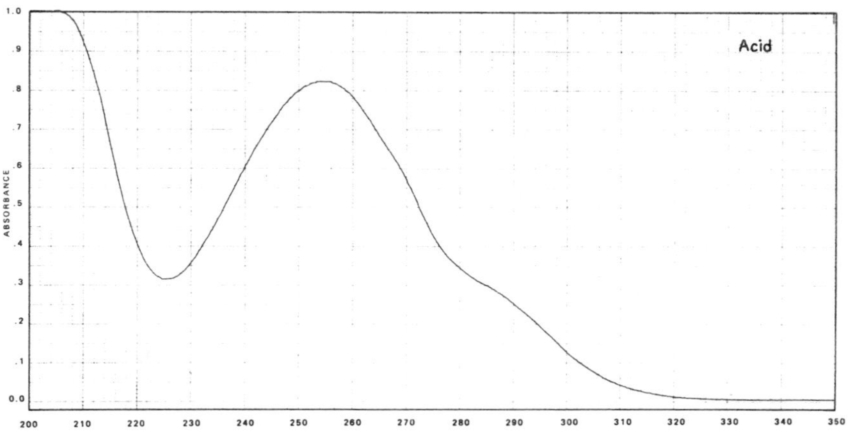

1-(N-PHENYLFORMIMIDOYL)PIPERIDINE

886

$C_{12}H_{16}N_2$
Mol. Wt. 188.27
B.P. 135-137°C/0.5mm

λ Max. mμ	a_m	Cell mm	Conc. g/L

Pure sample not available.

λ Max. mμ	a_m	Cell mm	Conc. g/L

N,N'-DIPHENYLFORMAMIDINE

887

$C_{13}H_{12}N_2$
Mol. Wt. 196.25
M.P. 130-132°C
Solvent: Methanol

λ Max. mμ	a_m	Cell mm	Conc. g/L
276.5	11100	1	0.100
227	10000	1	0.100

N,N'-DIPHENYLFORMAMIDINE

887

$C_{13}H_{12}N_2$
Mol. Wt. 196.25
M.P. 130-132°C
Solvent: Methanol HCl

λ Max. mμ	a_m	Cell mm	Conc. g/L
286	6810	1	0.100
270	6970	1	0.100

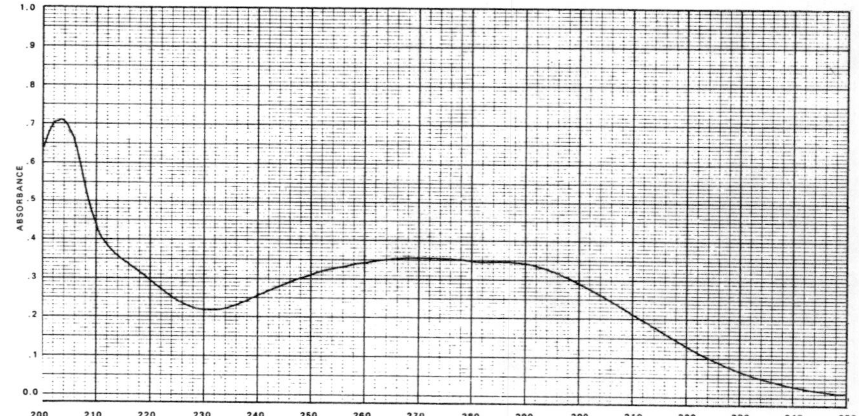

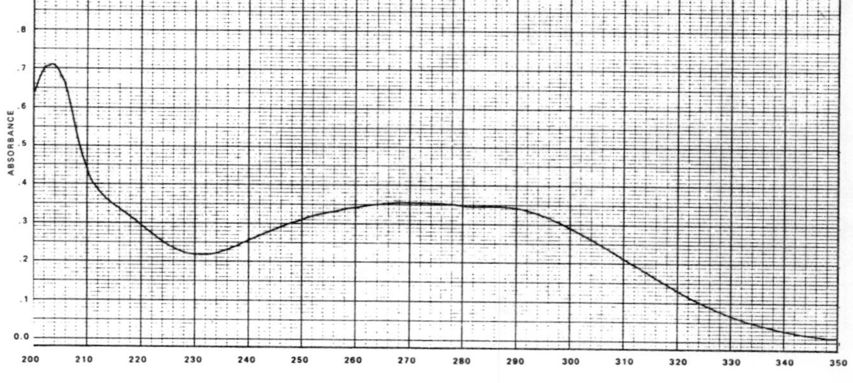

N,N'-DIPHENYLACETAMIDINE

888

$C_{14}H_{14}N_2$
Mol. Wt. 210.28
M.P. 132-133°C
Solvent: Methanol

λ Max. mμ	a_m	Cell mm	Conc. g/L
264	16800	1	0.100

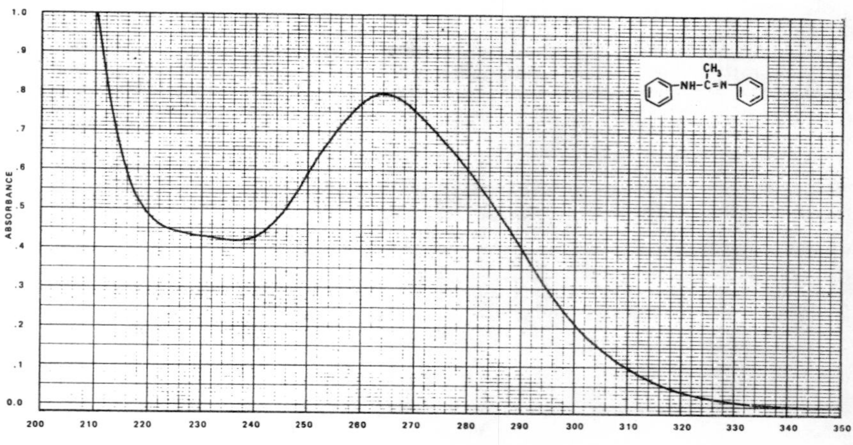

N,N'-DIPHENYLACETAMIDINE 888

$C_{14}H_{14}N_2$
Mol. Wt. 210.28
M.P. 132-133°C
Solvent: Methanol HCl

λ Max. mμ	a_m	Cell mm	Conc. g/L
239	10900	1	0.100

N-PHENYLBENZAMIDINE 889

$C_{13}H_{12}N_2$
Mol. Wt. 196.26
M.P. 116°C (lit.)
Solvent: Methanol

λ Max. mμ	a_m	Cell mm	Conc. g/L
222	15900	1	0.100

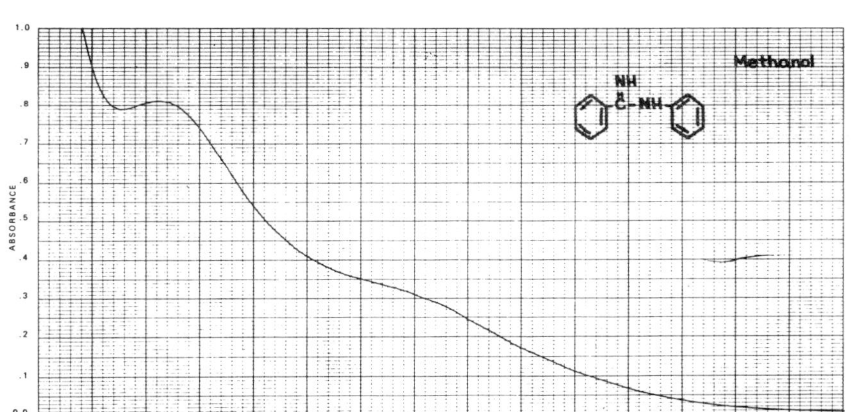

N-PHENYLBENZAMIDINE 889

$C_{13}H_{12}N_2$
Mol. Wt. 196.26
M.P. 116°C (lit.)
Solvent: Methanol HCl

λ Max. mμ	a_m	Cell mm	Conc. g/L
234	14500	1	0.100

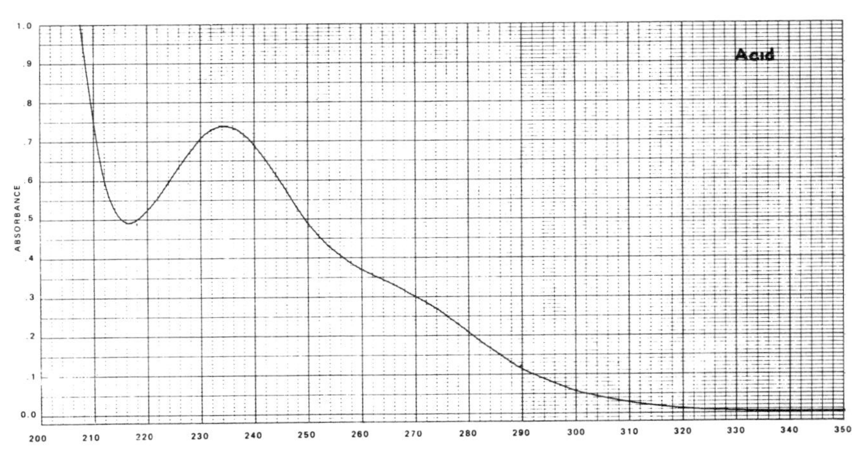

1,2,3-TRIPHENYLGUANIDINE 890

$C_{19}H_{17}N_3$
Mol. Wt. 287.37
M.P. 143-145°C
Solvent: Methanol

λ Max. mμ	a_m	Cell mm	Conc. g/L
268	22700	1	0.100

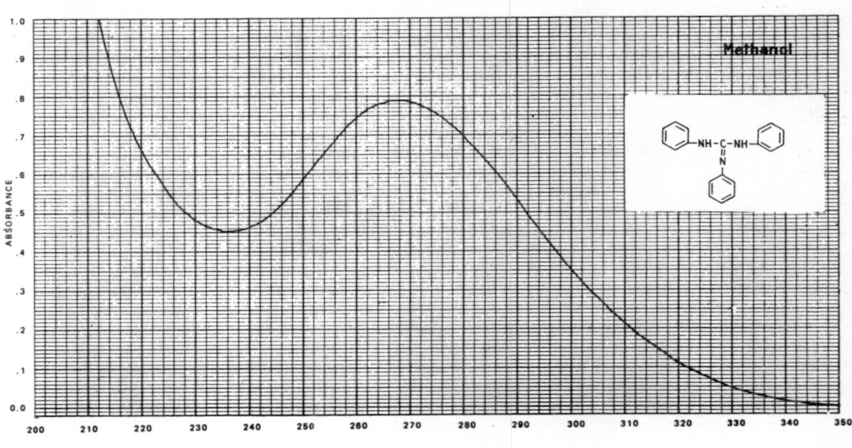

1,2,3-TRIPHENYLGUANIDINE 890

$C_{19}H_{17}N_3$
Mol. Wt. 287.37
M.P. 143-145°C
Solvent: Methanol HCl

λ Max. mμ	a_m	Cell mm	Conc. g/L
262	19500	1	0.100

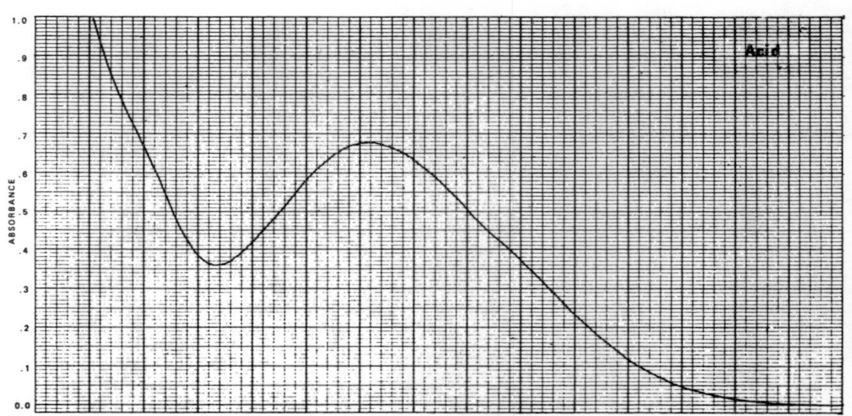

λ Max. mμ	a_m	Cell mm	Conc. g/L

Compounds 891 - 893 do not absorb in the near U.V.

SORBOHYDROXAMIC ACID 894

$C_6H_9NO_2$
Mol. Wt. 127.14
M.P. 131°C
Solvent: Methanol

λ Max. mμ	a_m	Cell mm	Conc. g/L
257	23200	1	0.0500

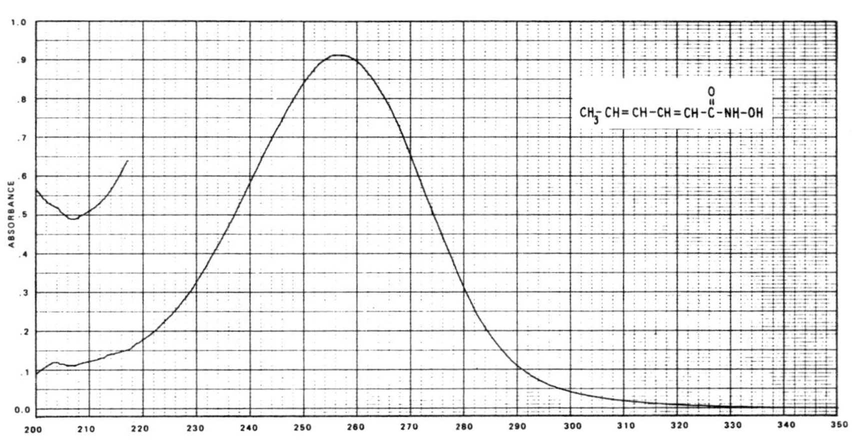

SORBOHYDROXAMIC ACID 894

$C_6H_9NO_2$
Mol. Wt. 127.14
M.P. 131°C
Solvent: Methanol KOH

λ Max. mμ	a_m	Cell mm	Conc. g/L
249	16400	1	0.0500

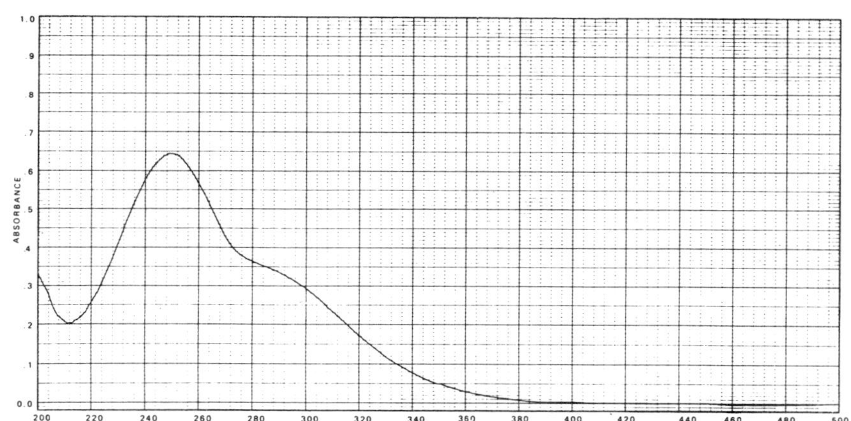

λ Max. mμ	a_m	Cell mm	Conc. g/L

ISONICOTINOHYDROXAMIC ACID 895

$C_6H_6N_2O_2$
Mol. Wt. 138.12
M.P. 161°C
Solvent: Methanol

λ Max. mμ	a_m	Cell mm	Conc. g/L
259	4180	2	0.100
x	x	1	0.100

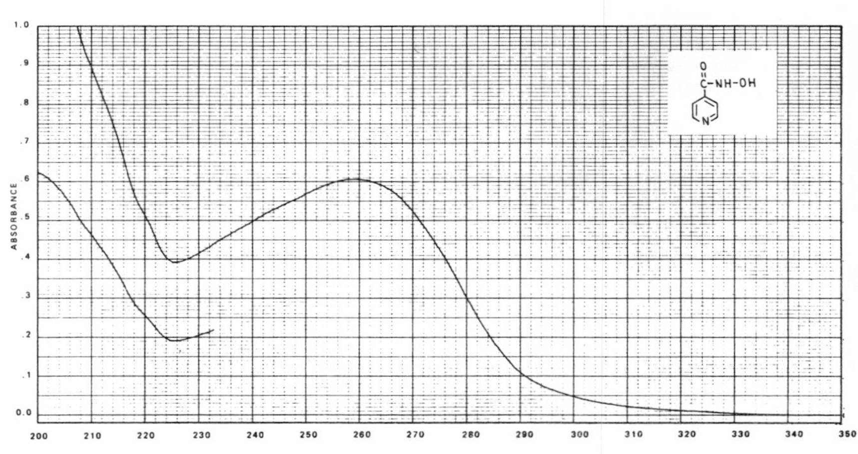

ISONICOTINOHYDROXAMIC ACID 895

$C_6H_6N_2O_2$
Mol. Wt. 138.12
M.P. 161°C
Solvent: Methanol KOH

λ Max. mμ	a_m	Cell mm	Conc. g/L
297	4490	2	0.100
235.5	3430	2	0.100
x	x	1	0.100

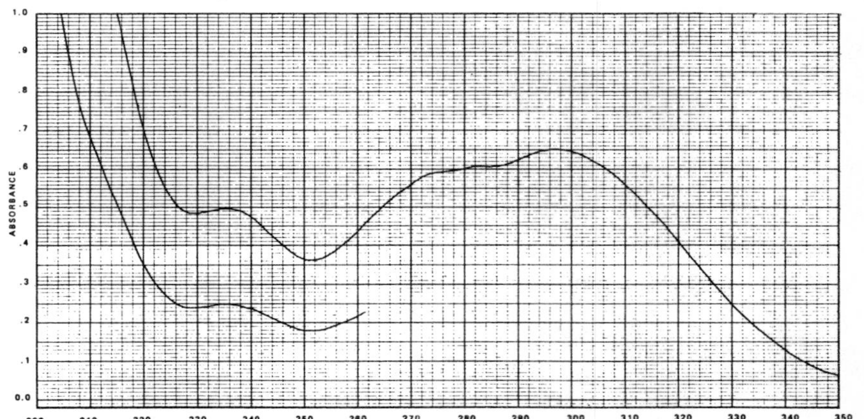

λ Max. mμ	a_m	Cell mm	Conc. g/L

AZO COMPOUNDS

The aromatic azo compounds display two major absorption bands in the near UV region in addition to a weaker band in the visible.

The azobenzenes do not display any significant changes in their UV spectra upon the addition of acid or base.

Compound	$\lambda_{max}(\epsilon_{max})$		$\lambda_{max}(\epsilon_{max})$		$\lambda_{max}(\epsilon_{max})$		Solvent	Spectra
Azobenzene	228	(13400)	314	(18200)	433	(729)	Methanol	896
m,m'-Azotoluene	232	(12400)	321	(16600)			Methanol	897
3,3'-Dichloroazobenzene	232	(14400)	314	(16700)	436	(565)	Methanol	898
p-Phenylazoaniline	245	(9270)	384	(25200)	----------		Methanol	899
N,N-Dimethyl-p-phenyl-azoaniline	253	(10400)	313	(4040)			Cyclohexane	900

AZOXY COMPOUNDS

The UV spectra of the aromatic azoxy compounds are quite similar to those of the parent azo benzenes except that the band in the visible region does not occur. The azoxybenzenes also show no significant change in band wavelength nor intensity upon the addition of acid or base to their methanol solutions.

The wavelength and intensity data for the two major bands of azoxybenzene and the 4,4'-dichloro derivative are given below.

Compound	$\lambda_{max}(\epsilon_{max})$		$\lambda_{max}(\epsilon_{max})$		Solvent	Spectrum
Azoxy benzene	232	(8680)	322	(14700)	Methanol	902
4,4'-Dichloroazoxy benzene	234	(13200)	329	(23600)	Methanol	903

THE TRIAZENES

The UV spectra of the aromatic triazenes vary significantly in appearance depending upon the number of phenyl groups present. The diphenyl triazenes appear to conbine the bands of the azo and aline compounds.

The spectra of the triazenes undergo marked changes in band position and intensity upon the addition of acid to their methanol solutions.

Compound	$\lambda_{max}(\epsilon_{max})$		$\lambda_{max}(\epsilon_{max})$		Solvent	Spectrum
3-Methyl-1-p-tolyltriazene	232	(4070)	280	(2610)	Methanol	904
1,3-Triphenyl triazene	236	(14900)	352	(15000)	Methanol	905
3,3-Dimethyl-1-phenyl-triazene	224	(10700)	285	(14000)	Cyclohexane	906

AZOBENZENE

$C_{12}H_{10}N_2$
Mol. Wt. 182.23
M.P. 67-68°C
Solvent: Methanol

λ Max. mμ	a_m	Cell mm	Conc. g/L
433	729	20	0.100
314	18200	2	0.0400
228	13400	2	0.0400

m,m'-AZOTOLUENE

$C_{14}H_{14}N_2$
Mol. Wt. 210.78
Solvent: Methanol

λ Max. mμ	a_m	Cell mm	Conc. g/L
321	16600	1	0.0800
232	12400	1	0.0800

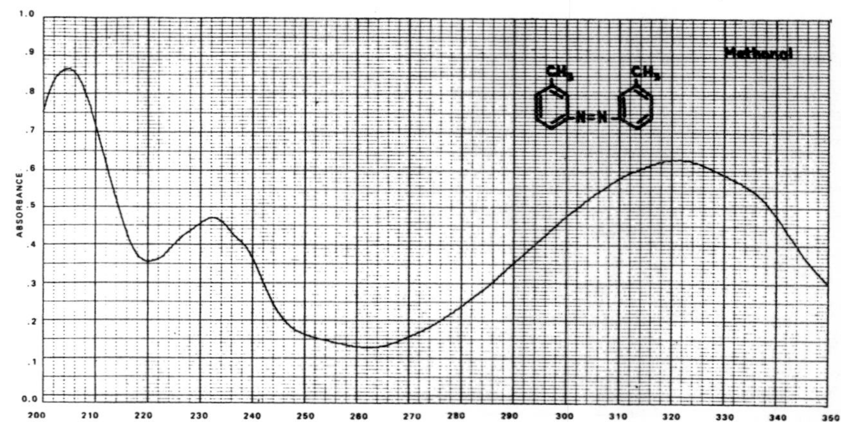

m,m'-AZOTOLUENE

$C_{14}H_{14}N_2$
Mol. Wt. 210.78
Solvent: Methanol HCl

λ Max. mμ	a_m	Cell mm	Conc. g/L
321.5	16500	1	0.0800
232	12100	1	0.0800

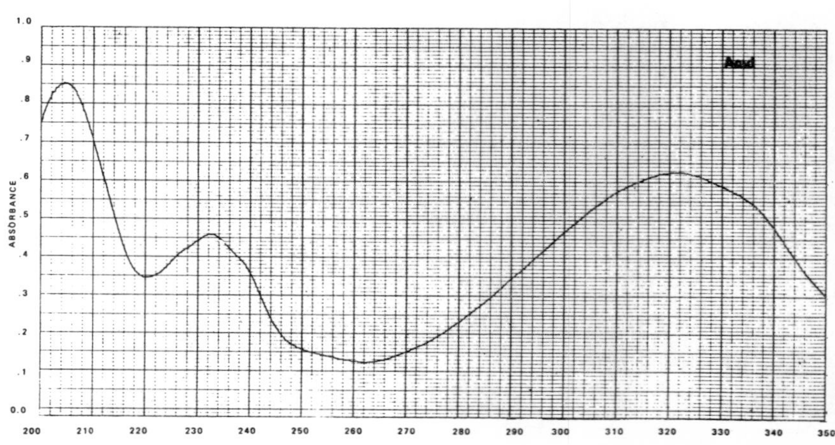

3,3'-DICHLOROAZOBENZENE

898

$C_{12}H_8Cl_2N_2$
Mol. Wt. 251.12
M.P. 103-104°C
Solvent: Methanol

λ Max. mμ	a_m	Cell mm	Conc. g/L
436	565	20	0.100
314	16700	1	0.100
232	14400	1	0.100

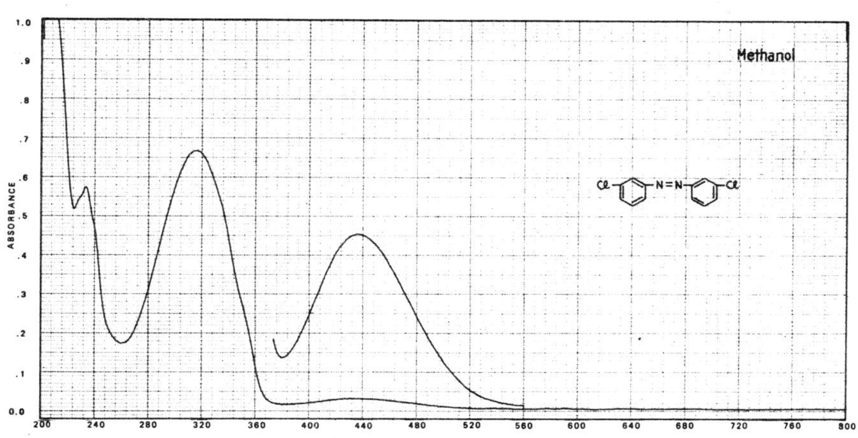

p-PHENYLAZO ANILINE (C.I.SOLVENT YELLOW 1)

899

$C_{12}H_{11}N_3$
Mol. Wt. 197.24
M.P. 125-126°C
Solvent: Methanol

λ Max. mμ	a_m	Cell mm	Conc. g/L
384	25200	2	0.0300
245	9270	2	0.0300

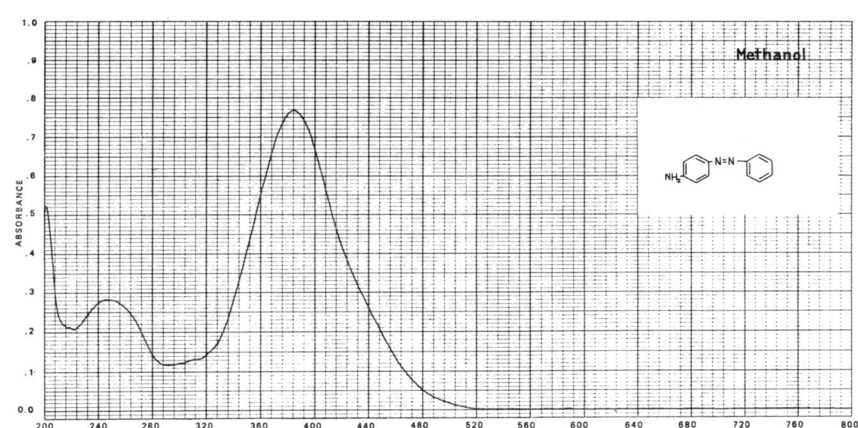

p-PHENYLAZO ANILINE (C.I.SOLVENT YELLOW 1)

899

$C_{12}H_{11}N_3$
Mol. Wt. 197.24
M.P. 125-126°C
Solvent: Methanol HCl

λ Max. mμ	a_m	Cell mm	Conc. g/L
496	13200	2	0.0300
316	17600	2	0.0300
228	11500	2	0.0300
224	11400	2	0.0300

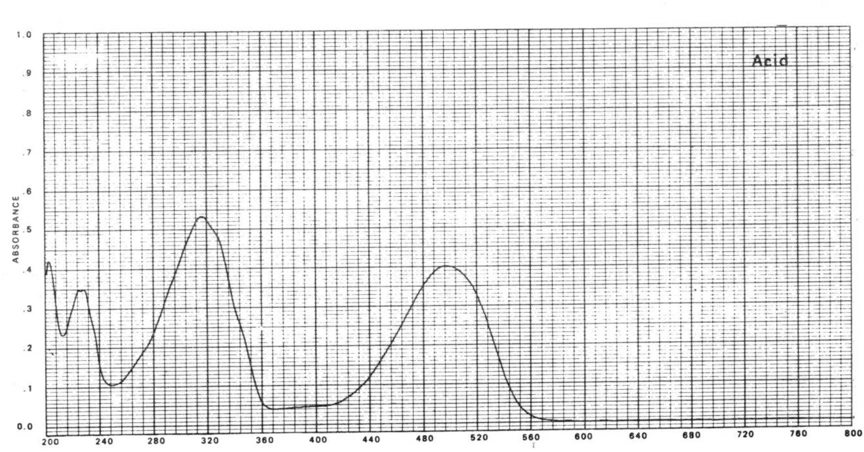

N,N-DIMETHYL-p-PHENYLAZOANILINE 900

$C_{14}H_{15}N_3$
Mol. Wt. 225.30
M.P. 117.5-118°C (lit.)
Solvent: Cyclohexane

λ Max. mμ	a_m	Cell mm	Conc. g/L
325	3580	10	0.068
312.5	4040	10	0.068
262	10000	10	0.034
252.5	10400	10	0.034

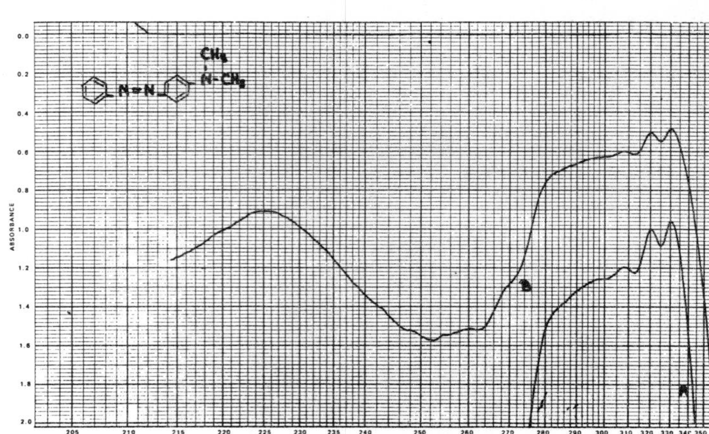

N,N-DIMETHYL-p[(p-AMINOPHENYL)AZO] ANILINE 901

$C_{14}H_{16}N_4$
Mol. Wt. 240.31
M.P. 185-187°C

λ Max. mμ	a_m	Cell mm	Conc. g/L

Pure sample not available.

AZOXYBENZENE 902

$C_{12}H_{10}N_2O$
Mol. Wt. 198.22
M.P. 36°C
Solvent: Methanol

λ Max. mμ	a_m	Cell mm	Conc. g/L
322	14700	10	0.010
260	7530	10	0.010
239	7530	10	0.010
232	8680	10	0.010

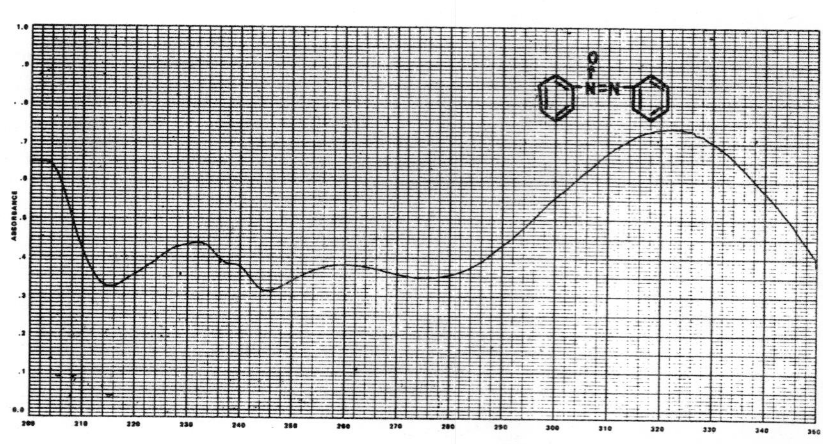

trans-4,4′-DICHLOROAZOXYBENZENE 903

$C_{12}H_8Cl_2N_2O$
Mol. Wt. 267.12
M.P. 158-159°C
Solvent: Methanol

λ Max. mμ	a_m	Cell mm	Conc. g/L
328.5	23600	1	0.100
234	13200	1	0.100

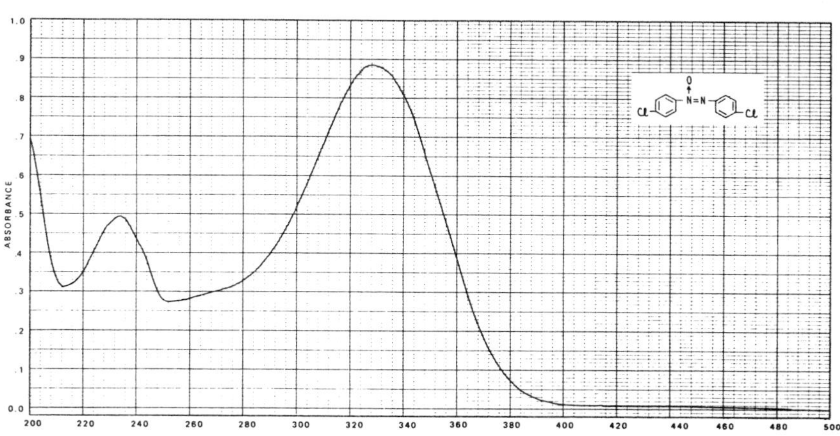

3-METHYL-1-p-TOLYLTRIAZENE 904

$C_8H_{11}N_3$
Mol. Wt. 149.20
M.P. 75-80°C
Solvent: Methanol

λ Max. mμ	a_m	Cell mm	Conc. g/L
280	2610	2	0.100
231.5	4070	2	0.100

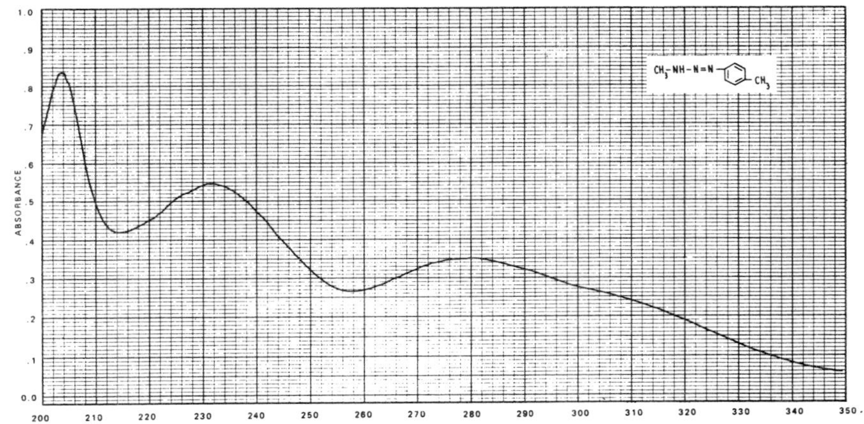

3-METHYL-1-p-TOLYLTRIAZENE 904

$C_8H_{11}N_3$
Mol. Wt. 149.20
M.P. 75-80°C
Solvent: Methanol HCl

λ Max. mμ	a_m	Cell mm	Conc. g/L
268.5	643	20	0.100
262.8	457	20	0.100
259.8	161	20	0.100
207	7400	1	0.100

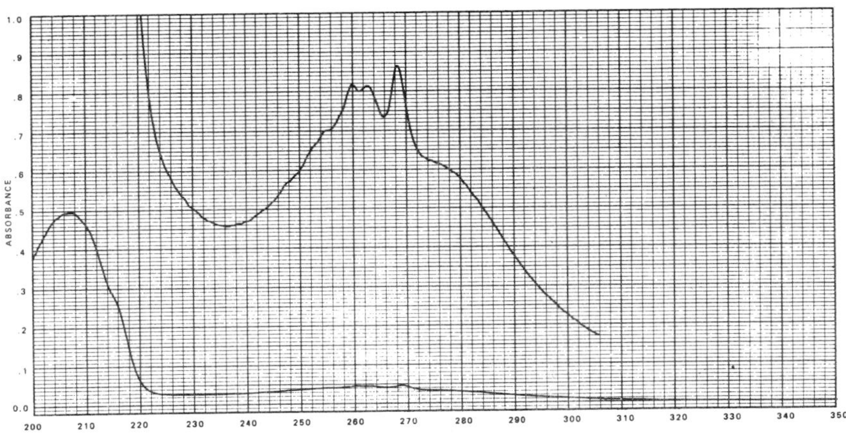

1,3-DIPHENYLTRIAZENE

905

$C_{12}H_{11}N_3$
Mol. Wt. 197.24
M.P. 96-98°C
Solvent: Methanol

λ Max. mμ	a_m	Cell mm	Conc. g/L
352	15000	1	0.100
292	6110	1	0.100
235.5	14900	1	0.100

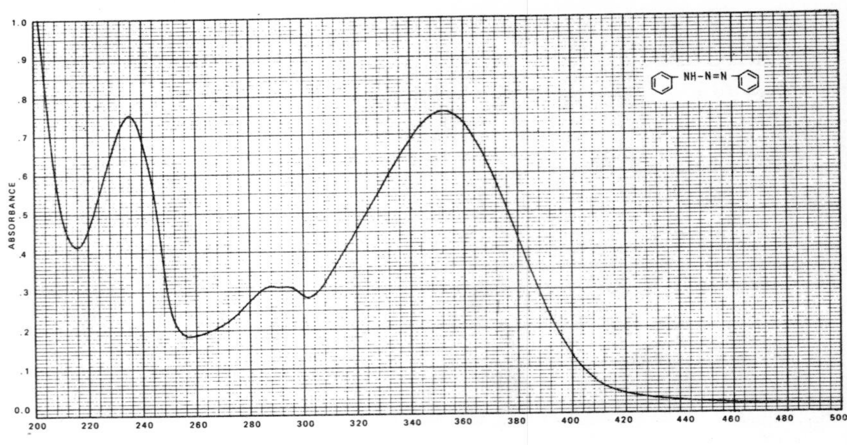

1,3-DIPHENYLTRIAZENE

905

$C_{12}H_{11}N_3$
Mol. Wt. 197.24
M.P. 96-98°C
Solvent: Methanol HCl

λ Max. mμ	a_m	Cell mm	Conc. g/L
318	256	10	0.100
278	1400	10	0.100
271	1640	10	0.100
265	1280	10	0.100
219	6600	2	0.100

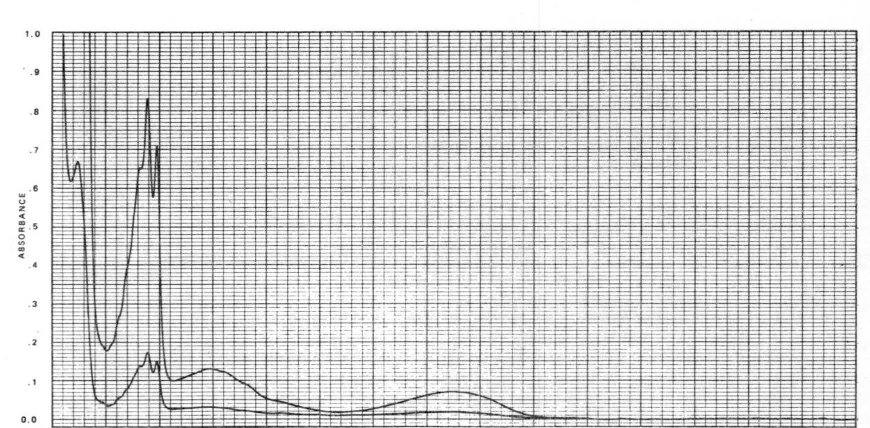

3,3-DIMETHYL-1-PHENYLTRIAZENE

906

$C_8H_{11}N_3$
Mol. Wt. 149.20
Solvent: Cyclohexane

λ Max. mμ	a_m	Cell mm	Conc. g/L
285	14000	10	0.009
224	10700	10	0.009
2205	10300	10	0.009

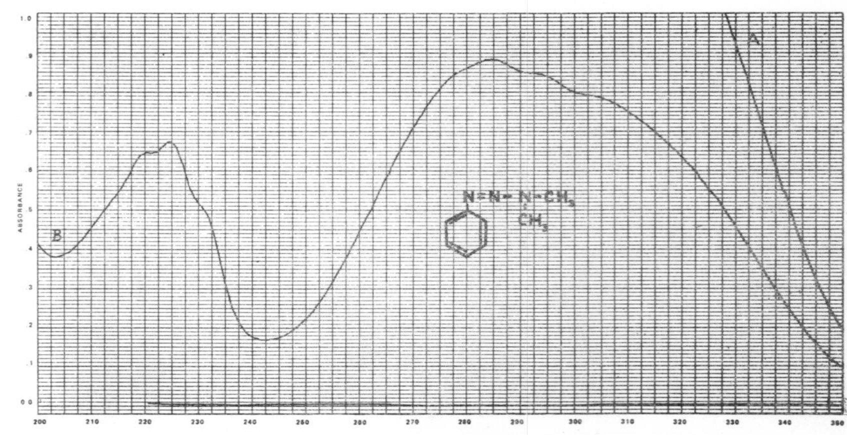

THE ISOCYANATES

Aliphatic Compounds

The aliphatic isocyanates do not display any maxima in the near UV region of the spectrum and, as a consequence, there are no spectra in this volume for compounds 907 through 911.

Aromatic Compounds

The phenyl isocyanates exhibit a major band near 226 mμ and a second much weaker band near 270 mμ which may show some superimposed fine structure.

The effects of additional ring substitution by other functional groups are similar to those of benzene.

Compound	$\lambda_{max}(\epsilon_{max})$	$\lambda_{max}(\epsilon_{max})$	Solvent	Spectrum
Isocyanic acid, phenyl ester	226 (11200)	270 (872)	Cyclohexane	912
Isocyanic acid, o-tolyl ester	229 (5130)	----------	Methanol	913
Isocyanic acid, o-fluoro-phenyl ester	226 (9950)	271 (1250)	Cyclohexane	916

ISOCYANIC ACID, PHENYL ESTER 912

C_7H_5NO

Mol. Wt. 119.12

B.P. 55-56°C/13mm

Solvent: Methanol

λ Max. mμ	a_m	Cell mm	Conc. g/L
276.5	609	10	0.100
269	872	10	0.100
226	11200	1	0.100

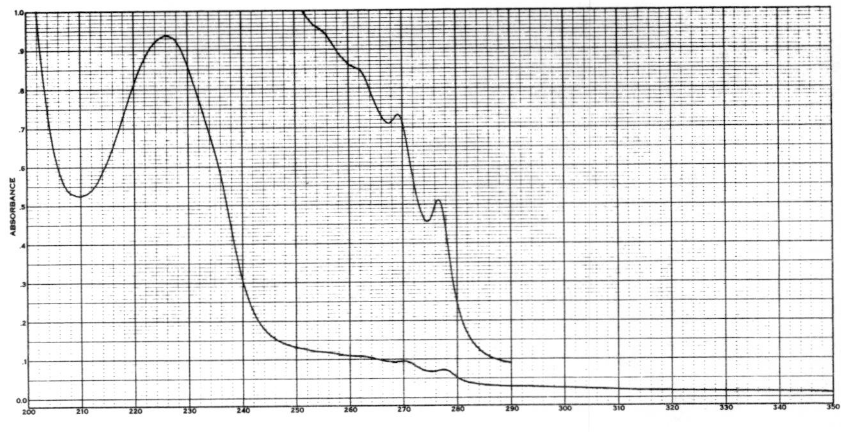

ISOCYANIC ACID, o-TOLYL ESTER 913

C_8H_7NO

Mol. Wt. 133.15

Solvent: Methanol

λ Max. mμ	a_m	Cell mm	Conc. g/L
229.0	5130	2.0	0.100
x	x	2.0	0.100

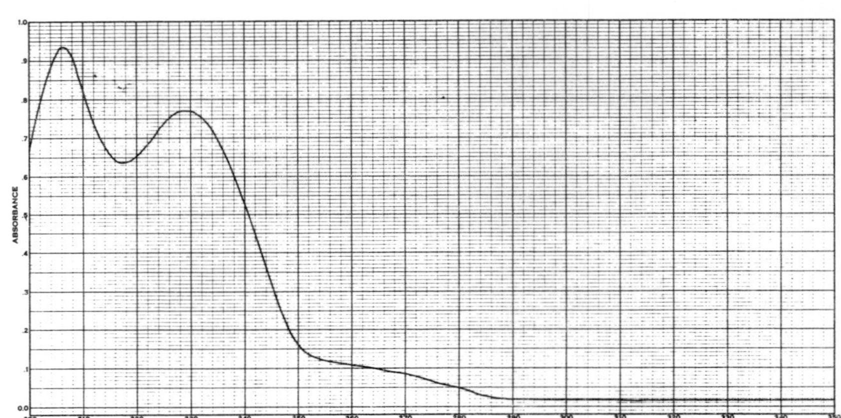

ISOCYANIC ACID, *a,a,a*-TRIFLUORO-o-TOLYL ESTER 914

$C_8H_4F_3NO$

Mol. Wt. 187.12

Solvent: Methanol

λ Max. mμ	a_m	Cell mm	Conc. g/L
272.5	1340	5	0.140
232	7390	1	0.140

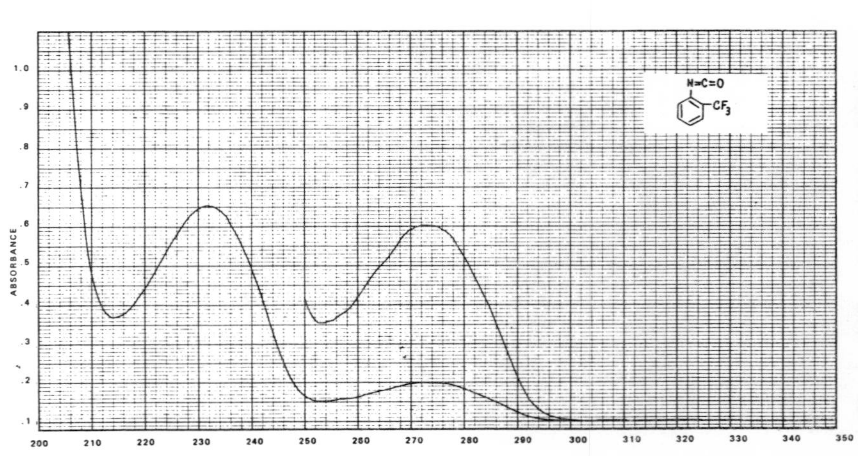

ISOCYANIC ACID, α,α,α-TRIFLUORO-m-TOLYL ESTER

915

$C_8H_4F_3NO$

Mol. Wt. 187.12

Solvent: Cyclohexane

λ Max. mμ	a_m	Cell mm	Conc. g/L
249	10800	1	0.100
x	x	1	0.100

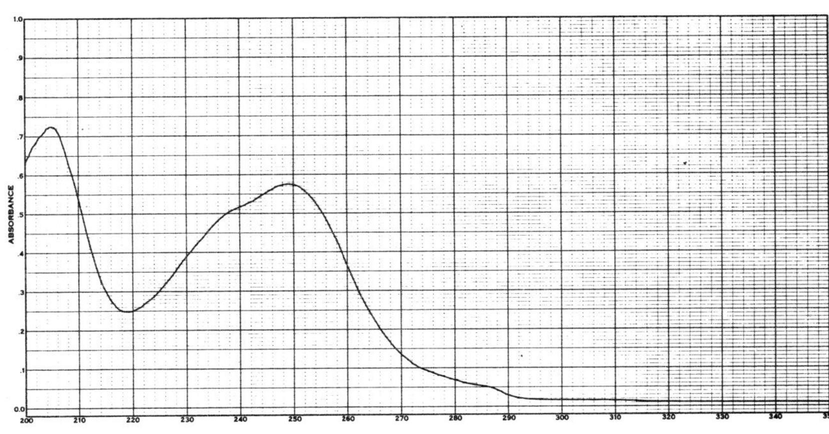

ISOCYANIC ACID, o-FLUOROPHENYL ESTER

916

C_7H_4FNO

Mol. Wt. 137.11

Solvent: Cyclohexane

λ Max. mμ	a_m	Cell mm	Conc. g/L
277.5	995	10	0.100
270.5	1250	10	0.100
226	9950	1	0.100

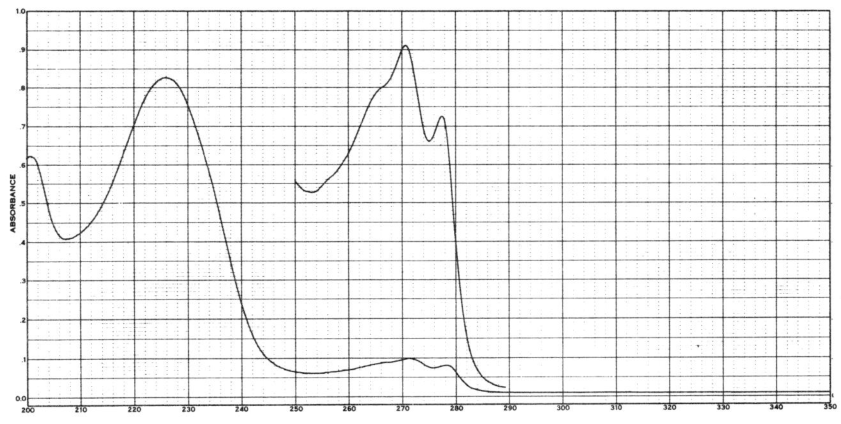

ISOCYANIC ACID, m-FLUOROPHENYL ESTER

917

C_7H_4FNO

Mol. Wt. 137.11

Solvent: Cyclohexane

λ Max. mμ	a_m	Cell mm	Conc. g/L
279	821	10	0.100
249.5	4350	2	0.100
x	x	2	0.100

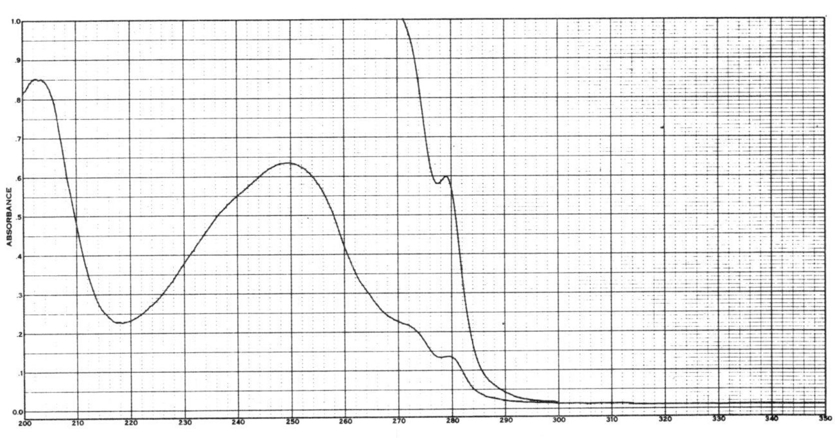

ISOCYANIC ACID, METHYLENEDI-p-PHENYLENE ESTER

918

$C_{15}H_{10}N_2O_2$
Mol. Wt. 250.26
Solvent: Methanol

λ Max. mμ	a_m	Cell mm	Conc. g/L
240	33300	1	0.070

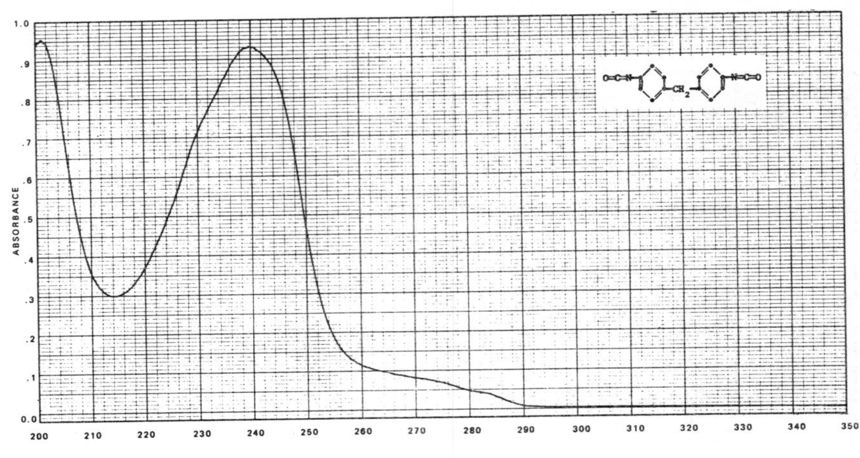

ISOCYANIC ACID, 2,5-XYLYL ESTER

919

C_9H_9NO
Mol. Wt. 147.18
M.P. 7-9°C
Solvent: Methanol

λ Max. mμ	a_m	Cell mm	Conc. g/L
275	809	5	0.1940
232	6850	1	0.1940

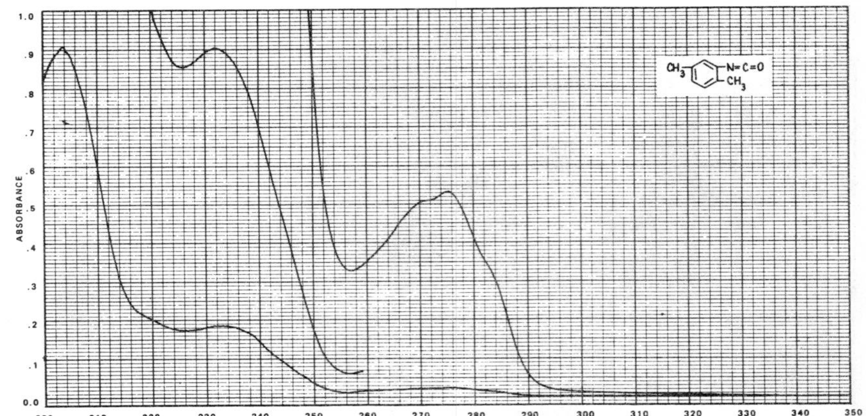

ISOCYANIC ACID, 2,5-DICHLOROPHENYL ESTER

920

$C_7H_3Cl_2NO$
Mol. Wt. 188.01
M.P. 26-28°C

λ Max. mμ	a_m	Cell mm	Conc. g/L

Pure sample not available.

ISOCYANIC ACID, 4-METHYL-m-PHENYLENE ESTER

921

$C_9H_6N_2O_2$
Mol. Wt. 174.16
B.P. 120°C/10mm
Solvent: Dioxane

λ Max. mμ	a_m	Cell mm	Conc. g/L
x	x	5	0.122
x	x	1	0.122

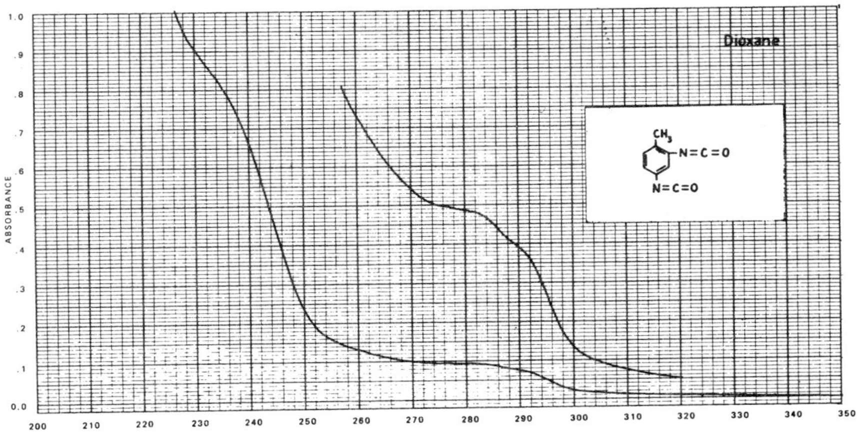

ISOCYANIC ACID, 1-NAPHTHYL ESTER

922

$C_{11}H_7NO$
Mol. Wt. 169.18
B.P. 118-21°C/3mm (lit.)
Solvent: Cyclohexane

λ Max. mμ	a_m	Cell mm	Conc. g/L
323	609	10	0.339
318	798	10	0.339
302	5490	10	0.034
290	7980	10	0.034
280.5	6870	10	0.034
226	68700	10	0.003

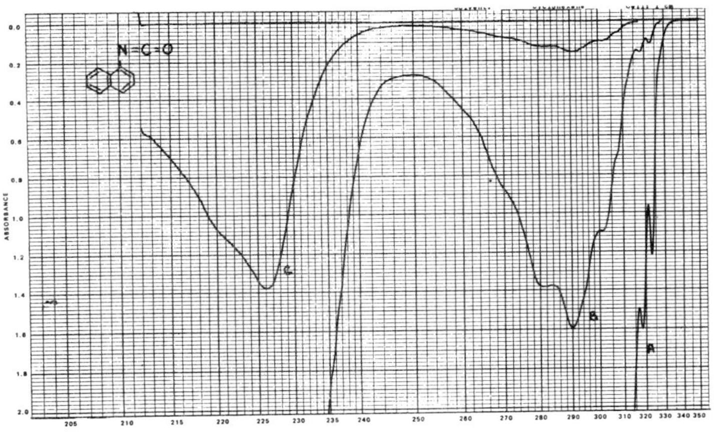

λ Max. mμ	a_m	Cell mm	Conc. g/L

NOTES

THE CARBODIIMIDES

Aliphatic Compounds

The cumulated system of the carbodiimides (—N=C=N—) absorbs near 270 mμ as an extremely weak band which may show some superimposed fine structure. The literature lists two maxima for diethylcarbodiimide one at 230 mμ (ϵ = 200) and one at 270 mμ (ϵ = 25).

Spectrum 924 displays one maximum near 271 mμ with an ϵ_{max} of 33 for dicyclohexyl carbodiimide in methanol solution.

Aromatic Compounds

The aromatic carbodiimides display an extremely strong band in the near UV region near 246 mμ with some weaker shoulders near 280 - 290 mμ.

Compound	$\lambda_{max}(\epsilon_{max})$	$\lambda_{max}(\epsilon_{max})$	Solvent	Spectrum
Di-o-tolylcarbodiimide	244 (25800)	288 (10225)	Methanol	927
Di-p-tolylcarbodiimide	247 (37000)	288 * (9180)	Methanol	928

* Shoulder

DIISOPROPYLCARBODIIMIDE 923

$C_7H_{14}N_2$
Mol. Wt. 126.20
B.P. 145-147°C

λ Max. mμ	a_m	Cell mm	Conc. g/L

Pure sample not available.

DICYCLOHEXYLCARBODIIMIDE 924

$C_{13}H_{22}N_2$
Mol. Wt. 206.34
B.P. 122-124°C/6mm M.P. 31-32°C
Solvent: Methanol

λ Max. mμ	a_m	Cell mm	Conc. g/L
271.0	32.8	20	0.5
x	x	2	0.5

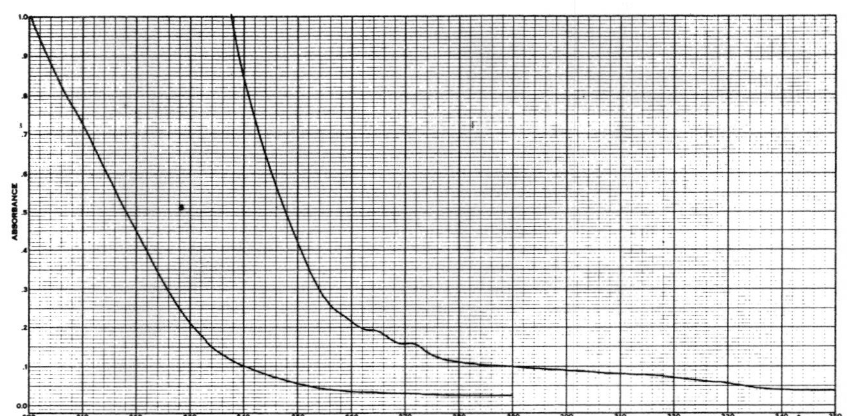

tert-BUTYL(TRIPHENYLMETHYL)CARBODIIMIDE 925

$C_{24}H_{24}N_2$
Mol. Wt. 340.47
M.P. 71-73°C

λ Max. mμ	a_m	Cell mm	Conc. g/L

Pure sample not available.

DITRITYLCARBODIIMIDE 926

$C_{39}H_{30}N_2$
Mol. Wt. 526.69
M.P. 210°C (lit.)

λ Max. mμ	a_m	Cell mm	Conc. g/L

Pure sample not available.

DI-o-TOLYLCARBODIIMIDE 927

$C_{15}H_{14}N_2$
Mol. Wt. 222.29
Solvent: Methanol

λ Max. mμ	a_m	Cell mm	Conc. g/L
244	25800	0.5	0.100
x	x	0.5	0.100

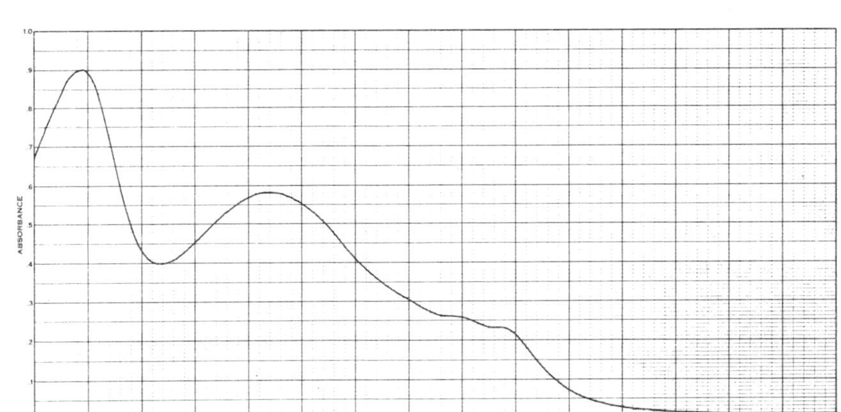

DI-p-TOLYLCARBODIIMIDE 928

$C_{15}H_{14}N_2$
Mol. Wt. 222.29
Solvent: Methanol

λ Max. mμ	a_m	Cell mm	Conc. g/L
247	37000	10	0.005

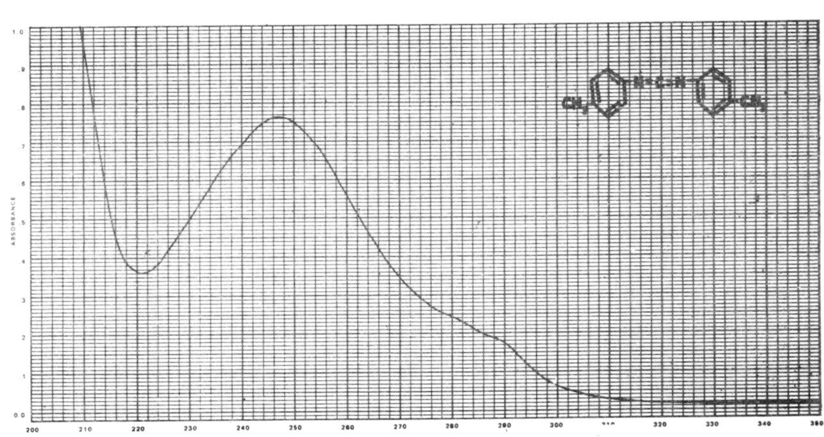

BIS(2,6-DIETHYLPHENYL)CARBODIIMIDE

$C_{21}H_{26}N_2$
Mol. Wt. 306.45
M.P. 192-194°C/0.4mm

λ Max. mμ	a_m	Cell mm	Conc. g/L

Pure sample not available.

λ Max. mμ	a_m	Cell mm	Conc. g/L

λ Max. mμ	a_m	Cell mm	Conc. g/L

THE ISOTHIOCYANATES

Aliphatic Compounds

The combination of two chromophores into the cumulated system —N=C=S gives rise to a weak absorption band in the range from 240 mμ to 255 mμ for the aliphatic isothiocyanates. The wavelength of this band is dependent on the type of aliphatic group present and it appears to shift to longer wavelength with increased branching of the aliphatic group.

A table of wavelength and intensity data for a series of aliphatic isothiocyanates is presented below.

Isothiocyanic acid,-	$\lambda_{max}(\epsilon_{max})$	Solvent	Spectrum
Heptyl ester	242 (1040)	Methanol	933
Allyl ester	243 (5100)	Methanol/KOH	936
Allyl ester	245 (757)	Methanol	936
Ethyl	249 (2570)	----------	Lit.
t-Butyl ester	251 (1310)	Methanol	932
1-Adamantyl ester	251 (1600)	Methanol	935

Aromatic Compounds

The spectra of the aromatic isothiocyanates in the near UV contain two major bands, a moderately intense band or shoulder near 223 mμ and a weaker band with fine structure superimposed near 275 mμ. The appearance of these spectra is similar to that of the aromatic isocyanates (—N=C=O).

The table presented below lists the wavelengths and intensities for a series of aromatic isothiocyanates examined in cyclohexane solution.

Isothiocyanic acid,-	$\lambda_{max}(\epsilon_{max})$	$\lambda_{max}(\epsilon_{max})$	$\lambda_{max}(\epsilon_{max})$	Spectrum
Phenyl ester	----------	269 (12100)	279 (12500)	938
o-Fluoro ester	222 (36100)	271 (10100)	281 (10900)	939
m-Fluoro ester	221 (30100)	271 (10200)	282 (10400)	940
p-Fluoro ester	222 (52200)	271 (22100)	280 (20400)	941

ISOTHIOCYANIC ACID, METHYL ESTER

930

C_2H_3NS

Mol. Wt. 73.12

M.P. 32-35°C

B.P. 118-120°C

λ Max. mμ	a_m	Cell mm	Conc. g/L

Pure sample not available.

ISOTHIOCYANIC ACID, BUTYL ESTER

931

C_5H_9NS

Mol. Wt. 115.20

B.P. 64-66°C/12mm

λ Max. mμ	a_m	Cell mm	Conc. g/L

Pure sample not available.

ISOTHIOCYANIC ACID, tert-BUTYL ESTER

932

C_5H_9NS

Mol. Wt. 115.20

M.P. 8-11°C

Solvent: Cyclohexane

λ Max. mμ	a_m	Cell mm	Conc. g/L
250.5	1310	1	0.5

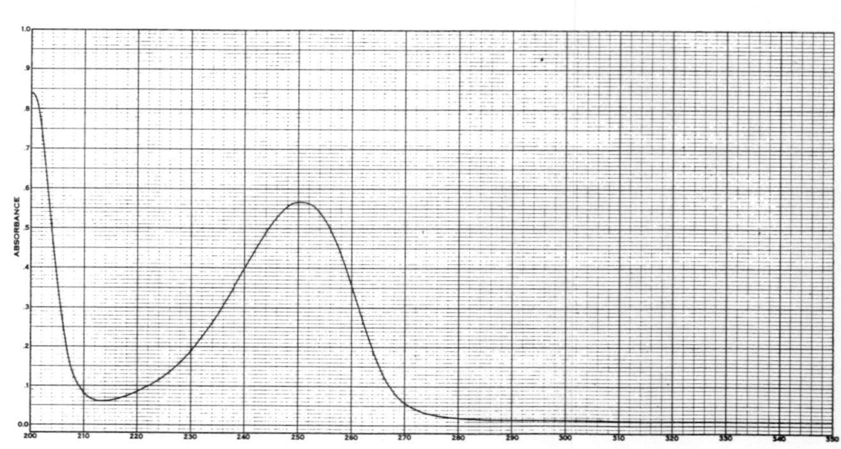

ISOTHIOCYANIC ACID, HEPTYL ESTER

933

$C_8H_{15}NS$

Mol. Wt. 157.28

B.P. 107-109°C/10mm

Solvent: Methanol

λ Max. mμ	a_m	Cell mm	Conc. g/L
242	1040	10	0.14320

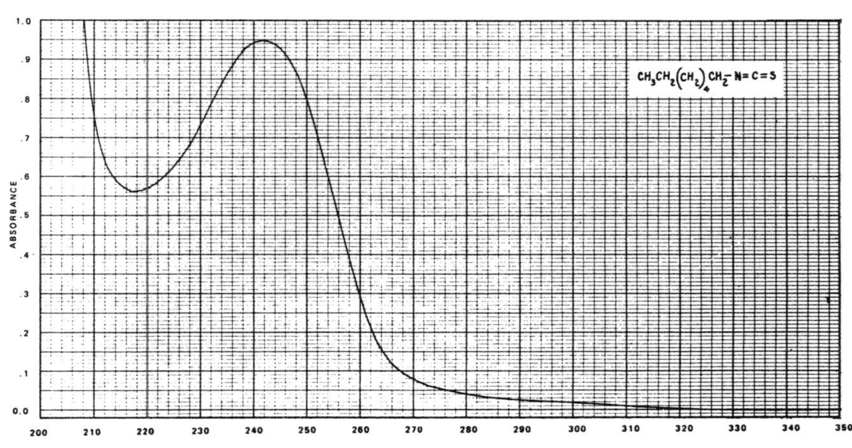

ISOTHIOCYANIC ACID, OCTADECYL ESTER

934

$C_{19}H_{37}NS$

Mol. Wt. 311.58

M.P. 24-28°C

λ Max. mμ	a_m	Cell mm	Conc. g/L

Pure sample not available.

ISOTHIOCYANIC ACID, 1-ADAMANTYL ESTER

935

$C_{11}H_{15}NS$

Mol. Wt. 193.31

M.P. 166.5-168°C

Solvent: Methanol

λ Max. mμ	a_m	Cell mm	Conc. g/L
250.5	1600	2	0.5

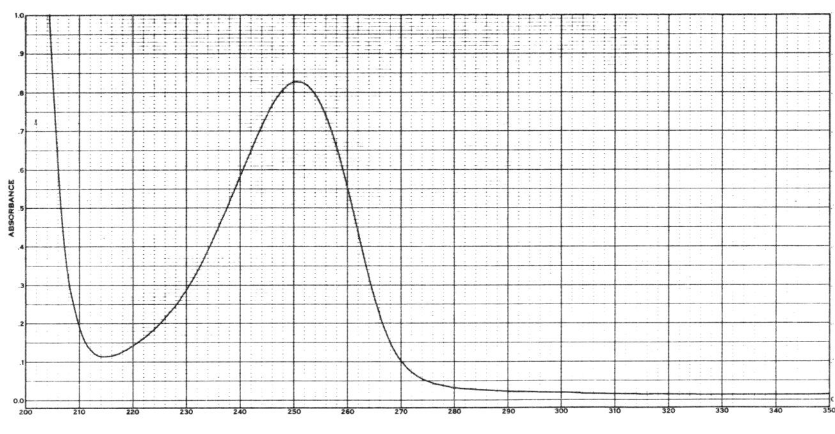

ISOTHIOCYANIC ACID, ALLYL ESTER

936

C_4H_5NS

Mol. Wt. 99.16

B.P. 150-152°C

Solvent: Methanol

λ Max. mμ	a_m	Cell mm	Conc. g/L
244.5	757	2	0.300

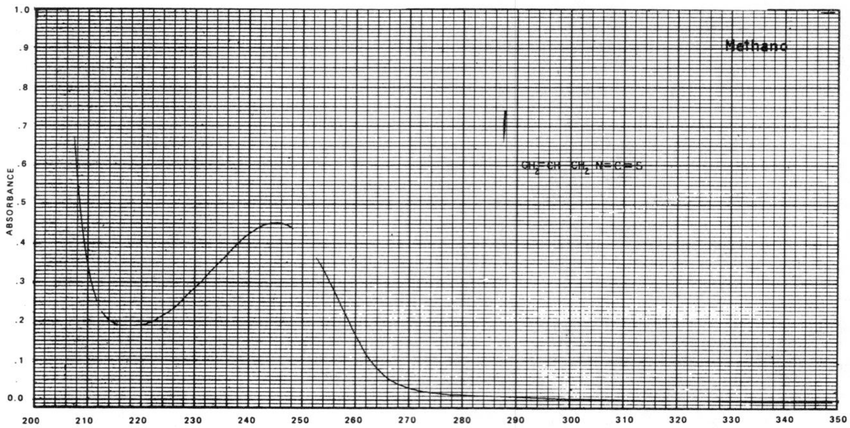

ISOTHIOCYANIC ACID, ALLYL ESTER

936

C_4H_5NS

Mol. Wt. 99.16

B.P. 150-152°C

Solvent: Methanol KOH

λ Max. mμ	a_m	Cell mm	Conc. g/L
242.5	5100	5	0.0300

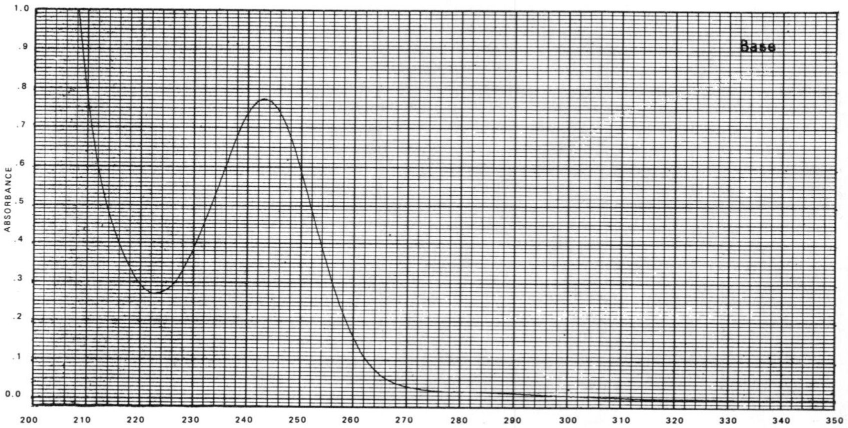

ISOTHIOCYANIC ACID, BENZYL ESTER

937

C_8H_7NS

Mol. Wt. 149.22

B.P. 114-116°C/5mm

λ Max. mμ	a_m	Cell mm	Conc. g/L

Pure sample not available.

ISOTHIOCYANIC ACID, PHENYL ESTER

938

C_7H_5NS
Mol. Wt. 135.19
B.R. 89-90°C/10mm (lit.)
Solvent: Cyclohexane

λ Max. mμ	a_m	Cell mm	Conc. g/L
279	12500	10	0.018
268.5	12100	10	0.018

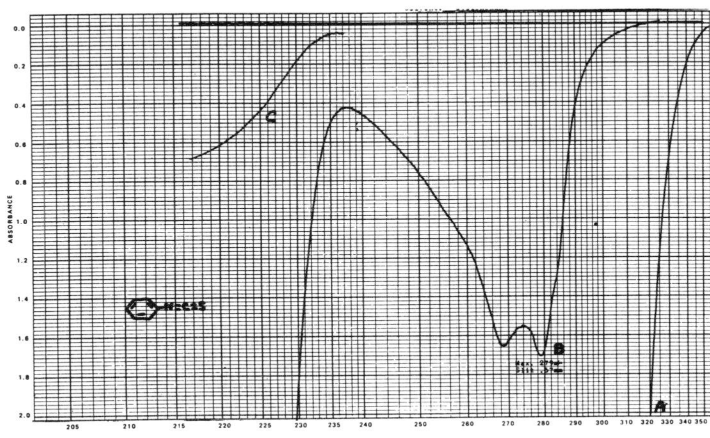

ISOTHIOCYANIC ACID, o-FLUOROPHENYL ESTER

939

C_7H_4FNS
Mol. Wt. 153.18
Solvent: Cyclohexane

λ Max. mμ	a_m	Cell mm	Conc. g/L
286	10400	2	0.443
281	10900	2	0.0443
270.5	10100	2	0.0443
221.5	36100	1	0.0222

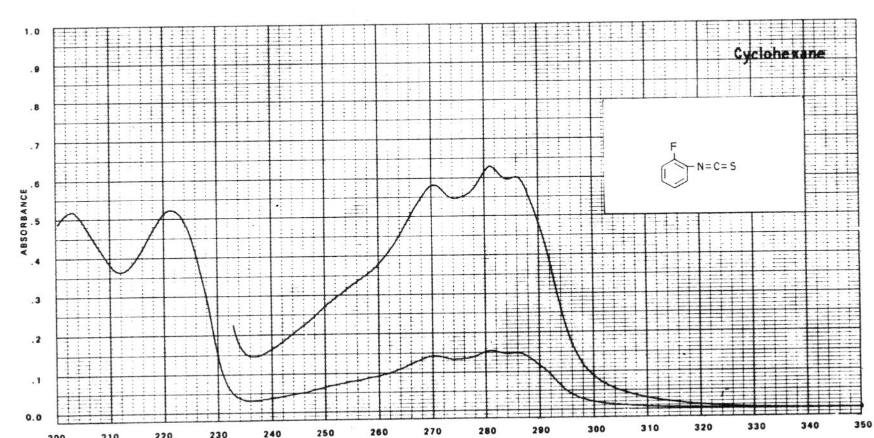

ISOTHIOCYANIC ACID, m-FLUOROPHENYL ESTER

940

C_7H_4FNS
Mol. Wt. 153.12
Solvent: Cyclohexane

λ Max. mμ	a_m	Cell mm	Conc. g/L
281.5	10400	2	0.0555
271	10200	2	0.0555
221	30100	1	0.0277

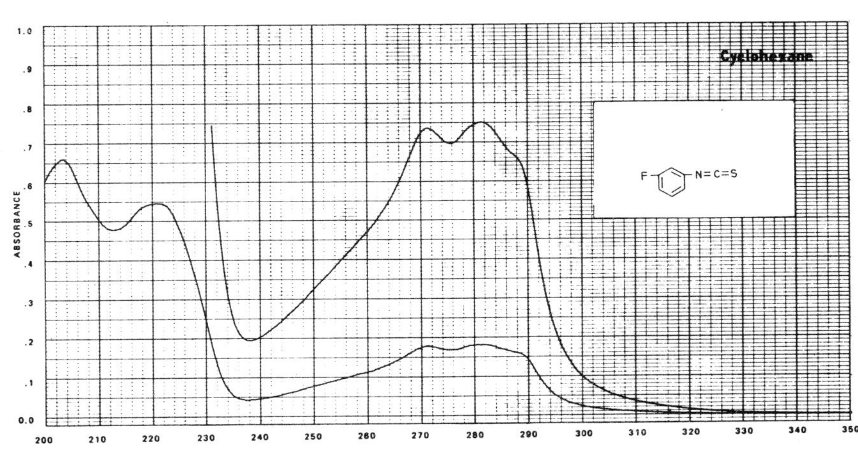

ISOTHIOCYANIC ACID, p-FLUOROPHENYL ESTER 941

C_7H_4FNS

Mol. Wt. 153.18

M.P. 23.5-25.5°C   B.P. 66°C/1.8mm (lit.)

Solvent: Cyclohexane

λ Max. mμ	a_m	Cell mm	Conc. g/L
280	20400	0.5	0.050
271	22100	0.5	0.050
221.5	52200	0.5	0.050
x	x	0.5	0.050

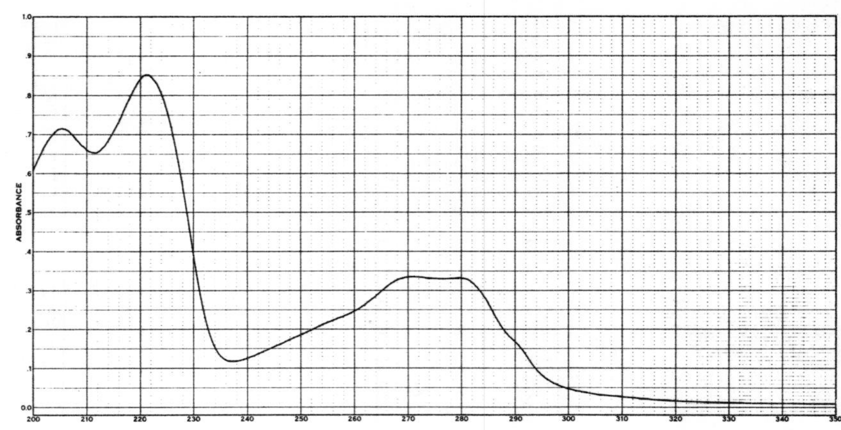

ISOTHIOCYANIC ACID, o-CHLOROPHENYL ESTER 942

C_7H_4ClNS

Mol. Wt. 169.63

M.P. 90°C/1mm

λ Max. mμ	a_m	Cell mm	Conc. g/L

Pure sample not available.

λ Max. mμ	a_m	Cell mm	Conc. g/L

THE NITRILES

Aliphatic Compounds

The aliphatic and olefinic nitriles are transparent in the near UV region. The nitrile group possesses a weak absorption band in the far UV near 170 mμ allowing acetonitrile to be used as as a solvent for the preparation of spectra in the near UV, with a cut-off wavelength of 210 mμ.

Aromatic Compounds

The cyano group has a bathochromic effect on the wavelengths observed for benzene and toluene, shifting the major bands to longer wavelength by about 20 mμ. A slight increase in band intensity is also observed. The near UV data for benzene, toluene and a series of benzonitriles is presented below.

Compound	$\lambda_{max}(\epsilon_{max})$	$\lambda_{max}(\epsilon_{max})$	Solvent	Spectrum
Benzene	204 (8800)	254 (250)	Hexane	Lit.
Toluene	208 (7900)	262 (260)	Hexane	Lit.
Benzonitrile	222 (10600)	270 (1010)	Methanol	983
2-Fluorobenzonitrile	223 (12000)	274 (1860)	Methanol	987
2-Methylbenzonitrile	227 (11000)	276 (1370)	Methanol	984
2-Chlorobenzonitrile	229 (10100)	278 (1460)	Methanol	990
2-Bromobenzonitrile	232 (9410)	281 (1510)	Methanol	992
2-Cyanobenzonitrile	237 (10400)	282 (1750)	Methanol	997

ACRYLONITRILE

966

C_3H_3N

Mol. Wt. 53.06

Solvent: Methanol

λ Max. mμ	a_m	Cell mm	Conc. g/L
x	x	10	0.100

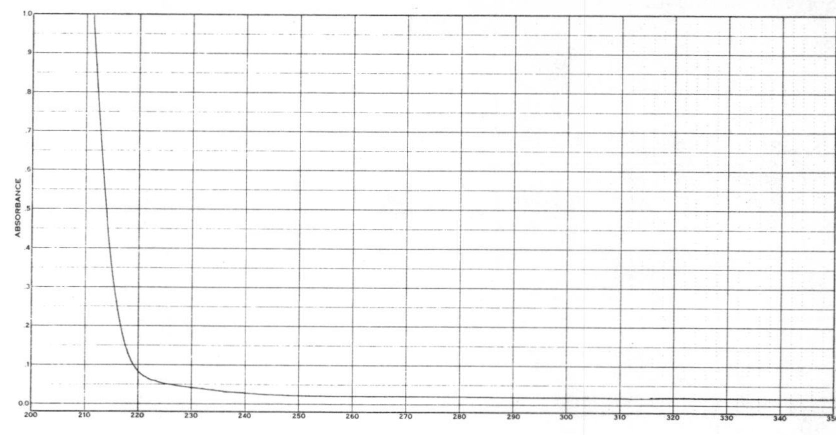

2-METHYLACRYLONITRILE

967

C_4H_5N

Mol. Wt. 67.09

λ Max. mμ	a_m	Cell mm	Conc. g/L

Pure sample not available.

3-BUTENENITRILE

968

C_4H_5N

Mol. Wt. 67.09

B.P. 117-119°C

λ Max. mμ	a_m	Cell mm	Conc. g/L

This compound does not produce maxima in the near UV.

(AMINOMETHYLENE) MALONONITRILE

969

$C_4H_3N_3$
Mol. Wt. 93.09
Solvent: Methanol

λ Max. mμ	a_m	Cell mm	Conc. g/L
343	2830	5	0.100
266	43100	0.5	0.100

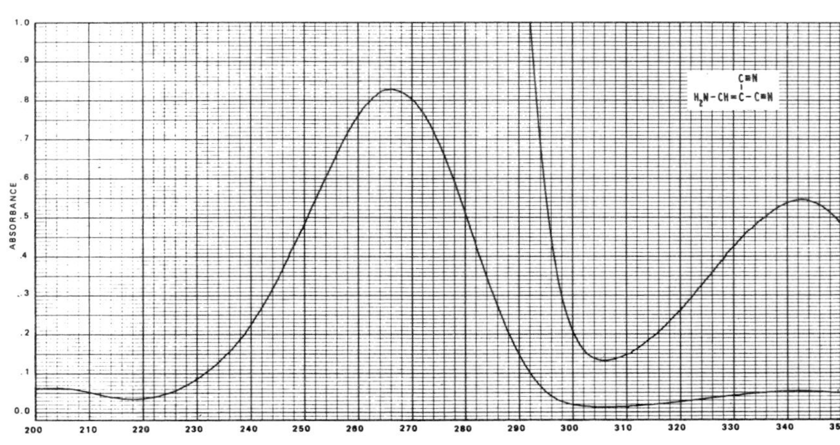

3-CYCLOHEXENE-1-CARBONITRILE

970

C_7H_9N
Mol. Wt. 107.16
B.P. 89-91°C/25mm

λ Max. mμ	a_m	Cell mm	Conc. g/L

This compound does not produce maxima in the near UV.

1-CYCLOHEXENE-1-CARBONITRILE

971

C_7H_9N
Mol. Wt. 107.16
Solvent: Cyclohexane

λ Max. mμ	a_m	Cell mm	Conc. g/L
250.5	14.5	20	0.5
x	x	0.5	0.25

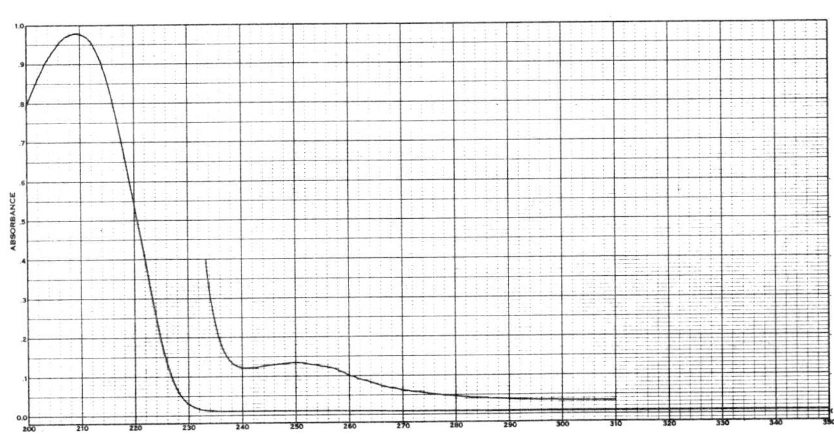

PHENYLACETONITRILE

972

C_8H_7N

Mol. Wt. 117.15

B.P. 233.4°C

Solvent: Methanol

λ Max. mμ	a_m	Cell mm	Conc. g/L
263	149	20	0.240
257	194	20	0.240
251	168	20	0.240
246.5	135	20	0.240
x	x	2	0.0480

HYDROCINNAMONITRILE

973

C_9H_9N

Mol. Wt. 131.18

Solvent: Methanol

λ Max. mμ	a_m	Cell mm	Conc. g/L
267	91.1	10	0.475
263.5	151	10	0.475
257.5	196	10	0.475
252	159	10	0.475
247	118	10	0.475

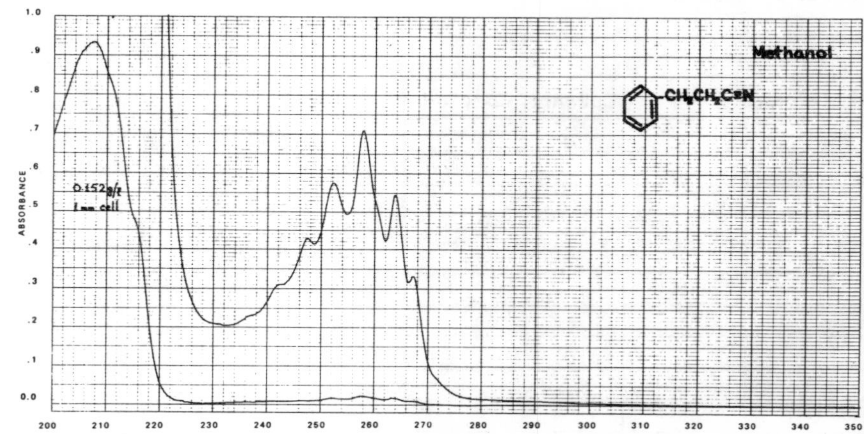

β,β-DIMETHYLHYDROCINNAMONITRILE

974

$C_{11}H_{13}N$

Mol. Wt. 159.23

B.P. 146°C/20mm

λ Max. mμ	a_m	Cell mm	Conc. g/L

Pure sample not available.

(DIMETHYLAMINO)PHENYLACETONITRILE

975

$C_{10}H_{12}N_2$
Mol. Wt. 160.22
B.P. 76-78^oC/0.8mm
Solvent: Methanol

λ Max. mμ	a_m	Cell mm	Conc. g/L
267	151	20	0.127
263	244	20	0.127
260.5	247	20	0.127
257	360	20	0.127
251	427	20	0.127

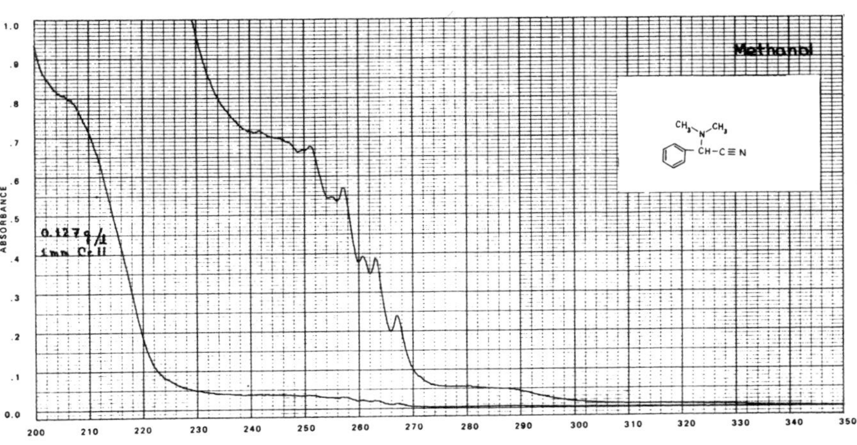

3,3'-(PHENYLIMINO)DIPROPIONITRILE

976

$C_{12}H_{13}N_3$
Mol. Wt. 199.26
Solvent: Methanol

λ Max. mμ	a_m	Cell mm	Conc. g/L
292.5	1790	10	0.100
249.5	13200	1	0.100

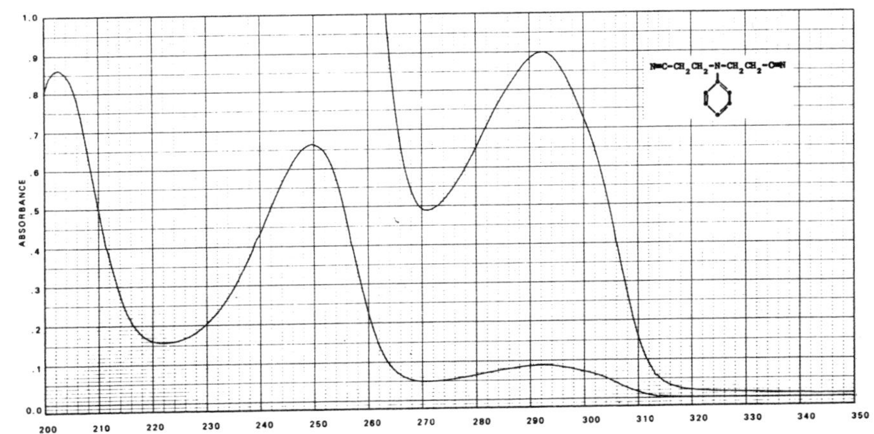

2,2-DIPHENYLBUTRONITRILE

977

$C_{16}H_{15}N$
Mol. Wt. 221.30
Solvent: Methanol

λ Max. mμ	a_m	Cell mm	Conc. g/L
256	1790	10	0.100
251.5	1850	10	0.100
x	x	1	0.100

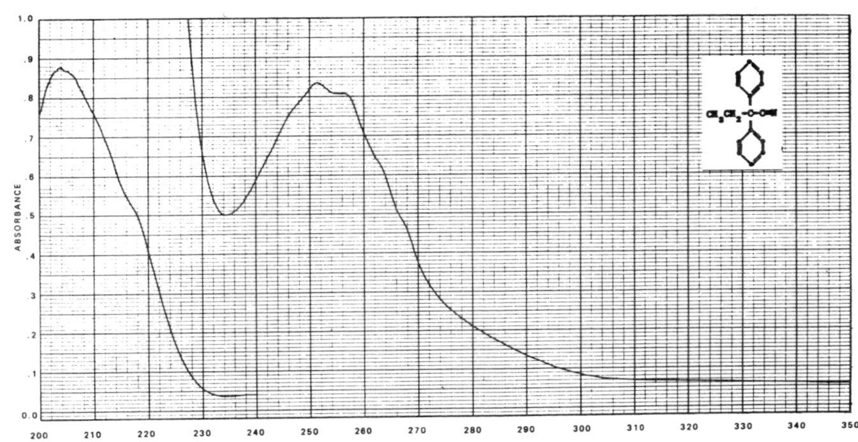

2,3,4-TRIPHENYLBUTYRONITRILE **978**

$C_{22}H_{19}N$
Mol. Wt. 297.40
M.P. 88-92°C

λ Max. mμ	a_m	Cell mm	Conc. g/L

Pure sample not available. .

3-PHENYL-1,3,5-PENTANETRICARBONITRILE **979**

$C_{14}H_{13}N_3$
Mol. Wt. 223.28
Solvent: Methanol

λ Max. mμ	a_m	Cell mm	Conc. g/L
256	207	40.0	0.100
251	168	40.0	0.100
x	x	4	0.100

(o-FLUOROPHENYL)ACETONITRILE **980**

C_8H_6FN
Mol. Wt. 135.14
B.P. 122-126°C/10mm (lit.)
Solvent: Methanol

λ Max. mμ	a_m	Cell mm	Conc. g/L
267	837	10	0.1263
261	877	10	0.1263
256	622	10	0.1263
x	x	1	0.1263

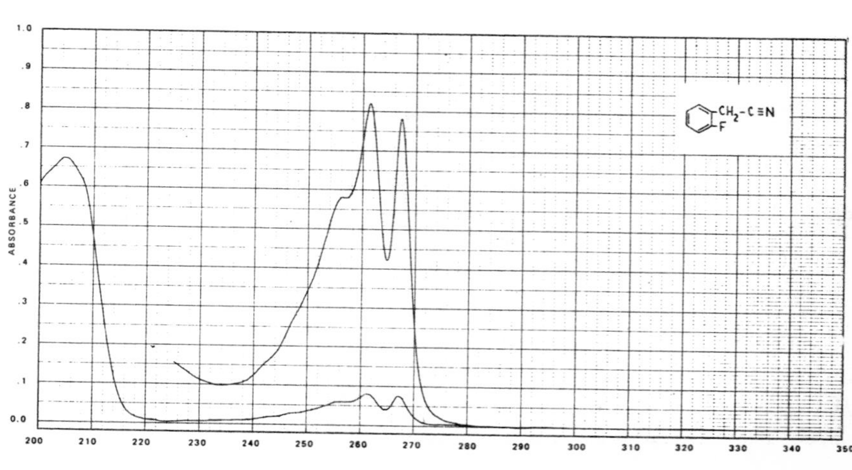

(p-CHLOROPHENYL)ACETONITRILE

981

C_8H_6ClN
Mol. Wt. 151.59
Solvent: Cyclohexane

λ Max. mμ	a_m	Cell mm	Conc. g/L
275	254	10	0.765
267	289	10	0.765
260	222	10	0.765
254	157	10	0.765

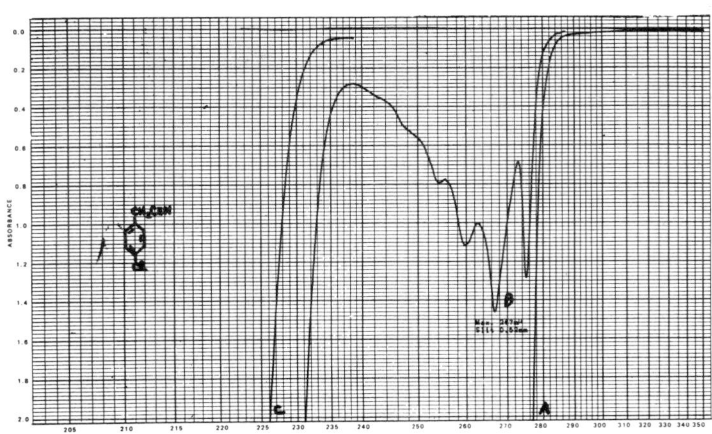

CINNAMONITRILE

982

C_9H_7N
Mol. Wt. 129.16
Solvent: Methanol

λ Max. mμ	a_m	Cell mm	Conc. g/L
272	39500	1	0.0490
221.5	25300	1	0.0490
216	29900	1	0.0490
211	24000	1	0.0490

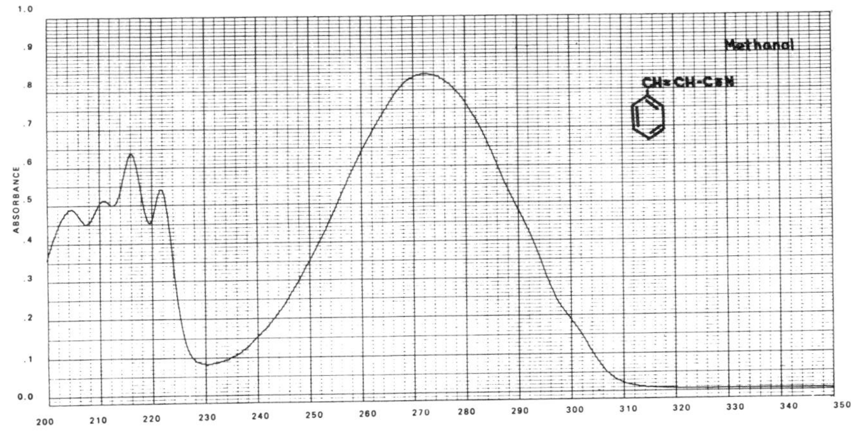

BENZONITRILE

983

C_7H_5N
Mol. Wt. 103.12
B.P. 188-189°C
Solvent: Methanol

λ Max. mμ	a_m	Cell mm	Conc. g/L
277	932	5	0.140
269.5	1010	5	0.140
263	804	5	0.140
230	9100	2	0.0380
222	10600	2	0.0380

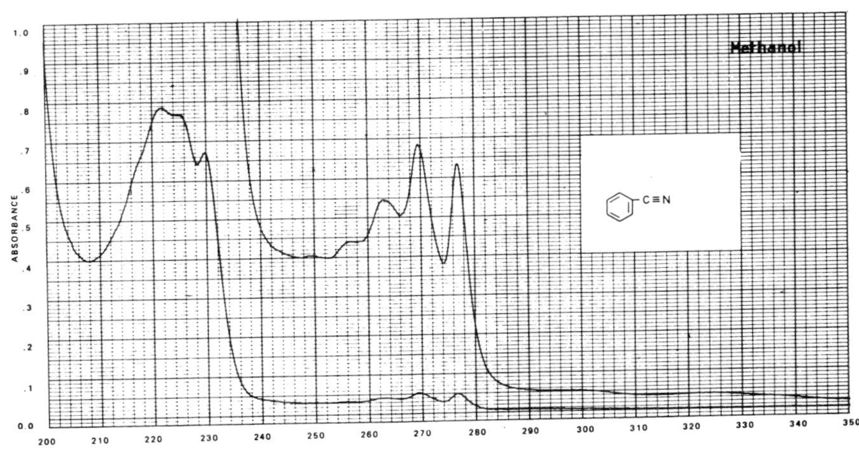

o-TOLUNITRILE

984

C_8H_7N

Mol. Wt. 117.15

M.P. -14 to -12°C

Solvent: Methanol

λ Max. mμ	$^a m$	Cell mm	Conc. g/L
283.5	1400	2	0.235
275.5	1370	2	0.235
227	11000	2	0.0470

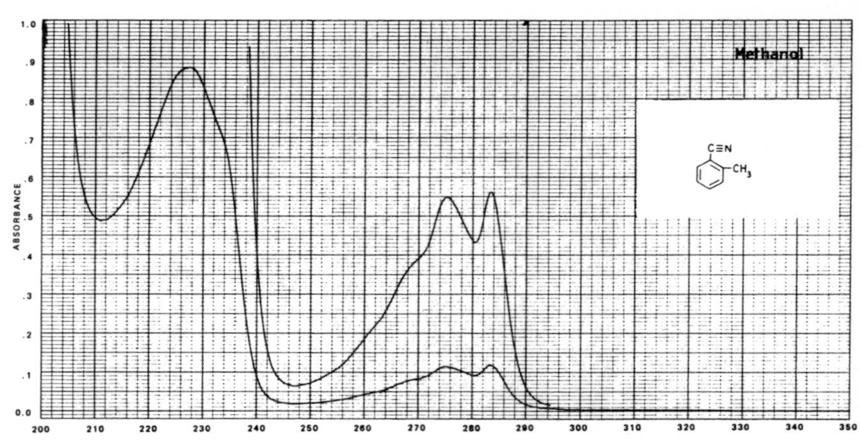

m-TOLUNITRILE

985

C_8H_7N

Mol. Wt. 117.15

B.P. 74-75°C/5mm

Solvent: Methanol

λ Max. mμ	$^a m$	Cell mm	Conc. g/L
283	1130	2	0.469
275	1130	2	0.469
227	11000	1	0.0938

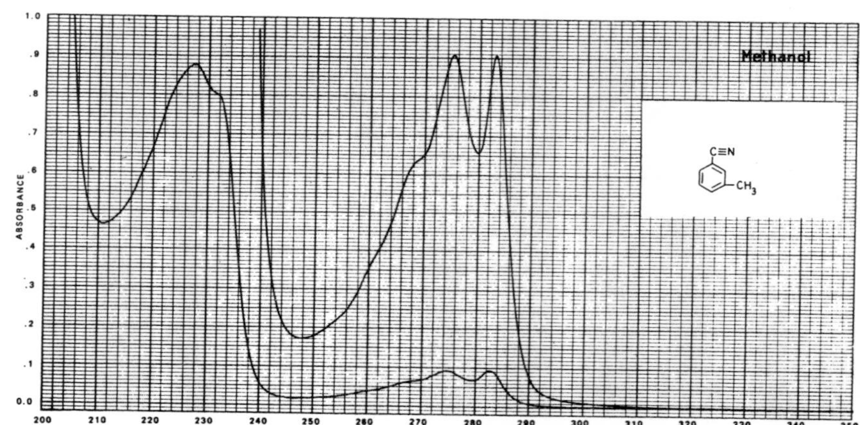

p-TOLUNITRILE

986

C_8H_7N

Mol. Wt. 117.15

M.P. 26-28°C

Solvent: Methanol

λ Max. mμ	$^a m$	Cell mm	Conc. g/L
278.5	445	2	0.334
272	570	2	0.334
266.5	789	2	0.334
258.5	1000	2	0.334
232	14700	1	0.0668

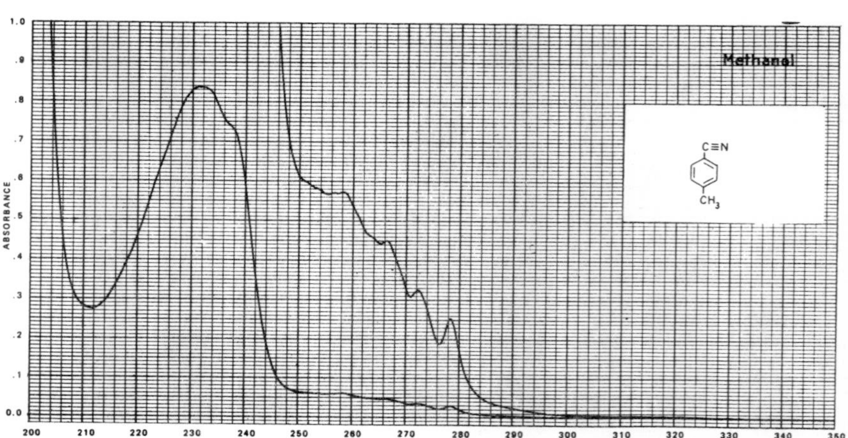

o-FLUOROBENZONITRILE

987

C_7H_4FN
Mol. Wt. 121.12
B.P. 92-95°C/22mm
Solvent: Methanol

λ Max. mμ	a_m	Cell mm	Conc. g/L
281.5	187	2	1.9850
273.5	186	2	1.9850
230	1020	1	0.9925
223	1200	1	0.9925

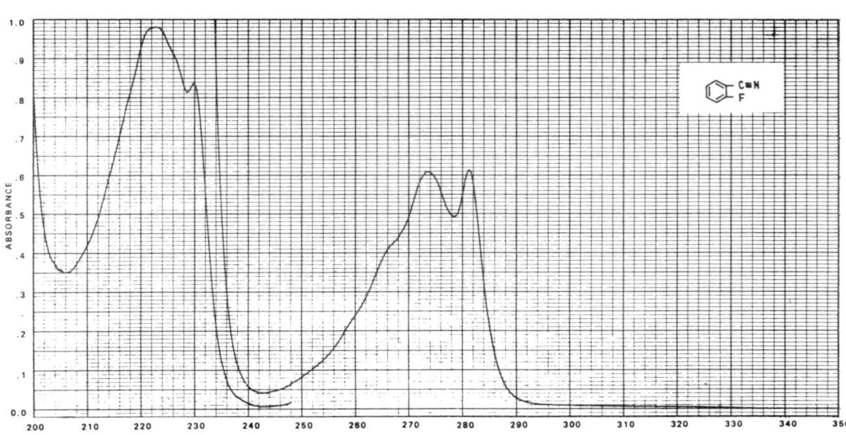

p-FLUOROBENZONITRILE

988

C_7H_4FN
Mol. Wt. 121.11
M.P. 32-34°C (lit.)
Solvent: Methanol

λ Max. mμ	a_m	Cell mm	Conc. g/L
270	200	10	0.266
262.5	336	10	0.266
257	319	10	0.266
224	12000	1	0.0800

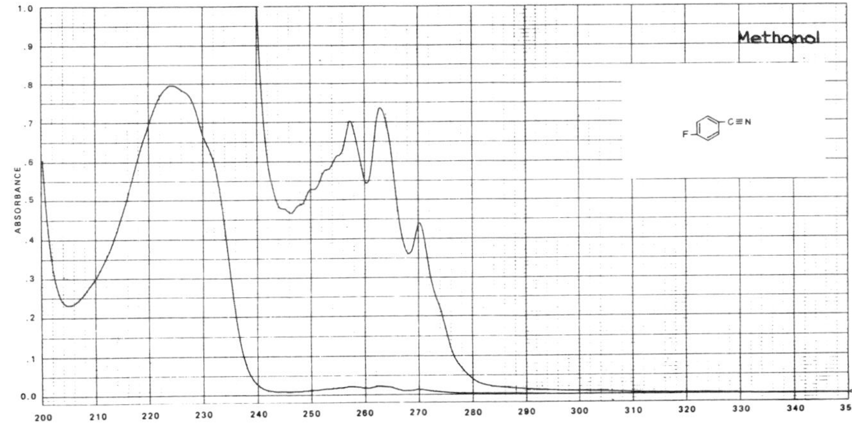

2,6-DIFLUOROBENZONITRILE

989

$C_7H_3F_2N$
Mol. Wt. 139.11
Solvent: Methanol

λ Max. mμ	a_m	Cell mm	Conc. g/L
335	20	20	0.100
303.5	149	20	0.100
273.5	1760	5	0.100
222	12500	1	0.100

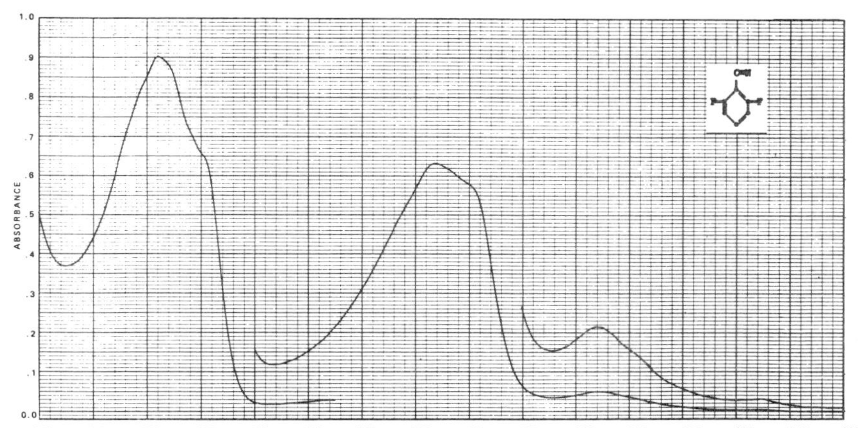

o-CHLOROBENZONITRILE

990

C_7H_4ClN

Mol. Wt. 137.57

M.P. 44-46°C (lit.)

Solvent: Methanol

λ Max. mμ	a_m	Cell mm	Conc. g/L
287	1460	5	0.100
278	1460	5	0.100
235	8540	1	0.100
229	10100	1	0.100

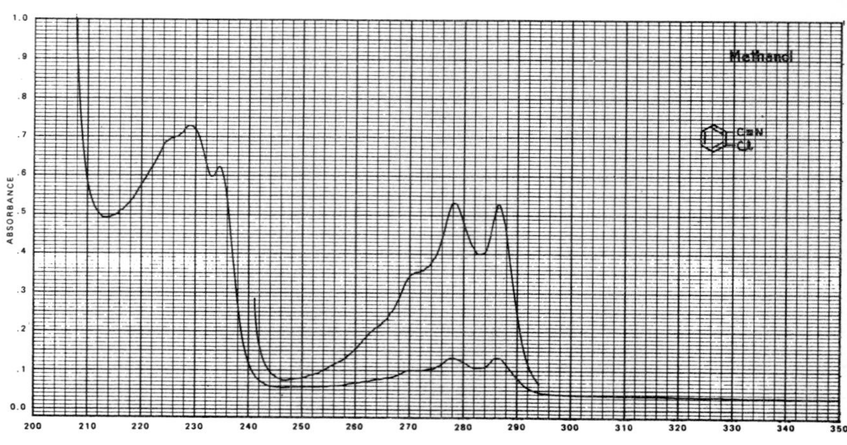

p-CHLOROBENZONITRILE

991

C_7H_4ClN

Mol. Wt. 137.57

M.P. 91-92°C

Solvent: Methanol

λ Max. mμ	a_m	Cell mm	Conc. g/L
280.5	411	20	0.100
275	463	20	0.100
269	598	20	0.100
261.5	510	20	0.100
235.5	19000	2	0.0200

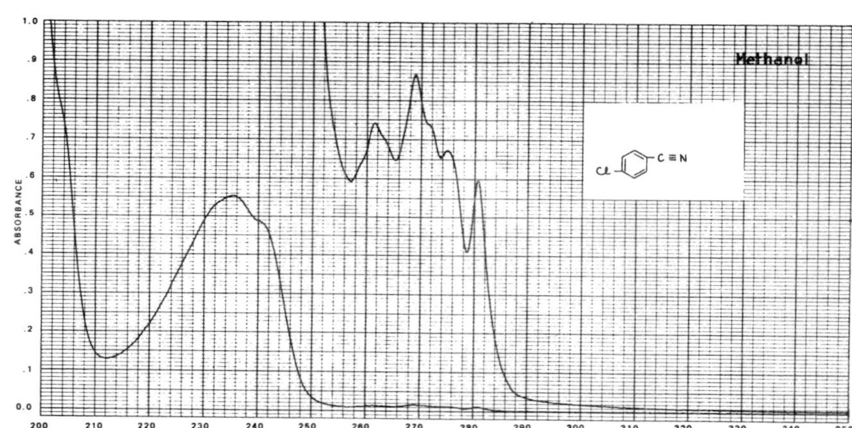

o-BROMOBENZONITRILE

992

C_7H_4BrN

Mol. Wt. 182.03

Solvent: Methanol

λ Max. mμ	a_m	Cell mm	Conc. g/L
289	1460	10	0.100
280.5	1510	10	0.100
237.5	7850	10	0.010
232	9410	10	0.010
227	9100	10	0.010

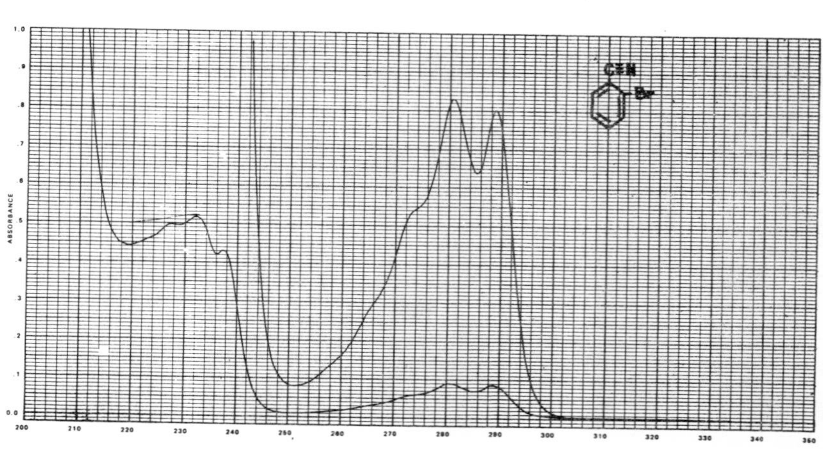

m-BROMOBENZONITRILE

993

C_7H_4BrN
Mol. Wt. 182.03
Solvent: Methanol

λ Max. mμ	a_m	Cell mm	Conc. g/L
288	912	10	0.1
280	997	10	0.1
272.5	697	10	0.1
229	10400	10	0.01
224	10300	10	0.01

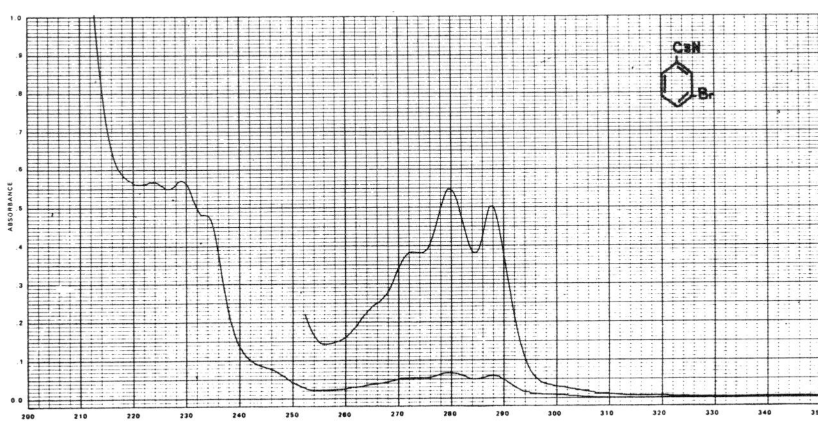

m-AMINOBENZONITRILE

994

$C_7H_6N_2$
Mol. Wt. 118.14
Solvent: Methanol

λ Max. mμ	a_m	Cell mm	Conc. g/L
317	2660	2.5	0.100
247	7470	0.5	0.050
216.5	28500	0.5	0.050

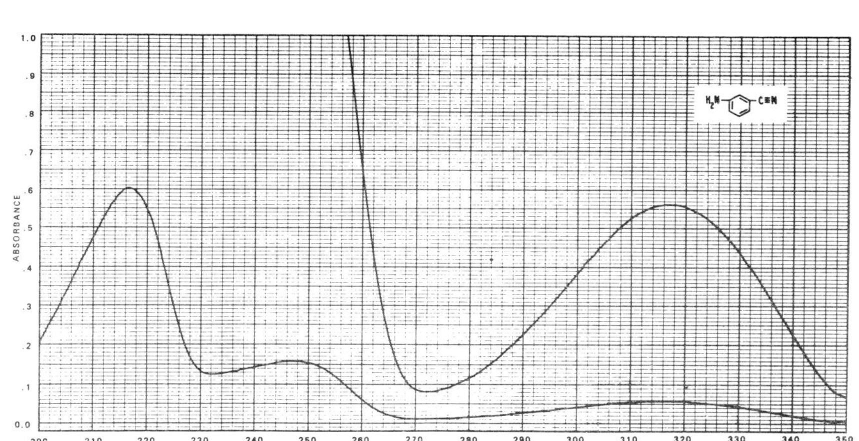

m-AMINOBENZONITRILE

994

$C_7H_6N_2$
Mol. Wt. 118.14
Solvent: Methanol HCl

λ Max. mμ	a_m	Cell mm	Conc. g/L
316	624	10	0.100
276	781	10	0.100
268	828	10	0.100
248	2530	1	0.050
217	16300	1	0.050

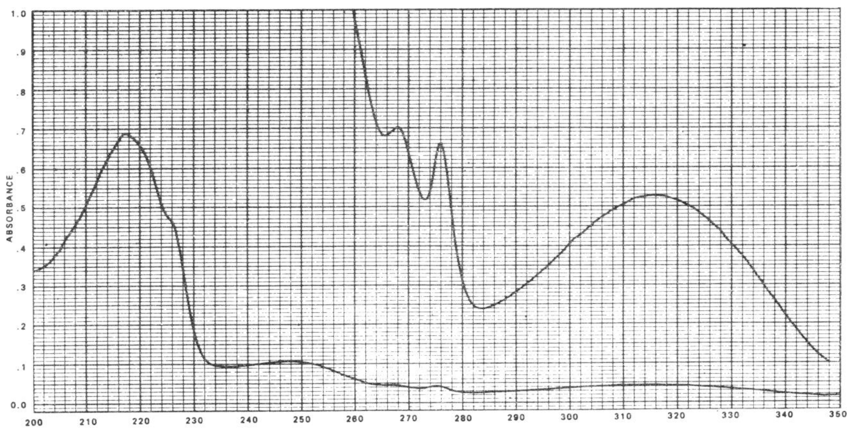

p-(DIETHYLAMINO)BENZONITRILE

995

$C_{11}H_{14}N_2$
Mol. Wt. 174.25
Solvent: Methanol

λ Max. mμ	a_m	Cell mm	Conc. g/L
345	3140	5	0.100
297	25400	0.5	0.100
219	8610	0.5	0.100

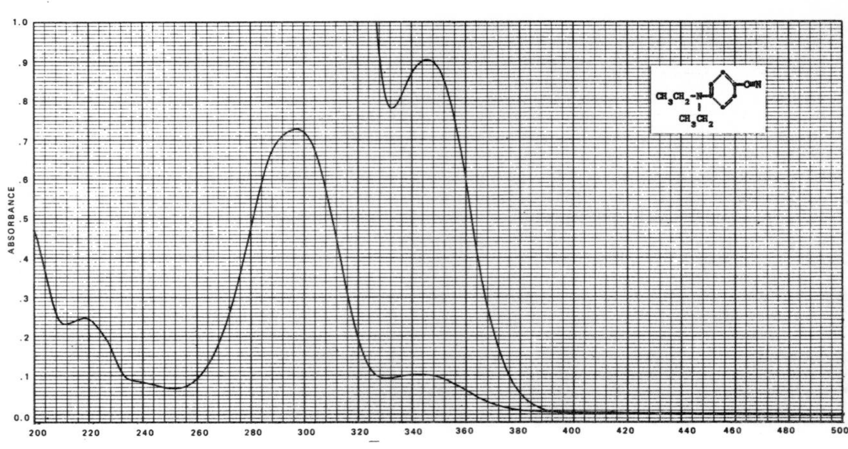

4,4'-BIPHENYLDICARBONITRILE

996

$C_{14}H_8N_2$
Mol. Wt. 204.23
M.P. 235-238°C
Solvent:

λ Max. mμ	a_m	Cell mm	Conc. g/L
274	45400	1	0.0200
218	18200	1	0.0200

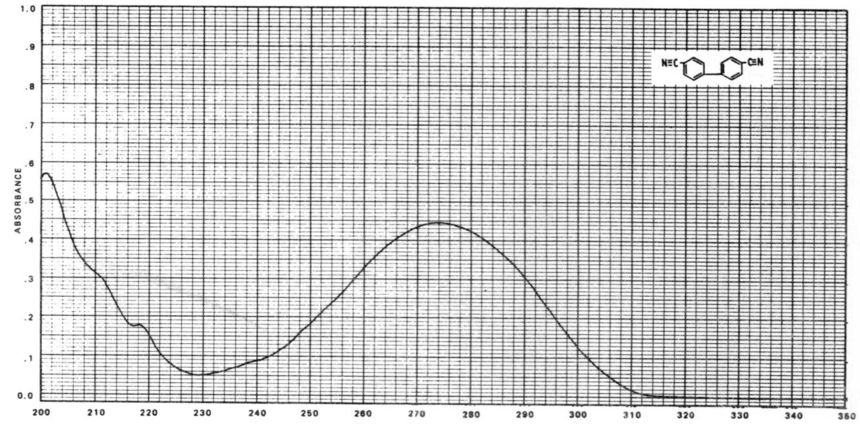

PHTHALONITRILE

997

$C_8H_4N_2$
Mol. Wt. 128.14
M.P. 140°C
Solvent: Methanol

λ Max. mμ	a_m	Cell mm	Conc. g/L
291	2090	10	0.03
281.5	1750	10	0.03
243	8070	10	0.01
236.5	10400	10	0.01
233	10100	10	0.01

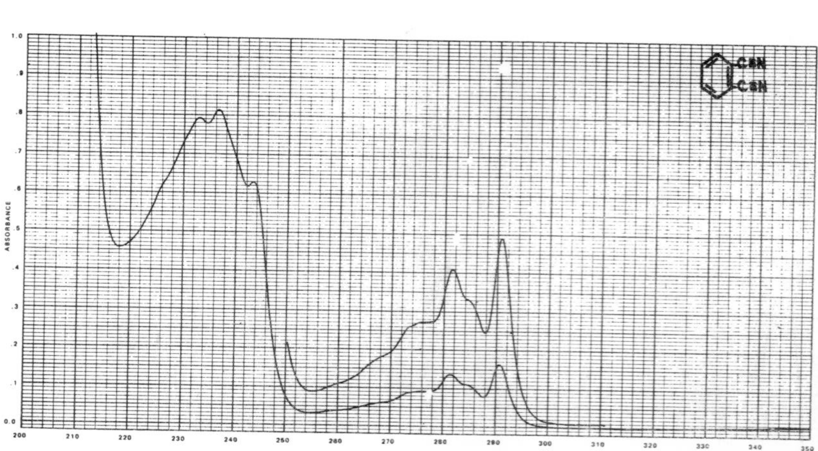

2-NAPHTHALENEACETONITRILE 998

$C_{12}H_9N$
Mol. Wt. 167.21
M.P. 82-84°C
Solvent: Methanol

λ Max. mμ	a_m	Cell mm	Conc. g/L
284.5	3350	2	0.100
275	4890	2	0.100
267	4500	2	0.100
223.5	11900	1	0.0100

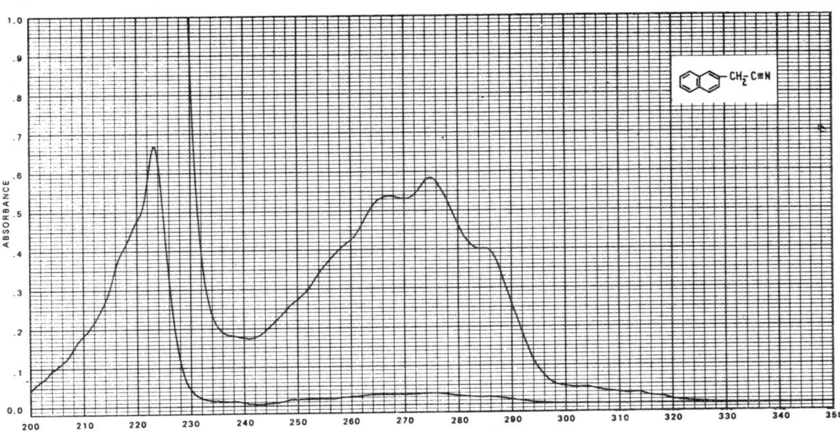

1-NAPHTHONITRILE 999

$C_{11}H_7N$
Mol. Wt. 153.19
M.P. 34-36°C
Solvent: Methanol

λ Max. mμ	a_m	Cell mm	Conc. g/L
322.3	2220	2	0.100
308.5	4990	2	0.100
296	6920	2	0.100
224	38500	1	0.0200
219	38300	1	0.0200

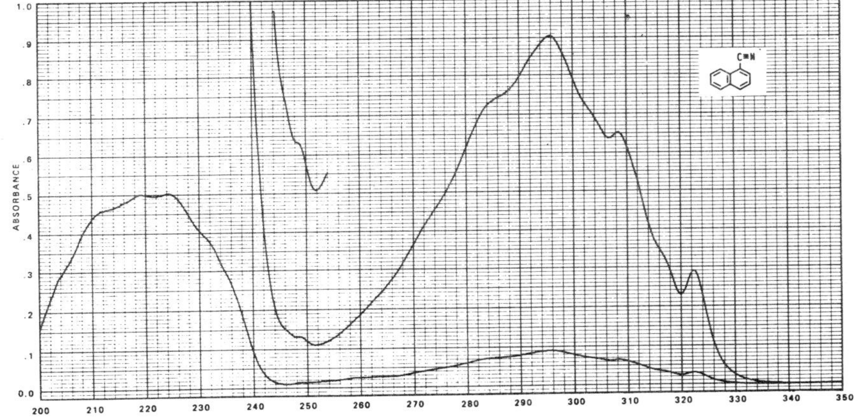

2-NAPHTHONITRILE 1000

$C_{11}H_7N$
Mol. Wt. 153.19
Solvent: Methanol

λ Max. mμ	a_m	Cell mm	Conc. g/L
330	1490	10	0.100
321.5	1040	10	0.100
315	1230	10	0.100
307.5	1060	10	0.100
280.5	6170	10	0.010
271.5	5470	10	0.010
234	77900	10	0.001

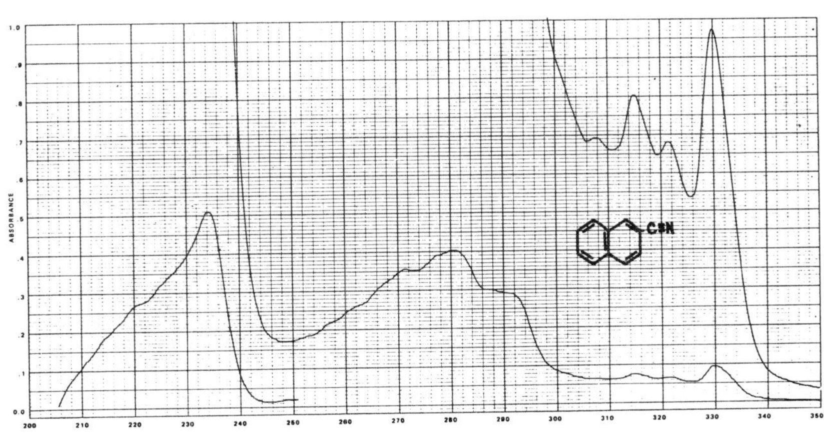

9-PHENANTHRENECARBONITRILE 1001

$C_{15}H_9N$
Mol. Wt. 203.45
Solvent: Methanol

λ Max. mμ	a_m	Cell mm	Conc. g/L
340	1040	10	0.100
311	14100	10	0.010
299	13600	10	0.010
274	11700	10	0.010
268.5	17100	10	0.010
258.5	52300	10	0.002
229.5	39800	10	0.002
211.5	30400	10	0.002

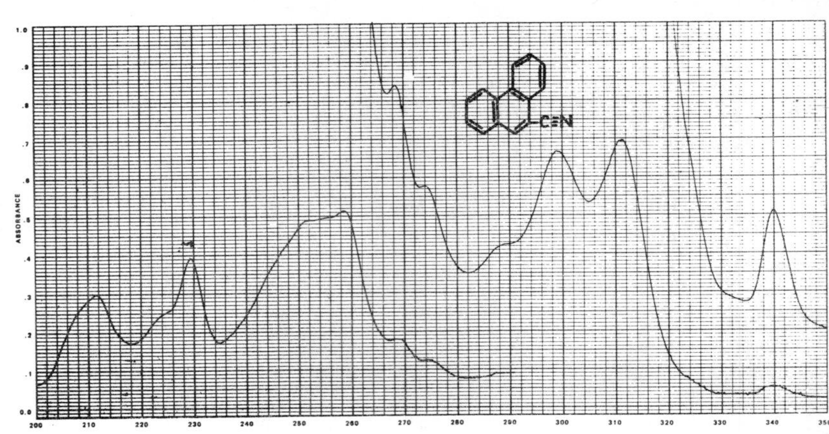

NICOTINONITRILE 1002

$C_6H_4N_2$
Mol. Wt. 104.11
Solvent: Methanol

λ Max. mμ	a_m	Cell mm	Conc. g/L
270	1800	10	0.065
263.5	2440	10	0.065
258	2260	10	0.065
216.7	10100	10	0.016

λ Max. mμ	a_m	Cell mm	Conc. g/L

THE CYANAMIDES

As spectra 1003 and 1004 illustrate, the aliphatic cyanamids do not display any maxima in the near UV region.

The spectrum of the dibenzyl derivative does not differ markedly from that of the parent compound, toluene.

THE THIOCYANATES

The thiocyanate chromophore produces very weak absorption band near 246 mμ. Substitution of the nitrile group by the sulfur atom results in a bathochromic shift similar to that observed for the olefinic chromophore when it is attached to a heteroatom containing a nonbonding electron pair such as sulfur.

DIMETHYLCYANAMIDE

1003

$C_3H_6N_2$
Mol. Wt. 70.09
B.P. 160°C
Solvent: Cyclohexane

λ Max. mμ	a_m	Cell mm	Conc. g/L
x	x	20	0.5
x	x	1	0.5

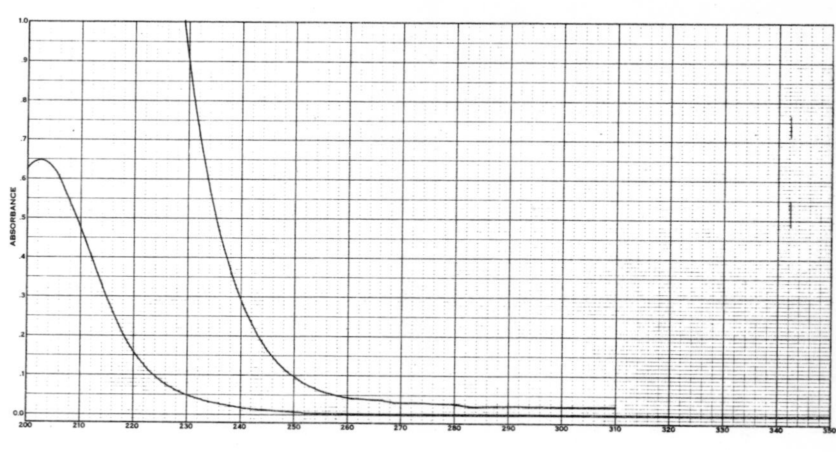

DIALLYLCYANAMIDE

1004

$C_7H_{10}N_2$
Mol. Wt. 122.17
B.P. 222°C
Solvent: Cyclohexane

λ Max. mμ	a_m	Cell mm	Conc. g/L
x	x	20	0.500
x	x	2	0.500

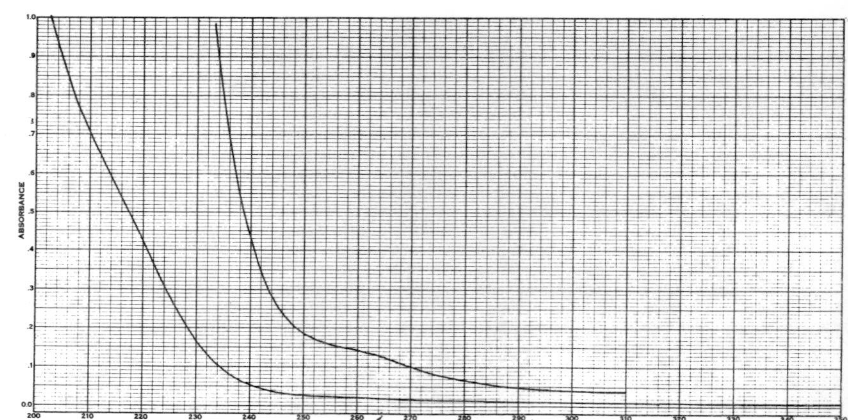

DIBENZYLCYANAMIDE

1005

$C_{15}H_{14}N_2$
Mol. Wt. 222.29
Solvent: Methanol

λ Max. mμ	a_m	Cell mm	Conc. g/L
267.5	248	10	0.700
264	388	10	0.700
258	491	10	0.700
252	432	10	0.700
247	381	10	0.700

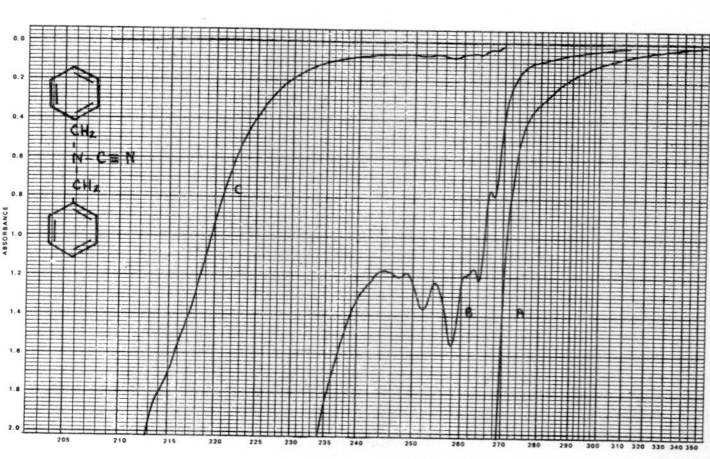

CYCLOHEXYL ISOCYANIDE 1006

$C_7H_{11}N$

Mol. Wt. 109.17

λ Max. mμ	a_m	Cell mm	Conc. g/L

Pure sample not available.

THIOCYANIC ACID, METHYL ESTER 1007

C_2H_3NS

Mol. Wt. 73.12

B.P. 130-132°C

Solvent: Methanol

λ Max. mμ	a_m	Cell mm	Conc. g/L
246.5	45.9	20	0.5
x	x	5	0.5

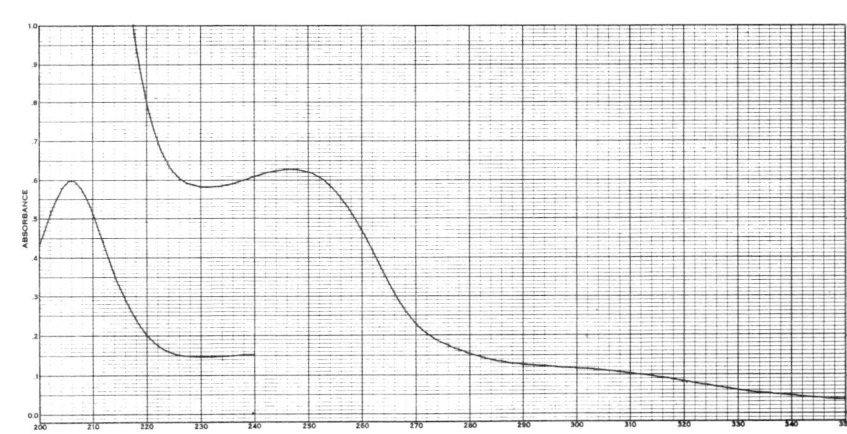

THIOCYANIC ACID, ETHYL ESTER 1008

C_3H_5NS

Mol. Wt. 87.14

B.P. 143-145°C

λ Max. mμ	a_m	Cell mm	Conc. g/L

Pure sample not available.

THIOCYANIC ACID, OCTYL ESTER 1010

$C_9H_{17}NS$

Mol. Wt. 171.31

λ Max. mμ	a_m	Cell mm	Conc. g/L

Pure sample not available.

THIOCYANIC ACID, BUTYL ESTER 1009

C_5H_9NS

Mol. Wt. 115.20

B.R. 180-183°C (lit.)

Solvent: Cyclohexane

λ Max. mμ	a_m	Cell mm	Conc. g/L
245	48.8	10	2.170

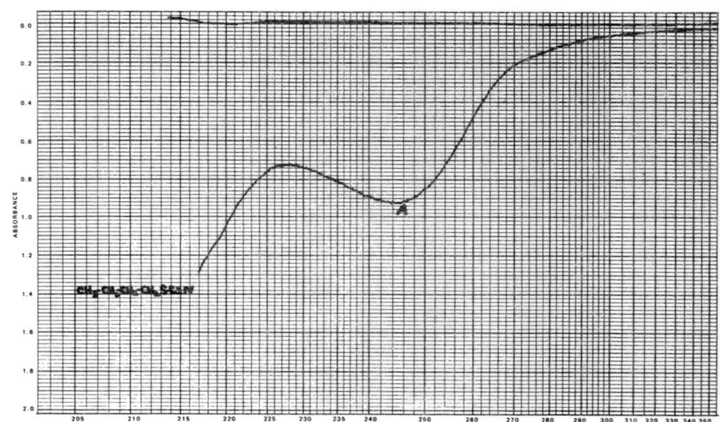

THIOCYANIC ACID, DECYL ESTER 1011

$C_{11}H_{21}NS$

Mol. Wt. 199.36

Solvent: Methanol

λ Max. mμ	a_m	Cell mm	Conc. g/L
246.2	50.4	20	0.5

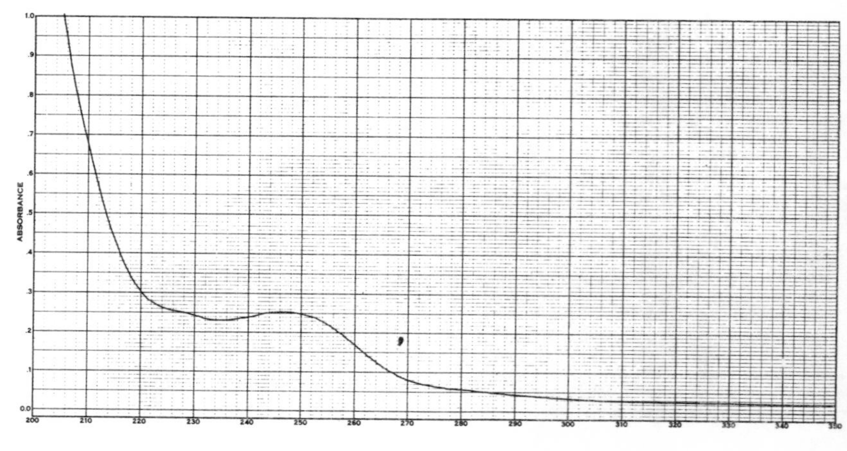

THIOCYANIC ACID, DODECYL ESTER 1012

$C_{13}H_{25}NS$
Mol. Wt. 227.41
B.P. 183-185°C/10mm

λ Max. mμ	a_m	Cell mm	Conc. g/L

Pure sample not available.

THIOCYANIC ACID, CHLOROMETHYL ESTER 1013

C_2H_2ClNS
Mol. Wt. 107.56

λ Max. mμ	a_m	Cell mm	Conc. g/L

Pure sample not available.

THIOCYANIC ACID, METHYLENE ESTER 1014

$C_3H_2N_2S_2$
Mol. Wt. 130.19
M.P. 104-106°C

λ Max. mμ	a_m	Cell mm	Conc. g/L

Pure sample not available.

THIOCYANIC ACID, ETHYLENE ESTER

1015

$C_4H_4N_2S_2$

Mol. Wt. 144.22

M.P. 88-90°C

Solvent: Dioxane

λ Max. mμ	a_m	Cell mm	Conc. g/L
244.0	174	10.0	0.5

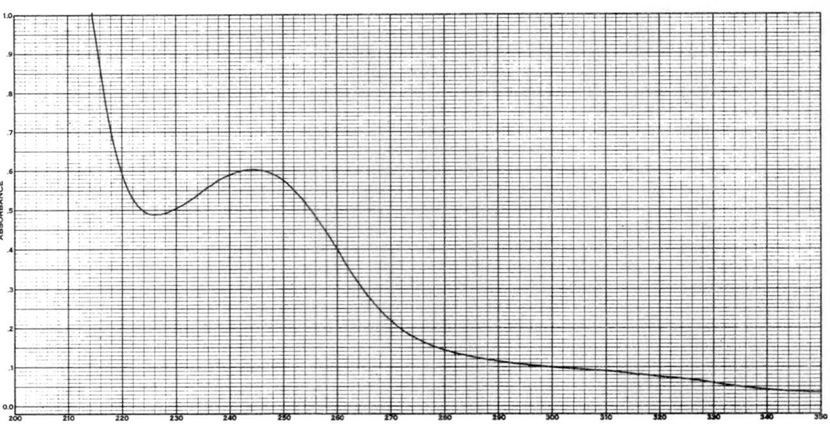

THIOCYANIC ACID, TETRAMETHYLENE ESTER

1016

$C_6H_8N_2S_2$

Mol. Wt. 172.27

B.P. 180-182°C/4mm

Solvent: Methanol

λ Max. mμ	a_m	Cell mm	Conc. g/L
257.5	157	20	0.5
x	x	5	0.25

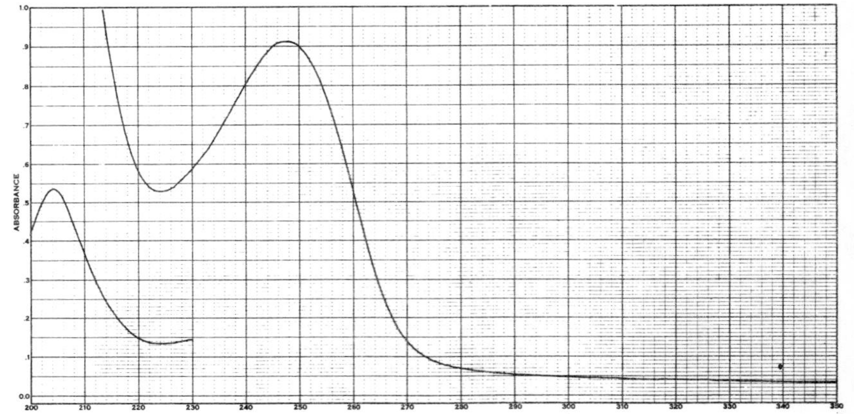

THIOCYANIC ACID, BENZYL ESTER

1017

C_8H_7NS

Mol. Wt. 149.22

Solvent: Methanol

λ Max. mμ	a_m	Cell mm	Conc. g/L
x	x	10	2.004
259.5	624	10	0.2004
x	x	10	0.020

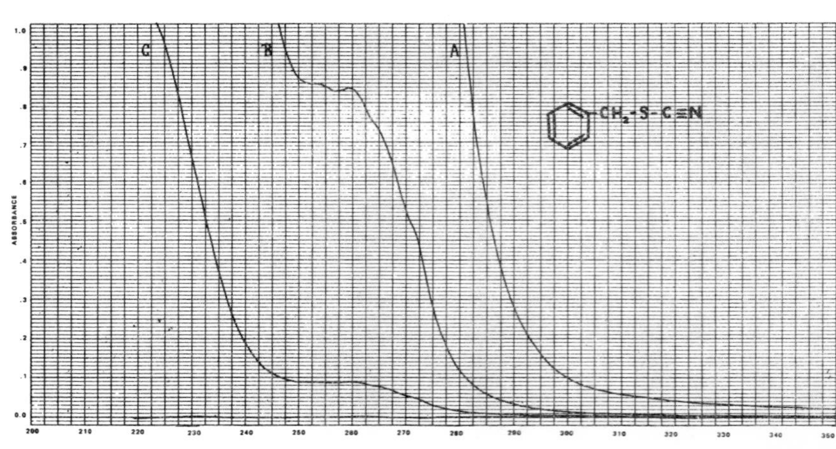

THIOCYANIC ACID, 2,6-DICHLOROBENZYL ESTER

1018

$C_8H_5Cl_2NS$
Mol. Wt. 218.11
M.P. 40-42°C
Solvent: Methanol

λ Max. mμ	a_m	Cell mm	Conc. g/L
286	579	20	0,100
277	676	20	0.100

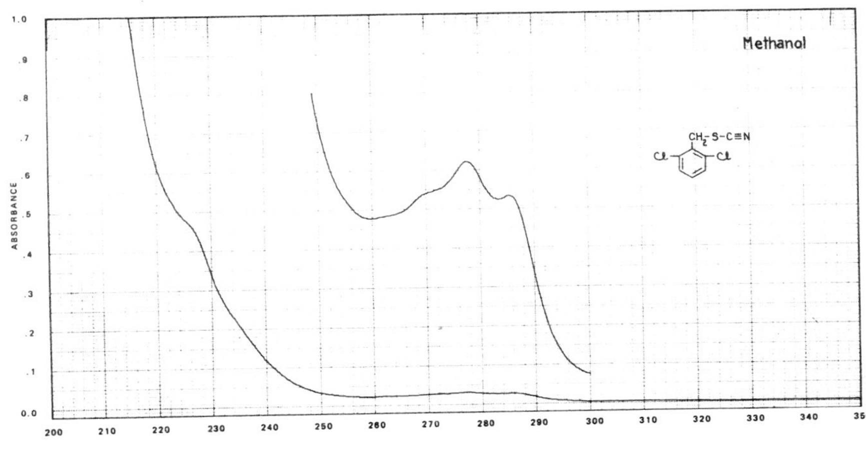

THIOCYANIC ACID, CINNAMYL ESTER

1019

$C_{10}H_9NS$
Mol. Wt. 175.26
Solvent: Methanol

λ Max. mμ	a_m	Cell mm	Conc. g/L
293	2280	10	0.05
257	16400	10	0.009

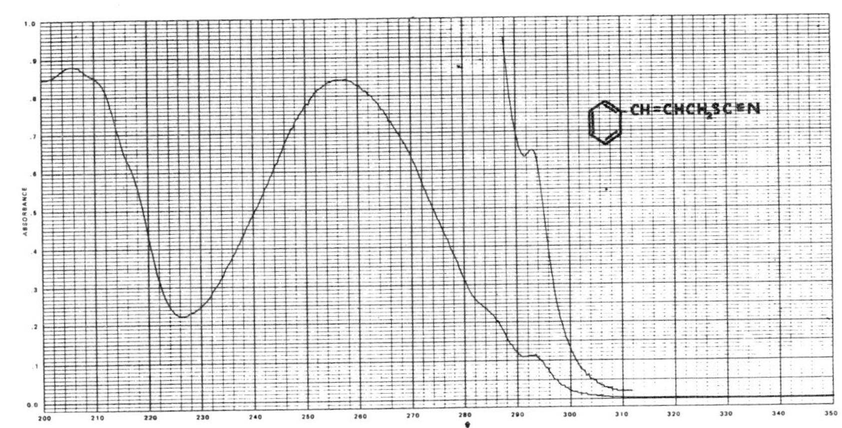

THIOCYANIC ACID, 5-INDOLINYL ESTER

1020

$C_9H_8N_2S$
Mol. Wt. 176.24
M.P. 60°C

λ Max. mμ	a_m	Cell mm	Conc. g/L

Pure sample not available.

NOTES

THE NITROSO COMPOUNDS

The aliphatic and aromatic nitroso compounds show absorption bands in both the near UV and visible regions of the spectrum.

t-Nitrosobutane displays two weak bands one at 300 mμ ($\epsilon = 100$) and the other at 665 mμ ($\epsilon = 20$), with a much stronger absorption at about 200 mμ ($\epsilon = 5000$). Upon dimerization of the aliphatic nitroso compounds a new band appears around 270 mμ.

Nitrosobenzene displays absorption bands at 219 mμ ($\epsilon = 5800$), 282 mμ ($\epsilon = 9300$), 306 mμ ($\epsilon = 8000$) and 750 mμ ($\epsilon = 45$) in acetonitrile solution (Lit.).

THE NITROSOAMINES

Aliphatic Compounds

The N-nitroso chromophore produces two major bands in the near UV. The more intense band absorbs at about 235 mμ while the weaker band which displays fine structure appears at about 370 mμ.

Aromatic Compounds

The aromatic nitrosoanilines produce UV spectra somewhat similar in appearance to that of aniline, i.e. the presence of a broad, relatively intense band at longer wavelength than that of benzene. These bands do not normally display any benzenoid fine structure.

Compound	$\lambda_{max}(\epsilon_{max})$	$\lambda_{max}(\epsilon_{max})$	Solvent	Spectrum
Benzene	204 (8800)	254 (250)	Hexane	Lit.
Aniline	230 (8200)	281 (1400)	Water	Lit.
N-Methyl-N-nitrosoaniline	- - - - - - - - - -	270 (7380)	Methanol	1031
N-Nitrosodiphenylamine	- - - - - - - - - -	262 (13600)	Methanol	1032

THE NITRITES

The UV spectra of the aliphatic nitrites characteristically contain two major bands, one at about 223 mμ and a second weaker band near 355 mμ. The band at 355 mμ normally shows considerable fine structure with as many as eight distinct maxima being observed. The wavelengths of these bands are as follows: 313, 322, 333, 343, 355, 369, 383 and 400 mμ.

THE NITRO COMPOUNDS

Aliphatic Compounds

The nitro chromophore produces a very weak absorption band in the region from 277 - 281 mμ ($\epsilon = 19 - 27$) as shown in spectra 1039 through 1044.

Aromatic Compounds

Nitrobenzene and its alkyl group substituted derivatives produce UV spectra containing a moderately strong band in the region from 250 - 275 mμ with an $\epsilon_{max} = 4000 - 12000$ (spectra 1046 - 1048).

2-METHYL-2-NITROSOPROPANE 1021

C_4H_9NP

Mol. Wt. 87.12

λ Max. mμ	a_m	Cell mm	Conc. g/L

This compound does not produce maxima in the near UV.

p-NITROSODIPHENYLAMINE 1022

$C_{12}H_{10}N_2O$

Mol. Wt. 198.23

M.P. 144-145°C

Solvent: Methanol

λ Max. mμ	a_m	Cell mm	Conc. g/L
425	28500	1	0.050
261.5	9870	1	0.050

p-NITROSODIPHENYLAMINE 1022

$C_{12}H_{10}N_2O$

Mol. Wt. 198.23

M.P. 144-145°C

Solvent: Methanol KOH

λ Max. mμ	a_m	Cell mm	Conc. g/L
378	295	10	0.050
295	1990	10	0.050
256	1980	10	0.050

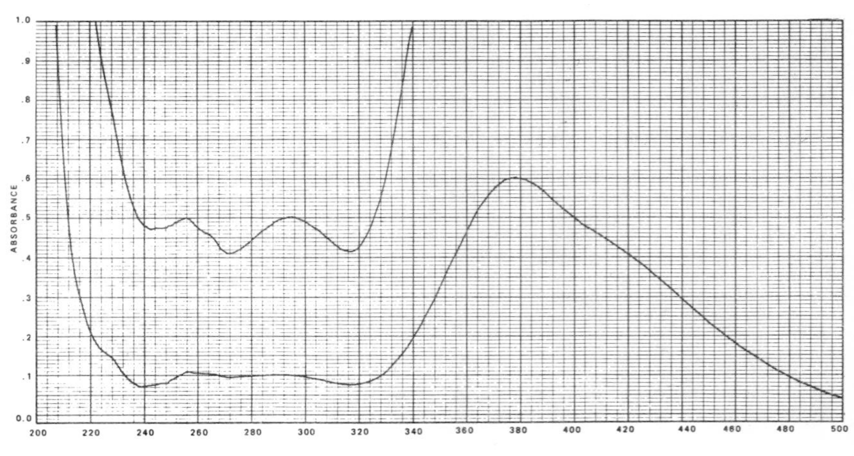

1022

p-NITROSODIPHENYLAMINE

$C_{12}H_{10}N_2O$
Mol. Wt. 198.23
M.P. 144-145°C
Solvent: Methanol HCl

λ Max. mμ	a_m	Cell mm	Conc. g/L
394	17500	1	0.10
260	2060	5	0.10

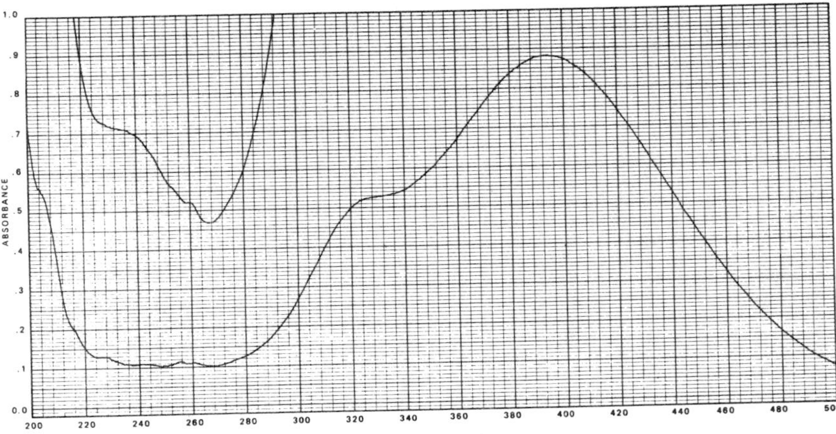

1023

N,N-DIMETHYL-p-NITROSOANILINE

$C_8H_{10}N_2O$
Mol. Wt. 150.18
M.P. 85°C (lit.)
Solvent: Methanol

λ Max. mμ	a_m	Cell mm	Conc. g/L
272.5	616	10	0.40
234	383	10	0.40

λ Max. mμ	a_m	Cell mm	Conc. g/L

N,N-DIETHYL-4-NITROSOANILINE

$C_{10}H_{14}N_2O$

Mol. Wt. 178.23

M.P. 82-83°C

Solvent: Methanol

λ Max. mμ	a_m	Cell mm	Conc. g/L
428.5	31800	1	0.0500
275	5570	2	0.100
238	3210	2	0.100

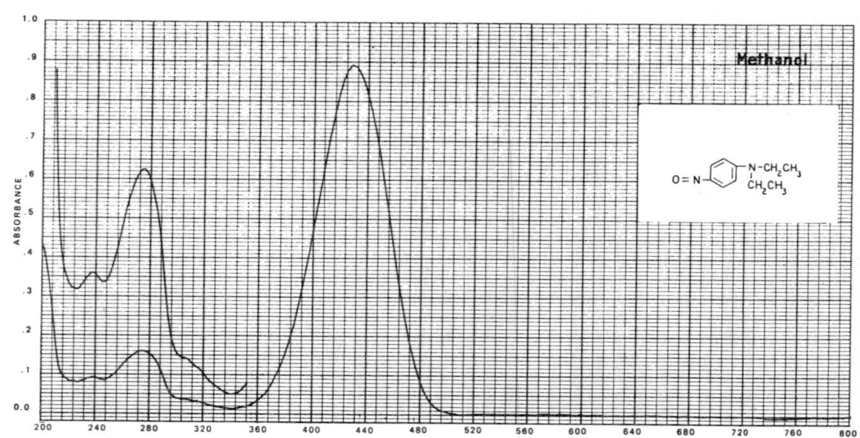

1024

N,N-DIETHYL-4-NITROSOANILINE

$C_{10}H_{14}N_2O$

Mol. Wt. 178.23

M.P. 82-83°C

Solvent: Methanol HCl

λ Max. mμ	a_m	Cell mm	Conc. g/L
362	22700	1	0.0500

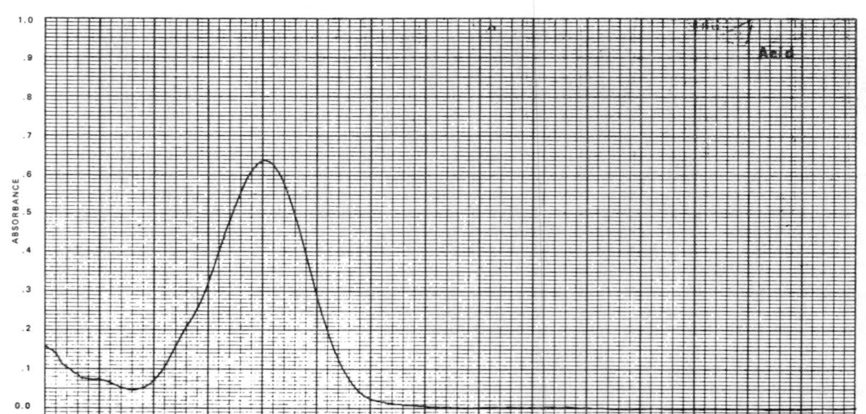

1025

N-NITROSODIMETHYLAMINE

$C_2H_6N_2O$

Mol. Wt. 74.08

B.P. 153°C/774mm

Solvent: Methanol

λ Max. mμ	a_m	Cell mm	Conc. g/L
373	102	10	0.5
361	123	10	0.5
231	5510	0.5	0.25

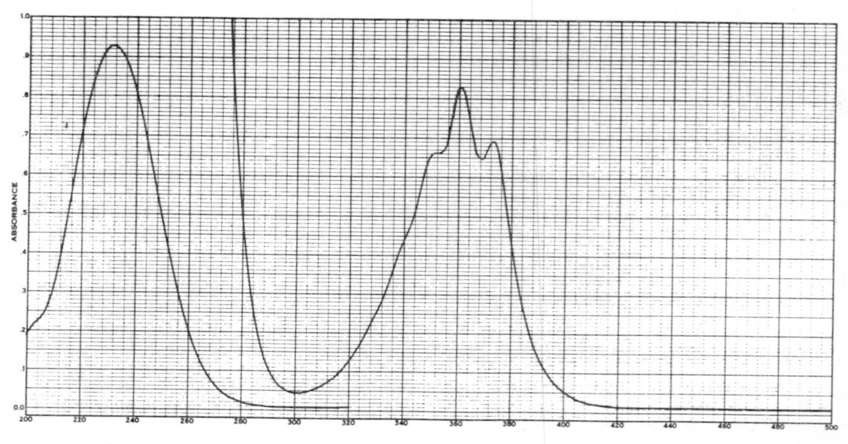

N-NITROSODIETHYLAMINE

1026

$C_4H_{10}N_2O$
Mol. Wt. 102.14
B.P. 59-60°C/8-9mm
Solvent: Methanol

λ Max. mμ	a_m	Cell mm	Conc. g/L
378	87.8	10	0.5
365	102	10	0.5
234	4850	0.5	0.25

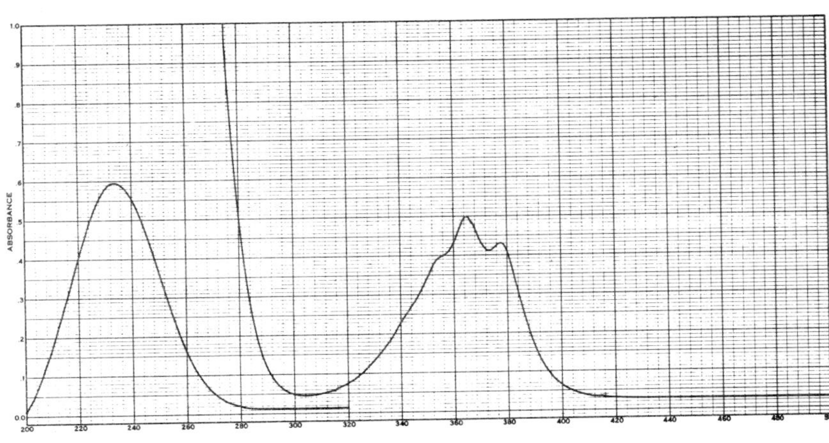

N-NITROSODIPROPYLAMINE

1027

$C_6H_{14}N_2O$
Mol. Wt. 130.19
B.P. 77-78°C/8mm

λ Max. mμ	a_m	Cell mm	Conc. g/L

Pure sample not available.

N-NITROSODICYCLOHEXYLAMINE

1028

$C_{12}H_{22}N_2O$
Mol. Wt. 210.32
M.P. 105-108°C
Solvent: Methanol

λ Max. mμ	a_m	Cell mm	Conc. g/L
386	90.4	20	0.5
372	98.8	20	0.5
238	6410	0.5	0.5

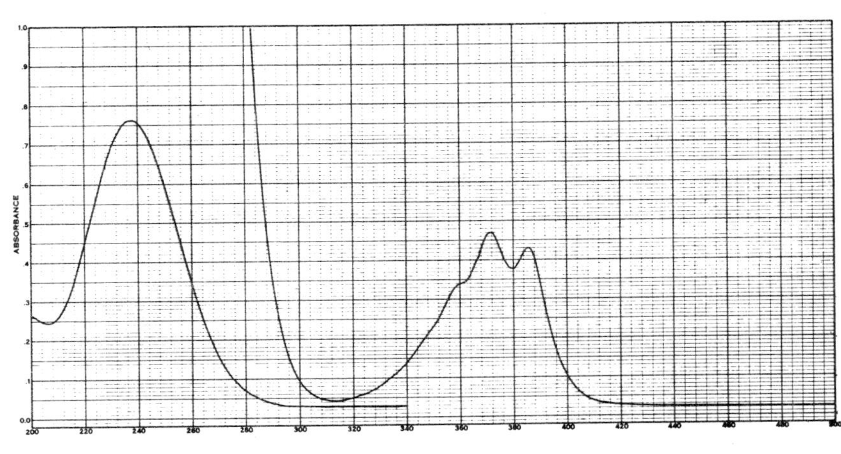

1-NITROSOPYRROLIDINE 1029

$C_4H_8N_2O$

Mol. Wt. 100.12

B.P. 74°C/4mm

λ Max. mμ	a_m	Cell mm	Conc. g/L

Pure sample not available.

1-NITROSOPIPERIDINE 1030

$C_5H_{10}N_2O$

Mol. Wt. 114.15

B.P. 216.5°C/760mm

Solvent: Methanol

λ Max. mμ	a_m	Cell mm	Conc. g/L
376	116	10	0.5
364	122	10	0.5
238	3360	0.5	0.5

N-METHYL-N-NITROSOANILINE 1031

$C_7H_8N_2O$

Mol. Wt. 136.15

M.P. 14-15°C

Solvent: Methanol

λ Max. mμ	a_m	Cell mm	Conc. g/L
270	7380	1	0.0970

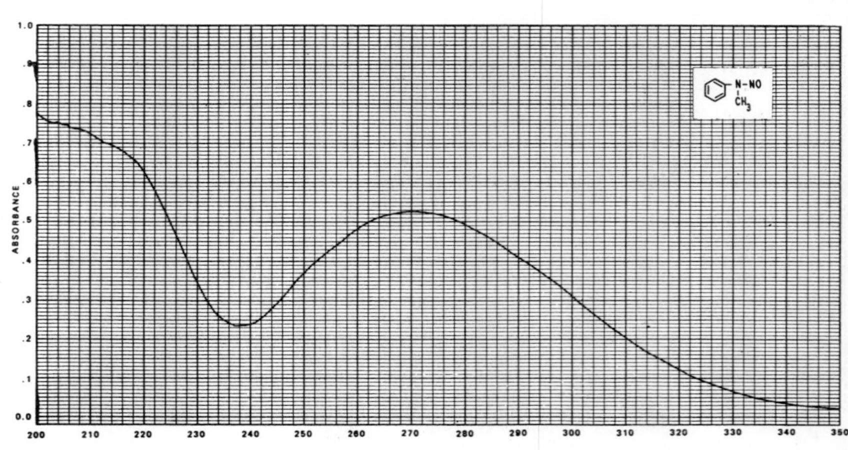

N-NITROSODIPHENYLAMINE 1032

$C_{12}H_{10}N_2O$
Mol. Wt. 198.23
M.P. 67-68°C (lit.)
Solvent: Methanol

λ Max. mμ	a_m	Cell mm	Conc. g/L
262	13600	10	0.0208

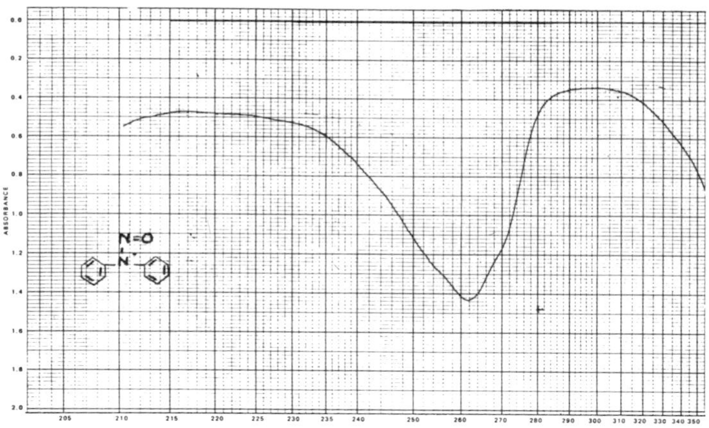

PROPYL NITRITE 1033

$C_3H_7NO_2$
Mol. Wt. 89.09

λ Max. mμ	a_m	Cell mm	Conc. g/L

Pure sample not available.

sec-BUTYL NITRITE 1034

$C_4H_9NO_2$
Mol. Wt. 103.12

λ Max. mμ	a_m	Cell mm	Conc. g/L

Pure sample not available.

ISOBUTYL NITRITE 1035

$C_4H_9NO_2$

Mol. Wt. 103.12

λ Max. mμ	a_m	Cell mm	Conc. g/L

Pure sample not available.

tert-BUTYL NITRITE 1036

$C_4H_9NO_2$

Mol. Wt. 103.12

B.P. 62-64°C

λ Max. mμ	a_m	Cell mm	Conc. g/L

Pure sample not available.

ISOPENTYL NITRITE 1037

$C_5H_{11}NO_2$

Mol. Wt. 117.15

B.P. 96.5-98.5°C

λ Max. mμ	a_m	Cell mm	Conc. g/L

Pure sample not available.

OCTYL NITRITE

1038

$C_8H_{17}NO_2$
Mol. Wt. 159.23
B.P. 52-53°C/6mm
Solvent: Methanol

λ Max. mμ	a_m	Cell mm	Conc. g/L
369	46.8	20	0.5
355	53.7	20	0.5
343	47.2	20	0.5
333	35.5	20	0.5
322	25.6	20	0.5
221	1000	2	0.5

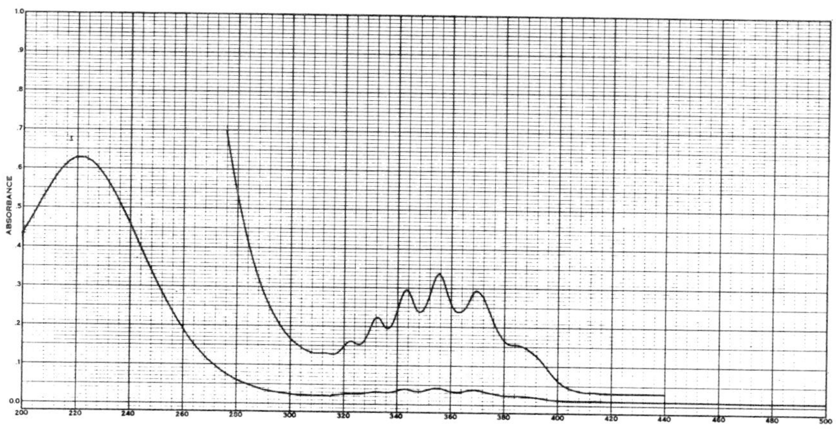

NITROMETHANE

1039

CH_3NO_2
Mol. Wt. 61.04
Solvent: Cyclohexane

λ Max. mμ	a_m	Cell mm	Conc. g/L
277	18.5	10	4.76
x	x	10	0.0476

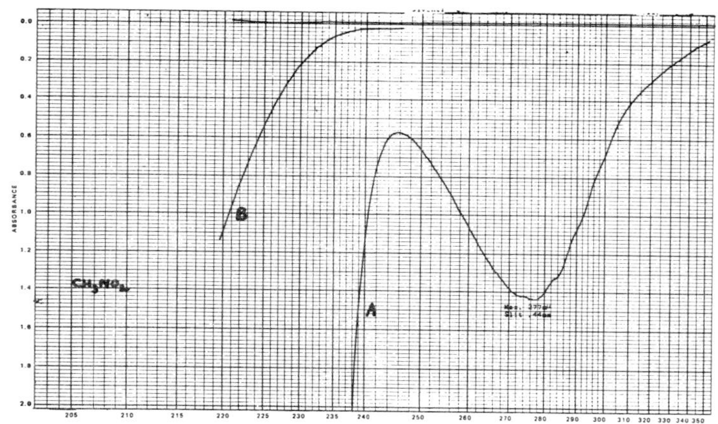

NITROETHANE

1040

$C_2H_5NO_2$
Mol. Wt. 75.07
Solvent: Cyclohexane

λ Max. mμ	a_m	Cell mm	Conc. g/L
277	20.8	10	4.64
x	x	10	0.0464

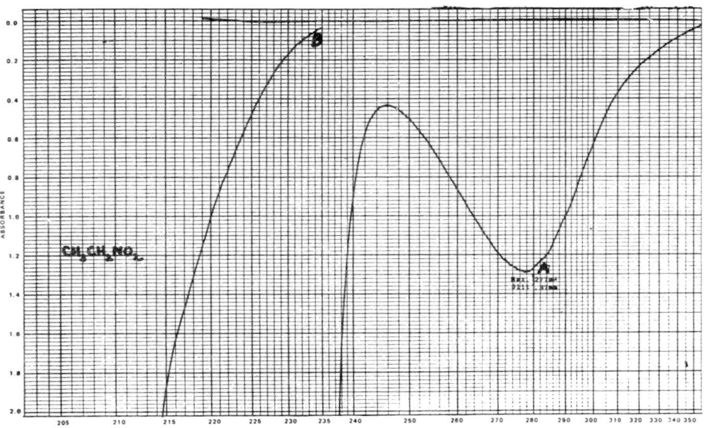

1-NITROPROPANE

1041

$C_3H_7NO_2$
Mol. Wt. 89.09
Solvent: Cyclohexane

λ Max. mμ	a_m	Cell mm	Conc. g/L
279.5	27.0	10	3.36
x	x	10	0.336

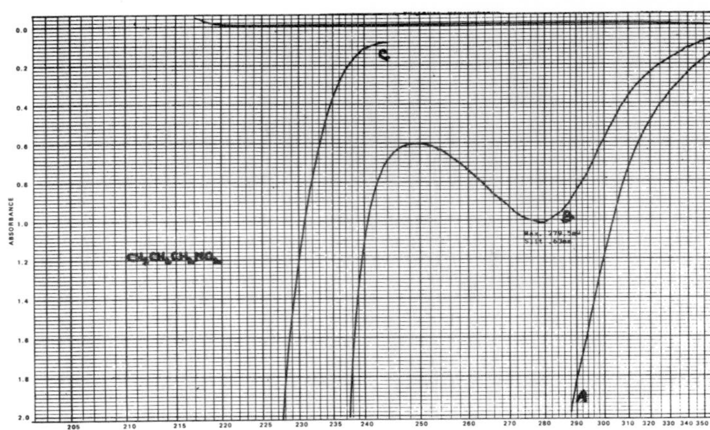

2-NITROPROPANE

1042

$C_3H_7NO_2$
Mol. Wt. 89.10
B.P. 102.30°C (lit.)
Solvent: Cyclohexane

λ Max. mμ	a_m	Cell mm	Conc. g/L
278	23.8	10	5.1680
x	x	10	0.0517

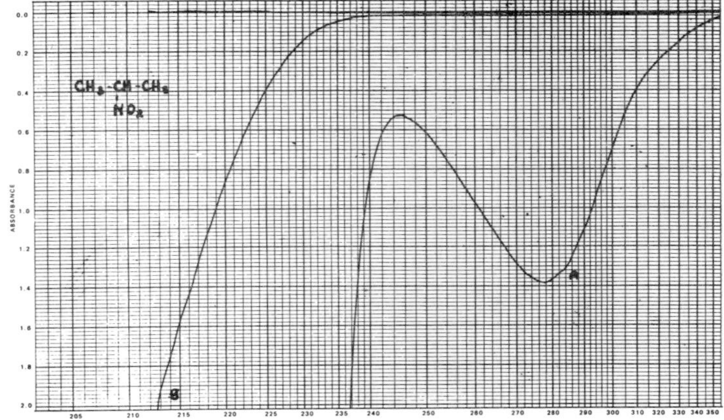

2-METHYL-2-NITROPROPANE

1043

$C_4H_9NO_2$
Mol. Wt. 103.12
M.P. 24-26°C

λ Max. mμ	a_m	Cell mm	Conc. g/L

Pure sample not available.

1-CHLORO-1-NITROETHANE

1044

$C_2H_4ClNO_2$

Mol. Wt. 109.52

B.P. 122-128.5°C (lit.)

Solvent: Cyclohexane

λ Max. mμ	a_m	Cell mm	Conc. g/L
281	27.3	10	6.0120
x	x	10	0.0601

NITROCYCLOHEXANE

1045

$C_6H_{11}NO_2$

Mol. Wt. 129.16

B.P. 205.5°C (dec.)

λ Max. mμ	a_m	Cell mm	Conc. g/L

Pure sample not available.

o-NITROTOLUENE

1046

$C_7H_7NO_2$

Mol. Wt. 137.14

B.P. 110-112°C/20mm (lit.)

Solvent: Methanol

λ Max. mμ	a_m	Cell mm	Conc. g/L
253.5	4330	1	0.190

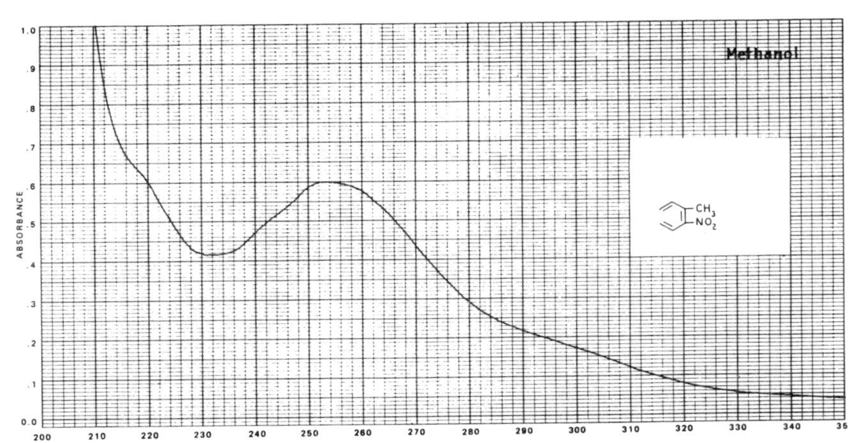

m-NITROTOLUENE 1047

$C_7H_7NO_2$

Mol. Wt. 137.14

B.P. 231°C (lit.)

Solvent: Methanol

λ Max. mμ	a_m	Cell mm	Conc. g/L
264	7700	1	0.143

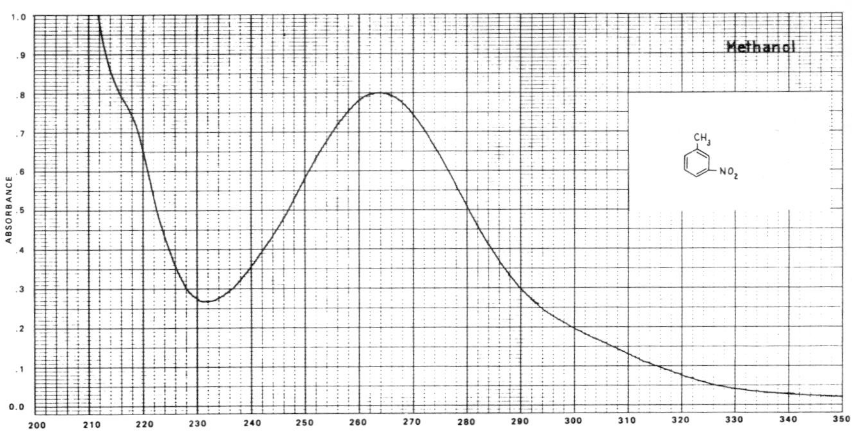

p-NITROTOLUENE 1048

$C_7H_7NO_2$

Mol. Wt. 137.14

M.P. 51-52°C

Solvent: Methanol

λ Max. mμ	a_m	Cell mm	Conc. g/L
273.5	11700	1	0.100
215	9440	1	0.100

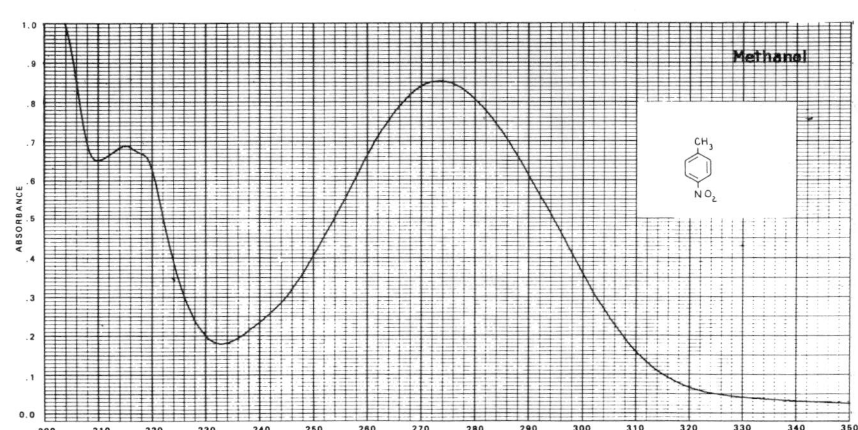

1-ETHYL-2-NITROBENZENE 1049

$C_8H_9NO_2$

Mol. Wt. 151.17

Solvent: Methanol

λ Max. mμ	a_m	Cell mm	Conc. g/L
257	4645	10	0.0096
205	14300	10	0.0096

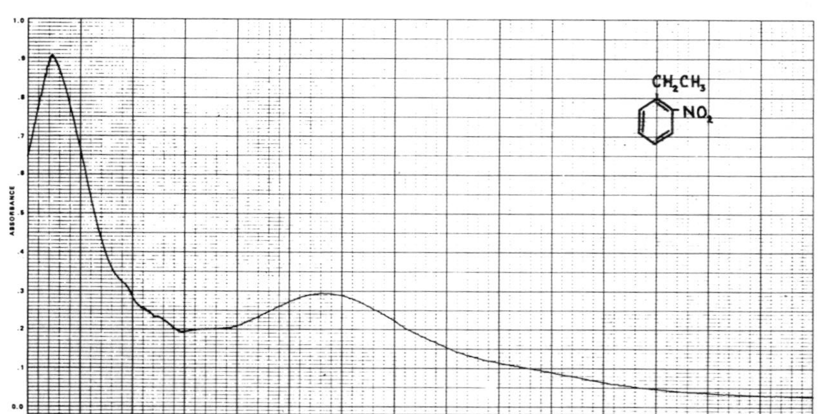

1-ETHYL-4-NITROBENZENE 1050

$C_8H_9NO_2$
Mol. Wt. 151.17
Solvent: Methanol

λ Max. mμ	a_m	Cell mm	Conc. g/L
274	21400	1	0.0500
215	16100	1	0.0500

2-NITROBIPHENYL 1051

$C_{12}H_9NO_2$
Mol. Wt. 199.21
B.P. 325°C
Solvent: Methanol

λ Max. mμ	a_m	Cell mm	Conc. g/L
231	16300	10	0.01

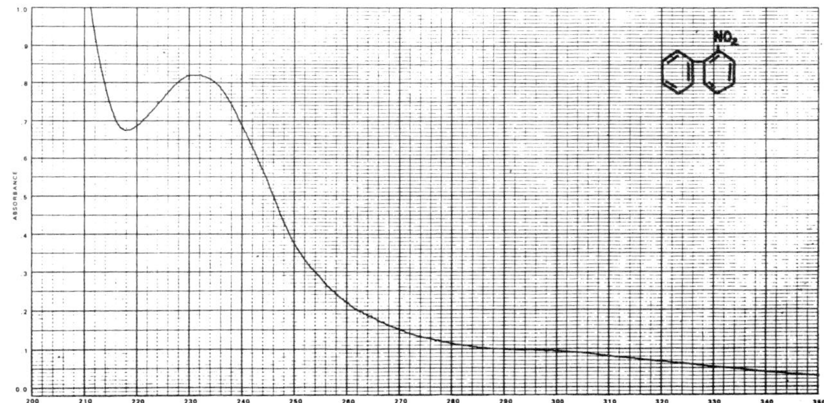

3-NITROBIPHENYL 1052

$C_{12}H_9NO_2$
Mol. Wt. 199.21
B.P. 140-146°C/9mm M.P. 58.5-61°C (lit.)
Solvent: Methanol

λ Max. mμ	a_m	Cell mm	Conc. g/L
248	26100	1	0.0700

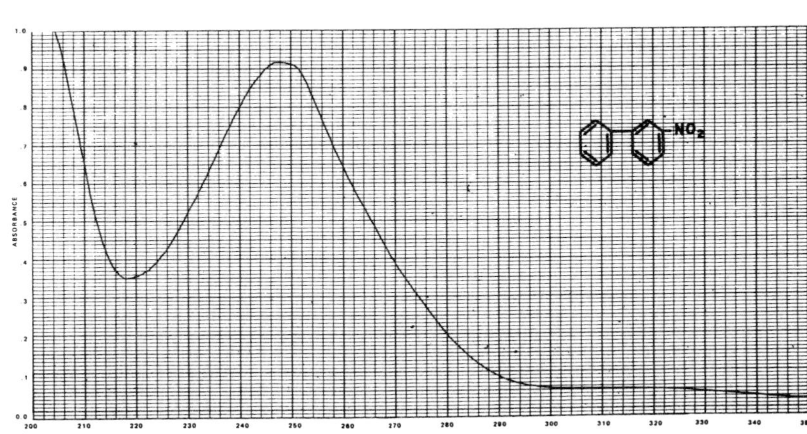

4-NITROBIPHENYL

1053

$C_{12}H_9NO_2$
Mol. Wt. 199.21
M.P. 113°C (lit.)
Solvent: Methanol

λ Max. mμ	a_m	Cell mm	Conc. g/L
305	14700	1	0.100
222	11600	1	0.100

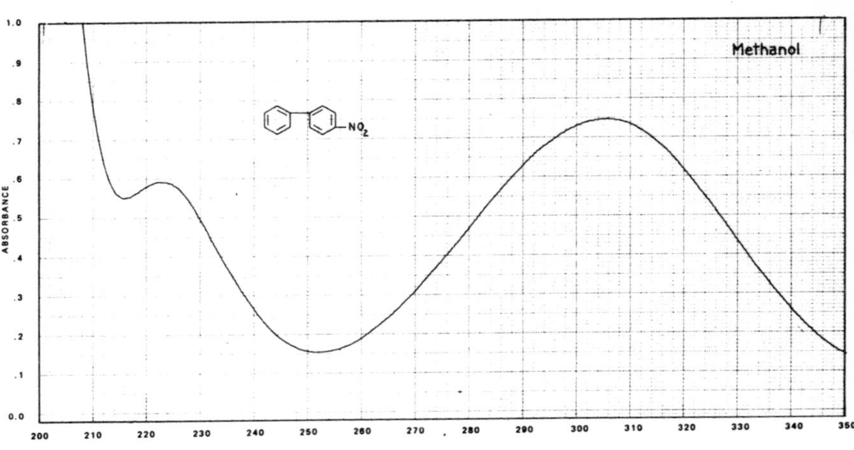

1-FLUORO-2-NITROBENZENE

1054

$C_6H_4FNO_2$
Mol. Wt. 141.10
B.P. 219-220°C
Solvent: Methanol

λ Max. mμ	a_m	Cell mm	Conc. g/L
301.5	2160	2	0.219
242	7420	1	0.109

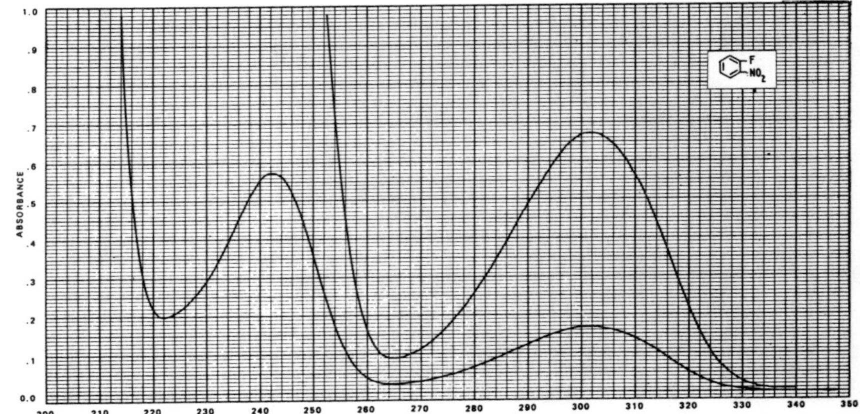
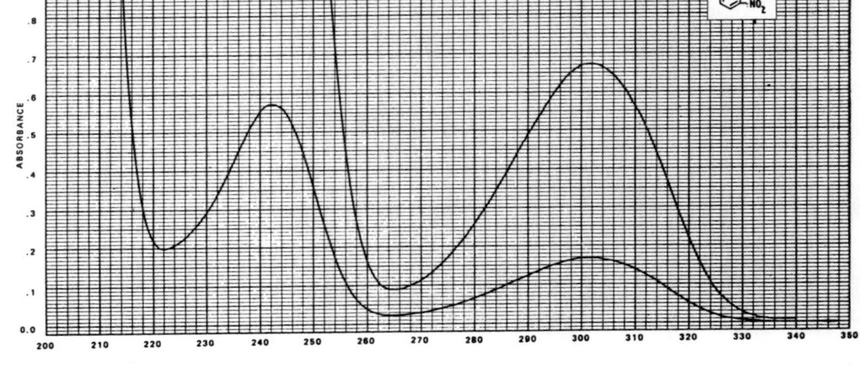

1-FLUORO-4-NITROBENZENE

1055

$C_6H_4FNO_2$
Mol. Wt. 141.10
M.P. 25-27°C (lit.)
Solvent: Methanol

λ Max. mμ	a_m	Cell mm	Conc. g/L
263	11900	1	0.100
211.5	14100	1	0.100

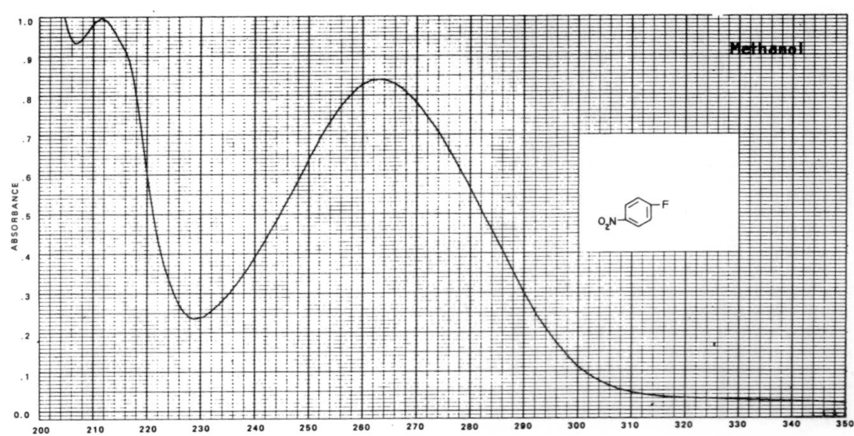

1-CHLORO-2-NITROBENZENE

1056

$C_6H_4ClNO_2$
Mol. Wt. 157.56
M.P. 31-32°C
Solvent: Methanol

λ Max. mμ	a_m	Cell mm	Conc. g/L
251	3620	1	0.100
209.5	14300	1	0.100

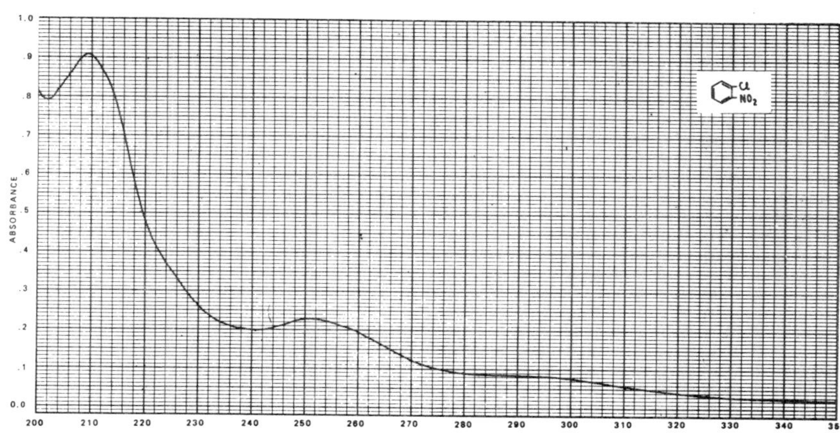

1-CHLORO-3-NITROBENZENE

1057

$C_6H_4ClNO_2$
Mol. Wt. 157.56
M.P. 43.9°C
Solvent: Methanol

λ Max. mμ	a_m	Cell mm	Conc. g/L
257	7230	10	0.01
206	19500	10	0.005

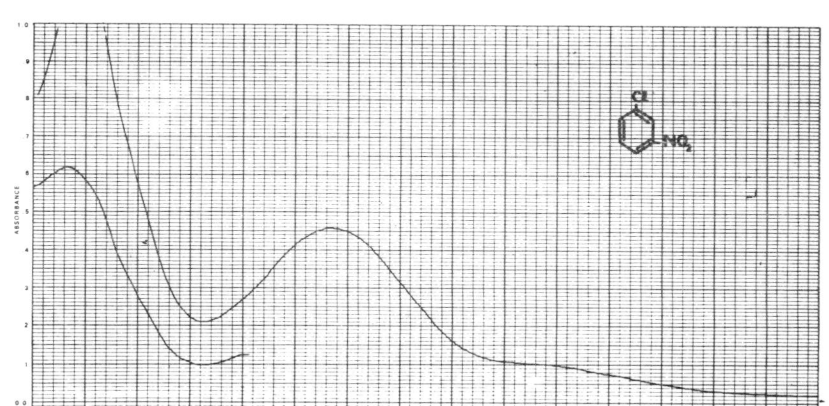

1-CHLORO-4-NITROBENZENE

1058

$C_6H_4ClNO_2$
Mol. Wt. 157.56
M.P. 82.5°C (lit.)
Solvent: Methanol

λ Max. mμ	a_m	Cell mm	Conc. g/L
269.5	10300	1	0.125
214.5	8140	1	0.125

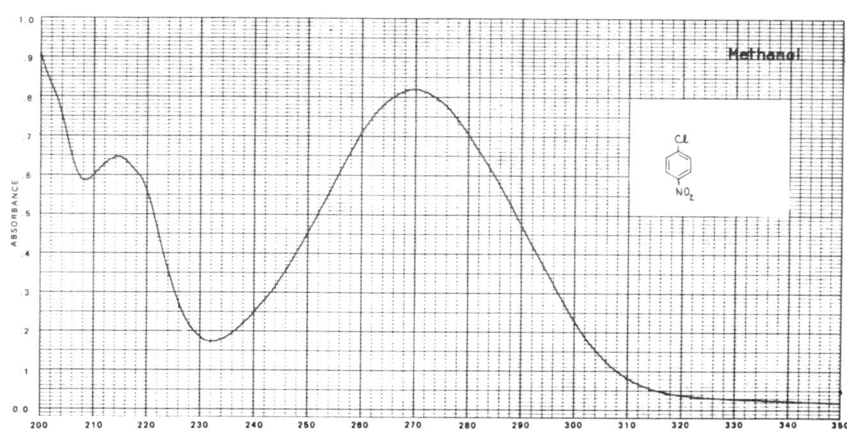

1-BROMO-2-NITROBENZENE

1059

$C_6H_4BrNO_2$
Mol. Wt. 202.01
M.P. 41-42°C
Solvent: Methanol

λ Max. mμ	a_m	Cell mm	Conc. g/L
291	1210	5	0.100
252	2850	5	0.100
208	13100	1	0.100

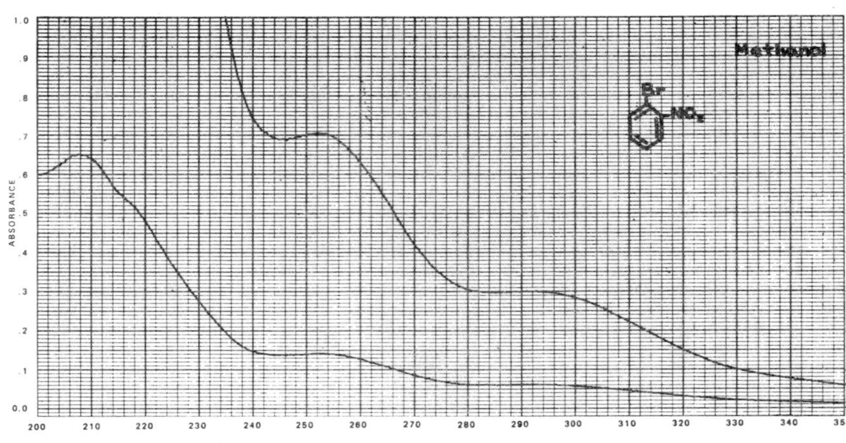

1-IODO-3-NITROBENZENE

1060

$C_6H_4INO_2$
Mol. Wt. 249.01
Solvent: Methanol

λ Max. mμ	a_m	Cell mm	Conc. g/L
258	6400	1	0.100
231.5	15400	1	0.100
210	8960	1	0.100

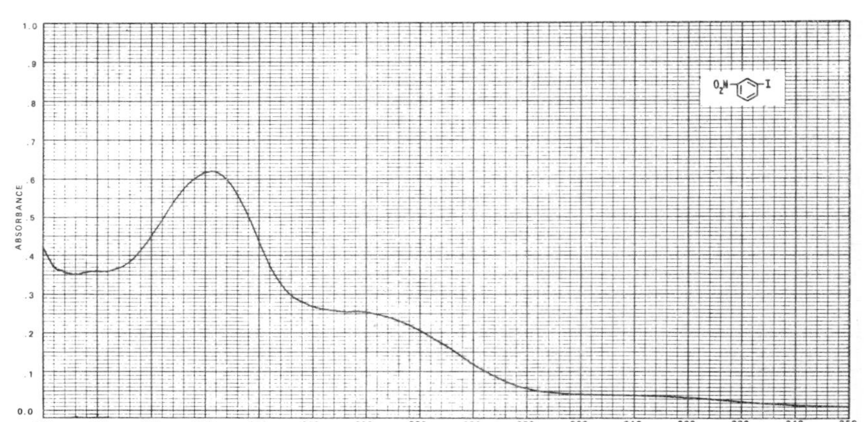

1-IODO-4-NITROBENZENE

1061

$C_6H_4INO_2$
Mol. Wt. 248.02
M.P. 170-171°C
Solvent: Methanol

λ Max. mμ	a_m	Cell mm	Conc. g/L
x	x	10	0.10
260	4300	10	0.02
230	10800	10	0.02

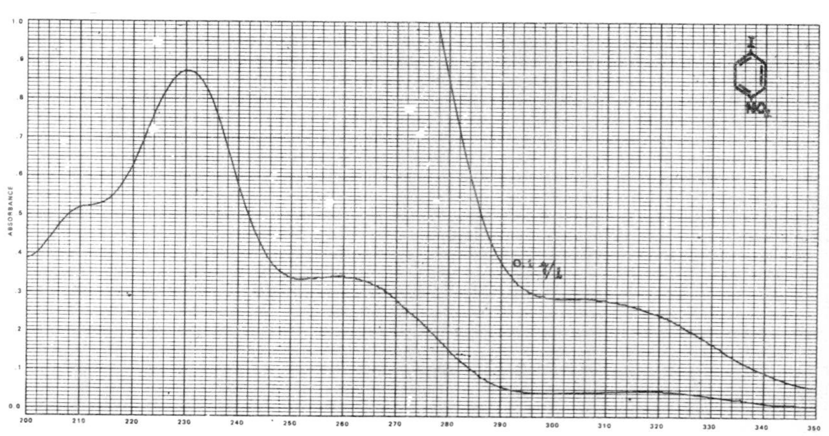

N-ETHYL-o-NITROANILINE

1062

$C_8H_{10}N_2O_2$
Mol. Wt. 166.18
B.P. 168°C/20mm

λ Max. mμ	a_m	Cell mm	Conc. g/L

Pure sample not available.

2-PENTANONE, (p-NITROPHENYL)HYDRAZONE

1063

$C_{11}H_{15}N_3O_2$
Mol. Wt. 221.26
M.P. 117°C
Solvent: Methanol

λ Max. mμ	a_m	Cell mm	Conc. g/L
392	20500	1	0.100
250	10400	1	0.100

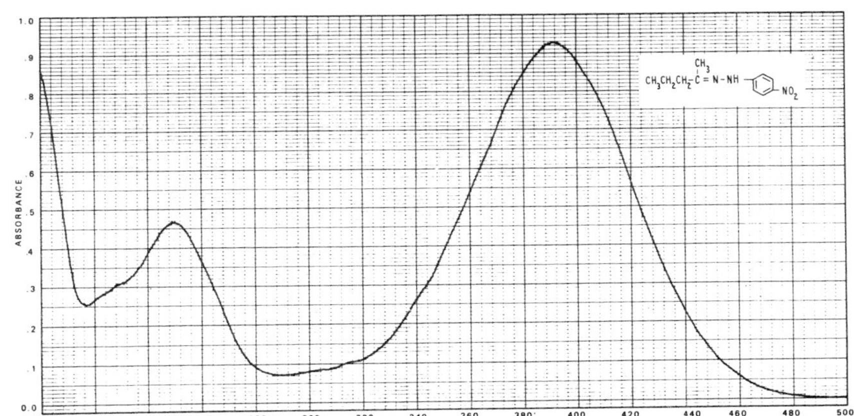

2-PENTANONE, (p-NITROPHENYL)HYDRAZONE

1063

$C_{11}H_{15}N_3O_2$
Mol. Wt. 221.26
M.P. 117°C
Solvent: Methanol HCl

λ Max. mμ	a_m	Cell mm	Conc. g/L
393.5	15300	1	0.100
250	7390	1	0.100
228	6330	1	0.100

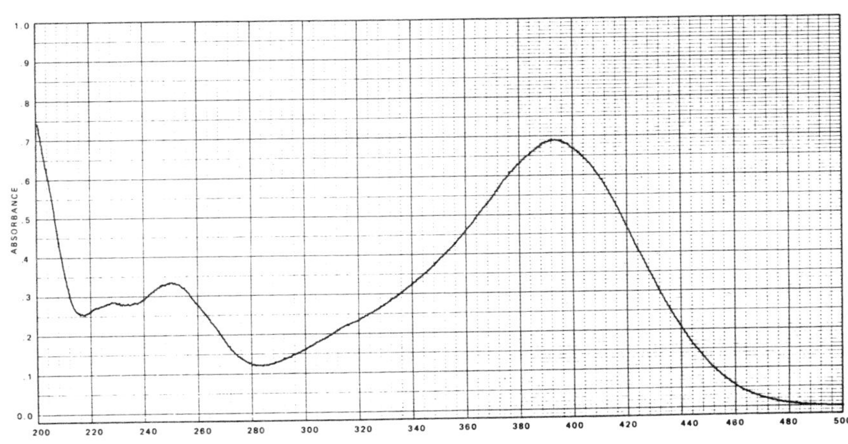

BENZALDEHYDE, (p-NITROPHENYL)HYDRAZONE

1064

$C_{13}H_{11}N_3O_2$
Mol. Wt. 241.25
M.P. 195-197°C
Solvent: Methanol

λ Max. mμ	a_m	Cell mm	Conc. g/L
400	32300	1	0.0500
328	59300	2	0.100
298	72400	2	0.100
227	14600	1	0.0500

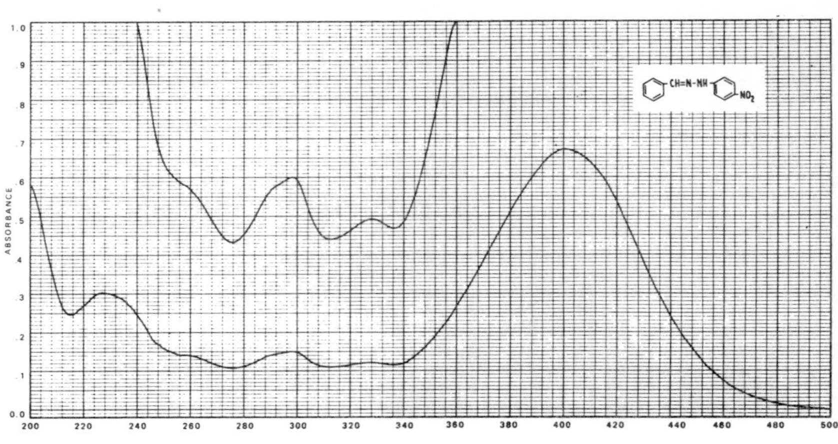

4-NITROAZOBENZENE

1065

$C_{12}H_9N_3O_2$
Mol. Wt. 227.23
M.P. 133-134°C
Solvent: Methanol

λ Max. mμ	a_m	Cell mm	Conc. g/L
329.5	25000	1	0.0700

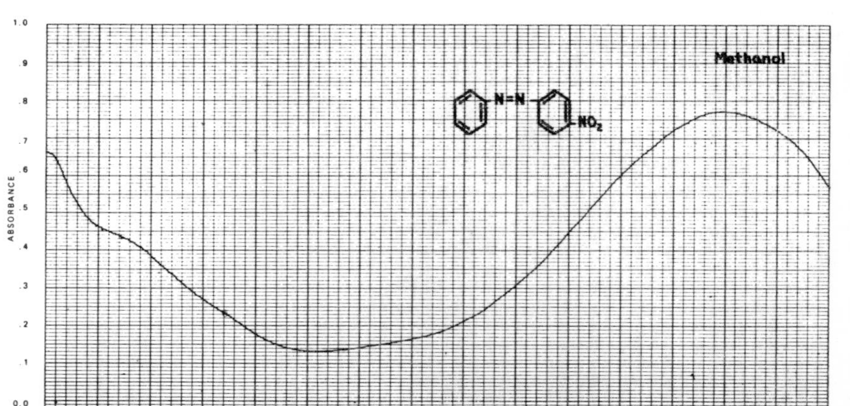

o-DINITROBENZENE

1066

$C_6H_4N_2O_4$
Mol. Wt. 168.11
M.P. 117-118°C B.P. 319°C/773mm
Solvent: Methanol

λ Max. mμ	a_m	Cell mm	Conc. g/L
436	127	20	0.100
x	x	1	0.100

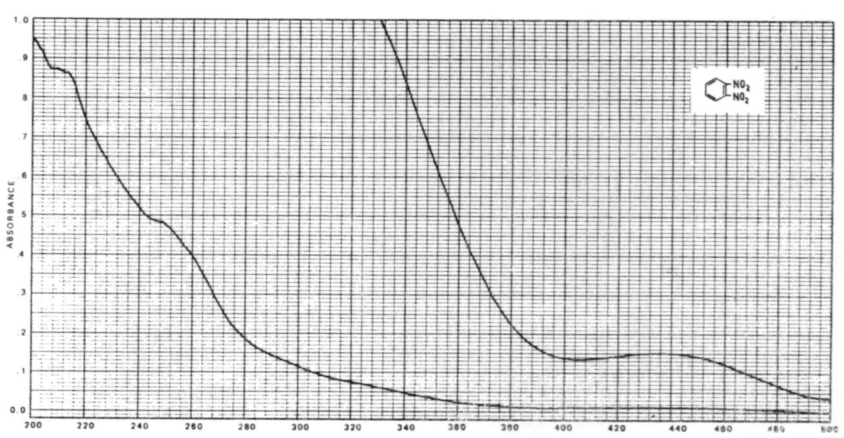

m-DINITROBENZENE

1067

$C_6H_4N_2O_4$

Mol. Wt. 168.11

M.P. 89-89.5°C

Solvent: Methanol

λ Max. mμ	a_m	Cell mm	Conc. g/L
233	18500	2	0.0200

4-NITRO-m-XYLENE

1068

$C_8H_9NO_2$

Mol. Wt. 151.17

Solvent: Methanol

λ Max. mμ	a_m	Cell mm	Conc. g/L
264.5	6730	1	0.206

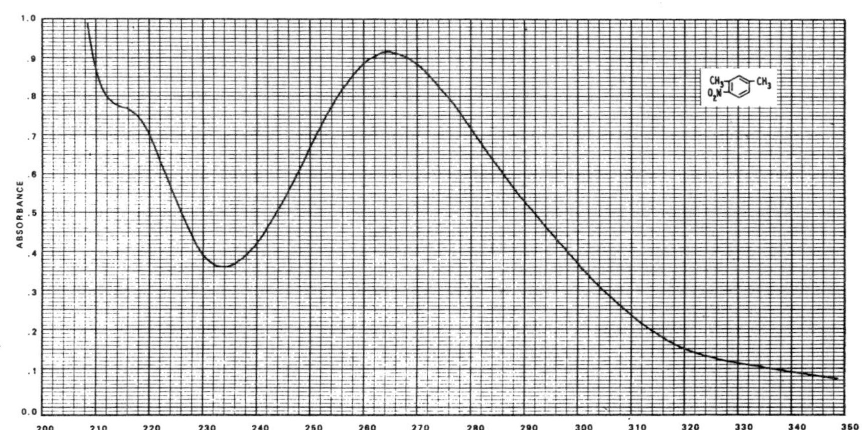

1,2-DICHLORO-4-NITROBENZENE

1069

$C_6H_3Cl_2NO_2$

Mol. Wt. 192.00

M.P. 40-42°C

Solvent: Methanol

λ Max. mμ	a_m	Cell mm	Conc. g/L
287	11400	1	0.100
225	6130	1	0.100

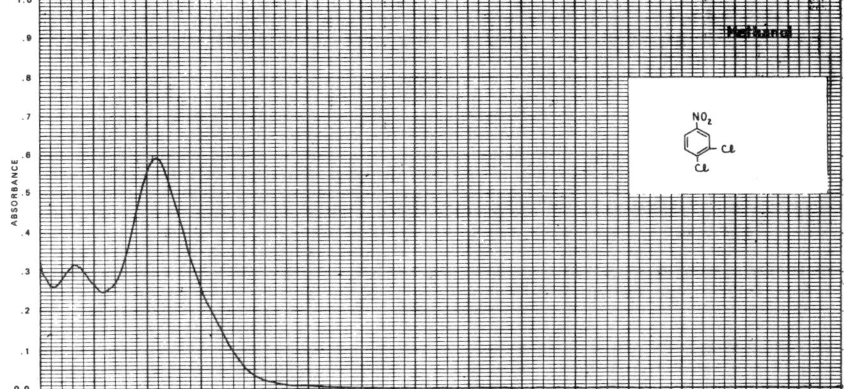

3-NITRO-p-TOLUIDINE

1070

$C_7H_8N_2O_2$
Mol. Wt. 152.16
Solvent: Methanol

λ Max. mμ	a_m	Cell mm	Conc. g/L
289	4870	10	0.0456
251	13000	10	0.0182
228	13500	10	0.0182

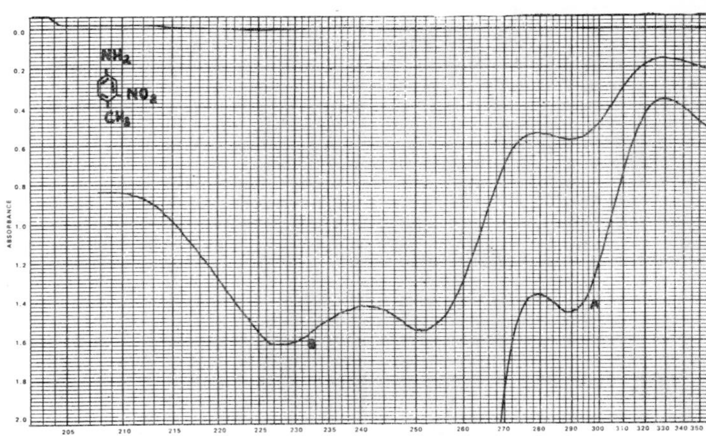

4-NITRO-m-TOLUIDINE

1071

$C_7H_8N_2O_2$
Mol. Wt. 152.15
M.P. 135°C
Solvent: Methanol

λ Max. mμ	a_m	Cell mm	Conc. g/L
372	12600	1	0.100
233	6060	1	0.100

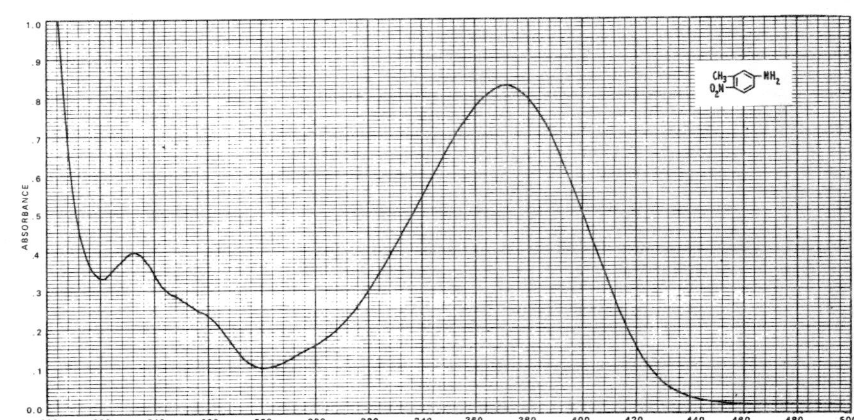

2,4-DINITRO-1-FLUOROBENZENE

1072

$C_6H_3FN_2O_4$
Mol. Wt. 186.10
Solvent: Methanol

λ Max. mμ	a_m	Cell mm	Conc. g/L
232	15100	1	0.115

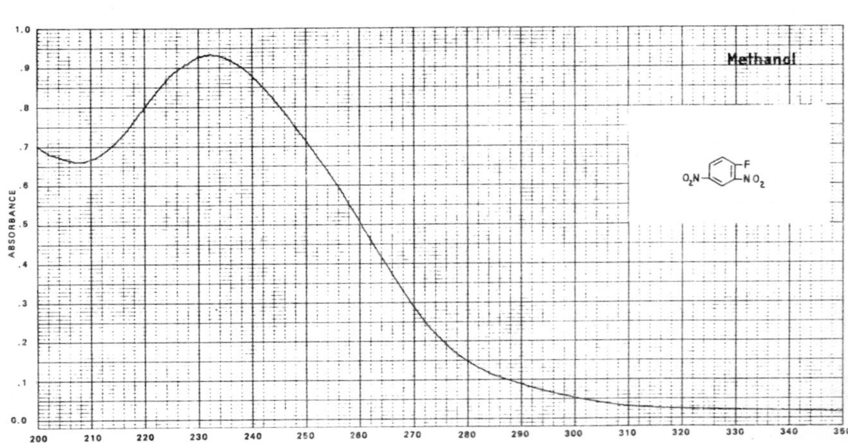

1-BROMO-2,4-DINITROBENZENE

1073

$C_6H_3BrN_2O_4$
Mol. Wt. 247.01
M.P. 70-72°C
Solvent: Methanol

λ Max. mμ	a_m	Cell mm	Conc. g/L
265	10800	1	0.100
239	9630	1	0.100

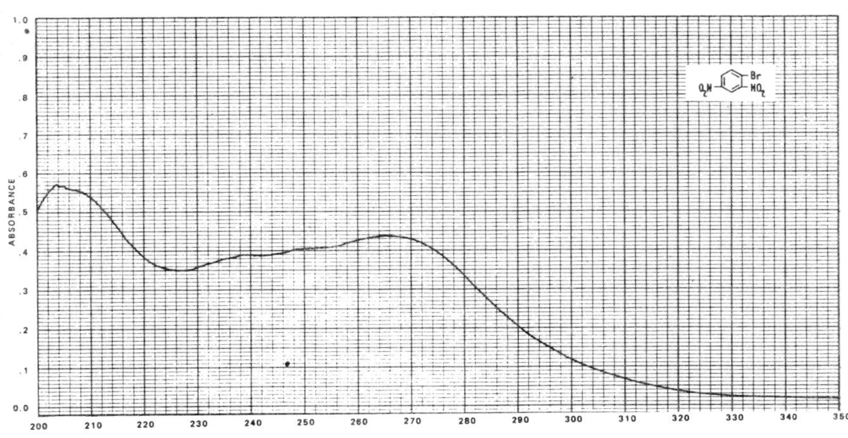

N,N-DIMETHYL-3,4-DINITROANILINE

1074

$C_8H_9N_3O_4$
Mol. Wt. 211.18
M.P. 177°C
Solvent: Methanol

λ Max. mμ	a_m	Cell mm	Conc. g/L
390	14500	1	0.100
228	12300	1	0.100

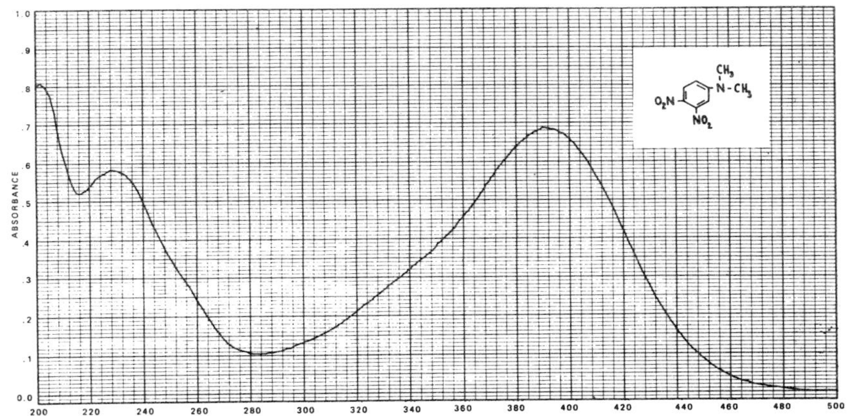

ACETONE,(2,4-DINITROPHENYL)HYDRAZONE

1075

$C_9H_{10}N_4O_4$
Mol. Wt. 238.21
M.P. 126.0°C
Solvent: Methanol

λ Max. mμ	a_m	Cell mm	Conc. g/L
227.5	15300	1	0.0800

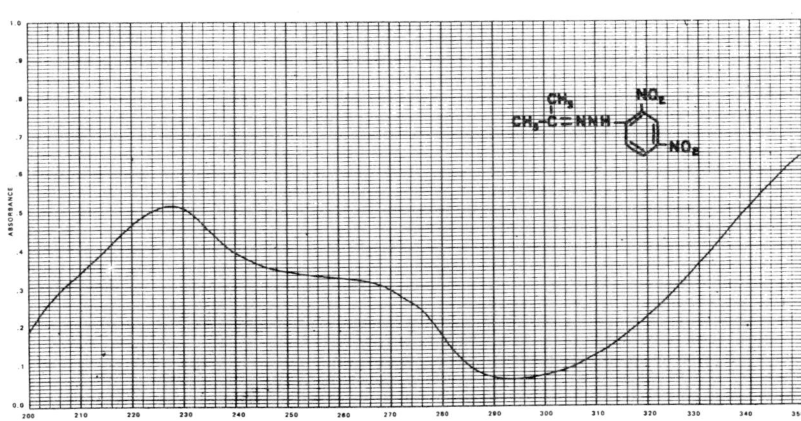

1,3,5-TRINITROBENZENE

1076

$C_6H_3O_6N_3$
Mol. Wt. 213.11
M.R. 121-122°C (lit.)
Solvent: Methanol

λ Max. mμ	a_m	Cell mm	Conc. g/L
x	x	10	1.00
223	31500	10	0.010

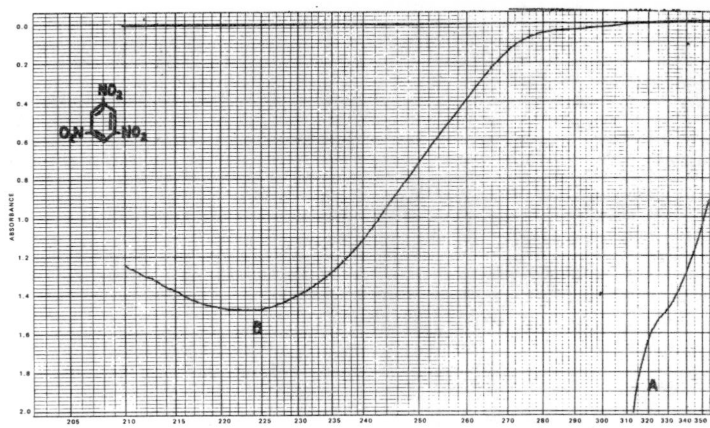

4-NITRO-2,6-XYLIDINE

1077

$C_8H_{10}N_2O_2$
Mol. Wt. 166.18
M.P. 164°C
Solvent: Methanol

λ Max. mμ	a_m	Cell mm	Conc. g/L
375	15100	1	0.100

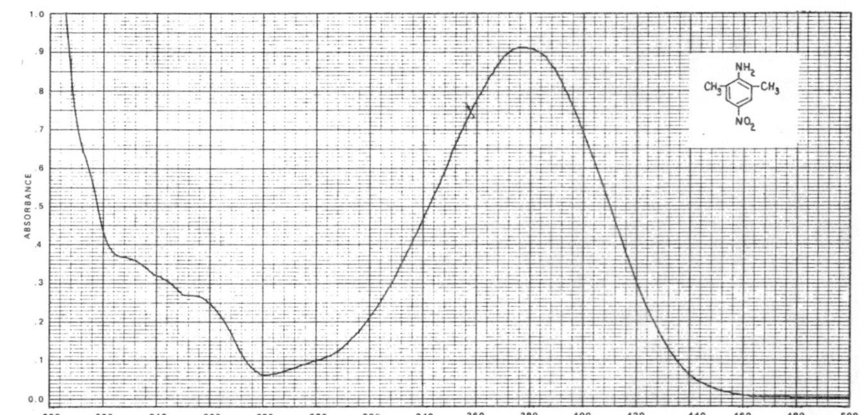

N-NITRODIISOBUTYLAMINE

1078

$C_8H_{18}N_2O_2$
Mol. Wt. 174.24
M.P. 81.5-82.5°C

λ Max. mμ	a_m	Cell mm	Conc. g/L

Pure sample not available.

1,4-DINITROPIPERAZINE **1079**

$C_4H_8N_4O_4$
Mol. Wt. 176.13
M.P. 207-212°C

λ Max. mμ	a_m	Cell mm	Conc. g/L

Pure sample not available.

PROPYL NITRATE **1080**

$C_3H_7NO_3$
Mol. Wt. 105.09
B.P. 108-110°C

λ Max. mμ	a_m	Cell mm	Conc. g/L

Pure sample not available.

ISOPROPYL NITRATE **1081**

$C_3H_7NO_3$
Mol. Wt. 105.09
B.P. 98-102°C

λ Max. mμ	a_m	Cell mm	Conc. g/L

Pure sample not available.

1082

NITRIC ACID, PENTYL ESTER

$C_5H_{11}NO_3$

Mol. Wt. 133.15

λ Max. mμ	a_m	Cell mm	Conc. g/L

Pure sample not available.

λ Max. mμ	a_m	Cell mm	Conc. g/L

λ Max. mμ	a_m	Cell mm	Conc. g/L

THE SILICON COMPOUNDS

Aliphatic Compounds

The aliphatic and olefinic silicon compounds do not display any maxima in the near UV and thus there are no spectra included in this volume for compounds 1083, 1085, 1086, 1087, 1092, 1093 and 1094.

Aromatic Compounds

The phenyl silicon compounds display two major bands in the near UV region. A stronger band or shoulder appears near 220 mμ and a weaker band with superimposed fine structure absorbs near 265 mμ. The fine structure may show as many as ten peaks with maxima at 244, 248, 250, 254, 258, 260, 264, 266, 271 and 273 mμ.

The table presented below lists the wavelength and intensity data for the two major bands of three phenyl silanes.

Compound	$\lambda_{max}(\epsilon_{max})$	$\lambda_{max}(\epsilon_{max})$	Solvent	Spectrum
Diphenylsilane	219 (18100)	264 (736)	Methanol	1084
Dibenzyldiphenylsilane	220 * (31400)	266 (1260)	Methanol	1088
Ethyltriphenylsilane	225 * (12300)	264 (1010)	Cyclohexane	1091

* Shoulder

HEXYLSILANE 1083

$C_6H_{16}Si$

Mol. Wt. 116.28

λ Max. mμ	a_m	Cell mm	Conc. g/L

This compound does not display any maxima in the near UV region.

DIPHENYLSILANE 1084

$C_{12}H_{12}Si$

Mol. Wt. 184.32

Solvent: Methanol

λ Max. mμ	a_m	Cell mm	Conc. g/L
271	578	10	0.1866
264.5	736	10	0.1866
260	687	10	0.1866
254.5	503	10	0.1866
219	18100	1	0.0933

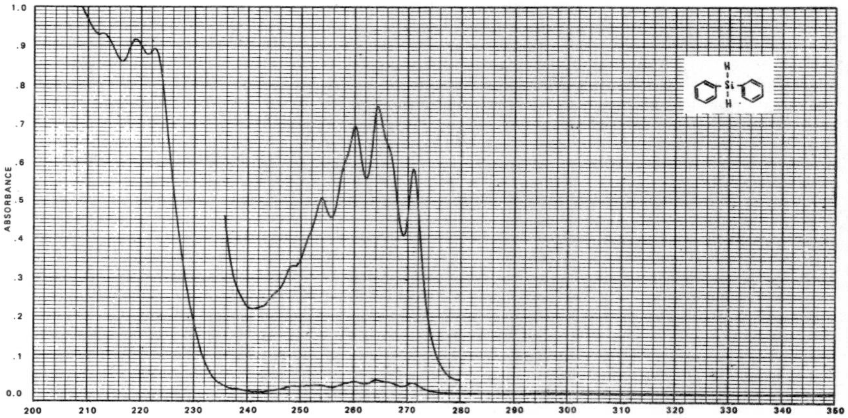

TETRAETHYLSILANE 1085

$C_8H_{20}Si$

Mol. Wt. 144.33

B.P. 155°C

λ Max. mμ	a_m	Cell mm	Conc. g/L

This compound does not display any maxima in the near UV region.

ALLYLTRIMETHYLSILANE 1086

$C_6H_{14}Si$
Mol. Wt. 114.26
B.P. 85-86°C

λ Max. mμ	a_m	Cell mm	Conc. g/L

This compound does not display any maxima in the near UV region.

DIALLYLDIMETHYLSILANE 1087

$C_8H_{16}Si$
Mol. Wt. 140.30
B.P. 68°C/50mm

λ Max. mμ	a_m	Cell mm	Conc. g/L

This compound does not display any maxima in the near UV region.

DIBENZYLDIPHENYL SILANE 1088

$C_{26}H_{24}Si$
Mol. Wt. 364.56
M.P. 63°C
Solvent: Methanol

λ Max. mμ	a_m	Cell mm	Conc. g/L
271	840	2	1.00
266	1260	2	1.00
260	1220	2	1.00
254	972	2	1.00
x	x	1	0.800

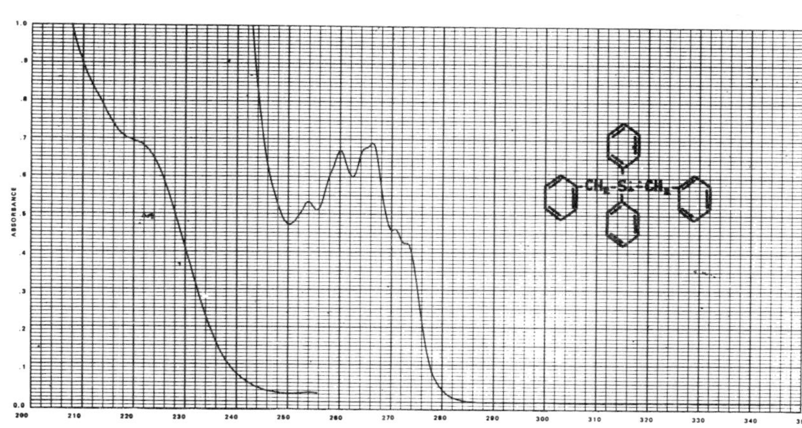

PHENYLTRIMETHYLSILANE 1089

$C_9H_{14}Si$
Mol. Wt. 150.29
B.P. 169-170°C

λ Max. mμ	a_m	Cell mm	Conc. g/L

Pure sample not available.

DIDODECYLDIPHENYLSILANE 1090

$C_{30}H_{60}Si$
Mol. Wt. 520.94
M.P. -40°C (lit.)
Solvent: Cyclohexane

λ Max. mμ	a_m	Cell mm	Conc. g/L
269	506	10	0.945
265	678	10	0.945
262.5	675	10	0.945
258.5	793	10	0.945
252.5	650	10	0.945
x	x	10	0.045

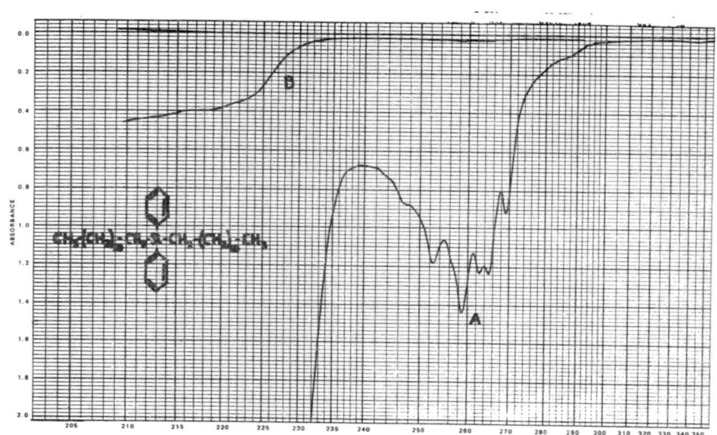

ETHYLTRIPHENYLSILANE 1091

$C_{20}H_{20}Si$
Mol. Wt. 288.42
M.P. 76°C
Solvent: Cyclohexane

λ Max. mμ	a_m	Cell mm	Conc. g/L
272	837	10	0.2256
267	968	10	0.2256
265	1010	10	0.2256
261	1050	10	0.2256
254.5	748	10	0.2256
x	x	10	0.0225

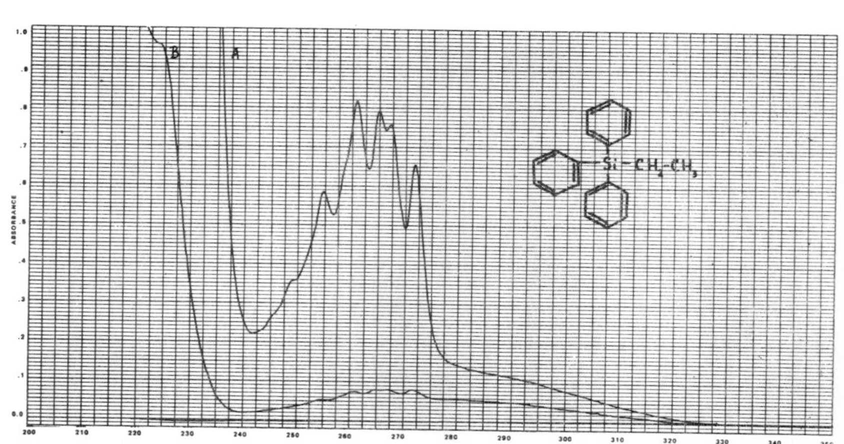

THE PHOSPHORUS COMPOUNDS

Aliphatic Compounds

The aliphatic phosphines, phosphonium halides and phosphine oxides do not display any maxima in the near UV and thus there are no spectra in this text for compounds 1095, 1101, 1103 nor 1104.

Aromatic Phosphine Compounds

The UV spectra of the aromatic phosphines display a rather broad band with no fine structure in the region from 248 to 275 mμ.

The table given below lists the wavelength and intensity data for a series of phosphines that were examined in methanol solution.

Compound	$\lambda_{max}(\epsilon_{max})$	$\lambda_{max}(\epsilon_{max})$	Spectrum
Ethyldiphenylphosphine	210 (20800)	248 (11500)	1096
Trimethylenebis(diphenylphosphine)	----------	252 (17400)	1097
Tri(p-tolyl)phosphine	----------	260 (13700)	1099
Tri(o-tolyl)phosphine	----------	275 (11400)	1098
Tri(p-chlorophenyl)phosphine	223 (26500)	263 (14300)	1100

Aromatic Phosphonium Compounds

The aromatic phosphonium compounds display two major bands, one near 225 mμ of higher intensity and one near 270 mμ which shows superimposed fine structure as maxima or shoulders near 254, 259, 266 and 272 mμ. The table given below lists the spectral data for a series of phosphonium halides examined in either methanol or ethanol solution.

Compound	$\lambda_{max}(\epsilon_{max})$	$\lambda_{max}(\epsilon_{max})$	Spectrum
Trimethylphenylphosphonium Iodide	218 (3150)	266 (1200)	Lit.
Methyltriphenylphosphonium Bromide	225 (27800)	267 (3150)	1102
Tetraphenylphosphonium Iodide	233 (23000)	269 (4750)	Lit.
Methyltri(o-tolyl)phosphonium Iodide	----------	274 (4350)	Lit.

Aromatic Phosphine Oxides

The UV spectra of the phosphine oxides contain a shoulder near 225 mμ and a band near 271 mμ which displays fine structure as either shoulders or maxima at 258, 265, 271 and 278 mμ.

The wavelength and intensity data for two phosphine oxides is given below.

Compound	$\lambda_{max}(\epsilon_{max})$	$\lambda_{max}(\epsilon_{max})$	Solvent	Spectrum
Tri(o-tolyl)phosphine Oxide	225 * (22400)	271 (3200)	Ethanol	Lit.
Tri(m-tolyl)phosphine Oxide	225 * (24300)	271 (3110)	Methanol	1106

*Shoulder

TRIBUTYLPHOSPHINE 1095

$C_{12}H_{27}P$
Mol. Wt. 202.32
M.P. 236°C

λ Max. mμ	a_m	Cell mm	Conc. g/L

This compound does not display any maxima in the near UV region.

DIPHENYLETHYLPHOSPHINE 1096

$C_{14}H_{15}P$
Mol. Wt. 214.25
B.P. 130-132°C/1mm
Solvent: Methanol

λ Max. mμ	a_m	Cell mm	Conc. g/L
248	11500	1	0.100
210	20800	1	0.100

TRIMETHYLENEBIS[DIPHENYLPHOSPHINE] 1097

$C_{27}H_{26}P_2$
Mol. Wt. 412.46
M.P. 55-57°C
Solvent: Methanol

λ Max. mμ	a_m	Cell mm	Conc. g/L
252	17400	1	0.100

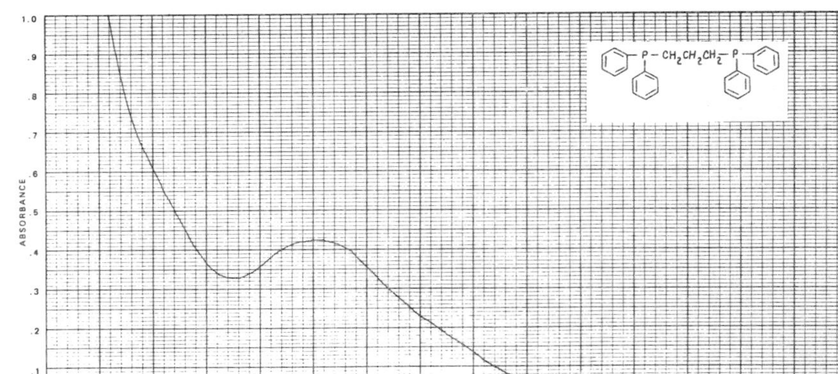

TRI-o-TOLYLPHOSPHINE 1098

$C_{21}H_{21}P$

Mol. Wt. 304.38

M.P. 120°C

Solvent: Methanol

λ Max. mμ	a_m	Cell mm	Conc. g/L
275	11400	1	0.100

TRI-p-TOLYLPHOSPHINE 1099

$C_{21}H_{21}P$

Mol. Wt. 304.38

M.P. 142°C

Solvent: Methanol

λ Max. mμ	a_m	Cell mm	Conc. g/L
260	13700	5	0.0400
x	x	1	0.0400

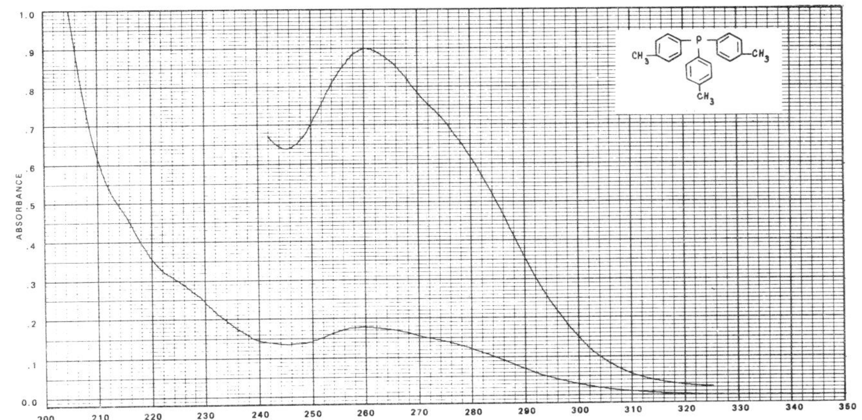

TRIS(p-CHLOROPHENYL)PHOSPHINE 1100

$C_{18}H_{12}Cl_3P$

Mol. Wt. 365.63

M.P. 90-93°C

Solvent: Methanol

λ Max. mμ	a_m	Cell mm	Conc. g/L
262.5	14300	1	0.100
223	26500	1	0.100

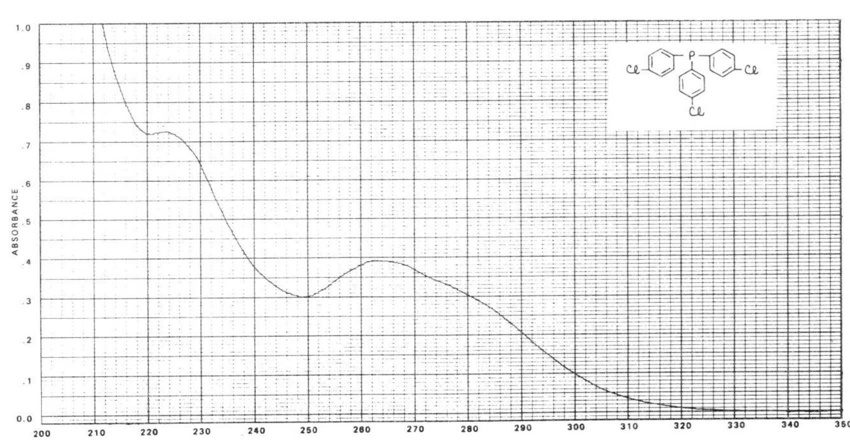

TETRAETHYLPHOSPHONIUM IODIDE

1101

$C_8H_{20}IP$

Mol. Wt. 274.13

M.P. 270°C

λ Max. mμ	a_m	Cell mm	Conc. g/L

This compound does not display any maxima in the near UV region.

METHYLTRIPHENYLPHOSPHONIUM BROMIDE

1102

$C_{19}H_{18}BrP$

Mol. Wt. 357.24

M.P. 229-232°C (lit.)

Solvent: Methanol

λ Max. mμ	a_m	Cell mm	Conc. g/L
274	2720	1	0.880
267	3150	1	0.880
261	2320	1	0.880
224.5	27800	1	0.0880

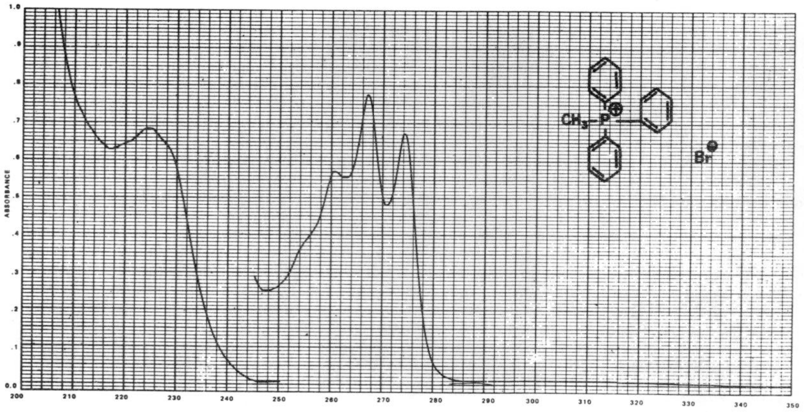

DIMETHYLDODECYLPHOSPHINE OXIDE

1103

$C_{14}H_{31}OP$

Mol. Wt. 246.38

M.P. 84-85°C

λ Max. mμ	a_m	Cell mm	Conc. g/L

This compound does not display any maxima in the near UV region.

DIMETHYLHEXADECYLPHOSPHINE OXIDE 1104

$C_{18}H_{39}OP$
Mol. Wt. 302.48
M.P. 93-94°C

λ Max. mμ	a_m	Cell mm	Conc. g/L

This compound does not display any maxima in the near UV region.

TRI-o-TOLYLPHOSPHINE OXIDE 1105

$C_{21}H_{21}OP$
Mol. Wt. 320.38
M.P. 150-151°C
Solvent: Methanol

λ Max. mμ	a_m	Cell mm	Conc. g/L
278.5	3090	10	0.08
271	3200	10	0.08
x	x	10	0.01

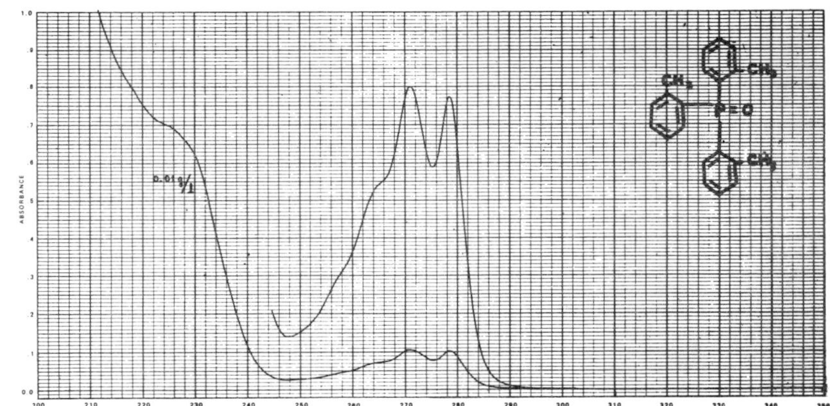

TRI-m-TOLYLPHOSPHINE OXIDE 1106

$C_{21}H_{21}OP$
Mol. Wt. 320.38
M.P. 143-144°C
Solvent: Methanol

λ Max. mμ	a_m	Cell mm	Conc. g/L
278.5	2950	10	0.10
271	3110	10	0.10
x	x	10	0.005

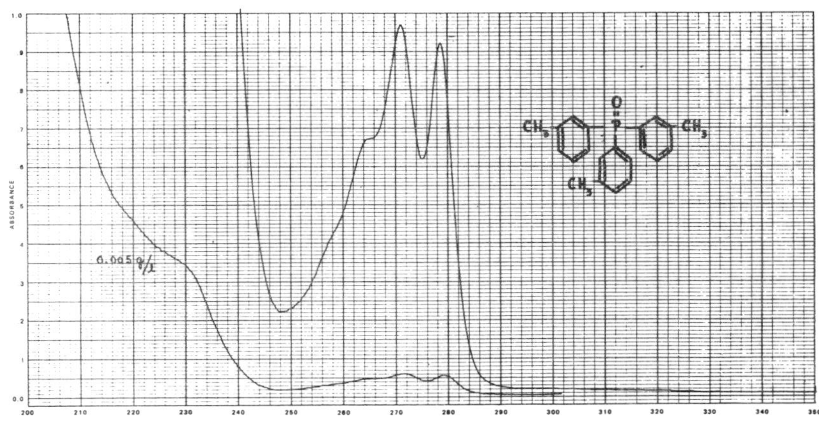

NOTES

THE SULFIDES AND THIOPHENES

Aliphatic Sulfides

The aliphatic sulfides containing the C—S—C linkage normally absorb below the solvent cut-off region of 220 mμ and thus there are no spectra in this volume for compounds 1107 through 1133.

Several of the saturated cyclic sulfides do display significant absorption bands at longer wavelength and four such compounds described in the literature possess the following maxima: ethylene sulfide, 258 (37); trimethylene sulfide, 333 (30,000); tetrahydrothiophene, 300 (40,000); tetrahydro-2H-thiopyran, 250 (40,000).

The Thiophenes

Thiophene and its derivatives formed with saturated substituents display an absorption band in the region from 230 to 243 mμ of moderate intensity (ϵ = 4000 - 9000). Thiophene itself, displays some superimposed fine structure but the substituted derivatives usually do not.

A list of several mono-substituted thiophenes is presented below.

Compound	$\lambda_{max}(\epsilon_{max})$	Solvent	Spectrum
Thiophene	232 (6040)	Methanol	1136
3-Methylthiophene	230 (4510)	Methanol	1137
2-Chlorothiophene	236 (7720)	Methanol	1138
2-Bromothiophene	235 (6670)	Methanol	1140
3-Bromothiophene	242 (8320)	Methanol	1141
2-Iodothiophene	243 (8420)	Methanol	1143

Aromatic Sulfides

The benzyl sulfides do not display any clear cut maxima in the near UV (spectra 1158 and 1159).

The alkyl-phenyl sulfides with the sulfide group bonded directly to the aromatic ring, exhibit a maximum in the region from 254 to 261 mμ as indicated below.

Compound	$\lambda_{max}(\epsilon_{max})$	Solvent	Spectrum
Methyl phenyl sulfide	254 (9900)	Heptane	Lit.
Bis(phenylthio)methane	257 (11000)	Methanol	1167
1-Bromophenyl methyl sulfide	261 (16900)	Methanol	1160
Benzyl-p-tolyl sulfide	254 (6950)	Methanol	1162
Phenethyl phenyl sulfide	255 (8750)	Methanol	1163
3-Phenylpropyl phenyl sulfide	255 (7620)	Methanol	1164

The diphenyl sulfides usually display three absorption bands at about 230, 250 and 274 mμ (spectra 1169, 1170 and 1171).

2-METHYL-2-THIAZOLINE 1134

C_4H_7NS

Mol. Wt. 101.17

B.P. 143-146°C

λ Max. mμ	a_m	Cell mm	Conc. g/L

Pure sample not available.

2-(BENZYLAMINO)-2-THIAZOLINE 1135

$C_{10}H_{12}N_2S$

Mol. Wt. 192.28

Solvent: Methanol

λ Max. mμ	a_m	Cell mm	Conc. g/L
x	x	1	0.100

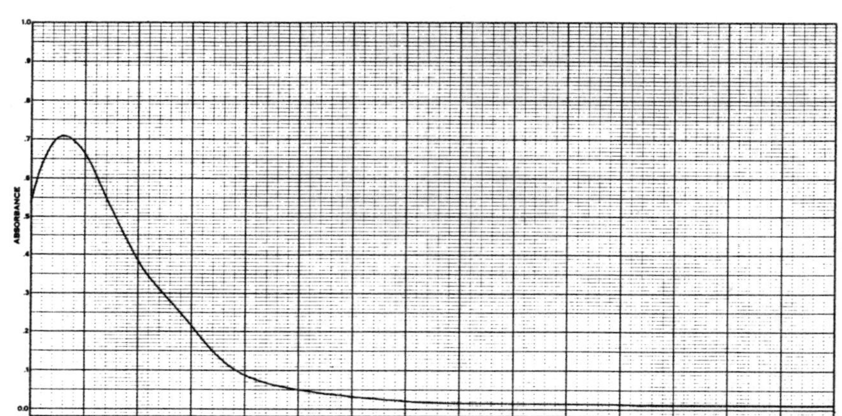

2-(BENZYLAMINO)-2-THIAZOLINE 1135

$C_{10}H_{12}N_2S$

Mol. Wt. 192.28

Solvent: Methanol HCl

λ Max. mμ	a_m	Cell mm	Conc. g/L
212.5	15000	1	2.100

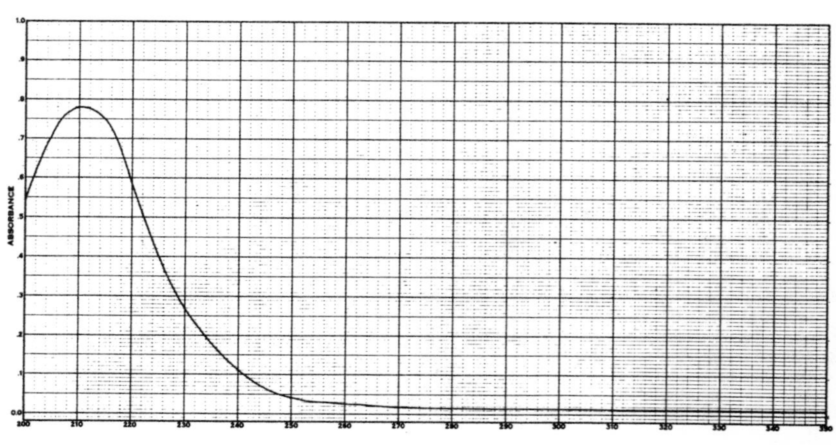

THIOPHENE

1136

C_4H_4S

Mol. Wt. 84.13

B.P. 84°C

Solvent: Methanol

λ Max. mμ	a_m	Cell mm	Conc. g/L
237	5560	10	0.0084
232.5	6040	10	0.0084

3-METHYLTHIOPHENE

1137

C_5H_6S

Mol. Wt. 98.17

B.P. 114°C/738mm

Solvent: Methanol

λ Max. mμ	a_m	Cell mm	Conc. g/L
230	4510	2	0.100

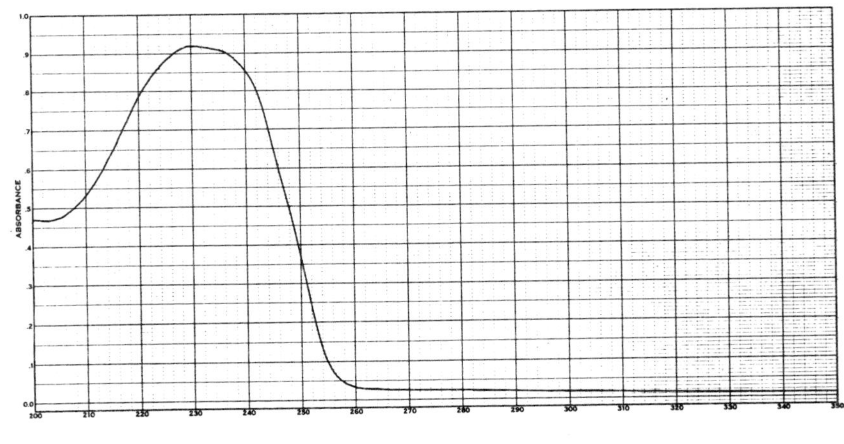

2-CHLOROTHIOPHENE

1138

C_4H_3ClS

Mol. Wt. 118.59

B.P. 126°C

Solvent: Methanol

λ Max. mμ	a_m	Cell mm	Conc. g/L
235.5	7720	10	0.0119

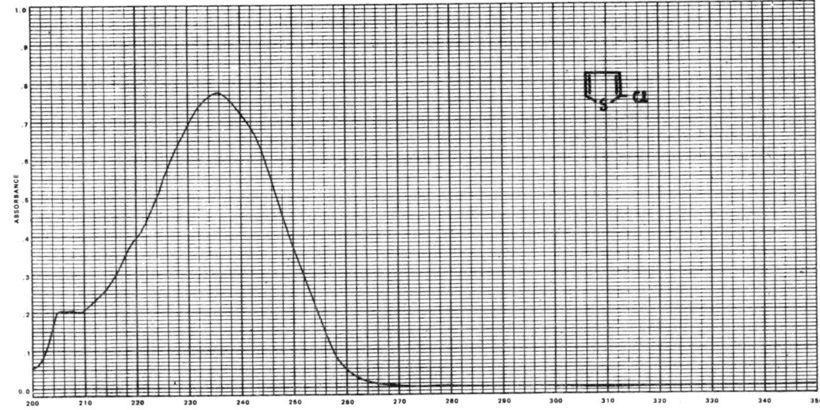

2,5-DICHLOROTHIOPHENE

1139

$C_4H_2Cl_2S$

Mol. Wt. 153.03

Solvent: Methanol

λ Max. mμ	a_m	Cell mm	Conc. g/L
243	5110	2	0.129

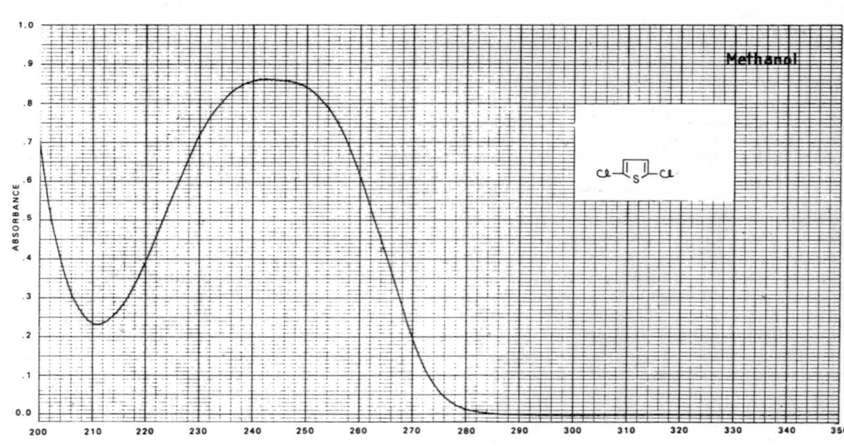

2-BROMOTHIOPHENE

1140

C_4H_3BrS

Mol. Wt. 163.04

B.P. 150-153°C

Solvent: Methanol

λ Max. mμ	a_m	Cell mm	Conc. g/L
235	6670	2	0.108

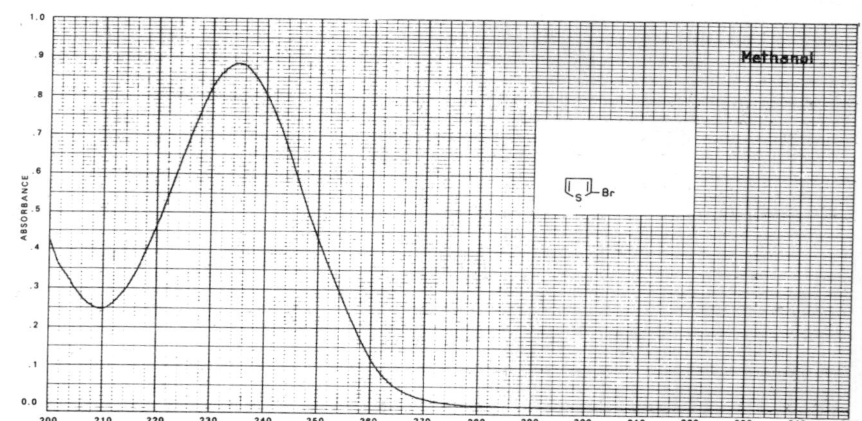

3-BROMOTHIOPHENE

1141

C_4H_3BrS

Mol. Wt. 163.04

B.P. 159-161°C

Solvent: Methanol

λ Max. mμ	a_m	Cell mm	Conc. g/L
242	8320	1	0.100

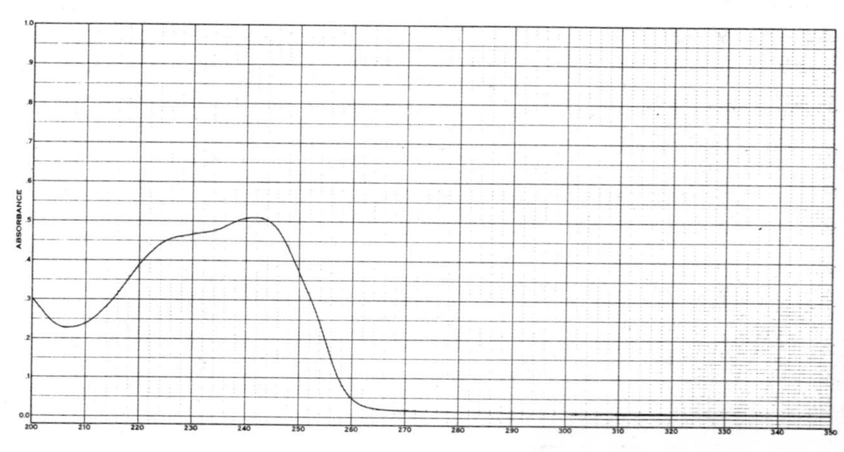

2,5-DIBROMOTHIOPHENE 1142

$C_4H_2Br_2S$

Mol. Wt. 241.93

B.P. 210.5-211.0°C

Solvent: Methanol

λ Max. mμ	a_m	Cell mm	Conc. g/L
250	8320	2	0.1100

2-IODOTHIOPHENE 1143

C_4H_3IS

Mol. Wt. 210.04

B.P. 65-66°C/10mm

Solvent: Methanol

λ Max. mμ	a_m	Cell mm	Conc. g/L
243	8420	1	0.1300

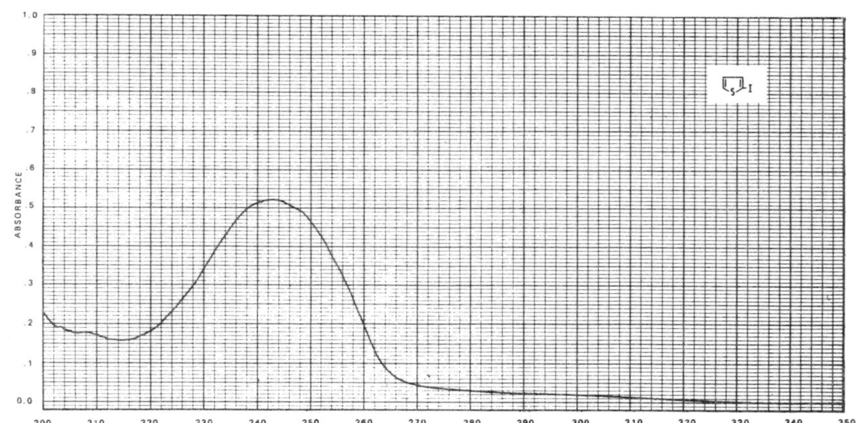

2-THIOPHENECARBONITRILE 1144

C_5H_3NS

Mol. Wt. 109.15

B.P. 75°C/10mm

Solvent: Methanol

λ Max. mμ	a_m	Cell mm	Conc. g/L
260	8610	1	0.0718
244	10100	1	0.0718

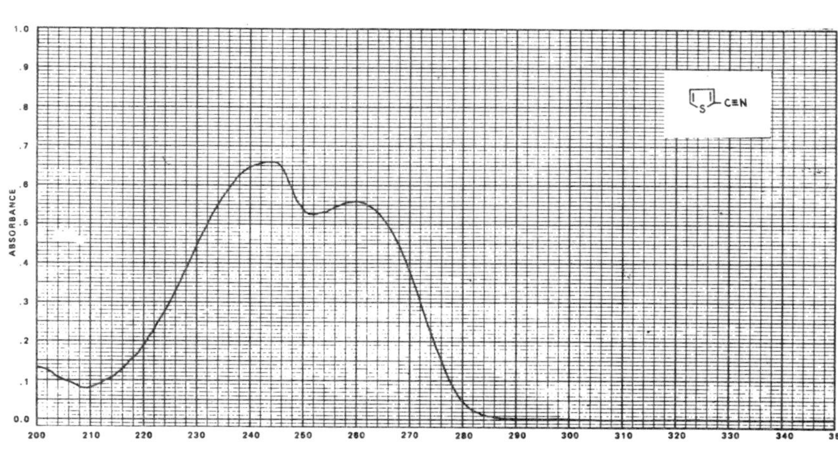

2-THIOPHENECARBOXALDEHYDE, anti-OXIME 1145

C_5H_5NOS

Mol. Wt. 127.17

Solvent: Methanol

λ Max. mμ	a_m	Cell mm	Conc. g/L
266.5	9230	1	0.100

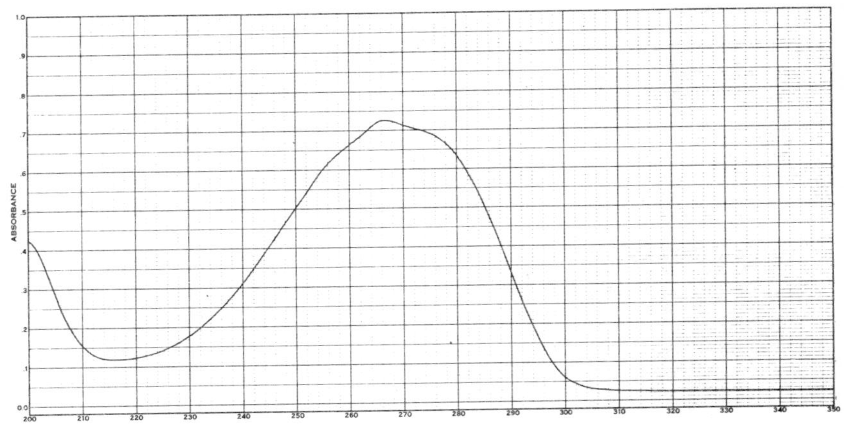

2-THIOPHENECARBOXALDEHYDE, anti-OXIME 1145

C_5H_5NOS

Mol. Wt. 127.17

Solvent: Methanol KOH

λ Max. mμ	a_m	Cell mm	Conc. g/L
292	7760	1	0.100
x	x	0.5	0.100

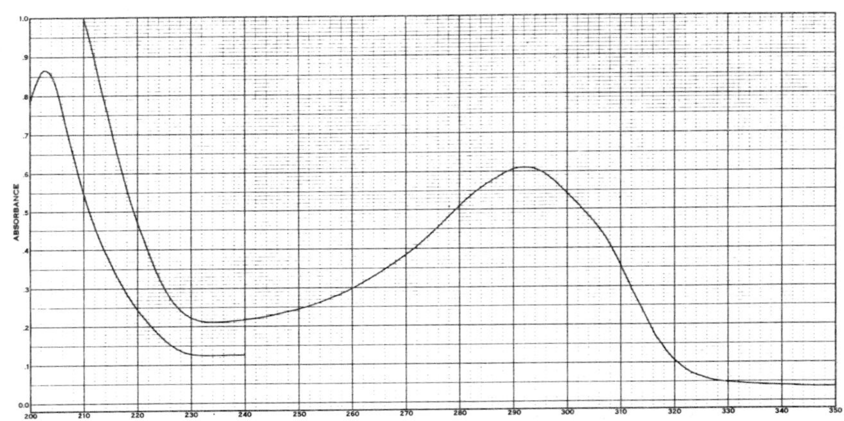

3-NITROTHIOPHENE 1146

$C_4H_3NO_2S$

Mol. Wt. 129.14

M.P. 75-76°C

Solvent: Methanol

λ Max. mμ	a_m	Cell mm	Conc. g/L
270	7300	1	0.100
211	10000	1	0.100

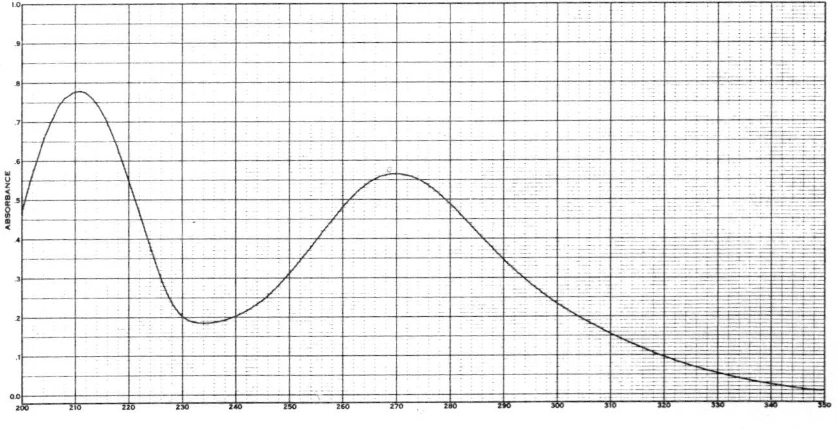

2,2'-METHYLENEDITHIOPHENE 1147

$C_9H_8S_2$

Mol. Wt. 180.29

M.P. 44-46°C

Solvent: Methanol

λ Max. mμ	a_m	Cell mm	Conc. g/L
235	7520	1	0.100

3-METHYLISOTHIAZOLE 1148

C_4H_5NS

Mol. Wt. 99.16

B.P. 134°C

M.P. −54°C

λ Max. mμ	a_m	Cell mm	Conc. g/L

Pure sample not available.

4-METHYLISOTHIAZOLE 1149

C_4H_5NS

Mol. Wt. 99.16

M.P. -39°C

Solvent: Methanol

λ Max. mμ	a_m	Cell mm	Conc. g/L
251	4310	2	0.0885

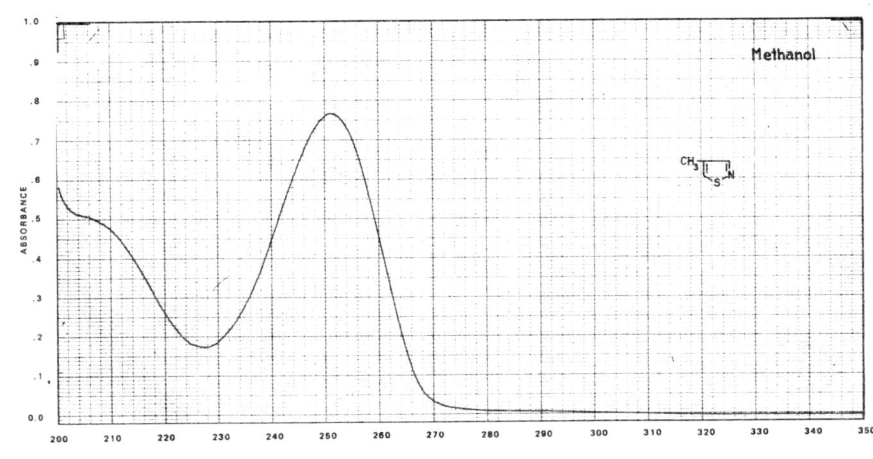

4-PHENYLISOTHIAZOLE

1150

C_9H_7NS

Mol. Wt. 161.23

Solvent: Methanol

λ Max. mμ	a_m	Cell mm	Conc. g/L
268.5	12100	1	0.100
241	12400	1	0.100
x	x	0.5	0.100

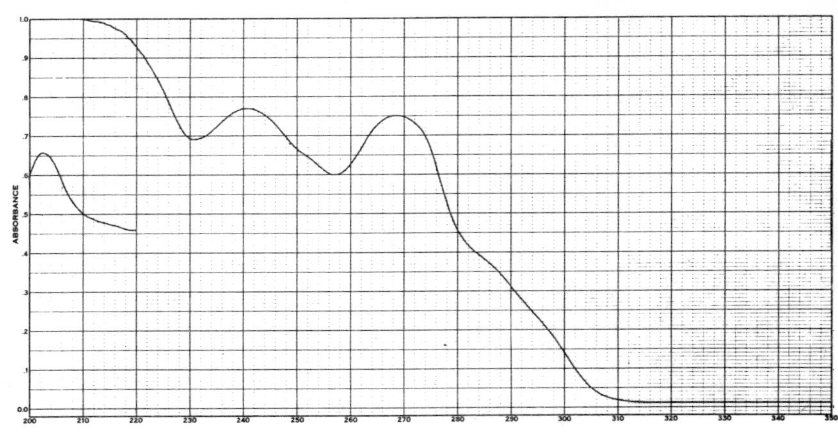

4,5-DIPHENYL-2-METHYLTHIAZOLE

1151

$C_{16}H_{13}NS$

Mol. Wt. 241.28

M.P. 187°C (lit.)

Solvent: Methanol

λ Max. mμ	a_m	Cell mm	Conc. g/L
284	9170	10	0.01
231	18300	10	0.01

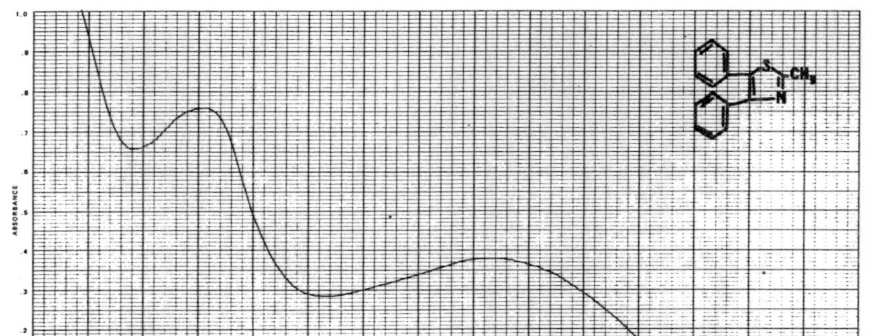

2-BROMOTHIAZOLE

1152

C_3H_2BrNS

Mol. Wt. 164.03

Solvent: Methanol

λ Max. mμ	a_m	Cell mm	Conc. g/L
243	4530	2	0.100

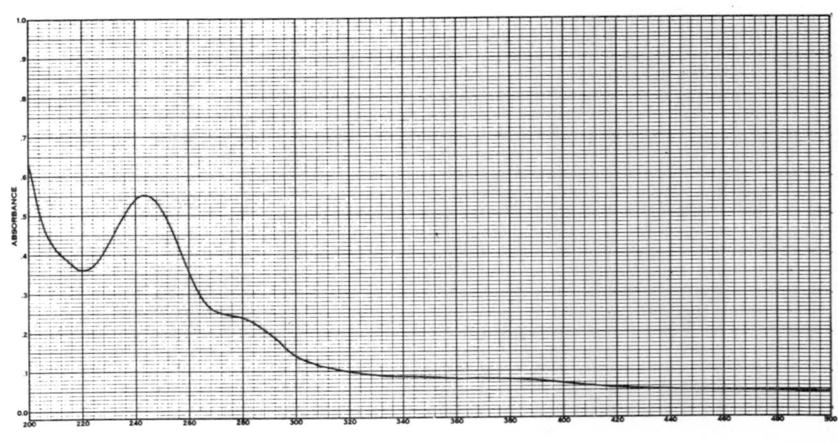

2-AMINOTHIAZOLE 1153

$C_3H_4N_2S$
Mol. Wt. 100.14
M.P. 92.2-93.3°C
Solvent: Methanol

λ Max. mμ	a_m	Cell mm	Conc. g/L
256	6610	10	0.010

2-AMINO-4-METHYLTHIAZOLE 1154

$C_4H_6N_2S$
Mol. Wt. 114.17
Solvent: Methanol

λ Max. mμ	a_m	Cell mm	Conc. g/L
258	731	1	0.100

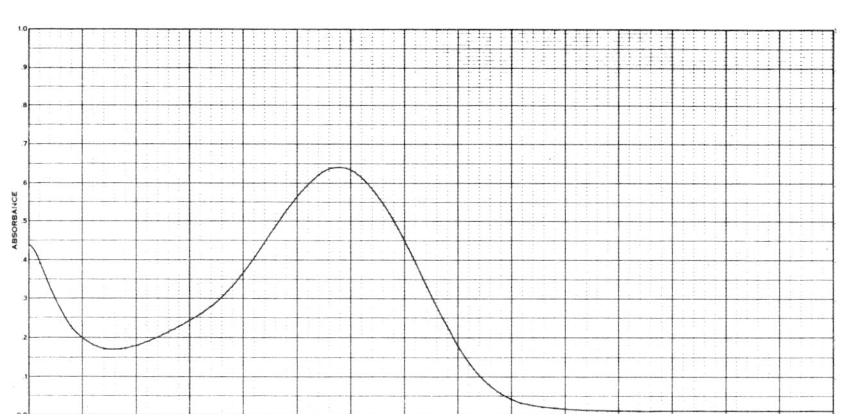

2-AMINO-4-METHYLTHIAZOLE 1154

$C_4H_6N_2S$
Mol. Wt. 114.17
Solvent: Methanol HCl

λ Max. mμ	a_m	Cell mm	Conc. g/L
259	9020	1	0.100
217	3350	1	0.100

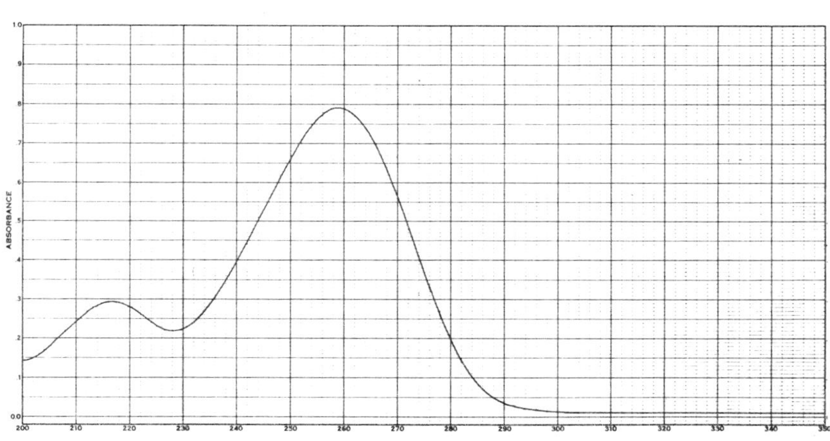

2-AMINO-5-ETHYL-1,3,4-THIADIAZOLE

1155

$C_4H_7N_3S$
Mol. Wt. 129.18
Solvent: Methanol

λ Max. mμ	a_m	Cell mm	Conc. g/L
254	7710	1	0.100

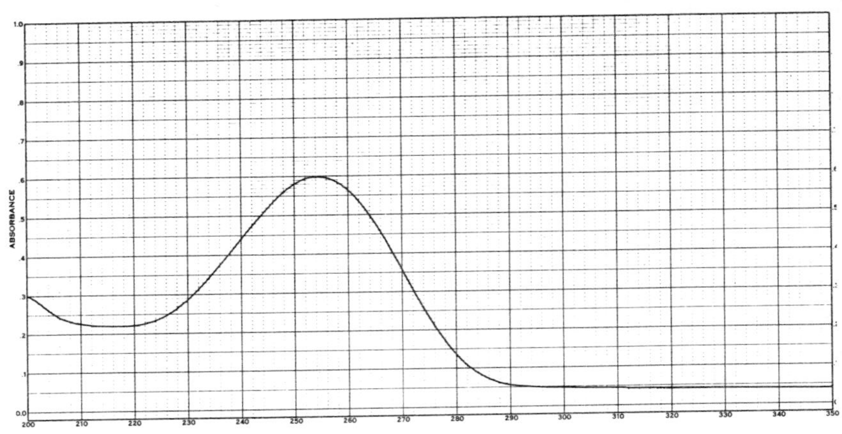

2-AMINO-5-ETHYL-1,3,4-THIADIAZOLE

1155

$C_4H_7N_3S$
Mol. Wt. 129.18
Solvent: Methanol HCl

λ Max. mμ	a_m	Cell mm	Conc. g/L
243.5	9030	1	0.100

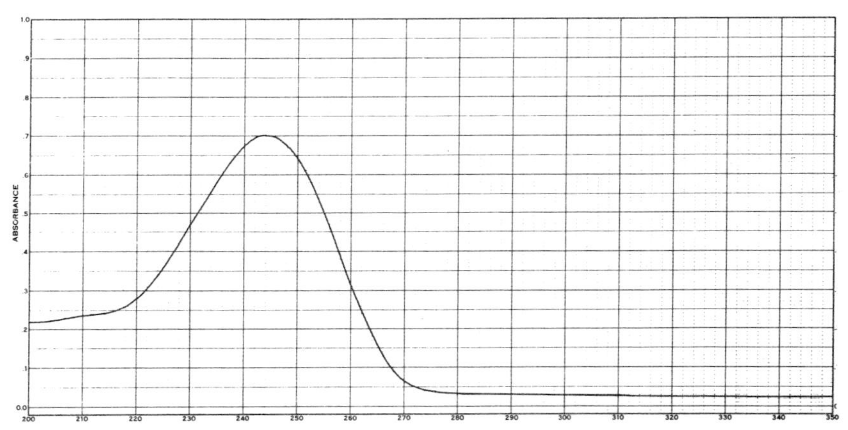

2-(ETHYLAMINO)-1,3,4-THIADIAZOLE

1156

$C_4H_7N_3S$
Mol. Wt. 129.18
M.P. 71-73°C
Solvent: Methanol

λ Max. mμ	a_m	Cell mm	Conc. g/L
264	7360	1	0.100
x	x	1	0.100

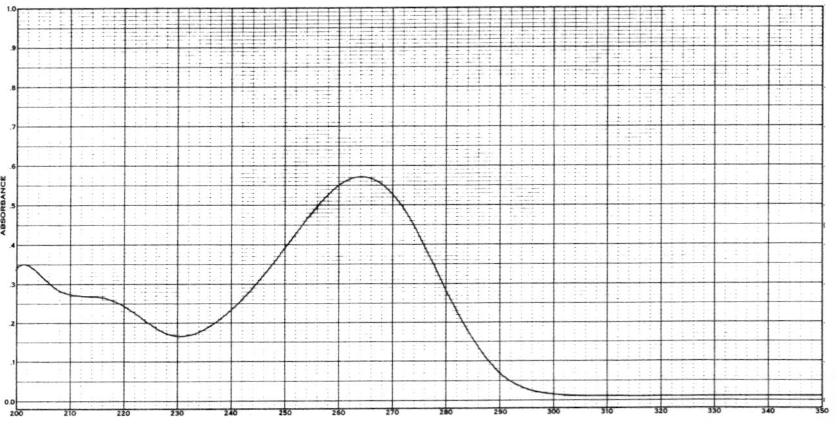

2-(ETHYLAMINO)-1,3,4-THIADIAZOLE

1156

$C_4H_7N_3S$
Mol. Wt. 129.18
M.P. 71-73°C
Solvent: Methanol HCl

λ Max. mμ	a_m	Cell mm	Conc. g/L
249	9020	1	0.100
214	4520	1	0.100

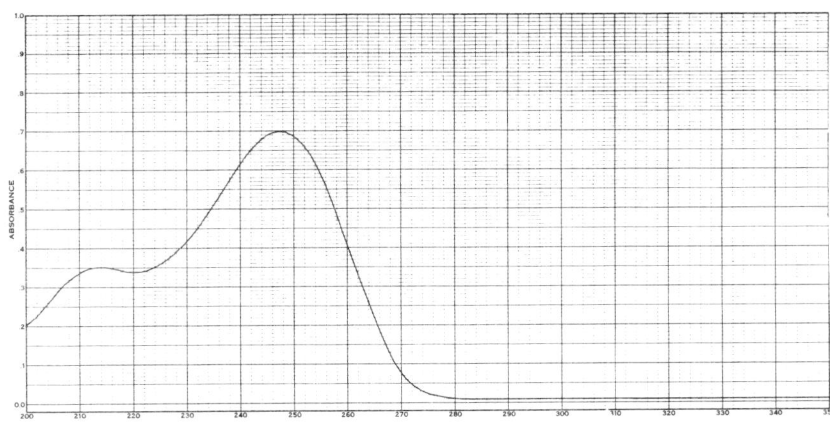

2,5-DIPHENYL-p-DITHIIN

1157

$C_{16}H_{12}S_2$
Mol. Wt. 268.40
M.P. 116-118°C
Solvent: Methanol

λ Max. mμ	a_m	Cell mm	Conc. g/L
306	8640	1	0.100
257.5	22300	1	0.100

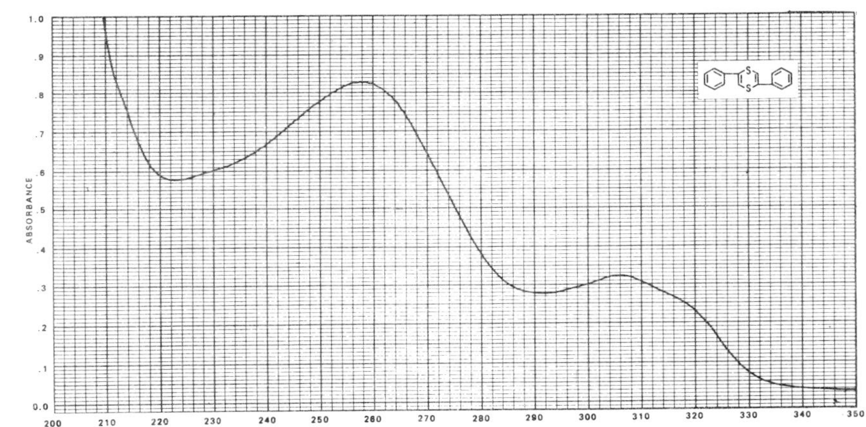

BENZYL METHYL SULFIDE

1158

$C_8H_{10}S$
Mol. Wt. 138.23
B.P. 78-79°C/15mm
Solvent: Methanol

λ Max. mμ	a_m	Cell mm	Conc. g/L
x	x	1	0.100

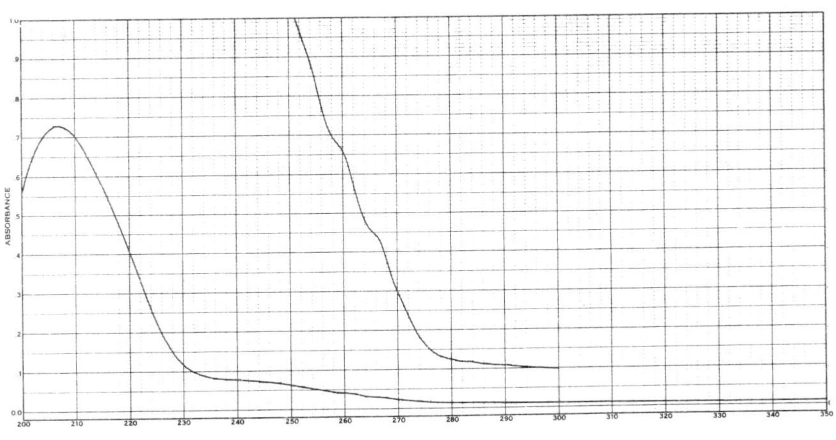

BENZYL ETHYL SULFIDE 1159

$C_9H_{12}S$

Mol. Wt. 152.26

Solvent: Methanol

λ Max. mμ	a_m	Cell mm	Conc. g/L
x	x	5	0.25
x	x	0.5	0.25

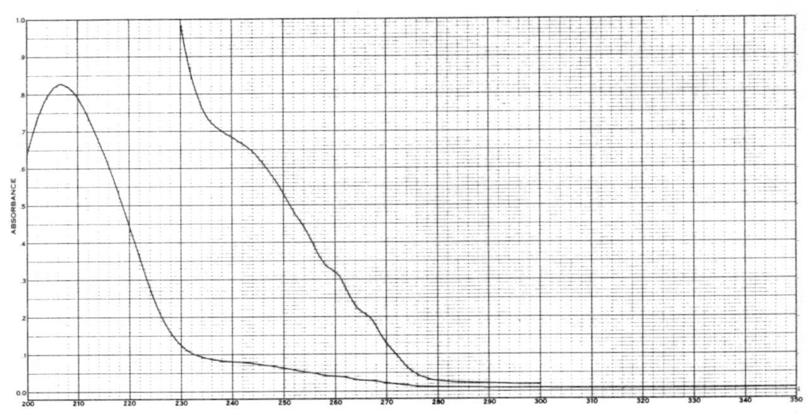

p-BROMOPHENYL METHYL SULFIDE 1160

C_7H_7BrS

Mol. Wt. 203.11

M.P. 37-38°C

Solvent: Methanol

λ Max. mμ	a_m	Cell mm	Conc. g/L
261	16900	1	0.0940

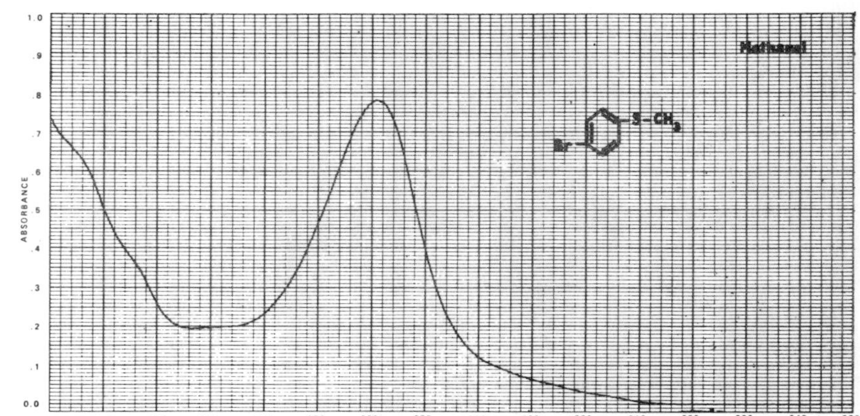

o-(METHYLTHIO)ANILINE 1161

C_7H_9NS

Mol. Wt. 139.22

Solvent: Methanol

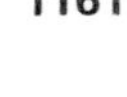

λ Max. mμ	a_m	Cell mm	Conc. g/L
301	2900	1	0.122
235	7600	1	0.122
206.5	24000	1	0.0488

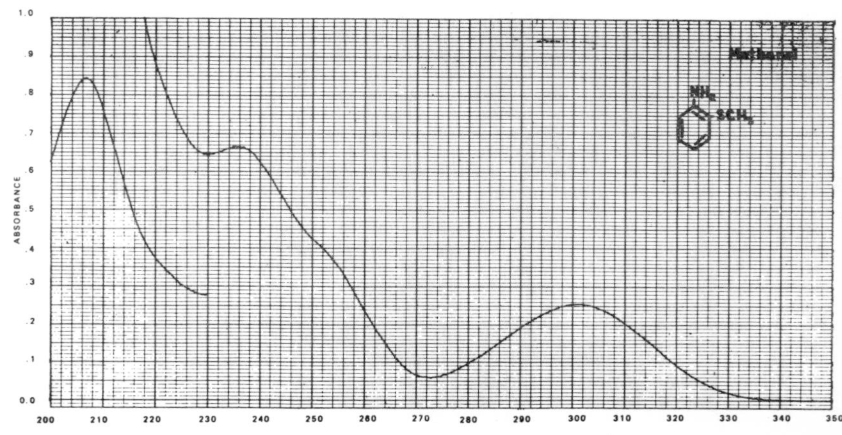

o-(METHYLTHIO)ANILINE

1161

C_7H_9NS

Mol. Wt. 139.22

Solvent: Methanol HCl

λ Max. mμ	a_m	Cell mm	Conc. g/L
251.5	5970	1	0.122

BENZYL p-TOLYL SULFIDE

1162

$C_{14}H_{14}S$

Mol. Wt. 214.33

Solvent: Methanol

λ Max. mμ	a_m	Cell mm	Conc. g/L
254	6950	2.5	0.100

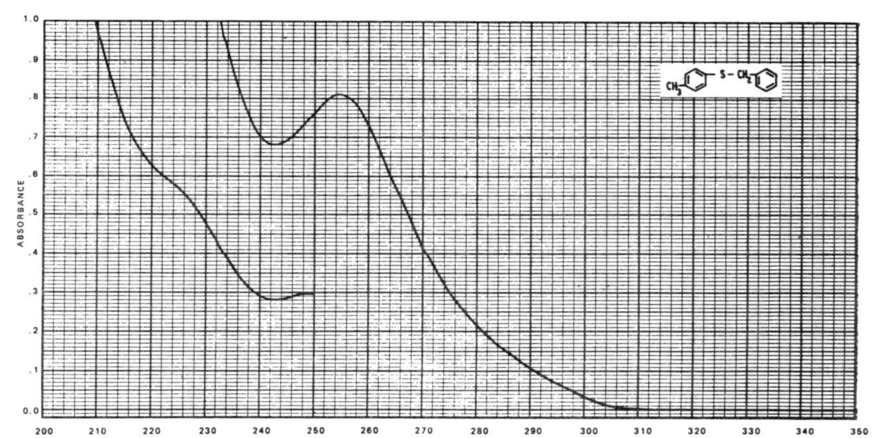

PHENETHYL PHENYL SULFIDE

1163

$C_{14}H_{14}S$

Mol. Wt. 214.33

Solvent: Methanol

λ Max. mμ	a_m	Cell mm	Conc. g/L
255	8750	1	0.124

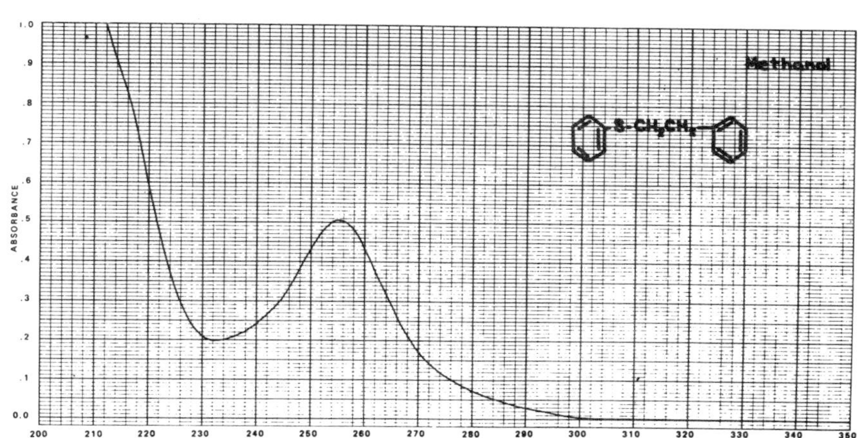

PHENYL 3-PHENYLPROPYL SULFIDE 1164

$C_{15}H_{16}S$
Mol. Wt. 228.36
Solvent: Methanol

λ Max. mμ	a_m	Cell mm	Conc. g/L
254.5	7620	1	0.0920

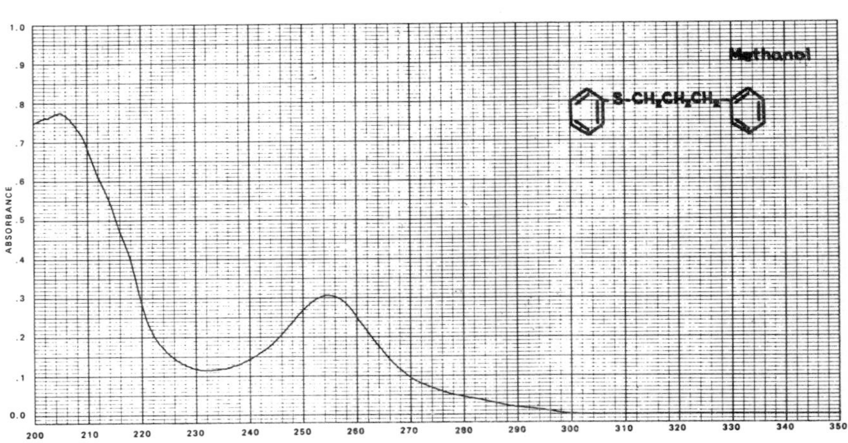

BENZYL p-CHLOROPHENYL SULFIDE 1165

$C_{13}H_{11}ClS$
Mol. Wt. 234.75
Solvent: Methanol

λ Max. mμ	a_m	Cell mm	Conc. g/L
260	10500	1	0.100

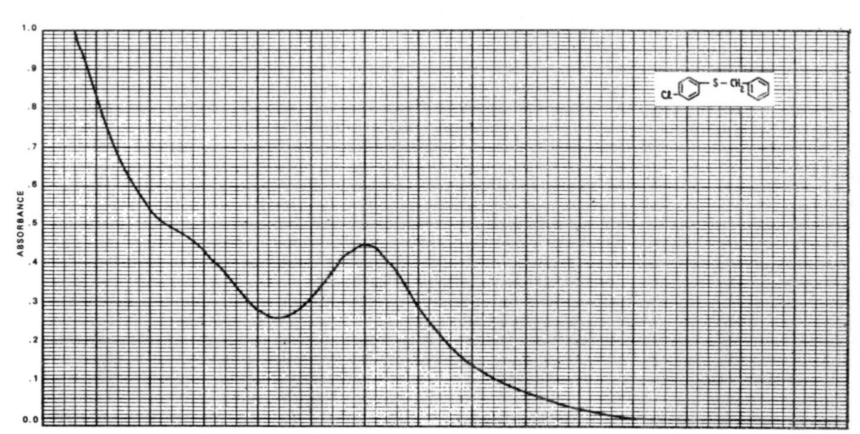

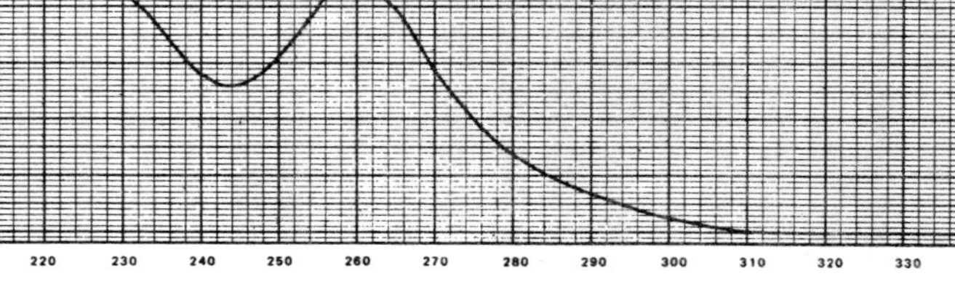

2,2-DIPHENYLVINYL PHENYL SULFIDE 1166

$C_{20}H_{16}S$
Mol. Wt. 288.41
M.P. 71-73°C
Solvent: Methanol

λ Max. mμ	a_m	Cell mm	Conc. g/L
308.5	18000	1	0.100

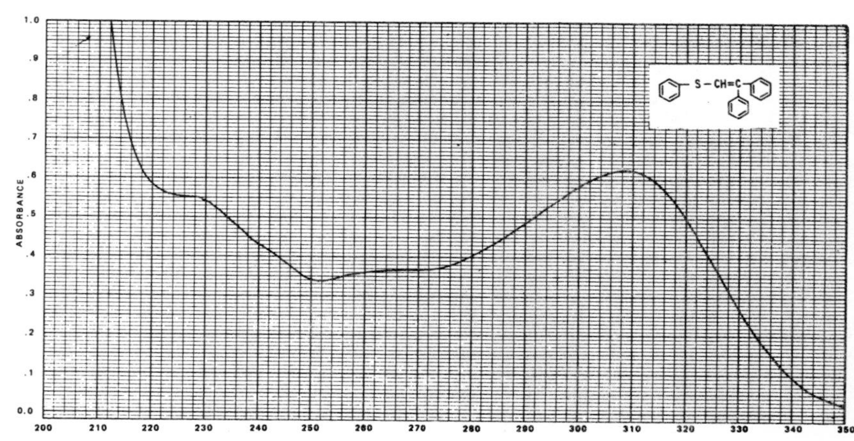

BIS(PHENYLTHIO)METHANE 1167

$C_{13}H_{12}S_2$
Mol. Wt. 232.37
Solvent: Methanol

λ Max. mμ	a_m	Cell mm	Conc. g/L
257	11000	1	0.100

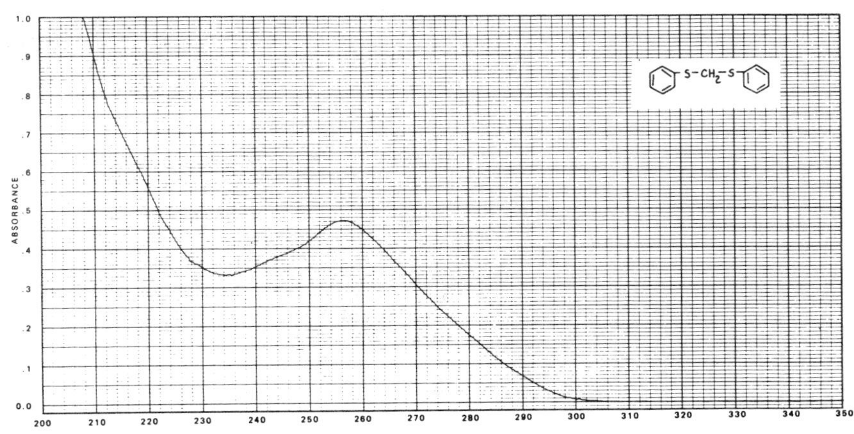

TETRATHIOORTHOCARBONIC ACID, TETRAPHENYL ESTER 1168

$C_{25}H_{20}S_4$
Mol. Wt. 448.69
M.P. 154-158°C

λ Max. mμ	a_m	Cell mm	Conc. g/L

Pure sample not available.

PHENYL SULFIDE 1169

$C_{12}H_{10}S$
Mol. Wt. 186.28
B.P. 96-100°C/0.1mm
Solvent: Methanol

λ Max. mμ	a_m	Cell mm	Conc. g/L
273	5350	2	0.0470
249.5	11400	2	0.0470
230	6360	2	0.0470

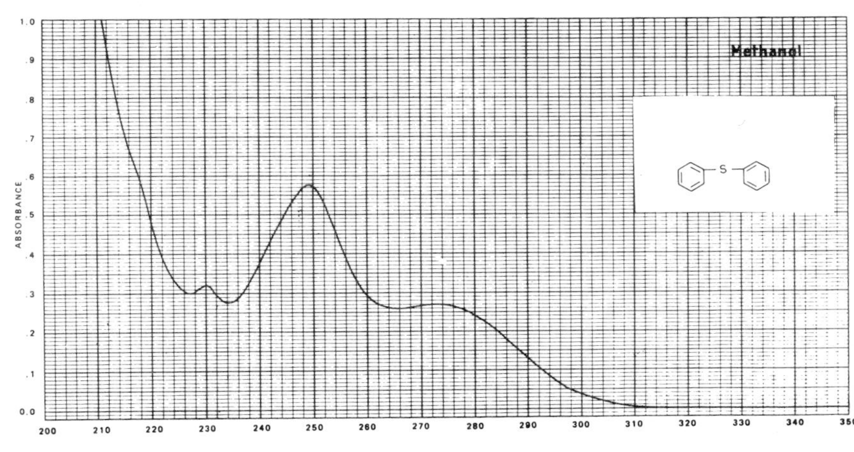

DI-p-TOLYL SULFIDE

1170

$C_{14}H_{14}S$
Mol. Wt. 214.33
M.P. 56.8-57.2°C
Solvent: Methanol

λ Max. mμ	a_m	Cell mm	Conc. g/L
274	6300	1	0.100
251.5	13700	1	0.100

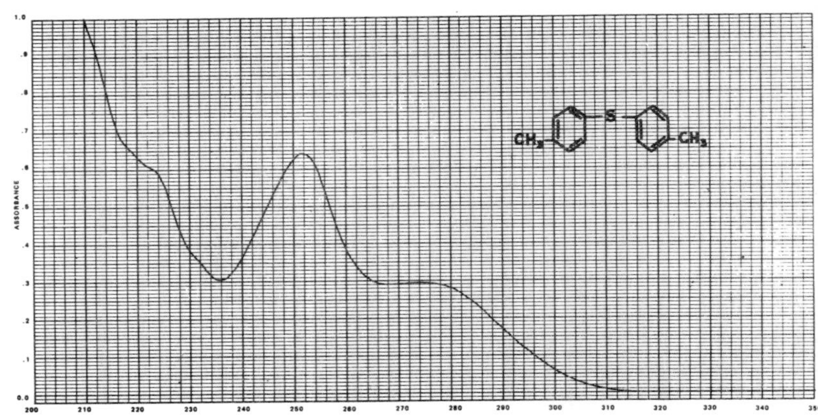

BIS(p-CHLOROPHENYL) SULFIDE

1171

$C_{12}H_8Cl_2S$
Mol. Wt. 255.17
Solvent: Methanol

λ Max. mμ	a_m	Cell mm	Conc. g/L
280.5	7350	1	0.100
256.5	14600	1	0.100
222	14600	1	0.100

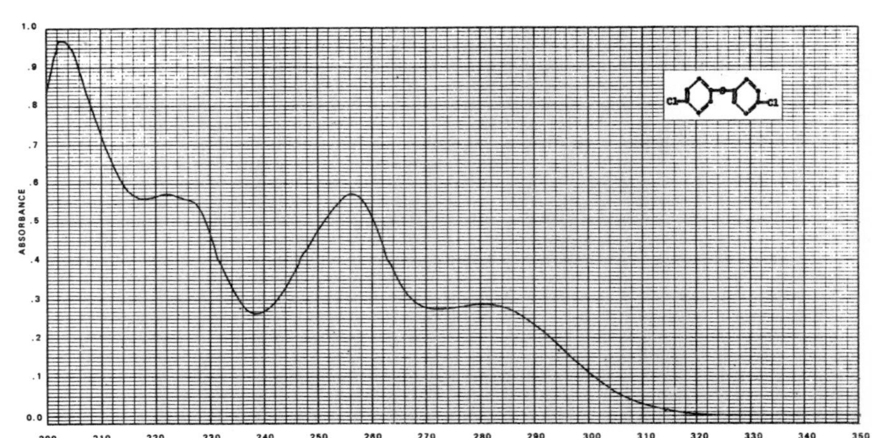

4-(PHENYLTHIO)PYRIDINE

1172

$C_{11}H_9NS$
Mol. Wt. 187.27
M.P. 0-5°C
Solvent: Methanol

λ Max. mμ	a_m	Cell mm	Conc. g/L
257	11200	1	0.109

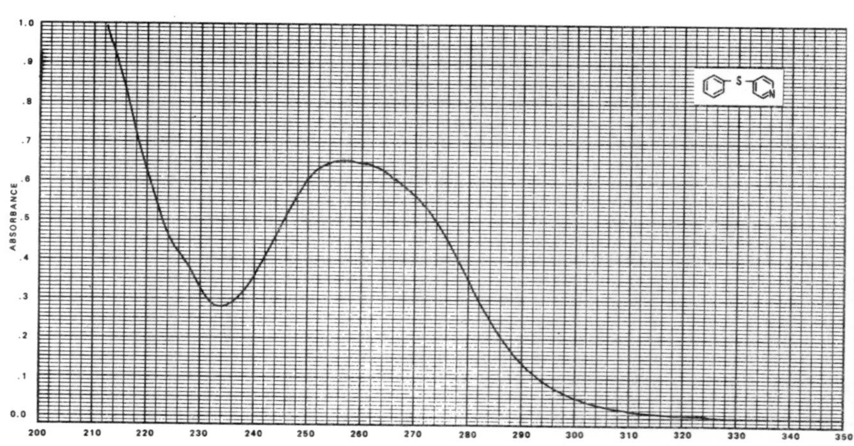

4-(PHENYLTHIO)PYRIDINE 1172

$C_{11}H_9NS$

Mol. Wt. 187.27

M.P. 0-5°C

Solvent: Methanol HCl

λ Max. mμ	^{a}m	Cell mm	Conc. g/L
291	16800	1	0.109
226.5	9900	1	0.109

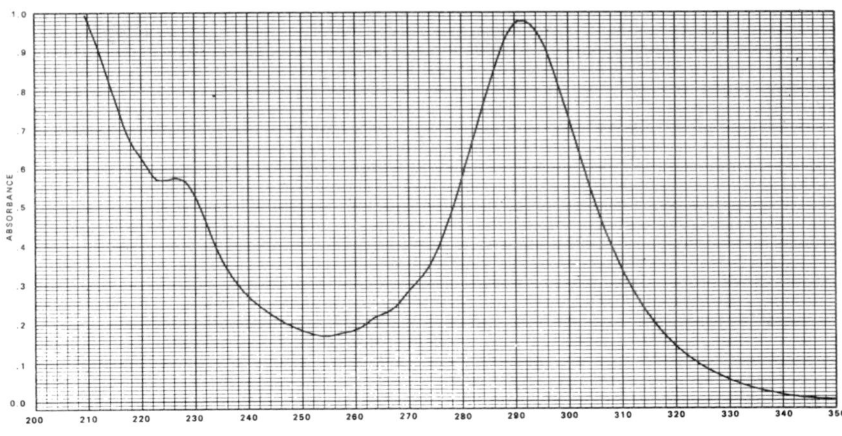

BENZYL 2-NAPHTHYL SULFIDE 1173

$C_{17}H_{14}S$

Mol. Wt. 250.37

M.P. 89.8-90.5^{o}C

Solvent: Methanol

λ Max. mμ	^{a}m	Cell mm	Conc. g/L
337.5	868	10	0.20
322.5	1080	10	0.20
283	8880	10	0.02
252.5	28100	10	0.005
217.5	45500	10	0.005

λ Max. mμ	^{a}m	Cell mm	Conc. g/L

2-(PHENYLTHIO)QUINOLINE

1174

$C_{15}H_{11}NS$

Mol. Wt. 237.33

M.P. 43-48°C

Solvent: Methanol

λ Max. mμ	a_m	Cell mm	Conc. g/L
338	7700	10	0.020
256	23100	2	0.020
212.5	49700	2	0.020

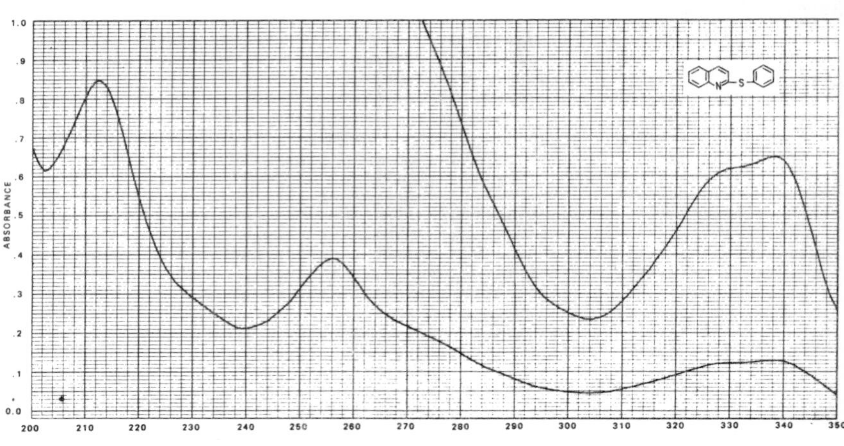

2-(PHENYLTHIO)QUINOLINE

1174

$C_{15}H_{11}NS$

Mol. Wt. 237.33

M.P. 43-48°C

Solvent: Methanol HCl

λ Max. mμ	a_m	Cell mm	Conc. g/L
349	14500	5	0.020
263	18400	5	0.020
211	65100	1	0.020

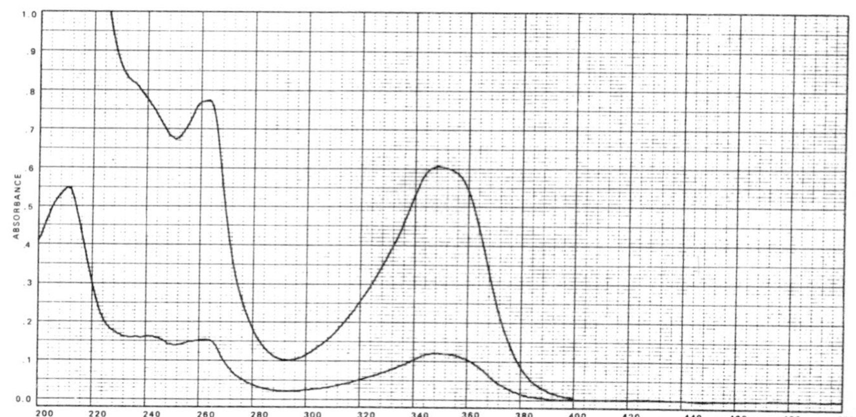

2-METHYLBENZOTHIAZOLE

1175

C_8H_7NS

Mol. Wt. 149.22

M.P. 13-15°C (lit.)

Solvent: Methanol

λ Max. mμ	a_m	Cell mm	Conc. g/L
292	1320	1	0.183
282	1550	1	0.183
251	6830	1	0.183
217.5	23100	1	0.0366

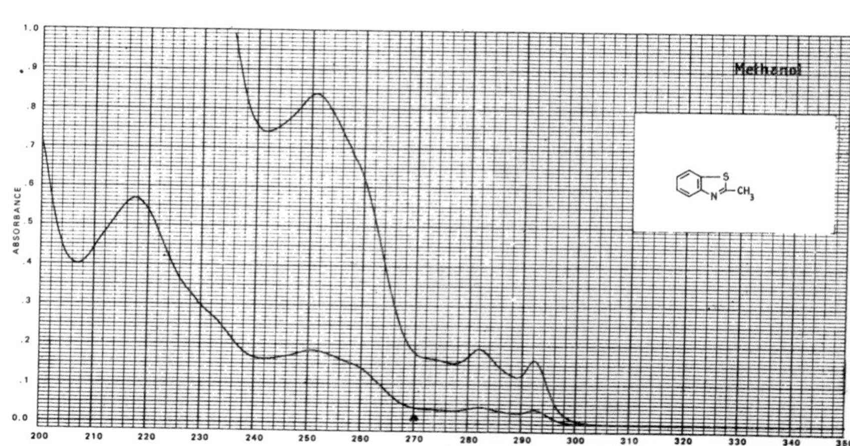

2-METHYLBENZOTHIAZOLE

1175

C_8H_7NS

Mol. Wt. 149.22

M.P. 13-15°C (lit.)

Solvent: Methanol HCl

λ Max. mμ	a_m	Cell mm	Conc. g/L
252.5	5220	5	0.0366
216	16900	2	0.0366

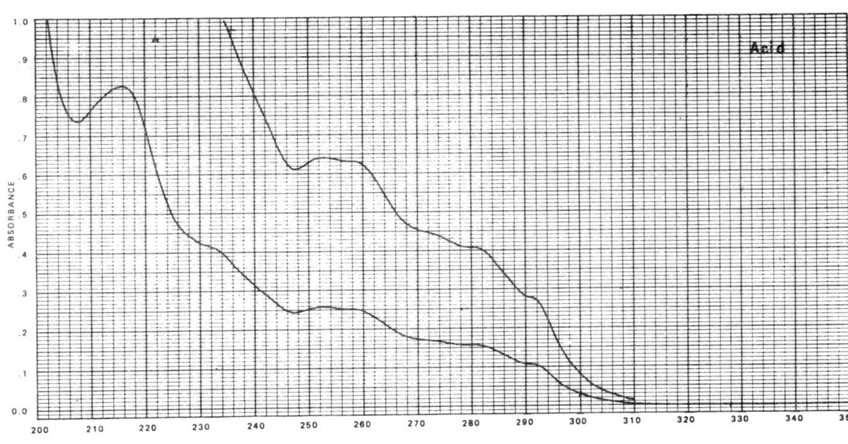

2-PHENYLBENZOTHIAZOLE

1176

$C_{13}H_9NS$

Mol. Wt. 211.29

M.P. 114°C

Solvent: Methanol

λ Max. mμ	a_m	Cell mm	Conc. g/L
296	18900	1	0.0800
254.5	7980	1	0.0800
246.5	8000	1	0.0800
225.5	20100	1	0.0800
206	37000	1	0.0400

λ Max. mμ	a_m	Cell mm	Conc. g/L

5-CHLORO-2-METHYLBENZOTHIAZOLE

1177

C_8H_6ClNS

Mol. Wt. 183.66

M.P. 68-70°C

Solvent: Methanol

λ Max. mμ	a_m	Cell mm	Conc. g/L
300	1510	10	0.117
289.5	1540	10	0.117
221.5	29900	1	0.059

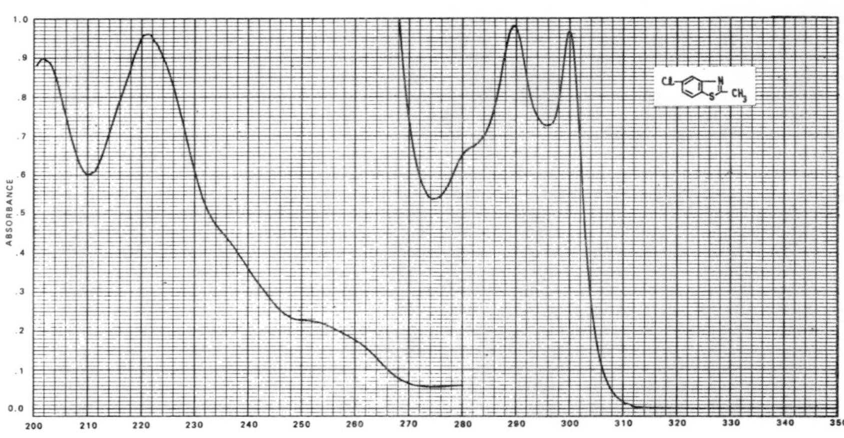

5-CHLORO-2-METHYLBENZOTHIAZOLE

1177

C_8H_6ClNS

Mol. Wt. 183.66

M.P. 68-70°C

Solvent: Methanol HCl

λ Max. mμ	a_m	Cell mm	Conc. g/L
299.5	1670	5	0.117
289	1840	5	0.117
280	1520	5	0.117
221.5	26800	1	0.059

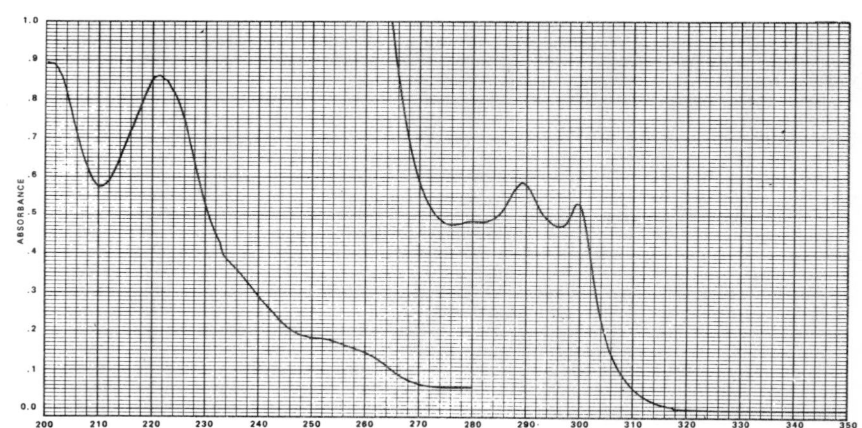

2,1,3-BENZOTHIADIAZOLE

1178

$C_6H_4N_2S$

Mol. Wt. 136.18

M.P. 42-44°C

Solvent: Methanol

λ Max. mμ	a_m	Cell mm	Conc. g/L
311	13400	1	0.0800
304.5	13600	1	0.0800
222	14100	1	0.0800

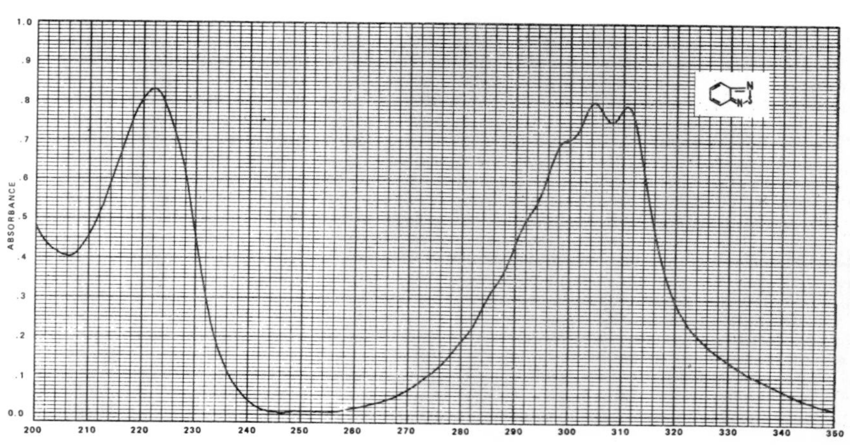

3-DIBENZOTHIOPHENAMINE 1179

$C_{12}H_9NS$
Mol. Wt. 199.28
M.P. 120-121°C
Solvent: Methanol

λ Max. mμ	a_m	Cell mm	Conc. g/L
302	12800	2	0.0320
282	15100	2	0.0320
240	51700	1	0.0320
204	23200	1	0.0320

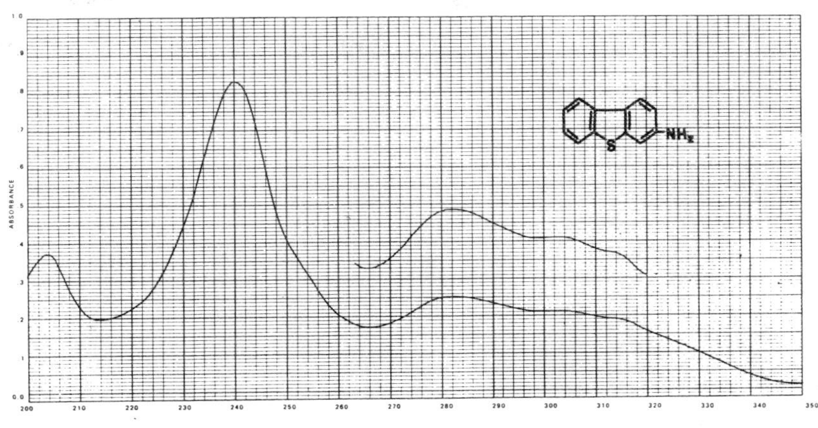

3-DIBENZOTHIOPHENAMINE 1179

$C_{12}H_9NS$
Mol. Wt. 199.28
M.P. 120-121°C
Solvent: Methanol HCl

λ Max. mμ	a_m	Cell mm	Conc. g/L
324	2720	5	0.0320
312	2370	5	0.0320
286	10300	5	0.0320
256	16800	1	0.0320
235.5	52900	1	0.0320

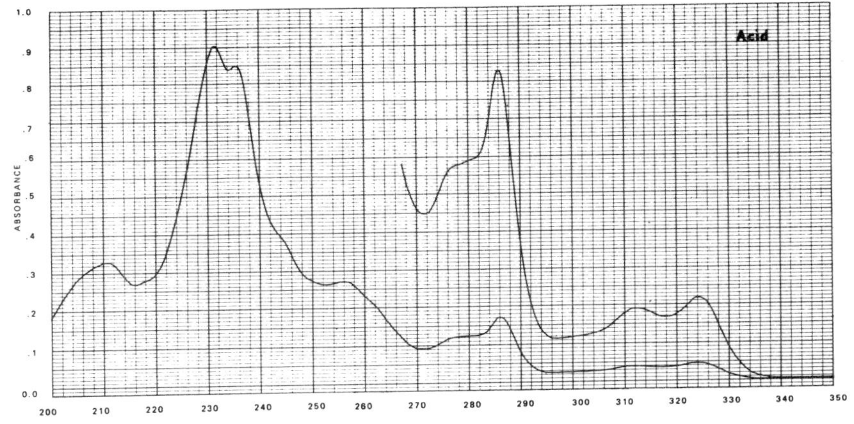

3,7-DINITRODIBENZOTHIOPHENE 1180

$C_{12}H_6N_2O_4S$
Mol. Wt. 274.26
M.P. 324-350°C (dec.)

λ Max. mμ	a_m	Cell mm	Conc. g/L

Pure sample not available.

PHENOTHIAZINE 1181

$C_{12}H_9NS$

Mol. Wt. 199.26

M.P. 185.1°C B.P. 371°C

Solvent: Methanol

λ Max. mμ	a_m	Cell mm	Conc. g/L
317.5	4660	10	0.0171
254	42500	10	0.0034

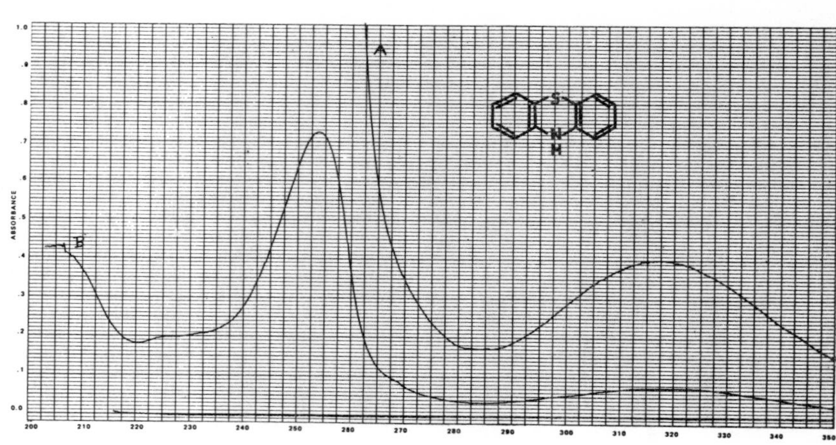

3-CHLOROPHENOTHIAZINE 1182

$C_{12}H_8ClNS$

Mol. Wt. 233.72

Solvent: Methanol

λ Max. mμ	a_m	Cell mm	Conc. g/L
322	6260	1	0.100
254	45100	0.5	0.100
x	x	0.5	0.100

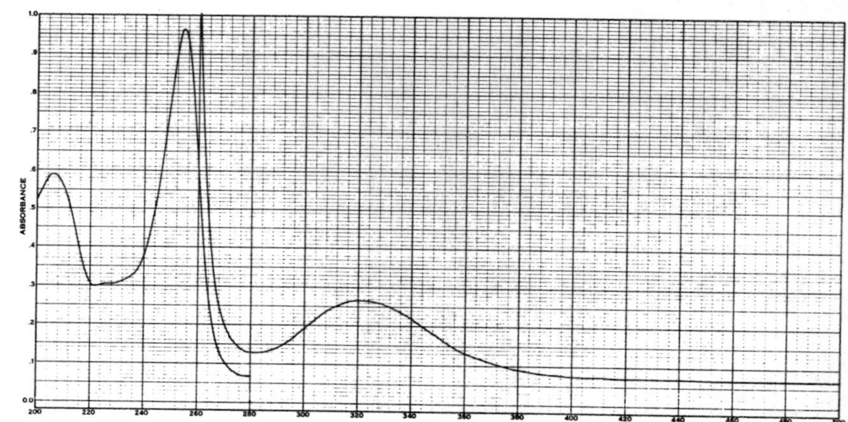

λ Max. mμ	a_m	Cell mm	Conc. g/L

THE DISULFIDES

Aliphatic Compounds

In contrast to the monosulfides, the aliphatic disulfides show the $n \rightarrow \sigma^*$ transition near 252 mμ well into the near UV region. This band is reported to be relatively unaffected by solvent changes and is not sensitive to the addition of acid or base.

Compound	$\lambda_{max}(\epsilon_{max})$	Solvent	Spectrum
Propyl disulfide	252 (475)	Ethanol	Lit.
Butyl disulfide	251 (348)	Methanol	1183
Isobutyl disulfide	252 (340)	Methanol	1185
Pentyl disulfide	250 (363)	Methanol	1187
Isopentyl disulfide	251 (361)	Methanol	1188

Aromatic Compounds

The aromatic disulfides display one major absorption band in the region from 239 - 248 mμ which appears at somewhat shorter wavelength than that of the aromatic monosulfides (254 - 261 mμ). One or more poorly resolved shoulders may be observed in the region from 260 - 310 mμ.

Compound	$\lambda_{max}(\epsilon_{max})$	Solvent	Spectrum
Methyl phenyl disulfide	238 (7880)	Methanol	1192
Ethyl phenyl disulfide	238 99900)	Methanol	1193
Diphenyl disulfide	240 (15800)	Dioxane	1194
p-Tolyl disulfide	241 (19100)	Methanol	1196
Bis-p-chlorophenyl disulfide	248 (23400)	Methanol	1197

BUTYL DISULFIDE 1183

$C_8H_{18}S_2$
Mol. Wt. 178.36
B.P. 110-112°C/13mm
Solvent: Methanol

λ Max. mμ	a_m	Cell mm	Conc. g/L
251	348	10	0.5

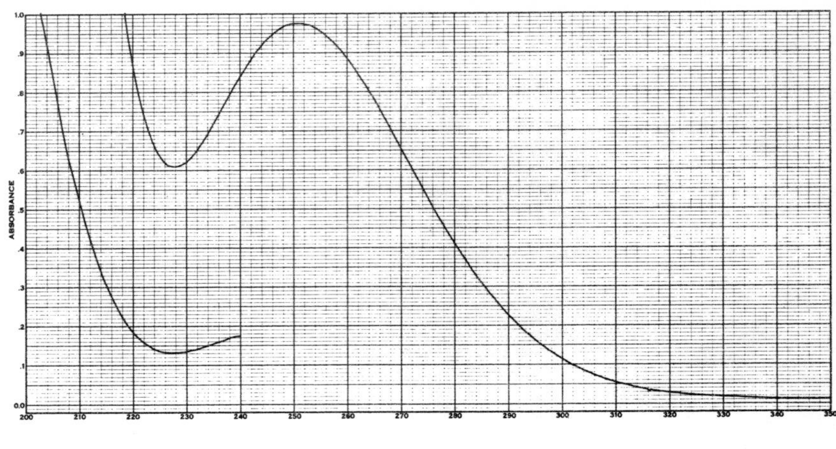

sec-BUTYL DISULFIDE 1184

$C_8H_{18}S_2$
Mol. Wt. 178.36

λ Max. mμ	a_m	Cell mm	Conc. g/L

Pure sample not available.

ISOBUTYL DISULFIDE 1185

$C_8H_{18}S_2$
Mol. Wt. 178.35
B.P. 82.5-85°C
Solvent: Methanol

λ Max. mμ	a_m	Cell mm	Conc. g/L
252	340	10	0.5
x	x	1	0.5

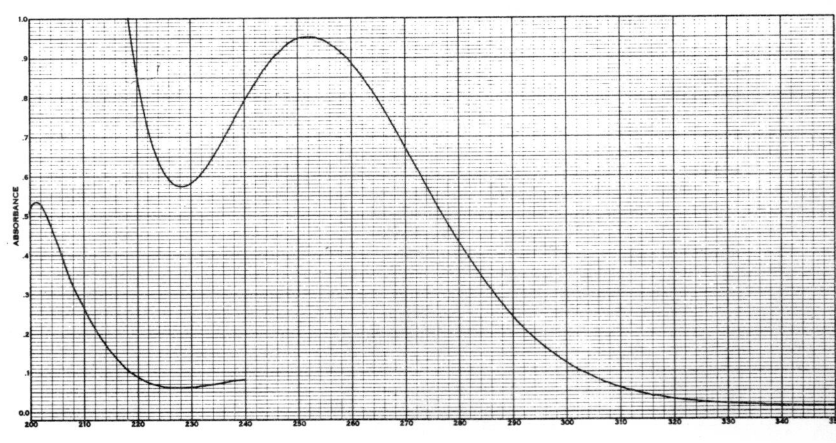

tert-BUTYL DISULFIDE 1186

$C_8H_{18}S_2$
Mol. Wt. 178.36
B.P. 198-204°C

λ Max. mμ	a_m	Cell mm	Conc. g/L

Pure sample not available.

AMYL DISULFIDE 1187

$C_{10}H_{22}S_2$
Mol. Wt. 206.42
B.P. 128-130°C/7mm
Solvent: Methanol

λ Max. mμ	a_m	Cell mm	Conc. g/L
250	363	10	0.5
x	x	2	0.5

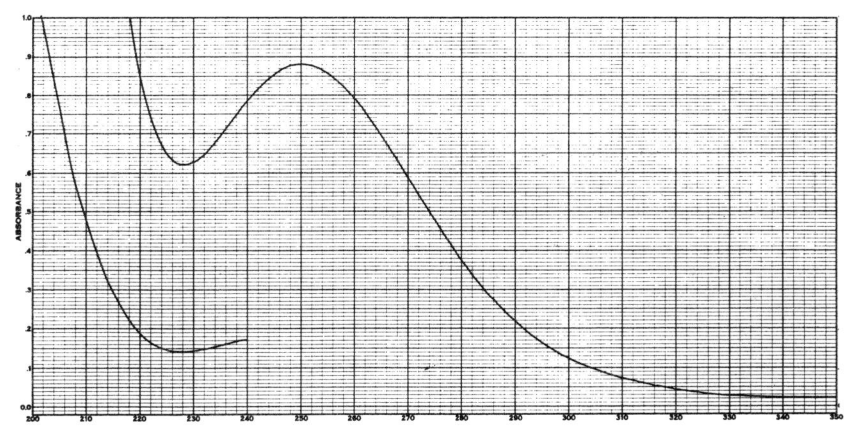

ISOPENTYL DISULFIDE 1188

$C_{10}H_{22}S_2$
Mol. Wt. 206.42
B.P. 124-126.5°C/10mm
Solvent: Methanol

λ Max. mμ	a_m	Cell mm	Conc. g/L
250.5	361	10	0.5
x	x	2	0.5

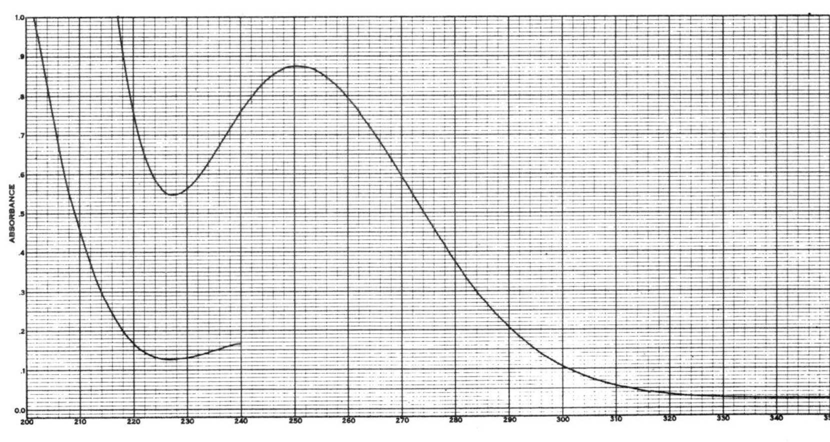

DODECYL DISULFIDE 1189

$C_{24}H_{50}S_2$
Mol. Wt. 402.79

λ Max. mμ	a_m	Cell mm	Conc. g/L

Pure sample not available.

ALLYL DISULFIDE 1190

$C_6H_{10}S_2$
Mol. Wt. 146.27

λ Max. mμ	a_m	Cell mm	Conc. g/L

Pure sample not available.

BENZYL DISULFIDE 1191

$C_{14}H_{14}S_2$
Mol. Wt. 246.40
M.P. 69-72°C
Solvent: Methanol

λ Max. mμ	a_m	Cell mm	Conc. g/L
x	x	1	0.100

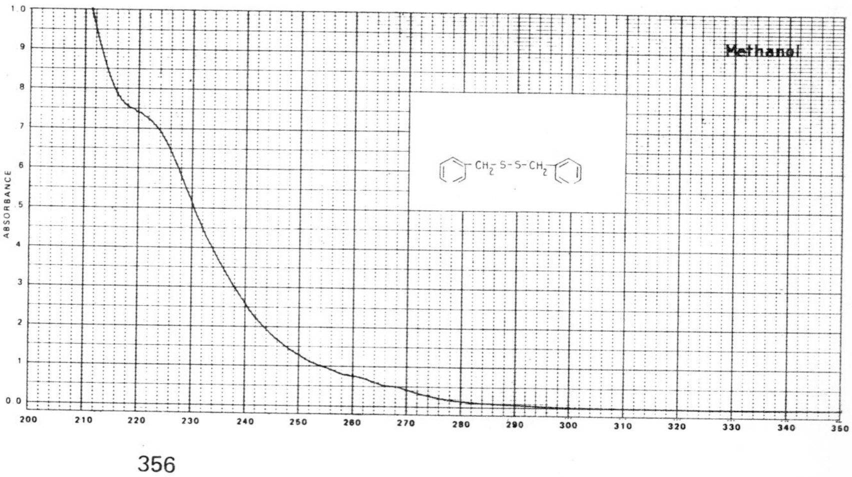

Methanol

$C_6H_5-CH_2-S-S-CH_2-C_6H_5$

ABSORBANCE 0.0 1 2 3 4 5 6 7 8 9 1.0

200 210 220 230 240 250 260 270 280 290 300 310 320 330 340 350

METHYL PHENYL DISULFIDE

1192

$C_7H_8S_2$
Mol. Wt. 156.27
B.P. 93-97°C/5mm
Solvent: Methanol

λ Max. mμ	a_m	Cell mm	Conc. g/L
238	7880	1	0.146

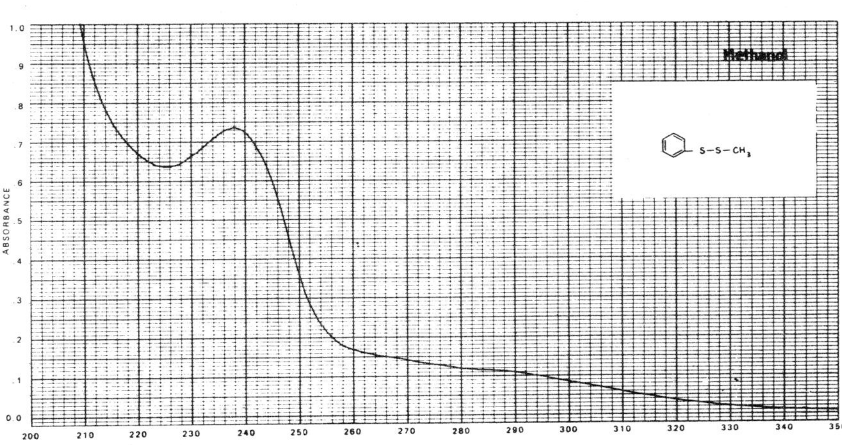

ETHYL PHENYL DISULFIDE

1193

$C_8H_{10}S_2$
Mol. Wt. 170.30
Solvent: Methanol

λ Max. mμ	a_m	Cell mm	Conc. g/L
238	9900	1	0.145

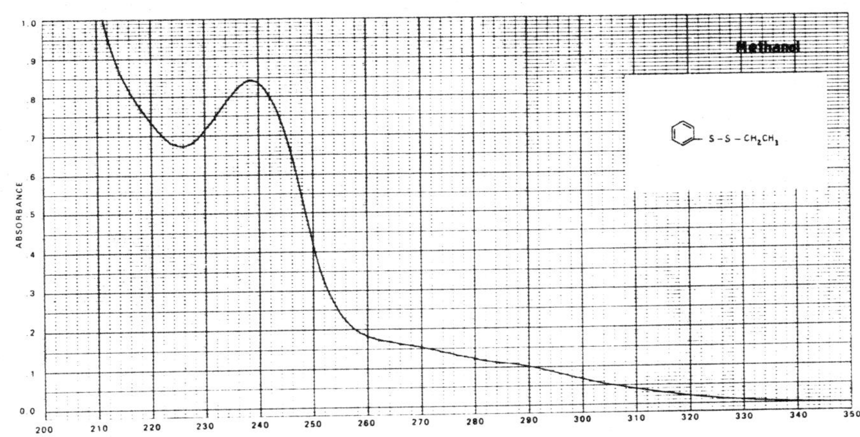

PHENYL DISULFIDE

1194

$C_{12}H_{10}S_2$
Mol. Wt. 218.34
M.P. 59-60°C
Solvent: Dioxane

λ Max. mμ	a_m	Cell mm	Conc. g/L
x	x	10	0.1968
240	15800	10	0.0197

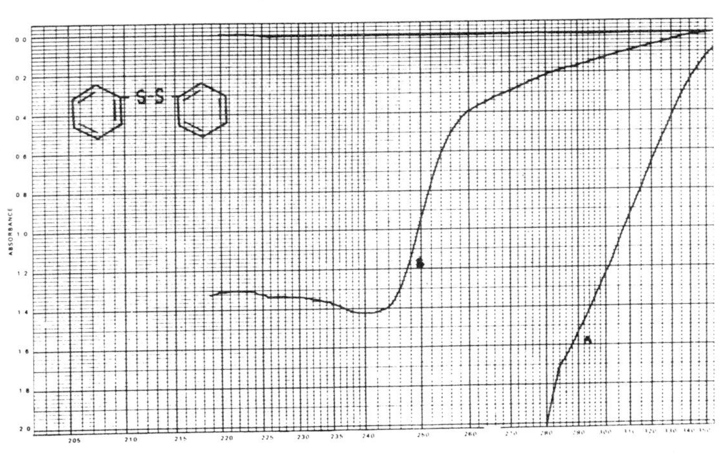

o-TOLYL DISULFIDE 1195

$C_{14}H_{14}S_2$
Mol. Wt. 246.60
Solvent: Methanol

λ Max. mμ	a_m	Cell mm	Conc. g/L
263	8130	1	0.100

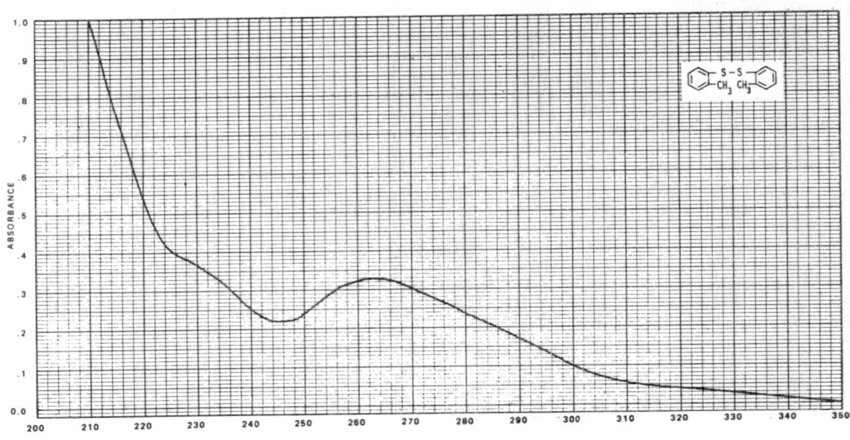

p-TOLYL DISULFIDE 1196

$C_{14}H_{14}S_2$
Mol. Wt. 246.40
M.P. 44-46°C
Solvent: Methanol

λ Max. mμ	a_m	Cell mm	Conc. g/L
241	19100	10	0.007

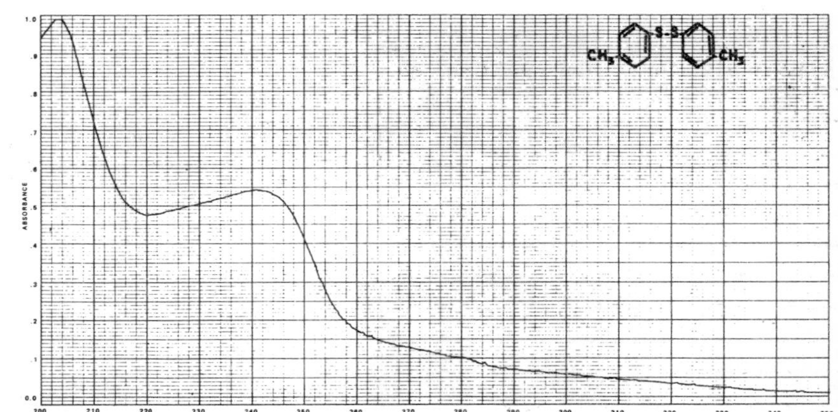

BIS(p-CHLOROPHENYL)DISULFIDE 1197

$C_{12}H_8Cl_2S_2$
Mol. Wt. 287.24
M.P. 71-72°C (lit.)
Solvent: Methanol

λ Max. mμ	a_m	Cell mm	Conc. g/L
x	x	10	0.344
x	x	10	0.0344
248	23400	10	0.0172

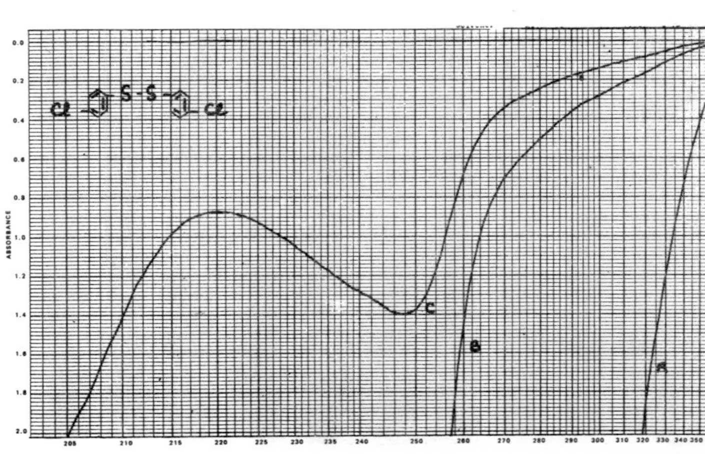

2,2′-DITHIODIANILINE 1198

$C_{12}H_{12}N_2S_2$

Mol. Wt. 248.36

M.P. 91-92°C

Solvent: Methanol

λ Max. mμ	a_m	Cell mm	Conc. g/L
335	8000	10	0.0439
x	x	10	0.0044

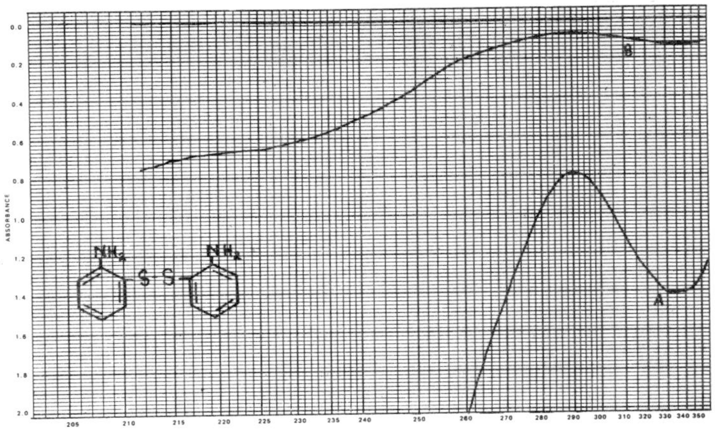

λ Max. mμ	a_m	Cell mm	Conc. g/L

λ Max. mμ	a_m	Cell mm	Conc. g/L

NOTES

THE THIOLS

Aliphatic Compounds

The major band for the aliphatic thiols absorbs below 210 mμ and thus there are no spectra in this volume for compounds 1199 through 1217.

Researchers have described a weak maximum or shoulder near 229 (ϵ = 165) for ethanethiol.

Aromatic Compounds

Benzenethiol and many of its derivatives display two major bands, the more intense maximum appears near 237 mμ and the weaker, which may show some additional shoulders or superimposed fine structure, is observed near 280 mμ.

Compound	$\lambda_{max}(\epsilon_{max})$	$\lambda_{max}(\epsilon_{max})$	Solvent	Spectrum
Benzenethiol	236 * (8300)	280 (610)	Heptane	Lit.
2-Methylbenzenethiol	237 (9030)	278 (979)	Methanol	1228
3-Methylbenzenethiol	239 (7170)	280 * (616)	Methanol	1229
4-Methylbenzenethiol	239 (10200)	282 (769)	Methanol	1230

* Shoulder

Upon the addition of base to the solution of a benzenethiol, the corresponding thiophenolate anion is formed with an attendant bathochromic shift to longer wavelengths by about 30 mμ and an increase in the intensity of the major band by about 50%.

Compound	$\lambda_{max}(\epsilon_{max})$	Solvent	Spectrum
4-Methylbenzenethiol	239 (10200)	Methanol	1230
4-Methylbenzenethiolate anion	266 (15600)	Methanol/KOH	1230
4-t-Butylbenzenethiol	239 (10400)	Methanol	1231
4-t-Butylbenzenethiolate anion	267 (16600)	Methanol/KOH	1231
4-Bromobenzenethiol	246 (27300)	Methanol	1235
4-Bromobenzenethiolate anion	277 (35200)	Methanol/KOH	1235

2-(PHENETHYLAMINO)ETHANETHIOL 1218

$C_{10}H_{15}NS$

Mol. Wt. 181.30

B.P. 130-135°C/1mm

Solvent: Methanol

λ Max. mμ	a_m	Cell mm	Conc. g/L
267.5	244	10	0.265
263.5	278	10	0.265
258	335	10	0.265
252.5	309	10	0.265
248	275	10	0.265

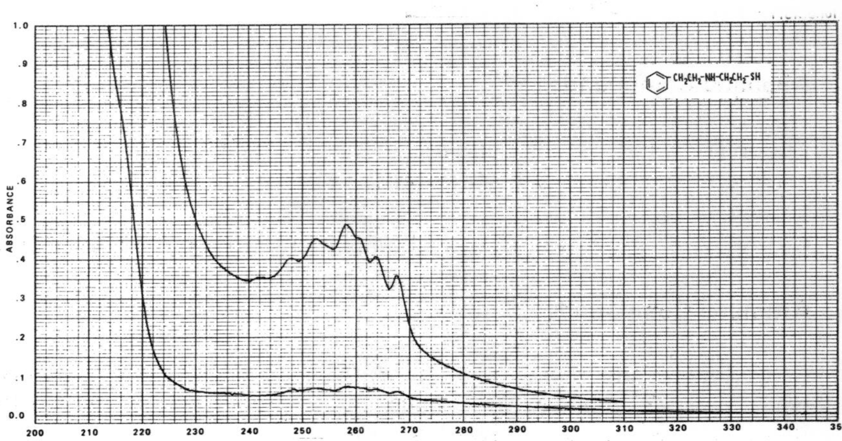

λ Max. mμ	a_m	Cell mm	Conc. g/L

Compounds 1219 through 1223 do not display any maxima in the near UV.

α-TOLUENETHIOL 1224

C_7H_8S

Mol. Wt. 124.20

Solvent: Cyclohexane

λ Max. mμ	a_m	Cell mm	Conc. g/L
x	x	10	1.78
269.5	181	10	0.534
262.5	273	10	0.534
x	x	10	0.0534
x	x	10	0.0178

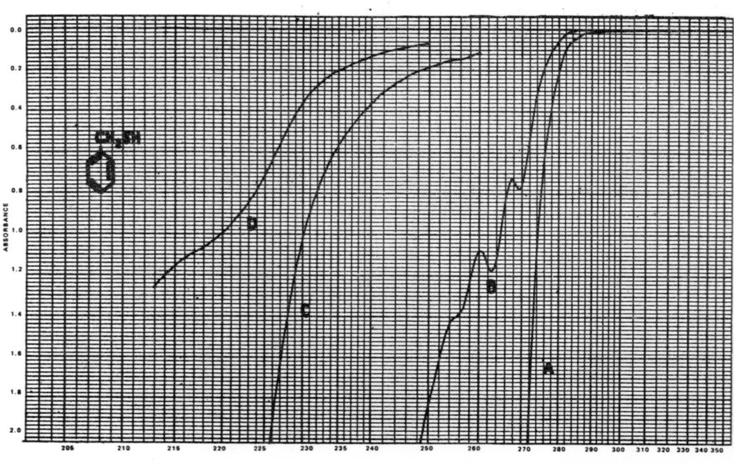

1225

p-CHLORO-α-TOLUENETHIOL

C_7H_7ClS
Mol. Wt. 158.65
B.P. 124°C/20mm
Solvent: Methanol

λ Max. mμ	a_m	Cell mm	Conc. g/L
277	224	20	0.1160
268.5	354	20	0.1160
223	10400	1	0.1160

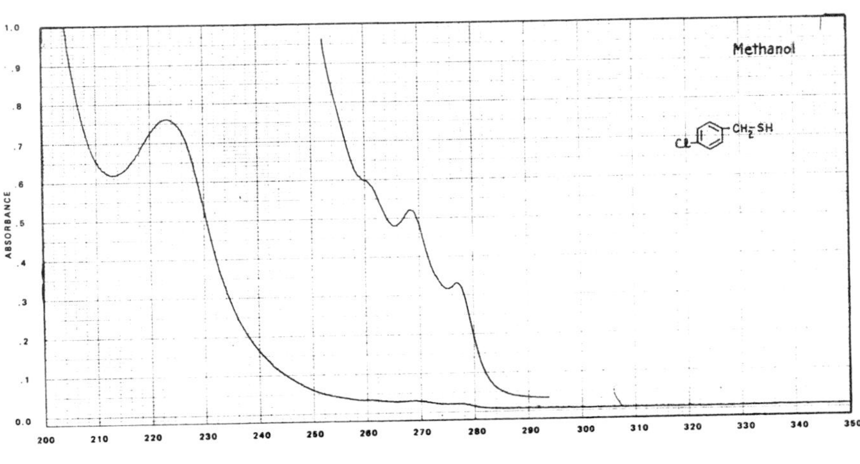

1225

p-CHLORO-α-TOLUENETHIOL

C_7H_7ClS
Mol. Wt. 158.65
B.P. 124°C/20mm
Solvent: Methanol KOH

λ Max. mμ	a_m	Cell mm	Conc. g/L
220	1590	1	0.5800

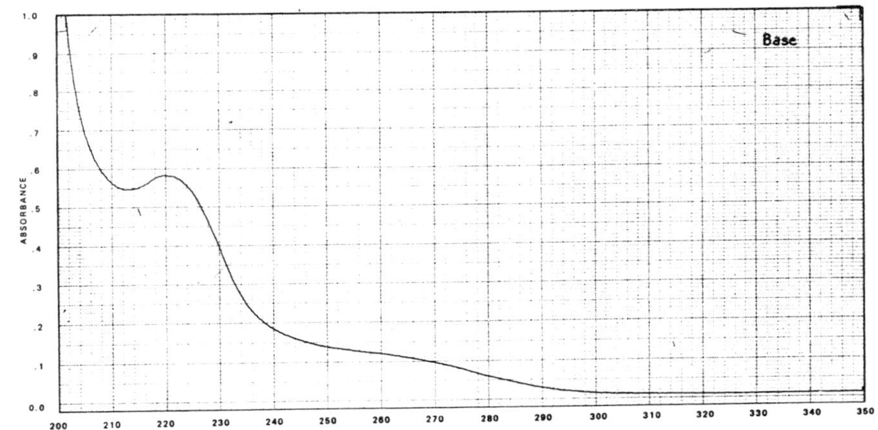

1226

TRIPHENYLMETHANETHIOL

$C_{19}H_{16}S$
Mol. Wt. 276.40
Solvent: Methanol

λ Max. mμ	a_m	Cell mm	Conc. g/L
x	x	0.5	0.100

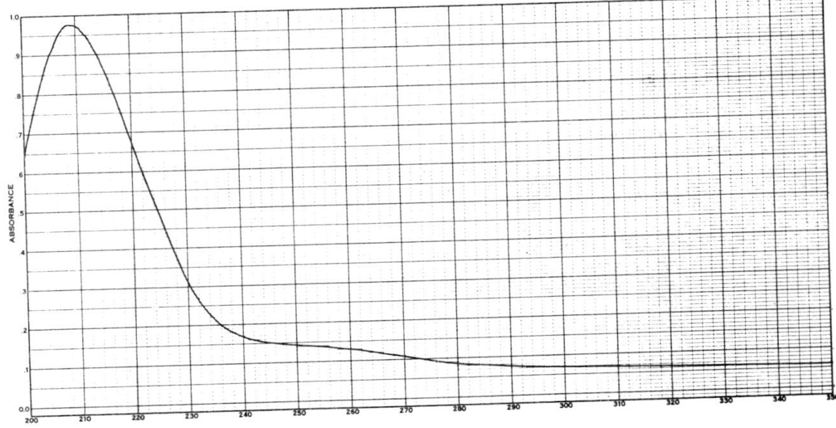

4,5-DIMETHYL-o-XYLENE-α,α-DITHIOL 1227

$C_{10}H_{14}S_2$

Mol. Wt. 198.35

M.P. 67-69°C

Solvent: Methanol

λ Max. mμ	a_m	Cell mm	Conc. g/L
272	45.6	20	0.100
x	x	1	0.100

o-TOLUENETHIOL 1228

C_7H_8S

Mol. Wt. 124.21

M.P. 10-12°C

Solvent: Methanol

λ Max. mμ	a_m	Cell mm	Conc. g/L
277	979	10	0.0406
270	955	10	0.0406
237	9030	1	0.0406

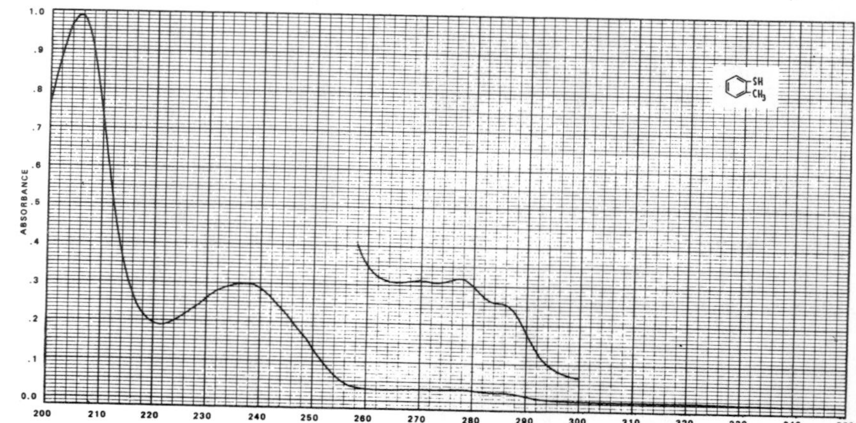

m-TOLUENETHIOL 1229

C_7H_8S

Mol. Wt. 124.21

B.P. 75-77°C/10mm

Solvent: Methanol

λ Max. mμ	a_m	Cell mm	Conc. g/L
x	x	10	0.119
239	7170	1	0.119

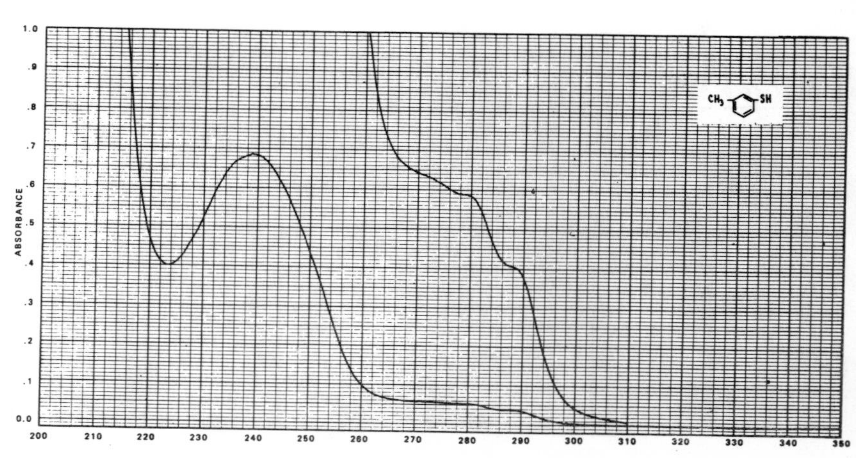

p-TOLUENETHIOL 1230

C_7H_8S

Mol. Wt. 124.21

M.P. 42-44°C B.P. 195°C (lit.)

Solvent: Methanol

λ Max. mμ	a_m	Cell mm	Conc. g/L
282.5	769	5	0.302
276	781	5	0.302
238.5	10200	2	0.0604

p-TOLUENETHIOL 1230

C_7H_8S

Mol. Wt. 124.21

M.P. 42-44°C B.P. 195°C (lit.)

Solvent: Methanol KOH

λ Max. mμ	a_m	Cell mm	Conc. g/L
266	7740	1	0.0604

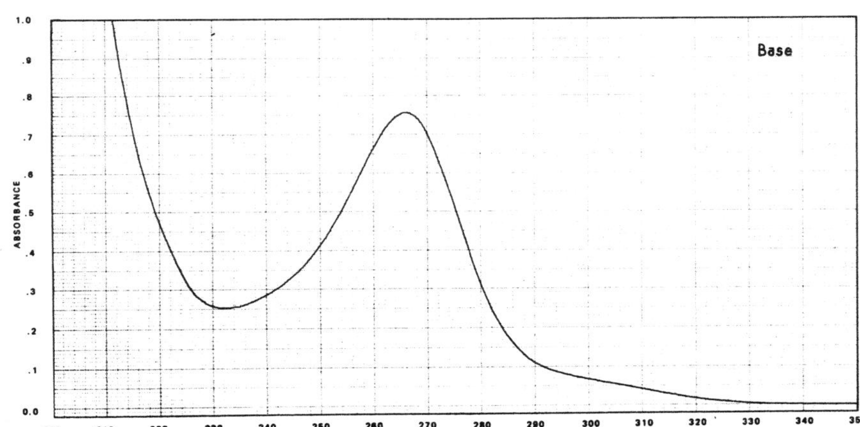

λ Max. mμ	a_m	Cell mm	Conc. g/L

p-tert-BUTYLBENZENETHIOL 1231

$C_{10}H_{14}S$

Mol. Wt. 166.29

Solvent: Methanol

λ Max. mμ	a_m	Cell mm	Conc. g/L
238.5	10400	2	0.0720

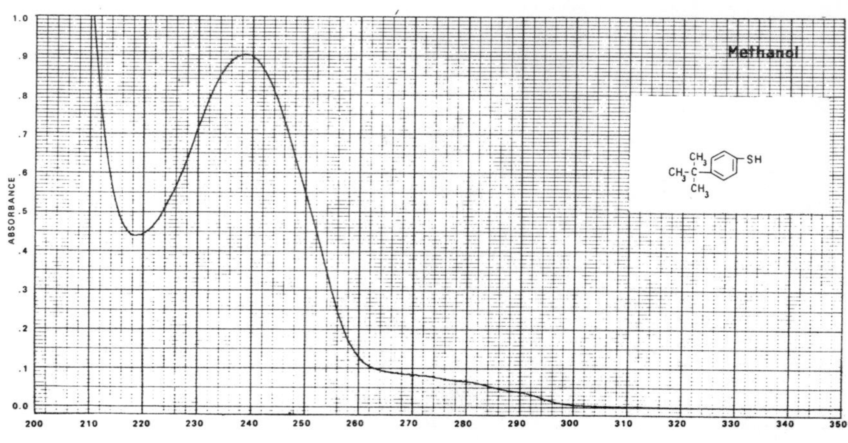

p-tert-BUTYLBENZENETHIOL 1231

$C_{10}H_{14}S$

Mol. Wt. 166.29

Solvent: Methanol KOH

λ Max. mμ	a_m	Cell mm	Conc. g/L
266.5	16600	1	0.0720

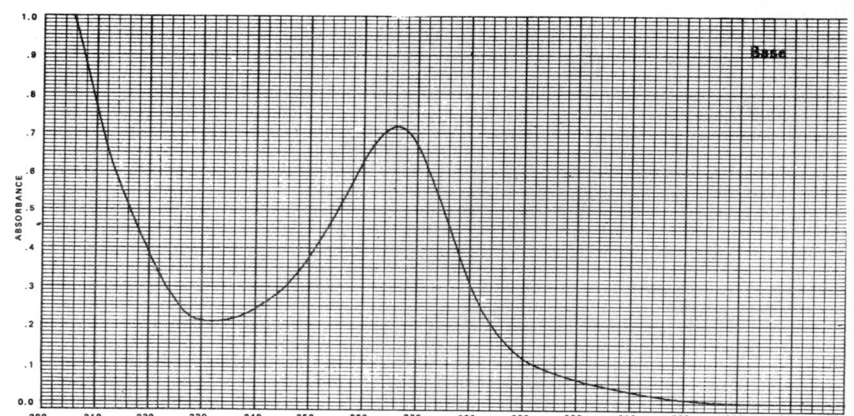

2,5-DICHLOROBENZENETHIOL 1232

$C_6H_4Cl_2S$

Mol. Wt. 179.07

Solvent: Methanol

λ Max. mμ	a_m	Cell mm	Conc. g/L
296	1400	10	0.0474
287	1660	10	0.0474
279	1600	10	0.0474
246	8310	1	0.0474
218	27600	1	0.0474

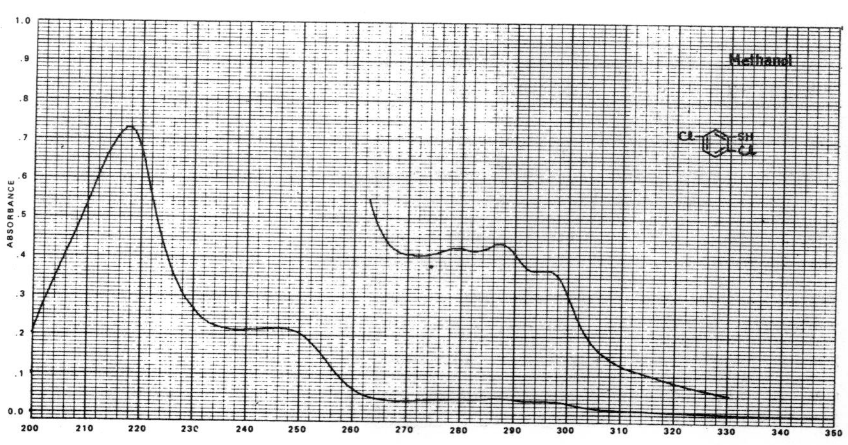

2,5-DICHLOROBENZENETHIOL

1232

$C_6H_4Cl_2S$
Mol. Wt. 179.07
Solvent: Methanol KOH

λ Max. mμ	a_m	Cell mm	Conc. g/L
277	8700	1	0.0474
217	21200	1	0.0474

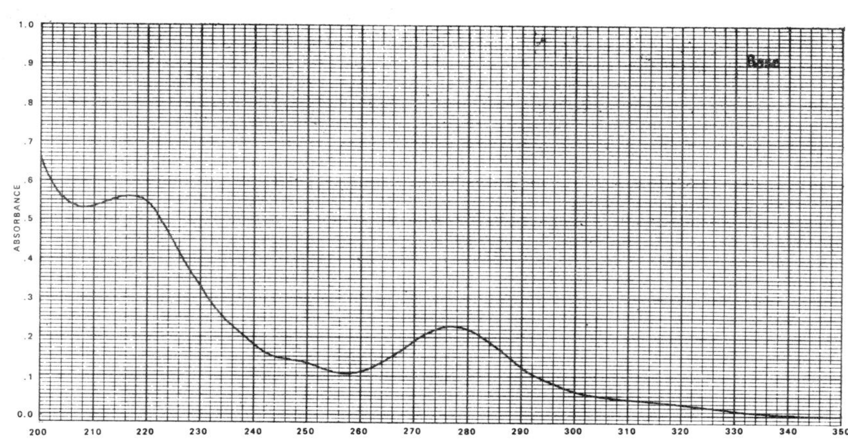

3,4-DICHLOROBENZENETHIOL

1233

$C_6H_4Cl_2S$
Mol. Wt. 179.07
Solvent: Methanol

λ Max. mμ	a_m	Cell mm	Conc. g/L
250	10300	1	0.0402
212	21000	1	0.0402

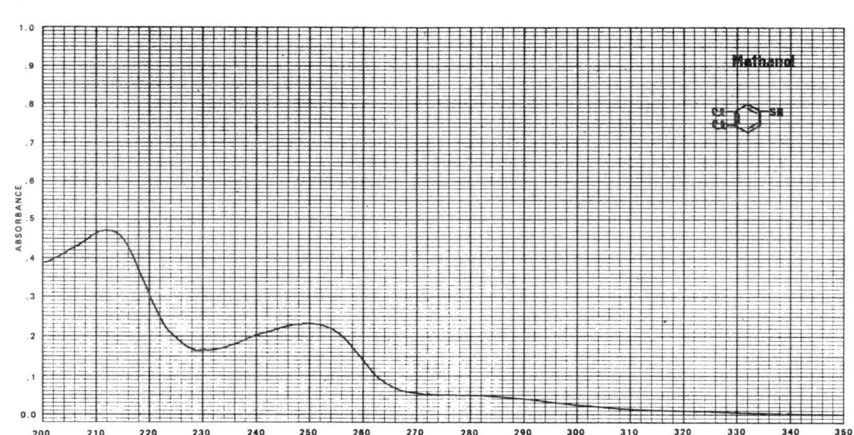

3,4-DICHLOROBENZENETHIOL

1233

$C_6H_4Cl_2S$
Mol. Wt. 179.07
Solvent: Methanol KOH

λ Max. mμ	a_m	Cell mm	Conc. g/L
280	19200	2	0.0440

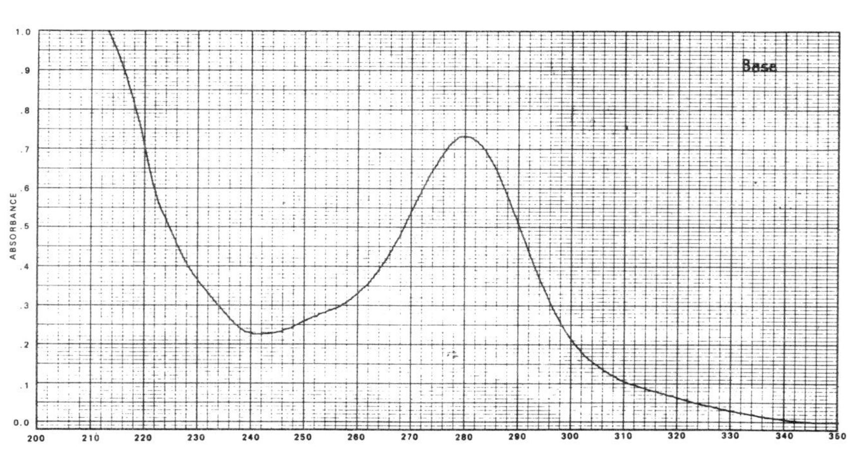

2,4,5-TRICHLOROBENZENETHIOL

1234

$C_6H_3Cl_3S$

Mol. Wt. 213.51

Solvent: Methanol

λ Max. mμ	a_m	Cell mm	Conc. g/L
296	1890	10	0.100
255	10900	1	0.0500
220	28600	1	0.0500

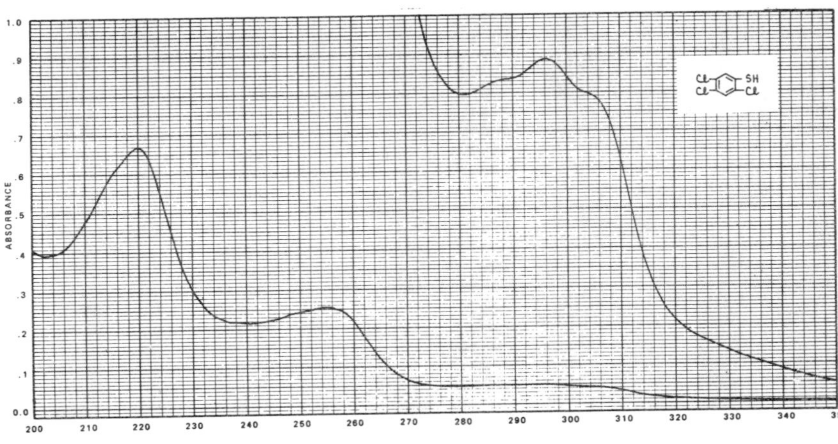

2,4,5-TRICHLOROBENZENETHIOL

1234

$C_6H_3Cl_3S$

Mol. Wt. 213.51

Solvent: Methanol KOH

λ Max. mμ	a_m	Cell mm	Conc. g/L
285	10700	1	0.100
258	6560	1	0.100

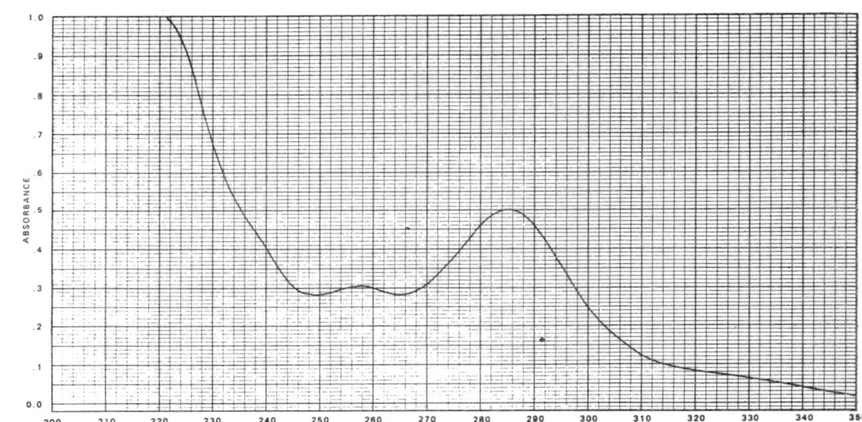
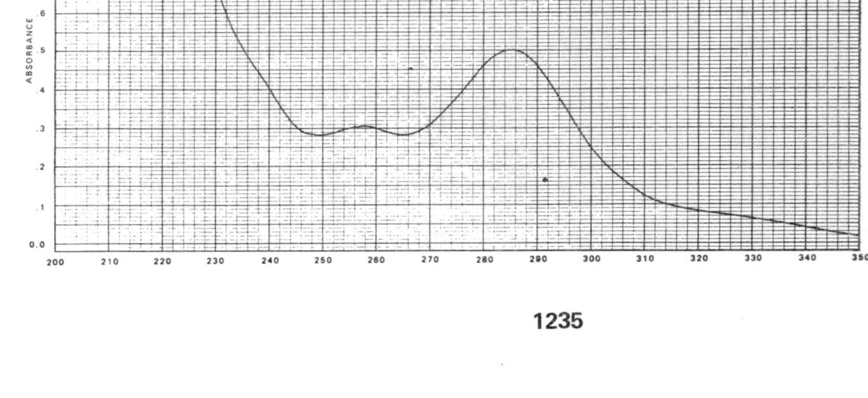

p-BROMOBENZENETHIOL

1235

C_6H_5BrS

Mol. Wt. 189.08

B.P. 230-232°C

Solvent: Methanol

λ Max. mμ	a_m	Cell mm	Conc. g/L
246	27300	1	0.0490

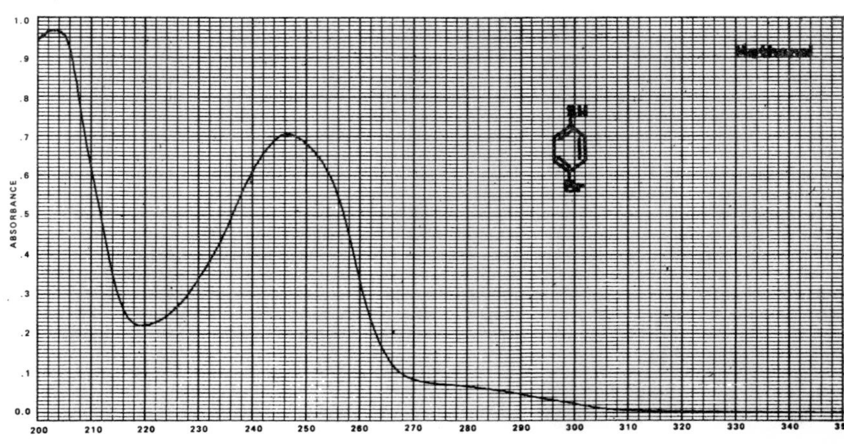

p-BROMOBENZENETHIOL 1235

C_6H_5BrS

Mol. Wt. 189.08

B.P. 230-232°C

Solvent: Methanol KOH

λ Max. mμ	$^a m$	Cell mm	Conc. g/L
276.5	35200	1	0.0490

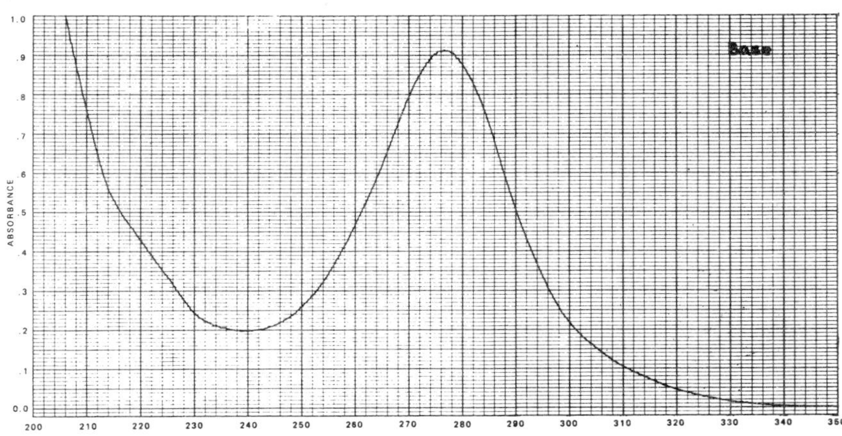

o-AMINOBENZENETHIOL 1236

C_6H_7NS

Mol. Wt. 125.11

B.P. 227.2°C (lit.)

Solvent: Methanol

λ Max. mμ	$^a m$	Cell mm	Conc. g/L
340	3020	10	0.0537
x	x	10	0.0107

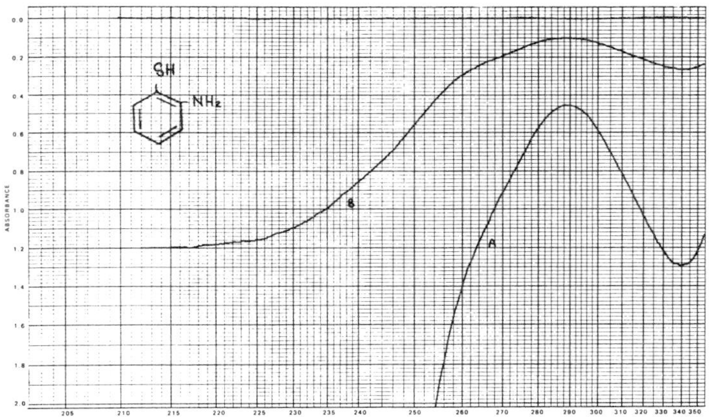

λ Max. mμ	$^a m$	Cell mm	Conc. g/L

m-AMINOBENZENETHIOL 1237

C_6H_7NS
Mol. Wt. 125.19
Solvent: Methanol

λ Max. mμ	a_m	Cell mm	Conc. g/L
298	2210	20	0.0213
220	25600	1	0.0213

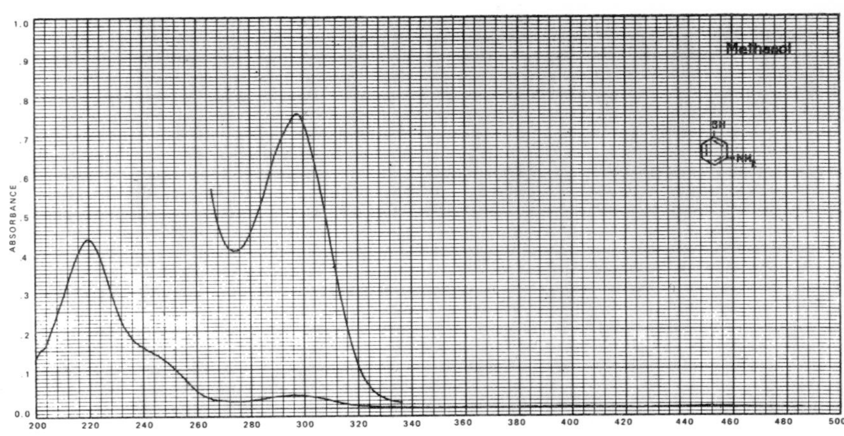

m-AMINOBENZENETHIOL 1237

C_6H_7NS
Mol. Wt. 125.19
Solvent: Methanol HCl

λ Max. mμ	a_m	Cell mm	Conc. g/L
244	10600	1	0.100

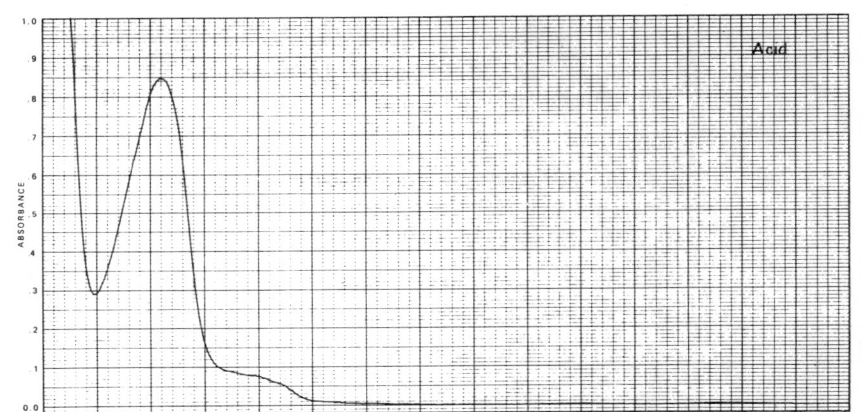

p-AMINOBENZENETHIOL 1238

C_6H_7NS
Mol. Wt. 125.20
Solvent: Methanol

λ Max. mμ	a_m	Cell mm	Conc. g/L
293	6930	10	0.0094
256	9060	10	0.0094

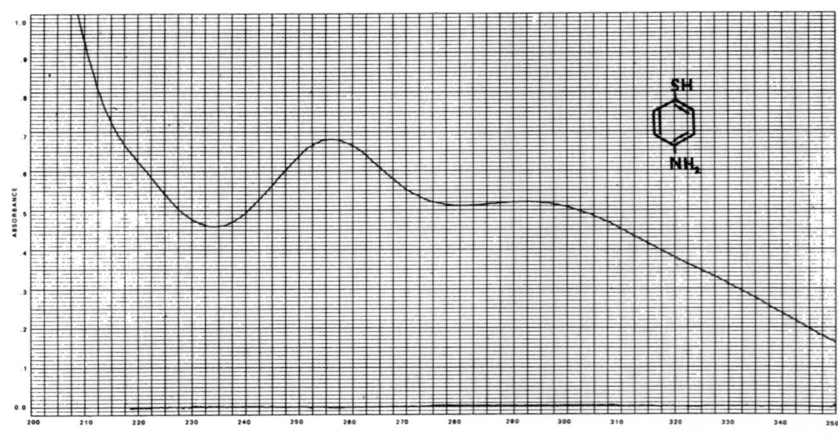

p-AMINOBENZENETHIOL 1238

C_6H_7NS

Mol. Wt. 125.20

Solvent: Methanol HCl

λ Max. mμ	a_m	Cell mm	Conc. g/L
244	8960	1	0.100

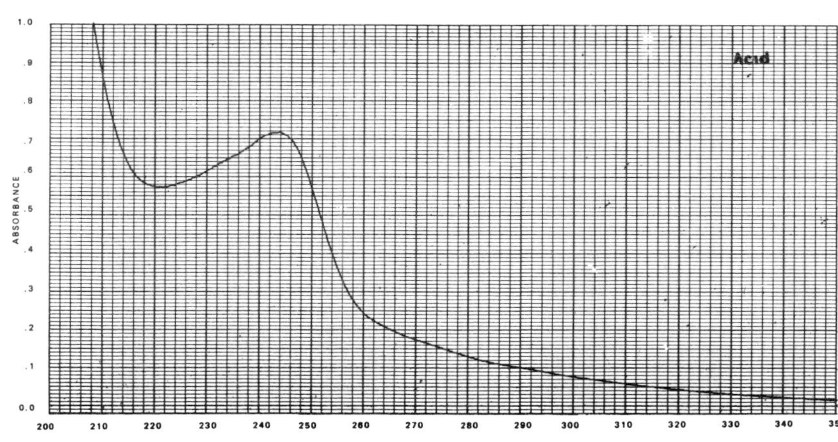

3,4-DITHIOLTOLUENE 1239

$C_7H_8S_2$

Mol. Wt. 156.27

M.P. 28-30°C

Solvent: Methanol

λ Max. mμ	a_m	Cell mm	Conc. g/L
297	1540	5	0.100
223	27400	0.5	0.100

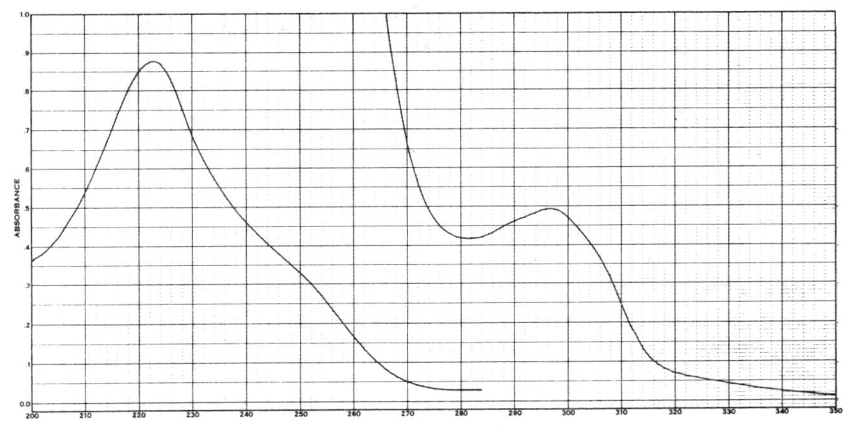

3,4-DITHIOLTOLUENE 1239

$C_7H_8S_2$

Mol. Wt. 156.27

Solvent: Methanol KOH

λ Max. mμ	a_m	Cell mm	Conc. g/L
317	3030	4	0.100
244	78200	0.5	0.100
x	x	0.5	0.100

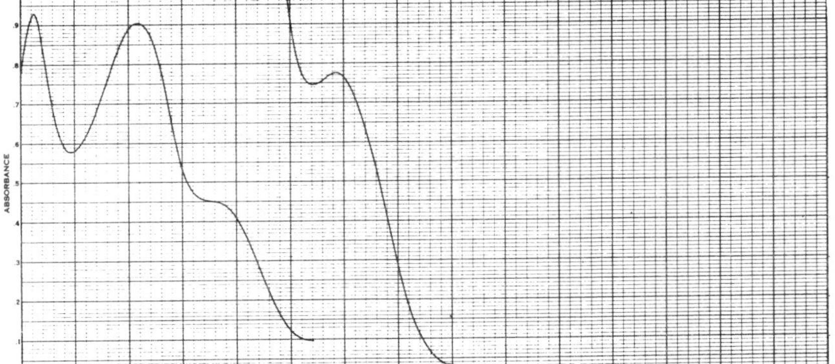

4-CHLORO-1,3-BENZENEDITHIOL

1240

$C_6H_5ClS_2$

Mol. Wt. 176.69

Solvent: Methanol

λ Max. mμ	a_m	Cell mm	Conc. g/L
308	1910	10	0.050
298.5	2310	10	0.050
231	39900	0.5	0.050

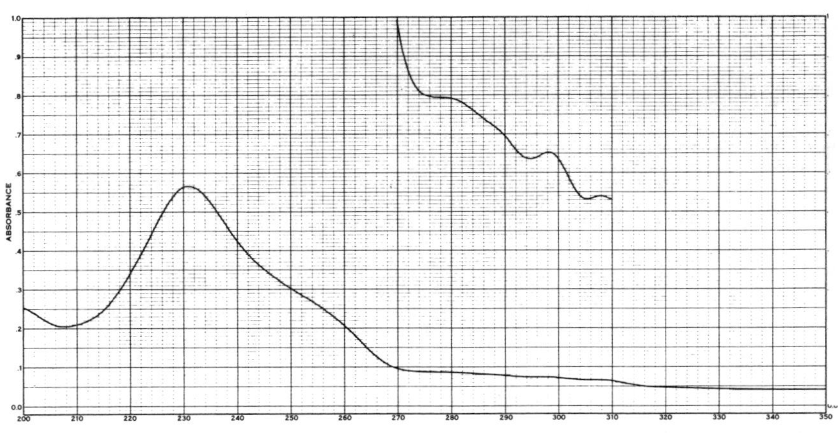

4-CHLORO-1,3-BENZENEDITHIOL

1240

$C_6H_5ClS_2$

Mol. Wt. 176.69

Solvent: Methanol KOH

λ Max. mμ	a_m	Cell mm	Conc. g/L
315.5	2660	10	0.050
260.5	45600	0.5	0.050
x	x	0.5	0.050

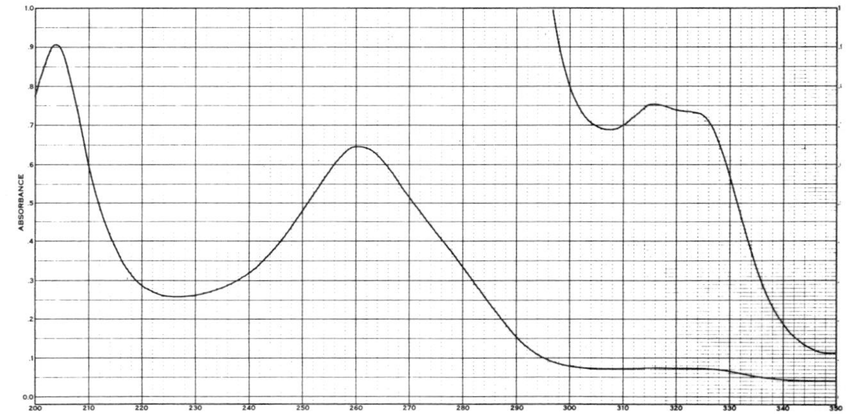

1-NAPHTHALENETHIOL

1241

$C_{10}H_8S$

Mol. Wt. 160.24

B.P. 130-131°C/5mm

Solvent: Methanol

λ Max. mμ	a_m	Cell mm	Conc. g/L
299	6470	1	0.159
220	41800	1	0.0319

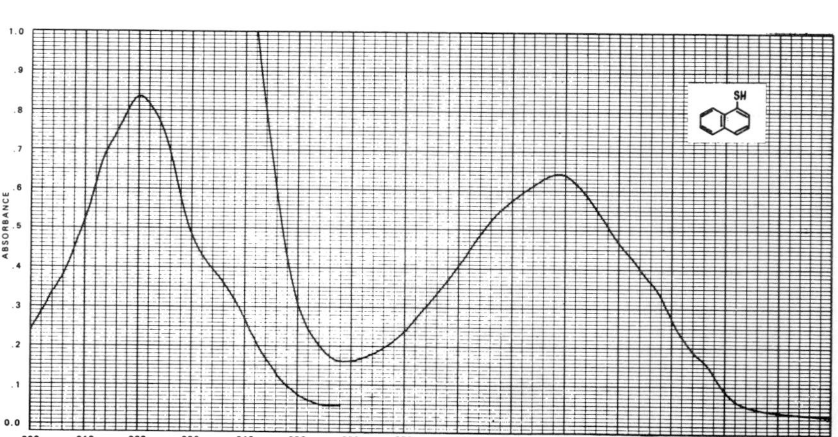

1-NAPHTHALENETHIOL

1241

$C_{10}H_8S$
Mol. Wt. 160.24
B.P. 130-131°C/5mm
Solvent: Methanol KOH

λ Max. mμ	a_m	Cell mm	Conc. g/L
340	7290	5	0.0159
251	13700	5	0.0159
210	46500	1	0.0159

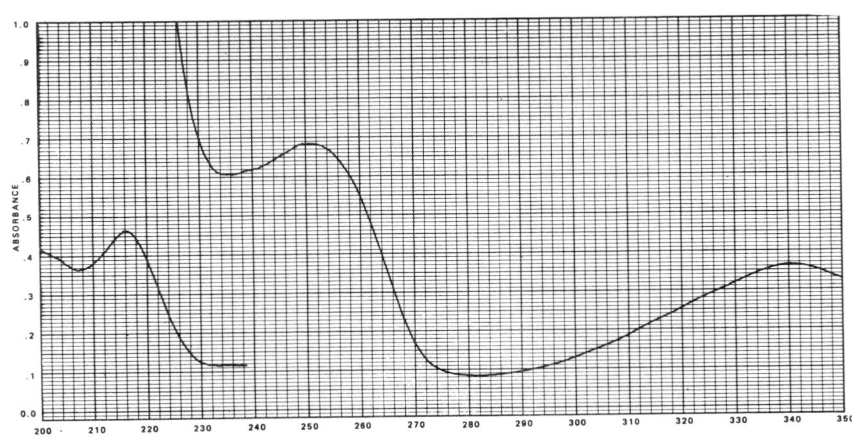

2-NAPHTHALENETHIOL

1242

$C_{10}H_8S$
Mol. Wt. 160.22
M.P. 81°C
Solvent: Methanol

λ Max. mμ	a_m	Cell mm	Conc. g/L
334	932	10	0.1840
320	1060	10	0.1840
291	5390	10	0.0184
281	9140	10	0.0184
241	36800	10	0.0055

λ Max. mμ	a_m	Cell mm	Conc. g/L

NOTES

THE SULFOXIDES

Aliphatic Compounds

The aliphatic sulfoxides do not absorb in the near UV (220 - 350 mμ) and thus there are no spectra in this section for compounds 1243 through 1246.

Aromatic Compounds

Dibenzyl sulfoxide (spectrum 1247) displays two major bands in the near UV. The more intense absorption occurs at 220 mμ and the weaker band appears at 260 mμ with superimposed benzenoid fine structure (253 mμ, 266 mμ, and 270 mμ).

The UV spectrogram of phenylsulfoxide (spectrum 1251) is similar in appearance to that of dibenzyl-sulfoxide although the 220 mμ band noted above shows a bathochromic shift of 12 mμ to 232 mμ. The fine structure is not as well resolved but occurs at approximately the same wavelengths (253 mμ, 260 mμ, 266 mμ and 272 mμ).

THE SULFONES

Aliphatic Compounds

The aliphatic sulfones do not produce any absorbance bands in the near ultraviolet region (220 mμ - 350 mμ) and thus there are no spectra in this section for compounds 1252 through 1256).

Aromatic Compounds

Few trends of spectral data can be obtained from the spectra presented in this text. The positions, intensities and appearance of the absorption bands of the sulfones are altered markedly with slight structural variations. The UV spectra of the sulfones do not show any significant changes upon the addition of either acid or base.

THE SULFONYL HALIDES

Aliphatic Compounds

The aliphatic sulfonyl halides do not display any maxima in the near UV region and, as a consequence, there are no spectra in this chapter for compounds 1280 through 1282.

Aromatic Compounds

The spectrum of α-toluenesulfonyl fluoride (compound 1279) displays one major absorption band near 260 mμ with associated vibrational fine structure appearing as well resolved maxima at 251, 256, 262 and 268 mμ. Due to their reactivity with alcohols, this spectrum probably represents that of the methyl ester, i.e. benzylsulfonic acid, methyl ester. Upon the addition of base to the sample, a new band appears at about 298 mμ.

DIBENZYL SULFOXIDE 1247

$C_{14}H_{14}OS$
Mol. Wt. 230.33
M.P. 135-137°C
Solvent: Methanol

λ Max. mμ	a_m	Cell mm	Conc. g/L
x	x	10	2.17
269.5	301	10	0.651
266	481	10	0.651
259.5	616	10	0.651
252.5	589	10	0.651
x	x	10	0.0651
219.5	20900	10	0.0195

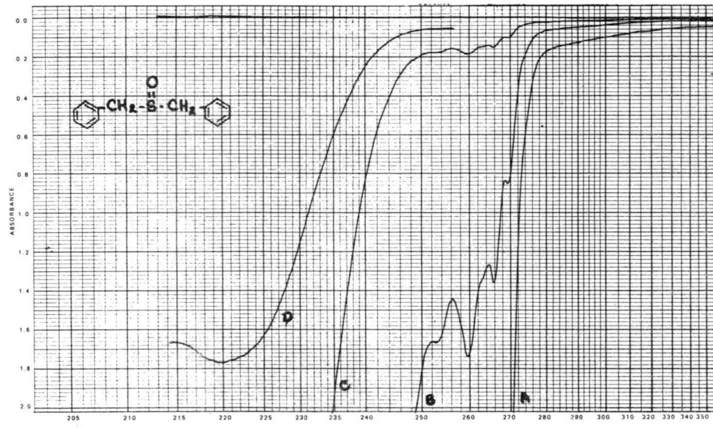

PHENYL PROPYL SULFOXIDE 1248

$C_9H_{12}OS$
Mol. Wt. 168.26
B.P. 80-83°C/0.02mm

λ Max. mμ	a_m	Cell mm	Conc. g/L

Pure sample not available.

p-IODOPHENYL METHYL SULFOXIDE 1249

C_7H_7IOS
Mol. Wt. 266.12
M.P. 110-111°C
Solvent: Methanol

λ Max. mμ	a_m	Cell mm	Conc. g/L
249	14500	10	0.01

p-CHLOROPHENYL 3-PENTYNYL SULFOXIDE

1250

$C_{11}H_{11}ClOS$
Mol. Wt. 226.73
Solvent: Methanol

λ Max. mμ	a_m	Cell mm	Conc. g/L
245	7730	2	0.100
221	11000	2	0.100

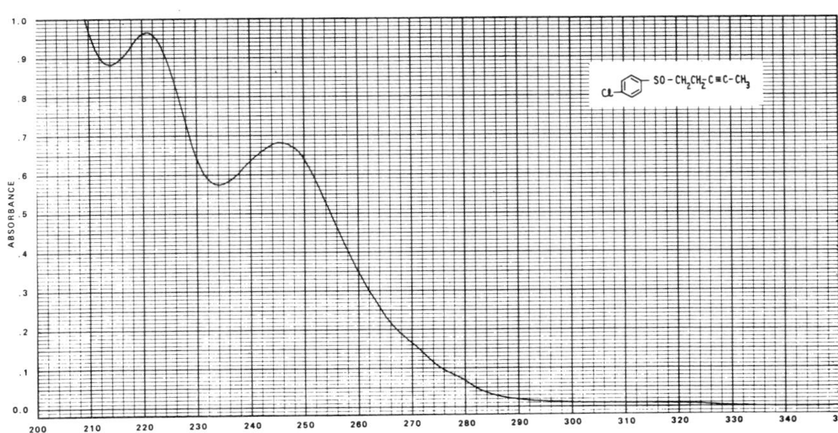

PHENYL SULFOXIDE

1251

$C_{12}H_{10}OS$
Mol. Wt. 202.29
M.P. 71-72°C
Solvent: Methanol

λ Max. mμ	a_m	Cell mm	Conc. g/L
273	1350	10	0.06
232	14200	10	0.01

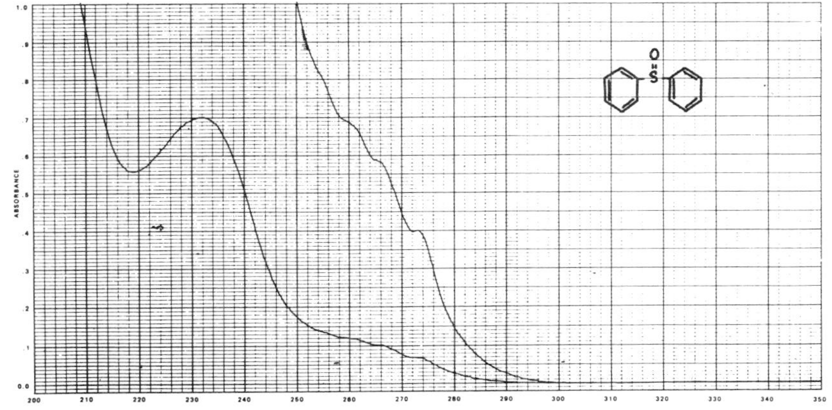

1252

λ Max. mμ	a_m	Cell mm	Conc. g/L

The aliphatic and olefinic sulfones (compounds 1252 through 1256) do not display any maxima in the near UV.

trans-CINNAMYL METHYL SULFONE 1257

$C_{10}H_{12}O_2S$
Mol. Wt. 196.27
M.P. 125-126°C
Solvent: Methanol

λ Max. mμ	a_m	Cell mm	Conc. g/L
292.5	1320	10	0.0700
282.5	2110	10	0.0700
254	20400	1	0.0700
216	13500	1	0.0700
210	21400	1	0.0700

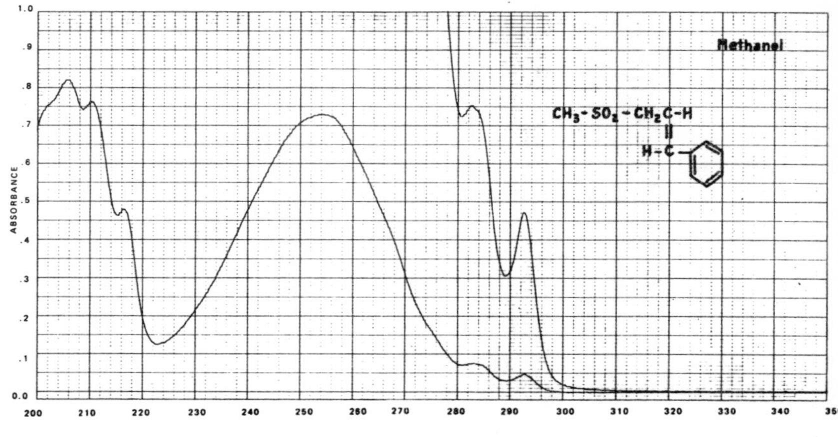

STYRYL SULFONE 1258

$C_{16}H_{14}O_2S$
Mol. Wt. 270.35
M.P. 99-100°C
Solvent: Methanol

λ Max. mμ	a_m	Cell mm	Conc. g/L
292	36700	5	0.0100

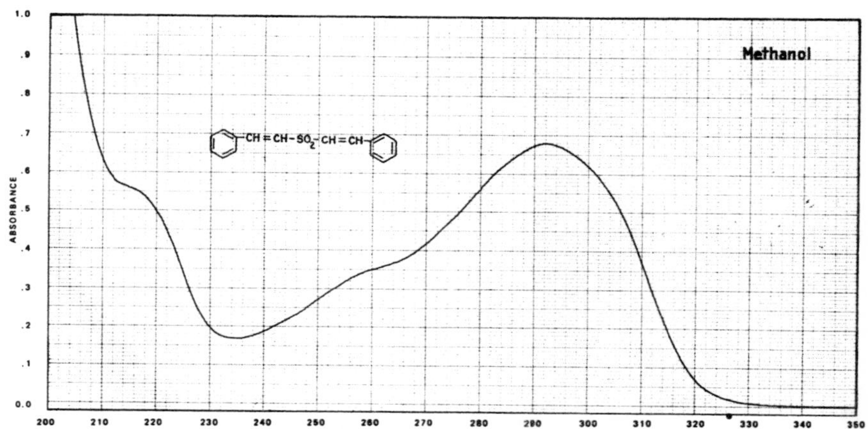

2,5-DIHYDRO-2,4-DIMETHYLTHIOPHENE, 1,1-DIOXIDE 1259

$C_6H_{10}O_2S$
Mol. Wt. 146.21
M.P. 40-43°C

λ Max. mμ	a_m	Cell mm	Conc. g/L

Pure sample not available.

3,4-DICHLOROTHIOPHENE-1,1-DIOXIDE

1260

$C_4H_2Cl_2O_2S$
Mol. Wt. 185.04
M.P. 112-113°C (d)
Solvent: Methanol

λ Max. mμ	a_m	Cell mm	Conc. g/L
301	401	10	0.300
233	4360	10	0.03

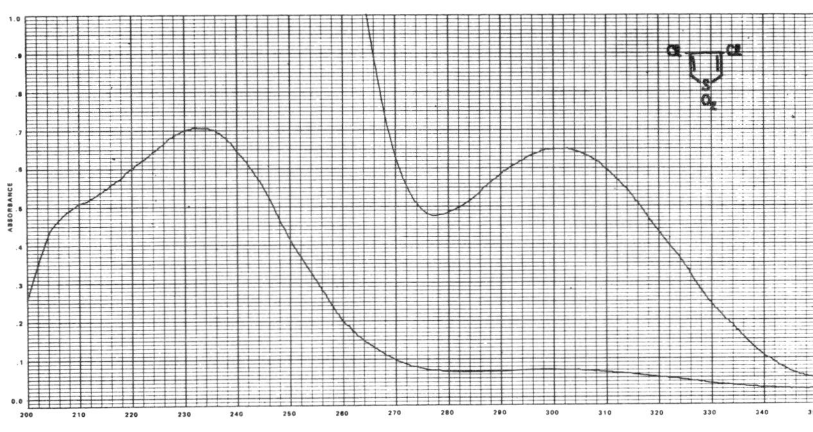

ALLYL PHENYL SULFONE

1261

$C_9H_{10}O_2S$
Mol. Wt. 182.24

λ Max. mμ	a_m	Cell mm	Conc. g/L

Pure sample not available.

ALLYL p-TOLYL SULFONE

1262

$C_{10}H_{12}O_2S$
Mol. Wt. 196.27
Solvent: Methanol

λ Max. mμ	a_m	Cell mm	Conc. g/L
261	10600	1	0.100

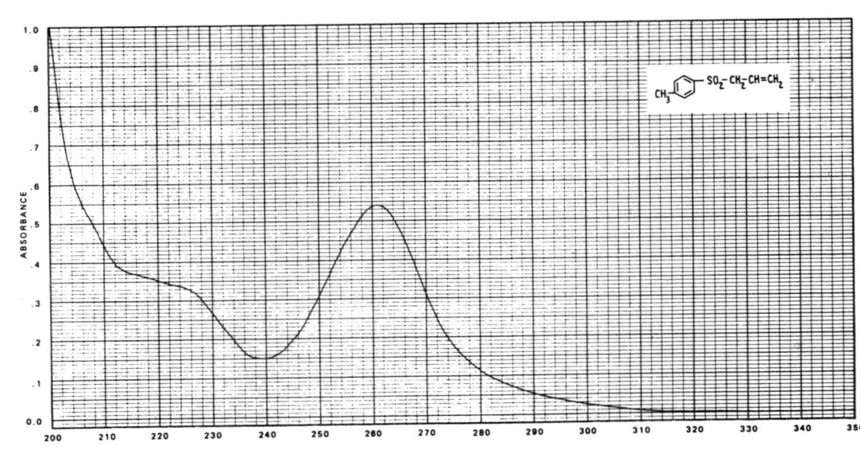

ALLYL p-CHLOROPHENYL SULFONE

1263

$C_9H_9ClO_2S$

Mol. Wt. 216.69

Solvent: Methanol

λ Max. mμ	a_m	Cell mm	Conc. g/L
273.5	464	20	0.100
265.5	575	20	0.100
262.5	564	20	0.100
255.5	472	20	0.100
227.5	16800	1	0.100

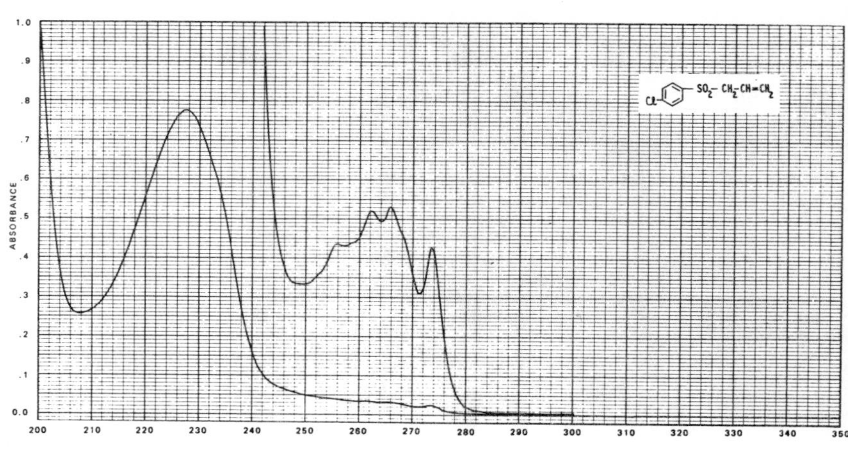

BIS(p-TOLYLSULFONYL)METHANE

1264

$C_{15}H_{16}O_4S_2$

Mol. Wt. 324.42

Solvent: Methanol

λ Max. mμ	a_m	Cell mm	Conc. g/L
273	938	10	0.100
262	1110	10	0.100
227	17400	1	0.100

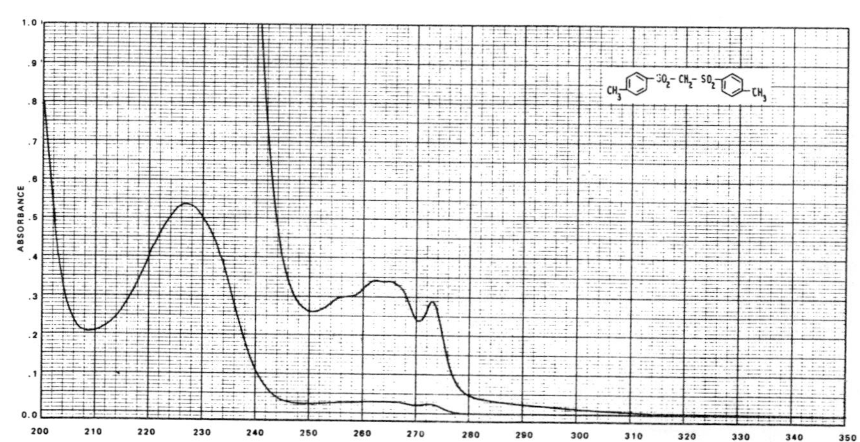

PHENYL 2-PROPYNYL SULFONE

1265

$C_9H_8O_2S$

Mol. Wt. 180.23

λ Max. mμ	a_m	Cell mm	Conc. g/L

Pure sample not available.

3,4-DICHLOROPHENYL 2-PROPYNYL SULFONE

1266

$C_9H_6Cl_2O_2S$
Mol. Wt. 249.12
Solvent: Methanol

λ Max. mμ	a_m	Cell mm	Conc. g/L
285.5	886	20	0.100
276.5	1080	20	0.100
232	12300	1	0.100

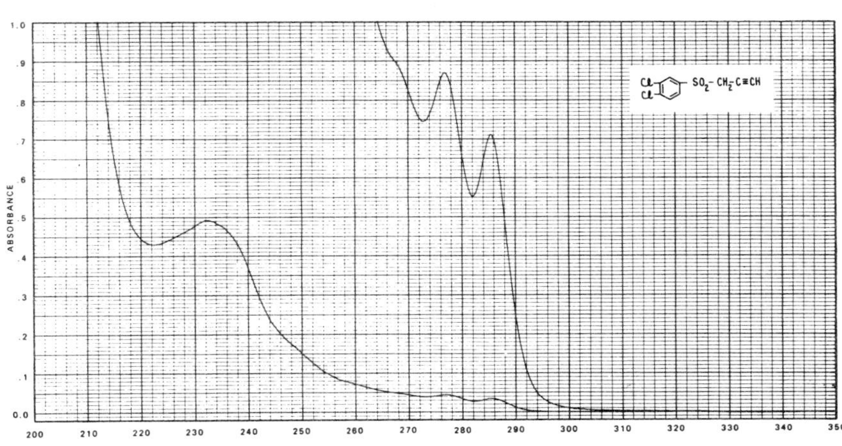

BENZYL p-TOLYL SULFONE

1267

$C_{14}H_{14}O_2S$
Mol. Wt. 246.33
Solvent: Methanol

λ Max. mμ	a_m	Cell mm	Conc. g/L
272	574	10	0.100
261	892	10	0.100
224	16600	1	0.100

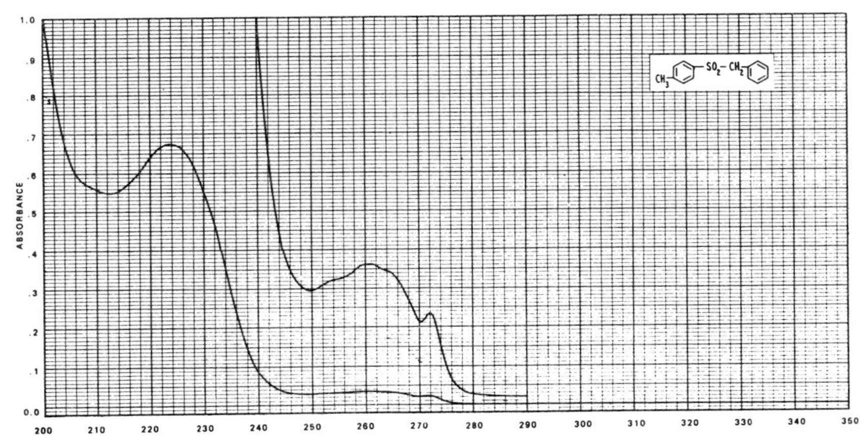

PHENYL p-TOLYL SULFONE

1268

$C_{13}H_{12}O_2S$
Mol. Wt. 232.30
Solvent: Methanol

λ Max. mμ	a_m	Cell mm	Conc. g/L
274	1290	5	0.100
266	2320	5	0.100
240	18100	1	0.100

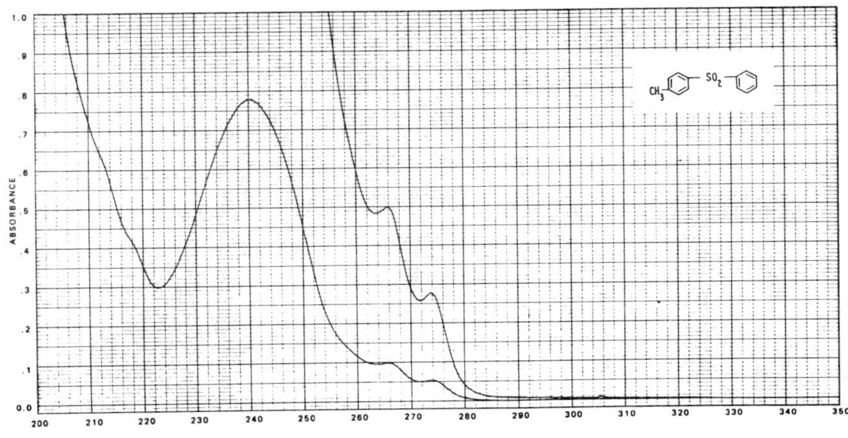

p-TOLYL SULFONE 1269

$C_{14}H_{14}O_2S$
Mol. Wt. 246.33
M.P. 158-159°C
Solvent: Methanol

λ Max. mμ	a_m	Cell mm	Conc. g/L
274.5	1180	20	0.100
244	20200	1	0.100
222	11000	1	0.100

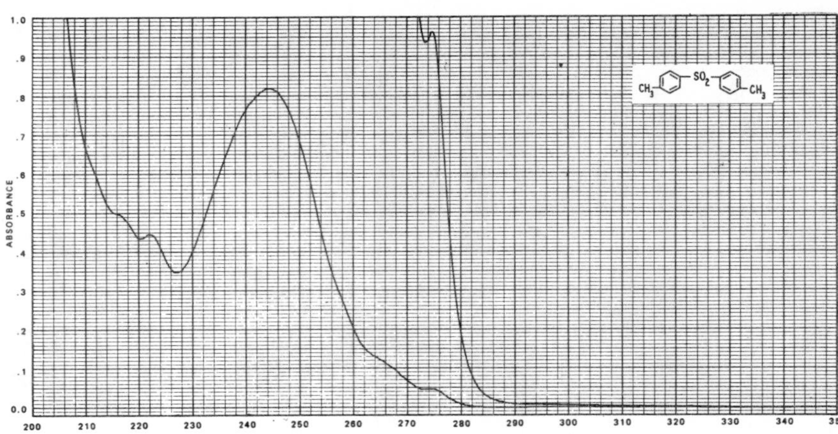

p-FLUOROPHENYL PHENYL SULFONE 1270

$C_{12}H_9FO_2S$
Mol. Wt. 236.27
M.P. 111-112°C
Solvent: Methanol

λ Max. mμ	a_m	Cell mm	Conc. g/L
274	851	10	0.100
266	1250	10	0.100
260	1480	10	0.100
235	15700	10	0.01

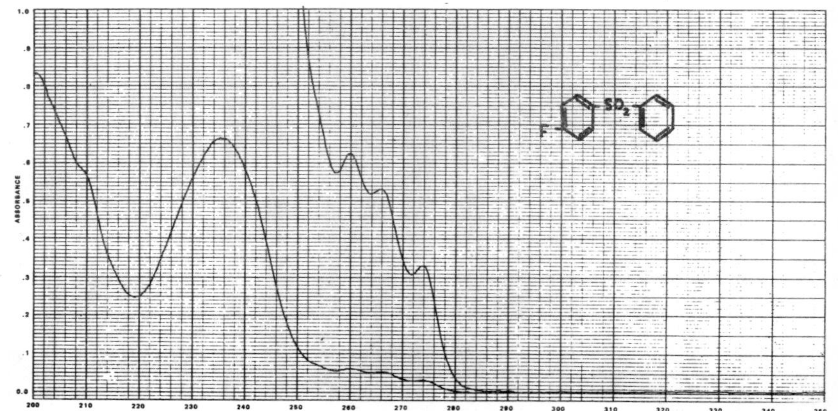

BIS(p-FLUOROPHENYL) SULFONE 1271

$C_{12}H_8F_2O_2S$
Mol. Wt. 254.26
M.P. 98-99°C
Solvent: Methanol

λ Max. mμ	a_m	Cell mm	Conc. g/L
259	1450	10	0.100
235	1560	1	0.100

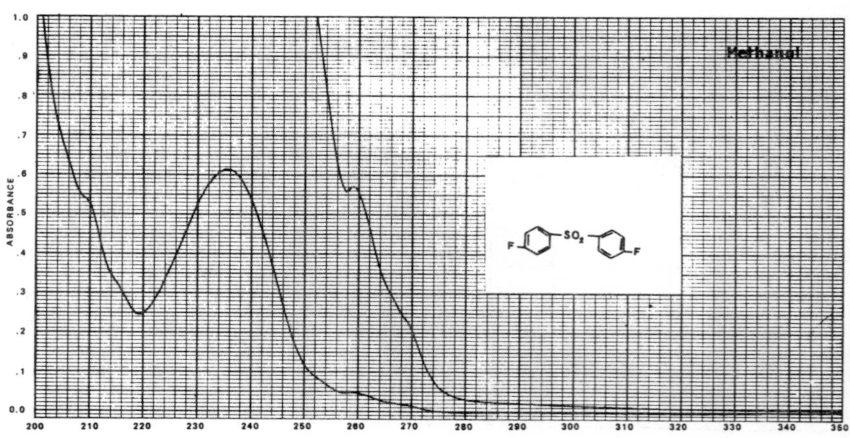

PHENYL α,α,α-TRIFLUORO-m-TOLYL SULFONE 1272

$C_{13}H_9F_3O_2S$

Mol. Wt. 286.27

M.P. 77-78°C

Solvent: Methanol

λ Max. mμ	a_m	Cell mm	Conc. g/L
273	1310	1	1.00
266	1910	1	1.00
260	1630	1	1.00
234	15100	1	0.100

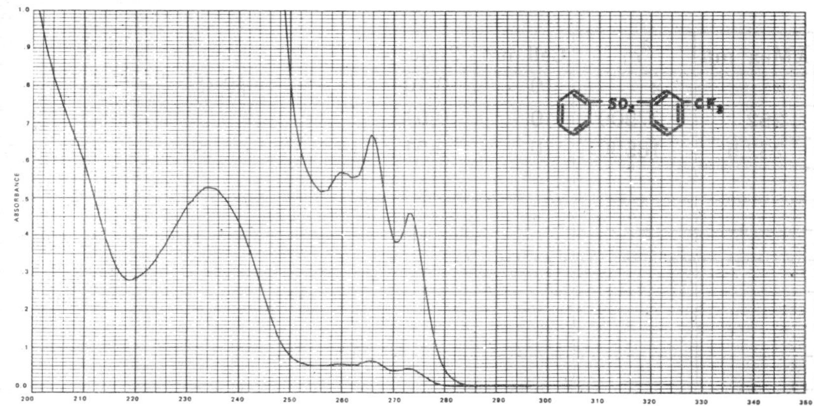

2,5-DICHLOROPHENYL PHENYL SULFONE 1273

$C_{12}H_8Cl_2O_2S$

Mol. Wt. 287.16

M.P. 145°C

Solvent: Methanol

λ Max. mμ	a_m	Cell mm	Conc. g/L
294	1500	10	0.10
285.5	1670	10	0.10
276	1730	10	0.10
268	1520	10	0.10
261	1190	10	0.10
226	24100	10	0.01

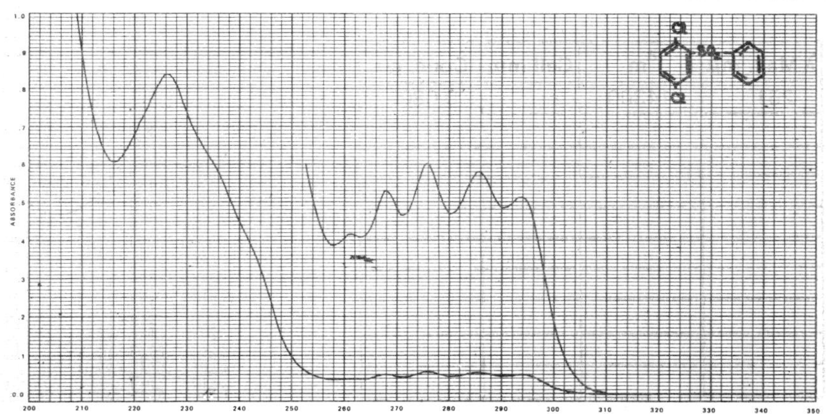

BIS(p-CHLOROPHENYL) SULFONE 1274

$C_{12}H_8Cl_2O_2S$

Mol. Wt. 287.17

M.P. 147°C

Solvent: Methanol

λ Max. mμ	a_m	Cell mm	Conc. g/L
277	1310	2	1.00
247.5	25900	1	0.0800
226	15000	1	0.0800

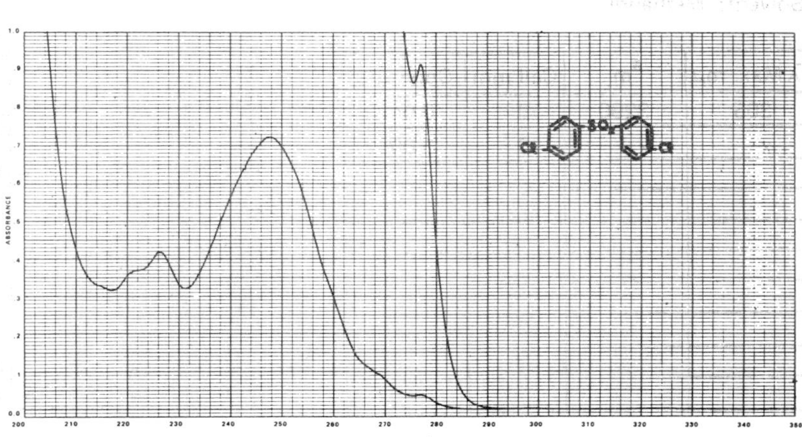

BIS(p-BROMOPHENYL)SULFONE

1275

$C_{12}H_8Br_2O_2S$
Mol. Wt. 376.08
M.P. 173°C
Solvent: Methanol

λ Max. mμ	a_m	Cell mm	Conc. g/L
x	x	10	0.10
252	27900	10	0.01
232.5	16500	10	0.01

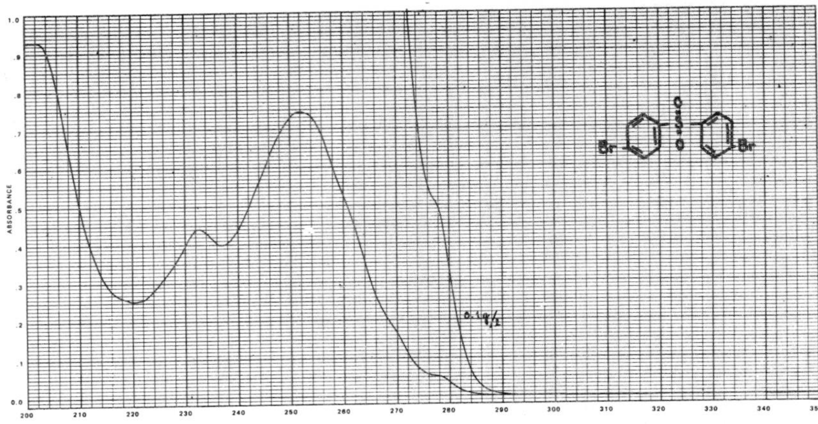

p-NITROPHENYL PHENYL SULFONE

1276

$C_{12}H_9NO_4S$
Mol. Wt. 263.28
M.P. 140-141°C
Solvent: Methanol

λ Max. mμ	a_m	Cell mm	Conc. g/L
261	14300	2	0.0800

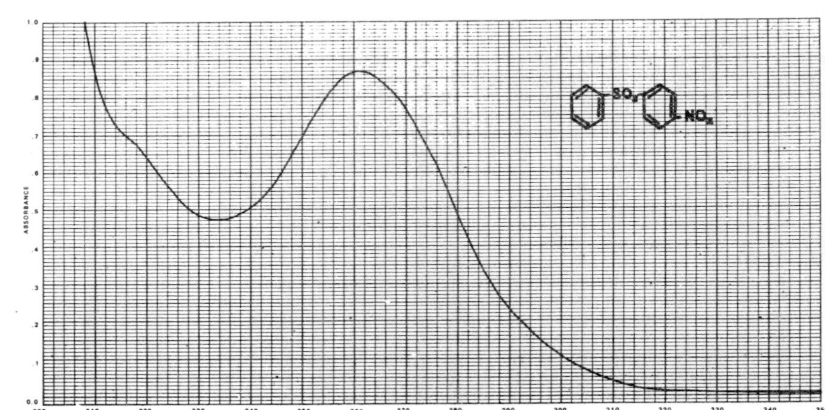

BENZO[b] THIOPHENE, 1,1-DIOXIDE

1277

$C_8H_6O_2S$
Mol. Wt. 166.20
M.P. 141-145°C
Solvent: Methanol

λ Max. mμ	a_m	Cell mm	Conc. g/L
305	3290	10	0.0423
x	x	10	0.0042

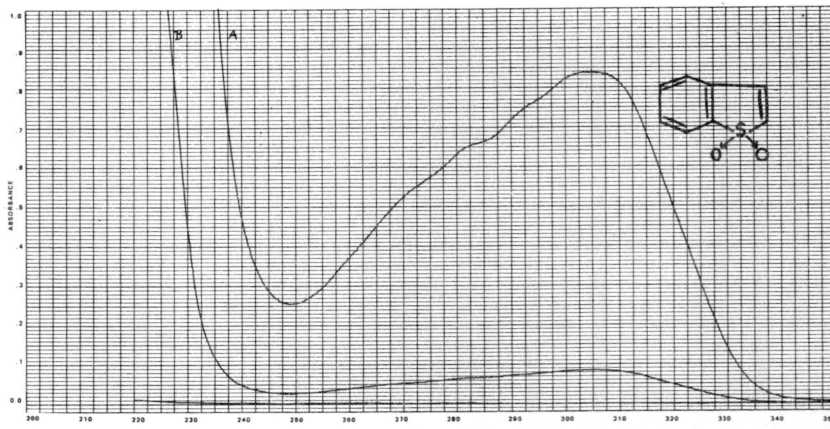

2-DIBENZOTHIOPHENAMINE, 5,5-DIOXIDE 1278

$C_{12}H_9NO_2S$
Mol. Wt. 231.28
M.P. 281°C
Solvent: Methanol

λ Max. mμ	a_m	Cell mm	Conc. g/L
315.5	4340	5	0.0700
287	8920	1	0.0700
266	30700	1	0.0700
236	20500	1	0.0700
228	23900	1	0.0700
209	22500	1	0.700

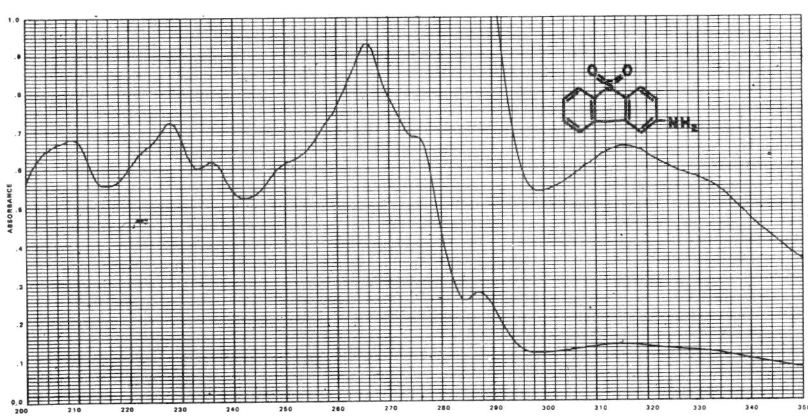

2-DIBENZOTHIOPHENAMINE, 5,5-DIOXIDE 1278

$C_{12}H_9NO_2S$
Mol. Wt. 231.28
M.P. 281°C
Solvent: Methanol HCl

λ Max. mμ	a_m	Cell mm	Conc. g/L
316	3420	5	0.0700
287.5	8000	1	0.0700
266	22800	1	0.0700
241.5	28200	1	0.0700
234	28100	1	0.0700

λ Max. mμ	a_m	Cell mm	Conc. g/L

α-TOLUENESULFONYL FLUORIDE

1279

$C_7H_7FO_2S$

Mol. Wt. 174.20

M.P. 93-94°C

Solvent: Methanol

λ Max. mμ	a_m	Cell mm	Conc. g/L
267.5	192	10	0.478
261.5	265	10	0.478
256.5	250	10	0.478
251	175	10	0.478
x	x	1	0.239

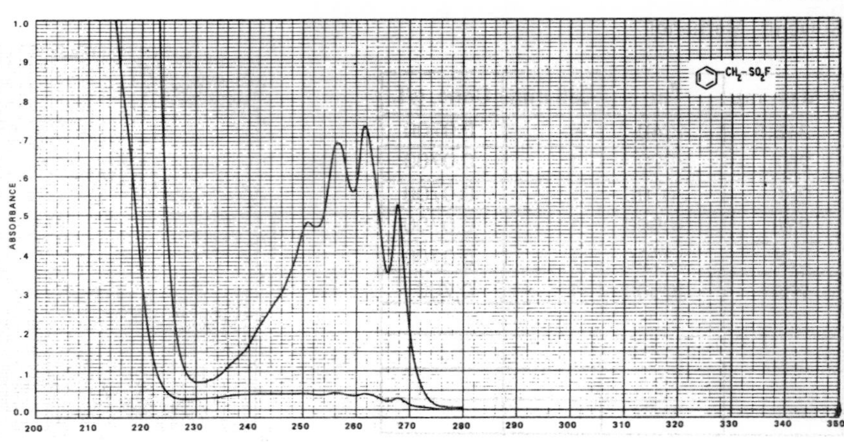

α-TOLUENESULFONYL FLUORIDE

1279

$C_7H_7FO_2S$

Mol. Wt. 174.20

M.P. 93-94°C

Solvent: Methanol KOH

λ Max. mμ	a_m	Cell mm	Conc. g/L
298	37	20	0.956
267.5	124	10	0.478
262	188	10	0.478
257	286	10	0.478
251.5	157	10	0.478

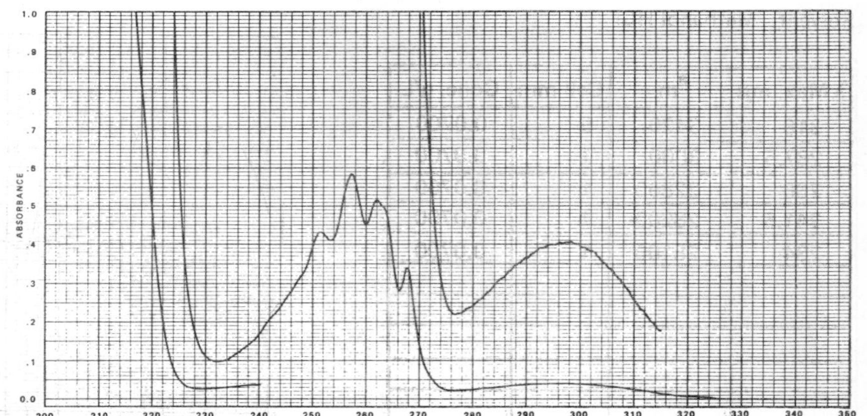

1280

λ Max. mμ	a_m	Cell mm	Conc. g/L

The aliphatic sulfonyl chlorides (compounds 1280 through 1282) do not display any maxima in the near UV.

p-TOLUENESULFONYL CHLORIDE 1283

$C_7H_7ClO_2S$

Mol. Wt. 190.65

M.P. 69-71°C

λ Max. mμ	a_m	Cell mm	Conc. g/L

Pure sample not available.

2,5-XYLENESULFONYL CHLORIDE 1284

$C_8H_9ClO_2S$

Mol. Wt. 204.68

Solvent: Cyclohexane

λ Max. mμ	a_m	Cell mm	Conc. g/L
287	3210	2	0.100
238.5	8480	2	0.100
x	x	1	0.100

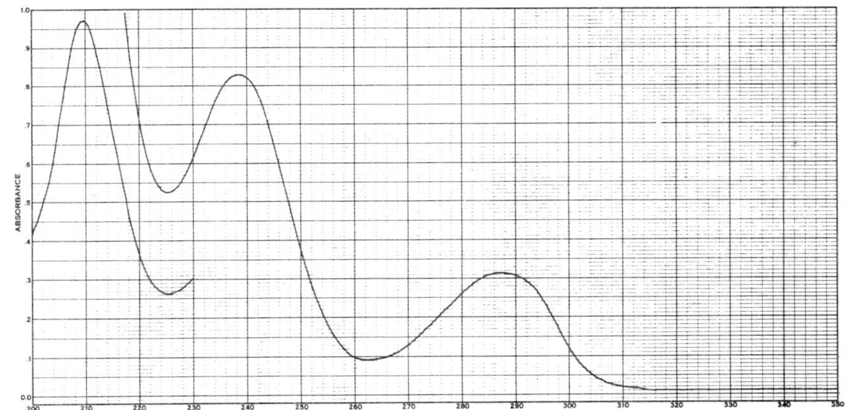

o-NITROBENZENESULFONYL CHLORIDE 1285

$C_6H_4ClNO_4S$

Mol. Wt. 221.62

Solvent: Dioxane

λ Max. mμ	a_m	Cell mm	Conc. g/L
x	x	4	0.100
x	x	1	0.100

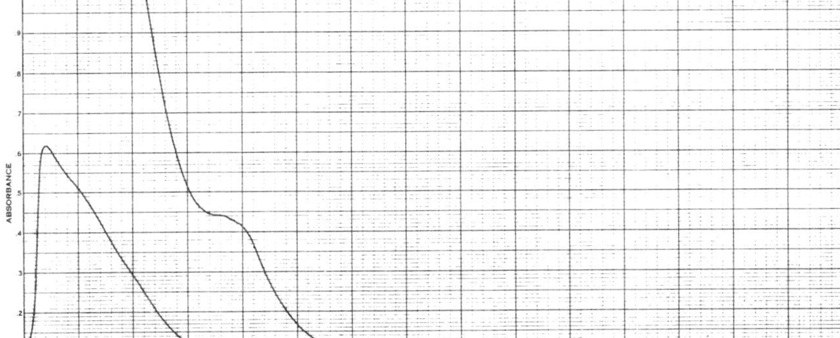

1-NAPHTHALENESULFONYL CHLORIDE **1286**

$C_{10}H_7ClO_2S$

Mol. Wt. 226.68

M.P. 67-69°C

Solvent: Cyclohexane

λ Max. mμ	a_m	Cell mm	Conc. g/L
321	3690	4	0.100
302.5	4910	4	0.100
235.5	18300	1	0.100
210.5	27700	0.5	0.100

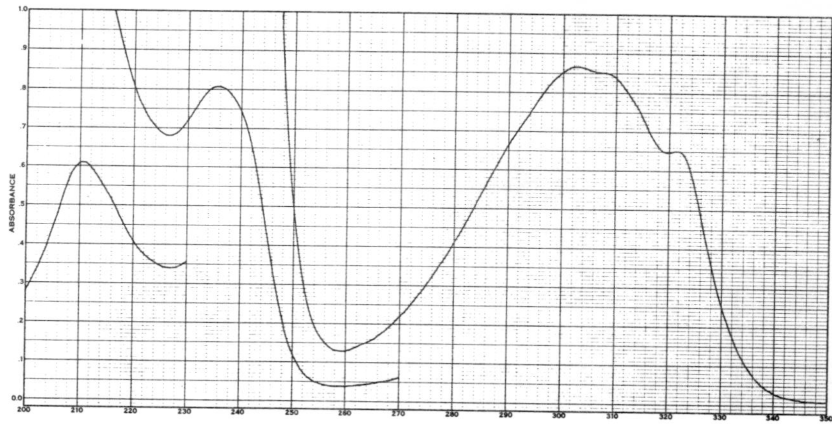

λ Max. mμ	a_m	Cell mm	Conc. g/L

λ Max. mμ	a_m	Cell mm	Conc. g/L

THE SULFONIC ACIDS

Aliphatic Compounds

The aliphatic sulfonic acids do not display any maxima in the near UV and as a consequence there are no spectra in this volume for compounds 1287 nor 1288.

Aromatic Compounds

Due to the presence of additional substituents, spectra 1289 through 1293 do not indicate the wavelengths nor maxima expected of the parent compound benzenesulfonic acid. Its spectrum is expected to be similar in appearance to that of the sodium salt (spectrum 1300).

THE SULFONIC ACID SALTS

Aliphatic Compounds

The alkyl sulfonates do not display any maxima in the near UV and as a result there are no spectra for compounds 1294 through 1299.

Aromatic Compounds

Benzenesulfonic acid displays two major absorption bands, a weak band displaying superimposed fine structure appears at about 264 mμ and series of unresolved shoulders is noted near 217 mμ (spectrum 1300). Several selected benzenesulfonates in methanol solution are listed below.

Compound	$\lambda_{max}(\epsilon_{max})$	$\lambda_{max}(\epsilon_{max})$	Spectrum
Benzenesulfonic acid, sodium salt	217 * (8750)	264 (361)	1300
2,4-Xylenesulfonic acid, sodium salt	223 (8770)	267 (401)	1301
p-Toluenesulfonic acid, barium salt	221 (106500)	262 (3200)	1302
p-Bromobenzenesulfonic acid, sodium salt	228 (12000)	265 (272)	1303

THE SULFONIC ACID ESTERS

Aliphatic Compounds

The aliphatic esters of alkyl sulfonic acids do not display any maxima in the near UV and thus there are no spectra in this volume for compounds 1314 through 1319.

Aromatic Compounds

The phenyl ester of methanesulfonic acid displays one major absorption band at 244 mμ with some fine structure extending the absorption band up to about 270 mμ (spectrum 1320).

The alkyl esters of benzenesulfonic acid display two major bands in the near UV region, one near 225 mμ and a weak band at 261 mμ which displays benzenoid fine structure (spectrum 1322).

4-BIPHENYLSULFONIC ACID 1289

$C_{12}H_{10}O_3S$
Mol. Wt. 234.28
Solvent: Methanol

λ Max. mμ	a_m	Cell mm	Conc. g/L
255.5	18300	1	0.100

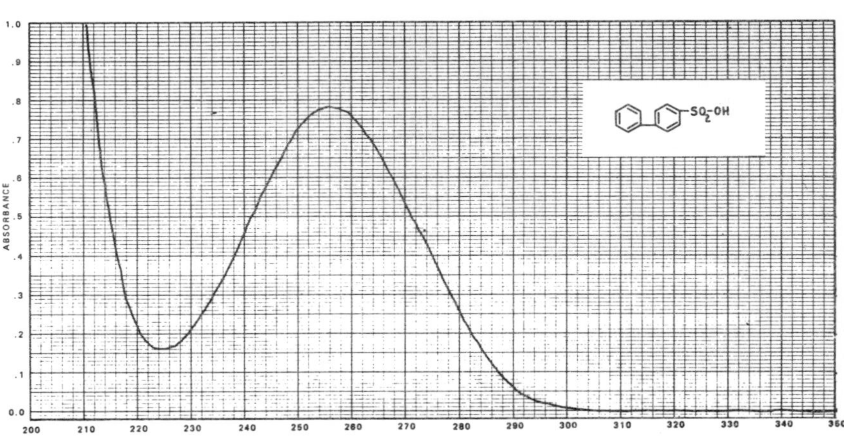

6-AMINO-m-TOLUENESULFONIC ACID 1290

$C_7H_9NO_3S$
Mol. Wt. 187.22
Solvent: Methanol

λ Max. mμ	a_m	Cell mm	Conc. g/L
307	313	20	0.100
275	418	20	0.100
266	422	20	0.100
245	1150	10	0.100
x	x	2	0.100

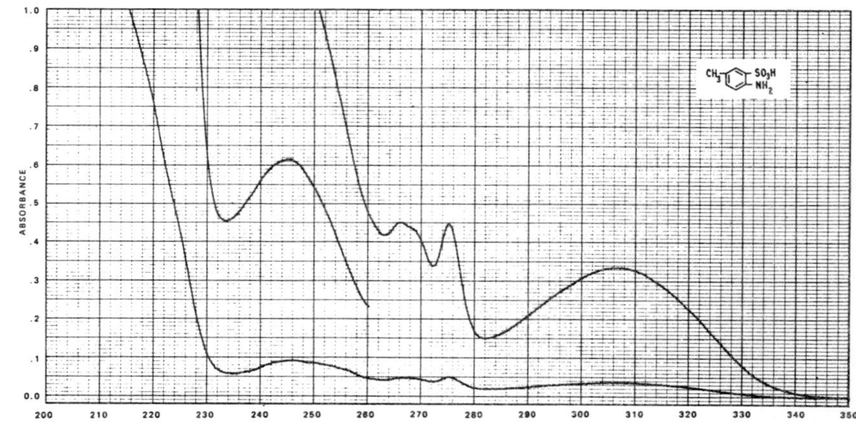

6-AMINO-m-TOLUENESULFONIC ACID 1290

$C_7H_9NO_3S$
Mol. Wt. 187.22
Solvent: Methanol KOH

λ Max. mμ	a_m	Cell mm	Conc. g/L
305	2670	2	0.100
243	8340	2	0.100

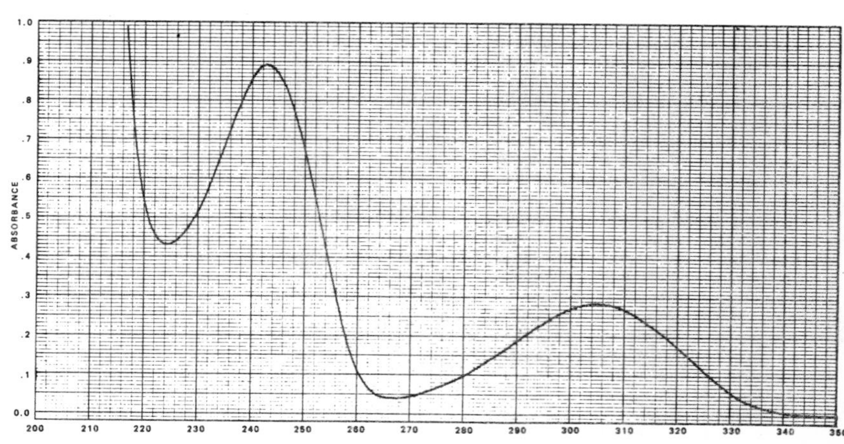

1290

6-AMINO-m-TOLUENESULFONIC ACID

$C_7H_9NO_3S$

Mol. Wt. 187.22

Solvent: Methanol HCl

λ Max. mμ	a_m	Cell mm	Conc. g/L
275	417	10	0.100
266.5	441	10	0.100
215	9010	2	0.100

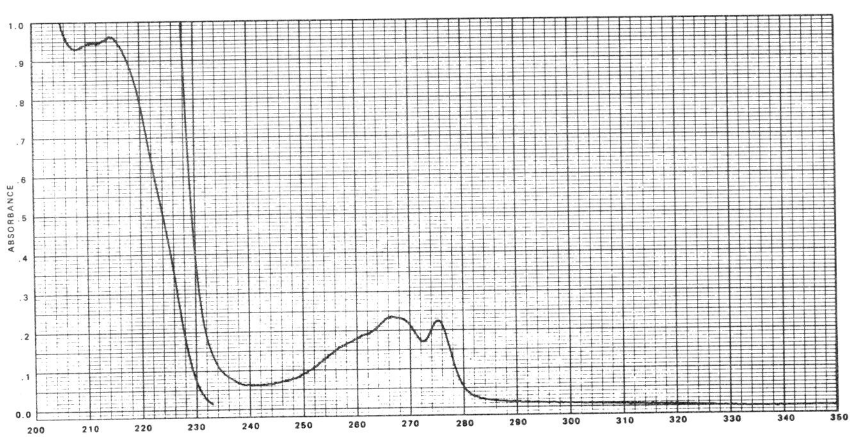

λ Max. mμ	a_m	Cell mm	Conc. g/L

λ Max. mμ	a_m	Cell mm	Conc. g/L

3-AMINO-p-TOLUENESULFONIC ACID

1291

$C_7H_9NO_3S$
Mol. Wt. 187.22
Solvent: Methanol

λ Max. mμ	a_m	Cell mm	Conc. g/L
295	247	20	0.100
268	199	20	0.100
218	10600	1	0.100

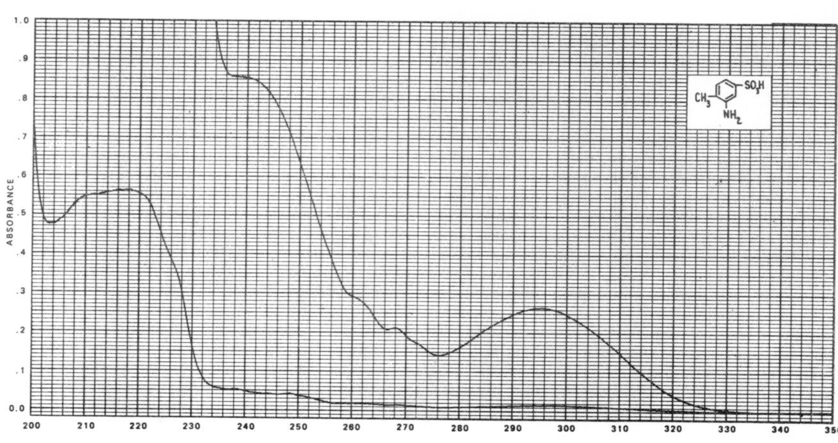

3-AMINO-p-TOLUENESULFONIC ACID

1291

$C_7H_9NO_3S$
Mol. Wt. 187.22
Solvent: Methanol KOH

λ Max. mμ	a_m	Cell mm	Conc. g/L
295	2480	2	0.100
239	6830	2	0.100

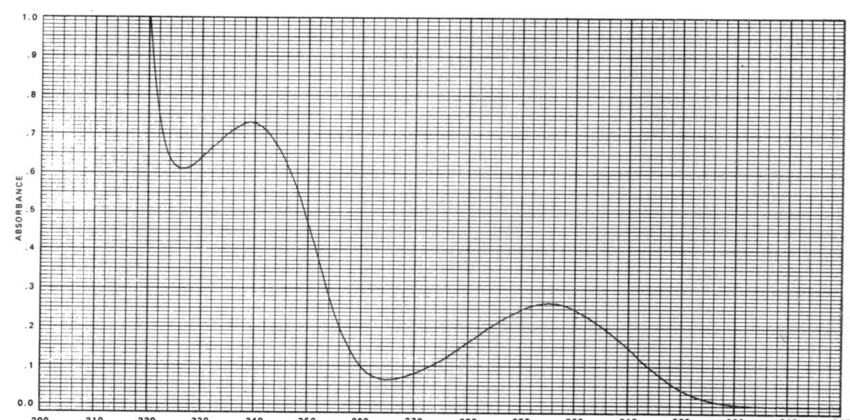

3-AMINO-p-TOLUENESULFONIC ACID

1291

$C_7H_9NO_3S$
Mol. Wt. 187.22
Solvent: Methanol HCl

λ Max. mμ	a_m	Cell mm	Conc. g/L
268	163	20	0.100
262	226	20	0.100
255	213	20	0.100
220.5	10800	1	0.100

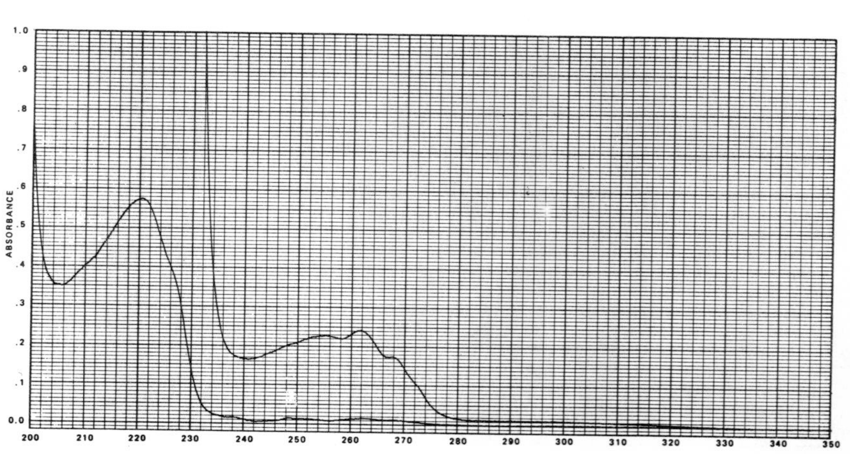

1-NAPHTHALENESULFONIC ACID, DIHYDRATE 1292

$C_{10}H_8O_3S{\cdot}2H_2O$

Mol. Wt. 244.27

Solvent: Methanol

λ Max. mμ	a_m	Cell mm	Conc. g/L
317	393	20	0.100
312.5	486	20	0.100
282.5	6990	2	0.100
274	6120	2	0.100
223.5	65300	1	0.100

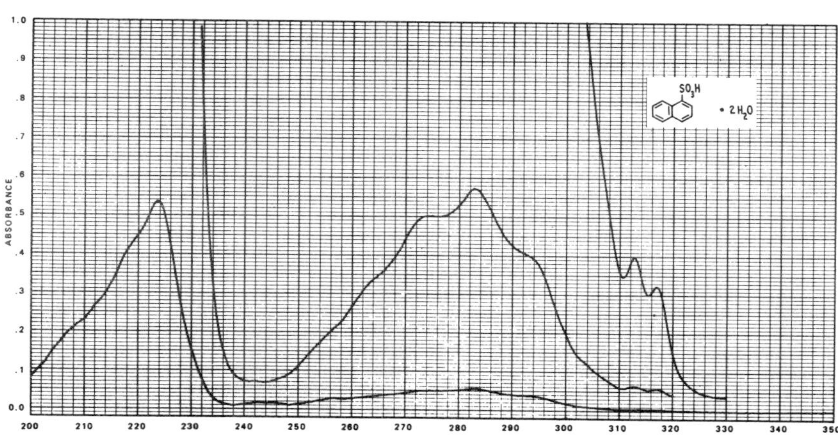

λ Max. mμ	a_m	Cell mm	Conc. g/L

λ Max. mμ	a_m	Cell mm	Conc. g/L

2-AMINO-1-NAPHTHALENESULFONIC ACID

1293

$C_{10}H_9NO_3S$

Mol. Wt. 223.25

Solvent: Methanol

λ Max. mμ	a_m	Cell mm	Conc. g/L
318	669	20	0.100
313.5	714	20	0.100
283	5900	5	0.0500
243.5	18600	1	0.0500
225	40900	1	0.0500

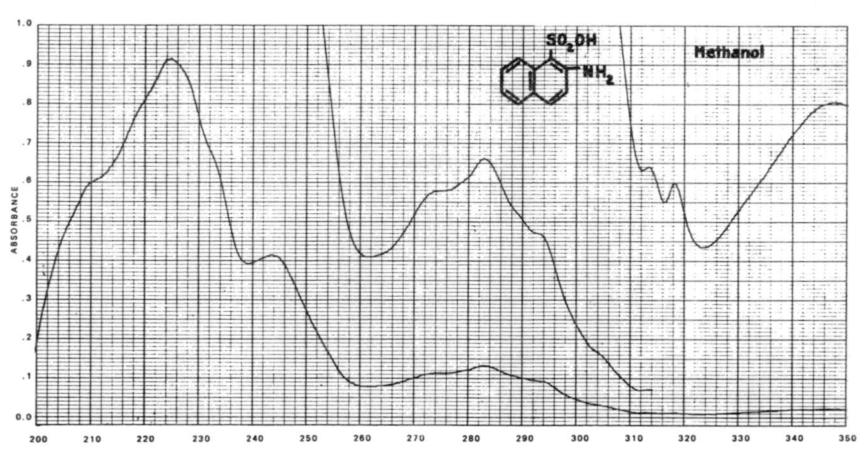

2-AMINO-1-NAPHTHALENESULFONIC ACID

1293

$C_{10}H_9NO_3S$

Mol. Wt. 223.25

Solvent: Methanol KOH

λ Max. mμ	a_m	Cell mm	Conc. g/L
294	4060	10	0.0250
282.5	6970	10	0.0250
272.5	6170	10	0.0250
244	54600	1	0.0250

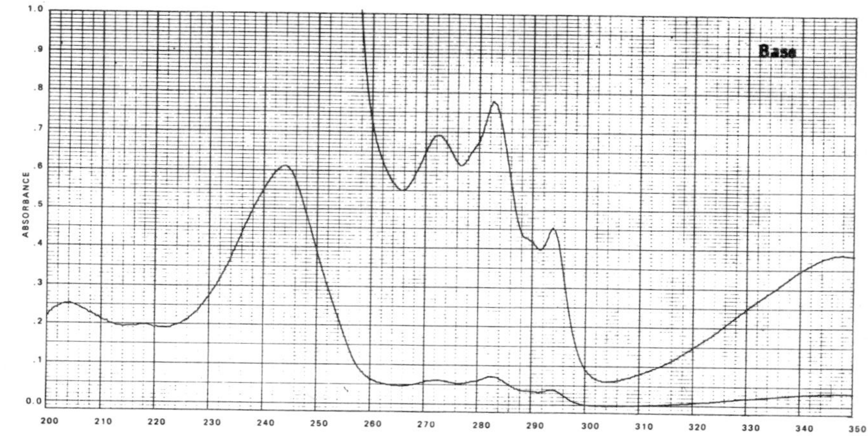

2-AMINO-1-NAPHTHALENESULFONIC ACID

1293

$C_{10}H_9NO_3S$

Mol. Wt. 223.25

Solvent: Methanol HCl

λ Max. mμ	a_m	Cell mm	Conc. g/L
318	525	20	0.100
285	2860	10	0.0500
224.5	25700	1	0.0500

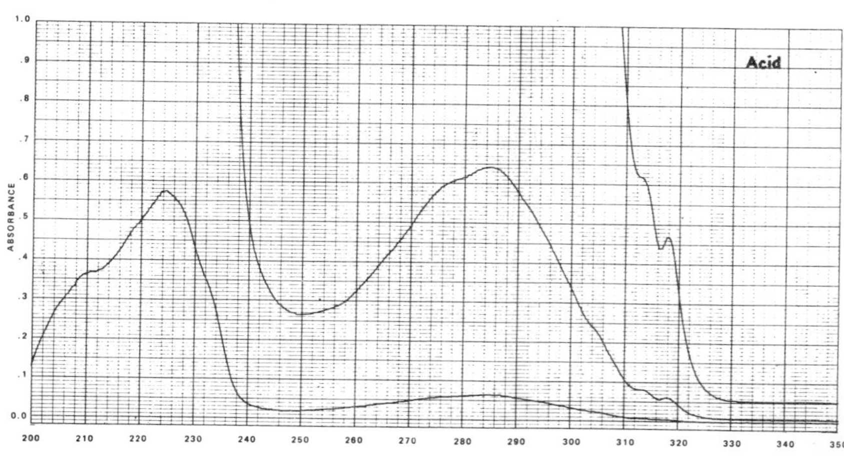

1294

λ Max. mμ	a_m	Cell mm	Conc. g/L

The aliphatic sulfonic acid salts (compounds 1294 through 1299) do not display any maxima in the near UV.

BENZENESULFONIC ACID, SODIUM SALT 1300

$C_6H_5O_3SNa$

Mol. Wt. 180.16

M.P. 450°C (d) (lit.)

Solvent: Methanol

λ Max. mμ	a_m	Cell mm	Conc. g/L
x	x	10	2.3280
270	302	10	0.6984
263.5	361	10	0.6984
259.5	310	10	0.6984
253	218	10	0.6984
247.5	130	10	0.6984
x	x	10	0.0070

2,4-XYLENESULFONIC ACID, SODIUM SALT 1301

$C_8H_9NaO_3S$

Mol. Wt. 208.21

Solvent: Methanol

λ Max. mμ	a_m	Cell mm	Conc. g/L
276	354	20	0.100
271	363	20	0.100
267	401	20	0.100
223	8770	1	0.100

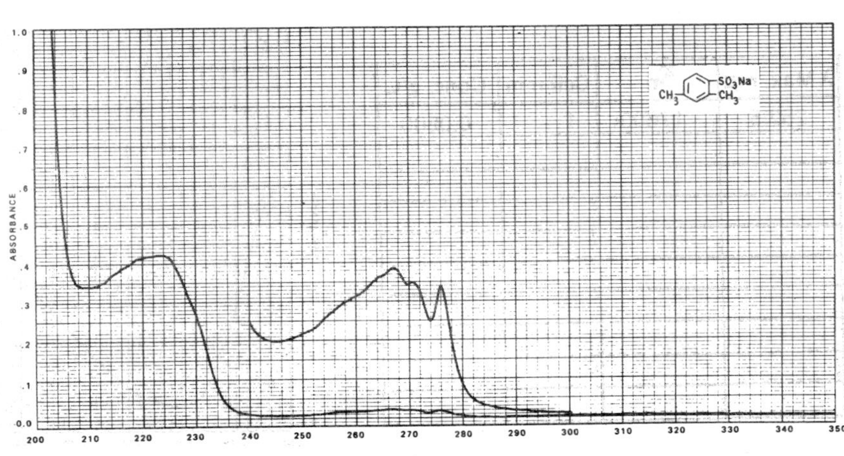

p-TOLUENESULFONIC ACID, BARIUM SALT 1302

$C_{14}H_{14}BaO_6S_2$
Mol. Wt. 479.73
Solvent: Methanol

λ Max. mμ	a_m	Cell mm	Conc. g/L
273.5	1820	10	0.100
268	2780	10	0.100
261.5	3200	10	0.100
256	2590	10	0.100
220.5	106500	2	0.0200

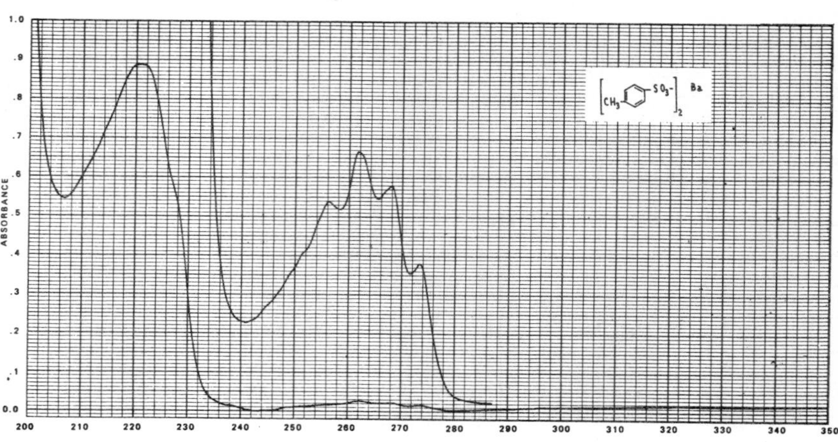

p-BROMOBENZENESULFONIC ACID, SODIUM SALT 1303

$C_6H_4O_3BrSNa$
Mol. Wt. 259.06
Solvent: Methanol

λ Max. mμ	a_m	Cell mm	Conc. g/L
270.5	179	20	0.100
264.5	272	20	0.100
258	259	20	0.100
228	12000	2	0.100

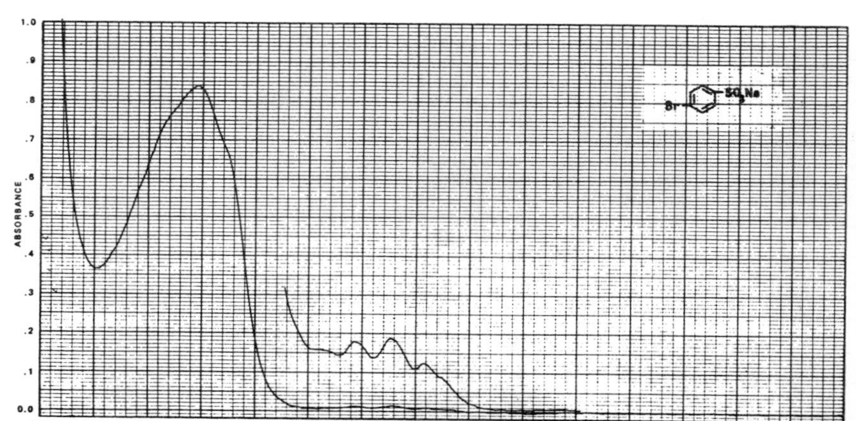

SULFANILIC ACID, SODIUM SALT, DIHYDRATE 1304

$C_6H_6NNaO_3S{\cdot}2H_2O$
Mol. Wt. 231.20
Solvent: Methanol

λ Max. mμ	a_m	Cell mm	Conc. g/L
252.5	17600	1	0.0500

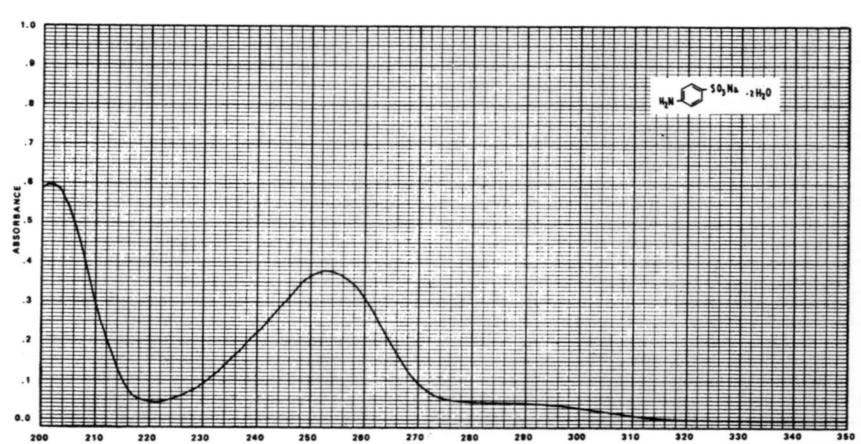

SULFANILIC ACID, SODIUM SALT, DIHYDRATE

1304

$C_6H_6NNaO_3S{\cdot}2H_2O$

Mol. Wt. 231.20

Solvent: Methanol HCl

λ Max. mμ	a_m	Cell mm	Conc. g/L
258	962	10	0.100
216	9970	1	0.100
210	9410	1	0.100

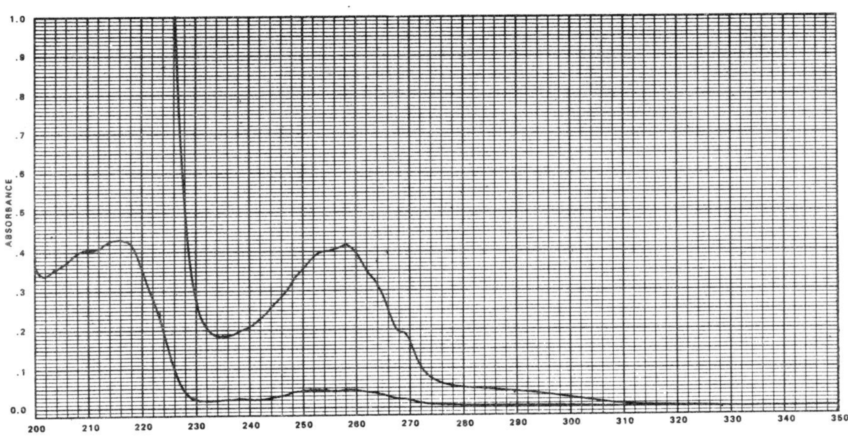

p-(PHENYLAZO)BENZENESULFONIC ACID, SODIUM SALT

1305

$C_{12}H_9N_2NaO_3S$

Mol. Wt. 284.27

Solvent: Methanol

λ Max. mμ	a_m	Cell mm	Conc. g/L
440	775	20	0.100
321	20500	1	0.100
230	1220	1	0.100

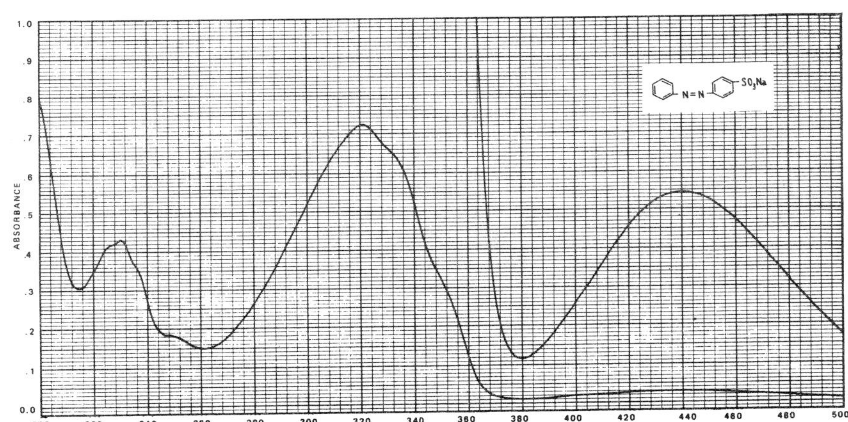

2-ANILINO-5-NITROBENZENESULFONIC ACID, SODIUM SALT

1306

$C_{12}H_9N_3NaO_5S$

Mol. Wt. 316.27

Solvent: Methanol

λ Max. mμ	a_m	Cell mm	Conc. g/L
377	19400	1	0.100
254	11000	1	0.100

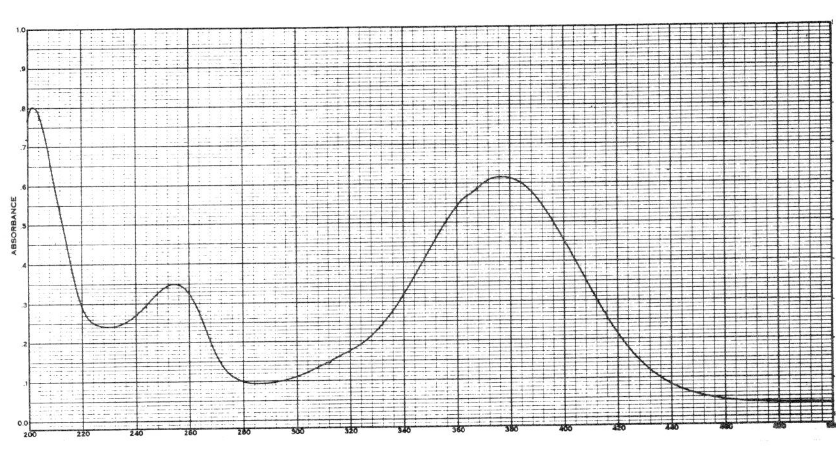

2,4-DINITROBENZENESULFONIC ACID, SODIUM SALT **1307**

$C_6H_3N_2NaO_7S$

Mol. Wt. 270.15

Solvent: Methanol

λ Max. mμ	a_m	Cell mm	Conc. g/L
258	10800	2	0.100

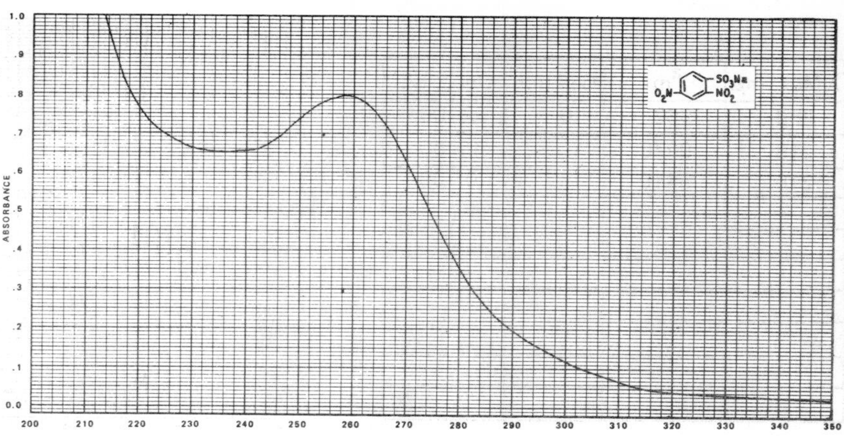

1,3,5-BENZENETRISULFONIC ACID, TRISODIUM SALT, TRIHYDRATE **1308**

$C_6H_3Na_3O_9S_3 \cdot 3H_2O$

Mol. Wt. 438.29

Solvent: Methanol

λ Max. mμ	a_m	Cell mm	Conc. g/L
260	2030	10	0.100

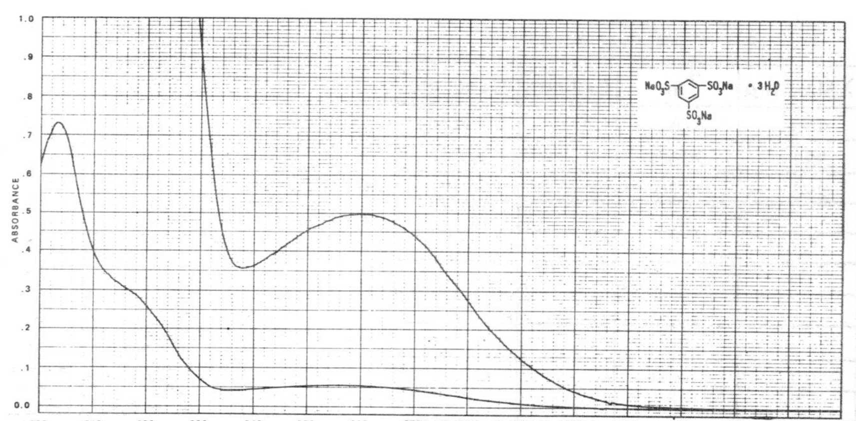

2-NAPHTHALENESULFONIC ACID, SODIUM SALT **1309**

$C_{10}H_7NaO_3S$

Mol. Wt. 230.22

Solvent: Methanol

λ Max. mμ	a_m	Cell mm	Conc. g/L
319	550	10	0.100
312	479	10	0.100
305	566	10	0.100
274	5070	1	0.100
227	102000	1	0.0200

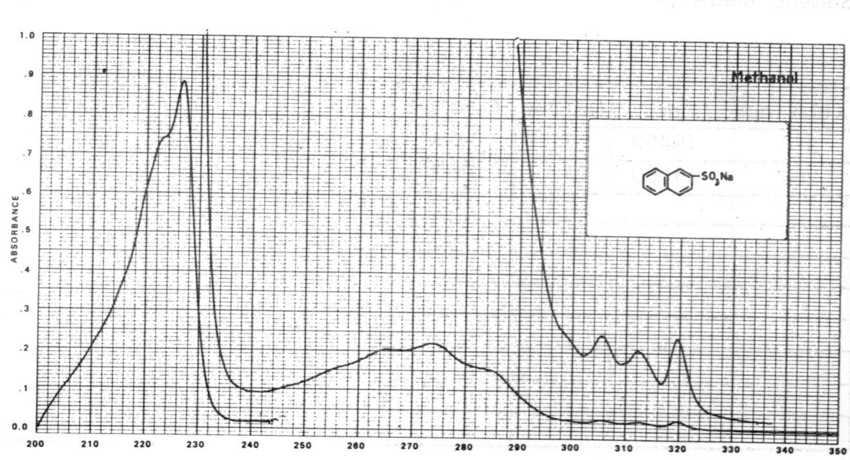

4-AMINO-1-NAPHTHALENESULFONIC ACID, SODIUM SALT, HEMIHYDRATE 1310

$C_{10}H_8NNaO_3S \cdot ½H_2O$
Mol. Wt. 254.24
Solvent: Methanol

λ Max. mμ	a_m	Cell mm	Conc. g/L
330	8060	2	0.100
245	18800	1	0.0500
215	33800	1	0.0500

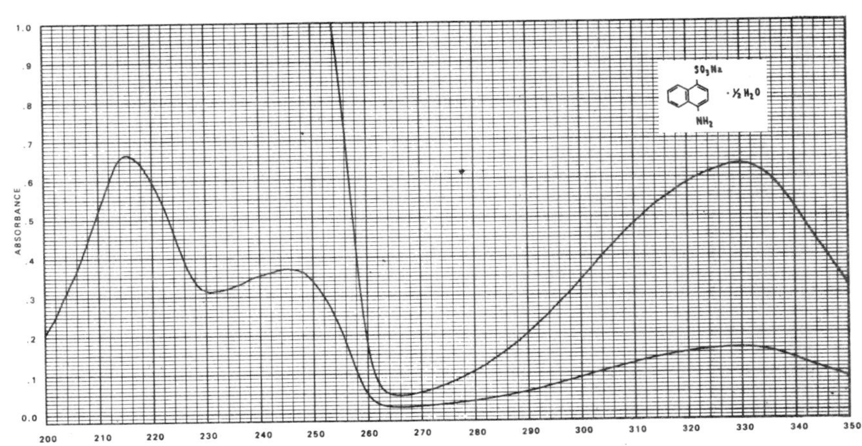

4-AMINO-1-NAPHTHALENESULFONIC ACID, SODIUM SALT, HEMIHYDRATE 1310

$C_{10}H_8NNaO_3S \cdot ½H_2O$
Mol. Wt. 254.24
Solvent: Methanol HCl

λ Max. mμ	a_m	Cell mm	Conc. g/L
314	572	2	0.100
285	6860	2	0.100
225.5	65500	1	0.0330

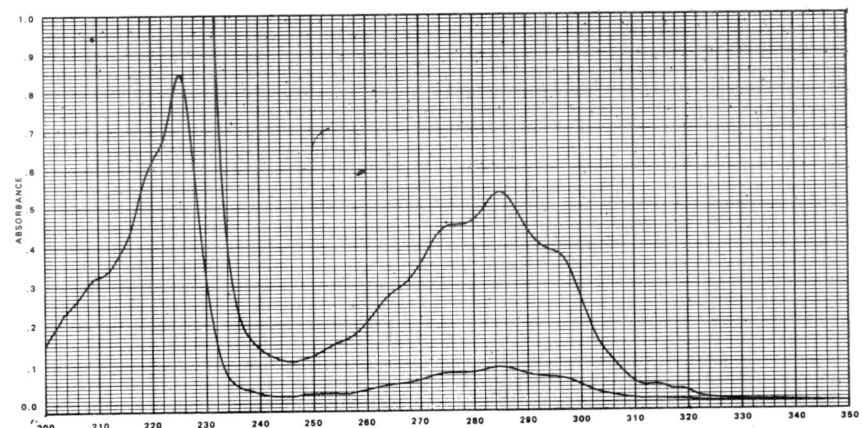

λ Max. mμ	a_m	Cell mm	Conc. g/L

2,7-NAPHTHALENEDISULFONIC ACID, DISODIUM SALT 1311

$C_{10}H_6Na_2O_6S_2$
Mol. Wt. 332.26
Solvent: Methanol

λ Max. mμ	a_m	Cell mm	Conc. g/L
266	5710	4	0.100
231.5	100000	0.5	0.050

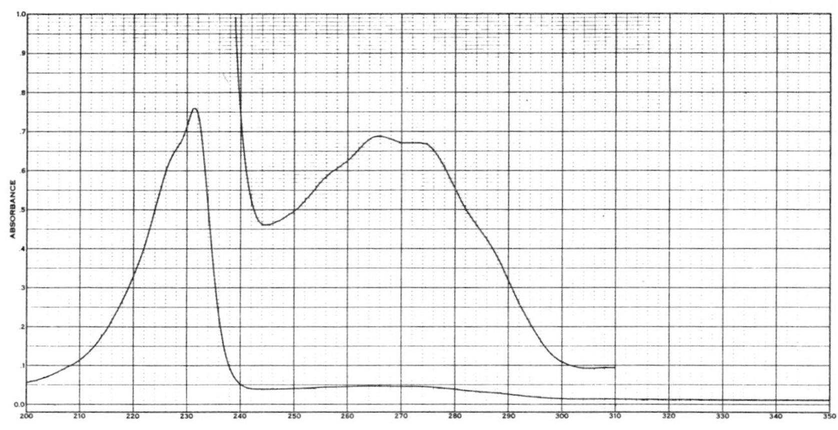

2,7-NAPHTHALENEDISULFONIC ACID, DISODIUM SALT 1311

$C_{10}H_6Na_2O_6S_2$
Mol. Wt. 332.26
Solvent: Methanol HCl

λ Max. mμ	a_m	Cell mm	Conc. g/L
265	5760	2	0.100
231.5	98000	0.5	0.050

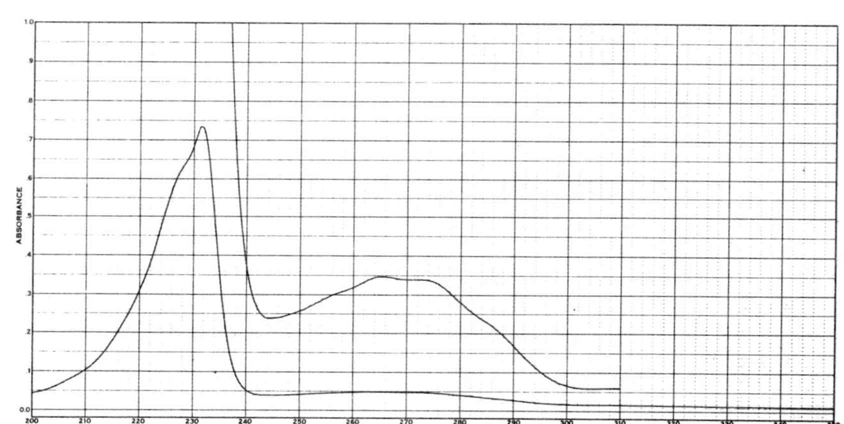

1-DODECYLPYRIDINIUM p-TOLUENESULFONATE 1312

$C_{17}H_{30}N \cdot C_7H_7O_3S$
Mol. Wt. 419.63
M.P. 138-140°C
Solvent: Methanol

λ Max. mμ	a_m	Cell mm	Conc. g/L
259	4780	5	0.100
218.5	15000	2	0.100

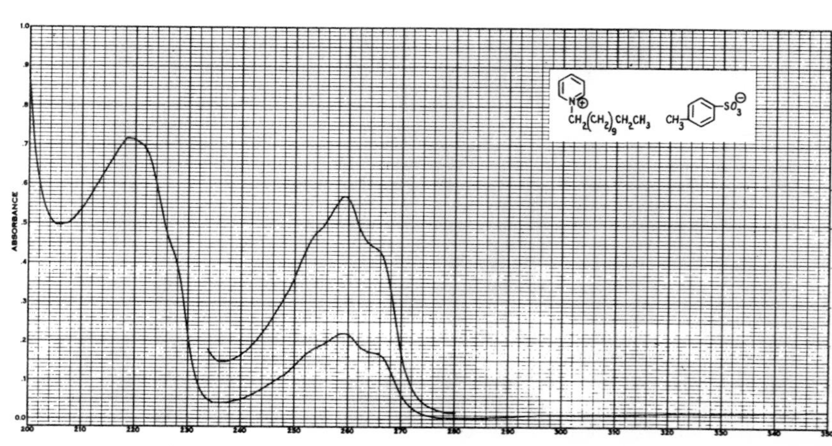

PHENYLTRIMETHYLAMMONIUM BENZENESULFONATE

1313

$C_{15}H_{19}NO_3S$
Mol. Wt. 293.39
M.P. 192-194°C
Solvent: Methanol

λ Max. mμ	a_m	Cell mm	Conc. g/L
269.5	440	20	0.100
263	651	20	0.100
258	733	20	0.100
253	651	20	0.100
216	8920	1	0.100

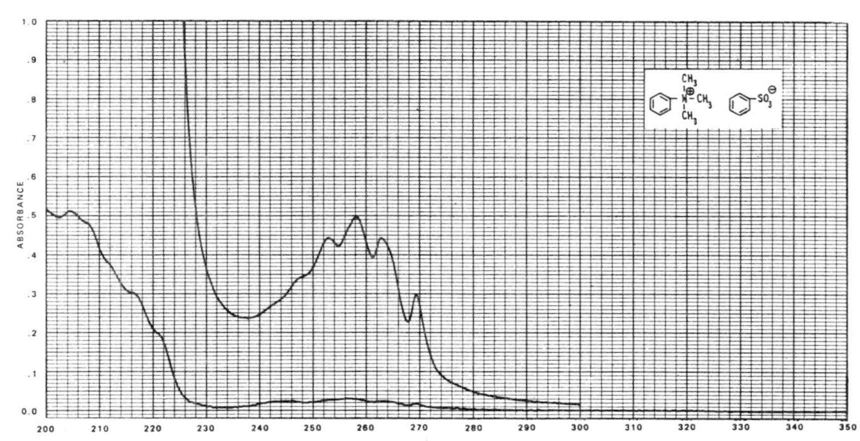

1314

λ Max. mμ	a_m	Cell mm	Conc. g/L

Compounds 1314 through 1319 do not display any maxima in the near UV.

METHANESULFONIC ACID, PHENYL ESTER

1320

$C_7H_8O_3S$
Mol. Wt. 172.20
M.P. 60-62°C
Solvent: Methanol

λ Max. mμ	a_m	Cell mm	Conc. g/L
261.5	503	4	0.308
255.5	707	4	0.308
244	974	4	0.308
x	x	0.5	0.308

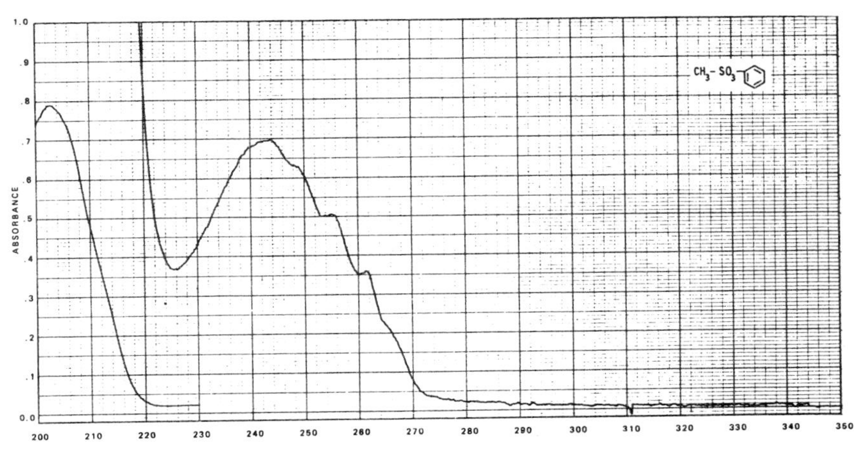

p-TOLUENESULFONIC ACID, ISOPROPYL ESTER 1321

$C_{10}H_{14}O_3S$
Mol. Wt. 214.27
M.R. 15-20°C (lit.)
Solvent: Methanol

λ Max. mμ	a_m	Cell mm	Conc. g/L
x	x	10	3.06
271.5	260	10	0.612
266	350	10	0.612
260.5	420	10	0.612
x	x	10	0.00612

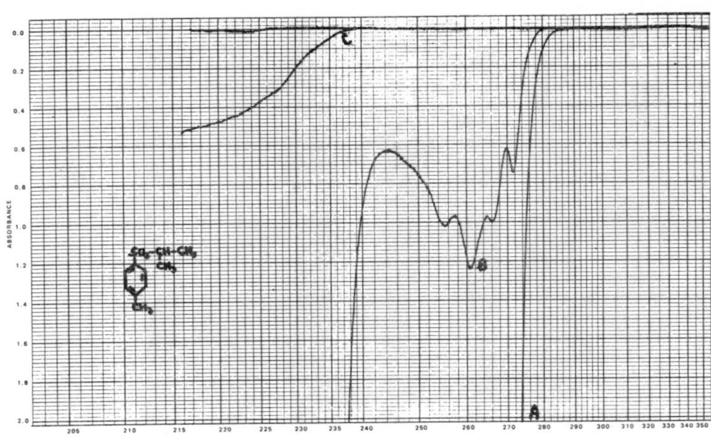

p-TOLUENESULFONIC ACID, BUTYL ESTER 1322

$C_{11}H_{16}O_3S$
Mol. Wt. 228.31
B.P. 174-175°C/10mm
Solvent: Methanol

λ Max. mμ	a_m	Cell mm	Conc. g/L
272	672	20	0.115
266	818	20	0.115
261	899	20	0.115
255.5	745	20	0.115
224.5	19000	1	0.115

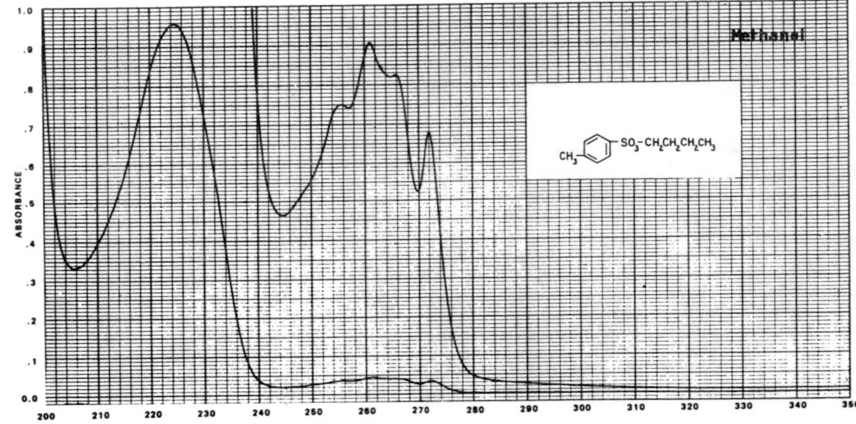

1323

λ Max. mμ	a_m	Cell mm	Conc. g/L

Compounds 1323 through 1330 do not display any maxima in the near UV.

THE THIOAMIDES

Aliphatic Compounds

The aliphatic thioamides exhibit a strong absorption band arising from the $\pi \rightarrow \pi^*$ transition of the thiocarbonyl chromophore (—C(=S)—) near 265 mμ. A second, much weaker band, has been reported for the $n \rightarrow \pi^*$ transition (325 mμ, ϵ_{max} = 77).

Aromatic Compounds

The dominant feature of the UV spectra of the aromatic thioamides is the band due to the thiocarbonyl chromophore as noted above. It is observed in the range from 255 to 272 mμ depending on the type of aromatic substitution and usually possesses an ϵ_{max} of about 10,000 (spectra 1332, 1333 and 1335).

Upon the addition of base, the thioamide bands undergo a blue shift to shorter wavelengths.

THE THIOUREAS

Aliphatic Compounds

The thiourea chromophore exhibits a relatively strong absorption band at 236 mμ which is shifted to longer wavelengths by increasing alkyl substitution. A table of several thioureas is given below.

Compound	$\lambda_{max}(\epsilon_{max})$	Solvent	Spectrum
1-Methylthiourea	241 (12800)	Methanol	1338
1,1-Dimethyl thiourea	243 (13800)	Ethanol	Lit.
Tetramethyl thiourea	256 (19400)	Ethanol	Lit.

Aromatic Compounds

The major band of the thioureas undergoes an additional shift to longer wavelength as the number and position of the phenyl substituents vary. Several examples are presented in the table presented below.

Compound	$\lambda_{max}(\epsilon_{max})$	$\lambda_{max}(\epsilon_{max})$	Solvent	Spectrum
1-Allyl-3-phenyl-2-thiourea	248 (13500)	262 * (12500)	Methanol	1350
1-Ethyl-3-phenyl-2-thiourea	250 (13500)	262 * (13200)	Methanol	1348
1,1-Diphenyl-2-Thiourea	255 (13200)		Methanol	1343
1-Phenyl-2-thiourea	264 (12500)		Methanol	1340
1,3-Diphenyl-2-thiourea	274 (19600)		Methanol	1351

THIOACETAMIDE

1331

C_2H_5NS
Mol. Wt. 75.13
M.P. 111-113°C
Solvent: Methanol

λ Max. mμ	a_m	Cell mm	Conc. g/L
265	11000	1	0.0500
210	3700	1	0.0500

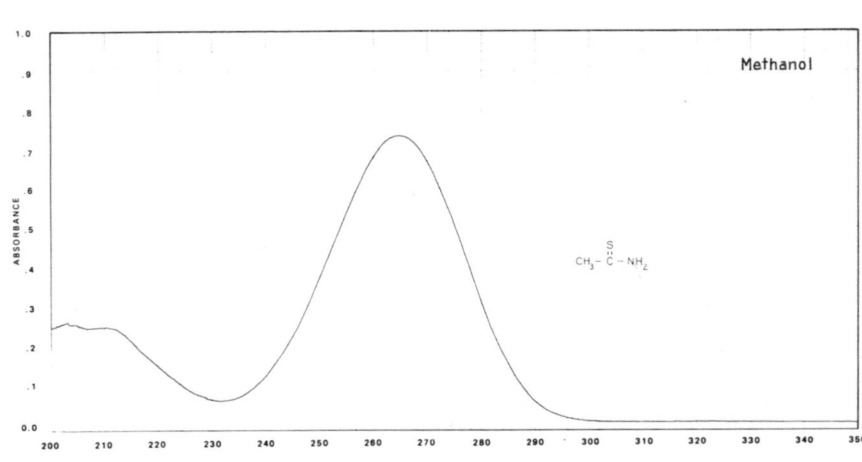

2-PHENYLTHIOACETAMIDE

1332

C_8H_9NS
Mol. Wt. 151.23
Solvent: Methanol

λ Max. mμ	a_m	Cell mm	Conc. g/L
266	10300	1	0.100

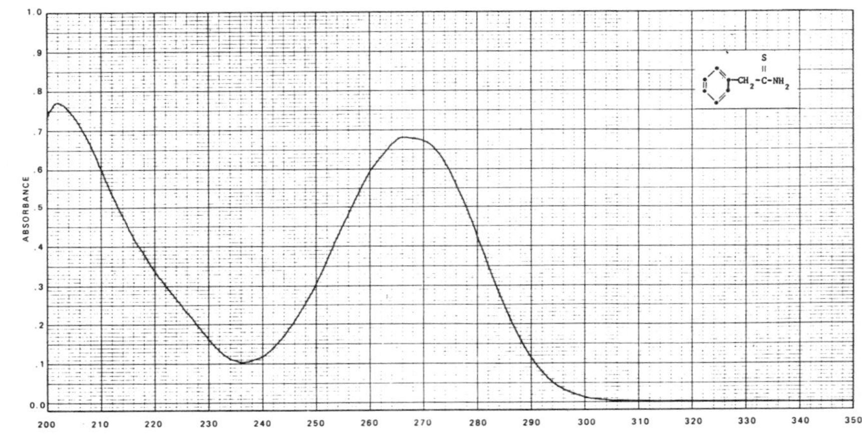

THIOBENZAMIDE

1333

C_7H_7NS
Mol. Wt. 137.20
M.P. 116-117°C (lit.)
Solvent: Methanol

λ Max. mμ	a_m	Cell mm	Conc. g/L
x	x	10	0.344
272	7260	10	0.0172
229	7100	10	0.0172

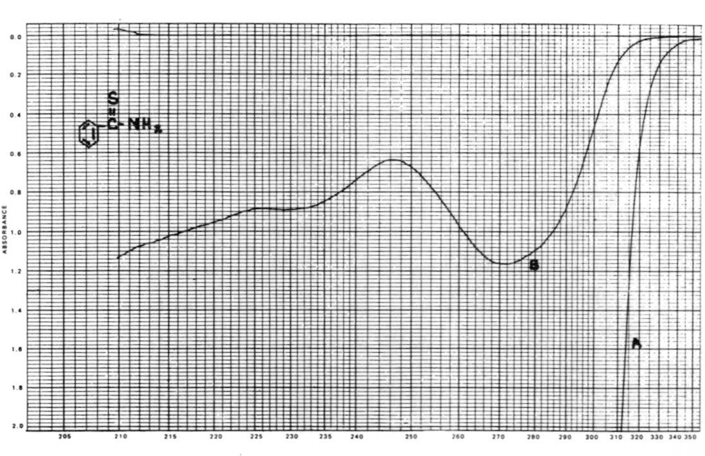

6-METHYLTHIOPICOLINAMIDE 1334

$C_7H_8N_2S$
Mol. Wt. 152.22
Solvent: Methanol

λ Max. mμ	a_m	Cell mm	Conc. g/L
359	98	40	0.100
308	72	40	0.100
231	2590	5	0.100
x	x	5	0.100

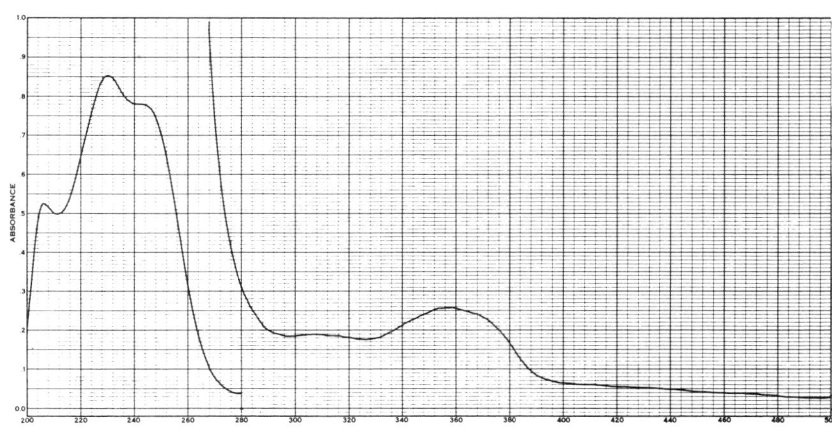

6-METHYLTHIOPICOLINAMIDE 1334

$C_7H_8N_2S$
Mol. Wt. 152.22
Solvent: Methanol HCl

λ Max. mμ	a_m	Cell mm	Conc. g/L
353	83	40	0.100
259	4810	2	0.100

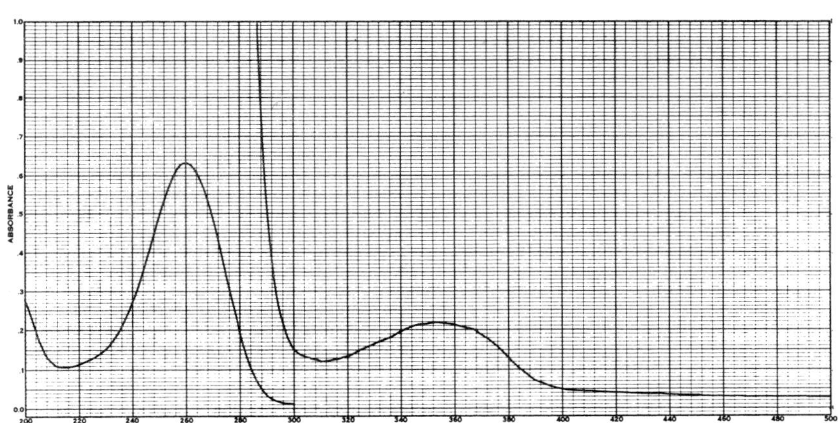

λ Max. mμ	a_m	Cell mm	Conc. g/L

THIOBENZANILIDE 1335

$C_{13}H_{11}NS$

Mol. Wt. 213.30

Solvent: Methanol

λ Max. mμ	a_m	Cell mm	Conc. g/L
x	x	20	0.100
313.5	8190	1	0.100
255	12700	1	0.100
232	14000	1	0.100
230	14000	1	0.100

THIOBENZANILIDE 1335

$C_{13}H_{11}NS$

Mol. Wt. 213.30

Solvent: Methanol KOH

λ Max. mμ	a_m	Cell mm	Conc. g/L
227	21000	1	0.100

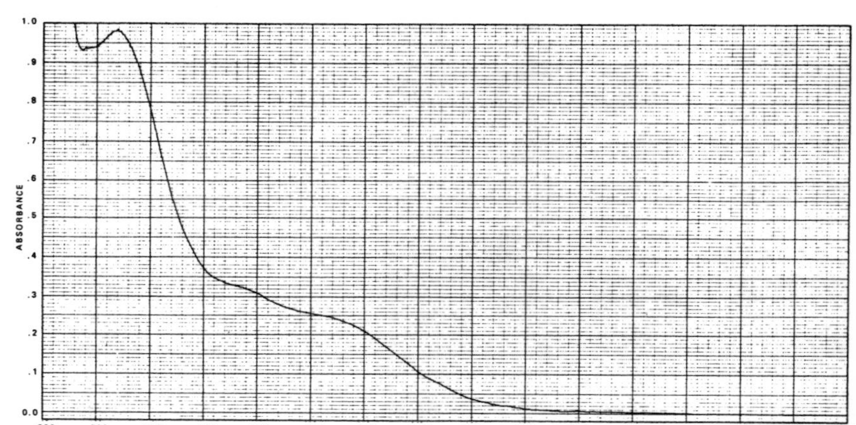

N,N-DIMETHYLTHIOFORMAMIDE 1336

C_3H_7NS

Mol. Wt. 89.16

B.P. 58-60°C/1mm

λ Max. mμ	a_m	Cell mm	Conc. g/L

Pure sample not available.

N,N-DIMETHYLTHIOACETAMIDE 1337

C_4H_9NS
Mol. Wt. 103.19
M.P. 73-75°C
Solvent: Methanol

λ Max. mμ	a_m	Cell mm	Conc. g/L
268.5	14400	0.5	0.1

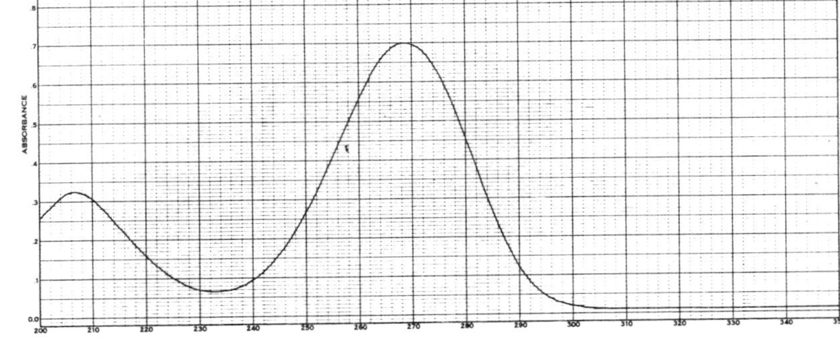

1-METHYL-2-THIOUREA 1338

$C_2H_6N_2S$
Mol. Wt. 90.15
Solvent: Methanol

λ Max. mμ	a_m	Cell mm	Conc. g/L
240.5	12800	10	0.005

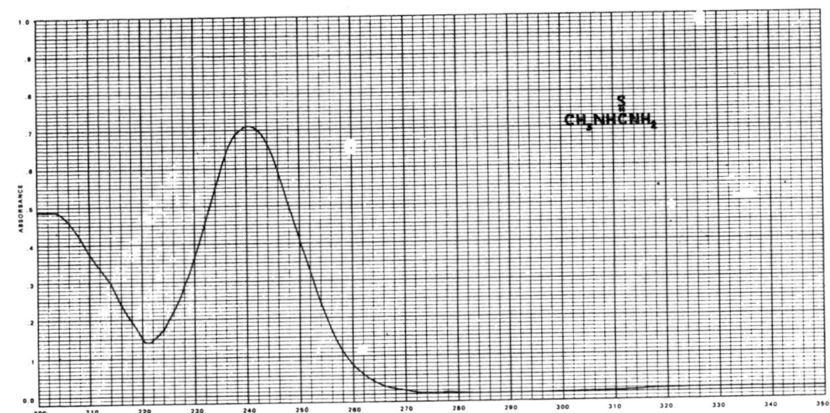

1-ETHYL-2-THIOUREA 1339

$C_3H_8N_2S$
Mol. Wt. 104.17
M.P. 110-112°C
Solvent: Methanol

λ Max. mμ	a_m	Cell mm	Conc. g/L
240.5	10500	0.5	0.1

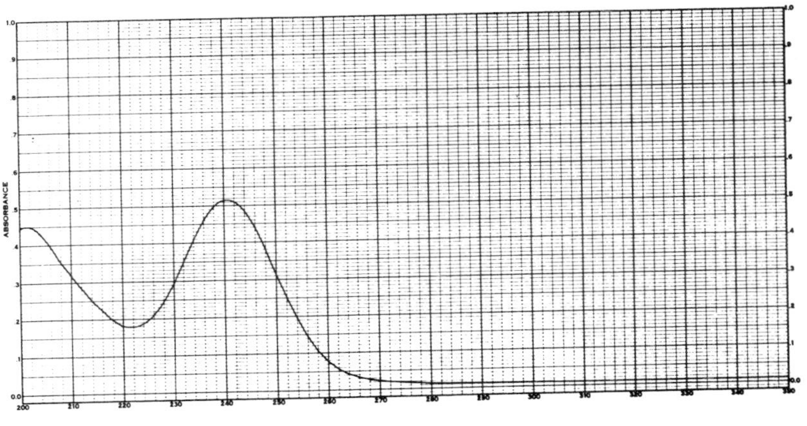

1-PHENYL-2-THIOUREA

1340

$C_7H_8N_2S$

Mol. Wt. 152.22

M.P. 153-154°C (lit.)

Solvent: Methanol

λ Max. mμ	a_m	Cell mm	Conc. g/L
264	12500	1	0.100

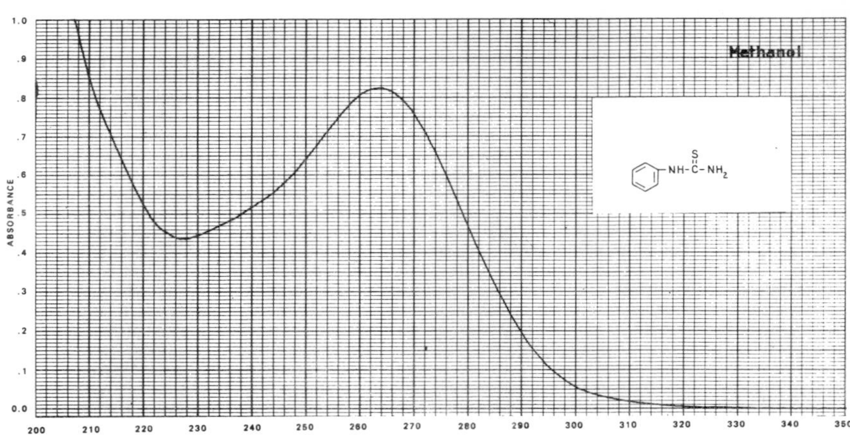

2-THIO-1-(o-TOLYL)UREA

1341

$C_8H_{10}N_2S$

Mol. Wt. 166.25

M.P. 160-161°C

Solvent: Methanol

λ Max. mμ	a_m	Cell mm	Conc. g/L
249.5	14300	10	0.010

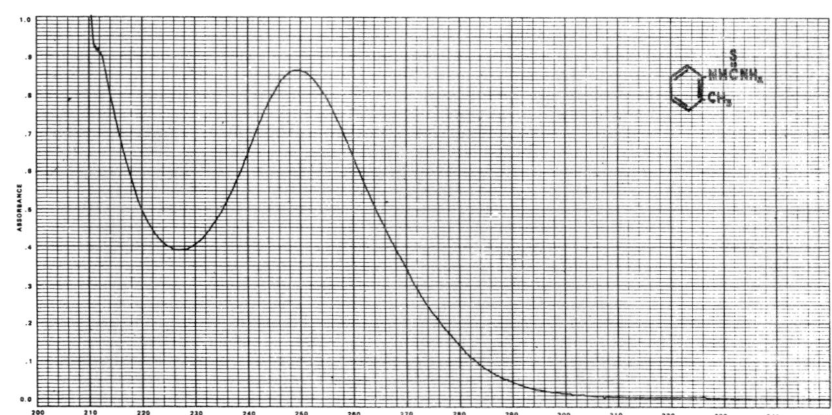

1-(1-NAPHTHYL)-2-THIOUREA

1342

$C_{11}H_{10}N_2S$

Mol. Wt. 202.28

M.P. 182-184°C

Solvent: Methanol

λ Max. mμ	a_m	Cell mm	Conc. g/L
290.5	5240	5	0.0500
212	41100	2	0.0200

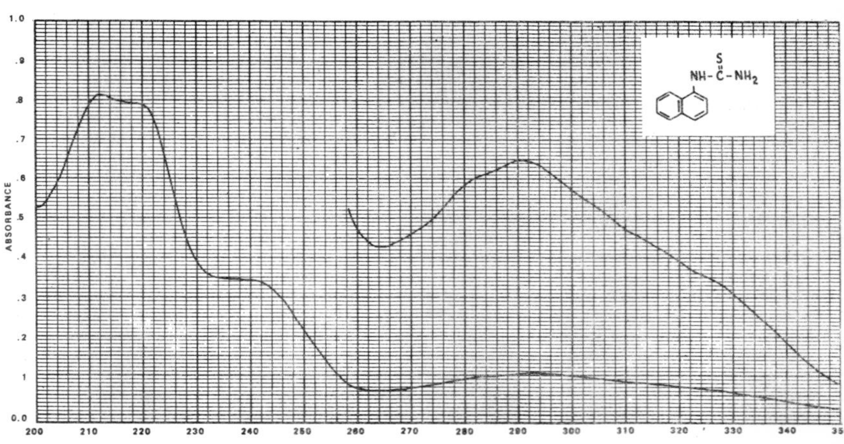

1-(1-NAPHTHYL)-2-THIOUREA 1342

$C_{11}H_{10}N_2S$
Mol. Wt. 202.28
M.P. 182-184°C
Solvent: Methanol HCl

λ Max. mμ	a_m	Cell mm	Conc. g/L
285	5790	5	0.0500
278	6600	5	0.0500
268	5700	5	0.0500
221	78500	1	0.0200

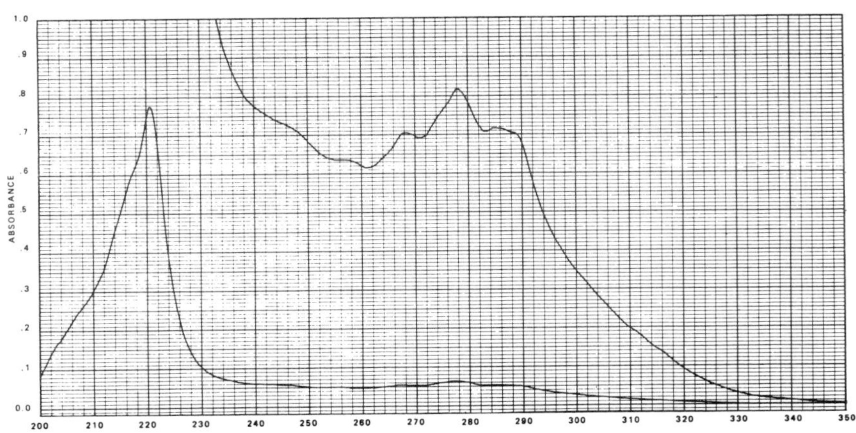

1,1-DIPHENYL-2-THIOUREA 1343

$C_{13}H_{12}N_2S$
Mol. Wt. 228.32
M.P. 219°C (dec.)
Solvent: Methanol

λ Max. mμ	a_m	Cell mm	Conc. g/L
255	13200	1	0.100

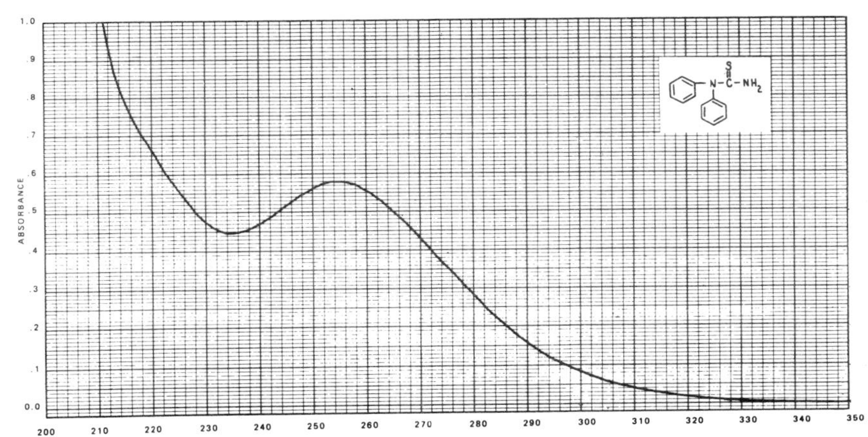

1,3-DIETHYL-2-THIOUREA 1344

$C_5H_{12}N_2S$
Mol. Wt. 132.23
M.P. 75°C

λ Max. mμ	a_m	Cell mm	Conc. g/L

Pure sample not available.

1,3-DIISOPROPYL-2-THIOUREA 1345

$C_7H_{16}N_2S$
Mol. Wt. 160.28
Solvent: Methanol

λ Max. mμ	a_m	Cell mm	Conc. g/L
241.2	11300	0.5	0.25

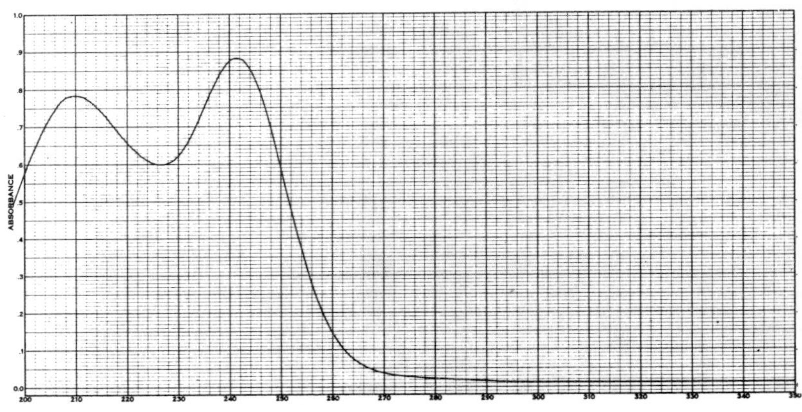

1,3-DIISOBUTYL-2-THIOUREA 1346

$C_9H_{20}N_2S$
Mol. Wt. 188.34
Solvent: Methanol

λ Max. mμ	a_m	Cell mm	Conc. g/L
240.5	12900	0.5	0.25

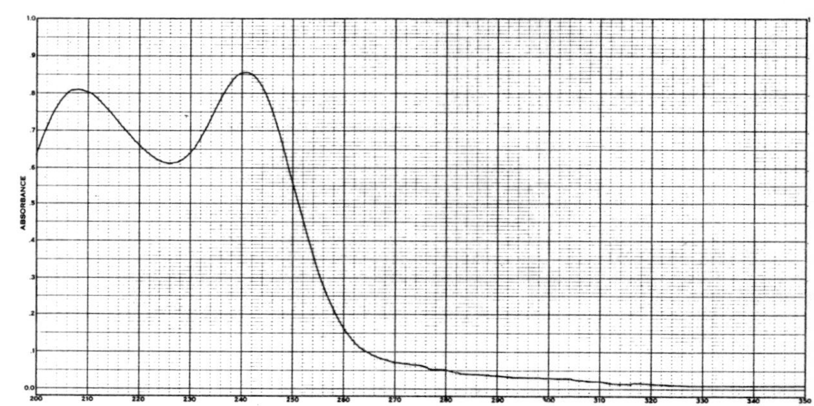

1,3-DIDECYL-2-THIOUREA 1347

$C_{21}H_{44}N_2S$
Mol. Wt. 356.66
M.P. 69-71°C

λ Max. mμ	a_m	Cell mm	Conc. g/L

Pure sample not available.

1-ETHYL-3-PHENYL-2-THIOUREA

1348

$C_9H_{12}N_2S$

Mol. Wt. 180.27

M.P. 102-104°C

Solvent: Methanol

λ Max. mμ	a_m	Cell mm	Conc. g/L
250	13500	1	0.100

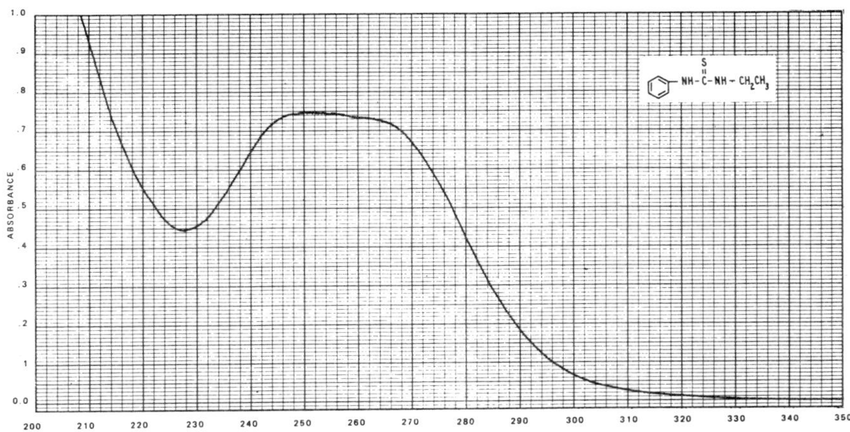

1-ISOPROPYL-3-PHENYL-2-THIOUREA

1349

$C_{10}H_{14}N_2S$

Mol. Wt. 194.30

M.P. 99°C

Solvent: Methanol

λ Max. mμ	a_m	Cell mm	Conc. g/L
247	14400	1	0.100
x	x	1	0.100

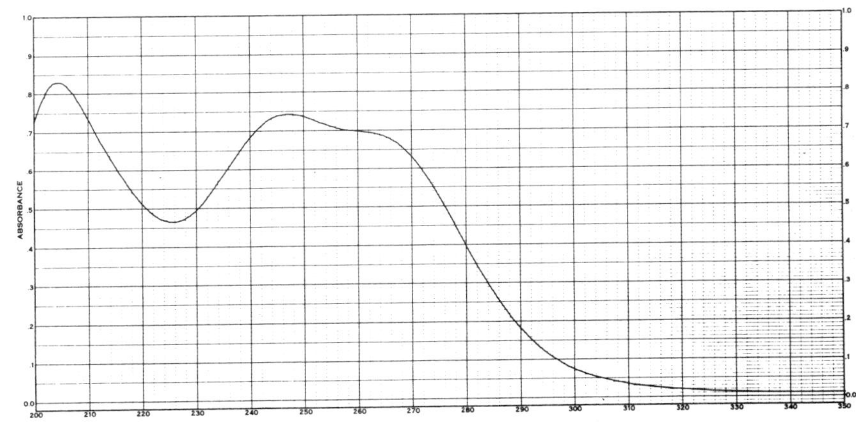

1-ALLYL-3-PHENYL-2-THIOUREA

1350

$C_{10}H_{12}N_2S$

Mol. Wt. 192.28

M.P. 98°C

Solvent: Methanol

λ Max. mμ	a_m	Cell mm	Conc. g/L
248	13500	1	0.100

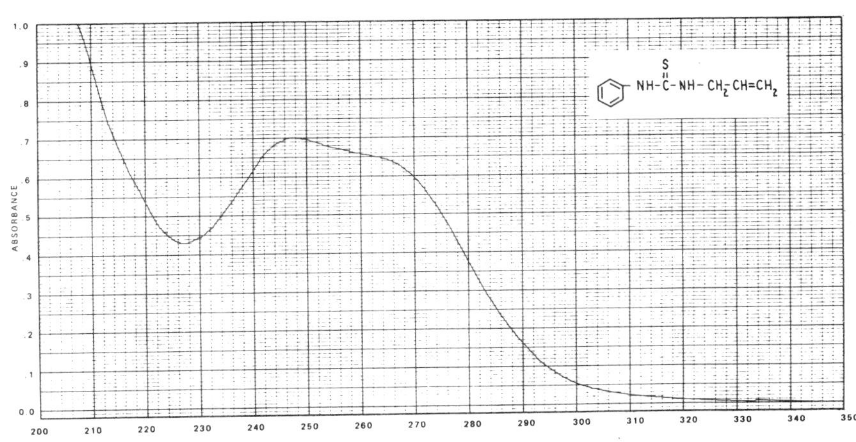

THIOCARBANILIDE

$C_{13}H_{12}N_2S$
Mol. Wt. 228.31
M.P. 153-154°C
Solvent: Methanol

λ Max. mμ	a_m	Cell mm	Conc. g/L
274	19600	10	0.010

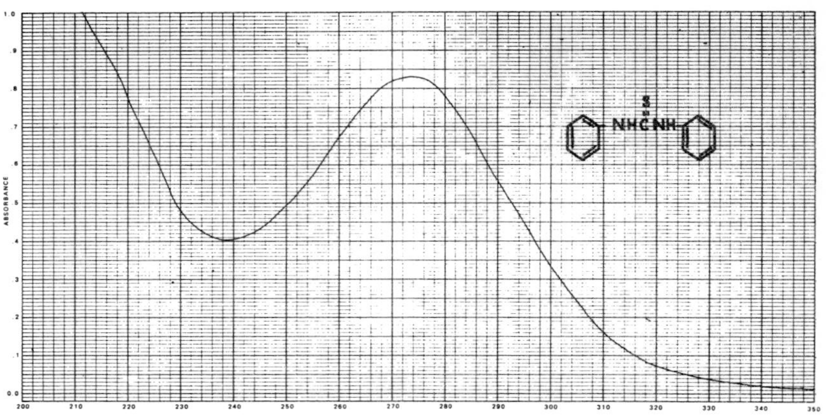

1-(o-CHLOROPHENYL)-3-PHENYL-2-THIOUREA 1352

$C_{13}H_{11}ClN_2S$
Mol. Wt. 262.76
M.P. 153-155°C
Solvent: Methanol

λ Max. mμ	a_m	Cell mm	Conc. g/L
272	18400	1	0.100

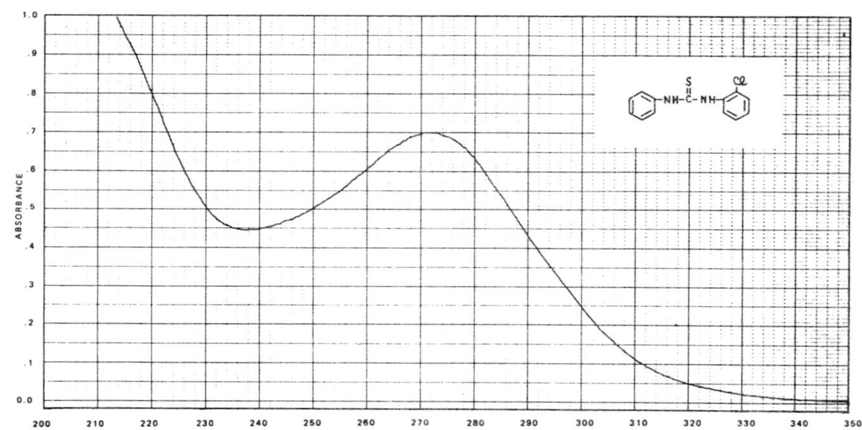

1-(o-CHLOROPHENYL)-3-PHENYL-2-THIOUREA 1352

$C_{13}H_{11}ClN_2S$
Mol. Wt. 262.76
M.P. 153-155°C
Solvent: Methanol KOH

λ Max. mμ	a_m	Cell mm	Conc. g/L
269	20400	1	0.100

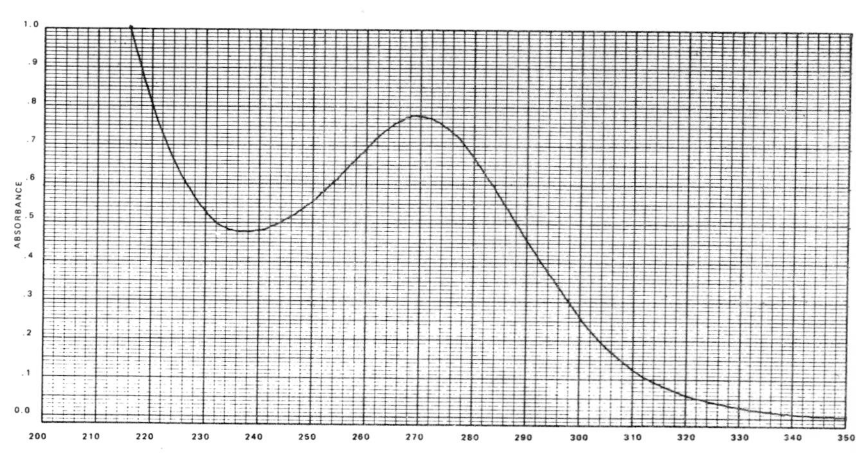

1,1-DIMETHYL-4-(2-NORBORNYL)-3-THIOSEMICARBAZIDE 1353

$C_{10}H_{19}N_3S$
Mol. Wt. 213.35
M.P. 152-153°C

λ Max. mμ	a_m	Cell mm	Conc. g/L

Pure sample not available.

3-(o-CHLOROPHENYL)-1,1-DIMETHYL-2-THIOUREA 1354

$C_9H_{11}ClN_2S$
Mol. Wt. 214.72
M.P. 146°C
Solvent: Methanol

λ Max. mμ	a_m	Cell mm	Conc. g/L
238.5	13900	1	0.0500
211	25800	1	0.0500

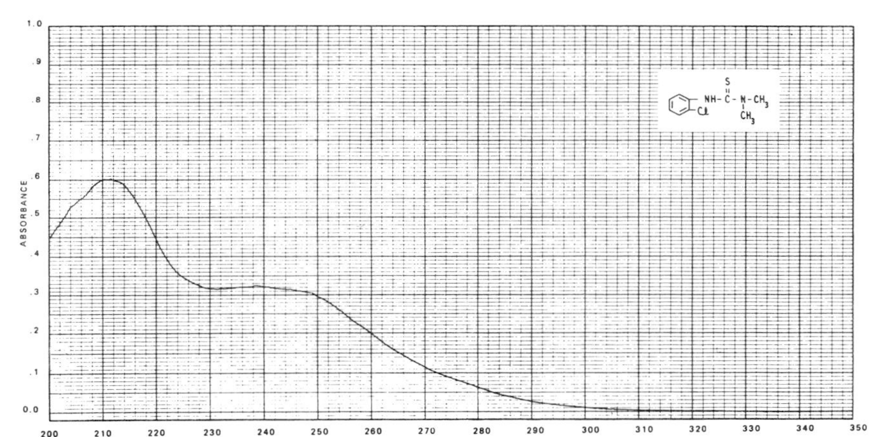

THIO-1-PIPERIDINECARBOXY-m-TOLUIDIDE 1355

$C_{13}H_{18}N_2S$
Mol. Wt. 234.36
M.P. 102°C
Solvent: Methanol

λ Max. mμ	a_m	Cell mm	Conc. g/L
254	16600	1	0.100
208.5	21300	1	0.100

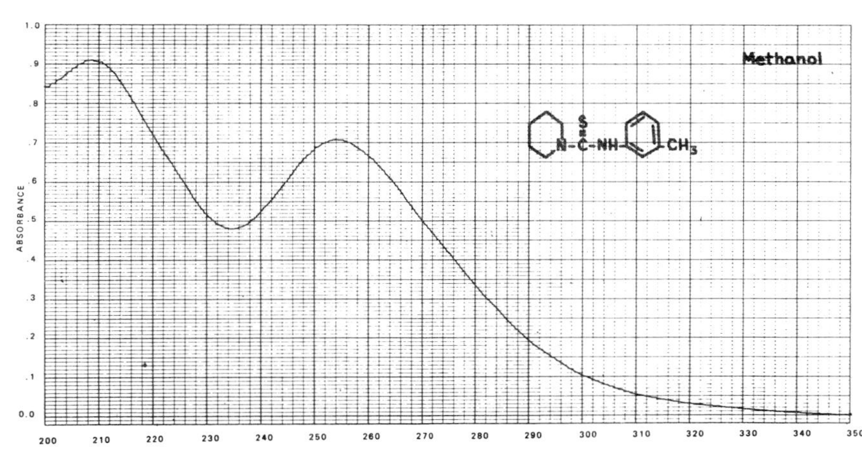

1,1,3,3-TETRAETHYL-2-THIOUREA 1356

$C_9H_{20}N_2S$

Mol. Wt. 188.34

B.P. 126-128°C/10mm

λ Max. mμ	a_m	Cell mm	Conc. g/L

Pure sample not available.

NAPHTH[2,3-d] IMIDAZOLINE-2-THIONE 1357

$C_{11}H_8N_2S$

Mol. Wt. 200.26

M.P. 305°C (dec.)

Solvent: Methanol

λ Max. mμ	a_m	Cell mm	Conc. g/L
344.5	32100	1	0.0200
331	18600	1	0.0200
274.5	63100	1	0.0200
219	52800	1	0.0200

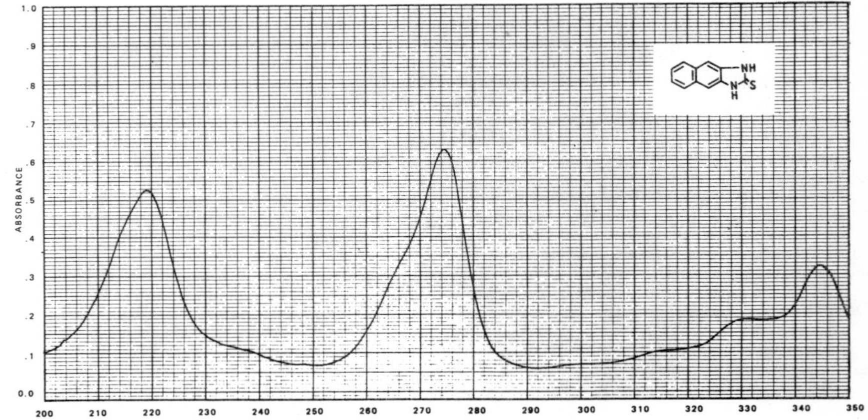

1,5-BIS-HEPTYLIDENE-3-THIOCARBOHYDRAZIDE 1358

$C_{15}H_{30}N_4S$

Mol. Wt. 298.50

M.P. 119°C

λ Max. mμ	a_m	Cell mm	Conc. g/L

Pure sample not available.

THE SULFONAMIDES

Aliphatic Compounds

The aliphatic sulfonamides do not display any absorption bands and thus there is no spectrum included in this volume for compound 1359.

Aromatic Compounds

The benzenesulfonamides, which possess a phenyl group bonded to the sulfur atom of the sulfonamide group, produce two major bands in the near UV region. A relatively strong band is observed near 225 mμ and a much weaker band is seen at about 265 mμ and displays benzenoid fine structure.

The spectra of the benzene sulfonamides do not change significantly upon the addition of base to the sample. The data for several benzene sulfonamides are listed in the table presented below.

Benzenesulfonamides

Compound	$\lambda_{max}(\epsilon_{max})$	$\lambda_{max}(\epsilon_{max})$	Solvent	Spectrum
Benzenesulfonamide	218 (9180)	264 (617)	Methanol	1361
o-Toluenesulfonamide		268 (1010)	Methanol	1362
p-Toluenesulfonamide	224 (10300)	268 (336)	Methanol	1363
N,N-Dimethyl-p-toluene-sulfonamide	229 (10900)	268 * (379)	Methanol	1375
2-Mesitylenesulfonamide	230 (9770)	275 (1250)	Methanol	1364

* Shoulder

The sulfonanilides, in which the phenyl group is bonded to the nitrogen atom of the sulfonamide group, also display two major bands but at slightly longer wavelength.

In addition, the fine structure that is apparent in the spectra of the benzenesulfonamides, is not observed in those of the sulfonanilides. The major bands of the compounds undergo a noticeable (12 mμ) shift to longer wavelength upon the addition of base to the methanol solution.

Compound	$\lambda_{max}(\epsilon_{max})$	$\lambda_{max}(\epsilon_{max})$	Solvent	Spectrum
p-Ethanesulfono-toluidide	228 (11600)	278 (669)	Methanol	1368
	248 (10900)	287 (1070)	Methanol/KOH	1368
4,4'-Dibromosulfanilide	241 (25500)	276 (2010)	Methanol	1378
	253 (27300)	----------	Methanol/KOH	1378

METHANESULFONAMIDE 1359

CH_5NO_2S

Mol. Wt. 95.12

M.P. 91-93°C

λ Max. mμ	a_m	Cell mm	Conc. g/L

Aliphatic sulfonamides do not display any maxima in the near UV region.

trans-2-PHENYLETHENESULFONAMIDE 1360

$C_8H_9NO_2S$

Mol. Wt. 183.23

Solvent: Methanol

λ Max. mμ	a_m	Cell mm	Conc. g/L
259	17600	1	0.100

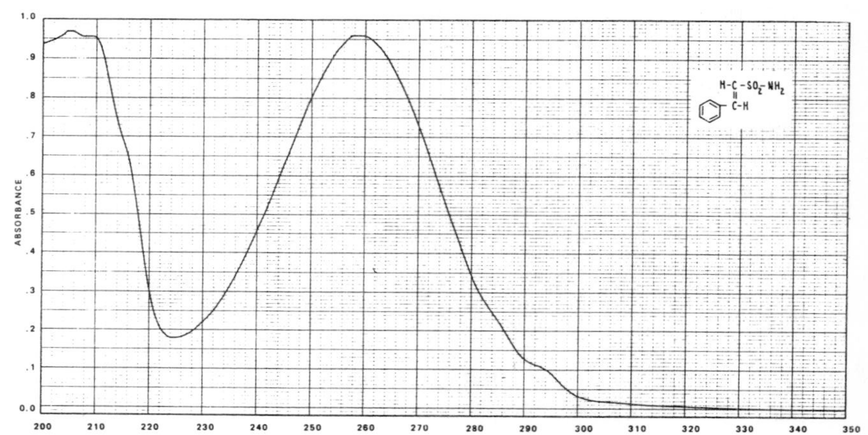

BENZENESULFONAMIDE 1361

$C_6H_7NO_2S$

Mol. Wt. 157.19

M.P. 152-154°C

Solvent: Methanol

λ Max. mμ	a_m	Cell mm	Conc. g/L
270.5	503	20	0.100
263.5	617	20	0.100
257.5	476	20	0.100
253	336	20	0.100
217.5	9180	1	0.100

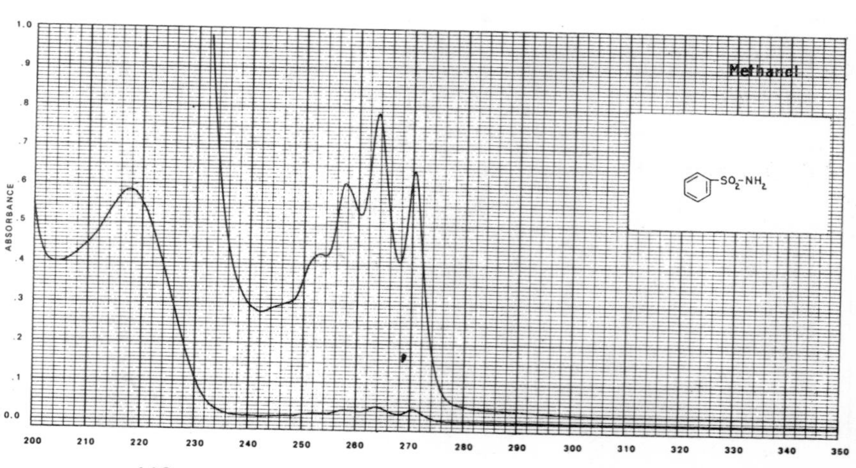

BENZENESULFONAMIDE 1361

$C_6H_7NO_2S$

Mol. Wt. 157.19

M.P. 152-154°C

Solvent: Methanol KOH

λ Max. mμ	a_m	Cell mm	Conc. g/L
270.5	411	20	0.100
263.5	570	20	0.100
257	591	20	0.100
216.5	7950	1	0.100

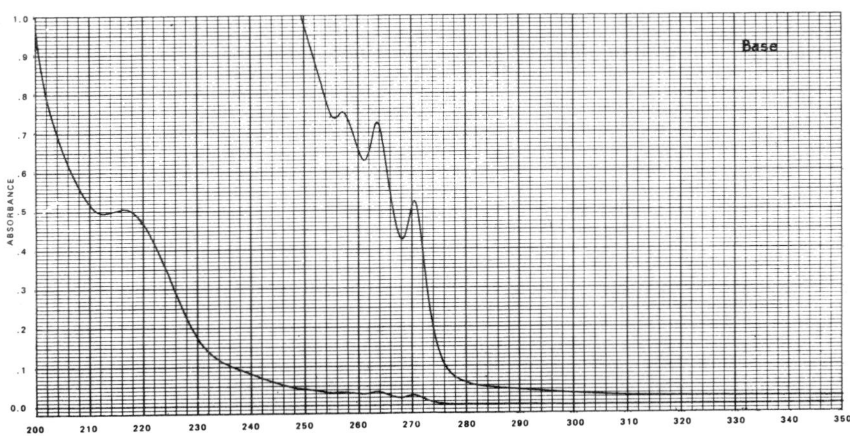

o-TOLUENESULFONAMIDE 1362

$C_7H_9NO_2S$

Mol. Wt. 171.22

Solvent: Methanol

λ Max. mμ	a_m	Cell mm	Conc. g/L
x	x	10	2.00
275	925	10	0.200
268	1010	10	0.200

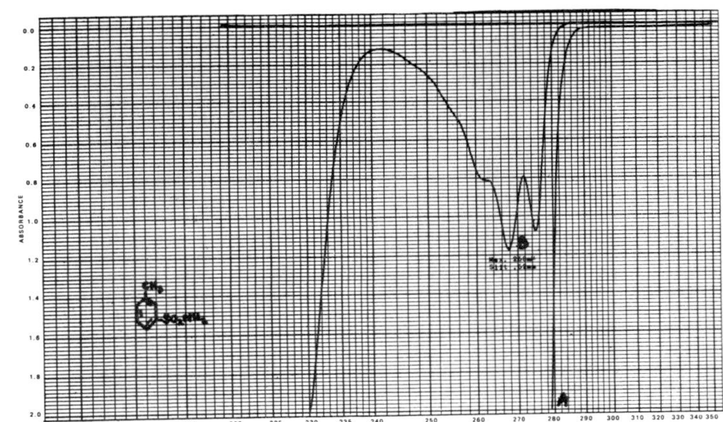

p-TOLUENESULFONAMIDE 1363

$C_7H_9NO_2S$

Mol. Wt. 171.22

M.P. 135-136°C

Solvent: Methanol

λ Max. mμ	a_m	Cell mm	Conc. g/L
273	257	20	0.100
267.5	336	20	0.100
262	434	20	0.100
256.5	370	20	0.100
224	10300	1	0.100

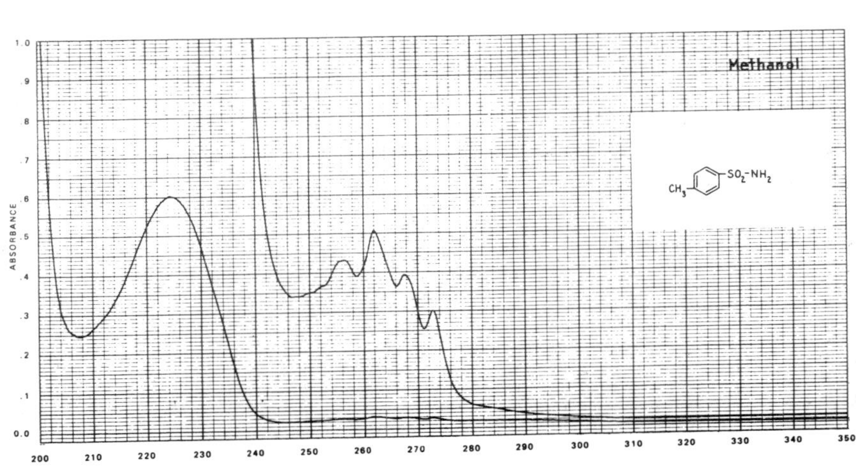

2-MESITYLENESULFONAMIDE 1364

$C_9H_{13}NO_2S$

Mol. Wt. 199.27

M.P. 140-144°C

Solvent: Methanol

λ Max. mμ	a_m	Cell mm	Conc. g/L
282.5	1310	10	0.100
274.5	1250	10	0.100
230	9770	2	0.100

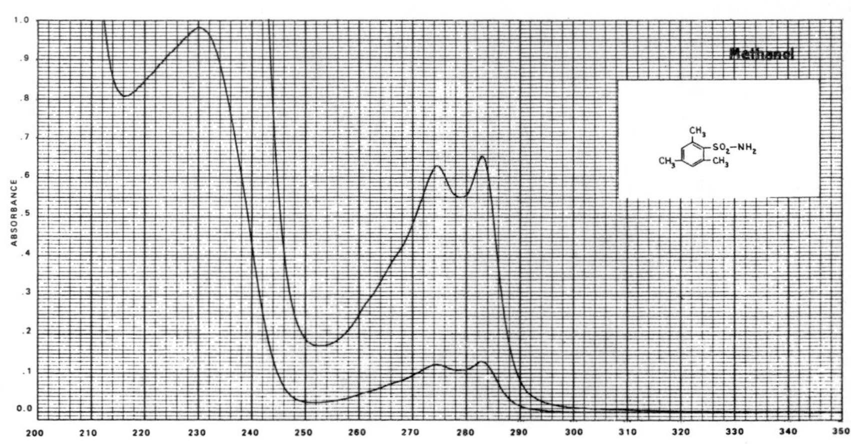

SULFANILAMIDE 1365

$C_6H_8N_2O_2S$

Mol. Wt. 172.21

M.P. 163°C

Solvent: Methanol

λ Max. mμ	a_m	Cell mm	Conc. g/L
262	3430	2	0.100

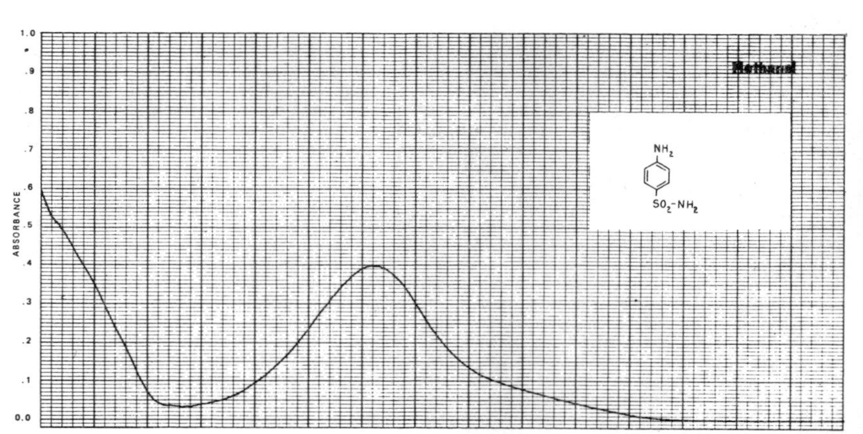

SULFANILAMIDE 1365

$C_6H_8N_2O_2S$

Mol. Wt. 172.21

M.P. 163°C

Solvent: Methanol HCl

λ Max. mμ	a_m	Cell mm	Conc. g/L
262.5	665	20	0.100
215	2140	5	0.100

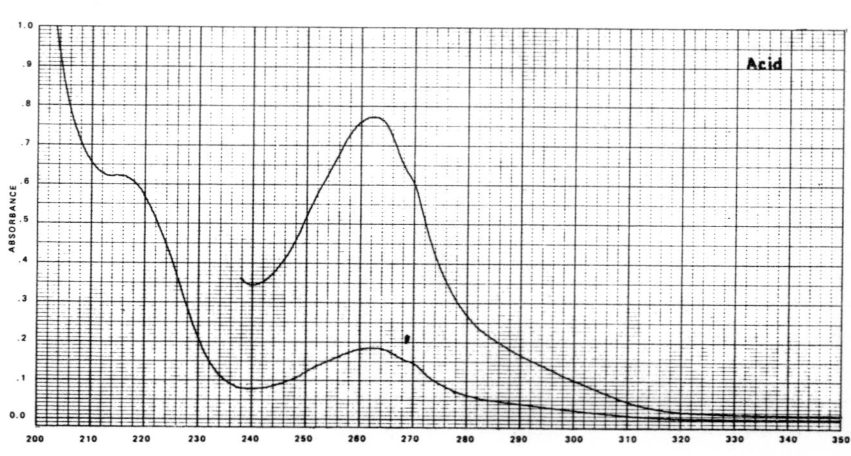

N^4-BENZYLIDENESULFANILAMIDE 1366

$C_{13}H_{12}N_2O_2S$
Mol. Wt. 260.32
Solvent: Methanol

λ Max. mμ	a_m	Cell mm	Conc. g/L
265	39700	0.5	0.100

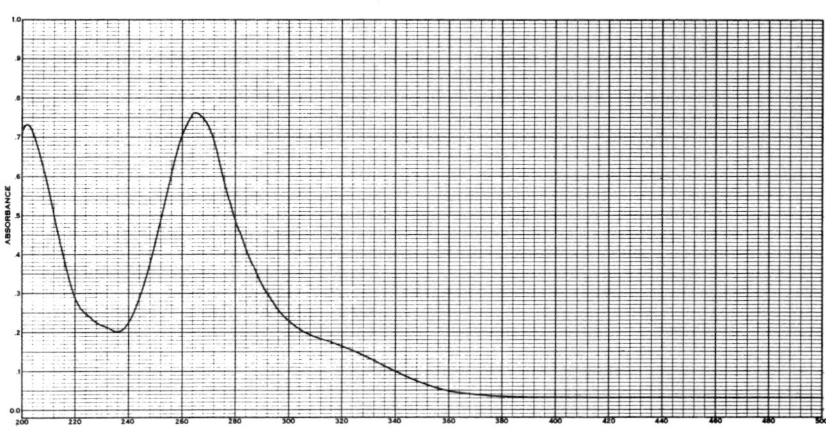

N^4-BENZYLIDENESULFANILAMIDE 1366

$C_{13}H_{12}N_2O_2S$
Mol. Wt. 260.32
Solvent: Methanol KOH

λ Max. mμ	a_m	Cell mm	Conc. g/L
263	32400	0.5	0.100

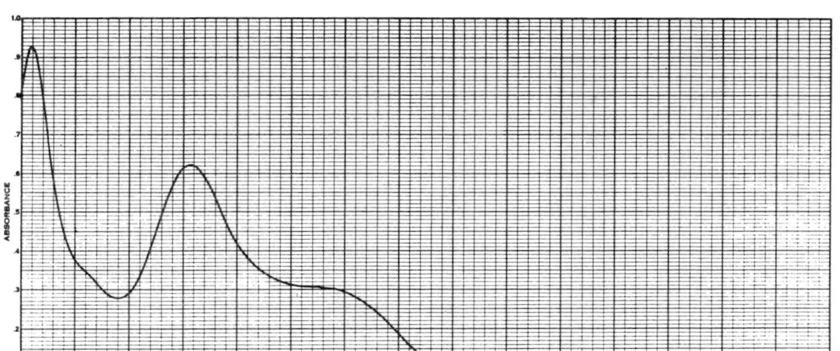

N^4-BENZYLIDENESULFANILAMIDE 1366

$C_{13}H_{12}N_2O_2S$
Mol. Wt. 260.32
Solvent: Methanol HCl

λ Max. mμ	a_m	Cell mm	Conc. g/L
249.5	7560	2	0.100
x	x	1	0.100

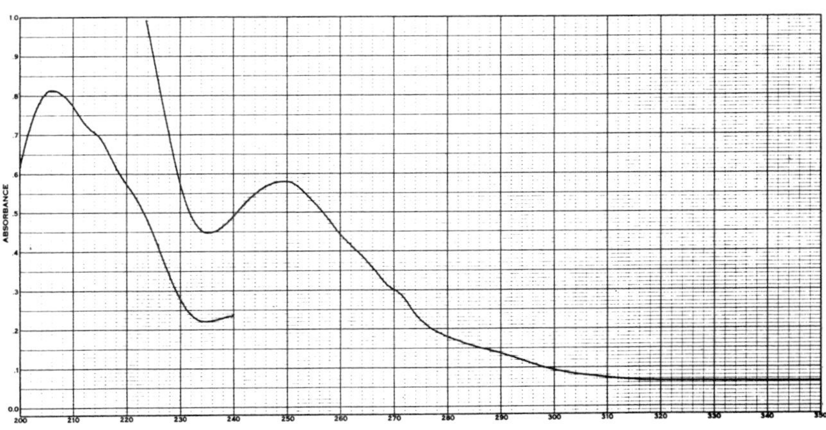

2-NAPHTHALENESULFONAMIDE

1367

$C_{10}H_9NO_2S$
Mol. Wt. 207.25
Solvent: Methanol

λ Max. mμ	a_m	Cell mm	Conc. g/L
323	827	10	0.100
313	605	10	0.100
308	701	10	0.100
275	4990	4	0.100
227	70500	0.5	0.050

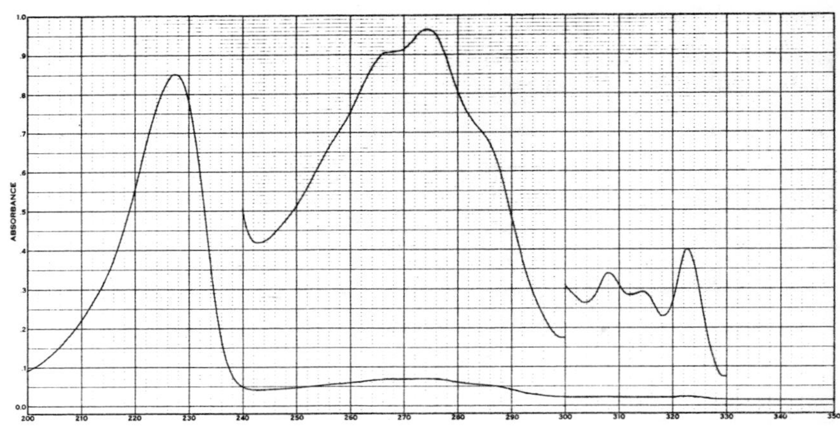

2-NAPHTHALENESULFONAMIDE

1367

$C_{10}H_9NO_2S$
Mol. Wt. 207.25
Solvent: Methanol KOH

λ Max. mμ	a_m	Cell mm	Conc. g/L
321	405	20	0.100
307	519	20	0.100
275	5620	2	0.100
265	5530	2	0.100
224.5	56800	0.5	0.050

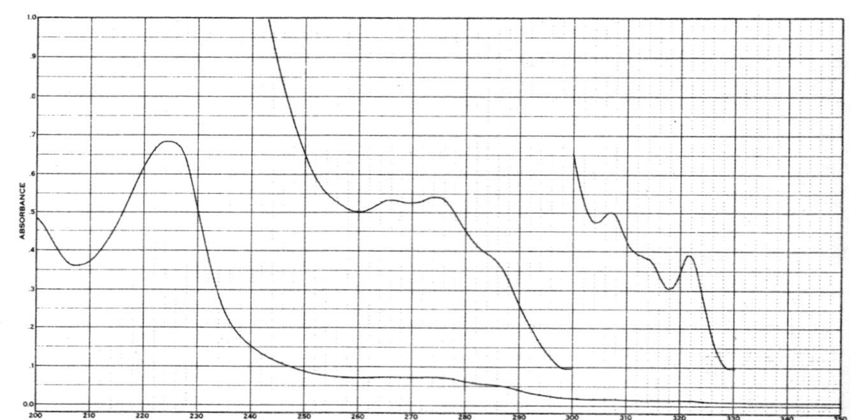

ETHANESULFONO-p-TOLUIDIDE

1368

$C_9H_{13}NO_2S$
Mol. Wt. 199.27
M.P. 81°C
Solvent: Methanol

λ Max. mμ	a_m	Cell mm	Conc. g/L
277.5	669	20	0.100
228	11600	1	0.100

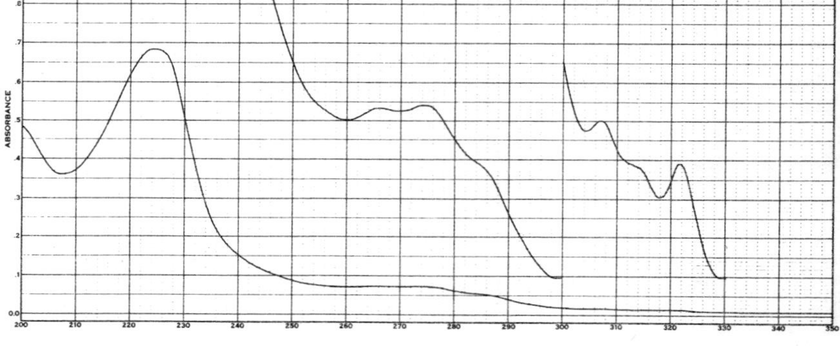

ETHANESULFONO-p-TOLUIDIDE 1368

$C_9H_{13}NO_2S$

Mol. Wt. 199.27

M.P. 81°C

Solvent: Methanol KOH

λ Max. mμ	a_m	Cell mm	Conc. g/L
287	1070	10	0.100
248	10900	1	0.100

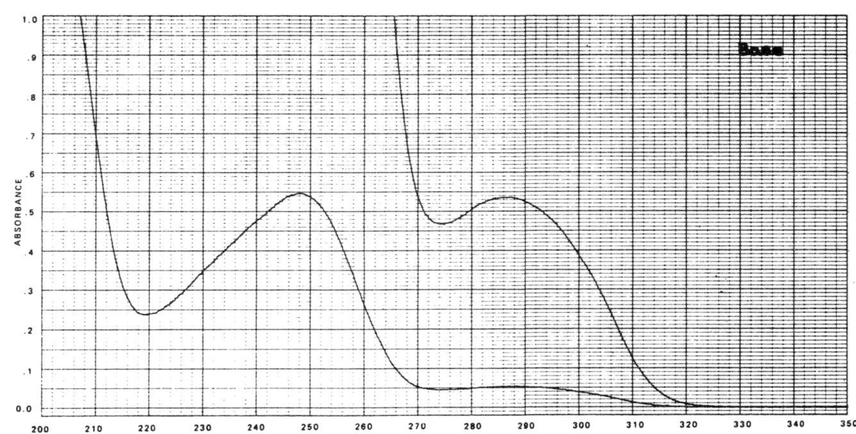

N-(2-HYDROXYETHYL)-N-(3-HYDROXYPROPYL)-p-TOLUENESULFONAMIDE 1369

$C_{12}H_{19}NO_4S$

Mol. Wt. 273.35

Solvent: Methanol

λ Max. mμ	a_m	Cell mm	Conc. g/L
231	12300	2	0.100

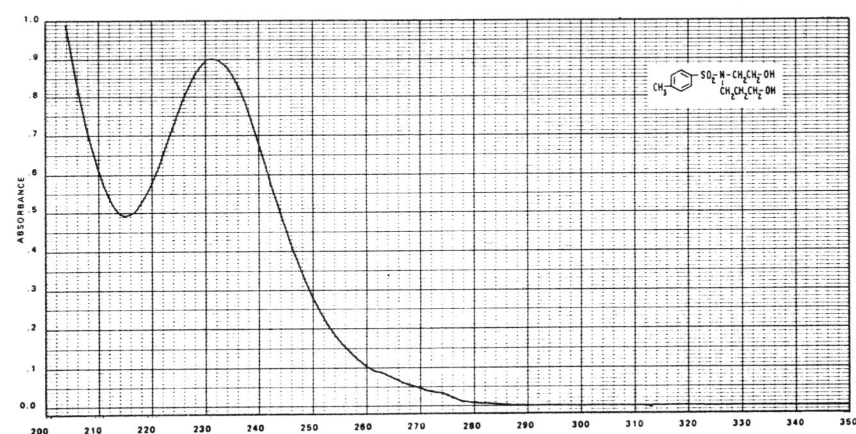

λ Max. mμ	a_m	Cell mm	Conc. g/L

p-TOLUENESULFONANILIDE 1370

$C_{13}H_{13}NO_2S$
Mol. Wt. 247.32
M.P. 100-101°C
Solvent: Methanol

λ Max. mμ	a_m	Cell mm	Conc. g/L
223.5	14700	1	0.100

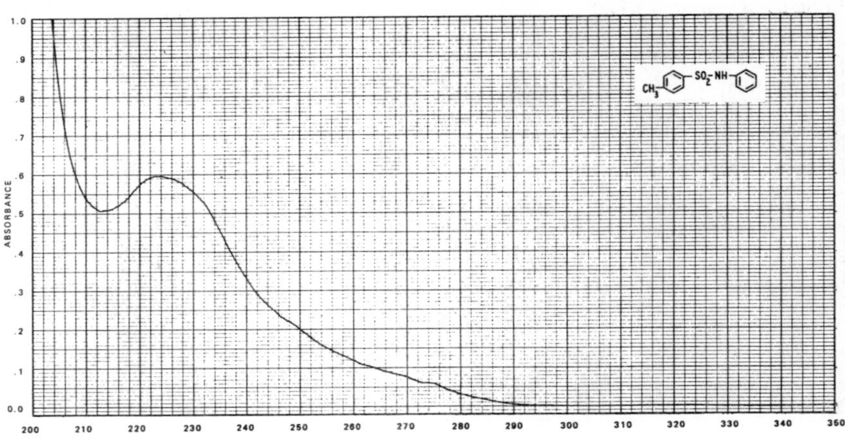

p-TOLUENESULFONANILIDE 1370

$C_{13}H_{13}NO_2S$
Mol. Wt. 247.32
M.P. 100-101°C
Solvent: Methanol KOH

λ Max. mμ	a_m	Cell mm	Conc. g/L
246	12300	1	0.100
222.5	13700	1	0.100

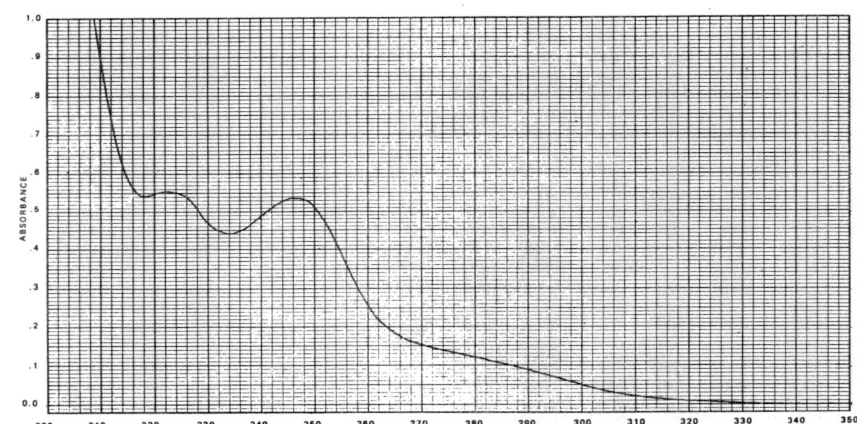

o-BENZENESULFONOTOLUIDIDE 1371

$C_{13}H_{13}NO_2S$
Mol. Wt. 247.32
Solvent: Methanol

λ Max. mμ	a_m	Cell mm	Conc. g/L
267	1200	10	0.100
260	1590	10	0.100
x	x	1	0.100

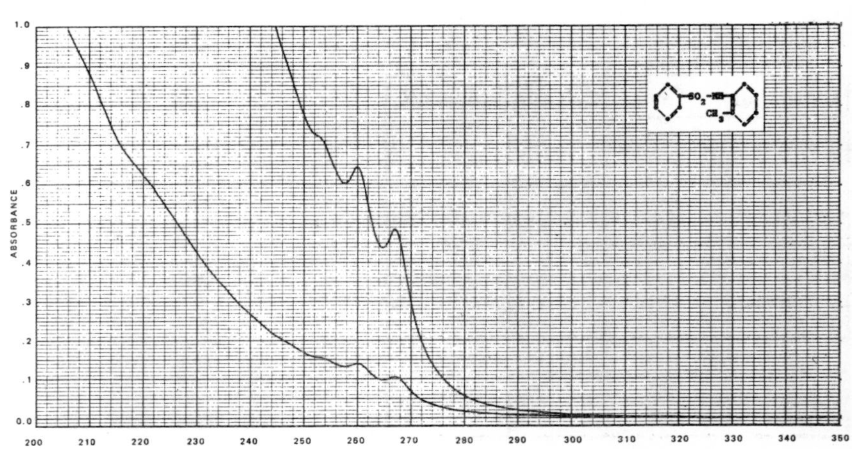

o-BENZENESULFONOTOLUIDIDE 1371

$C_{13}H_{13}NO_2S$
Mol. Wt. 247.32
Solvent: Methanol KOH

λ Max. mμ	$^a m$	Cell mm	Conc. g/L
238	16100	1	0.100

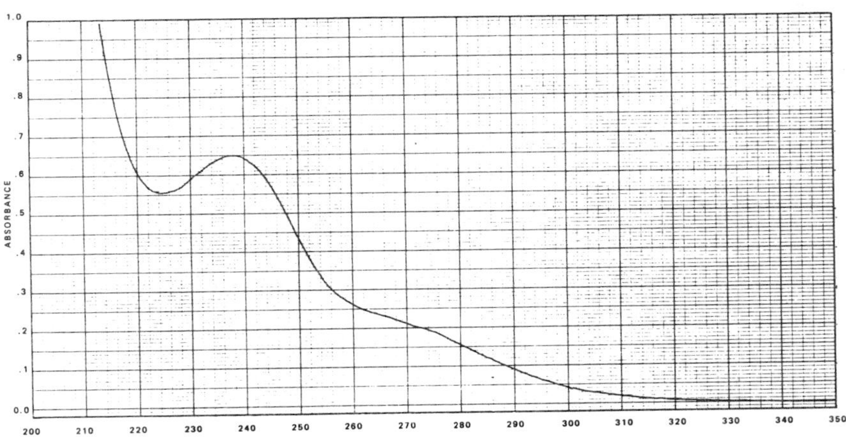

p-TOLUENESULFONO-2′,6′-XYLIDIDE 1372

$C_{15}H_{17}NO_2S$
Mol. Wt. 275.37
M.P. 137°C
Solvent: Methanol

λ Max. mμ	$^a m$	Cell mm	Conc. g/L
x	x	1	0.100

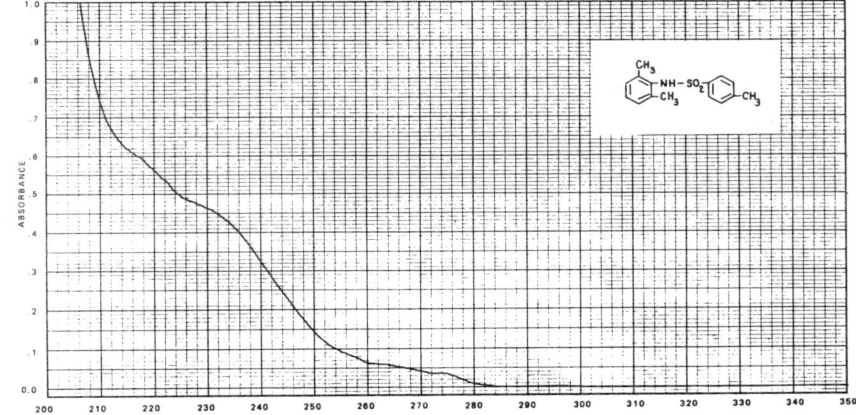

1373

λ Max. mμ	$^a m$	Cell mm	Conc. g/L

Compounds 1373 and 1374 do not display any maxima in the near UV.

N,N-DIMETHYL-p-TOLUENESULFONAMIDE 1375

$C_9H_{13}NO_2S$
Mol. Wt. 199.27
M.P. 80-82°C
Solvent: Methanol

λ Max. mμ	a_m	Cell mm	Conc. g/L
273	279	20	0.100
262	569	20	0.100
229	10900	1	0.100

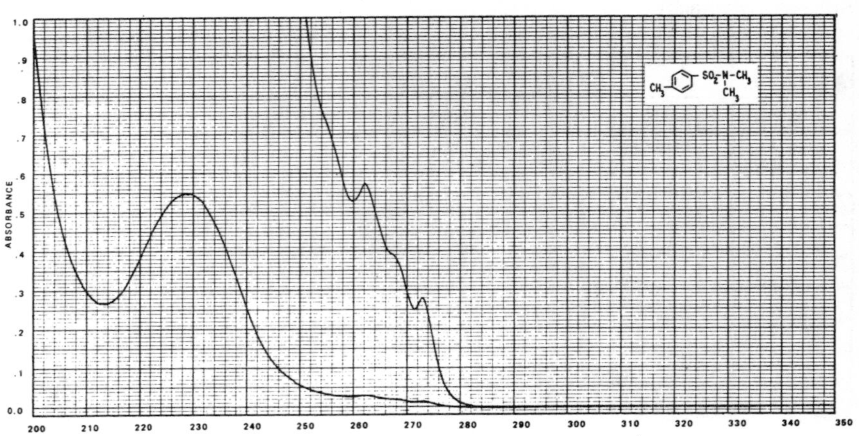

1,3-BIS(PHENYLSULFONYL)IMIDAZOLIDINE 1376

$C_{15}H_{16}N_2O_4S_2$
Mol. Wt. 352.43
Solvent: Methanol

λ Max. mμ	a_m	Cell mm	Conc. g/L
272	982	20	0.100
265.5	1230	20	0.100
259	999	20	0.100
223	13400	2	0.100

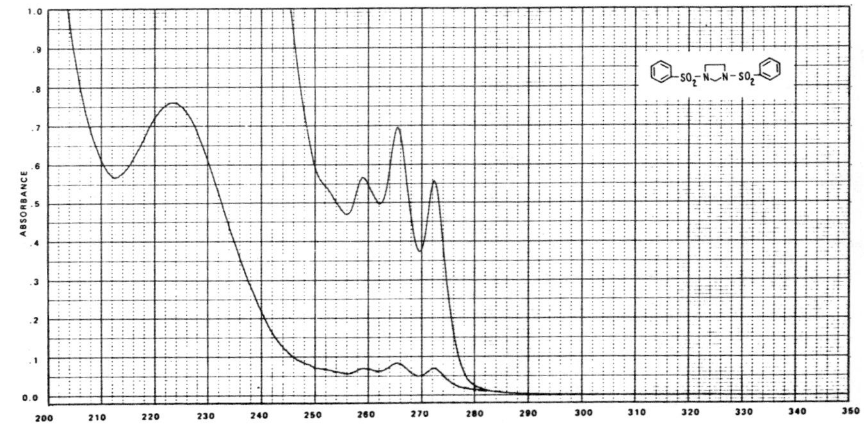

N,N′-DICYCLOHEXYLSULFAMIDE 1377

$C_{12}H_{24}N_2O_2S$
Mol. Wt. 260.40
M.P. 155-157°C

λ Max. mμ	a_m	Cell mm	Conc. g/L

This compound does not display any maxima in the near UV.

1378

4,4'-DIBROMOSULFANILIDE

$C_{12}H_{10}Br_2N_2O_2S$
Mol. Wt. 406.11
M.P. 122-123°C
Solvent: Methanol

λ Max. mμ	a_m	Cell mm	Conc. g/L
276	2010	20	0.100
240.5	25500	1	0.100

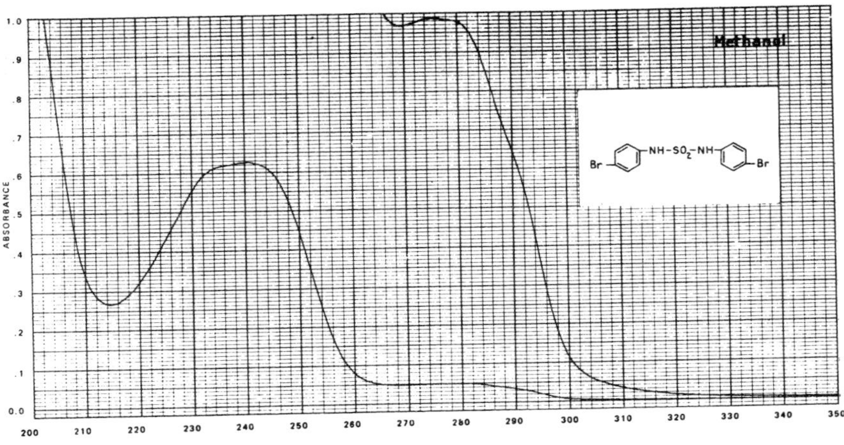

1378

4,4'-DIBROMOSULFANILIDE

$C_{12}H_{10}Br_2N_2O_2S$
Mol. Wt. 406.11
M.P. 122-123°C
Solvent: Methanol KOH

λ Max. mμ	a_m	Cell mm	Conc. g/L
253	27300	1	0.100

λ Max. mμ	a_m	Cell mm	Conc. g/L

NOTES

Aliphatic Compounds

The aliphatic and olefinic ethers do not produce any maxima in the near UV region, although very weak inflections may be detected at about 225 mμ. This lack of significant absorption has allowed the use of ethyl ether, tetrahydrofuran and 1,4-dioxane as solvents for the preparation of the spectra of other compounds in the near UV region of the spectrum.

Because of their lack of absorption, there are no spectra included in this chapter for compounds 1379 through 1446.

Aromatic Compounds

The benzyl ethers, whose structures contain an insulating carbon atom between the oxygen linkage and the phenyl group, produce UV absorption similar in appearance to that of toluene, i.e. a weak band at about 260 mμ with superimposed fine structure (242, 247, 252, 258, 264 and 267 mμ) and an unresolved shoulder near 215 mμ.

Compound	$\lambda_{max}(\epsilon_{max})$	Solvent	Spectrum
Benzyl methyl ether	258 (219)	Methanol	1479
Ethyl trityl ether	258 (875)	Methanol	1481
Benzyl ether	258 (393)	Cyclohexane	1482

For the phenyl ethers, in whose molecular structures the phenyl group is bonded directly to the oxygen atom, strong bathochromic and hypsochromic effects are observed. In addition, only two or three of the fine structure maxima are clearly resolved (266, 271 and 278 mμ). Neither the benzyl nor phenyl ethers undergo changes in their UV spectra upon the addition of acid or base.

The wavelength and intensity values for anisole, phenetole and several para substituted anisoles are listed in the table shown below.

Compound	$\lambda_{max}(\epsilon_{max})$	$\lambda_{max}(\epsilon_{max})$	Solvent	Spectrum
Anisole	220 (7940)	271 (1830)	Methanol	1488
Phenetole	220 (6400)	271 (1440)	Methanol	1489
p-Methylanisole	222 (8540)	278 (1850)	Methanol	1496
p-Chloroanisole	227 (11200)	280 (1660)	Methanol	1511
p-Bromoanisole	226 (14200)	280 (1580)	Methanol	1516
p-Iodoanisole	233 (18500)	280 (1450)	Methanol	1521
1,4-Dimethoxybenzene	225 (9670)	289 (3080)	Methanol	1547

(EPOXYETHYL)BENZENE 1447

C_8H_8O

Mol. Wt. 120.15

Solvent: Cyclohexane

λ Max. mμ	a_m	Cell mm	Conc. g/L
x	x	10	2.23
267	162	10	0.670
260.5	222	10	0.670
255	186	10	0.670
250.5	158	10	0.670
x	x	10	0.0670

1448

λ Max. mμ	a_m	Cell mm	Conc. g/L

The alicyclic ethers (compounds 1448 through 1452) do not display any maxima in the near UV.

6,6a-DIHYDRO-1aH-OXIRENO[a] INDENE 1453

C_9H_8O

Mol. Wt. 132.16

B.P. 98°C/6mm

Solvent: Methanol

λ Max. mμ	a_m	Cell mm	Conc. g/L
266	637	10	0.179
260	701	10	0.179
253	576	10	0.179
246	527	10	0.179

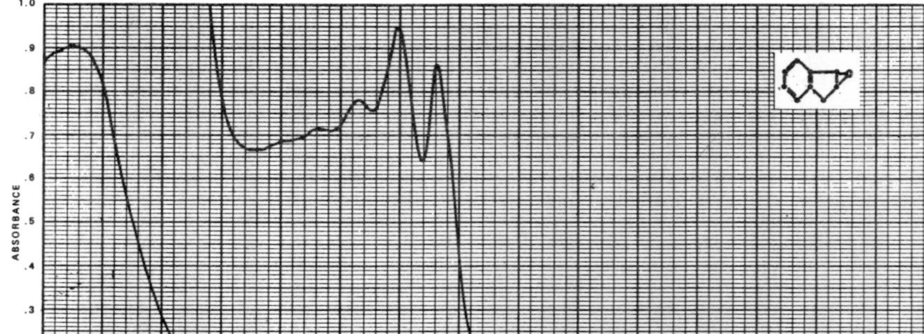

1454

λ Max. mμ	a_m	Cell mm	Conc. g/L

The alicyclic ethers (compounds 1454 through 1467) do not display any maxima in the near UV.

4-m-TOLYLMORPHOLINE 1468

$C_{11}H_{15}NO$

Mol. Wt. 177.25

M.P. 31-36°C

Solvent: Methanol

λ Max. mμ	a_m	Cell mm	Conc. g/L
285	3440	10	0.050
249.5	24400	1	0.050

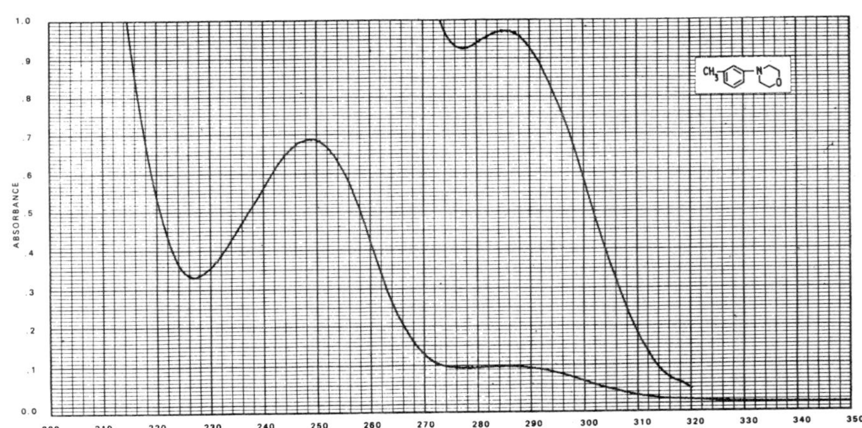

4-m-TOLYLMORPHOLINE 1468

$C_{11}H_{15}NO$

Mol. Wt. 177.25

M.P. 31-36°C

Solvent: Methanol HCl

λ Max. mμ	a_m	Cell mm	Conc. g/L
321	322	10	0.050
268.5	3130	10	0.050
262	3520	10	0.050
258	3220	10	0.050
243	3010	10	0.050

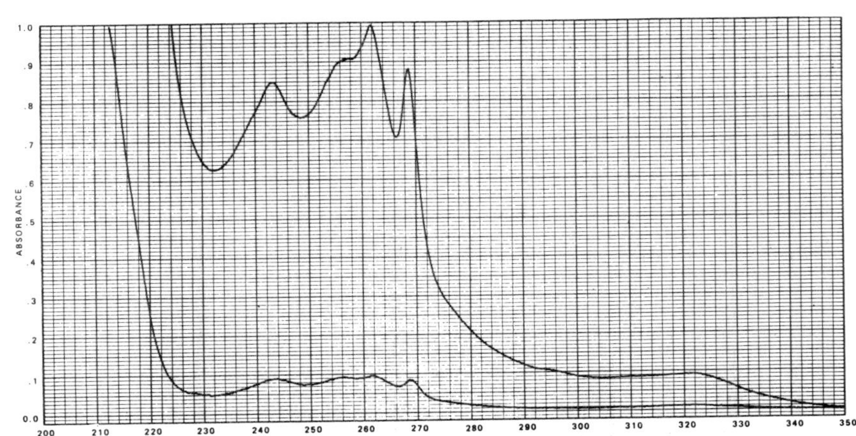

1469

λ Max. mμ	a_m	Cell mm	Conc. g/L

The alicyclic ethers (compounds 1469 through 1478) do not display any maxima in the near UV.

BENZYL METHYL ETHER

1479

$C_8H_{10}O$
Mol. Wt. 122.17
B.P. 58-60°C/10mm
Solvent: Methanol

λ Max. mμ	a_m	Cell mm	Conc. g/L
267	106	10	0.2230
263.5	161	10	0.2230
257.5	219	10	0.2230
251.5	221	10	0.2230
248	203	10	0.2230

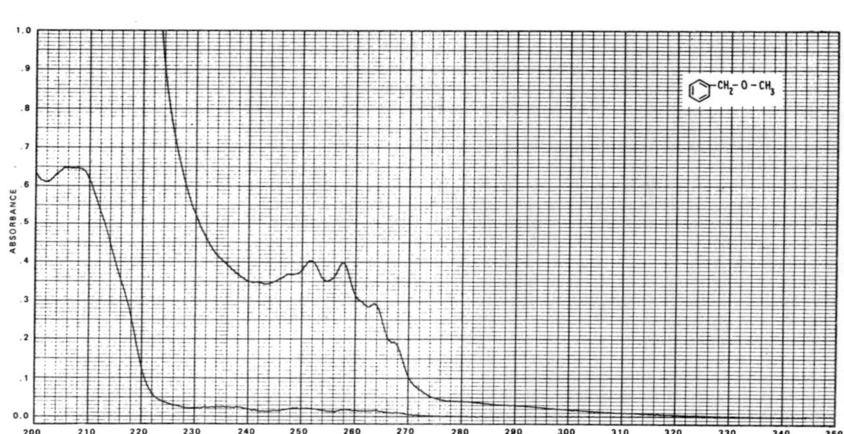

4-ETHOXY-4-PHENYLBUTYRONITRILE

1480

$C_{12}H_{15}NO$
Mol. Wt. 189.26
Solvent: Methanol

λ Max. mμ	a_m	Cell mm	Conc. g/L
263	399	5	0.453
257	531	5	0.453
251	545	5	0.453
247	508	5	0.453
206	9120	1	0.181

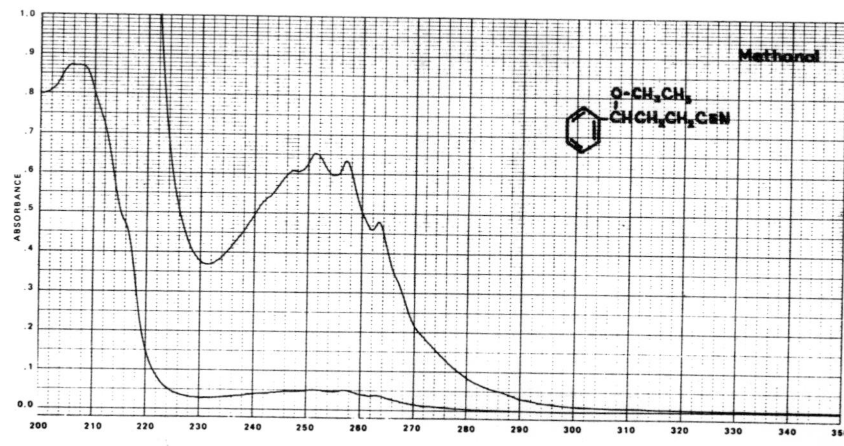

ETHYL TRITYL ETHER

1481

$C_{21}H_{20}O$

Mol. Wt. 288.39

M.P. 83°C (lit.)

Solvent: Methanol

λ Max. mμ	a_m	Cell mm	Conc. g/L
267.5	554	20	0.100
258	875	20	0.100
253.5	829	20	0.100
x	x	1	0.100

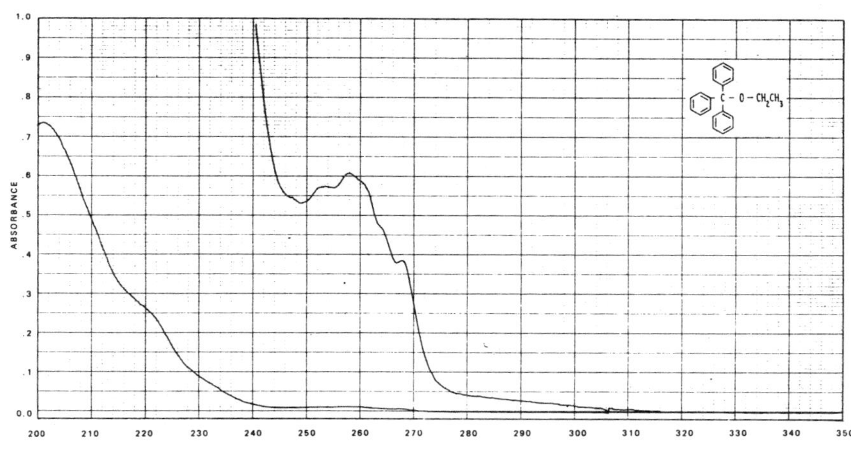

BENZYL ETHER

1482

$C_{14}H_{14}O$

Mol. Wt. 198.27

M.R. 1.5-3.5°C (lit.)

Solvent: Cyclohexane

λ Max. mμ	a_m	Cell mm	Conc. g/L
x	x	10	2.37
264	312	10	0.711
258	393	10	0.711
252	353	10	0.711
x	x	10	0.035

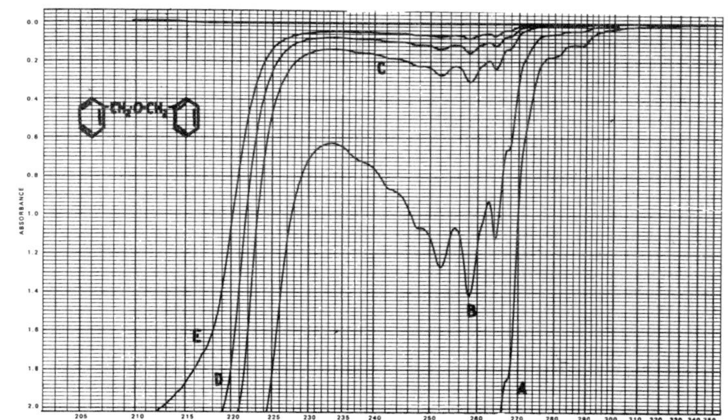

BIS(α-METHYLBENZYL)ETHER

1483

$C_{16}H_{18}O$

Mol. Wt. 226.32

Solvent: Methanol

λ Max. mμ	a_m	Cell mm	Conc. g/L
266.5	248	10	0.392
263.5	468	10	0.392
257	518	10	0.392
251.5	168	10	0.392
247	428	10	0.392
242	389	10	0.392
207	16700	10	0.0098

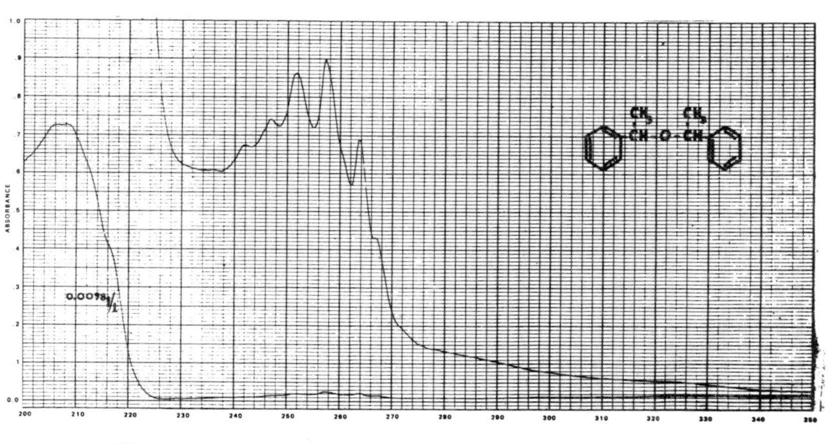

METHYL PHENETHYL ETHER 1484

$C_9H_{12}O$

Mol. Wt. 136.20

B.P. 195°C/760mm

Solvent: Methanol

λ Max. mμ	a_m	Cell mm	Conc. g/L
265.5	122	40	0.100
256.5	194	40	0.100
251	175	40	0.100
x	x	1	0.100

ACETALDEHYDE, DIPHENETHYL ACETAL 1485

$C_{18}H_{22}O_2$

Mol. Wt. 270.37

Solvent: Methanol

λ Max. mμ	a_m	Cell mm	Conc. g/L
267.5	276	10	0.542
264	329	10	0.542
260.5	372	10	0.542
258	422	10	0.542
252.5	385	10	0.542
247.5	284	10	0.542
207.5	15900	10	0.0136

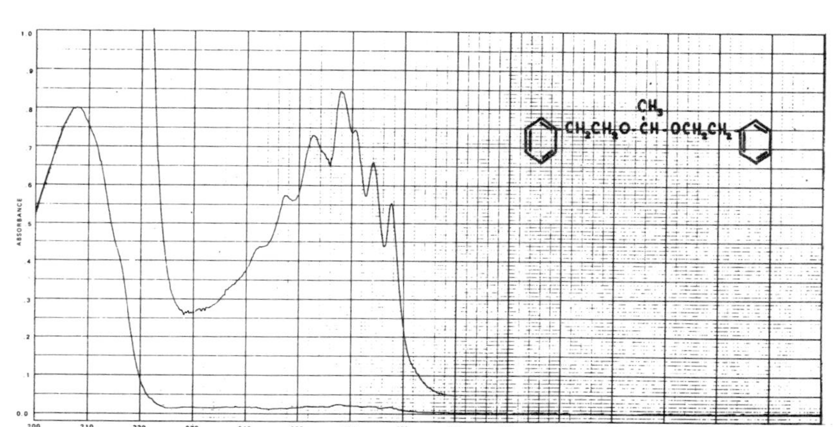

DIMETHOXYDIPHENYLMETHANE 1486

$C_{15}H_{16}O_2$

Mol. Wt. 228.29

M.P. 105-107°C

Solvent: Methanol

λ Max. mμ	a_m	Cell mm	Conc. g/L
245.5	4260	5	0.100
x	x	1	0.100

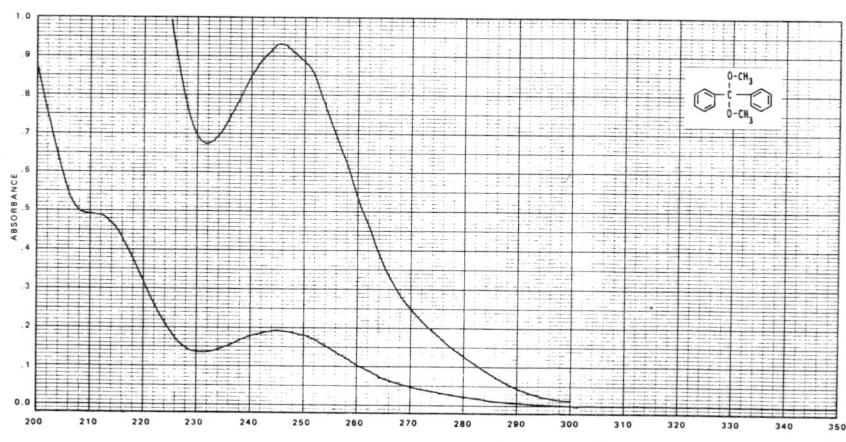

ORTHOBENZOIC ACID, TRIMETHYL ESTER 1487

$C_{10}H_{14}O_3$
Mol. Wt. 182.22
Solvent: Methanol

λ Max. mμ	a_m	Cell mm	Conc. g/L
280	54	10	0.422
267	234	10	0.422
263	252	10	0.422
260.5	283	10	0.422
256.5	267	10	0.422

ANISOLE 1488

C_7H_8O
Mol. Wt. 108.13
Solvent: Methanol

λ Max. mμ	a_m	Cell mm	Conc. g/L
x	x	10	2.07
277.5	1570	10	0.104
270.5	1830	10	0.104
x	x	10	0.0207

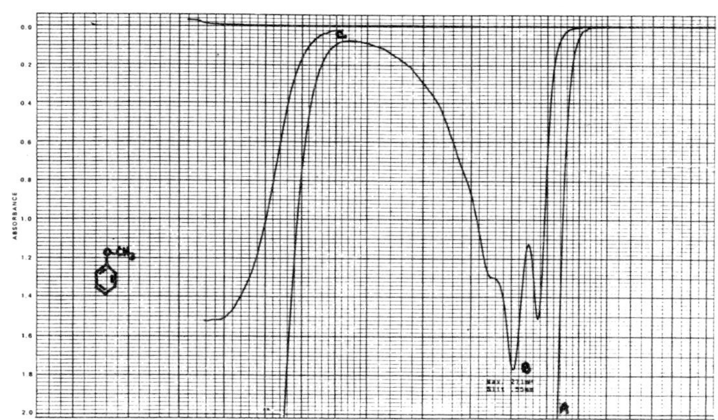

PHENETOLE 1489

$C_8H_{10}O$
Mol. Wt. 122.17
Solvent: Methanol

λ Max. mμ	a_m	Cell mm	Conc. g/L
277.5	1190	5	0.140
271	1440	5	0.140
220	6400	1	0.140

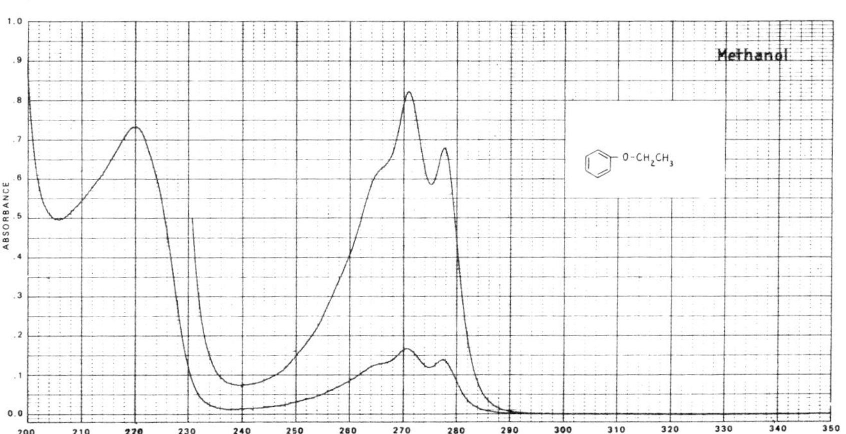

PHENYL PROPYL ETHER 1490

$C_9H_{12}O$

Mol. Wt. 136.20

B.P. 96-97°C/35mm

Solvent: Methanol

λ Max. mμ	$^a m$	Cell mm	Conc. g/L
278.5	4740	1	0.0500
271.5	5670	1	0.0500
220.5	25900	1	0.0500

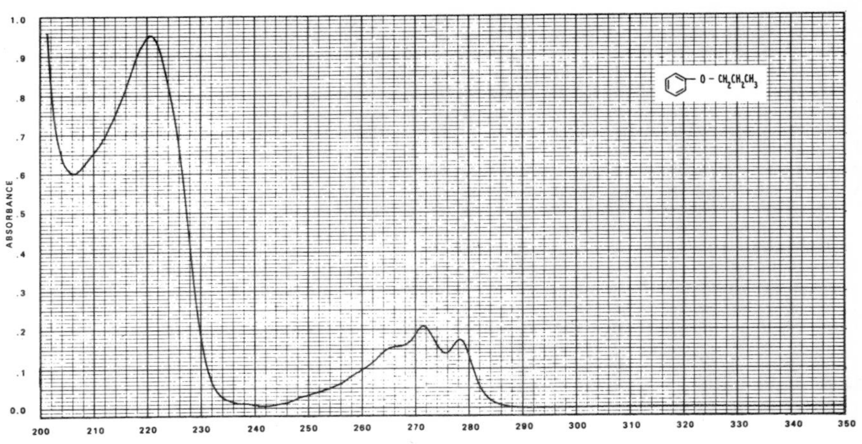

β-BROMOPHENETOLE 1491

C_8H_9BrO

Mol. Wt. 201.07

M.P. 30-31°C B.P. 117-122°C/11mm

Solvent: Methanol

λ Max. mμ	$^a m$	Cell mm	Conc. g/L
276.5	1290	10	0.100
270	1570	10	0.100
264.5	1170	10	0.100
219	16900	1	0.100

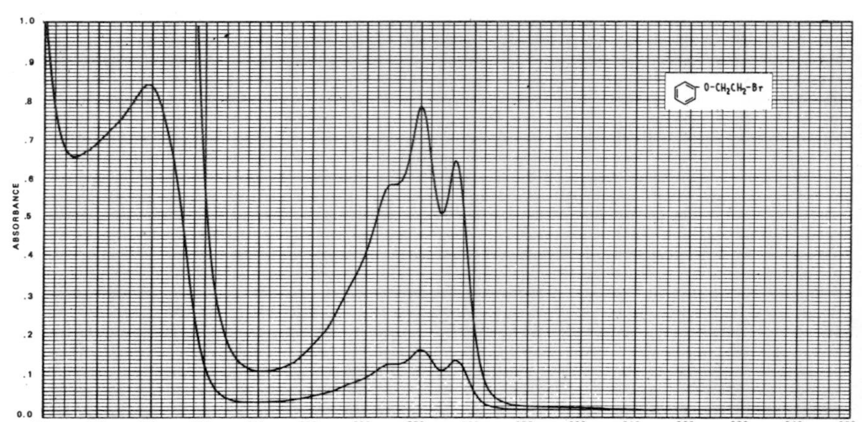

(2-METHOXYETHOXY)BENZENE 1492

$C_9H_{12}O_2$

Mol. Wt. 152.20

B.P. 219°C

Solvent: Methanol

λ Max. mμ	$^a m$	Cell mm	Conc. g/L
277	2270	5	0.0620
270.5	2700	5	0.0620
219	12500	1	0.0620

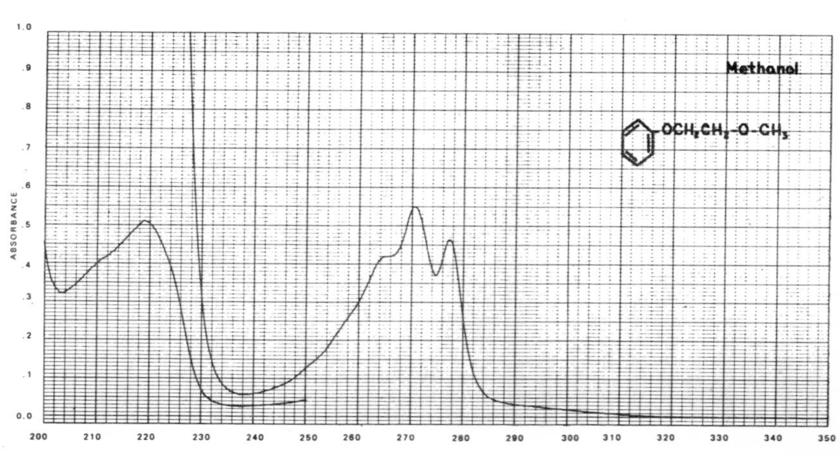

ORTHOFORMIC ACID, DIETHYL PHENYL ESTER 1493

$C_{11}H_{16}O_3$
Mol. Wt. 196.25
B.P. 103-104.5°C/10mm
Solvent: Methanol

λ Max. mμ	a_m	Cell mm	Conc. g/L
273	1640	10	0.100
267.5	1570	10	0.100
211.5	7750	2	0.100

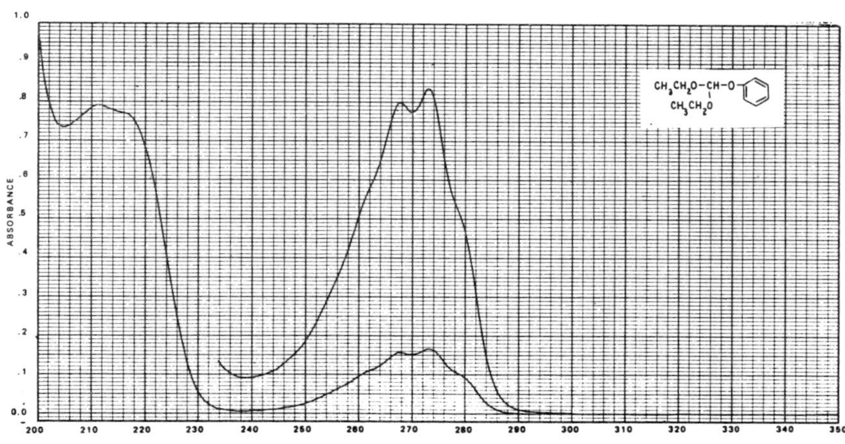

o-METHYLANISOLE 1494

$C_8H_{10}O$
Mol. Wt. 122.17
B.P. 170-172°C
Solvent: Methanol

λ Max. mμ	a_m	Cell mm	Conc. g/L
278	1620	5	0.0980
271.5	1750	5	0.0980
216	6270	1	0.0980

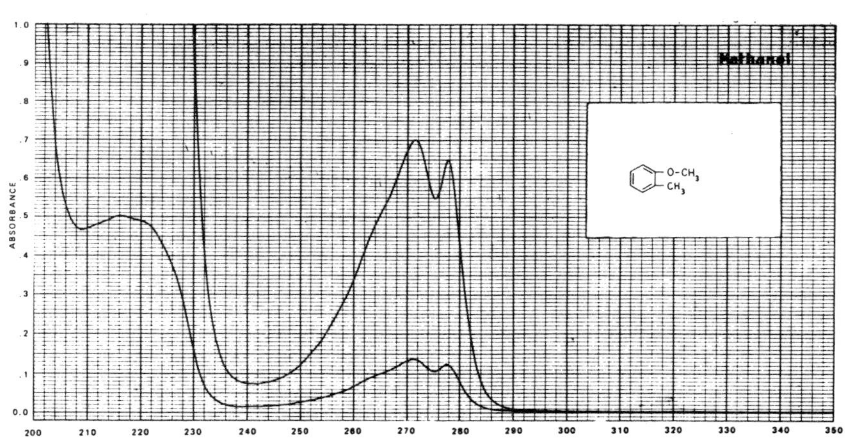

m-METHYLANISOLE 1495

$C_8H_{10}O$
Mol. Wt. 122.17
B.P. 102-103°C/100mm
Solvent: Methanol

λ Max. mμ	a_m	Cell mm	Conc. g/L
279	1430	2	0.228
272	1510	2	0.228
216.5	6590	2	0.0456

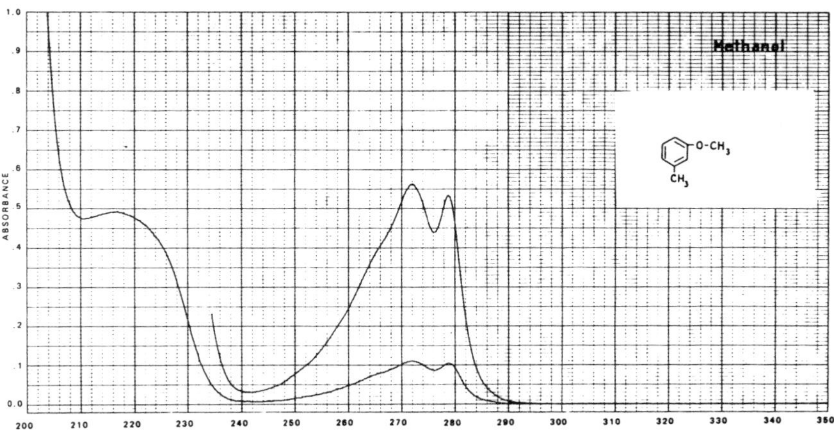

p-METHYLANISOLE

1496

$C_8H_{10}O$
Mol. Wt. 122.16
Solvent: Methanol

λ Max. mμ	a_m	Cell mm	Conc. g/L
x	x	10	1.66
284.5	1540	10	0.0830
278	1850	10	0.0830
x	x	10	0.0083

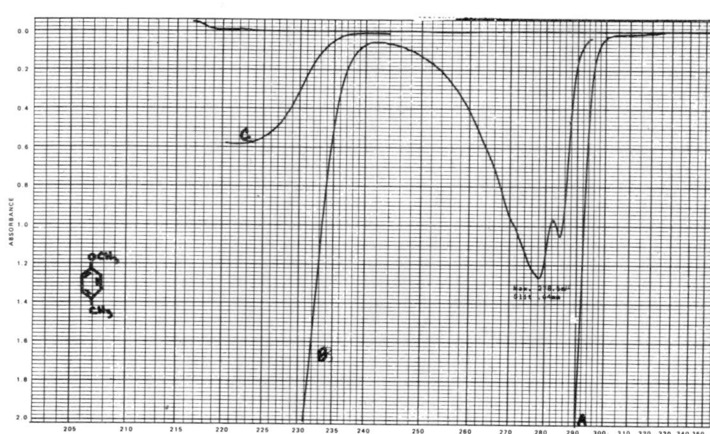

p-ETHYLANISOLE

1497

$C_9H_{12}O$
Mol. Wt. 136.20
Solvent: Methanol

λ Max. mμ	a_m	Cell mm	Conc. g/L
283	1570	5	0.103
276.5	1930	5	0.103
223.5	10100	1	0.103

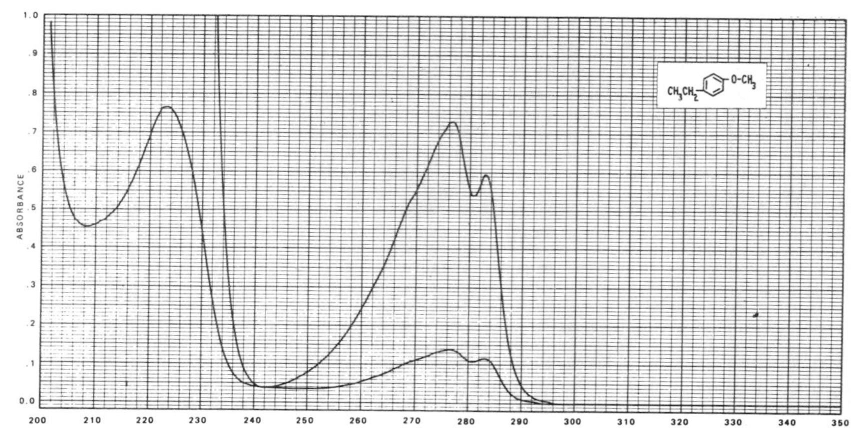

o-METHYLPHENETOLE

1498

$C_9H_{12}O$
Mol. Wt. 136.19
B.P. 55-56°C/5mm
Solvent: Methanol

λ Max. mμ	a_m	Cell mm	Conc. g/L
277.5	1430	2	0.238
271.5	1580	2	0.238
215.5	6670	2	0.0476

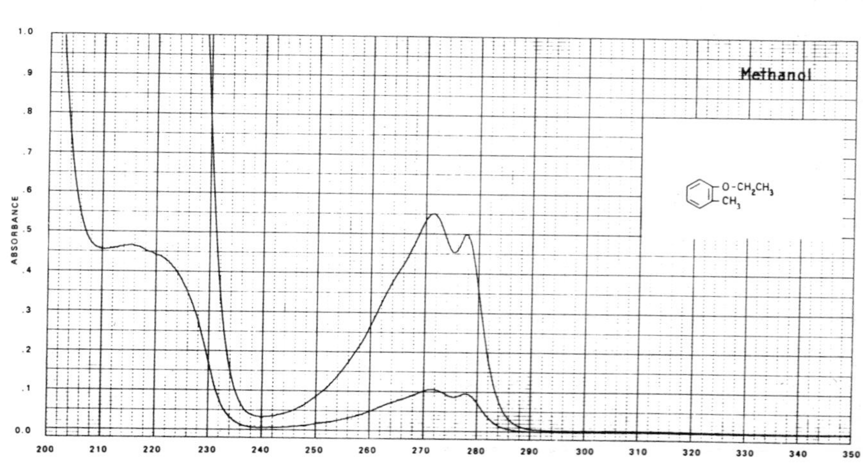

m-METHYLPHENETOLE

1499

$C_9H_{12}O$

Mol. Wt. 136.19

B.R. 63-64°C/5mm (lit.)

Solvent: Cyclohexane

λ Max. mμ	a_m	Cell mm	Conc. g/L
x	x	10	1.66
280	1560	10	0.133
273	1538	10	0.133
216	6550	10	0.0266

p-METHYLPHENETOLE

1500

$C_9H_{12}O$

Mol. Wt. 136.20

B.P. 63-64°C/10mm (lit.)

Solvent: Cyclohexane

λ Max. mμ	a_m	Cell mm	Conc. g/L
286	1810	10	0.1203
279.5	1930	10	0.1203
224.5	8170	10	0.0241

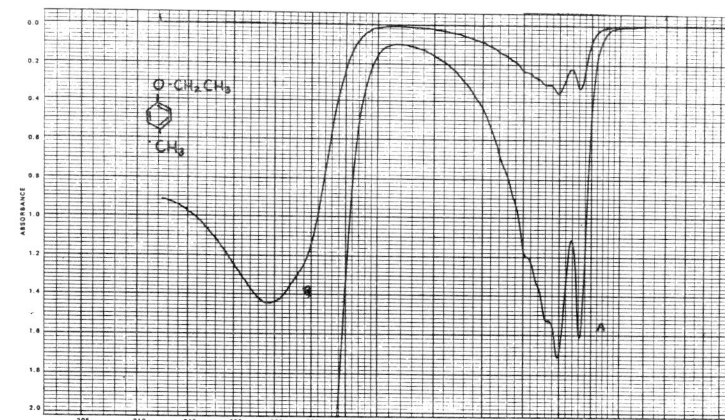

p-PROPYLANISOLE

1501

$C_{10}H_{14}O$

Mol. Wt. 150.22

B.P. 67°C/2mm

Solvent: Methanol

λ Max. mμ	a_m	Cell mm	Conc. g/L
284	1520	5	0.1335
277	1820	5	0.1335
224	9110	1	0.1335

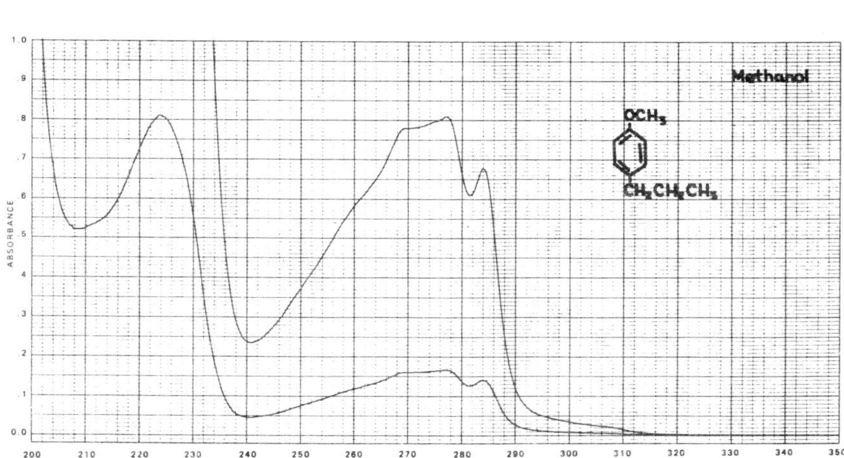

4-CHLOROBUTYL m-TOLYL ETHER

1502

$C_{11}H_{15}ClO$
Mol. Wt. 198.69
Solvent: Methanol

λ Max. mμ	a_m	Cell mm	Conc. g/L
274	1520	2	0.450
267	1640	2	0.450
213	7230	1	0.225

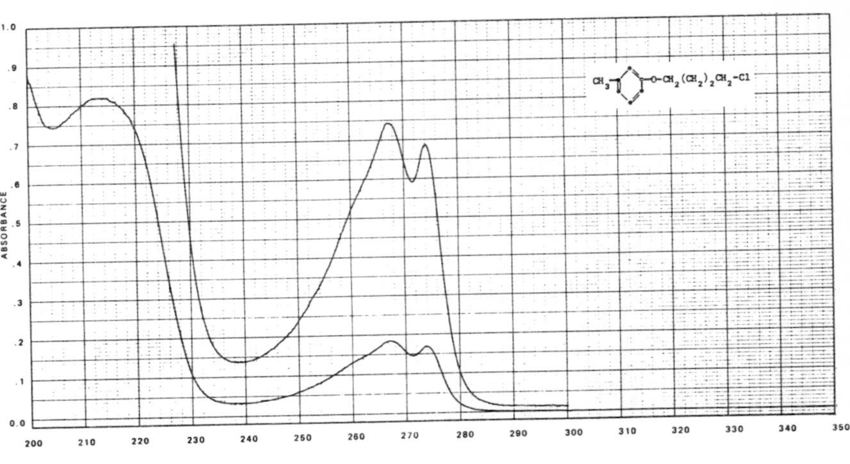

p-(2-BROMOETHYL)ANISOLE

1503

$C_9H_{11}BrO$
Mol. Wt. 215.10
Solvent: Methanol

λ Max. mμ	a_m	Cell mm	Conc. g/L
282	2060	5	0.100
275.5	2460	5	0.100
226.5	16000	1	0.100

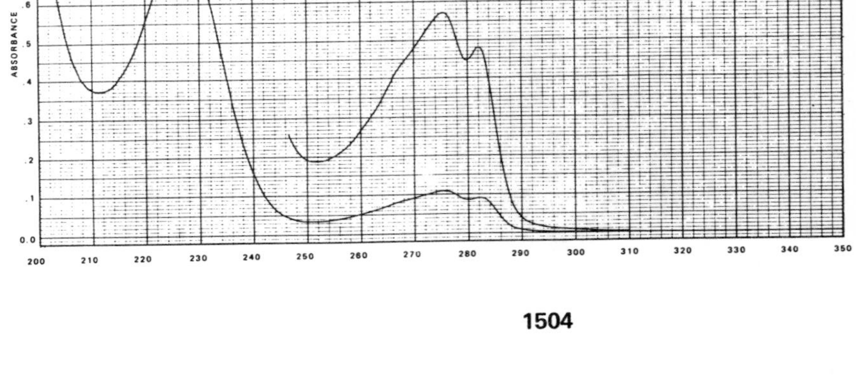

o-METHOXYBENZYLAMINE

1504

$C_8H_{11}NO$
Mol. Wt. 137.18
Solvent: Methanol

λ Max. mμ	a_m	Cell mm	Conc. g/L
306	198	20	0.194
276	1810	1	0.194
271	1970	1	0.194
217	6880	1	0.194

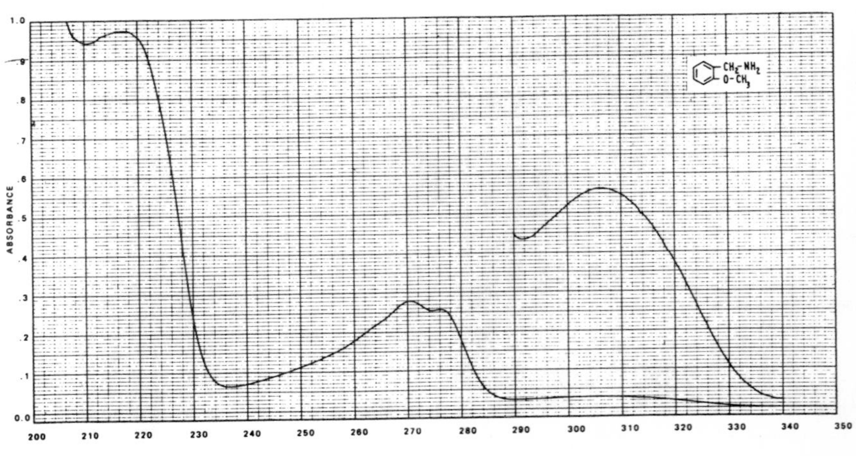

m-METHOXYBENZYLAMINE 1505

$C_8H_{11}NO$

Mol. Wt. 137.18

Solvent: Methanol

λ Max. mμ	a_m	Cell mm	Conc. g/L
280.5	1640	10	0.068
273	1790	10	0.068
217	7670	2	0.068

p-PROPENYLANISOLE 1506

$C_{10}H_{12}O$

Mol. Wt. 148.21

M.P. 22.5°C B.P. 235.3°C (lit.)

Solvent: Cyclohexane

λ Max. mμ	a_m	Cell mm	Conc. g/L
x	x	10	1.572
259	2110	10	0.0943

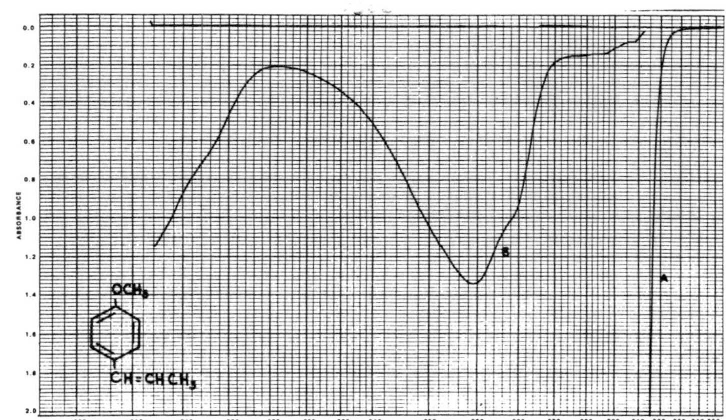

o-PHENYLANISOLE 1507

$C_{13}H_{12}O$

Mol. Wt. 184.24

M.P. 28-30°C

Solvent: Methanol

λ Max. mμ	a_m	Cell mm	Conc. g/L
283.5	4540	1	0.127
246	11100	1	0.127

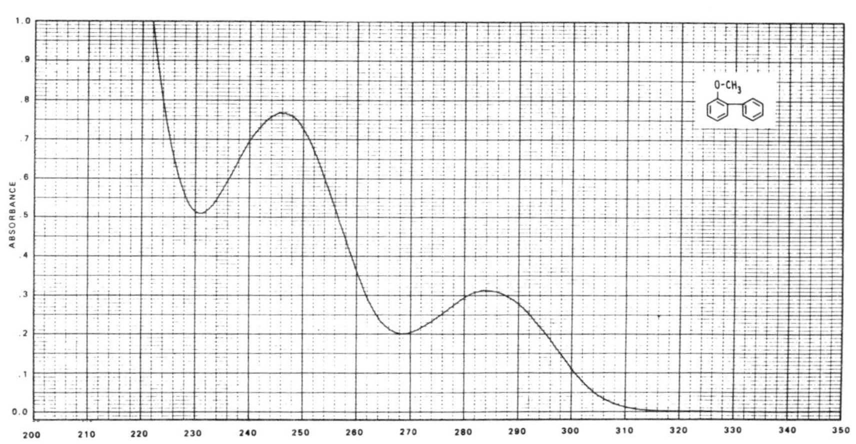

p-PHENYLANISOLE 1508

$C_{13}H_{12}O$

Mol. Wt. 184.24

Solvent: Methanol

λ Max. mμ	a_m	Cell mm	Conc. g/L
323	768	20	0.100
309	691	20	0.100
260	16700	1	0.100

o-CHLOROANISOLE 1509

C_7H_7ClO

Mol. Wt. 142.58

B.P. 199.5-200°C (lit.)

Solvent: Cyclohexane

λ Max. mμ	a_m	Cell mm	Conc. g/L
x	x	10	1.96
282.5	2750	10	0.0784
274.5	2590	10	0.0784
223	8010	10	0.0235
218	8130	10	0.0235

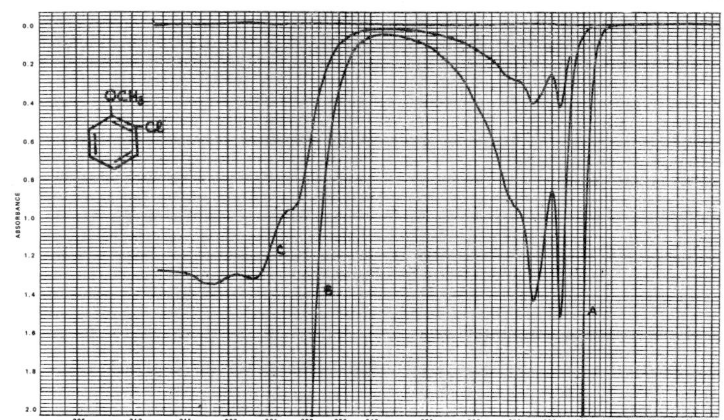

m-CHLOROANISOLE 1510

C_7H_7ClO

Mol. Wt. 142.59

B.P. 193°C

Solvent: Methanol

λ Max. mμ	a_m	Cell mm	Conc. g/L
282	1830	5	0.1252
274.5	1980	5	0.1252
219.5	6810	1	0.1252

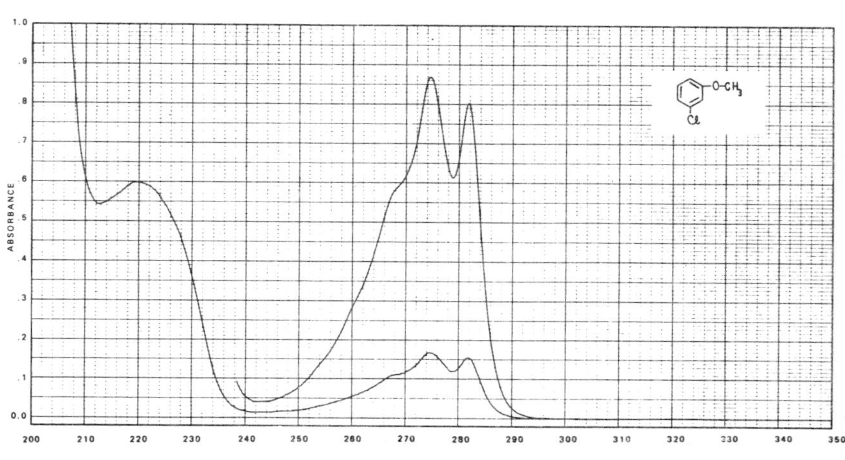

p-CHLOROANISOLE 1511

C_7H_7ClO

Mol. Wt. 142.59

B.P. 198°C

Solvent: Methanol

λ Max. mμ	a_m	Cell mm	Conc. g/L
288	1360	2	0.258
280.5	1660	2	0.258
227	11200	2	0.0516

o-CHLOROPHENETOLE 1512

C_8H_9ClO

Mol. Wt. 156.61

B.P. 82-83°C/10mm

Solvent: Methanol

λ Max. mμ	a_m	Cell mm	Conc. g/L
281.5	1850	1	0.159
274.5	2090	1	0.159
218.5	7250	1	0.159

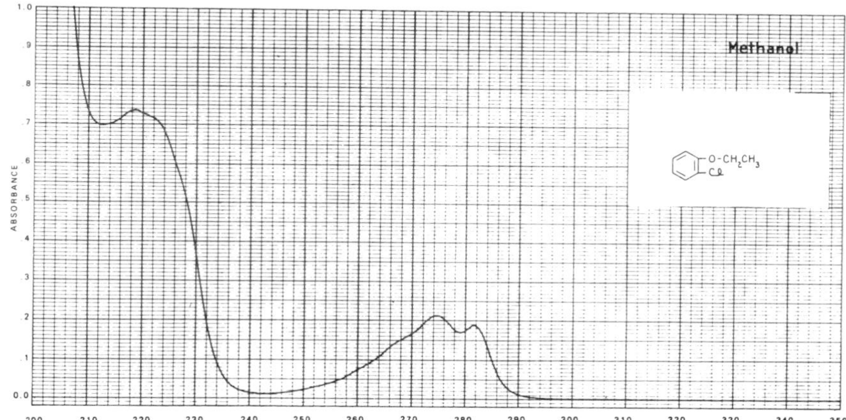

p-CHLOROPHENETOLE 1513

C_8H_9ClO

Mol. Wt. 156.61

B.P. 84-86°C/10mm

Solvent: Methanol

λ Max. mμ	a_m	Cell mm	Conc. g/L
288	2770	2	0.100
280.5	3430	2	0.100
228.5	25200	1	0.0500

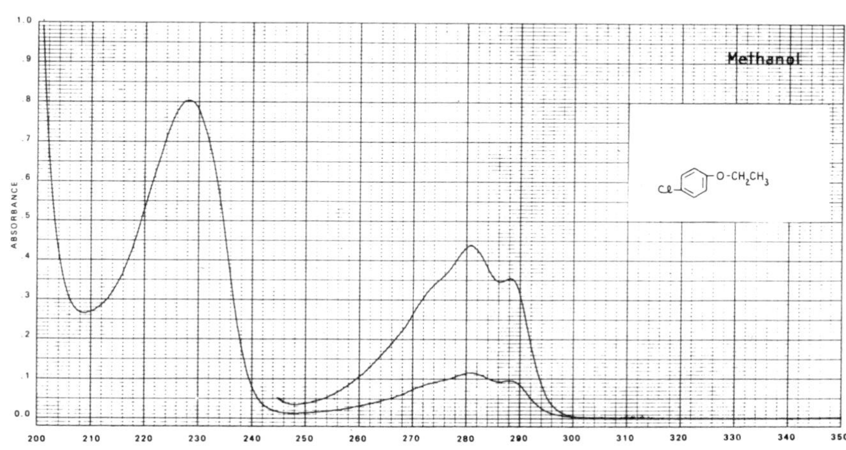

o-BROMOANISOLE

1514

C_7H_7BrO

Mol. Wt. 187.04

M.P. 2-4°C

Solvent: Methanol

λ Max. mμ	a_m	Cell mm	Conc. g/L
282.5	2260	1	0.6210
275	2470	1	0.6210
x	x	1	0.1240

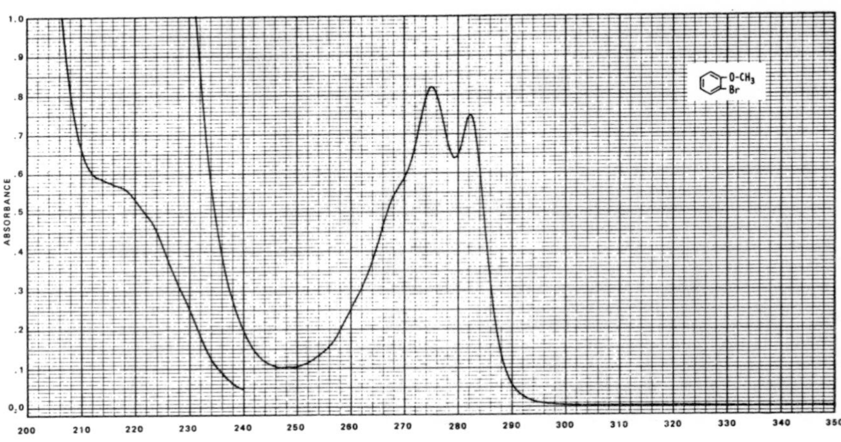

m-BROMOANISOLE

1515

C_7H_7BrO

Mol. Wt. 187.04

Solvent: Methanol

λ Max. mμ	a_m	Cell mm	Conc. g/L
282.5	2040	5	0.0860
275	2240	5	0.0860
x	x	1	0.0860

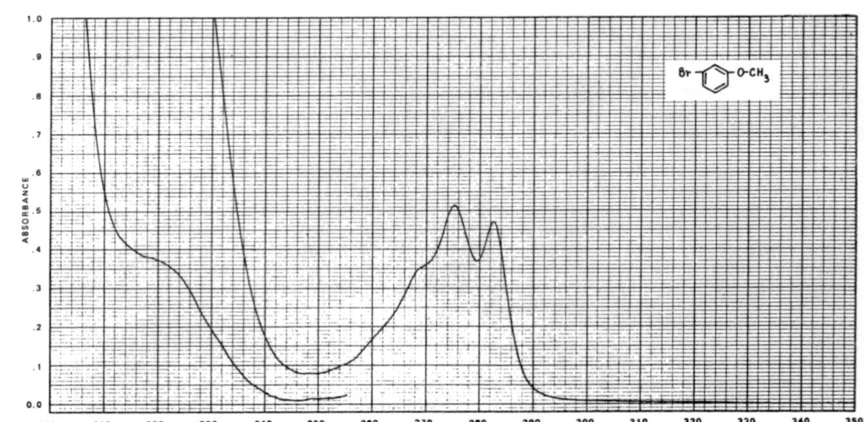

p-BROMOANISOLE

1516

C_7H_7BrO

Mol. Wt. 187.04

M.P. 12-13°C

Solvent: Methanol

λ Max. mμ	a_m	Cell mm	Conc. g/L
288	1280	2	0.367
280.5	1580	2	0.367
226.5	14200	1	0.0733

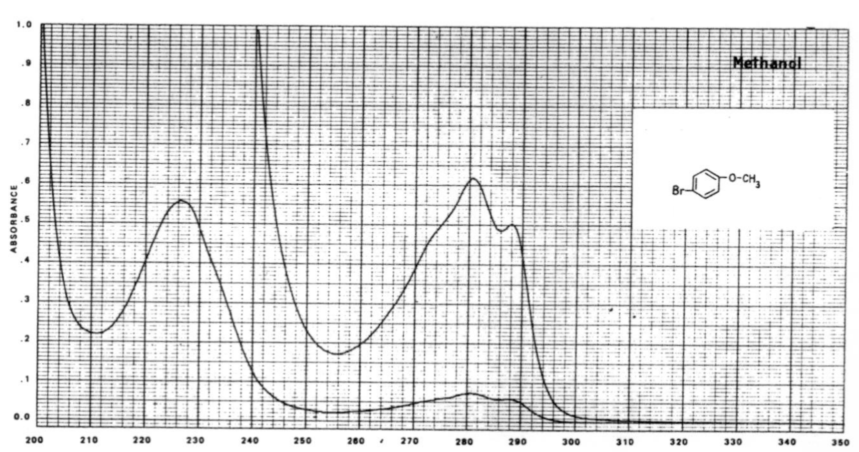

o-BROMOPHENETOLE 1517

C_8H_7BrO

Mol. Wt. 201.07

B.P. 122-125°C/22mm

Solvent: Methanol

λ Max. mμ	a_m	Cell mm	Conc. g/L
282.5	2990	4	0.100
275.5	3360	4	0.100
x	x	1	0.100

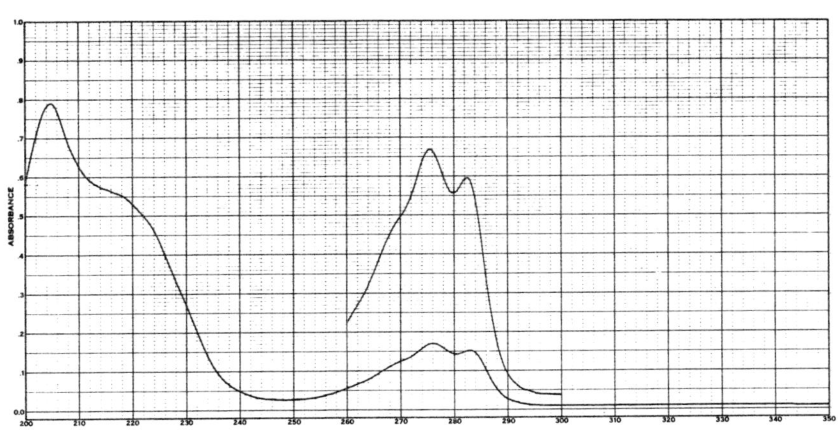

p-BROMOPHENETOLE 1518

C_8H_9BrO

Mol. Wt. 201.08

B.P. 73-74°C/3mm

Solvent: Methanol

λ Max. mμ	a_m	Cell mm	Conc. g/L
288	1080	2	0.428
281	1330	2	0.428
227.5	11200	2	0.0428

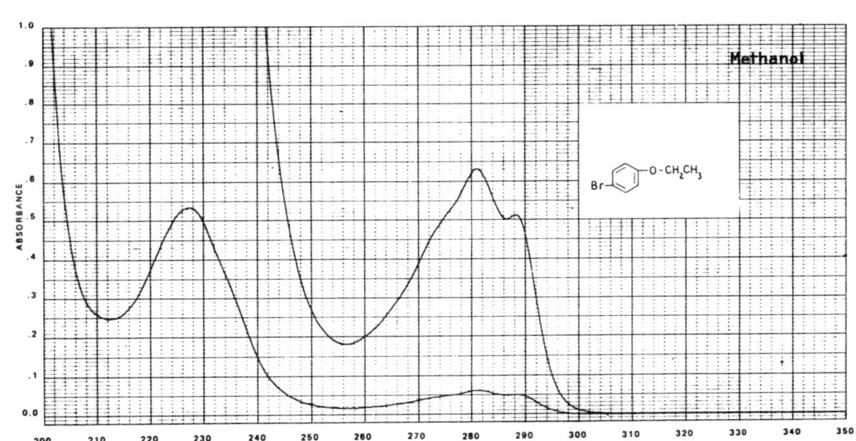

o-IODOANISOLE 1519

C_7H_7IO

Mol. Wt. 234.04

B.P. 239-241°C

Solvent: Methanol

λ Max. mμ	a_m	Cell mm	Conc. g/L
285	2660	1	0.1990
277	2860	1	0.1990
229.5	9130	1	0.1990

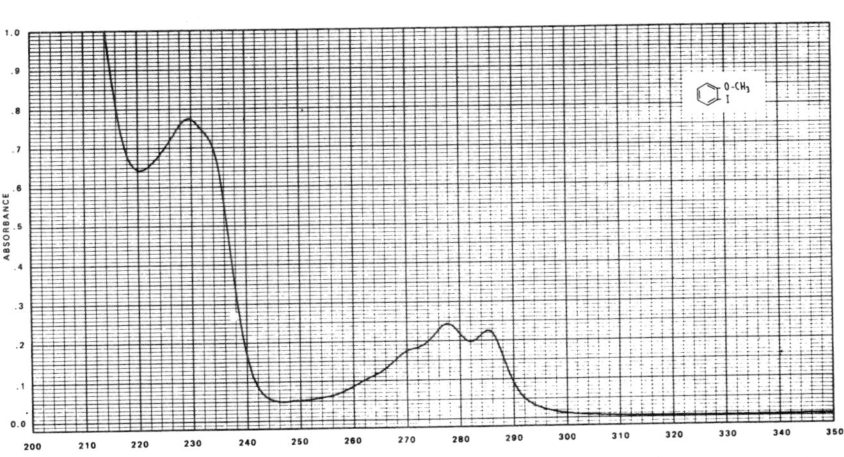

m-IODOANISOLE

1520

C_7H_7IO

Mol. Wt. 234.04

B.P. 128-129°C/27mm

Solvent: Methanol

λ Max. mμ	a_m	Cell mm	Conc. g/L
284.5	2350	1	0.8500
277	2510	1	0.8500
x	x	1	0.0850

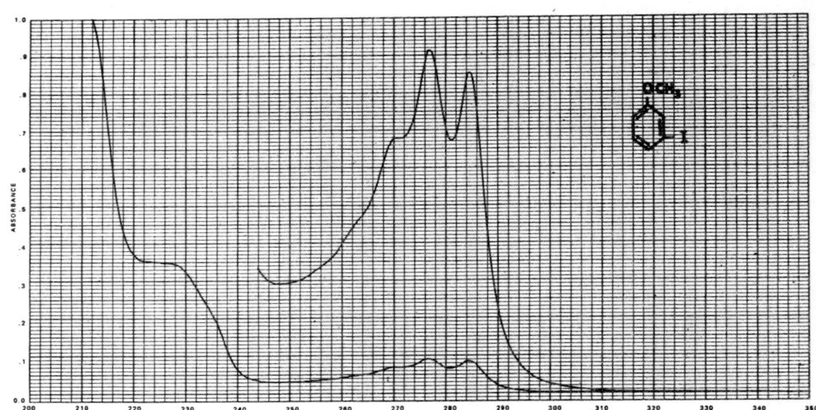

p-IODOANISOLE

1521

C_7H_7IO

Mol. Wt. 234.04

M.P. 51-52°C

Solvent: Methanol

λ Max. mμ	a_m	Cell mm	Conc. g/L
280.5	1450	10	0.100
233	18500	1	0.100

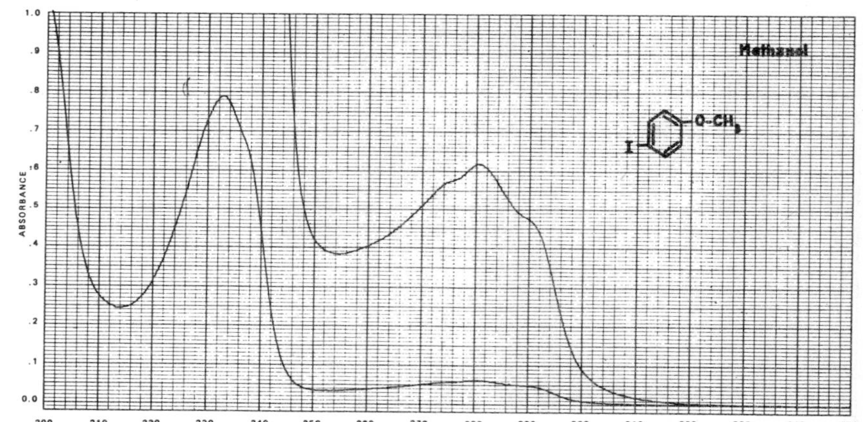

m-PHENETIDINE

1522

$C_8H_{11}NO$

Mol. Wt. 137.18

B.P. 124-126°C/7mm

Solvent: Methanol

λ Max. mμ	a_m	Cell mm	Conc. g/L
286.5	2200	2	0.1230
235	6550	1	0.1230
206	36000	1	0.0246

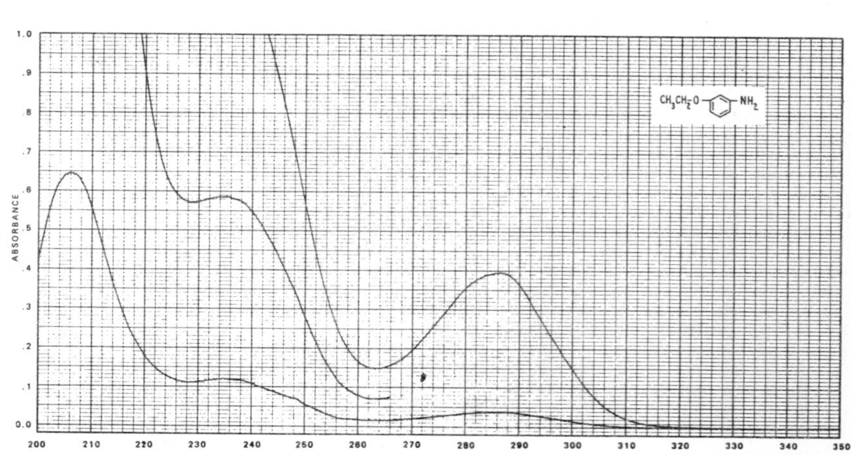

1522

m-PHENETIDINE

$C_8H_{11}NO$

Mol. Wt. 137.18

B.P. 124-126°C/7mm

Solvent: Methanol HCl

λ Max. mμ	a_m	Cell mm	Conc. g/L
278	1810	5	0.1230
272	2060	5	0.1230
222.5	9150	1	0.1230

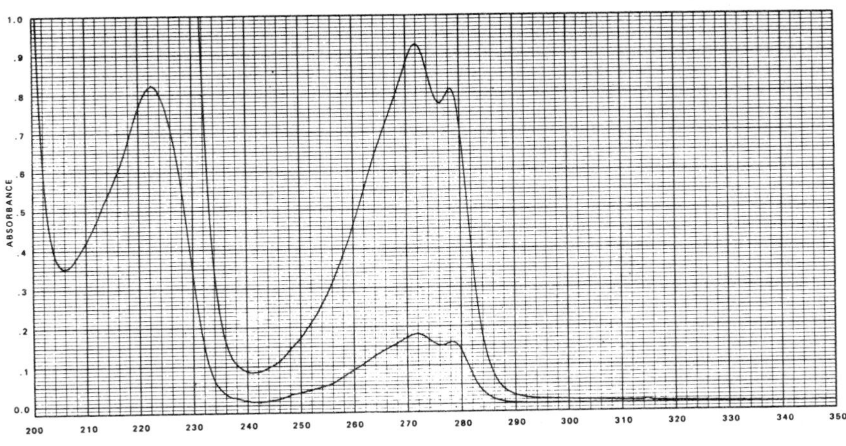

1523

N-METHYL-p-ANISIDINE

$C_8H_{11}NO$

Mol. Wt. 137.18

Solvent: Methanol

λ Max. mμ	a_m	Cell mm	Conc. g/L
266	12900	1	0.100

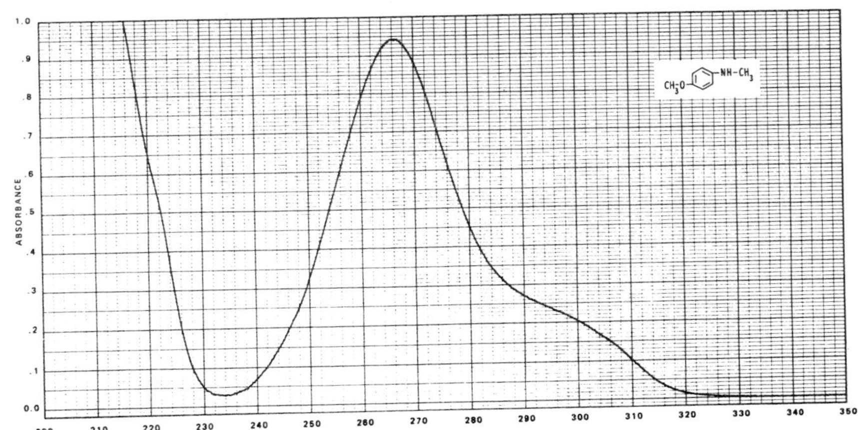

λ Max. mμ	a_m	Cell mm	Conc. g/L

N,N-DIMETHYL-p-ANISIDINE

1524

$C_9H_{13}NO$

Mol. Wt. 151.21

M.P. 47°C

Solvent: Methanol

λ Max. mμ	a_m	Cell mm	Conc. g/L
307	1750	5	0.100
245	11700	1	0.100

N,N-DIMETHYL-p-ANISIDINE

1524

$C_9H_{13}NO$

Mol. Wt. 151.21

M.P. 47°C

Solvent: Methanol HCl

λ Max. mμ	a_m	Cell mm	Conc. g/L
279	1220	5	0.100
272	1420	5	0.100
224	11600	1	0.100

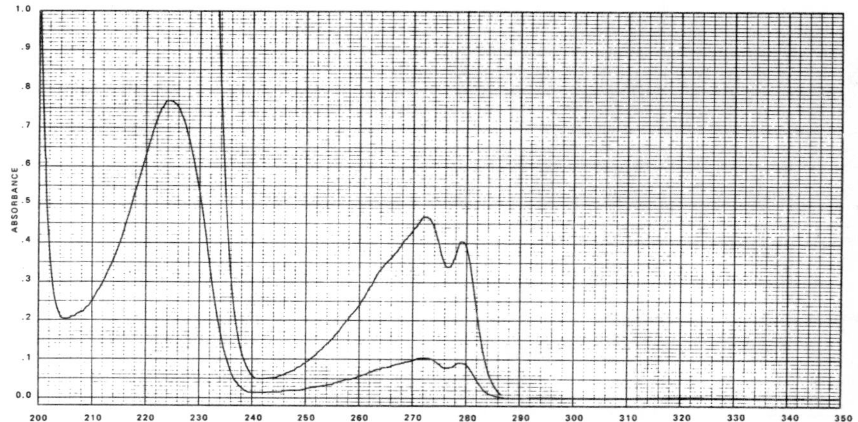

N,N-DIETHYL-m-PHENETIDINE

1525

$C_{12}H_{19}NO$

Mol. Wt. 193.29

B.P. 145-147°C/13mm

Solvent: Methanol

λ Max. mμ	a_m	Cell mm	Conc. g/L
300	7250	2	0.1080
259.5	12200	1	0.0540
212.5	24300	1	0.0540

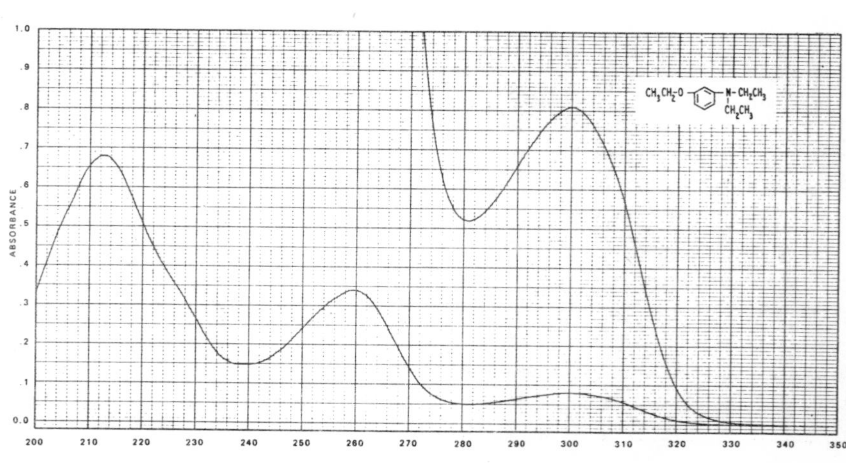

N,N-DIETHYL-m-PHENETIDINE

1525

$C_{12}H_{19}NO$

Mol. Wt. 193.29

B.P. 145-147°C/13mm

Solvent: Methanol HCl

λ Max. mμ	a_m	Cell mm	Conc. g/L
280	2210	5	0.1080
274	2440	5	0.1080
224	8950	1	0.1080

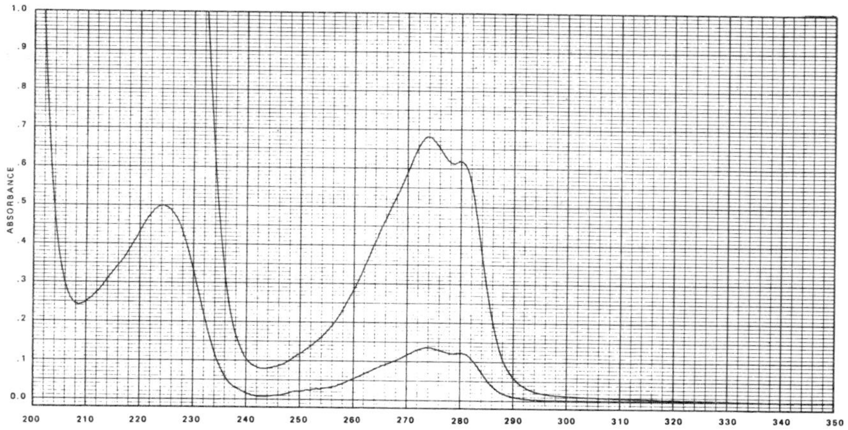

o-ANISIDINE, HYDROCHLORIDE

1526

$C_7H_9NO \cdot HCl$

Mol. Wt. 159.62

M.P. 229°C (dec.)

Solvent: Methanol

λ Max. mμ	a_m	Cell mm	Conc. g/L
276	1880	5	0.100
270	2040	5	0.100
217	6940	1	0.100

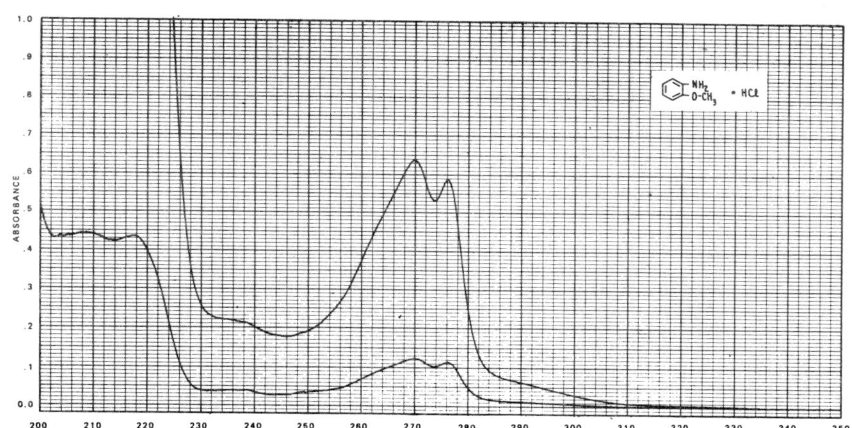

λ Max. mμ	a_m	Cell mm	Conc. g/L

o-METHOXYPHENYLHYDRAZINE, HYDROCHLORIDE

1527

$C_7H_{10}N_2O \cdot HCl$
Mol. Wt. 174.63
Solvent: Methanol

λ Max. mμ	a_m	Cell mm	Conc. g/L
278.0	2850	2	0.100
230.0	7640	2	0.100

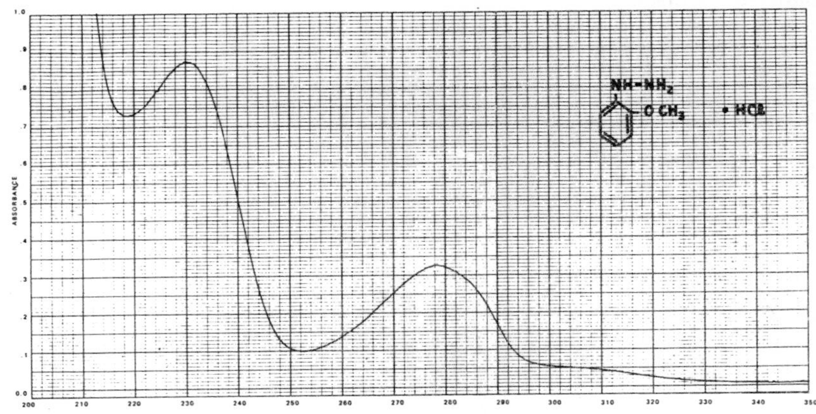

o-METHOXYPHENYLHYDRAZINE, HYDROCHLORIDE

1527

$C_7H_{10}N_2O \cdot HCl$
Mol. Wt. 174.63
Solvent: Methanol KOH

λ Max. mμ	a_m	Cell mm	Conc. g/L
285	3000	2	0.100
240	8050	2	0.100

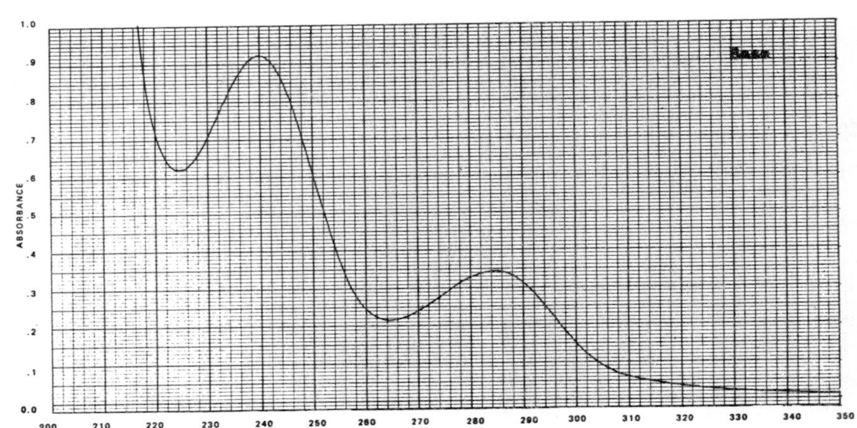

N-(p-METHOXYBENZYLIDENE)ANILINE

1528

$C_{14}H_{13}NO$
Mol. Wt. 211.27
M.P. 63-64°C
Solvent: Methanol

λ Max. mμ	a_m	Cell mm	Conc. g/L
309	16200	1	0.100
287.5	17300	1	0.100
282	17300	1	0.100
222	15500	1	0.100

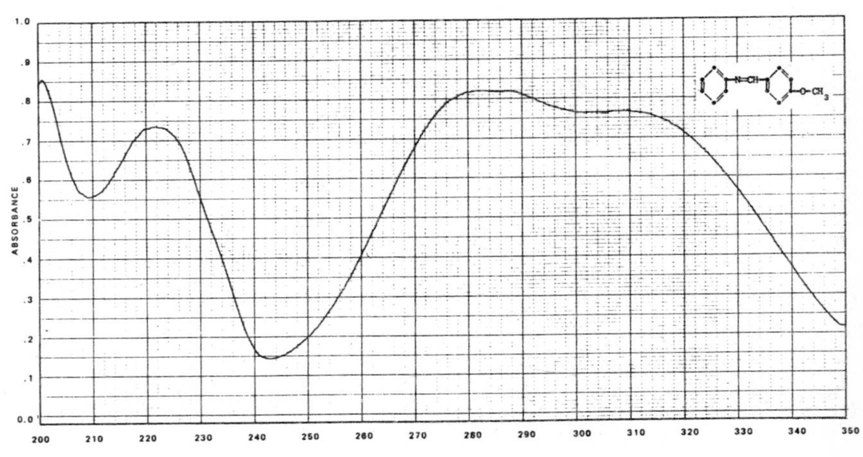

N-(-METHOXYBENZYLIDENE)ANILINE 1528

$C_{14}H_{13}NO$
Mol. Wt. 211.27
M.P. 63-64°C
Solvent: Methanol HCl

λ Max. mμ	a_m	Cell mm	Conc. g/L
278	12100	1	0.100
273	12100	1	0.100
218.5	10600	1	0.100

o-ANISALDEHYDE, OXIME 1529

$C_8H_9NO_2$
Mol. Wt. 151.17
Solvent: Methanol

λ Max. mμ	a_m	Cell mm	Conc. g/L
304	5500	2	0.100
252.5	11500	1	0.0500
210.5	17800	1	0.0500

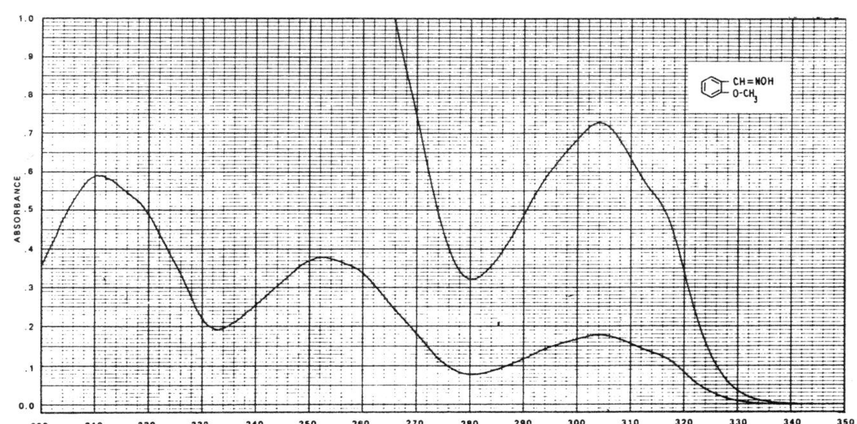

o-ANISALDEHYDE, OXIME 1529

$C_8H_9NO_2$
Mol. Wt. 151.17
Solvent: Methanol KOH

λ Max. mμ	a_m	Cell mm	Conc. g/L
306	7500	1	0.100
264.5	9430	1	0.100

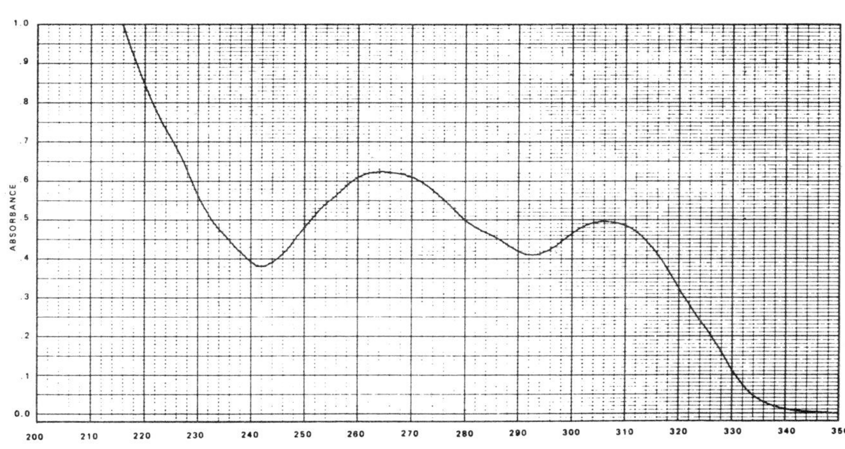

o-NITROANISOLE 1530

$C_7H_7NO_3$
Mol. Wt. 153.13
M.P. 9-10°C
Solvent: Methanol

λ Max. mμ	a_m	Cell mm	Conc. g/L
321	9620	10	0.0113
258	12900	10	0.0113
232	18800	10	0.0011
225	19500	10	0.0011
211	55800	10	0.0011
207	56000	10	0.0011

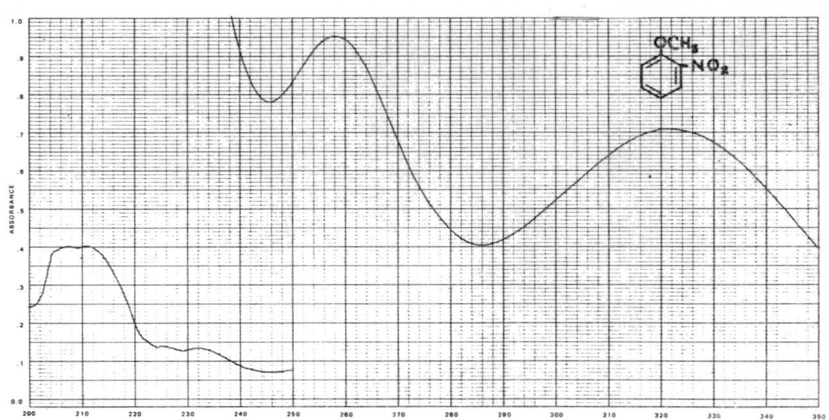

m-NITROANISOLE 1531

$C_7H_7NO_3$
Mol. Wt. 153.14
M.P. 36-38°C
Solvent: Methanol

λ Max. mμ	a_m	Cell mm	Conc. g/L
325	2080	5	0.075
267	6200	1	0.075
227	10600	1	0.075
211	13700	1	0.075

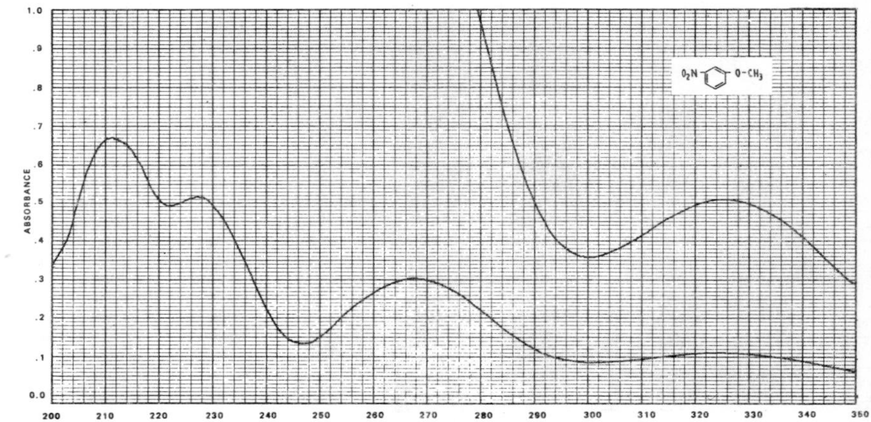

p-NITROANISOLE 1532

$C_7H_7NO_3$
Mol. Wt. 153.14
M.P. 52-53°C
Solvent: Methanol

λ Max. mμ	a_m	Cell mm	Conc. g/L
305	10600	1	0.100
227	7180	1	0.100

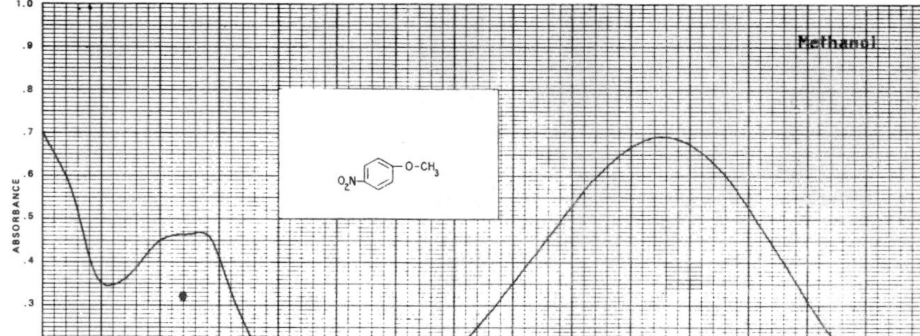

4-NITROPHENETOLE 1533

$C_8H_9NO_3$

Mol. Wt. 167.16

M.P. 57-58°C

Solvent: Methanol

λ Max. mμ	a_m	Cell mm	Conc. g/L
307	11900	10	0.01
227	8360	10	0.01

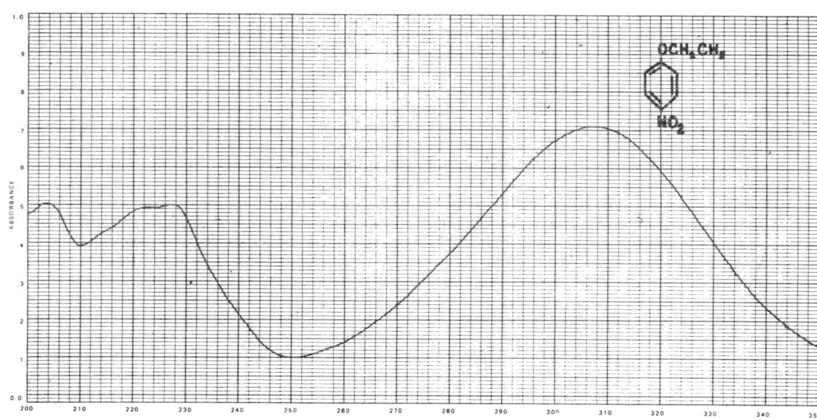

1-BUTOXY-2-NITROBENZENE 1534

$C_{10}H_{16}NO_3$

Mol. Wt. 195.22

Solvent: Methanol

λ Max. mμ	a_m	Cell mm	Conc. g/L
324	2190	10	0.0552
259	3020	10	0.0552
213	13900	10	0.0055

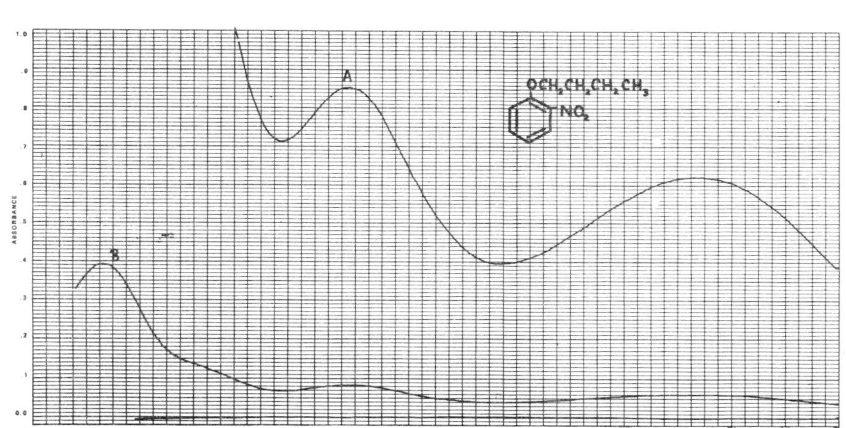

λ Max. mμ	a_m	Cell mm	Conc. g/L

m-METHOXYBENZENETHIOL 1535

C_7H_8OS

Mol. Wt. 140.21

B.P. 223-226°C

Solvent: Methanol

λ Max. mμ	a_m	Cell mm	Conc. g/L
290	2070	5	0.09905
282.5	2410	5	0.09905
213	27900	1	0.049525

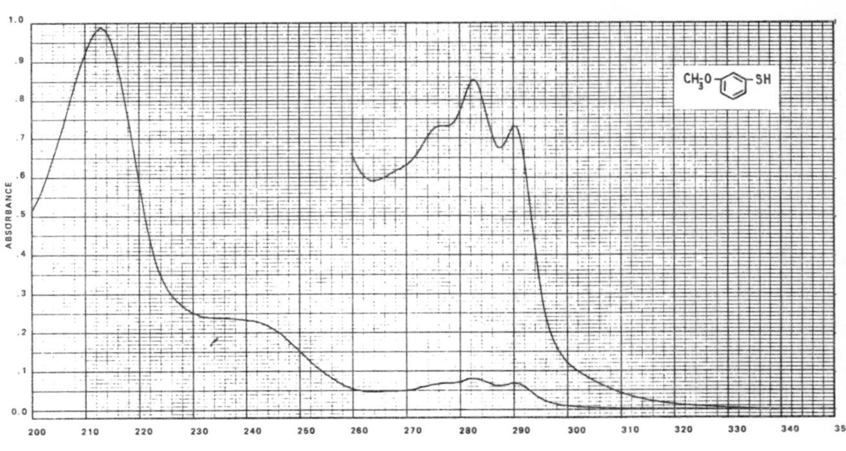

m-METHOXYBENZENETHIOL 1535

C_7H_8OS

Mol. Wt. 140.21

B.P. 223-226°C

Solvent: Methanol KOH

λ Max. mμ	a_m	Cell mm	Conc. g/L
266.5	11900	1	0.049525
212	23000	1	0.049525

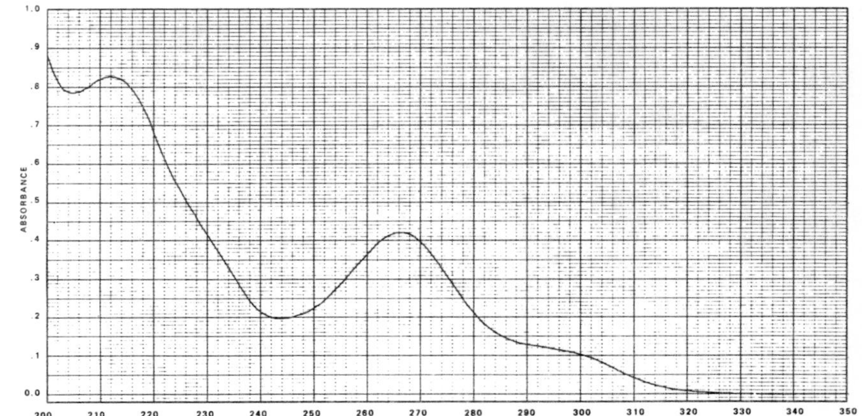

p-METHOXYBENZENETHIOL 1536

C_7H_8OS

Mol. Wt. 140.21

Solvent: Methanol

λ Max. mμ	a_m	Cell mm	Conc. g/L
243.8	10900	1	0.100
x	x	1	0.100

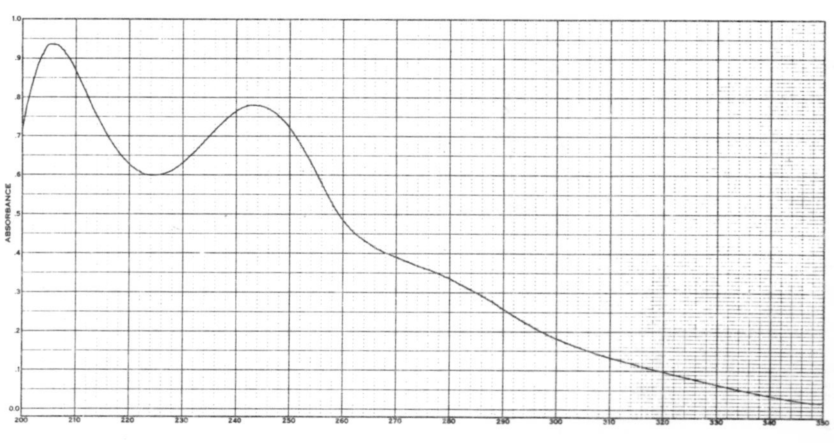

p-METHOXYBENZENETHIOL 1536

C_7H_8OS

Mol. Wt. 140.21

Solvent: Methanol KOH

λ Max. mμ	a_m	Cell mm	Conc. g/L
245	8480	1	0.100

4,4'-SULFONYLDIANISOLE 1537

$C_{14}H_{14}O_4S$

Mol. Wt. 278.33

Solvent: Methanol

λ Max. mμ	a_m	Cell mm	Conc. g/L
258.5	27600	1	0.0800
235.5	17700	1	0.0800

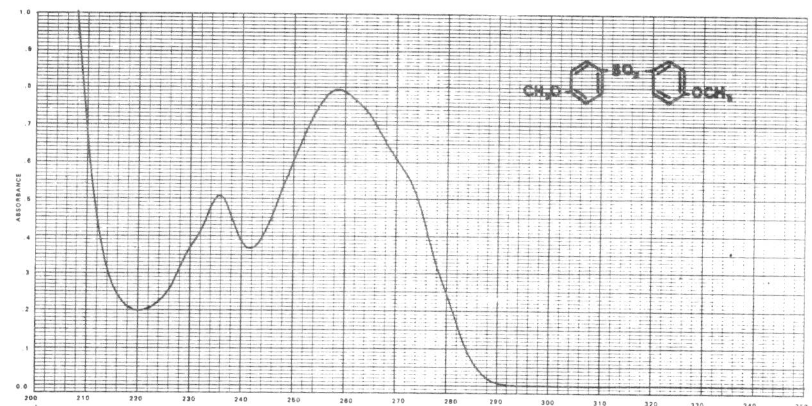

p-METHOXYBENZENESULFONYL CHLORIDE 1538

$C_7H_7ClO_3S$

Mol. Wt. 206.65

Solvent: Methanol

λ Max. mμ	a_m	Cell mm	Conc. g/L
280	1210	5	0.132
271	1610	5	0.132
263	1690	5	0.132
231	12800	1	0.132

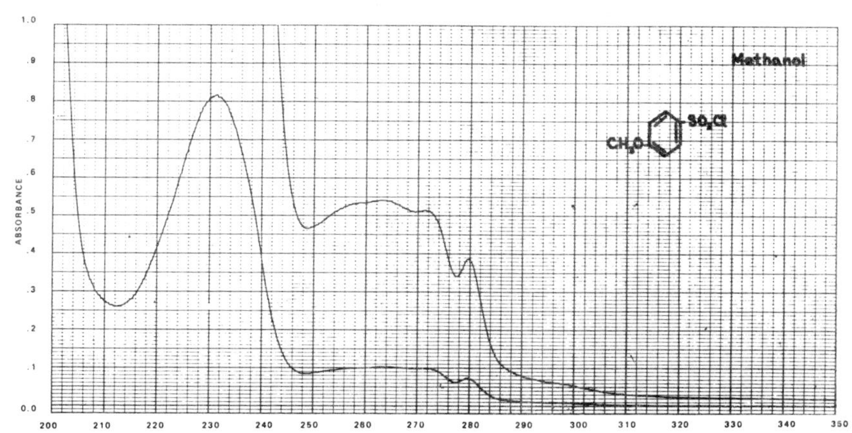

2,2-BIS[p-(ALLYLOXY)PHENYL] PROPANE

1539

$C_{21}H_{24}O_2$

Mol. Wt. 308.42

Solvent: Methanol

λ Max. mμ	a_m	Cell mm	Conc. g/L
283	2680	2	0.4381
276.5	3030	2	0.4381
228	17600	0.5	0.2191
205	20200	0.5	0.2191

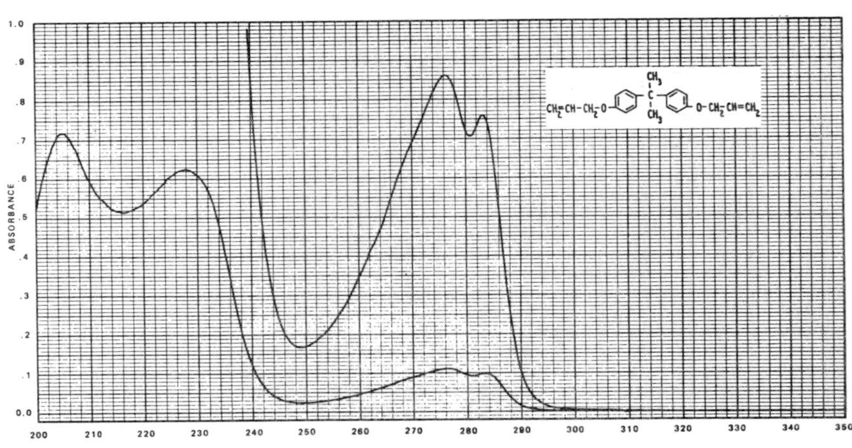

1,2-EPOXY-3-(m-TOLYLOXY)PROPANE

1540

$C_{10}H_{12}O_2$

Mol. Wt. 164.20

B.P. 122-123°C/8mm (lit.)

Solvent: Methanol

λ Max. mμ	a_m	Cell mm	Conc. g/L
278.5	1440	2	0.453
271.5	1520	2	0.453
217	7080	1	0.226

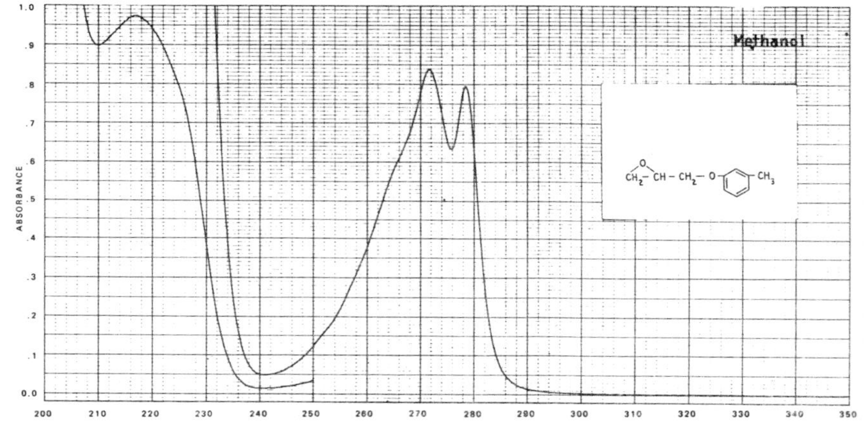

PHENYL ETHER

1541

$C_{12}H_{10}O$

Mol. Wt. 170.21

M.P. 25-27°C

Solvent: Methanol

λ Max. mμ	a_m	Cell mm	Conc. g/L
295	9170	1	0.0800
285.5	16100	1	0.0800
280	17400	1	0.0800
248.5	19500	1	0.0800
217	39000	1	0.0400
207	39600	1	0.0400

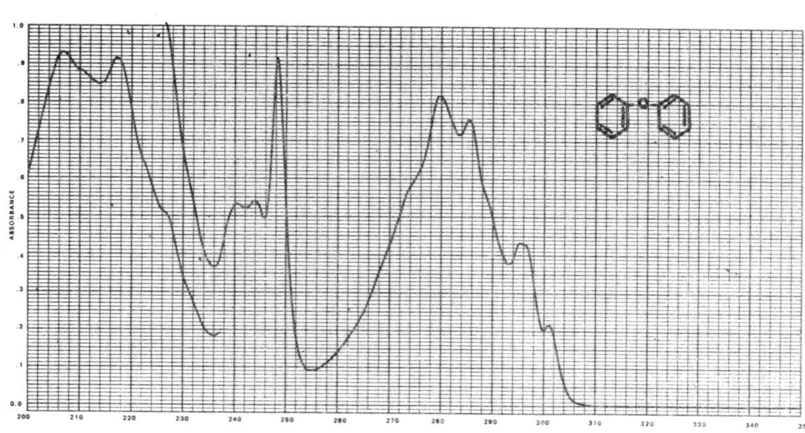

p-BROMOPHENYL PHENYL ETHER 1542

$C_{12}H_9BrO$
Mol. Wt. 249.11
Solvent: Cyclohexene

608 UV

λ Max. mμ	a_m	Cell mm	Conc. g/L
x	x	10	1.93
288.5	990	10	0.193
277.5	1940	10	0.193
269.5	1940	10	0.193
235	16800	10	0.0193

o-NITROPHENYL PHENYL ETHER 1543

$C_{12}H_9NO_3$
Mol. Wt. 215.21
M.P. 55-58°C
Solvent: Methanol

λ Max. mμ	a_m	Cell mm	Conc. g/L
312	2090	2	0.3290
x	x	1	0.0658

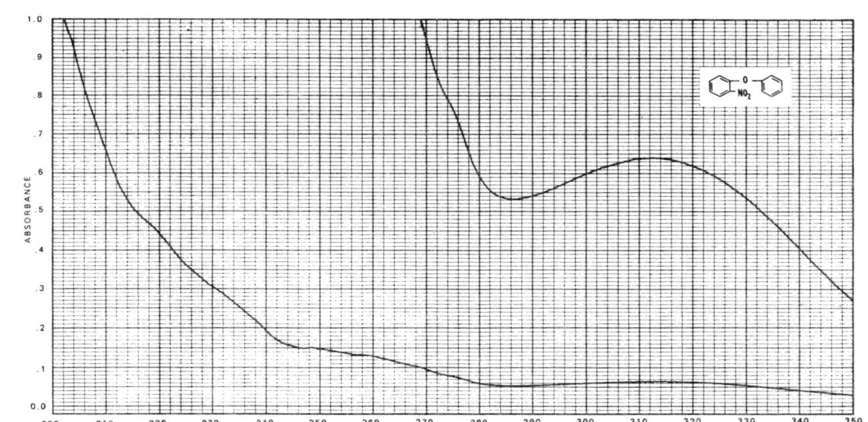

m-NITROPHENYL PHENYL ETHER 1544

$C_{12}H_9NO_3$
Mol. Wt. 215.21
B.P. 194-196°C/11mm
Solvent: Methanol

λ Max. mμ	a_m	Cell mm	Conc. g/L
318	911	10	0.120
263.5	4310	4	0.120
x	x	1	0.060

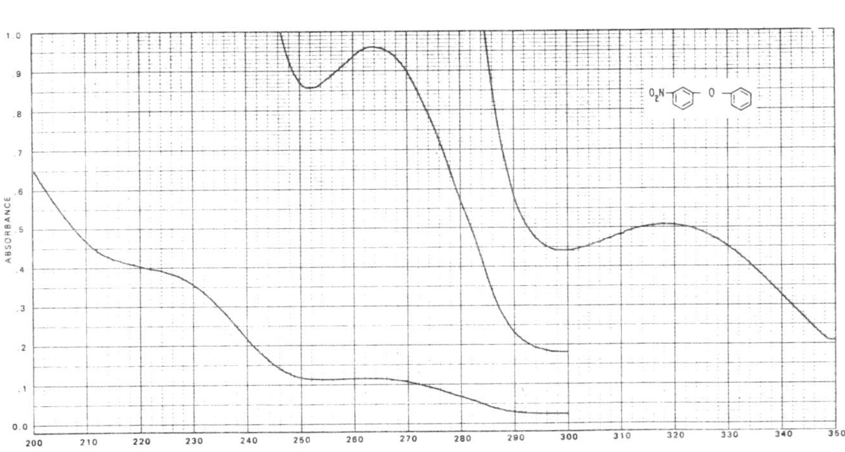

o-DIMETHOXYBENZENE

1545

$C_8H_{10}O_2$

Mol. Wt. 138.17

Solvent: Methanol

λ Max. mμ	a_m	Cell mm	Conc. g/L
274.3	3920	1	0.286
225	11700	2	0.0572

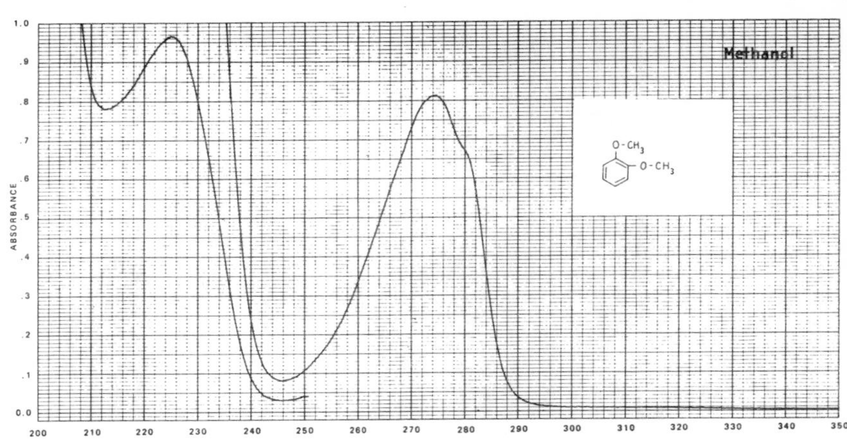

m-DIMETHOXYBENZENE

1546

$C_8H_{10}O_2$

Mol. Wt. 138.17

Solvent: Methanol

λ Max. mμ	a_m	Cell mm	Conc. g/L
x	x	10	2.13
279	2090	10	0.0852
273	2310	10	0.0852
x	x	10	0.0085

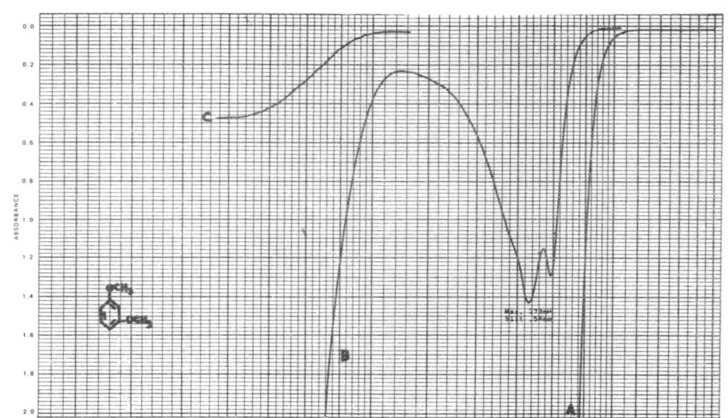

p-DIMETHOXYBENZENE

1547

$C_8H_{10}O_2$

Mol. Wt. 138.17

M.P. 53-55°C B.P. 210-212°C

Solvent: Methanol

λ Max. mμ	a_m	Cell mm	Conc. g/L
289	3080	1	0.100
225	9670	1	0.100

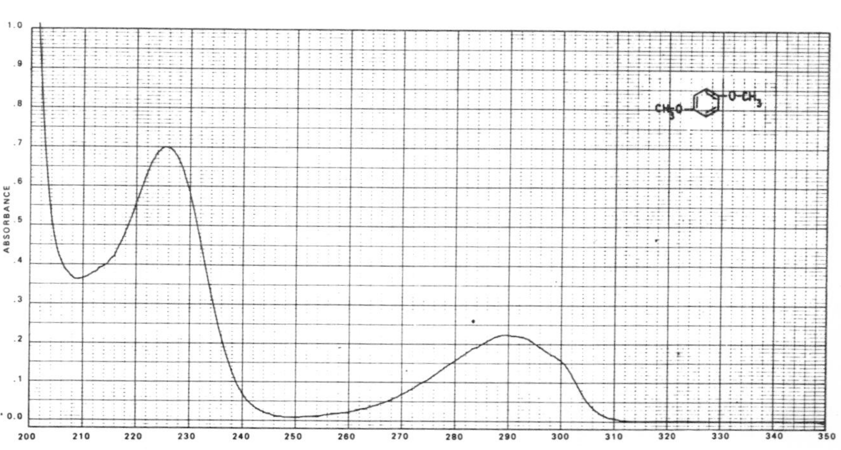

1-METHOXY-4-PHENOXYBENZENE

1548

$C_{12}H_{12}O_2$
Mol. Wt. 200.24
M.P. 5-9°C
Solvent: Methanol

λ Max. mμ	a_m	Cell mm	Conc. g/L
279	2510	5	0.1180
271	2460	5	0.1180
228	2720	1	0.1180

4,4′-OXYDIANISOLE

1549

$C_{14}H_{14}O_3$
Mol. Wt. 230.27
M.P. 102-104°C
Solvent: Methanol

λ Max. mμ	a_m	Cell mm	Conc. g/L
285	4070	2	0.190
281	4170	2	0.190
230.5	17400	1	0.095

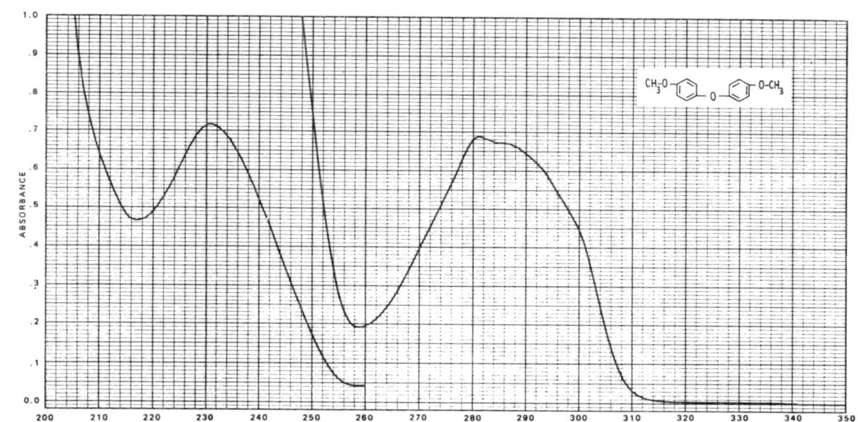

m-DIPHENOXYBENZENE

1550

$C_{18}H_{14}O_2$
Mol. Wt. 262.31
M.P. 60-62°C
Solvent: Methanol

λ Max. mμ	a_m	Cell mm	Conc. g/L
277	3270	5	0.100
270	3280	5	0.100

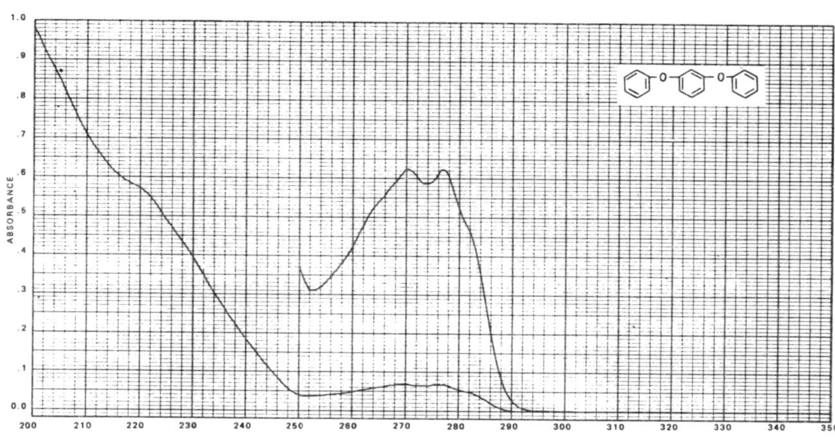

2,3-DIMETHYLANISOLE 1551

$C_9H_{12}O$

Mol. Wt. 136.20

B.P. 195°C

Solvent: Methanol

λ Max. mμ	a_m	Cell mm	Conc. g/L
279	1450	5	0.1233
273.5	1380	5	0.1233
270.5	1390	5	0.1233
x	x	1	0.1233

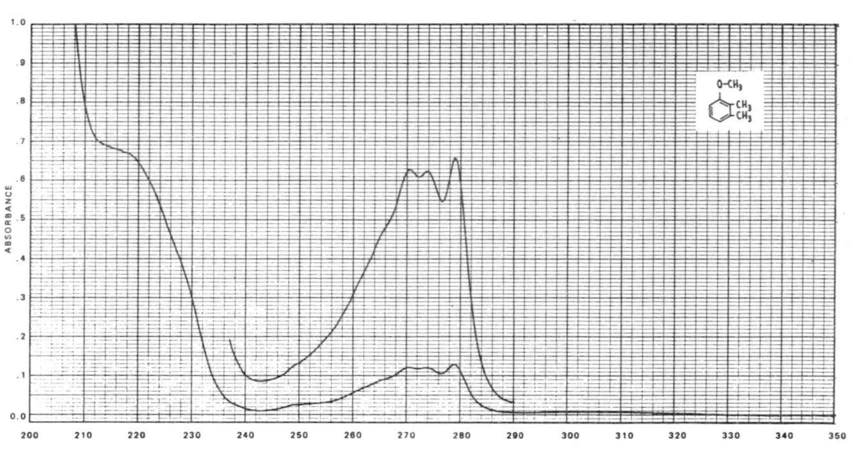

2,4-DIMETHYLANISOLE 1552

$C_9H_{12}O$

Mol. Wt. 136.20

B.P. 188°C

Solvent: Methanol

λ Max. mμ	a_m	Cell mm	Conc. g/L
284	1700	5	0.110
278	1900	5	0.110
223	6710	1	0.110
218.5	6770	1	0.110

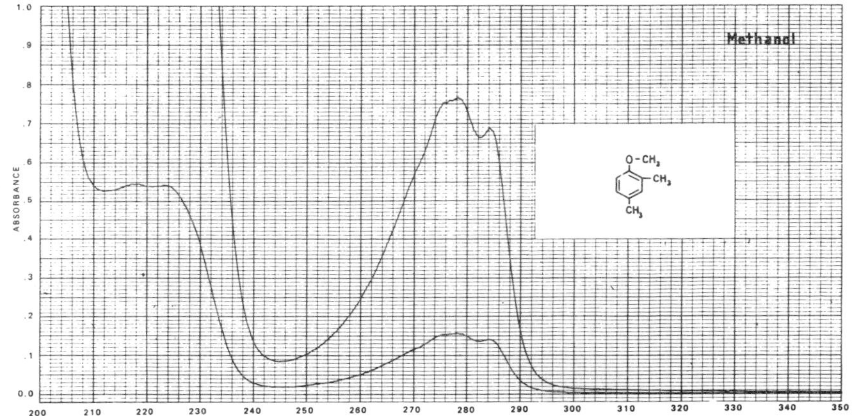

2,6-DICHLOROANISOLE 1553

$C_7H_6Cl_2O$

Mol. Wt. 177.03

Solvent: Methanol

λ Max. mμ	a_m	Cell mm	Conc. g/L
278.5	429	20	0.1390
271	461	20	0.1390
x	x	1	0.1390

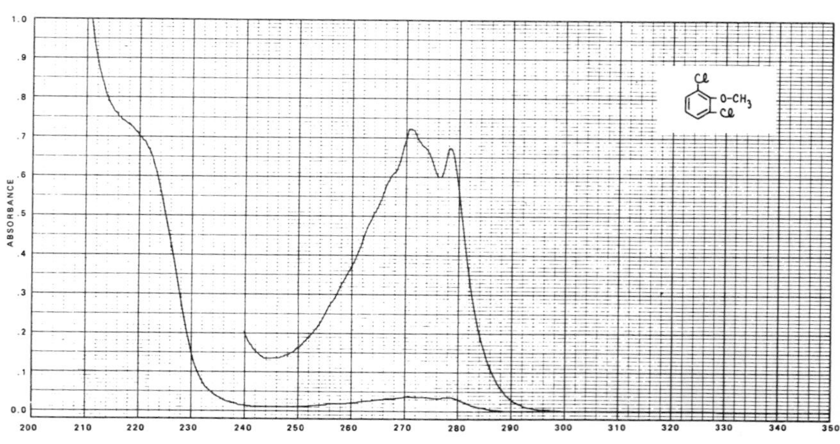

p-CHLORO-o-ANISIDINE 1554

C_7H_8ClNO

Mol. Wt. 157.60

Solvent: Methanol

λ Max. mμ	a_m	Cell mm	Conc. g/L
x	x	10	2.00
294	3920	10	0.0400
243	8200	10	0.0200

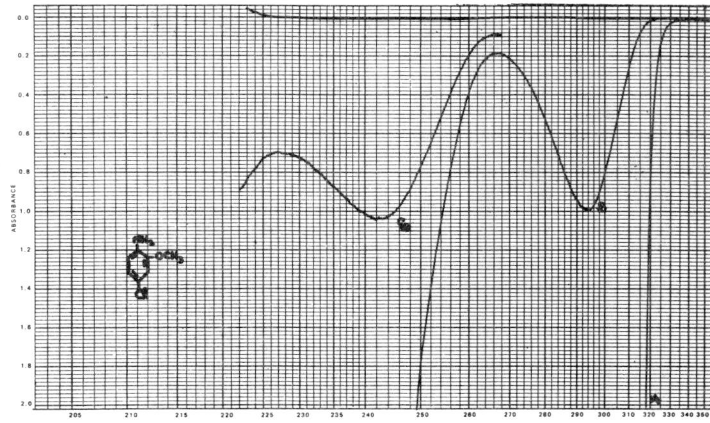

2,4-DINITROANISOLE 1555

$C_7H_6N_2O_5$

Mol. Wt. 198.14

M.P. 95.5-96°C

Solvent: Methanol

λ Max. mμ	a_m	Cell mm	Conc. g/L
290	10900	1	0.100
251.5	7430	2	0.100
213	14000	1	0.100

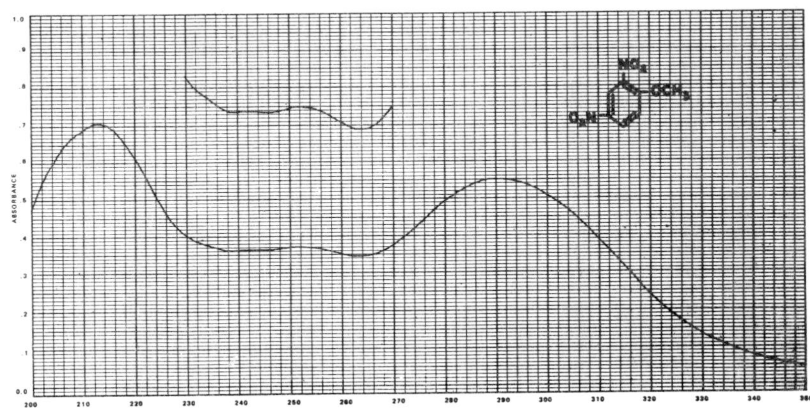

2,6-DINITROANISOLE 1556

$C_7H_6N_2O_5$

Mol. Wt. 198.14

M.P. 118°C

Solvent: Methanol

λ Max. mμ	a_m	Cell mm	Conc. g/L
302	1890	5	0.100
230	10400	1	0.100

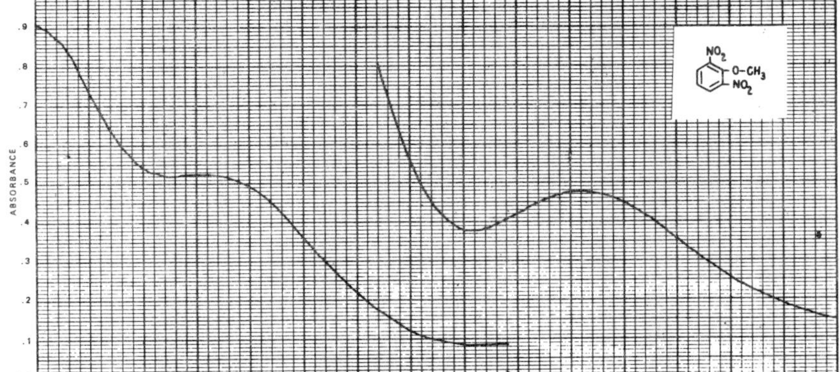

2,4-DINITROPHENETOLE

1557

$C_8H_8N_2O_5$

Mol. Wt. 212.16

M.P. 83-85.5°C

Solvent: Methanol

λ Max. mμ	a_m	Cell mm	Conc. g/L
293	11000	1	0.100
252	6960	1	0.100
214	13800	1	0.100

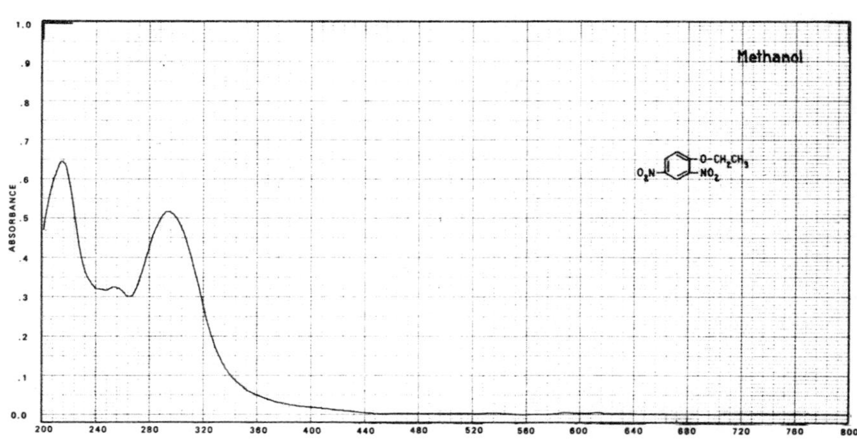

2,5-DIMETHOXYTOLUENE

1558

$C_9H_{12}O_2$

Mol. Wt. 152.19

M.P. 19-20°C

Solvent: Methanol

λ Max. mμ	a_m	Cell mm	Conc. g/L
289	5390	1	0.100
226.5	12800	1	0.100

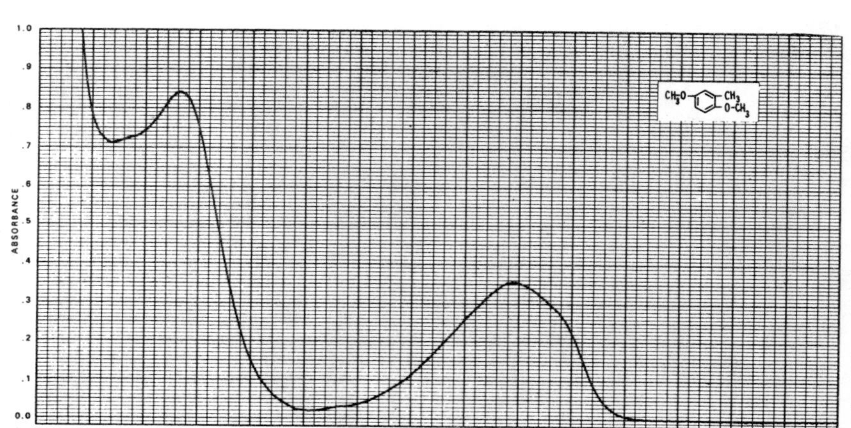

1,2-DIMETHOXY-4-PROPENYLBENZENE

1559

$C_{11}H_{14}O_2$

Mol. Wt. 178.23

Solvent: Methanol

λ Max. mμ	a_m	Cell mm	Conc. g/L
256.5	17800	1	0.100
211.5	13800	1	0.100

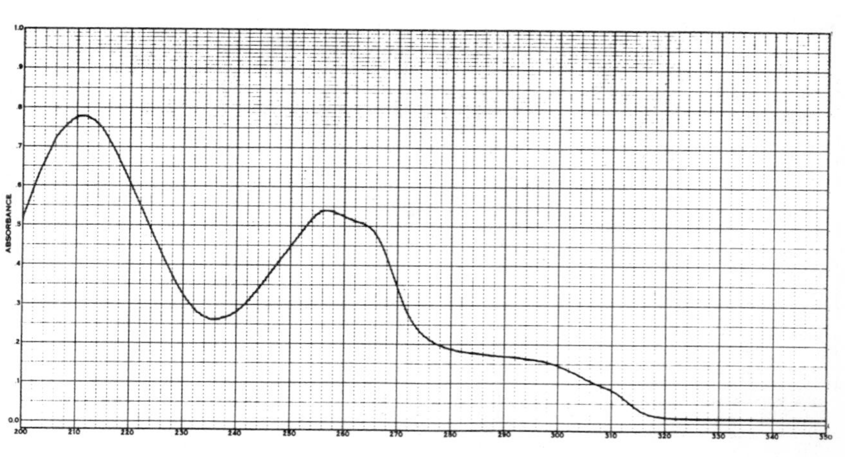

4-ALLYL-1,2-DIMETHOXYBENZENE 1560

$C_{11}H_{14}O_2$
Mol. Wt. 178.23
Solvent: Methanol

λ Max. mμ	a_m	Cell mm	Conc. g/L
280	2940	10	0.0492
230	8070	10	0.0098

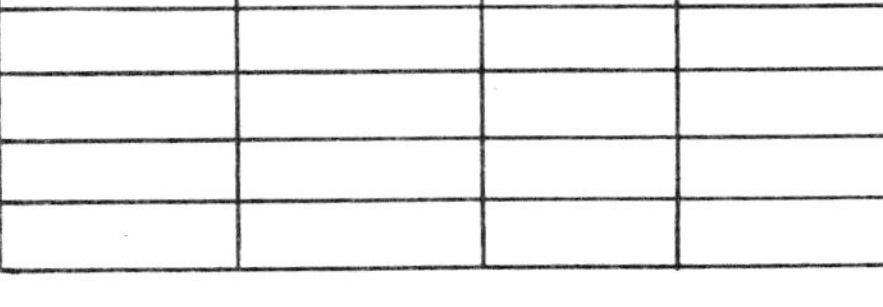

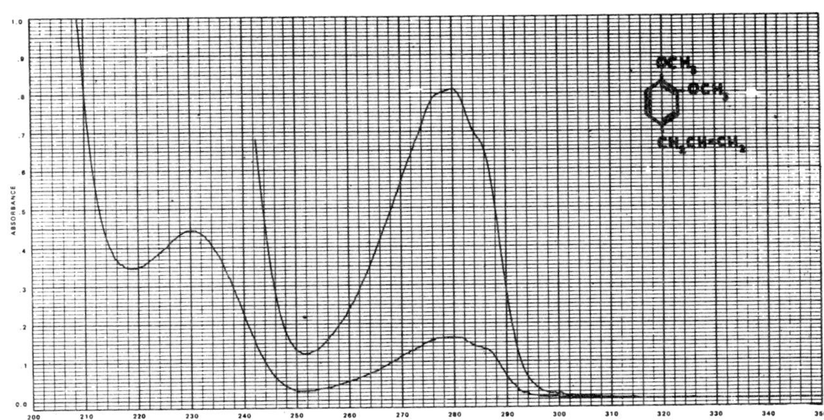

3,4-DIETHOXYANILINE 1561

$C_{10}H_{15}NO_2$
Mol. Wt. 181.24
M.P. 47-49°C B.P. 132-135°C/0.45mm
Solvent: Methanol

λ Max. mμ	a_m	Cell mm	Conc. g/L
294	2790	1	0.125
238.5	7340	1	0.125

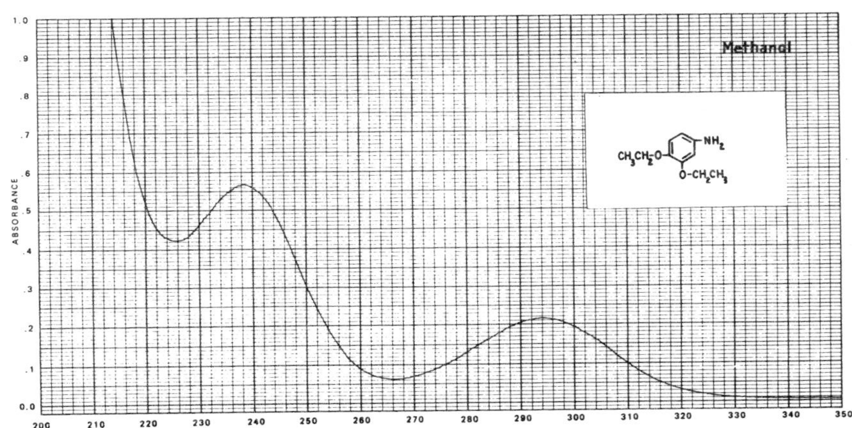

3,4-DIETHOXYANILINE 1561

$C_{10}H_{15}NO_2$
Mol. Wt. 181.24
M.P. 47-49°C B.P. 132-135°C/0.45mm
Solvent: Methanol HCl

λ Max. mμ	a_m	Cell mm	Conc. g/L
278	2700	1	0.125
230	6820	1	0.125

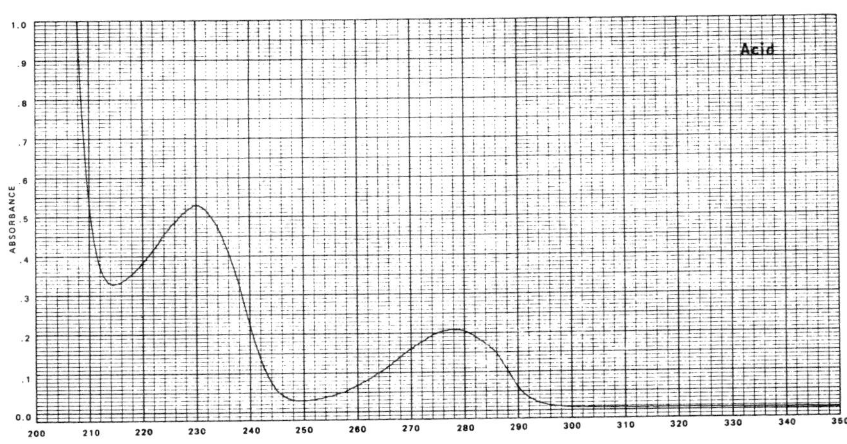

2,5-DIBUTOXYANILINE

1562

$C_{14}H_{23}NO_2$
Mol. Wt. 237.35
Solvent: Cyclohexane

λ Max. mμ	a_m	Cell mm	Conc. g/L
x	x	10	1.4480
296	4670	10	0.0724
x	x	10	0.0072

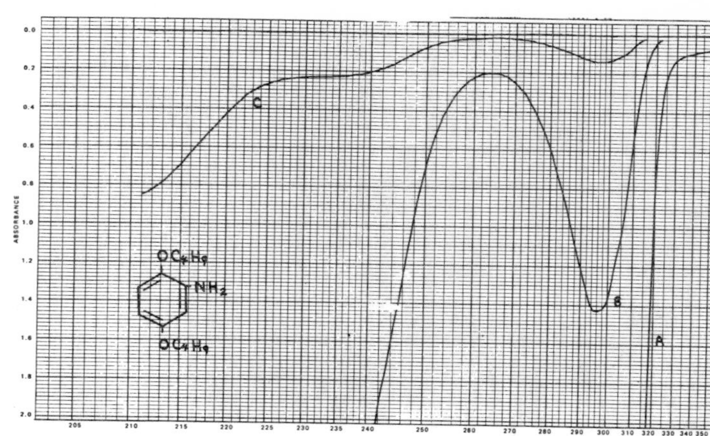

VERATRONITRILE

1563

$C_9H_9NO_2$
Mol. Wt. 163.18
Solvent: Methanol

λ Max. mμ	a_m	Cell mm	Conc. g/L
293	4680	10	0.010
286	4900	10	0.020
254.5	15600	10	0.010
216.5	31000	10	0.004

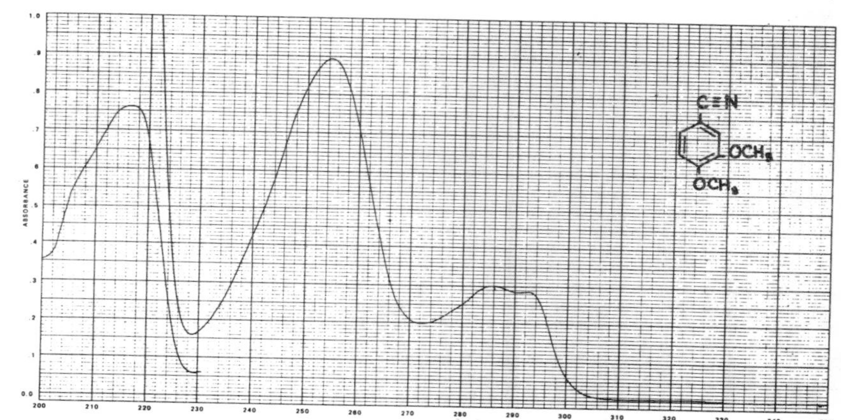

1,3-DIMETHOXY-4-NITROBENZENE

1564

$C_8H_9NO_4$
Mol. Wt. 183.16
Solvent: Methanol

λ Max. mμ	a_m	Cell mm	Conc. g/L
325	3210	2	0.100
286	2730	2	0.100
237	3350	2	0.100
212	5720	2	0.100

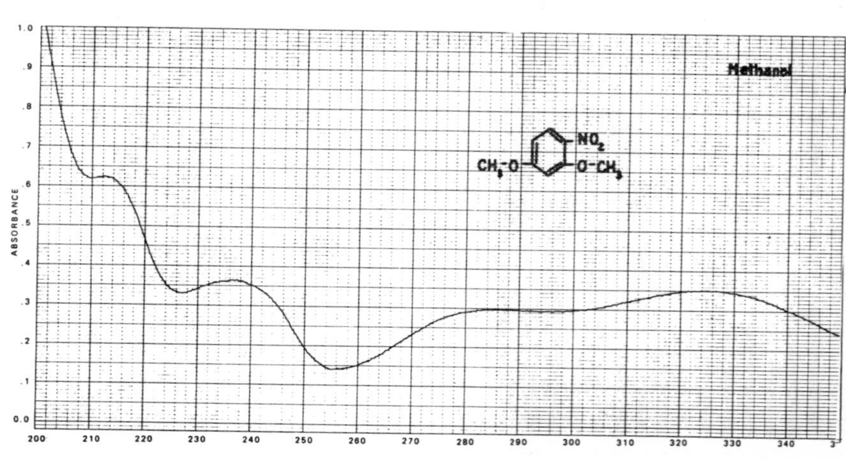

1,2,3-TRIMETHOXYBENZENE

1565

$C_9H_{12}O_3$
Mol. Wt. 168.19
M.P. 43-45°C
Solvent: Methanol

λ Max. mμ	a_m	Cell mm	Conc. g/L
x	x	1	0.100
267	696	20	0.100

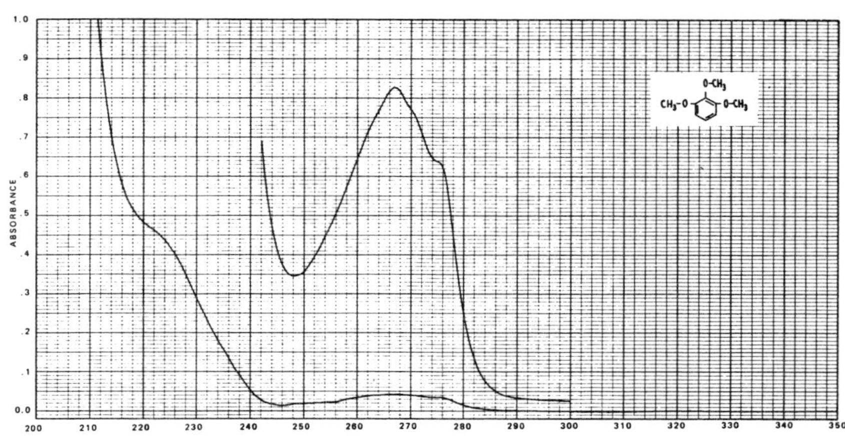

2,4,6,-TRICHLOROANISOLE

1566

$C_7H_5Cl_3O$
Mol. Wt. 211.48
Solvent: Cyclohexane

λ Max. mμ	a_m	Cell mm	Conc. g/L
x	x	10	2.00
287	869	10	0.400
279	825	10	0.400
x	x	10	0.040

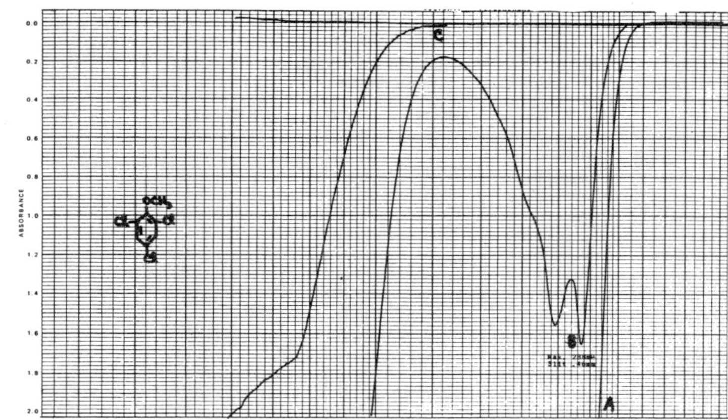

2,4,6-TRIBROMOANISOLE

1567

$C_7H_5Br_3O$
Mol. Wt. 344.84
M.P. 85-87°C
Solvent: Methanol

λ Max. mμ	a_m	Cell mm	Conc. g/L
289	762	20	0.100
281.5	745	20	0.100
210.5	41500	1	0.0500

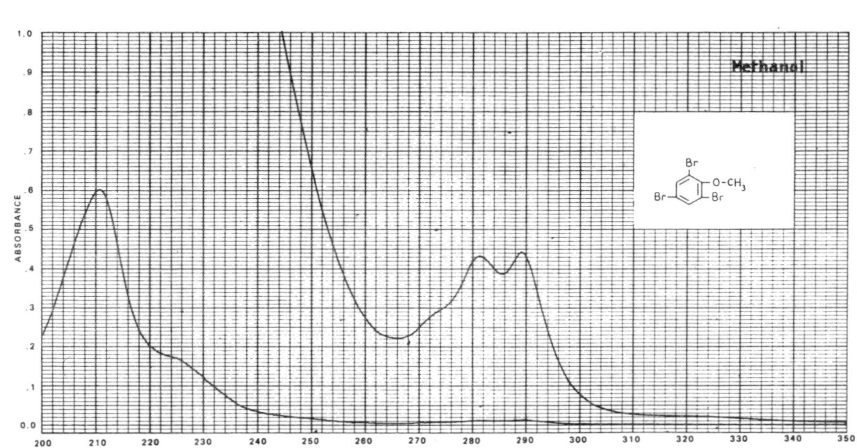

2,4,6-TRINITROANISOLE 1568

$C_7H_5N_3O_7$

Mol. Wt. 243.13

Solvent: Methanol

λ Max. mμ	a_m	Cell mm	Conc. g/L
225	12700	1	0.100

2,4,6-TRINITROANISOLE 1568

$C_6H_5N_3O_7$

Mol. Wt. 243.13

Solvent: Methanol KOH

λ Max. mμ	a_m	Cell mm	Conc. g/L
484	12700	1	0.100
411	19300	1	0.100
247	7970	1	0.100

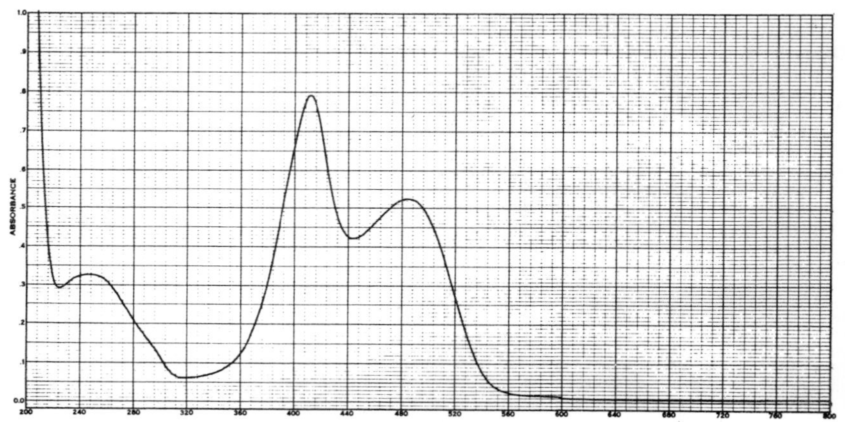

1-METHOXYNAPHTHALENE 1569

$C_{11}H_{10}O$

Mol. Wt. 158.20

B.P. 124°C/4mm

Solvent: Methanol

λ Max. mμ	a_m	Cell mm	Conc. g/L
320	2510	1	0.1079
306	3980	1	0.1079
293	6020	1	0.1079
231	34100	1	0.0215
212	46600	1	0.0215

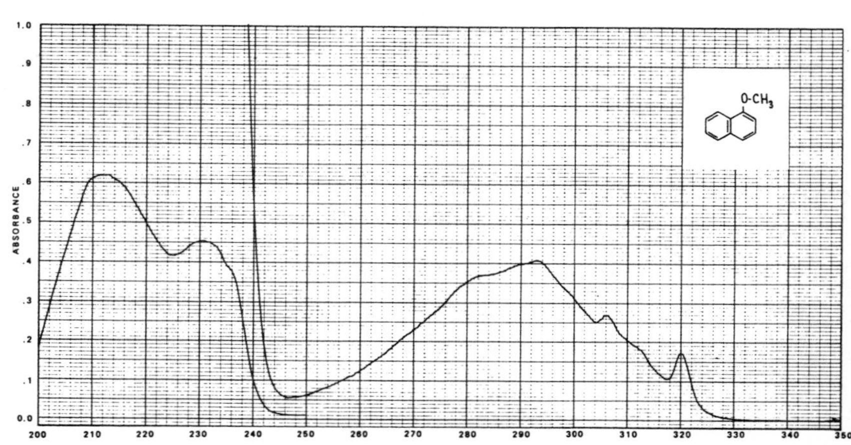

1-ETHOXYNAPHTHALENE

1570

$C_{12}H_{12}O$
Mol. Wt. 172.23
B.P. 143-145°C/12mm

λ Max. mμ	a_m	Cell mm	Conc. g/L

Pure sample not available.

2-ETHOXYNAPHTHALENE

1571

$C_{12}H_{12}O$
Mol. Wt. 172.23
Solvent: Methanol

λ Max. mμ	a_m	Cell mm	Conc. g/L
327.5	1880	2	0.100
281.5	2960	2	0.100
271	4460	2	0.100
261	4070	2	0.100
226	72600	2	0.0100

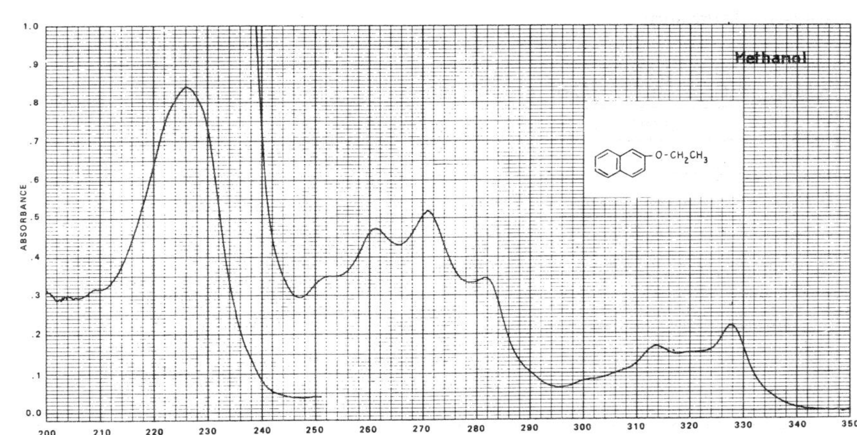

2-BENZYLOXYNAPHTHALENE

1572

$C_{17}H_{14}O$
Mol. Wt. 234.30
M.P. 99.5-100.5°C
Solvent: Methanol

λ Max. mμ	a_m	Cell mm	Conc. g/L
327	1870	10	0.04
319	1270	10	0.04
313	1420	10	0.04
282	3040	10	0.04
271	4780	10	0.04
261	4770	10	0.04
252	3780	10	0.04
228.5	78100	10	0.003

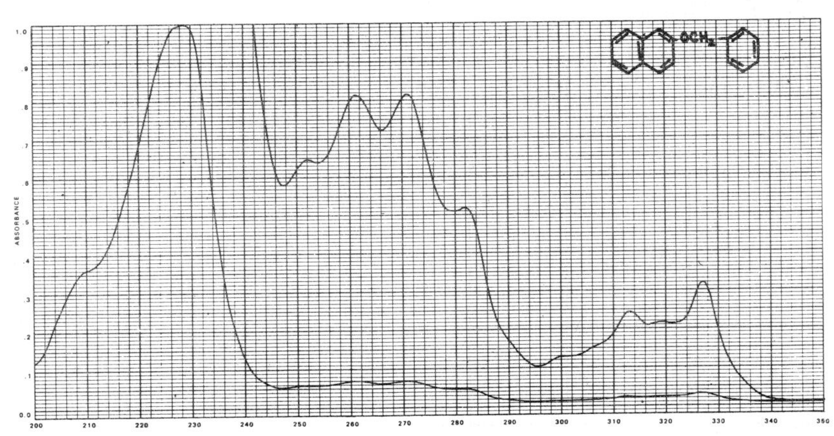

FURAN

1573

C_4H_4O

Mol. Wt. 68.08

Solvent: Methanol

λ Max. mμ	a_m	Cell mm	Conc. g/L
x	x	2	0.100

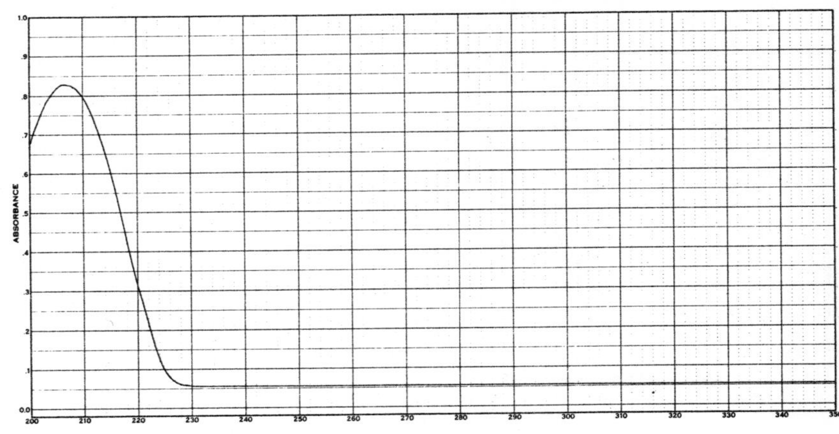

2-METHYLFURAN

1574

C_5H_6O

Mol. Wt. 82.10

B.P. 65.45-65.55°C

Solvent: Methanol

λ Max. mμ	a_m	Cell mm	Conc. g/L
213	8690	10	0.005

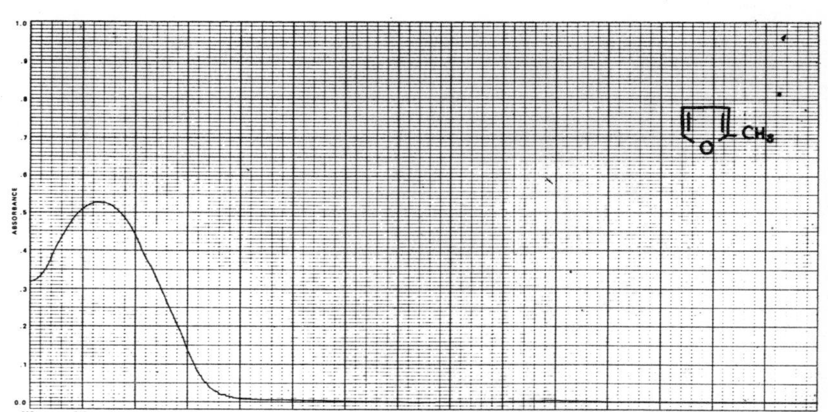

2,5-DIMETHYLFURAN

1575

C_6H_8O

Mol. Wt. 96.13

B.P. 92-94°C

Solvent: Methanol

λ Max. mμ	a_m	Cell mm	Conc. g/L
219	6230	1	0.0900

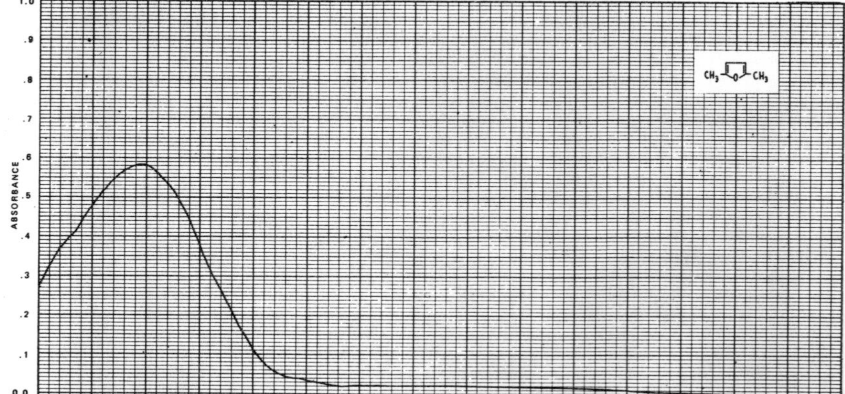

2-FURONITRILE 1576

C_5H_3NO

Mol. Wt. 93.09

Solvent: Methanol

λ Max. mμ	a_m	Cell mm	Conc. g/L
239.5	11000	1	0.075

2-FURANMETHANETHIOL 1577

C_5H_6OS

Mol. Wt. 114.17

Solvent: Methanol

λ Max. mμ	a_m	Cell mm	Conc. g/L
221	5480	1	0.100

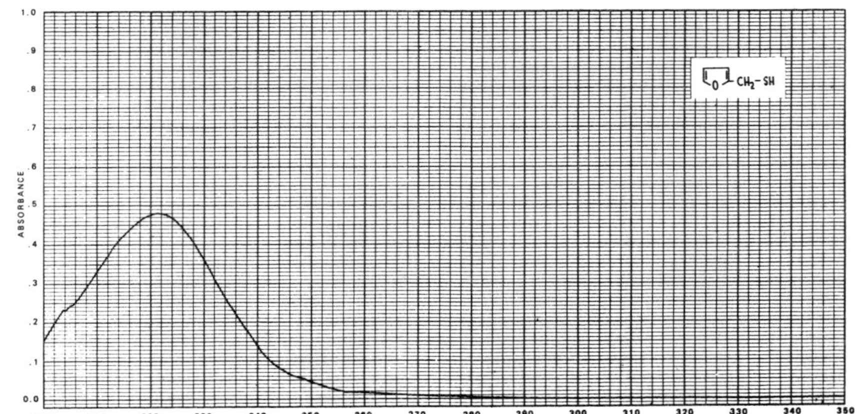

2-(2-NITROVINYL)FURAN 1578

$C_9H_5NO_3$

Mol. Wt. 139.11

M.R. 76-77°C (lit.)

Solvent: Methanol

λ Max. mμ	a_m	Cell mm	Conc. g/L
340	11800	10	0.0208
228	4280	10	0.0208

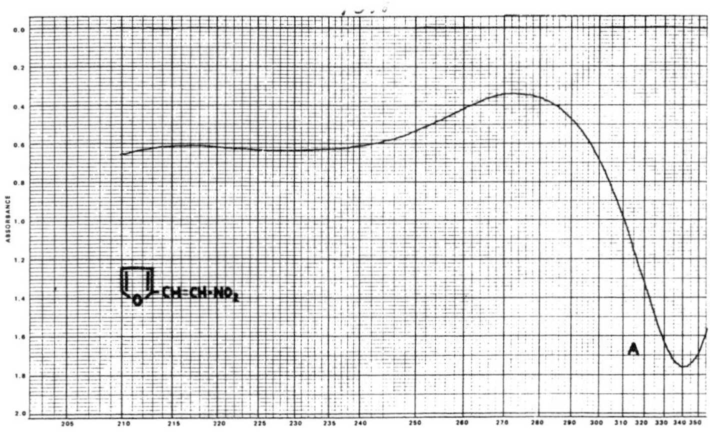

3-METHYLISOXAZOLE

C_4H_5NO
Mol. Wt. 83.09
B.P. 118°C
Solvent: Methanol

λ Max. mμ	a_m	Cell mm	Conc. g/L
208.5	3540	2	0.100

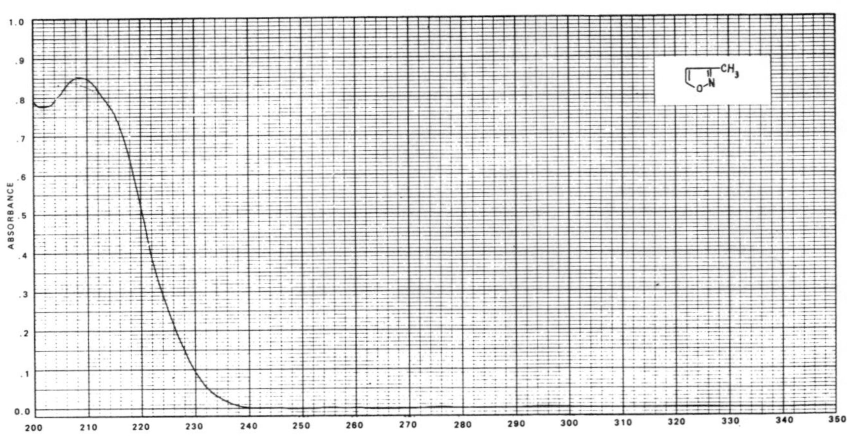

2-(m-CHLOROPHENYL)-5-PHENYLOXAZOLE

1580

$C_{15}H_{10}ClNO$
Mol. Wt. 255.71
M.P. 107°C
Solvent: Methanol

λ Max. mμ	a_m	Cell mm	Conc. g/L
307.5	26700	10	0.009
205.5	25900	10	0.009

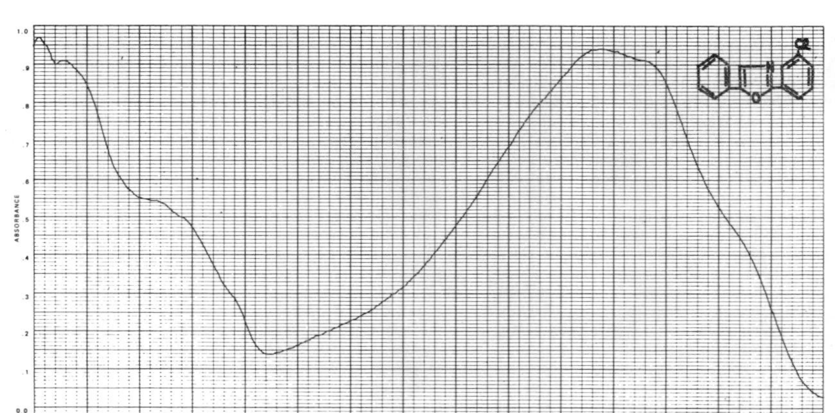

2-(HEXADECYLOXY)PYRIDINE

1581

$C_{21}H_{37}NO$
Mol. Wt. 319.54
Solvent: Methanol

λ Max. mμ	a_m	Cell mm	Conc. g/L
272	4140	2	0.100
215	8930	2	0.100

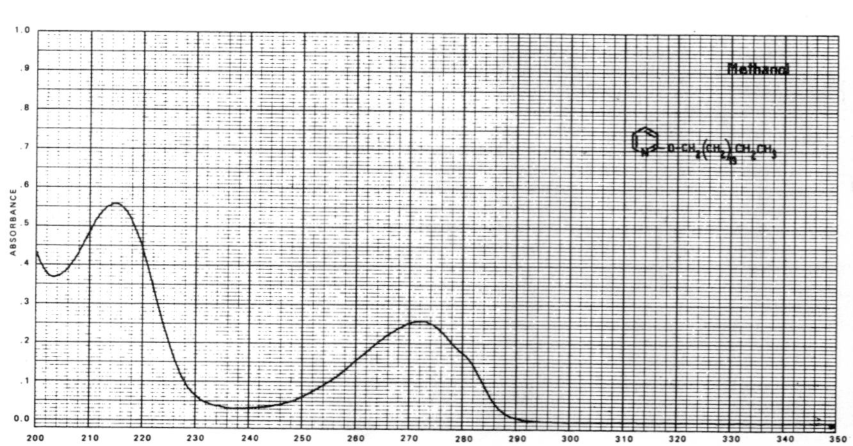

2-(HEXADECYLOXY)PYRIDINE 1581

$C_{21}H_{37}NO$
Mol. Wt. 319.54
Solvent: Methanol HCl

λ Max. mμ	a_m	Cell mm	Conc. g/L
280	15400	1	0.100

METHOXYPYRAZINE 1582

$C_5H_6N_2O$
Mol. Wt. 110.12
Solvent: Methanol

λ Max. mμ	a_m	Cell mm	Conc. g/L
276.5	5200	1	0.100

METHOXYPYRAZINE 1582

$C_5H_6N_2O$
Mol. Wt. 110.12
Solvent: Methanol HCl

λ Max. mμ	a_m	Cell mm	Conc. g/L
277	5130	1	0.100

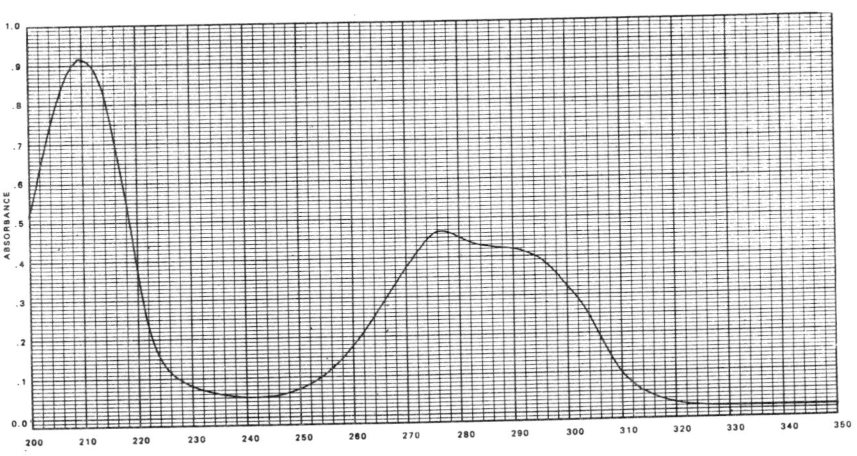

3-METHOXYPHENOTHIAZINE

1583

$C_{13}H_{11}NOS$

Mol. Wt. 229.30

Solvent: Methanol

λ Max. mμ	a_m	Cell mm	Conc. g/L
313	4630	5	0.070
247.5	31700	1	0.070
206.5	25600	1	0.070

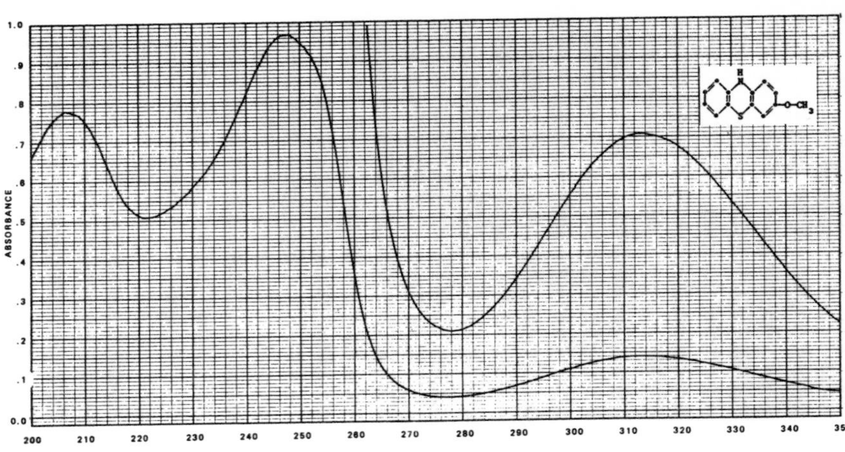

BENZOFURAN

1584

C_8H_6O

Mol. Wt. 118.14

B.P. 173-175°C

Solvent: Methanol

λ Max. mμ	a_m	Cell mm	Conc. g/L
281	2860	5	0.0636
274.5	2590	5	0.0636
269	1870	5	0.0636
243	10800	1	0.0636

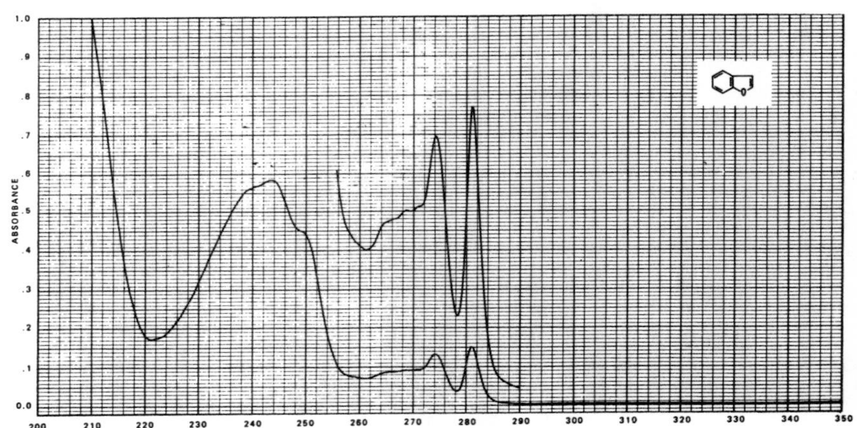

2,5,6-TRIMETHYLBENZOXAZOLE

1585

$C_{10}H_{11}NO$

Mol. Wt. 161.21

Solvent: Dioxane

λ Max. mμ	a_m	Cell mm	Conc. g/L
285.5	5340	1	0.100
279.5	5130	1	0.100
275.5	5010	1	0.100
236	11100	1	0.100

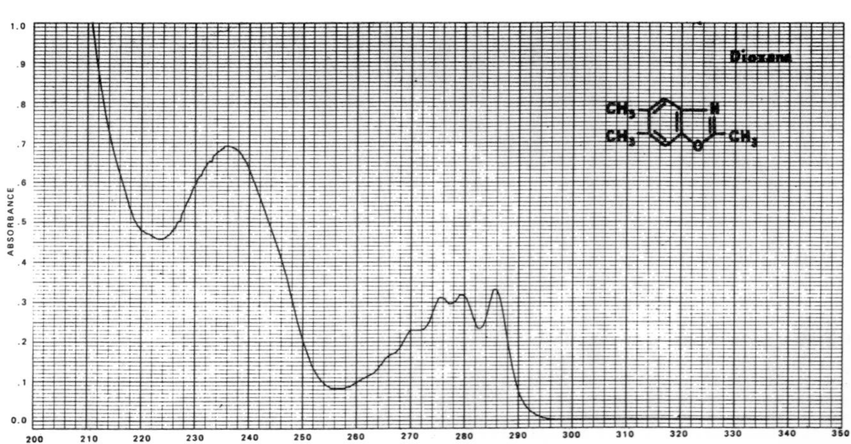

PHENOXATHIIN 1586

$C_{12}H_8OS$

Mol. Wt. 200.25

M.P. 56-58°C

Solvent: Methanol

λ Max. mμ	a_m	Cell mm	Conc. g/L
293	3710	10	0.03
x	x	10	0.01
236	28700	10	0.004
221.5	45300	10	0.004

PHENOXATHIIN, 10,10-DIOXIDE 1587

$C_{12}H_8O_3S$

Mol. Wt. 232.26

Solvent: Methanol

λ Max. mμ	a_m	Cell mm	Conc. g/L
293.5	4820	2	0.100
286.5	4300	2	0.100
216	40300	1	0.0500

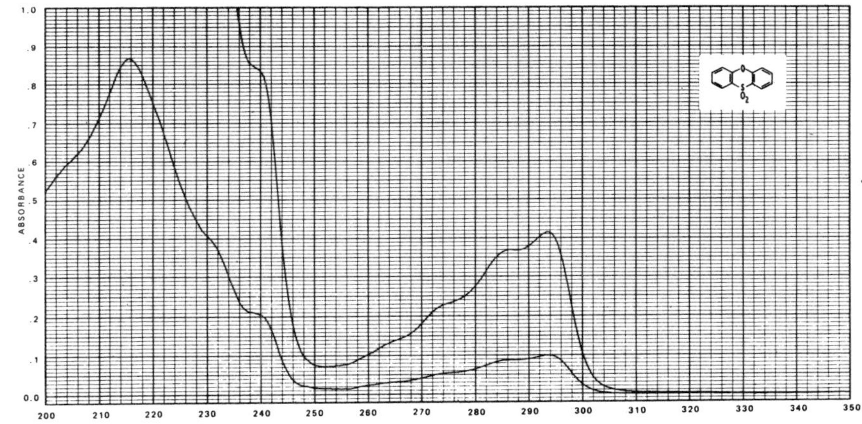

1,3-BENZODIOXOLE 1588

$C_7H_6O_2$

Mol. Wt. 122.12

B.P. 62°C/13mm

Solvent: Methanol

λ Max. mμ	a_m	Cell mm	Conc. g/L
282.5	3240	1	0.215
231	3050	1	0.215

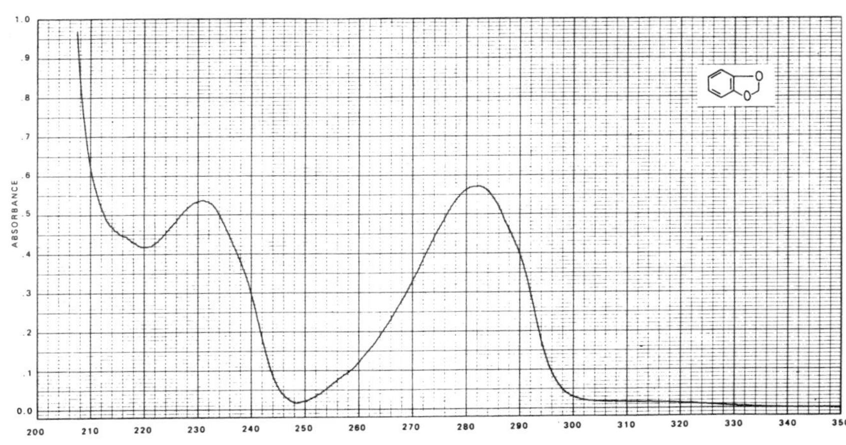

ISOCHROMAN **1589**

$C_9H_{10}O$
Mol. Wt. 134.18
Solvent: Methanol

λ Max. mμ	a_m	Cell mm	Conc. g/L
272	578	10	0.175
264.5	550	10	0.175
258.5	439	10	0.175
x	x	1	0.175

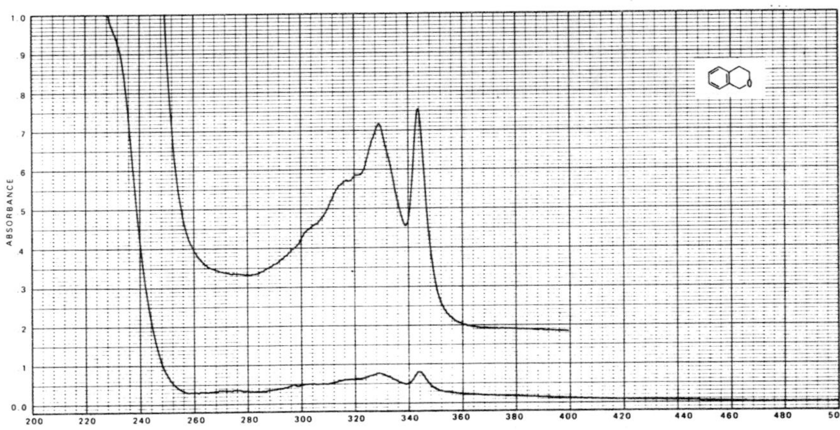

1,4-BENZODIOXAN **1590**

$C_8H_8O_2$
Mol. Wt. 136.15
Solvent: Methanol

λ Max. mμ	a_m	Cell mm	Conc. g/L
284	2240	1	0.110
278	2530	1	0.110
218	5640	1	0.110

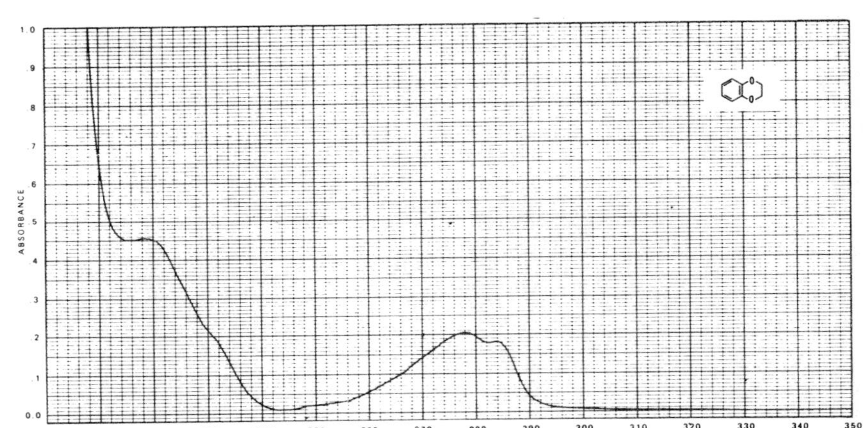

DIBENZO-p-DIOXIN **1591**

$C_{12}H_8O_2$
Mol. Wt. 184.20
Solvent: Methanol

λ Max. mμ	a_m	Cell mm	Conc. g/L
289	3960	2	0.100
227	43700	2	0.0200
224	44000	2	0.0200

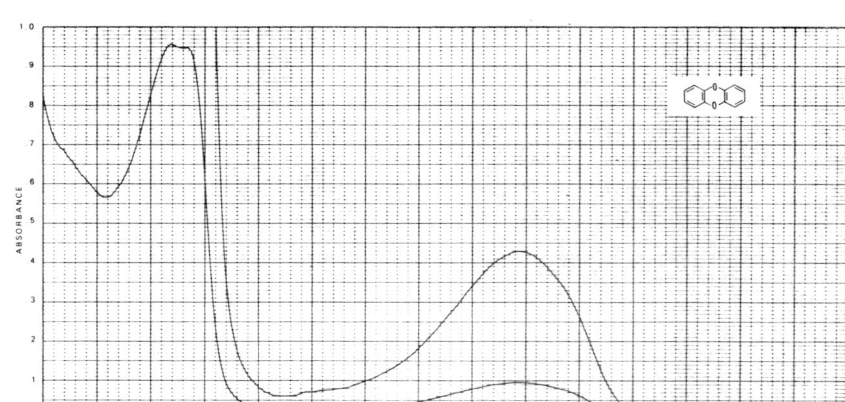

λ Max. mμ	a_m	Cell mm	Conc. g/L

Compounds 1592 and 1593 do not display any maxima in the near UV.

DIMETHOXYDIPHENYLSILANE

1594

$C_{14}H_{16}O_2Si$
Mol. Wt. 244.37
B.P. 191°C/53mm
Solvent: Methanol

λ Max. mμ	a_m	Cell mm	Conc. g/L
270	598	20	0.125
263.5	779	20	0.125
258.5	684	20	0.125
252.5	498	20	0.125
214	18000	1	0.100

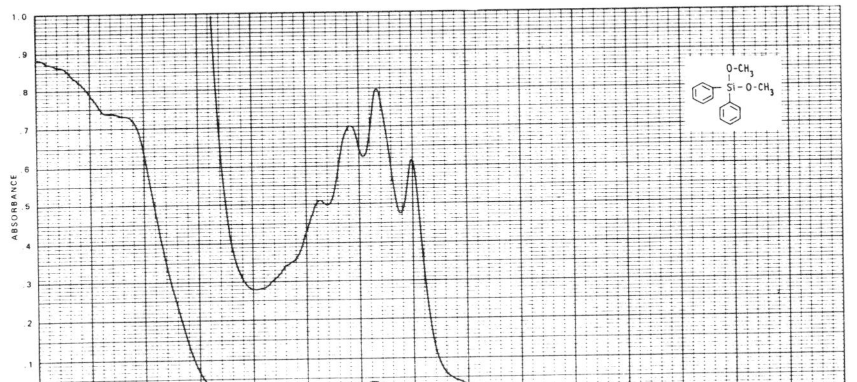

1595

λ Max. mμ	a_m	Cell mm	Conc. g/L

The aliphatic silicon and phosphorus ethers (compounds 1595 through 1607) do not display any maxima in the near UV.

PHENYL PHOSPHITE

1608

$C_{18}H_{15}O_3P$
Mol. Wt. 310.30
Solvent: Methanol

λ Max. mμ	a_m	Cell mm	Conc. g/L
263.5	2030	10	0.0908
x	x	10	0.0091

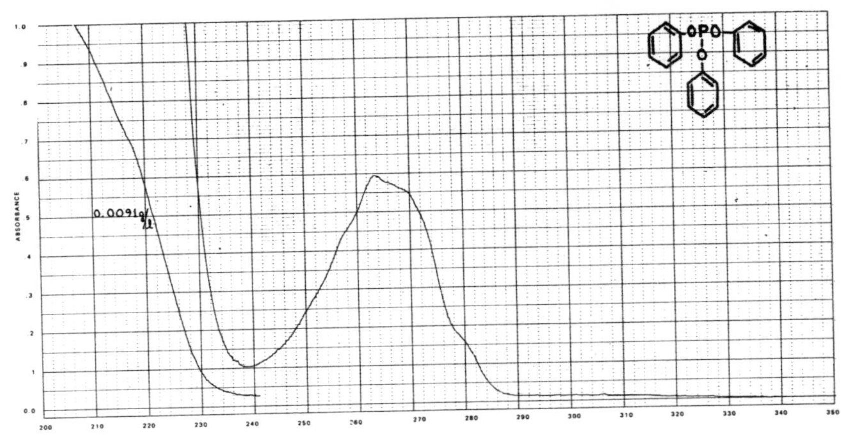

1609

λ Max. mμ	a_m	Cell mm	Conc. g/L

The aliphatic and alicyclic peroxides (compounds 1609 and 1610) do not display any maxima in the near UV.

λ Max. mμ	a_m	Cell mm	Conc. g/L

PRIMARY ALCOHOLS

Aliphatic Compounds

The aliphatic primary alcohols do not produce any maxima in the near UV. Methanol, ethanol and isopropanol are used extensively as solvents for the preparation of spectra of other compounds and have a near ultraviolet cut-off wavelength of 210 - 215 mμ when using 1 cm cells.

Aromatic Compounds

The near ultraviolet spectra of benzyl alcohol is very similar to that of the benzyl ethers as expected.

A weak band with benzenoid fine structure occurs at 252 - 258 mμ.

The UV spectra of the simple benzyl alcohols do not change upon the addition of acid or base unless a reactive substituent is also present.

The spectral data for benzyl alcohol and three para substituted derivatives is given below.

Compound	$\lambda_{max}(\epsilon_{max})$	$\lambda_{max}(\epsilon_{max})$	Solvent	Spectrum
Benzyl alcohol	- - - - - - - - - -	252 (233)	Methanol	1700
p-Methylbenzyl alcohol	217 (9090)	265 (771)	Methanol	1713
p-Fluorobenzyl alcohol	- - - - - - - - - -	264 (757)	Methanol	1716
p-Methoxybenzyl alcohol	226 (10400)	274 (1490)	Methanol	1723

Furfuryl Alcohol

Furfuryl alcohol produces two absorption bands, a very weak band near 270 mμ and a stronger band near 216 mμ which probably arises from the diene absorption.

1-(DIPHENYLPHOSPHINYL)-1-BUTANOL 1659

$C_{16}H_{19}O_2P$

Mol. Wt. 274.30

M.P. 112-115°C

Solvent: Methanol

λ Max. mμ	a_m	Cell mm	Conc. g/L
272	1170	10	0.100
265	1430	10	0.100
259.5	1090	10	0.100
222	18100	1	0.100

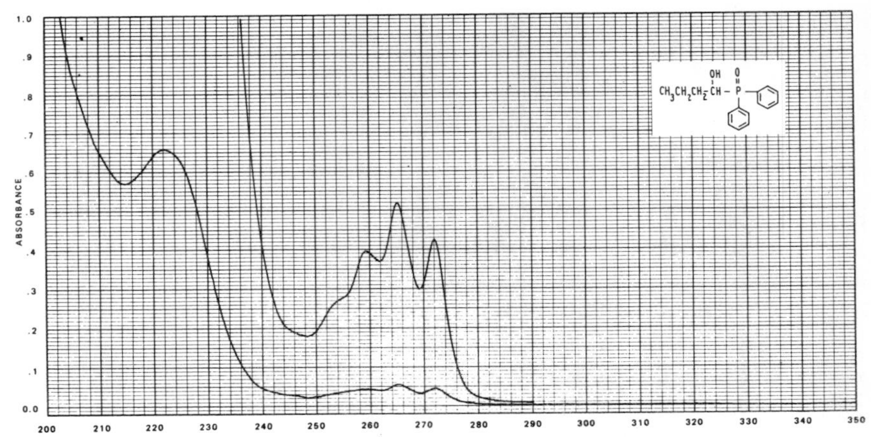

1660

λ Max. mμ	a_m	Cell mm	Conc. g/L

The substituted primary alcohols (compounds 1660 - 1677) do not display any maxima in the near UV.

2-THIOPHENEETHANOL 1678

C_6H_8OS

Mol. Wt. 128.19

Solvent: Methanol

λ Max. mμ	a_m	Cell mm	Conc. g/L
233	5920	2	0.100

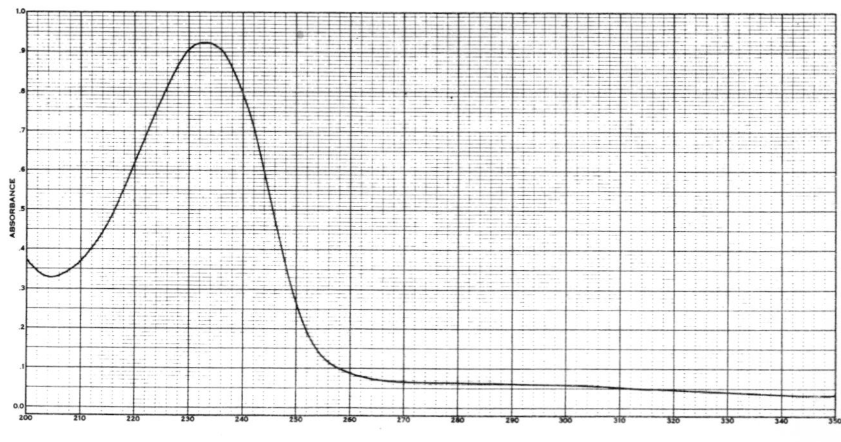

1679

λ Max. mμ	a_m	Cell mm	Conc. g/L

The primary alcohols (compounds 1679 through 1699) do not display any maxima in the near UV.

1700

BENZYL ALCOHOL

C_7H_8O

Mol. Wt. 108.14

B.P. 204.7°C (lit.)

Solvent: Methanol

λ Max. mμ	a_m	Cell mm	Conc. g/L
266.5	112	20	0.215
263	165	20	0.215
257	229	20	0.215
251.5	233	20	0.215
x	x	1	0.215

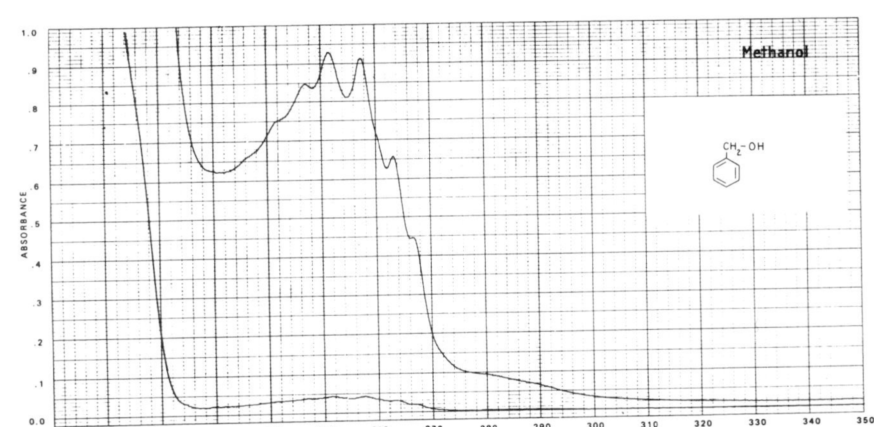

1701

PHENETHYL ALCOHOL

$C_8H_{10}O$

Mol. Wt. 122.17

Solvent: Cyclohexane

λ Max. mμ	a_m	Cell mm	Conc. g/L
x	x	10	2.13
267	138	10	0.640
263.5	160	10	0.640
258	212	10	0.640
252.5	168	10	0.640
247.5	115	10	0.640
x	x	10	0.0064

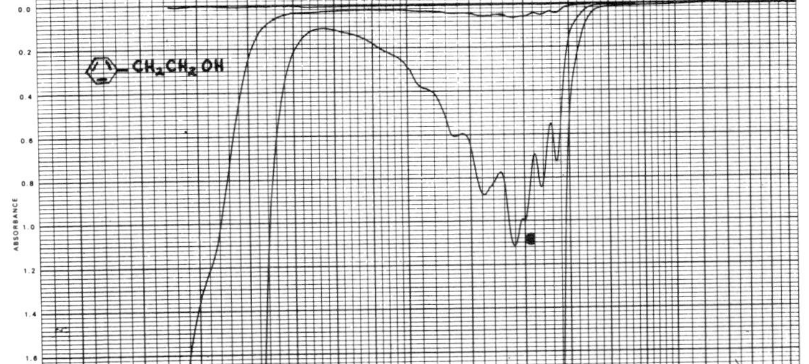

3-PHENYL-1-PROPANOL 1702

$C_9H_{12}O$

Mol. Wt. 136.20

Solvent: Methanol

λ Max. mμ	a_m	Cell mm	Conc. g/L
268	166	10	0.438
264	157	10	0.438
261	206	10	0.438
259	200	10	0.438
254.5	175	10	0.438
253	177	10	0.438
248	141	10	0.438
243	109	10	0.438
x	x	1	0.438

2-(BENZYLMETHYLAMINO)ETHANOL 1703

$C_{10}H_{15}NO$

Mol. Wt. 165.24

Solvent: Methanol

λ Max. mμ	a_m	Cell mm	Conc. g/L
256	635	20	0.100
250	697	20	0.100
x	x	1	0.100

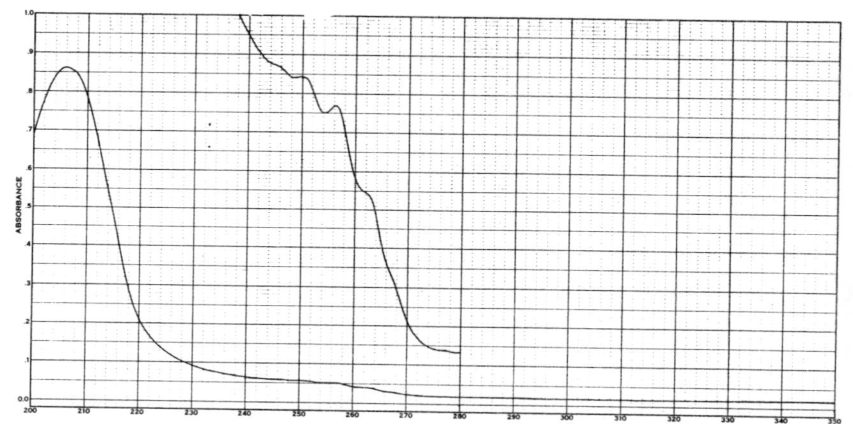

2-(DIBENZYLAMINO)ETHANOL 1704

$C_{16}H_{19}NO$

Mol. Wt. 241.34

Solvent: Methanol

λ Max. mμ	a_m	Cell mm	Conc. g/L
263.5	424	10	0.279
257.5	591	10	0.279
251	634	10	0.279
212	8450	1	0.279

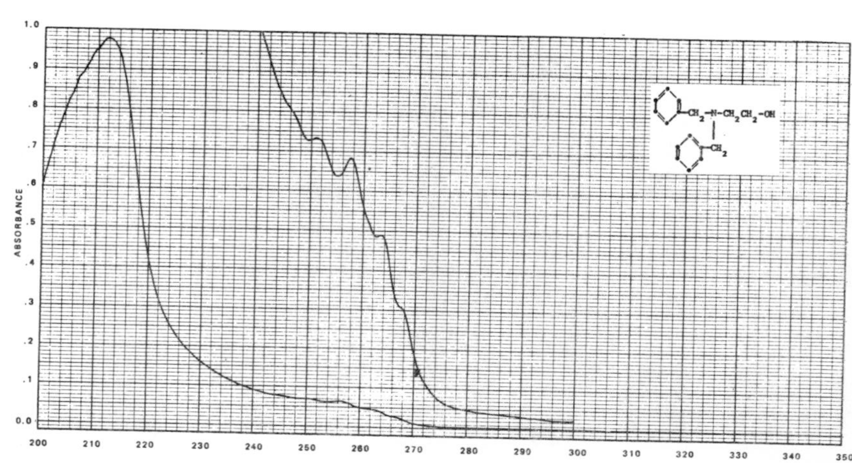

2-(BENZYLOXY)ETHANOL

1705

$C_9H_{12}O_2$
Mol. Wt. 152.19
Solvent: Methanol

λ Max. mμ	a_m	Cell mm	Conc. g/L
257	252	20	0.100
251	234	20	0.100
215	2720	5	0.100

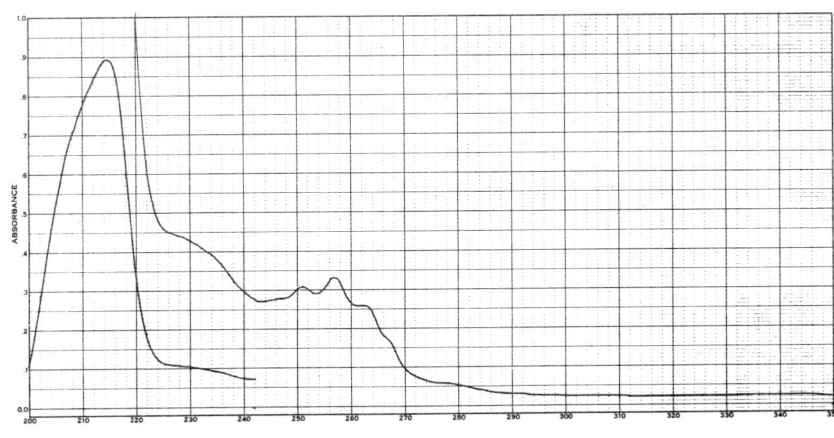

2-(N-ETHYLANILINO)ETHANOL

1706

$C_{10}H_{15}NO$
Mol. Wt. 165.23
Solvent: Methanol

λ Max. mμ	a_m	Cell mm	Conc. g/L
x	x	10	2.220
301	2200	10	0.1110
257.5	15600	10	0.0111

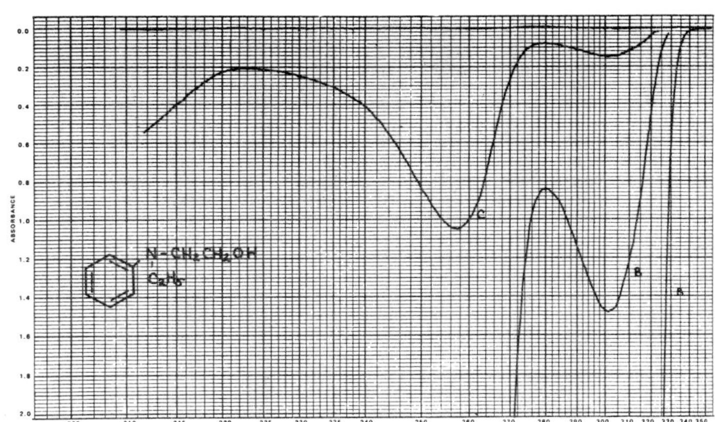

2[(p-CHLOROBENZYLIDENE)AMINO] ETHANOL

1707

$C_9H_{10}ClNO$
Mol. Wt. 183.64
M.P. ∿70°C
Solvent: Methanol

λ Max. mμ	a_m	Cell mm	Conc. g/L
289	1200	10	0.100
252	16300	1	0.100
207	16700	1	0.100

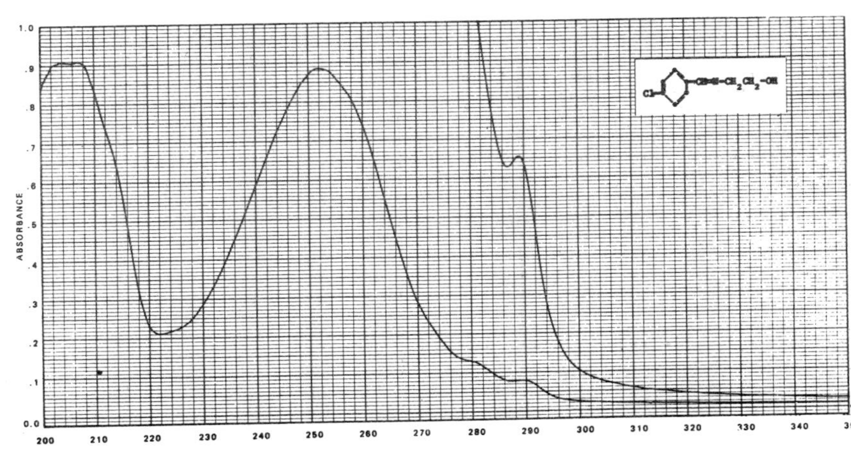

2-(p-TOLYLTHIO)ETHANOL 1708

$C_9H_{12}OS$

Mol. Wt. 168.26

B.P. 158-160°C/10mm

Solvent: Methanol

λ Max. mμ	a_m	Cell mm	Conc. g/L
253.5	6370	2	0.100

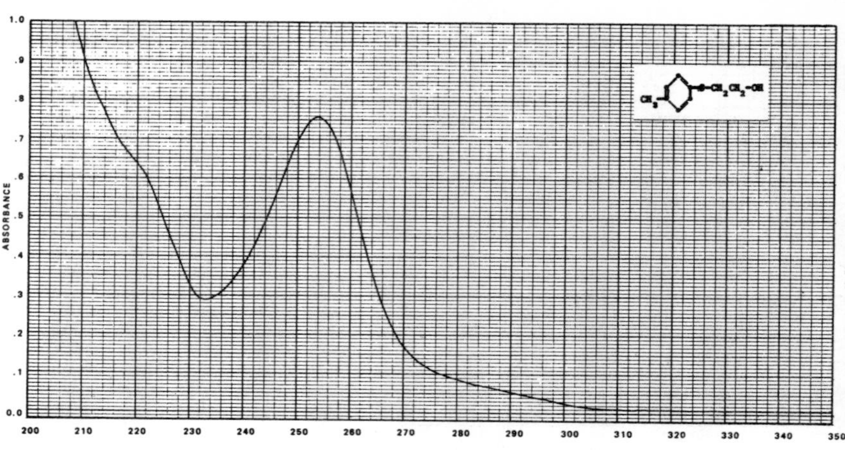

p-TOLYLSULFONYLMETHANOL 1709

$C_8H_{10}O_3S$

Mol. Wt. 186.23

M.P. 93-95°C (lit.)

Solvent: Methanol

λ Max. mμ	a_m	Cell mm	Conc. g/L
x	x	10	1.94
x	x	10	0.194
242	4670	10	0.0582
222	11000	10	0.0194

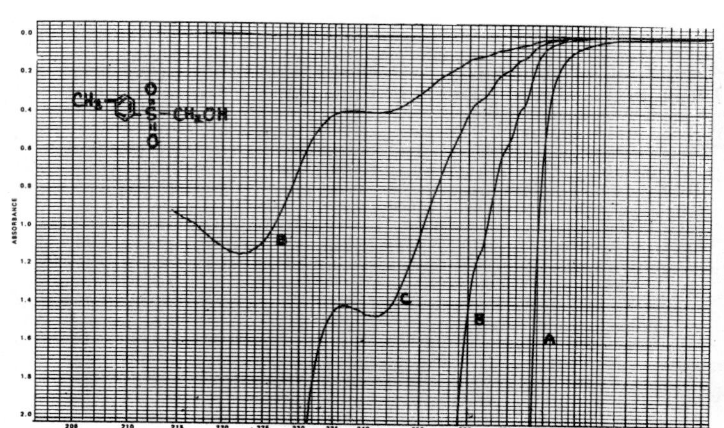

2-PHENOXYETHANOL 1710

$C_8H_{10}O_2$

Mol. Wt. 138.17

Solvent: Methanol

λ Max. mμ	a_m	Cell mm	Conc. g/L
277	1420	1	0.174
270.3	1690	1	0.174
219.5	7140	1	0.174

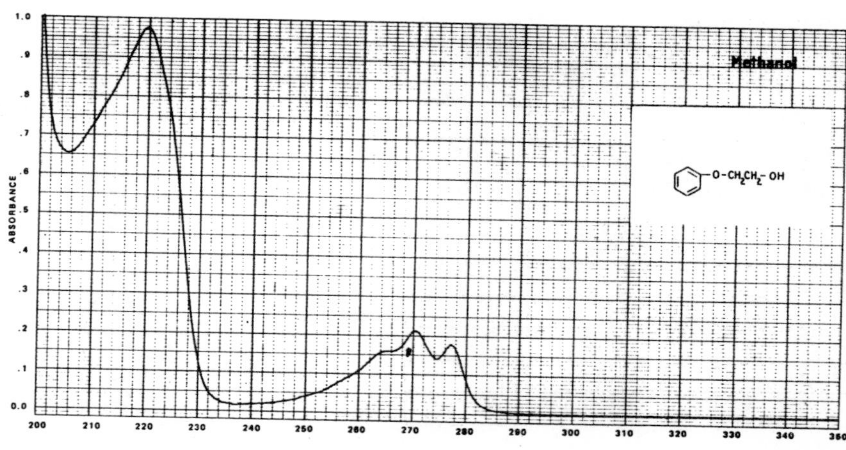

CINNAMYL ALCOHOL

1711

$C_9H_{10}O$
Mol. Wt. 134.17
Solvent: Methanol

λ Max. mμ	a_m	Cell mm	Conc. g/L
x	x	10	2.00
291	1340	10	0.100
282	1720	10	0.100
250.5	12000	10	0.0100

3-PHENYL-2-BUTEN-1-ol

1712

$C_{10}H_{12}O$
Mol. Wt. 148.21
Solvent: Methanol

λ Max. mμ	a_m	Cell mm	Conc. g/L
243.5	14600	1	0.100
x	x	1	0.100

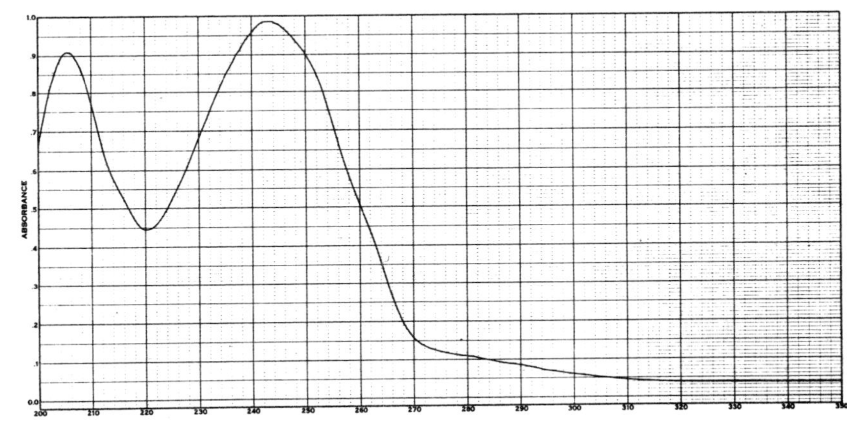

p-METHYL BENZYL ALCOHOL

1713

$C_8H_{10}O$
Mol. Wt. 122.17
M.P. 60-61°C
Solvent: Methanol

λ Max. mμ	a_m	Cell mm	Conc. g/L
273	621	10	0.100
265	771	10	0.100
217	9090	1	0.100

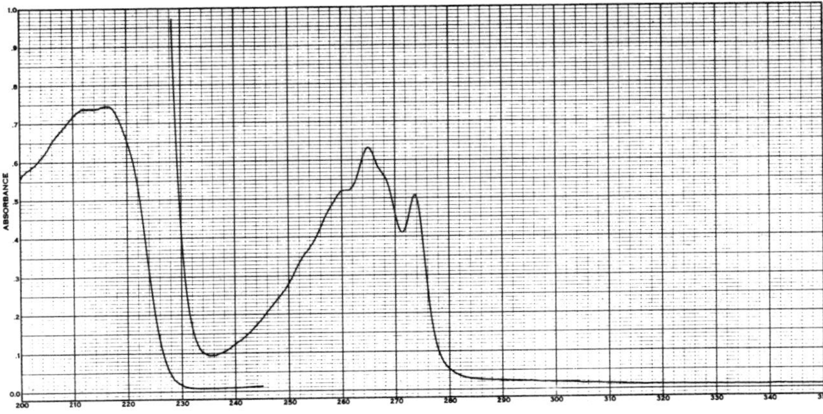

p-CYMEN-7-OL

1714

$C_{10}H_{14}O$
Mol. Wt. 150.22
B.P. 127-129°C/10mm
Solvent: Methanol

λ Max. mμ	^{a}m	Cell mm	Conc. g/L
271.5	261	10	0.208
262.5	383	10	0.208
258	349	10	0.208
218	8570	1	0.104
213.5	8260	1	0.104

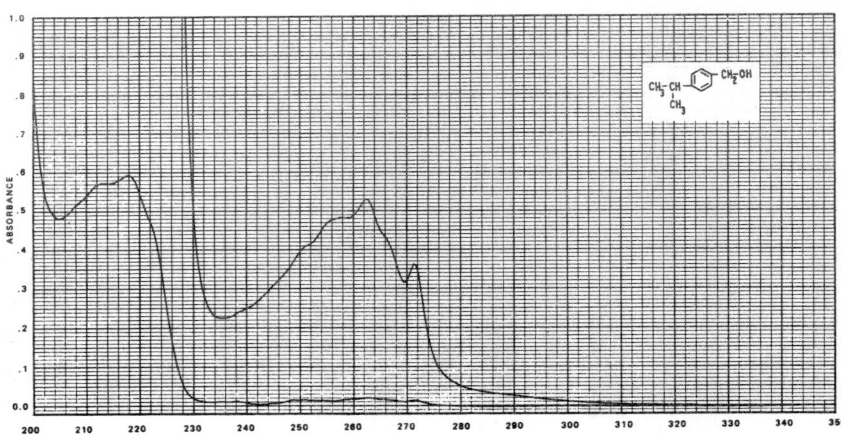

o-FLUOROBENZYL ALCOHOL

1715

C_7H_7FO
Mol. Wt. 126.13
Solvent: Methanol

λ Max. mμ	^{a}m	Cell mm	Conc. g/L
268.5	751	2	0.3772
262	815	2	0.3772
205.5	3950	2	0.07544

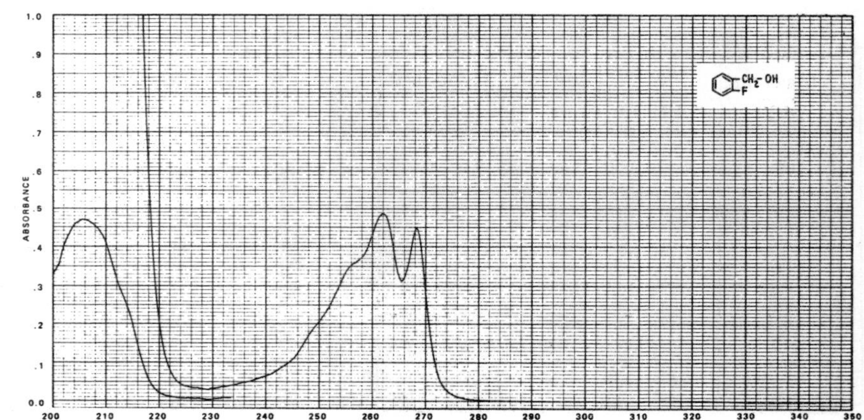

p-FLUOROBENZYL ALCOHOL

1716

C_7H_7FO
Mol. Wt. 126.13
M.P. 23°C B.P. 76-78°C/13mm
Solvent: Methanol

λ Max. mμ	^{a}m	Cell mm	Conc. g/L
271	657	5	0.22290
264.5	757	5	0.22290
x	x	1	0.11145

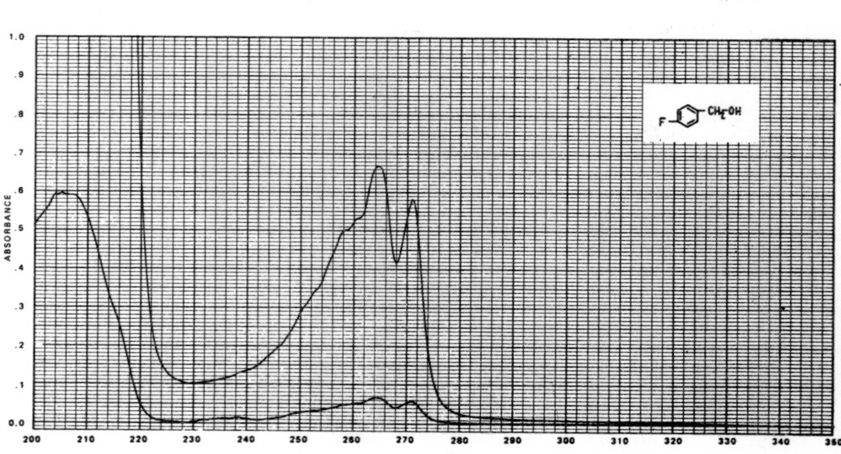

o-CHLOROBENZYL ALCOHOL

1717

C_7H_7ClO

Mol. Wt. 142.59

M.P. 69-71°C

Solvent: Methanol

λ Max. mμ	a_m	Cell mm	Conc. g/L
270	182	20	0.100
263	249	20	0.100
212	8030	1	0.100

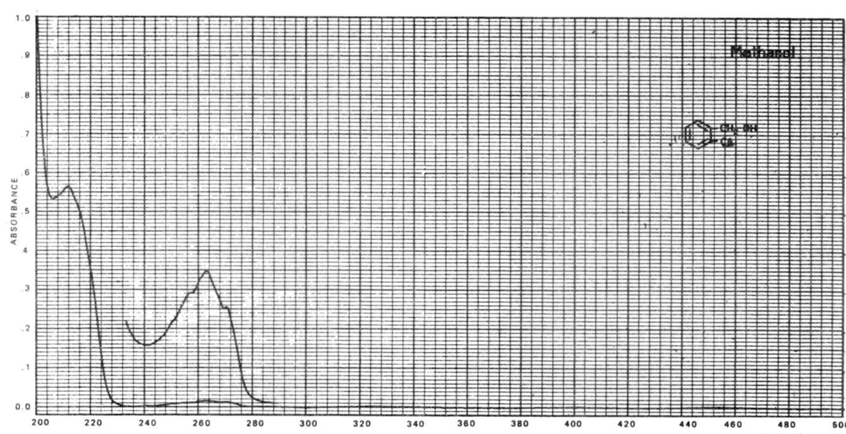

p-AMINOPHENETHYL ALCOHOL

1718

$C_8H_{11}NO$

Mol. Wt. 137.18

M.P. 105-108°C

Solvent: Methanol

λ Max. mμ	a_m	Cell mm	Conc. g/L
289	1480	5	0.100
236	9630	1	0.100

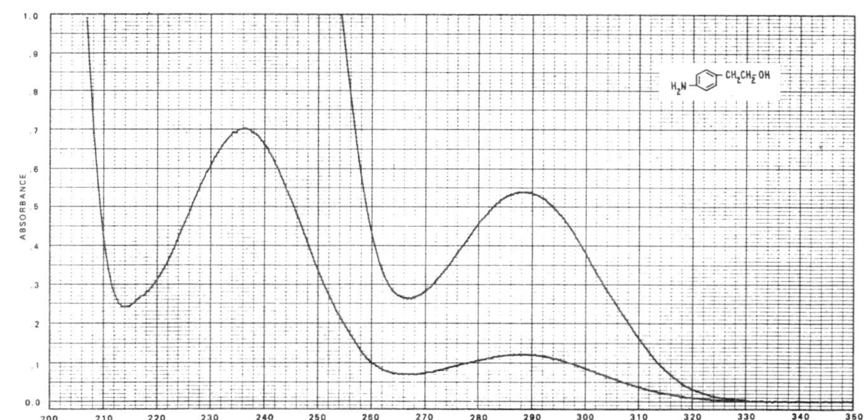

p-AMINOPHENETHYL ALCOHOL

1718

$C_8H_{11}NO$

Mol. Wt. 137.18

M.P. 105-108°C

Solvent: Methanol HCl

λ Max. mμ	a_m	Cell mm	Conc. g/L
268	197	10	0.100
259.5	260	10	0.100
209	7540	1	0.100

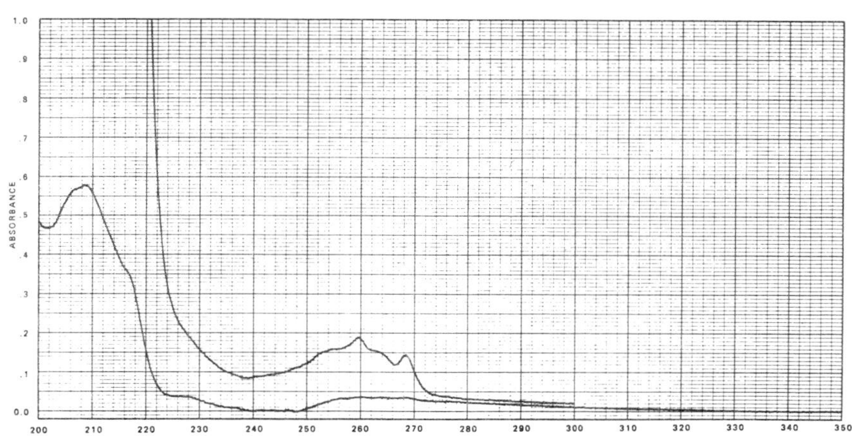

o-NITROBENZYL ALCOHOL

1719

$C_7H_7NO_3$

Mol. Wt. 153.14

M.P. 74°C (lit.)

Solvent: Methanol

λ Max. mμ	a_m	Cell mm	Conc. g/L
260.0	5800	2	0.100

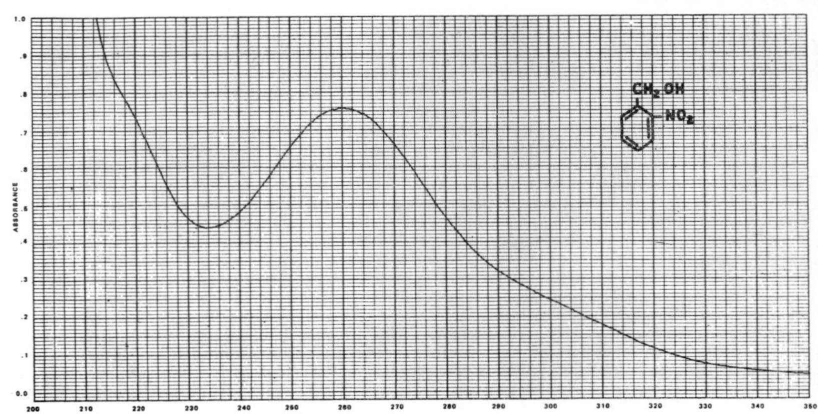

m-NITROBENZYL ALCOHOL

1720

$C_7H_7NO_3$

Mol. Wt. 153.14

M.P. 30-32°C

Solvent: Methanol

λ Max. mμ	a_m	Cell mm	Conc. g/L
262	7210	1	0.1130

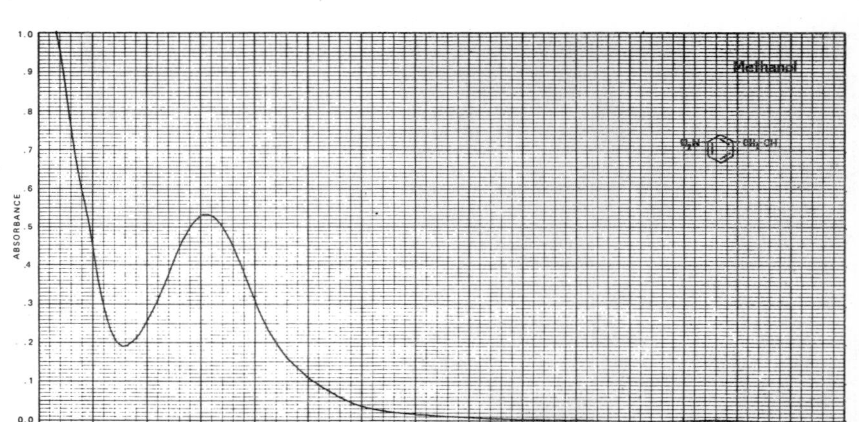

p-NITROBENZYL ALCOHOL

1721

$C_7H_7NO_3$

Mol. Wt. 153.14

Solvent: Methanol

λ Max. mμ	a_m	Cell mm	Conc. g/L
270.5	8790	1	0.100
214	6650	1	0.100

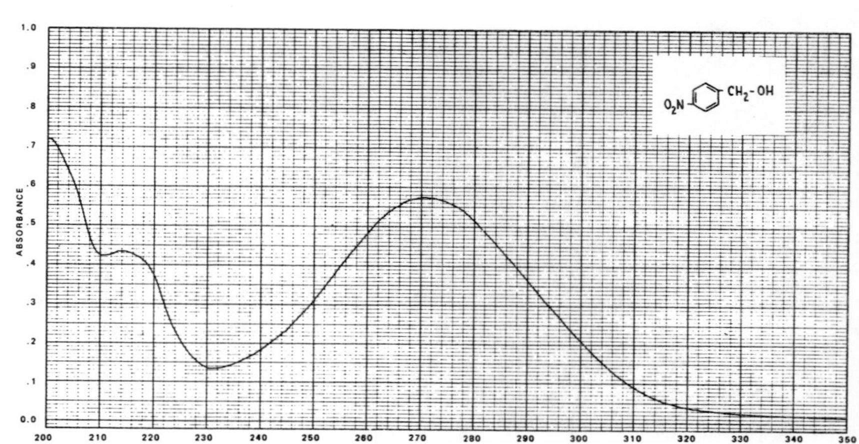

o-METHOXYBENZYL ALCOHOL

1722

$C_8H_{10}O_2$
Mol. Wt. 138.17
B.P. 290°C
Solvent: Methanol

λ Max. mμ	a_m	Cell mm	Conc. g/L
275.5	1780	5	0.110
270.5	1830	5	0.110
220	6530	1	0.110

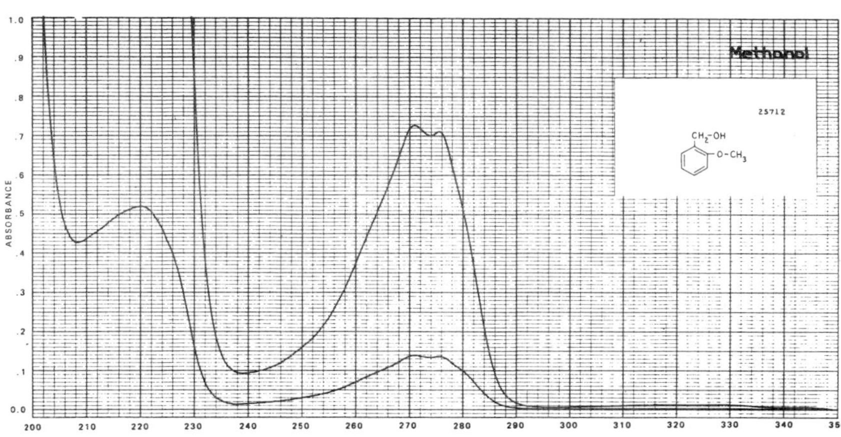

p-METHOXYBENZYL ALCOHOL

1723

$C_8H_{10}O_2$
Mol. Wt. 138.17
M.P. 23-25°C
Solvent: Methanol

λ Max. mμ	a_m	Cell mm	Conc. g/L
280	1270	5	0.121
274.5	1490	5	0.121
225.5	10400	1	0.121

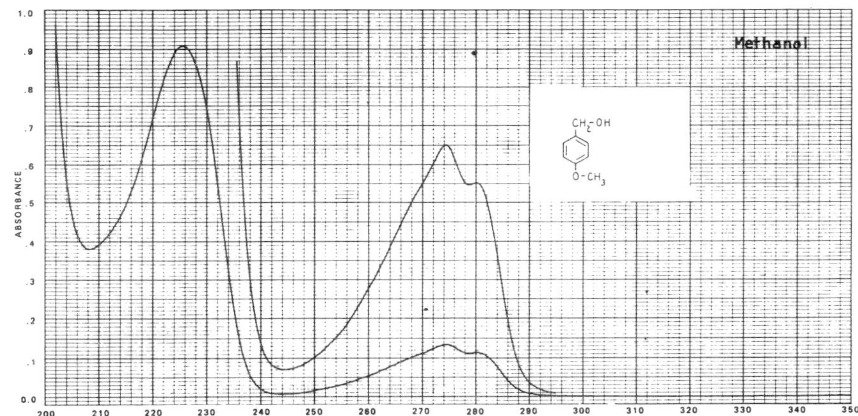

3-(p-NITROPHENYL)-2-PROPEN-1-OL

1724

$C_9H_9NO_3$
Mol. Wt. 179.18
M.P. 127-129°C
Solvent: Methanol

λ Max. mμ	a_m	Cell mm	Conc. g/L
302	12400	1	0.100
220	10600	1	0.100

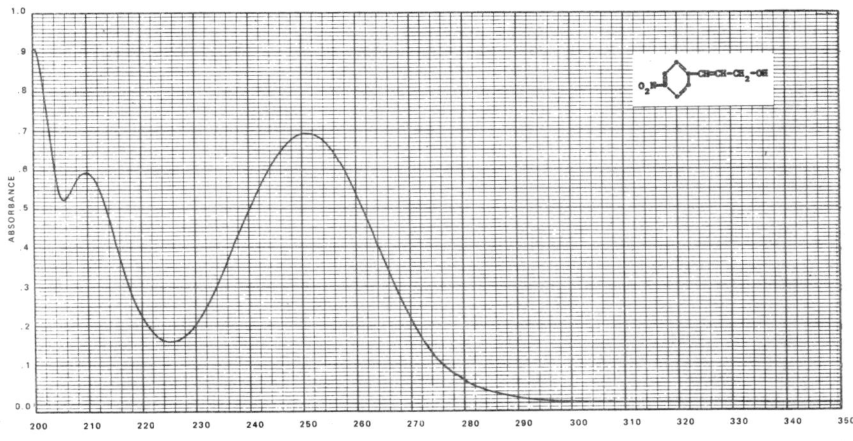

1-NAPHTHALENEETHANOL 1725

$C_{12}H_{12}O$
Mol. Wt. 172.23
Solvent: Methanol

λ Max. mμ	a_m	Cell mm	Conc. g/L
288	1560	5	0.100
281	2240	5	0.100
271	1910	5	0.100
223	19000	5	0.100

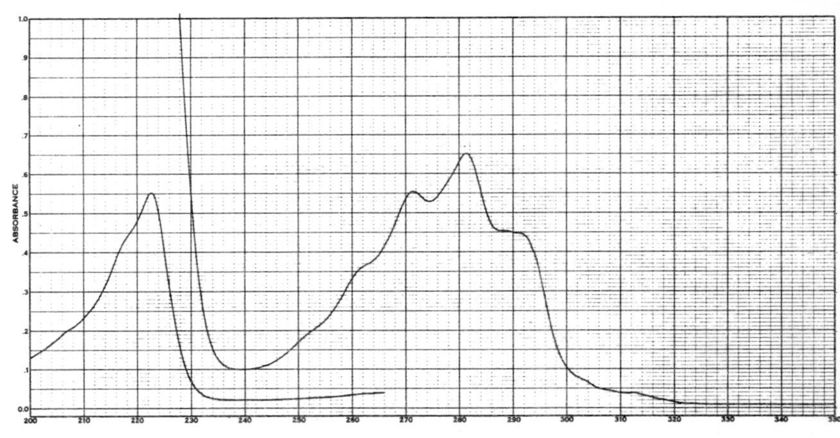

2-(2-NAPHTHYLOXY)ETHANOL 1726

$C_{12}H_{12}O_2$
Mol. Wt. 188.23
M.P. 64°C (lit.)
Solvent: Methanol

λ Max. mμ	a_m	Cell mm	Conc. g/L
327.0	1680	5	0.100
319.5	1160	5	0.100
313.0	1290	5	0.100
282.0	2730	5	0.100
271.0	4060	2	0.100
261.0	3760	2	0.100

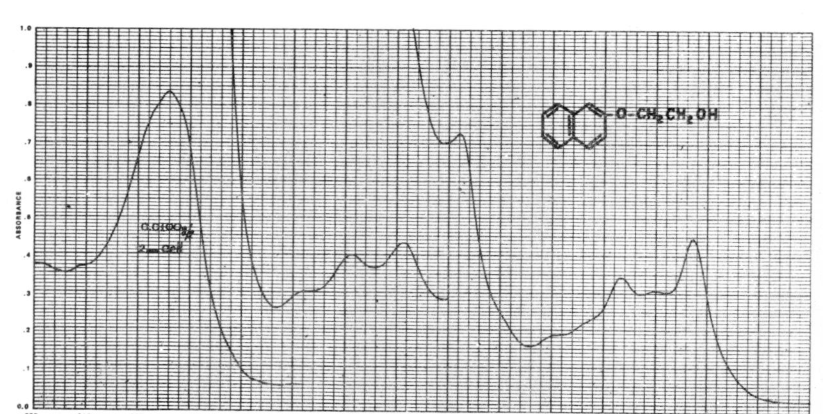

FLUORENE-9-METHANOL 1727

$C_{14}H_{12}O$
Mol. Wt. 196.25
M.P. 102-104°C
Solvent: Methanol

λ Max. mμ	a_m	Cell mm	Conc. g/L
300	7100	1	0.100
289	5490	1	0.100
265	19600	1	0.100
228	6670	1	0.100
220.5	16800	1	0.100

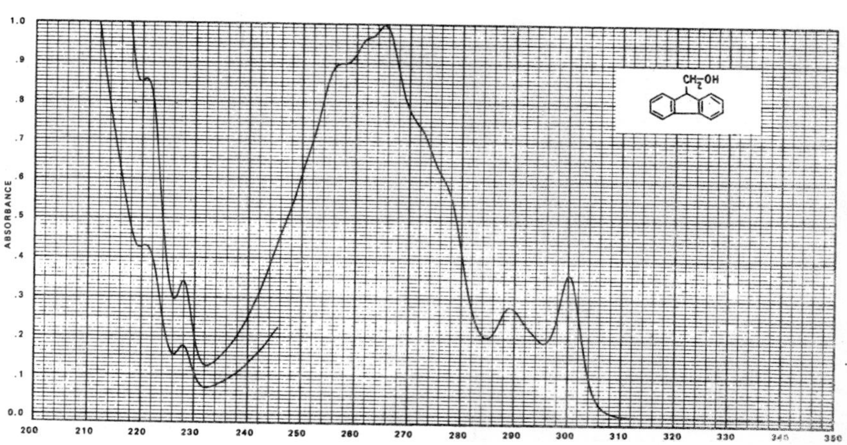

2-PYRIDINEMETHANOL

C_6H_7NO

Mol. Wt. 109.13

B.P. 112-113^oC/16mm

Solvent: Methanol

λ Max. mμ	a_m	Cell mm	Conc. g/L
267	2460	2	0.1183
261	3400	2	0.1183
255.5	2970	2	0.1183

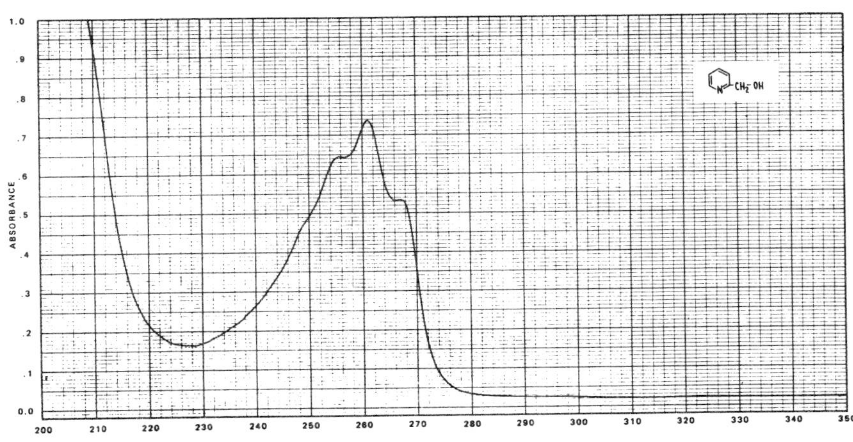

1728

2-PYRIDINEMETHANOL

C_6H_7NO

Mol. Wt. 109.13

B.P. 112-113^oC/16mm

Solvent: Methanol HCl

λ Max. mμ	a_m	Cell mm	Conc. g/L
262.5	6660	1	0.1183

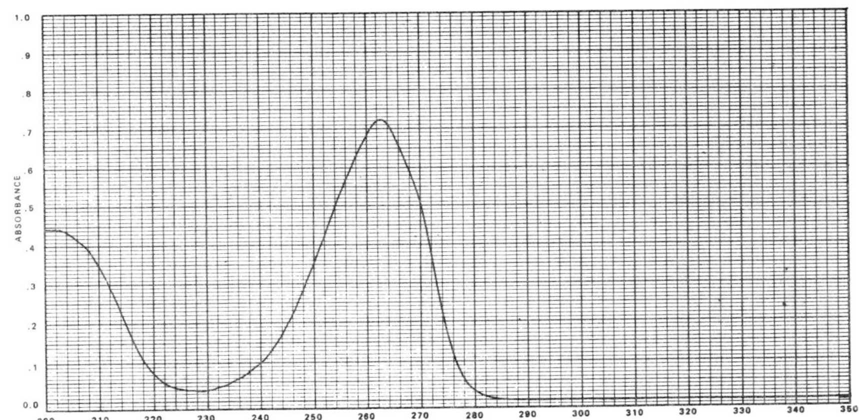

λ Max. mμ	a_m	Cell mm	Conc. g/L

4-PYRIDINEMETHANOL

1729

C_6H_7NO

Mol. Wt. 109.13

B.P. 140-142°C/12mm

Solvent: Methanol

λ Max. mμ	a_m	Cell mm	Conc. g/L
256	2160	2	0.100

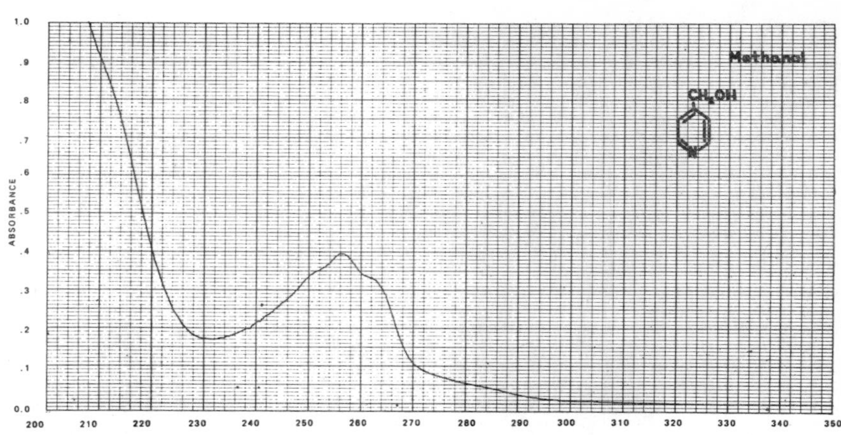

4-PYRIDINEMETHANOL

1729

C_6H_7NO

Mol. Wt. 109.13

B.P. 140-142°C/12mm

Solvent: Methanol HCl

λ Max. mμ	a_m	Cell mm	Conc. g/L
254	4790	2	0.100
218.5	4200	2	0.100

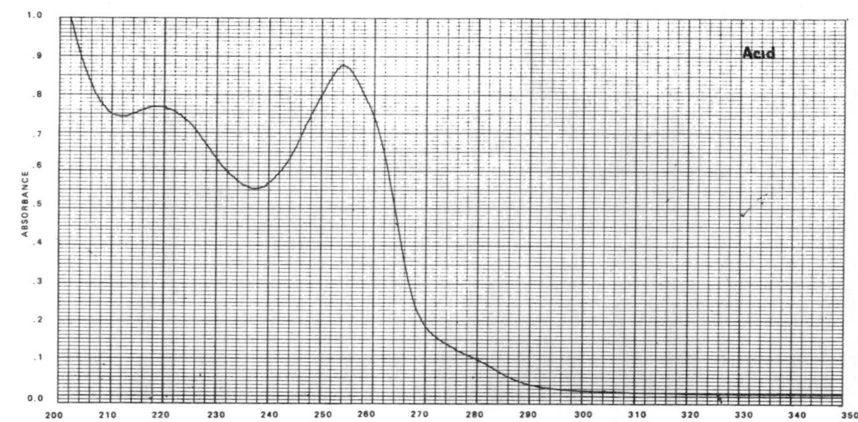

2-BENZIMIDAZOLEMETHANOL

1730

$C_8H_8N_2O$

Mol. Wt. 148.17

M.P. 170-172°C

Solvent: Methanol

λ Max. mμ	a_m	Cell mm	Conc. g/L
280.5	5030	2	0.100
274	5330	2	0.100
244	4390	2	0.100
x	x	1	0.100

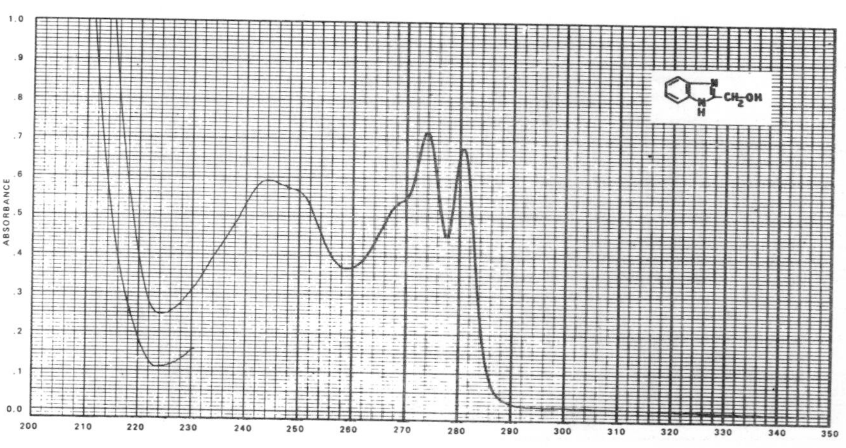

2-BENZIMIDAZOLEMETHANOL

1730

$C_8H_8N_2O$
Mol. Wt. 148.17
M.P. 170-172°C
Solvent: Methanol HCl

λ Max. mμ	a_m	Cell mm	Conc. g/L
275	7290	1	0.100
269	6670	1	0.100
237	3290	1	0.100

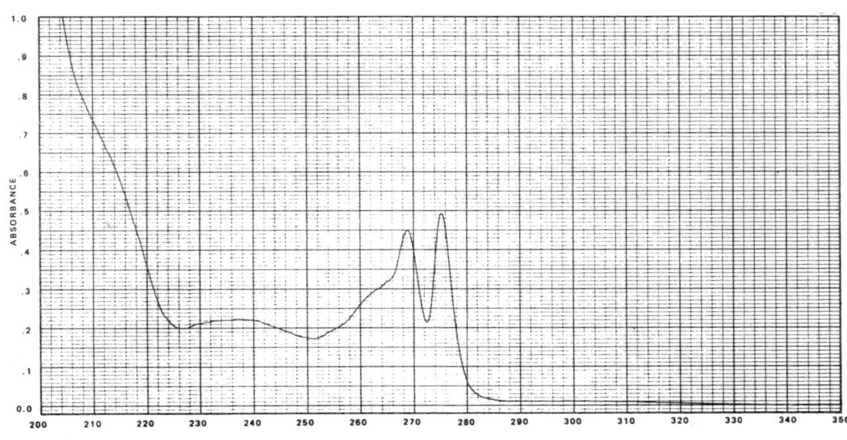

3-QUINOLINEMETHANOL

1731

$C_{10}H_9NO$
Mol. Wt. 159.18
M.P. 83.5-84°C
Solvent: Methanol

λ Max. mμ	a_m	Cell mm	Conc. g/L
316	3500	10	0.04
303	3060	10	0.04
290	3030	10	0.04
278	3350	10	0.04
232.5	33200	10	0.004
228.5	35400	10	0.004
207	39100	10	0.004

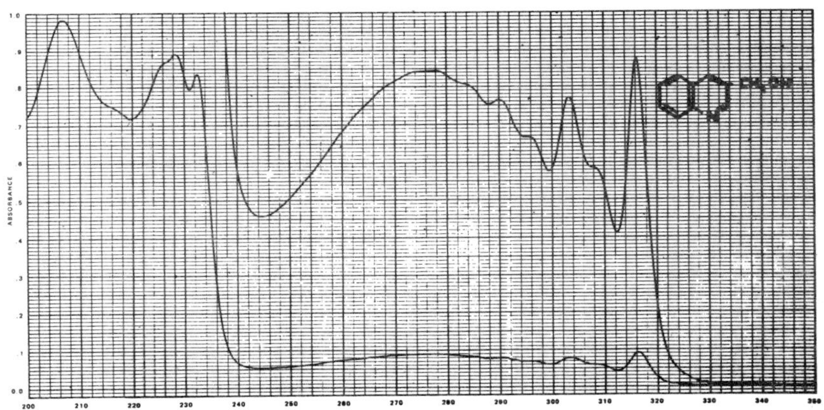

λ Max. mμ	a_m	Cell mm	Conc. g/L

5-PHENYL-2-PYRIMIDINEETHANOL 1732

$C_{12}H_{12}N_2O$

Mol. Wt. 200.24

M.P. 92-97°C

Solvent: Methanol

λ Max. mμ	a_m	Cell mm	Conc. g/L
246	16000	1	0.100

5-PHENYL-2-PYRIMIDINEETHANOL 1732

$C_{12}H_{12}N_2O$

Mol. Wt. 200.24

M.P. 92-97°C

Solvent: Methanol HCl

λ Max. mμ	a_m	Cell mm	Conc. g/L
258	13400	1	0.100

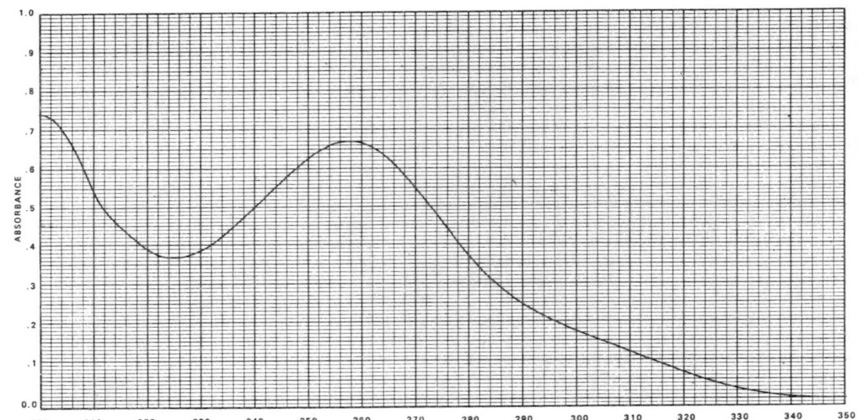

FURFURYL ALCOHOL 1733

$C_5H_6O_2$

Mol. Wt. 98.10

B.P. 171°C/750mm (lit.)

Solvent: Methanol

λ Max. mμ	a_m	Cell mm	Conc. g/L
270	51.9	10	2.31
216	5620	10	0.028

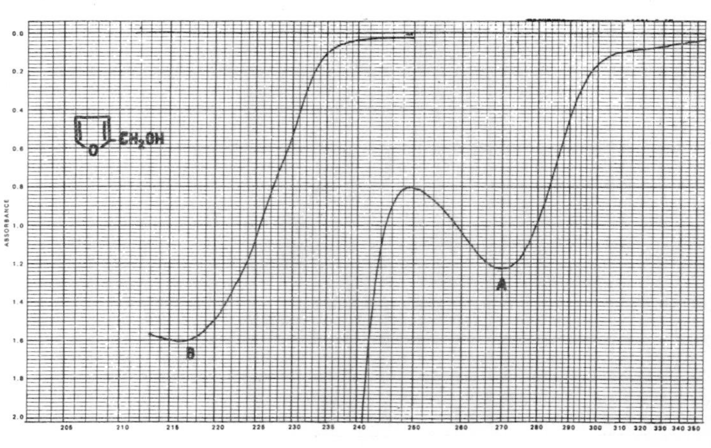

PIPERONYL ALCOHOL

$C_8H_8O_3$

Mol. Wt. 152.15

M.P. 51°C (lit.)

Solvent: Methanol

λ Max. mμ	a_m	Cell mm	Conc. g/L
285.5	3770	2	0.100
235	4180	2	0.100

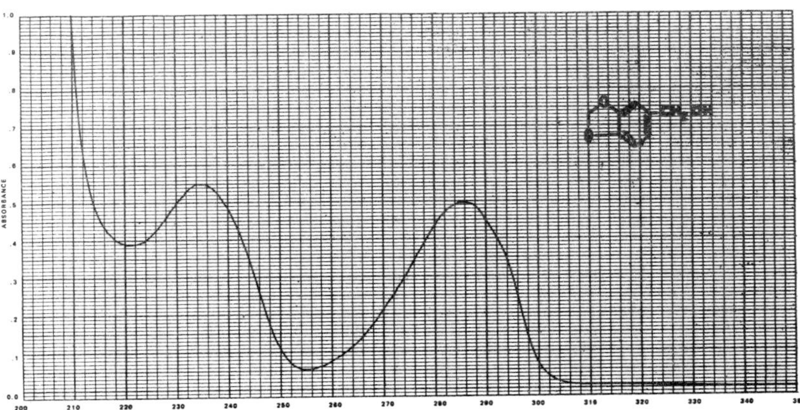

λ Max. mμ	a_m	Cell mm	Conc. g/L

λ Max. mμ	a_m	Cell mm	Conc. g/L

NOTES

THE SECONDARY ALCOHOLS

Aliphatic Compounds

As with the primary alcohols, the aliphatic and alicyclic secondary alcohols do not display any maxima in the near UV region of the spectrum. As a consequence, there are no spectra in this chapter for compounds 1735 through 1773.

Aromatic Compounds

The aromatic secondary alcohols give rise to two distinct types of patterns in the UV region depending upon whether the structure is that of an alkyl phenyl methanol or a diphenyl secondary alcohol.

The alkyl phenyl methanols, such as compounds 1788 and 1789, produce spectra with a major band at 246 mμ with associated fine structure at 242, 251, 257, 263 and 267 mμ. These two compounds also display a shoulder near 216 mμ and a weak band or shoulder at about 280 mμ.

The diphenyl secondary alcohols, such as compounds 1776 and 1790, give rise to spectra with a major band at about 259 mμ with superimposed fine structure appearing as maxima or shoulders at 248, 253, 264 and 268 mμ. In addition, a shoulder is often observed at about 219 mμ.

The UV spectra of the secondary alcohols do not show any significant changes upon the addition of acid or base.

trans-2-PHENYLCYCLOHEXANOL 1774

$C_{12}H_{16}O$
Mol. Wt. 176.26
Solvent: Methanol

λ Max. mμ	a_m	Cell mm	Conc. g/L
267.5	244	20	0.100
263.5	264	20	0.100
258	330	20	0.100
252	321	20	0.100
248	301	20	0.100

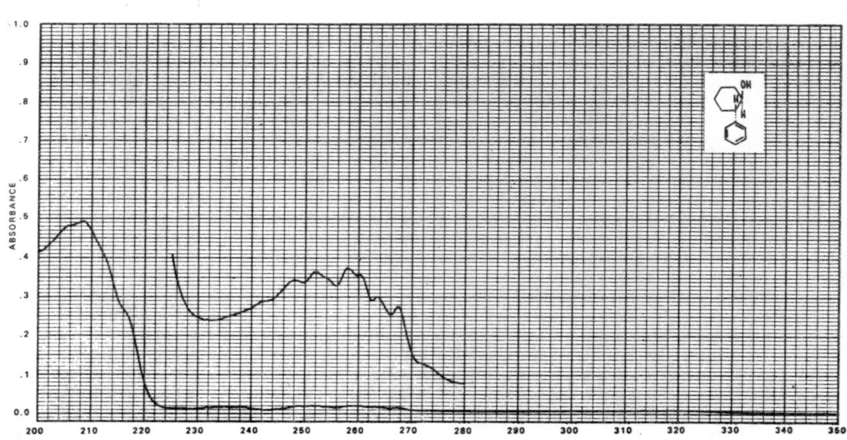

cis-2-PHENYLCYCLOHEXANOL 1775

$C_{12}H_{16}O$
Mol. Wt. 176.26
Solvent: Methanol

λ Max. mμ	a_m	Cell mm	Conc. g/L
281	152	10	0.2471
267	216	10	0.2471
263	249	10	0.2471
257	364	10	0.2471
251	426	10	0.2471

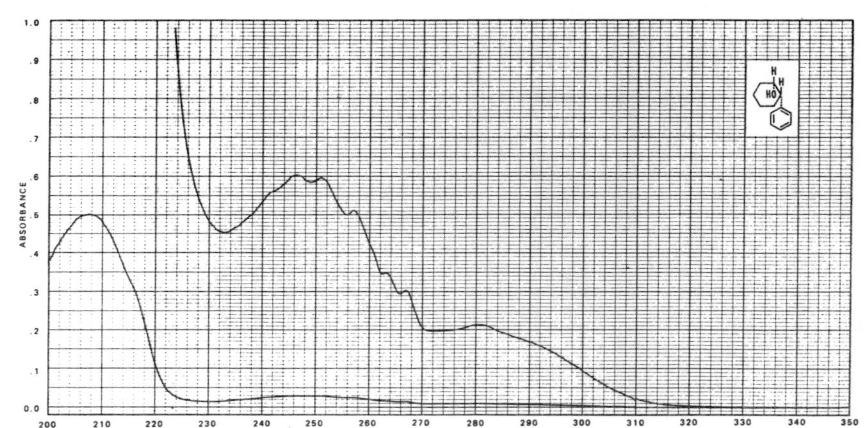
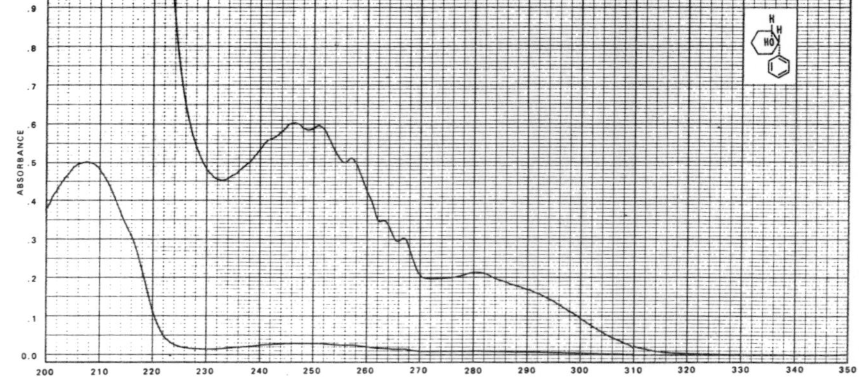

2,2-DIPHENYLCYCLOHEXANOL 1776

$C_{18}H_{20}O$
Mol. Wt. 252.36
M.P. 82-83°C
Solvent: Methanol

λ Max. mμ	a_m	Cell mm	Conc. g/L
268	580	2	1.00
260	767	2	1.00
254	738	2	1.00
219	10700	1	0.0800

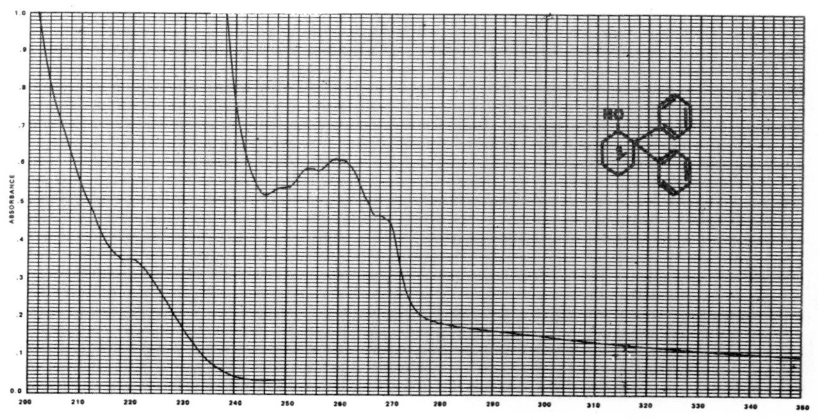

1777

λ Max. mμ	a_m	Cell mm	Conc. g/L

The alicyclic and olefinic alcohols (compounds 1777 through 1787) do not display any maxima in the near UV.

α-ETHYLBENZYL ALCOHOL **1788**

$C_9H_{12}O$

Mol. Wt. 136.20

B.P. 103°C/14mm

Solvent: Methanol

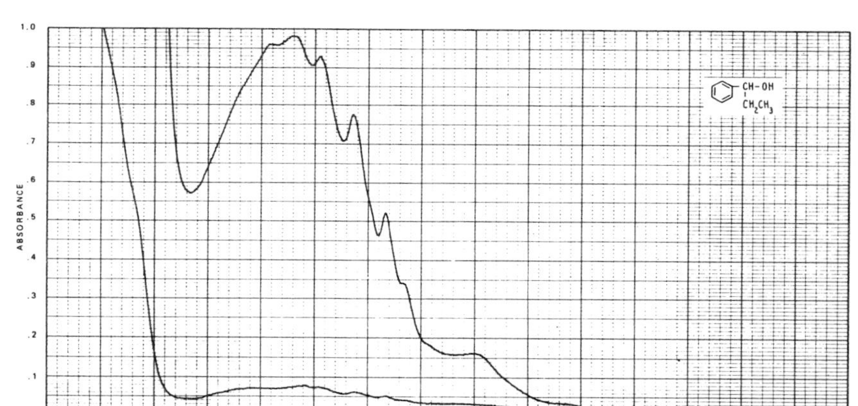

λ Max. mμ	a_m	Cell mm	Conc. g/L
280	62	10	0.353
263	201	10	0.353
257	299	10	0.353
251	359	10	0.353
246	378	10	0.353

α-CYCLOPROPYLBENZYL ALCOHOL **1789**

$C_{10}H_{12}O$

Mol. Wt. 148.21

B.P. 121°C/12mm

Solvent: Methanol

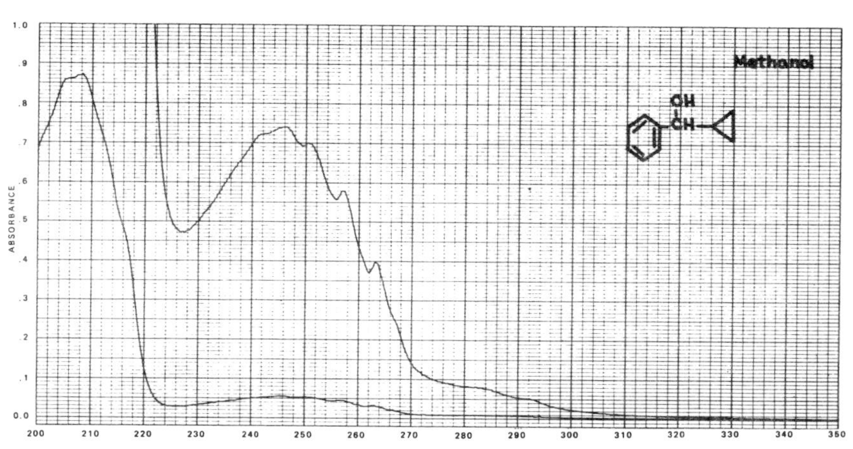

λ Max. mμ	a_m	Cell mm	Conc. g/L
263	310	10	0.190
257	452	10	0.190
250	546	10	0.190
246	577	10	0.190
208	8480	1	0.152

BENZHYDROL 1790

$C_{13}H_{12}O$
Mol. Wt. 184.24
M.P. 67-68°C
Solvent: Methanol

λ Max. mμ	a_m	Cell mm	Conc. g/L
263.5	395	5	0.500
258	520	5	0.500
252.5	472	5	0.500
242	304	5	0.500
x	x	1	0.100

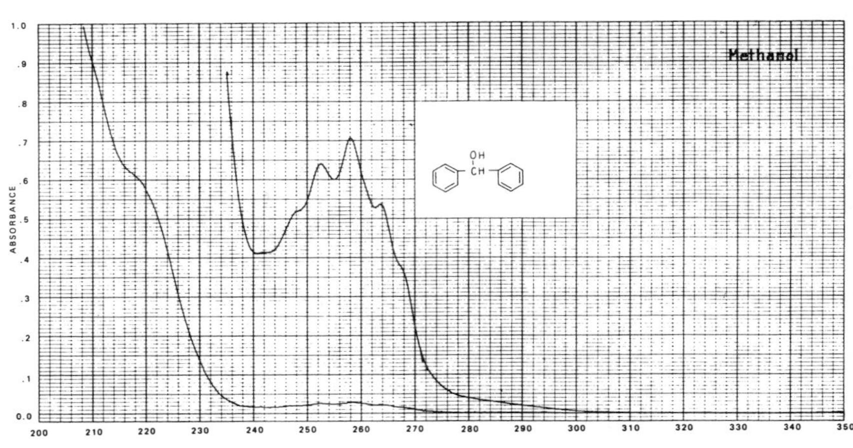

1,2-DIPHENYLETHANOL 1791

$C_{14}H_{14}O$
Mol. Wt. 198.27
Solvent: Methanol

λ Max. mμ	a_m	Cell mm	Conc. g/L
257	1490	10	0.100
252	1540	10	0.100
210.5	19000	1	0.100

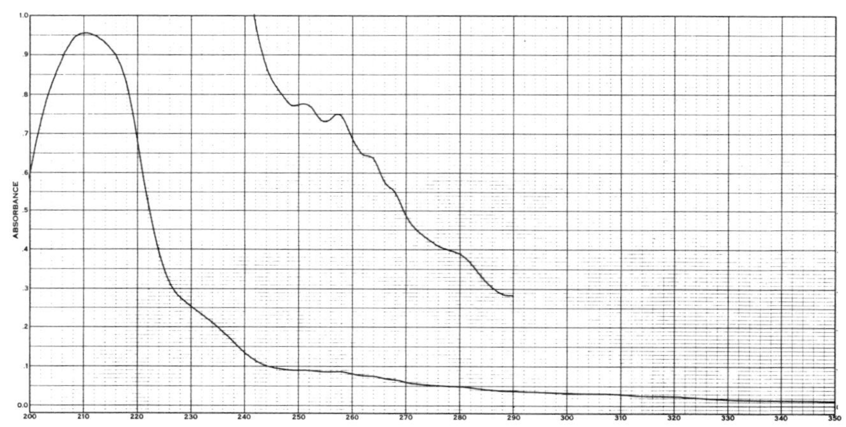

1-PHENOXY-2-PROPANOL 1792

$C_9H_{12}O_2$
Mol. Wt. 152.19
M.P. 13-17°C
Solvent: Methanol

λ Max. mμ	a_m	Cell mm	Conc. g/L
277.5	1430	5	0.142
270.5	1680	5	0.142
220	8160	1	0.142

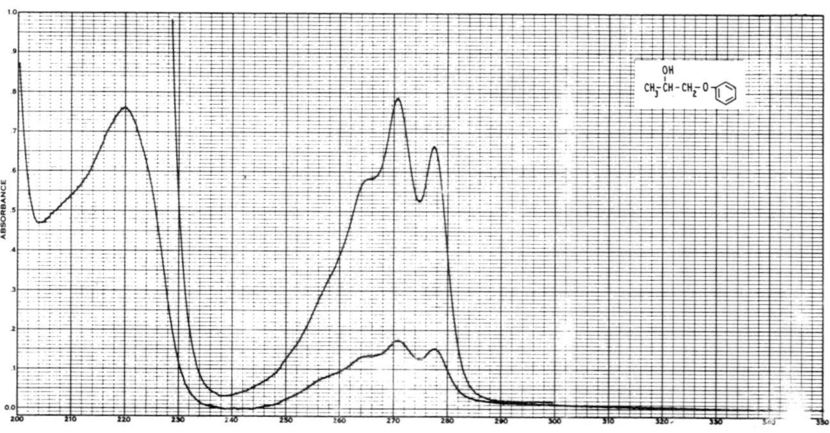

2,5-DICHLORO-α-METHYLBENZYL ALCOHOL

1793

$C_8H_8Cl_2O$
Mol. Wt. 191.06
Solvent: Methanol

λ Max. mμ	a_m	Cell mm	Conc. g/L
281	358	40	0.100
273	432	40	0.100
224	11200	1	0.100
x	x	1	0.100

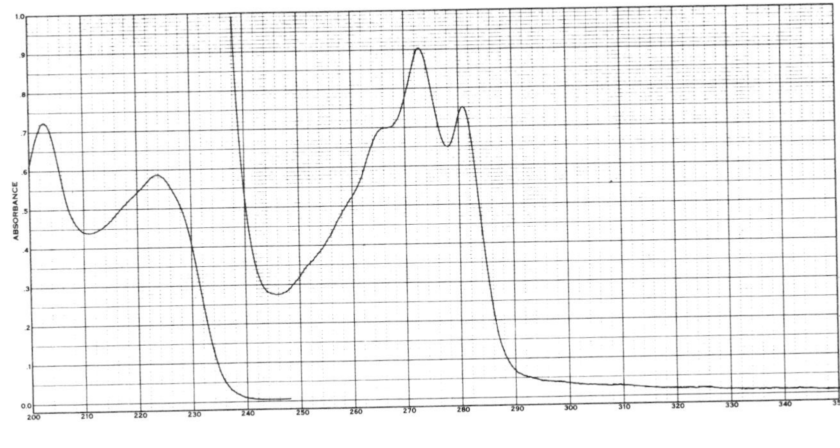

QUININE

1794

$C_{20}H_{24}N_2O_2$
Mol. Wt. 324.43
Solvent: Methanol

λ Max. mμ	a_m	Cell mm	Conc. g/L
330	5730	4	0.100
278	4650	4	0.100
229	35200	0.5	0.100

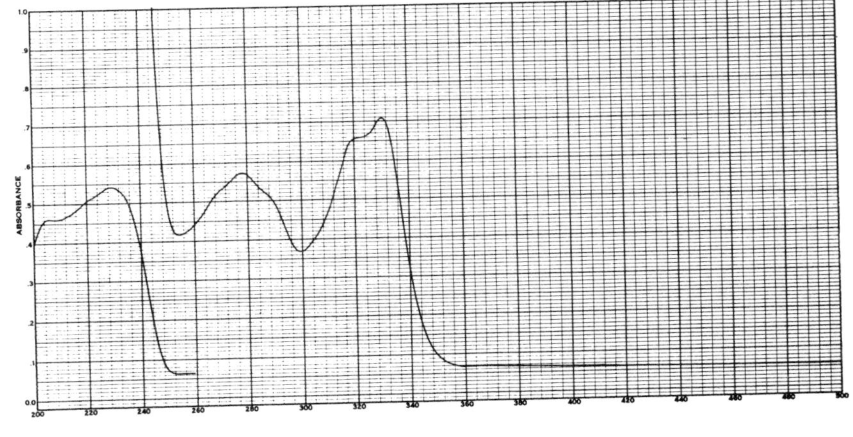

QUININE

1794

$C_{20}H_{24}N_2O_2$
Mol. Wt. 324.43
Solvent: Methanol HCl

λ Max. mμ	a_m	Cell mm	Conc. g/L
348	6720	1	0.100
314	4380	5	0.100
251	30700	1	0.100

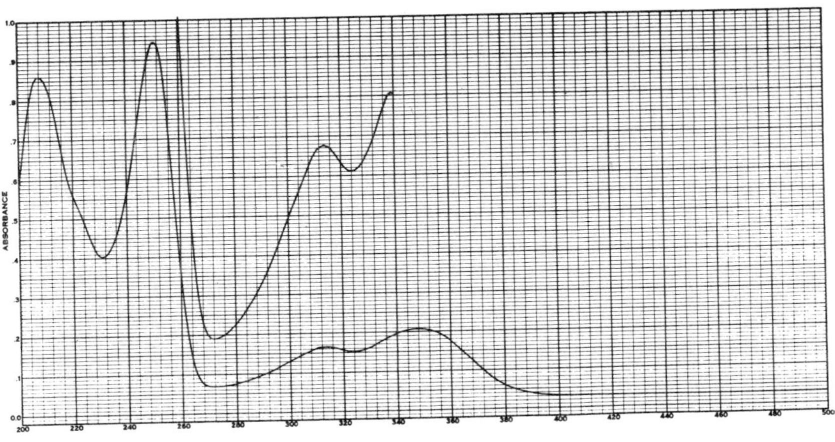

NOTES

THE TERTIARY ALCOHOLS

Aliphatic Compounds

Due to the fact that the aliphatic tertiary alcohols do not display any maxima in the near ultraviolet, there are no spectra in this section for compounds 1795 through 1816.

Aromatic Compounds

The aromatic tertiary alcohols produce ultraviolet spectra that are similar in band position and shape but with widely different intensities, increasing with the number of phenyl groups as expected.

The major absorption band occurs at about 258 mμ with superimposed fine structure appearing as maxima or inflections at about 237, 242, 247, 252, 264 and 268 mμ.

The wavelength and intensity data for three aromatic tertiary alcohols is provided in the table presented below.

Compound	$\lambda_{max}(\epsilon_{max})$	Solvent	Spectrum
α,α-Dimethylbenzyl Alcohol	258 (180)	Methanol	1817
1,1-Diphenyloctanol	258 (649)	Methanol	1820
Triphenylmethanol	258 (3330)	Methanol	1822

Acetylenic Compounds

The spectrum of 2,7-dimethyl-3,5-octadiyne-2,7-diol (compound 1859) is of special interest because of the pattern produced by the two conjugated acetylenic linkages.

The λ_{max} occurs near 241 mμ with additional well defined maxima at 218, 229 and 254 mμ.

The band positions and intensities are similar to those reported for the spectrum of 3,5-octadiyne (λ_{max} = 239, ϵ_{max} =340).

The ultraviolet spectra of the aromatic and conjugated acetylenic tertiary alcohols do not show any significant changes upon the addition of acid or base.

α,α-DIMETHYLBENZYL ALCOHOL

1817

$C_9H_{12}O$

Mol. Wt. 136.20

Solvent: Methanol

λ Max. mμ	a_m	Cell mm	Conc. g/L
267.5	78.3	10	0.60
264.5	134	10	0.60
258	180	10	0.60
252.5	162	10	0.60
247.5	139	10	0.60
242.5	200	10	0.60
209.5	6760	10	0.01

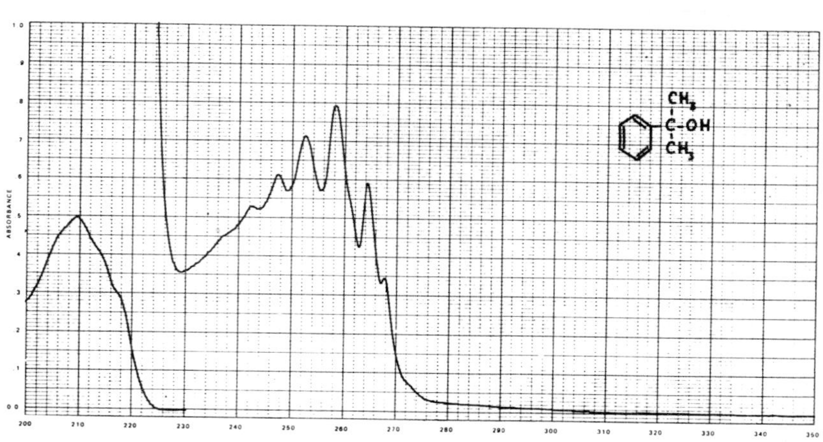

α,α-DIETHYLBENZYL ALCOHOL

1818

$C_{11}H_{16}O$

Mol. Wt. 164.25

B.P. 80°C/2mm

λ Max. mμ	a_m	Cell mm	Conc. g/L

Pure sample not available.

2-PHENYL-3-BUTYN-2-OL

1819

$C_{10}H_{10}O$

Mol. Wt. 146.18

M.P. 49°C

Solvent: Methanol

λ Max. mμ	a_m	Cell mm	Conc. g/L
262.5	151	10	0.500
256.5	196	10	0.500
251	152	10	0.500
246.5	106	10	0.500
207.5	7400	10	0.010

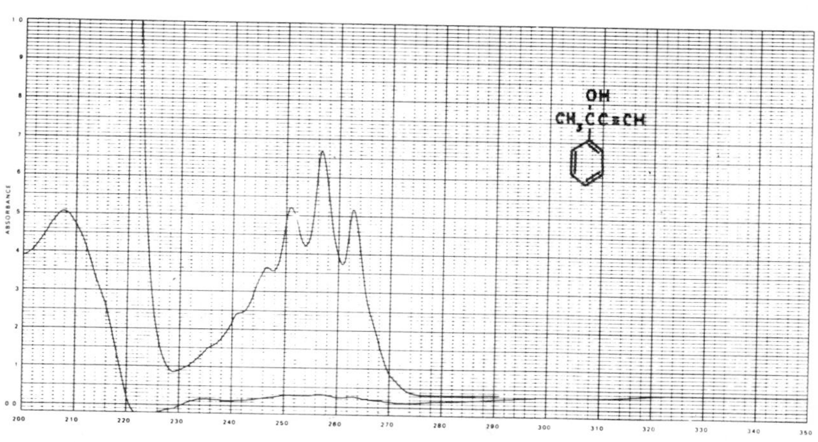

1820

α-OCTYLBENZHYDROL

$C_{21}H_{28}O$

Mol. Wt. 296.46

B.P. 194-200°C/0.02mm

Solvent: Methanol

λ Max. mμ	a_m	Cell mm	Conc. g/L
258	649	40	0.100
252	671	40	0.100
248	646	40	0.100
x	x	2	0.100

1821

1-(p-TOLYL)CYCLOHEXANOL

$C_{13}H_{18}O$

Mol. Wt. 190.29

Solvent: Methanol

λ Max. mμ	a_m	Cell mm	Conc. g/L
266	800	5	0.253
257	1110	5	0.253
251	1170	5	0.253
x	x	1	0.253

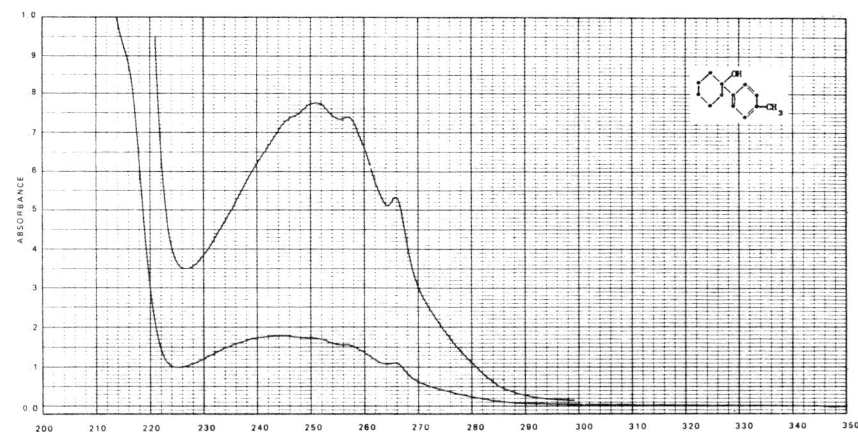

1822

TRIPHENYLMETHANOL

$C_{19}H_{16}O$

Mol. Wt. 260.34

M.P. 161-162°C

Solvent: Methanol

λ Max. mμ	a_m	Cell mm	Conc. g/L
264	2510	5	0.100
258.5	3330	5	0.100
252.5	2910	5	0.100
x	x	1	0.0200

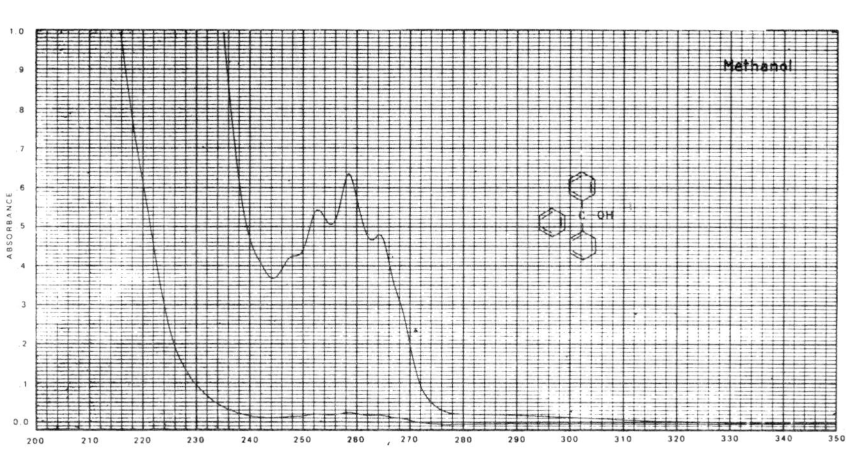

λ Max. mμ	a_m	Cell mm	Conc. g/L

The aliphatic polyols and carbohydrates (compounds 1823 through 1858 and 1861 through 1874) do not produce any maxima in the near UV.

2,7-DIMETHYL-3,5-OCTADIYNE-2,7-DIOL **1859**

$C_{10}H_{14}O_2$

Mol. Wt. 166.22

M.P. 132.5°C

Solvent: Methanol

λ Max. mμ	a_m	Cell mm	Conc. g/L
254.0	244	2	1.00
241.0	381	2	1.00
229.0	365	2	1.00
218.5	281	2	1.00

p-XYLENE-α,α'-DIOL **1860**

$C_8H_{10}O_2$

Mol. Wt. 138.16

M.P. 118°C

Solvent: Methanol

λ Max. mμ	a_m	Cell mm	Conc. g/L
271.5	151	10	0.40
262	265	10	0.40
218	8700	10	0.01

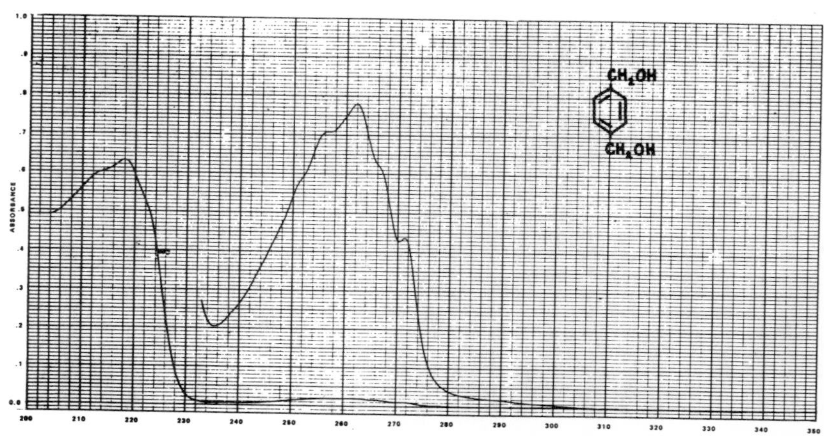

THE PHENOLS

The substitution of benzene by the polar —OH group which contains unshared electrons shifts the benzene absorption bands to longer wavelength and also results in an increase in their intensity. The wavelength of the major band of phenol although not significantly altered by examination in different solvents, is quite sensitive to the addition of base resulting in the formation of the phenolate anion with a resulting shift to longer wavelength and the disappearance of fine structure.

The spectral data for phenol in several solvents and the phenolate anion are listed below.

Compound	$\lambda_{max}(\epsilon_{max})$	$\lambda_{max}(\epsilon_{max})$	Solvent	Spectrum
Phenol	- - - - - - - - - -	270 (2690)	Cyclohexane	1875
	211 (6000)	271 (2200)	Heptane	Lit.
	211 (5900)	270 (1500)	Water	Lit.
Phenolate anion	235 (9900)	287 (2600)	Water/NaOH	Lit.

The wavelengths and intensities of the 271 mμ bands are extremely similar to those observed for anisole (spectrum 1488, page 433).

The table of para substituted compounds presented below illustrates the effect of alkyl and halogen substitution on the wavelength of the major bands of phenol and the phenolate anion.

Compound	$\lambda_{max}(\epsilon_{max})$	$\lambda_{max}(\epsilon_{max})$	Solvent	Spectrum
p-Pentyl phenol	224 (7290)	280 (1780)	Methanol	1884
	241 (8240)	295 (2010)	Methanol/KOH	1884
p-Fluoro phenol	217 (3860)	281 (2650)	Methanol	1891
	233 (4940)	301 (2420)	Methanol/KOH	1891
p-Bromo phenol	226 (12100)	283 (1930)	Methanol	1895
	245 (15600)	300 (2670)	Methanol/KOH	1895
p-Iodophenol	233 (15300)	283 (1440)	Methanol	1898
	249 (18200)	297 (2190)	Methanol/KOH	1898

PHENOL

1875

C_6H_6O

Mol. Wt. 94.11

M.P. 41°C (lit.)

Solvent: Cyclohexane

λ Max. mμ	^{a}m	Cell mm	Conc. g/L
x	x	10	2.19
276.5	2340	10	0.058
270	2690	10	0.058
264	1630	10	0.058
x	x	10	0.006

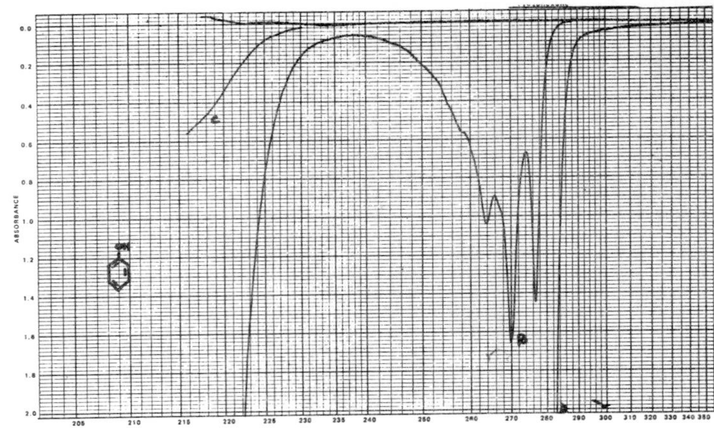

o-CRESOL

1876

C_7H_8O

Mol. Wt. 108.14

M.P. 30-31°C

Solvent: Methanol

λ Max. mμ	^{a}m	Cell mm	Conc. g/L
272.5	1820	1	0.142
214	6030	1	0.142

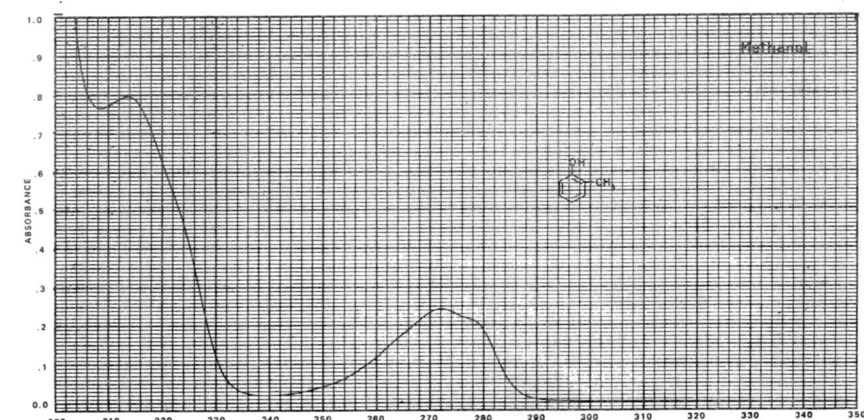

o-CRESOL

1876

C_7H_8O

Mol. Wt. 108.14

M.P. 30-31°C

Solvent: Methanol KOH

λ Max. mμ	^{a}m	Cell mm	Conc. g/L
282	1990	1	0.142
238	5510	1	0.142

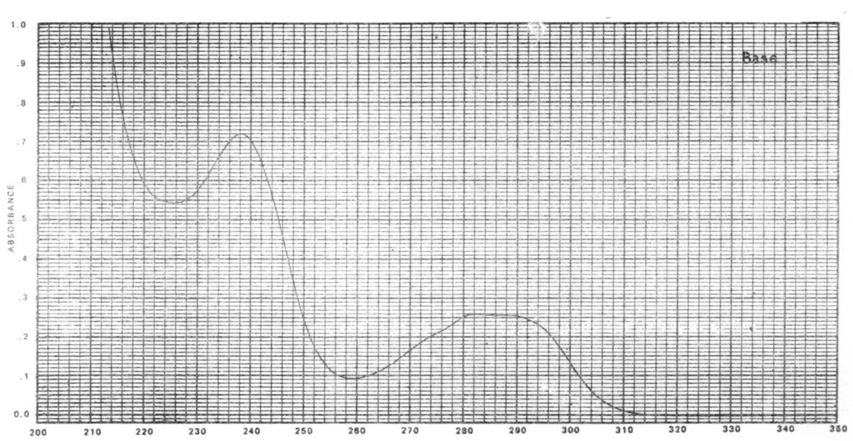

m-CRESOL

C_7H_8O

Mol. Wt. 108.13

B.P. 202.8°C (lit.)

Solvent: Methanol

λ Max. mμ	^{a}m	Cell mm	Conc. g/L
x	x	10	2.84
273	1570	10	0.0852
x	x	10	0.00852

1877

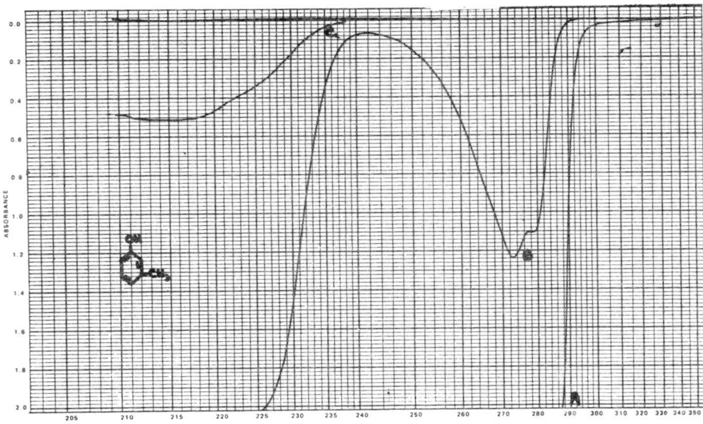

p-CRESOL

C_7H_8O

Mol. Wt. 108.13

Solvent: Methanol

λ Max. mμ	^{a}m	Cell mm	Conc. g/L
x	x	10	1.86
278	1950	10	0.0743

1878

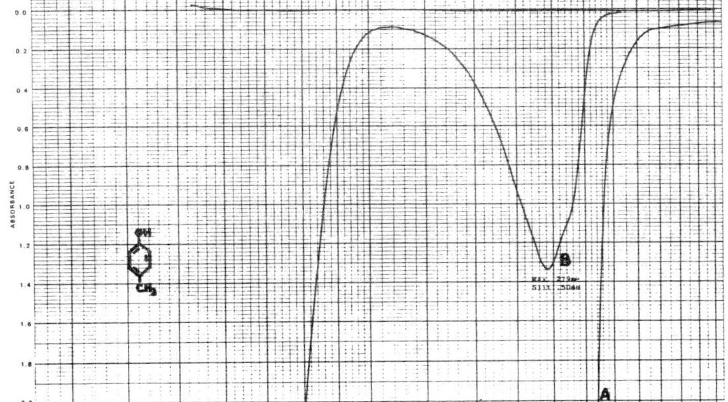

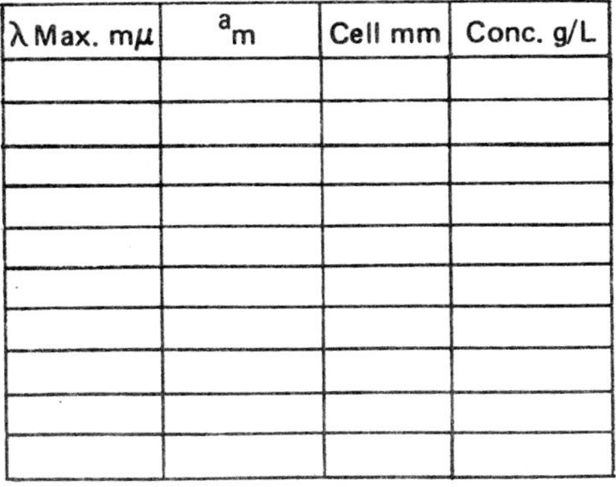

λ Max. mμ	^{a}m	Cell mm	Conc. g/L

o-ETHYLPHENOL

1879

$C_8H_{10}O$
Mol. Wt. 122.17
B.P. 87-89°C/10mm
Solvent: Methanol

λ Max. mμ	a_m	Cell mm	Conc. g/L
273.5	1940	1	0.3510
215	6770	1	0.0702

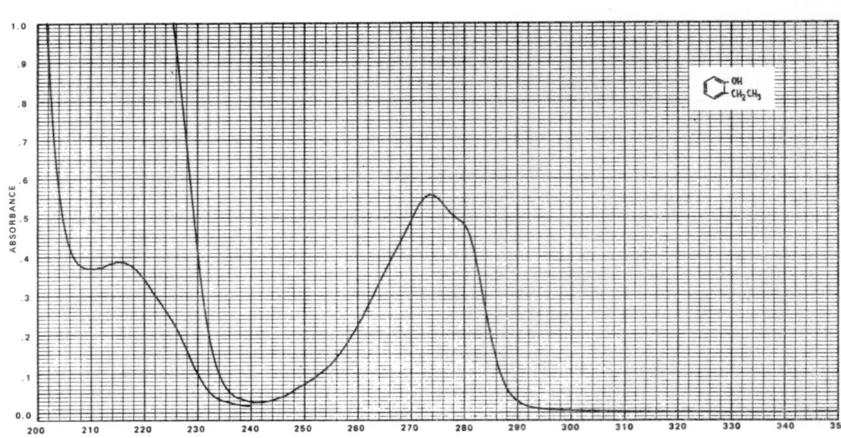

o-ETHYLPHENOL

1879

$C_8H_{10}O$
Mol. Wt. 122.17
B.P. 87-89°C/10mm
Solvent: Methanol KOH

λ Max. mμ	a_m	Cell mm	Conc. g/L
274	1930	1	0.3510
x	x	1	0.0702

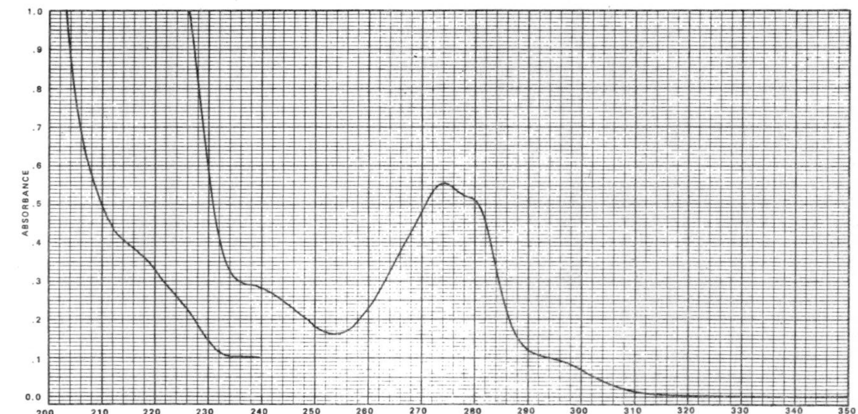

m-ETHYLPHENOL

1880

$C_8H_{10}O$
Mol. Wt. 122.17
M.P. -4°C   B.P. 214°C/752mm (lit.)
Solvent: Methanol

λ Max. mμ	a_m	Cell mm	Conc. g/L
279	1680	1	0.2569
274	1900	1	0.2569
216	6690	1	0.1289

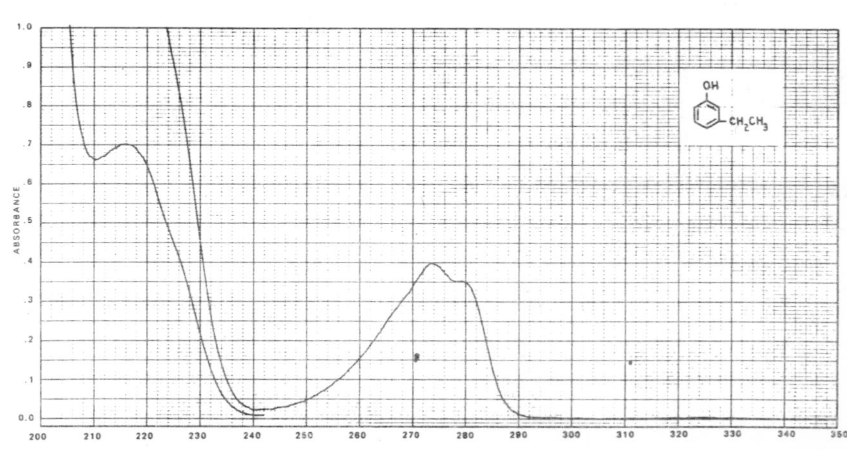

m-ETHYLPHENOL 1880

$C_8H_{10}O$

Mol. Wt. 122.17

M.P. -4°C B.P. 214°C/752mm (lit.)

Solvent: Methanol KOH

λ Max. mμ	a_m	Cell mm	Conc. g/L
289	2290	1	0.1289
239	7050	1	0.1289

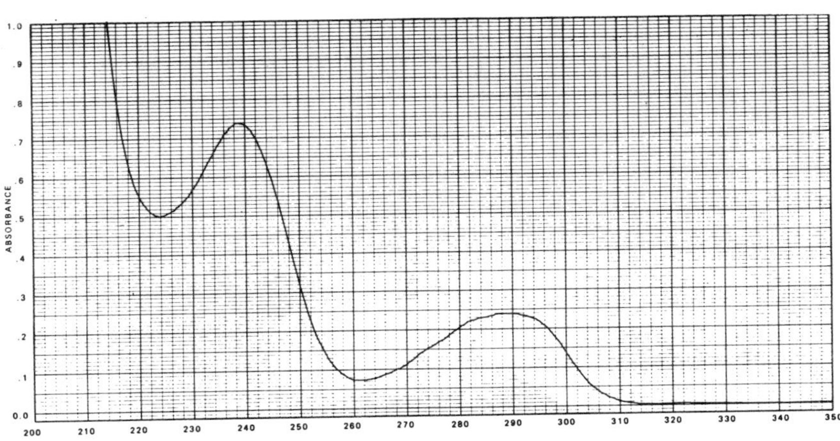

p-ISOPROPYLPHENOL 1881

$C_9H_{12}O$

Mol. Wt. 136.19

Solvent: Cyclohexane

λ Max. mμ	a_m	Cell mm	Conc. g/L
x	x	10	1.80
287	2150	10	0.090
280	2240	10	0.090
274	1570	10	0.090
223	7280	10	0.0271

λ Max. mμ	a_m	Cell mm	Conc. g/L

o-tert-BUTYLPHENOL 1882

$C_{10}H_{14}O$
Mol. Wt. 150.22
B.P. 224°C M.P. -7°C
Solvent: Methanol

λ Max. mμ	a_m	Cell mm	Conc. g/L
279.5	2000	2	0.2940
273	2260	2	0.2940
216	5830	1	0.1470

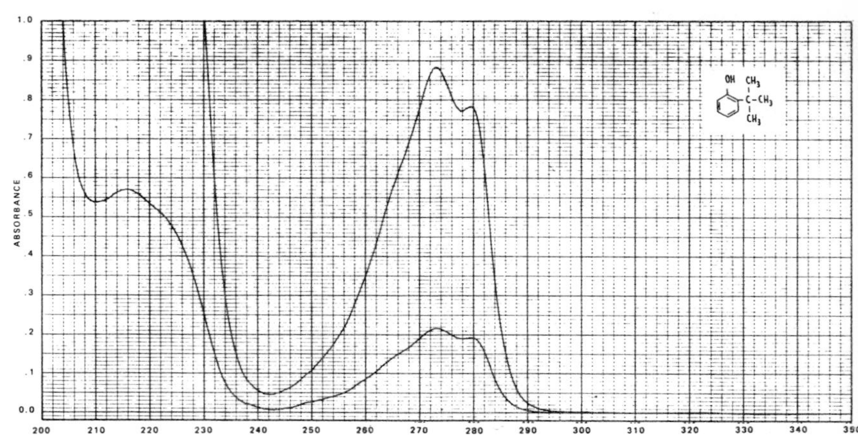

o-tert-BUTYLPHENOL 1882

$C_{10}H_{14}O$
Mol. Wt. 150.22
B.P. 224°C M.P. -7°C
Solvent: Methanol KOH

λ Max. mμ	a_m	Cell mm	Conc. g/L
279.5	2000	2	0.2940
273	2170	2	0.2940
245	726	2	0.2940
213	6090	1	0.1470

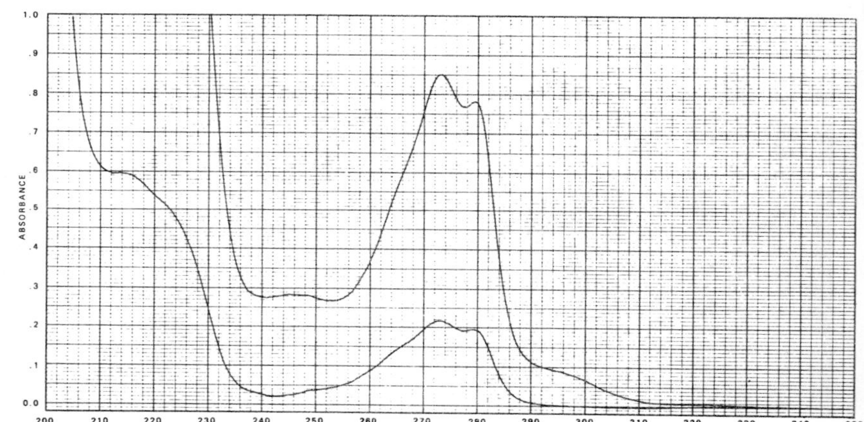

p-tert-BUTYLPHENOL 1883

$C_{10}H_{14}O$
Mol. Wt. 150.21
Solvent: Cyclohexane

λ Max. mμ	a_m	Cell mm	Conc. g/L
x	x	10	1.8320
283.5	2030	10	0.1099
276.5	2050	10	0.1099
270.5	1430	10	0.1099
220	6930	10	0.0330

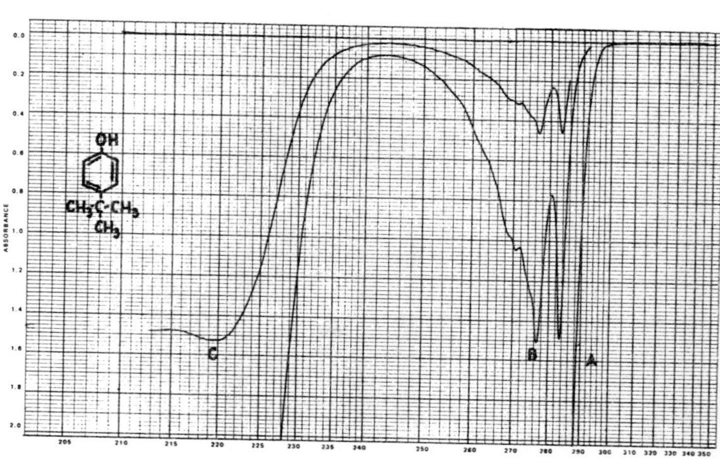

p-PENTYLPHENOL

1884

$C_{11}H_{16}O$
Mol. Wt. 164.25
M.P. 20-22°C
Solvent: Methanol

λ Max. mμ	a_m	Cell mm	Conc. g/L
279.5	1780	1	0.196
224	7290	1	0.196

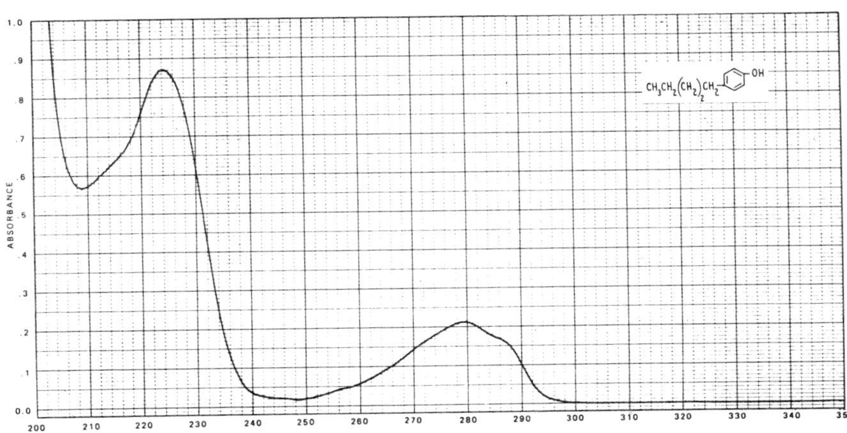

p-PENTYLPHENOL

1884

$C_{11}H_{16}O$
Mol. Wt. 164.25
M.P. 20-22°C
Solvent: Methanol KOH

λ Max. mμ	a_m	Cell mm	Conc. g/L
295	2010	5	0.137
241	8240	1	0.137

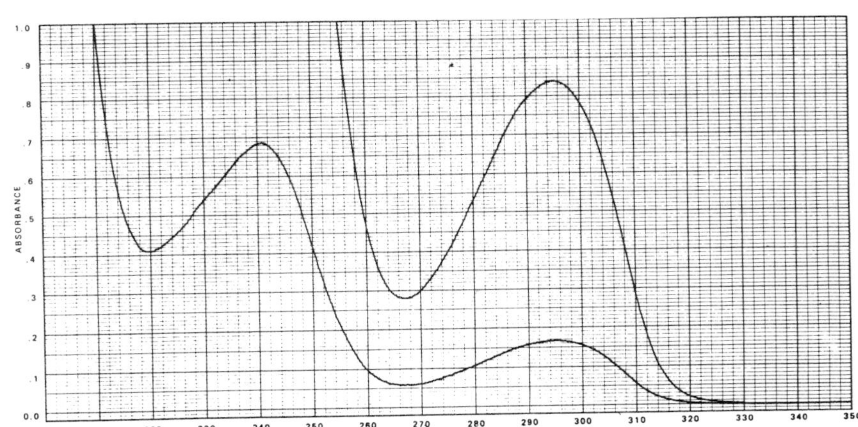

λ Max. mμ	a_m	Cell mm	Conc. g/L

p-tert-PENTYLPHENOL

$C_{11}H_{16}O$

Mol. Wt. 164.25

M.P. 89-93°C

Solvent: Methanol

1885

λ Max. mμ	$^a{}_m$	Cell mm	Conc. g/L
276.5	1790	2	0.100
222.5	8130	2	0.100

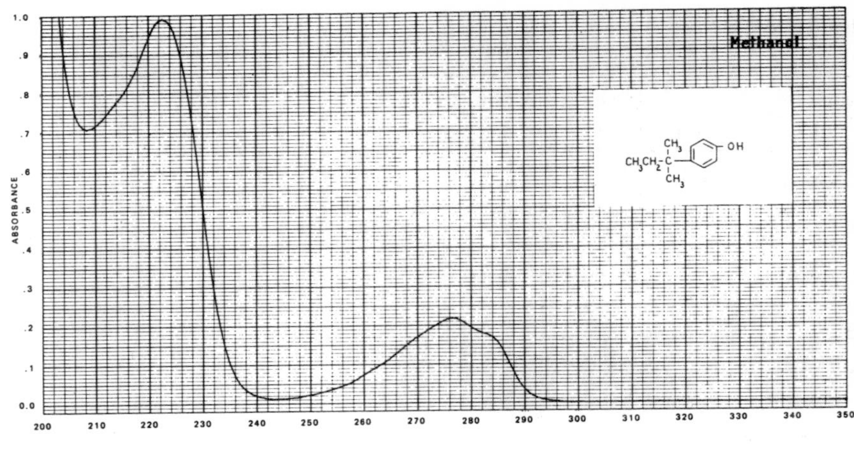

p-tert-PENTYLPHENOL

$C_{11}H_{16}O$

Mol. Wt. 164.25

M.P. 89-93°C

Solvent: Methanol KOH

1885

λ Max. mμ	$^a{}_m$	Cell mm	Conc. g/L
286	1900	1	0.500
238.5	9200	1	0.100

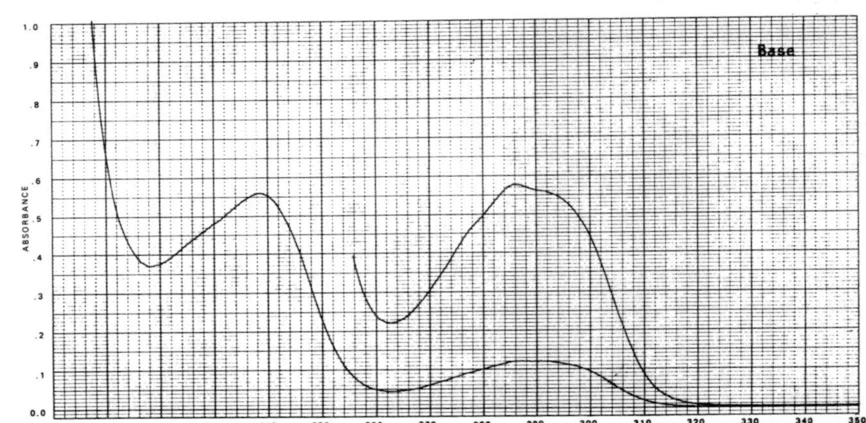

λ Max. mμ	$^a{}_m$	Cell mm	Conc. g/L

p-(1,1,3,3-TETRAMETHYLBUTYL)PHENOL

1886

$C_{14}H_{22}O$
Mol. Wt. 206.33
Solvent: Methanol

λ Max. mμ	a_m	Cell mm	Conc. g/L
278	1660	10	0.0800
223.5	7760	2	0.0800

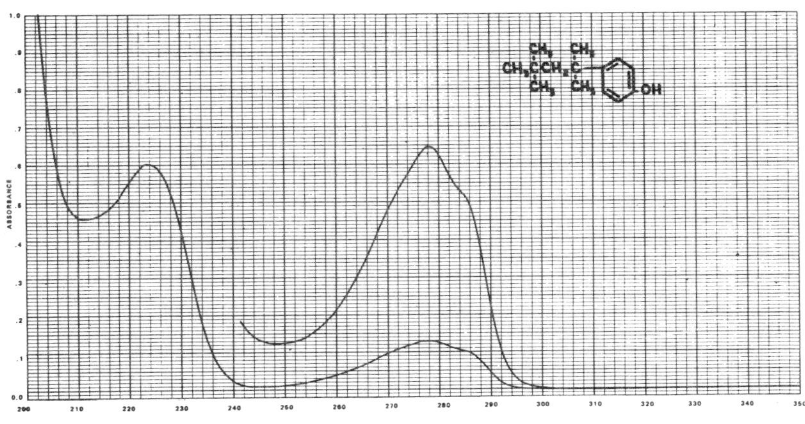

p-(1,1,3,3-TETRAMETHYLBUTYL)PHENOL

1886

$C_{14}H_{22}O$
Mol. Wt. 206.33
Solvent: Methanol KOH

λ Max. mμ	a_m	Cell mm	Conc. g/L
286.5	1700	10	0.0800
237	6840	2	0.0800
229	6960	2	0.0800

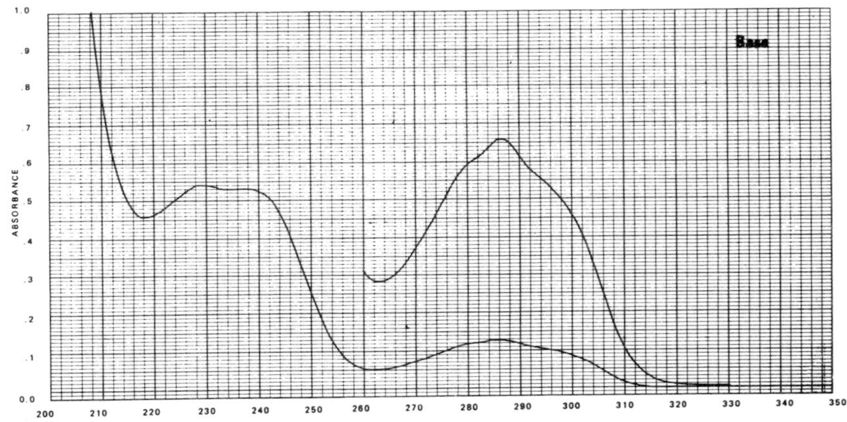

p-CYCLOHEXYLPHENOL

1887

$C_{12}H_{16}O$
Mol. Wt. 176.26
F.P. 126°C (lit.)
Solvent: Cyclohexane

λ Max. mμ	a_m	Cell mm	Conc. g/L
x	x	10	2.2920
284.5	1820	10	0.1375
278	2000	10	0.1375
275	1670	10	0.1375
272	1520	10	0.1375
221	6920	10	0.0275

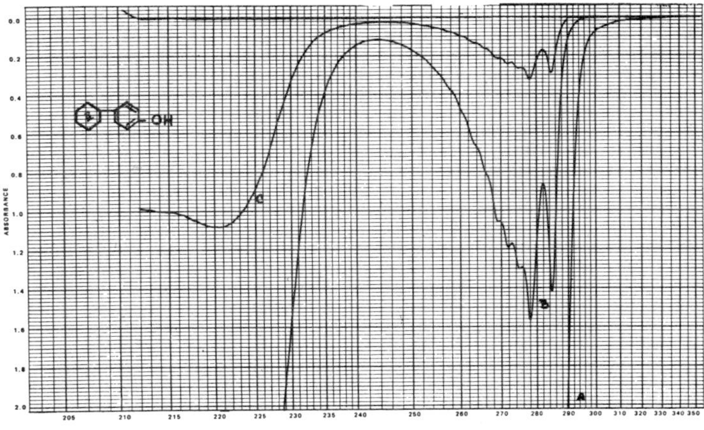

4,4'-METHYLENEDIPHENOL

1888

$C_{13}H_{12}O_2$
Mol. Wt. 200.24
Solvent: Methanol

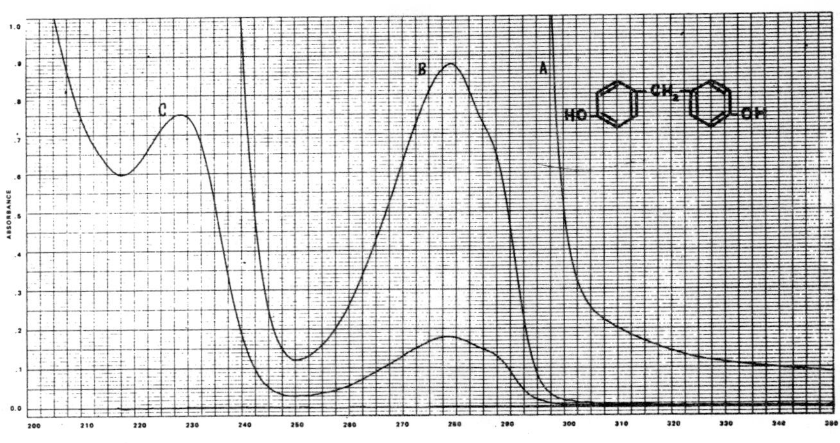

λ Max. mμ	a_m	Cell mm	Conc. g/L
x	x	10	1.680
279	3490	10	0.0504
228	14900	10	0.0101

p-PHENYLPHENOL

1889

$C_{12}H_{10}O$
Mol. Wt. 170.21
M.P. 165°C
Solvent: Methanol

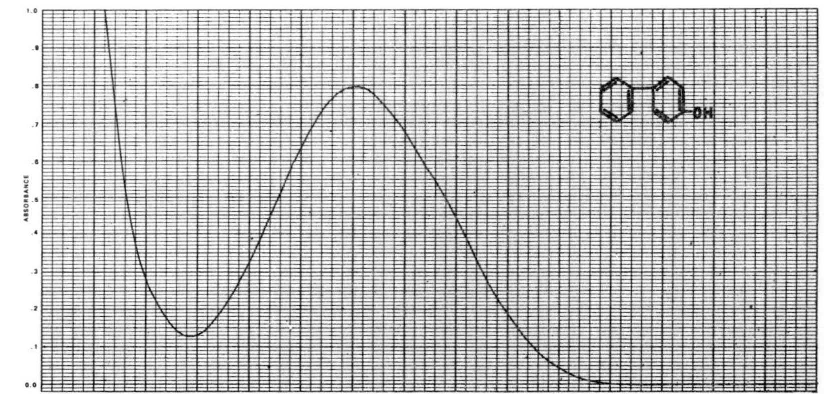

λ Max. mμ	a_m	Cell mm	Conc. g/L
260.5	18100	1	0.0750

p-PHENYLPHENOL

1889

$C_{12}H_{10}O$
Mol. Wt. 170.21
M.P. 165°C
Solvent: Methanol KOH

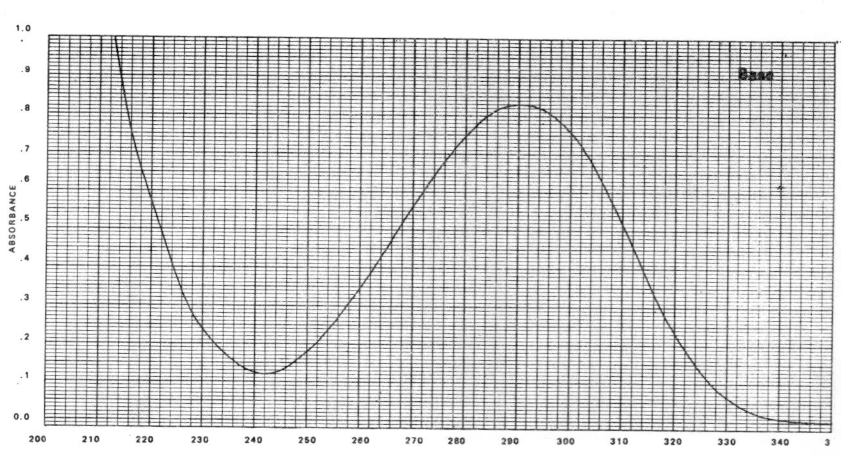

λ Max. mμ	a_m	Cell mm	Conc. g/L
290.5	18800	1	0.0750

o-FLUOROPHENOL 1890

C_6H_5FO

Mol. Wt. 112.11

B.P. 149-151°C

Solvent: Methanol

λ Max. mμ	a_m	Cell mm	Conc. g/L
269	1520	10	0.02
211.5	5170	10	0.02

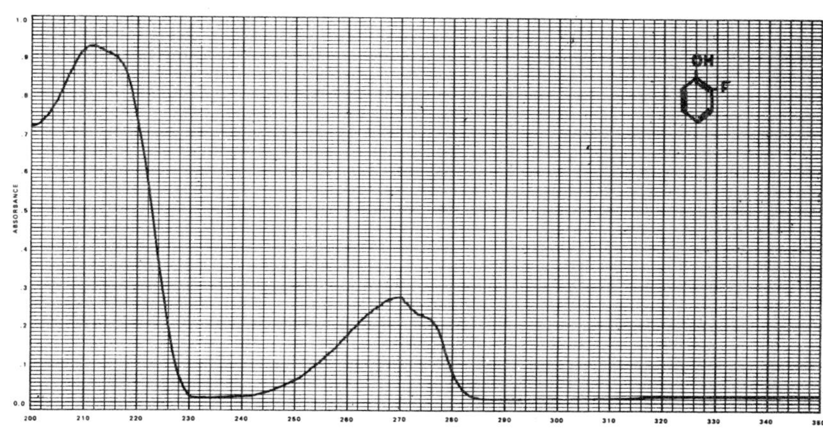

p-FLUOROPHENOL 1891

C_6H_5FO

Mol. Wt. 112.10

M.P. 47-49°C

Solvent: Methanol

λ Max. mμ	a_m	Cell mm	Conc. g/L
281	2650	1	0.1390
217	3860	1	0.1390
210	4360	1	0.1390

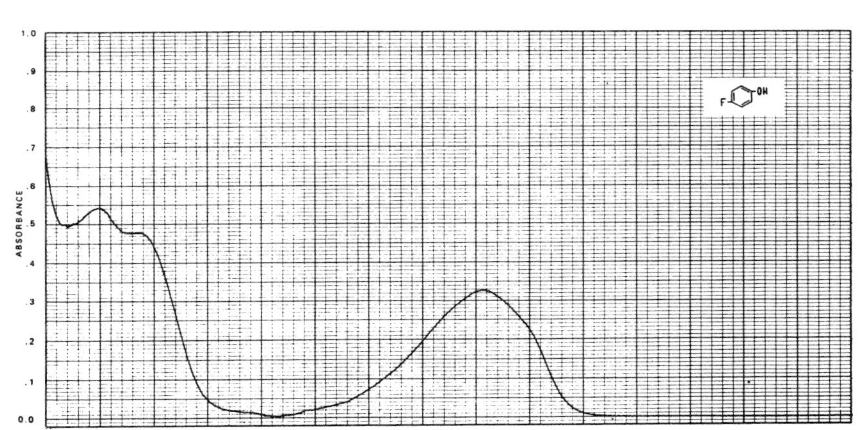

p-FLUOROPHENOL 1891

C_6H_5FO

Mol. Wt. 112.10

M.P. 47-49°C

Solvent: Methanol KOH

λ Max. mμ	a_m	Cell mm	Conc. g/L
301	2420	1	0.1390
233	4940	1	0.1390

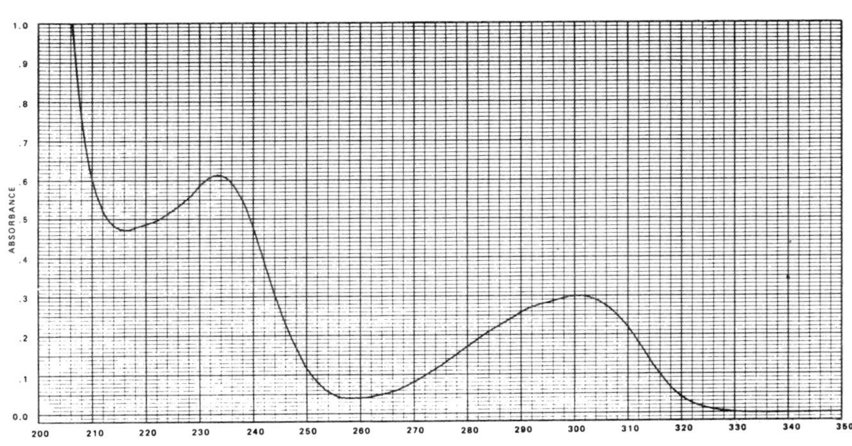

o-CHLOROPHENOL 1892

C_6H_5ClO
Mol. Wt. 128.56
M.R. 65-69°C (lit.)
Solvent: Cyclohexane

λ Max. mμ	a_m	Cell mm	Conc. g/L
x	x	10	2.89
281	2440	10	0.0865
273.5	2350	10	0.0865
x	x	10	0.0289

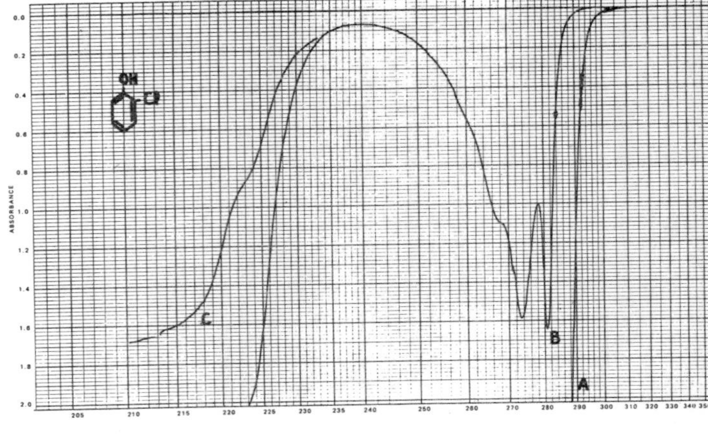

p-CHLOROPHENOL 1893

C_6H_5ClO
Mol. Wt. 128.56
M.P. 43°C B.P. 217°C/760mm
Solvent: Methanol

λ Max. mμ	a_m	Cell mm	Conc. g/L
284	1810	10	0.02
228	9260	10	0.010

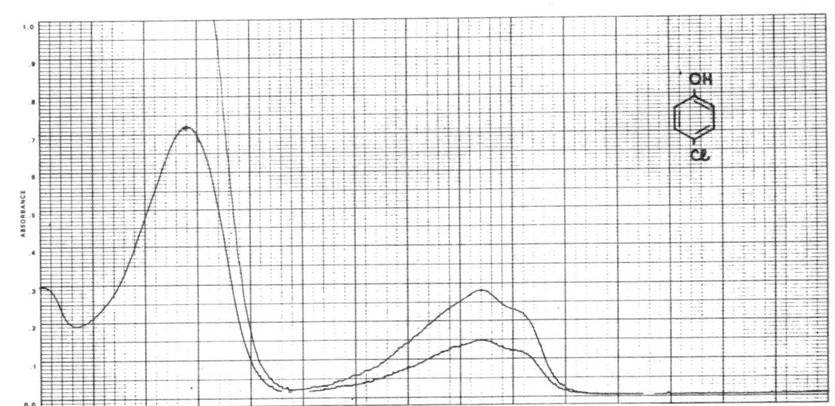

ó-BROMOPHENOL 1894

C_6H_5BrO
Mol. Wt. 173.02
B.P. 193-195°C
Solvent: Methanol

λ Max. mμ	a_m	Cell mm	Conc. g/L
276.5	2670	5	0.0800
x	x	1	0.0800

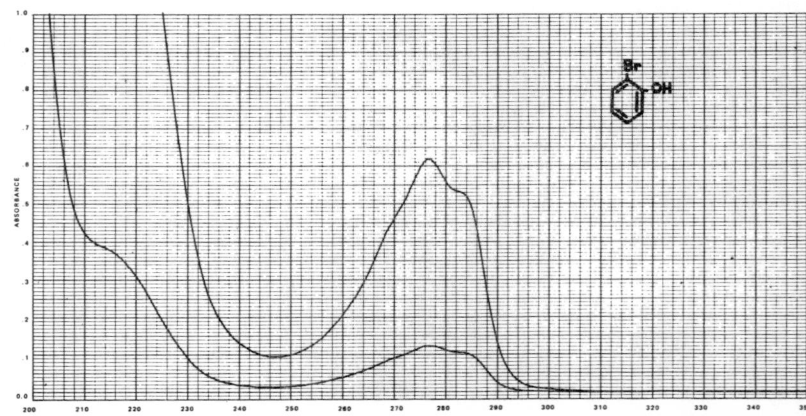

o-BROMOPHENOL

1894

C_6H_5BrO

Mol. Wt. 173.02

B.P. 193-195°C

Solvent: Methanol KOH

λ Max. mμ	a_m	Cell mm	Conc. g/L
295.5	3980	5	0.0800
240	8800	1	0.0800

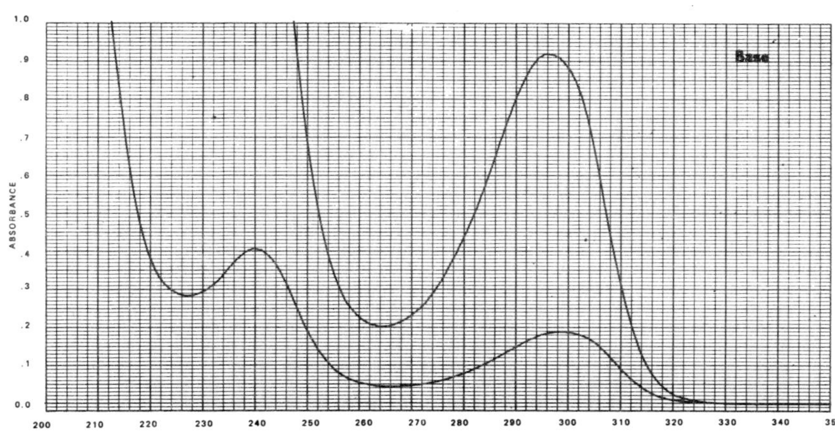

p-BROMOPHENOL

1895

C_6H_5BrO

Mol. Wt. 173.02

M.P. 64-66°C

Solvent: Methanol

λ Max. mμ	a_m	Cell mm	Conc. g/L
282.5	1930	1	0.500
226	12100	1	0.100

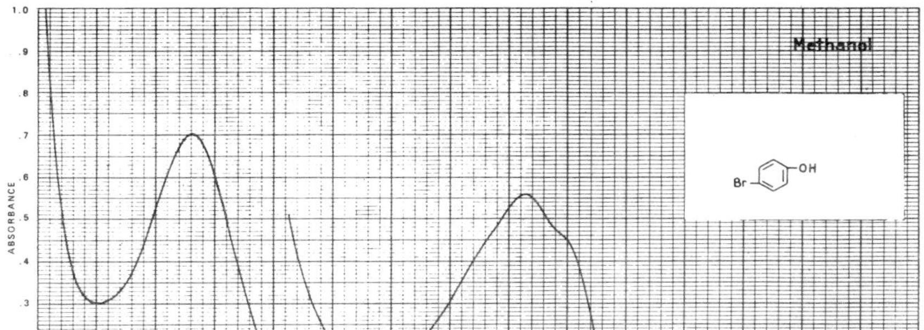

p-BROMOPHENOL

1895

C_6H_5BrO

Mol. Wt. 173.02

M.P. 64-66°C

Solvent: Methanol KOH

λ Max. mμ	a_m	Cell mm	Conc. g/L
299.5	2670	1	0.500
244.5	15600	1	0.100

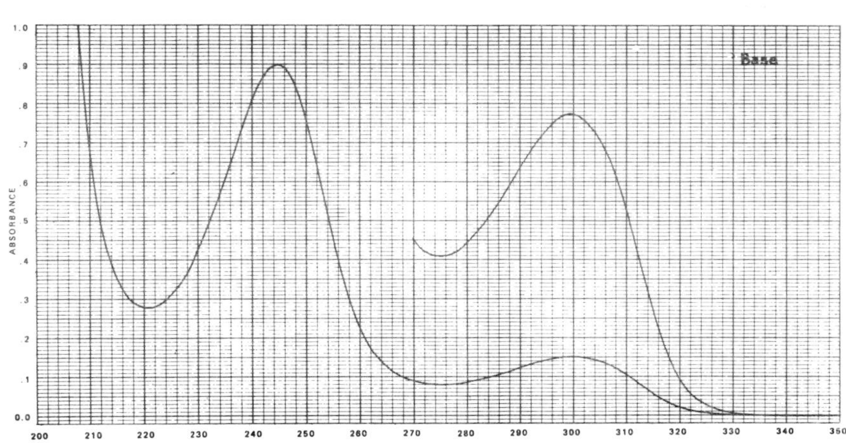

o-IODOPHENOL 1896

C_6H_5IO

Mol. Wt. 220.01

M.P. 41-43°C

Solvent: Methanol

λ Max. mμ	a_m	Cell mm	Conc. g/L
287	3190	2	0.100
280	3630	2	0.100
227	9080	2	0.100

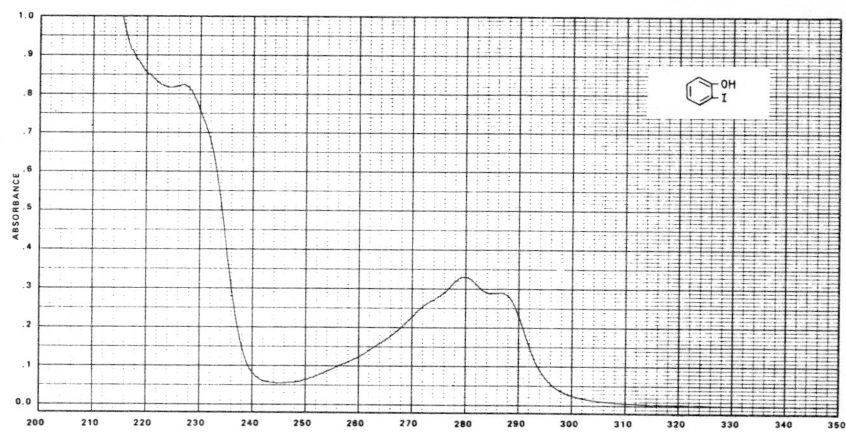

o-IODOPHENOL 1896

C_6H_5IO

Mol. Wt. 220.01

M.P. 41-43°C

Solvent: Methanol KOH

λ Max. mμ	a_m	Cell mm	Conc. g/L
298	4360	1	0.100
241	9020	1	0.100

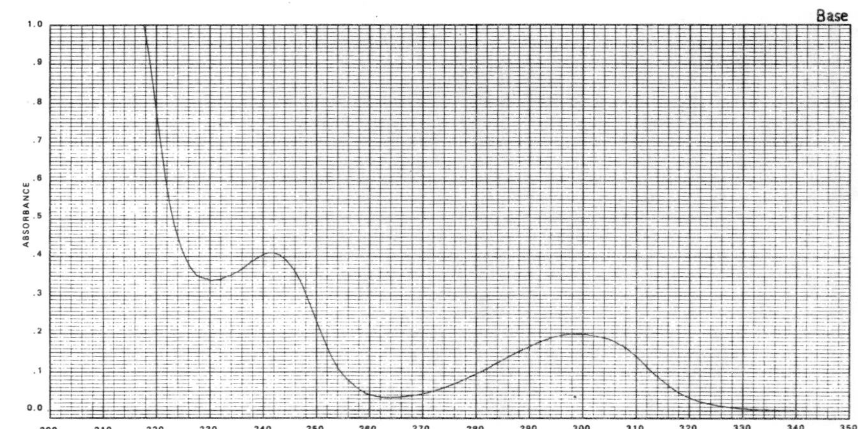

m-IODOPHENOL 1897

C_6H_5IO

Mol. Wt. 220.01

M.P. 40-42°C

Solvent: Methanol

λ Max. mμ	a_m	Cell mm	Conc. g/L
284	2460	5	0.125
277	2800	5	0.125
227	9420	1	0.125
223	9450	1	0.125

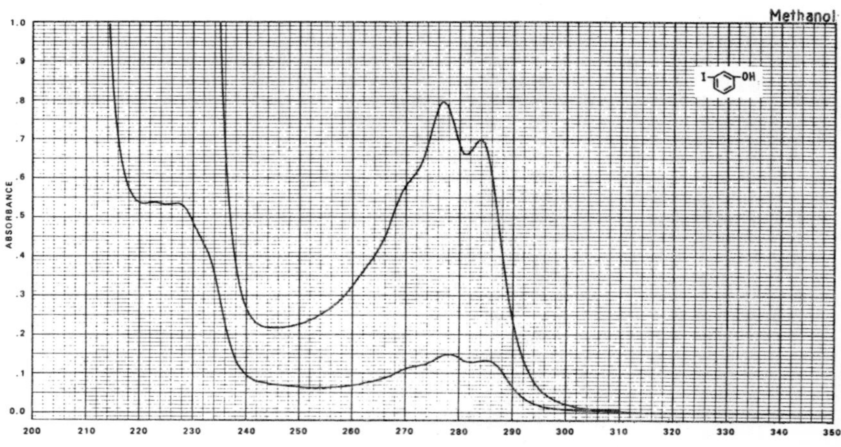

m-IODOPHENOL

C_6H_5IO

Mol. Wt. 220.01

M.P. 40-42°C

Solvent: Methanol KOH

λ Max. mμ	a_m	Cell mm	Conc. g/L
293	3260	10	0.062
241.5	9940	1	0.062

1897

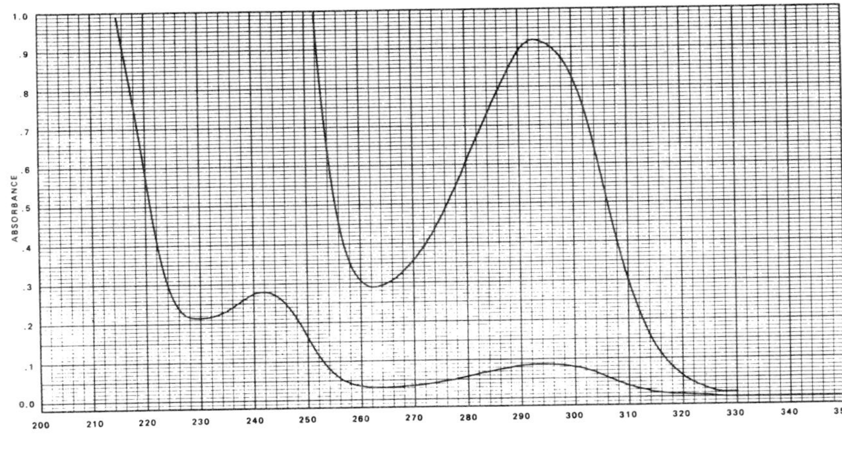

p-IODOPHENOL

C_6H_5IO

Mol. Wt. 220.01

Solvent: Methanol

λ Max. mμ	a_m	Cell mm	Conc. g/L
282.5	1440	10	0.111
232.5	15300	1	0.111

1898

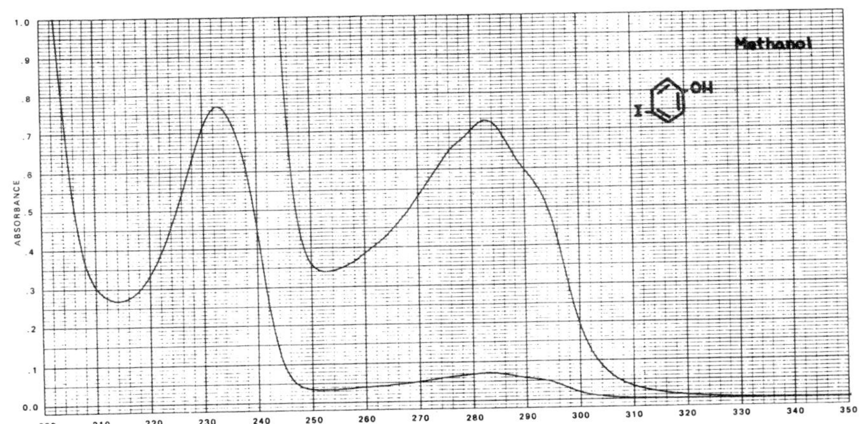

p-IODOPHENOL

C_6H_5IO

Mol. Wt. 220.01

Solvent: Methanol KOH

λ Max. mμ	a_m	Cell mm	Conc. g/L
297	2190	5	0.111
249	18200	1	0.111

1898

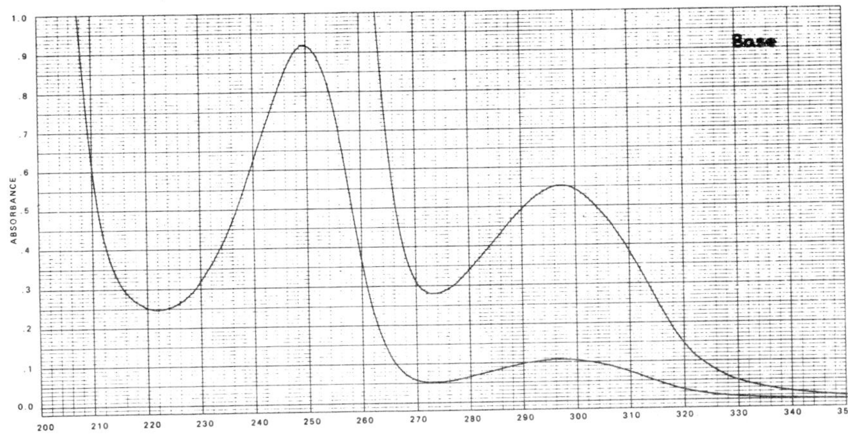

m-AMINOPHENOL 1899

C_6H_7NO

Mol. Wt. 109.12

M.P. 122-123°C (lit.)

Solvent: Methanol

λ Max. mμ	a_m	Cell mm	Conc. g/L
x	x	10	2.1080
287	2090	10	0.0632
x	x	10	0.0063

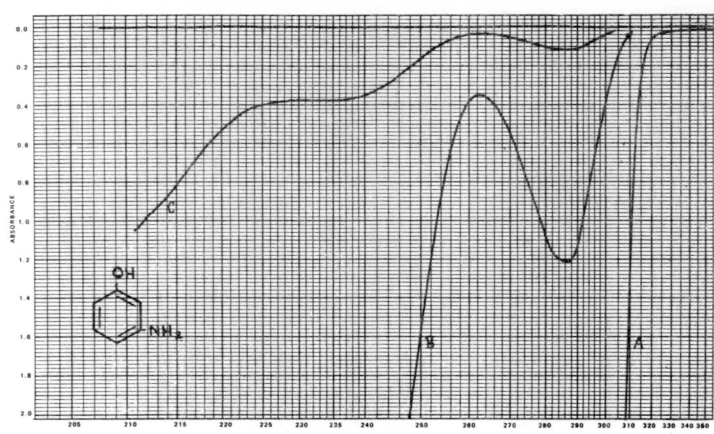

m-(DIMETHYLAMINO)PHENOL 1900

$C_8H_{11}NO$

Mol. Wt. 137.18

Solvent: Methanol

λ Max. mμ	a_m	Cell mm	Conc. g/L
x	x	10	2.01
290	206	10	0.0604
251	11200	10	0.00604

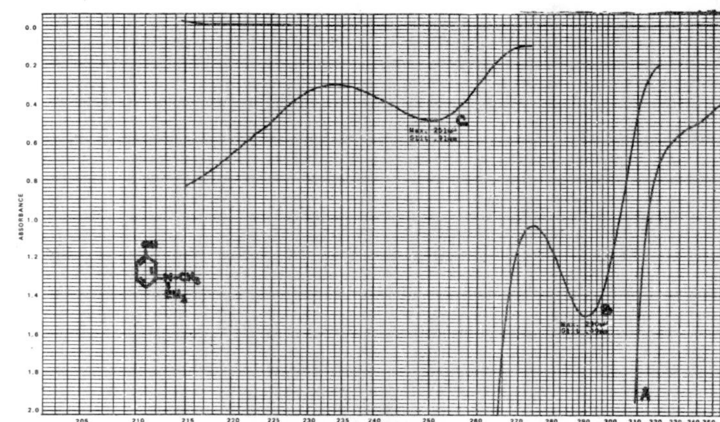

α,α-BIS[p-(DIMETHYLAMINO)PHENOL]-p-CRESOL 1901

$C_{23}H_{26}N_2O$

Mol. Wt. 346.48

M.P. 166-168°C

Solvent: Methanol

λ Max. mμ	a_m	Cell mm	Conc. g/L
262.5	32400	1	0.100

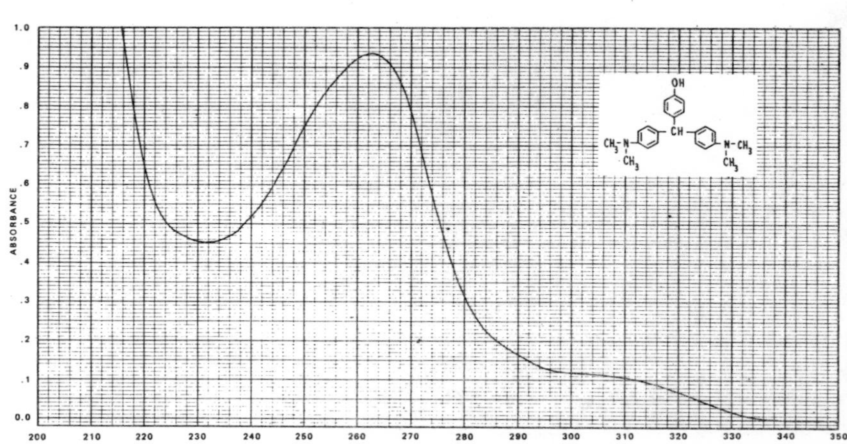

a,a-BIS[p-(DIMETHYLAMINO)PHENOL-p-CRESOL **1901**

$C_{23}H_{26}N_2O$
Mol. Wt. 346.48
M.P. 166-168°C
Solvent: Methanol KOH

λ Max. mμ	a_m	Cell mm	Conc. g/L
259.5	35600	1	0.0500

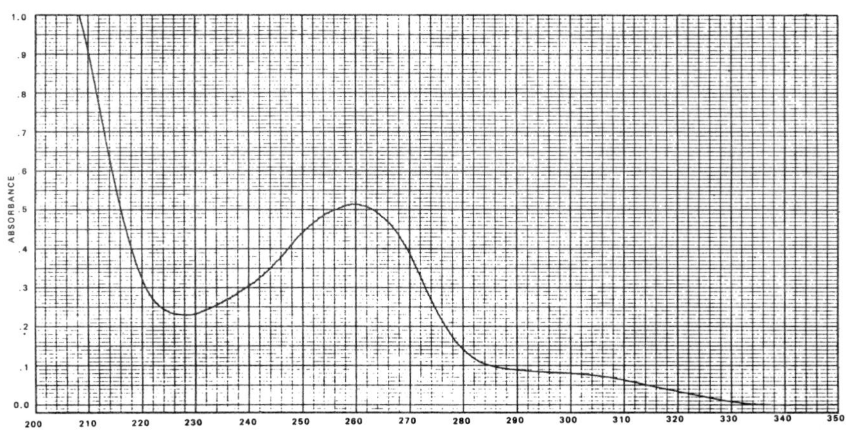

a,a-BIS[p-(DIMETHYLAMINO)PHENOL]-p-CRESOL **1901**

$C_{23}H_{26}N_2O$
Mol. Wt. 346.48
M.P. 166-168°C
Solvent: Methanol HCl

λ Max. mμ	a_m	Cell mm	Conc. g/L
280.5	2160	10	0.100
270	2200	10	0.100
x	x	1	0.100

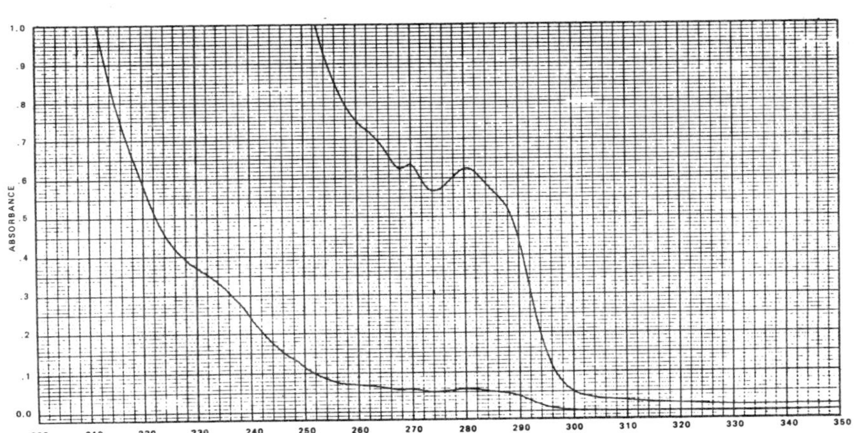

λ Max. mμ	a_m	Cell mm	Conc. g/L

p-HYDROXYHYDROCINNAMONITRILE 1902

C_9H_9NO

Mol. Wt. 138.11

Solvent: Methanol

λ Max. mμ	a_m	Cell mm	Conc. g/L
277.5	1620	10	0.07
225	7970	10	0.01

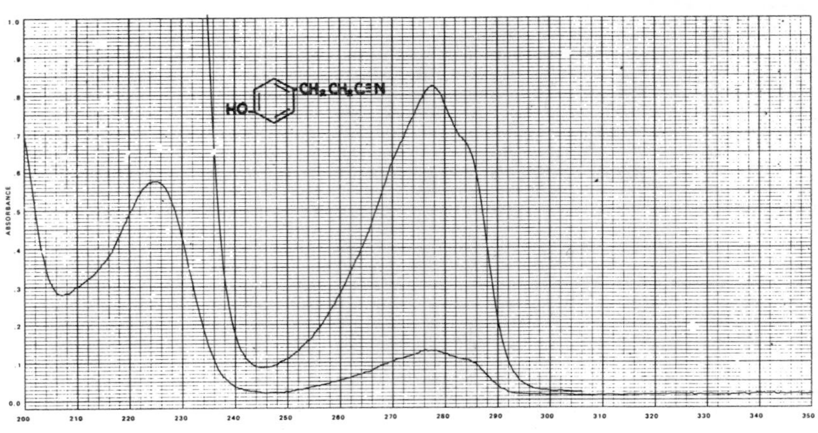

p-HYDROXYHYDROCINNAMONITRILE 1902

C_9H_9NO

Mol. Wt. 138.11

Solvent: Methanol KOH

λ Max. mμ	a_m	Cell mm	Conc. g/L
294	2210	5	0.100
244	10700	1	0.100

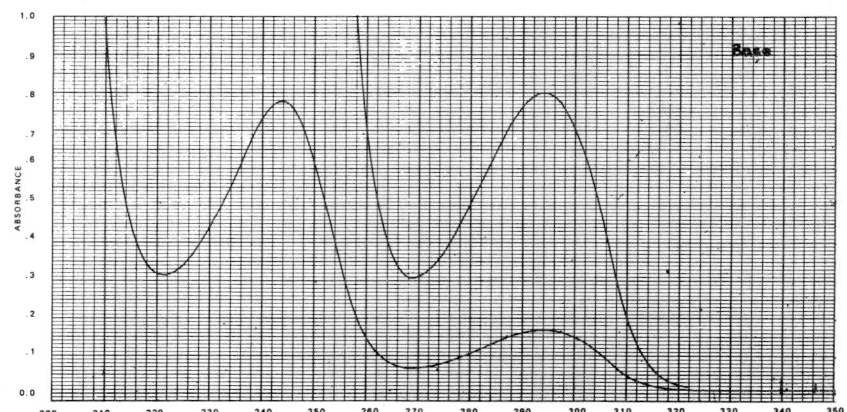

o-NITROPHENOL 1903

$C_6H_5NO_3$

Mol. Wt. 139.11

M.P. 42°C

Solvent: Methanol

λ Max. mμ	a_m	Cell mm	Conc. g/L
345	3330	1	0.100
272	6300	1	0.100

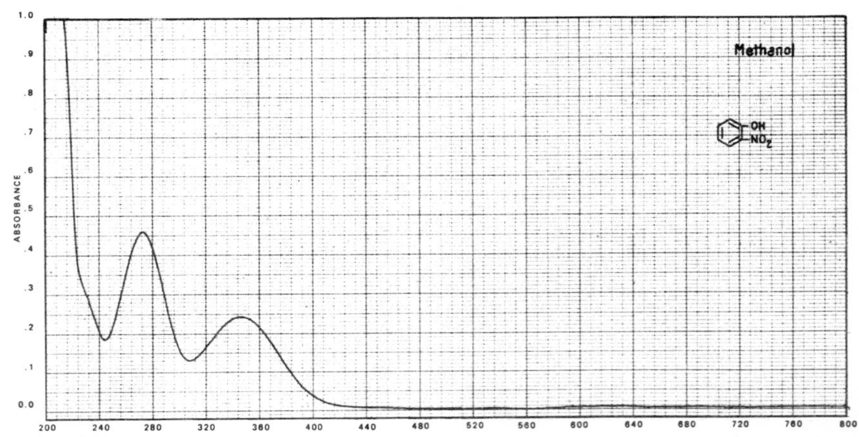

o-NITROPHENOL 1903

$C_6H_5NO_3$
Mol. Wt. 139.11
M.P. 42°C
Solvent: Methanol KOH

λ Max. mμ	a_m	Cell mm	Conc. g/L
408	4870	1	0.100
276	3990	1	0.100
230	16900	1	0.0500

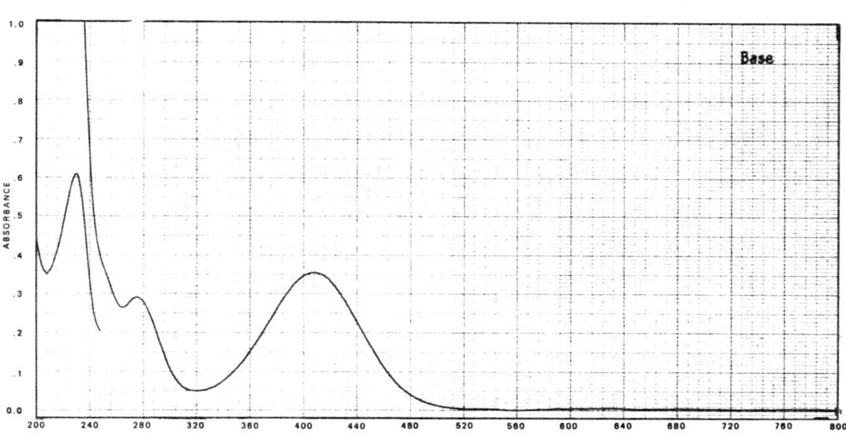

m-NITROPHENOL 1904

$C_6H_5O_3N$
Mol. Wt. 139.11
Solvent: Methanol

λ Max. mμ	a_m	Cell mm	Conc. g/L
330	2020	10	0.080
268.5	5980	10	0.020
229	9600	10	0.020

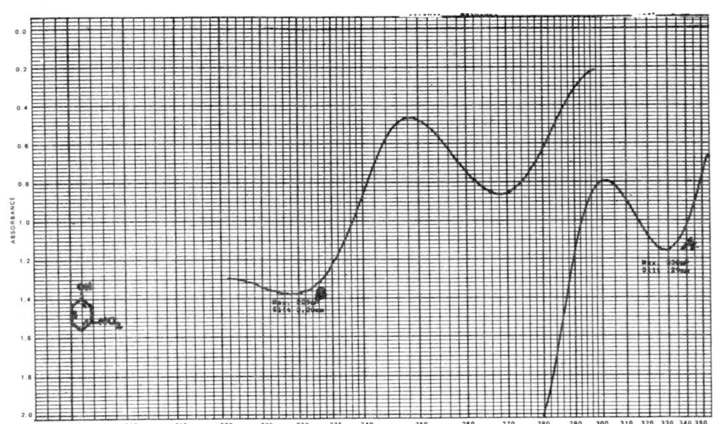

λ Max. mμ	a_m	Cell mm	Conc. g/L

p-NITROPHENOL

1905

$C_6H_5NO_3$

Mol. Wt. 139.11

M.P. 112-113°C

Solvent: Methanol

λ Max. mμ	a_m	Cell mm	Conc. g/L
311	11000	1	0.100
228	7510	1	0.100

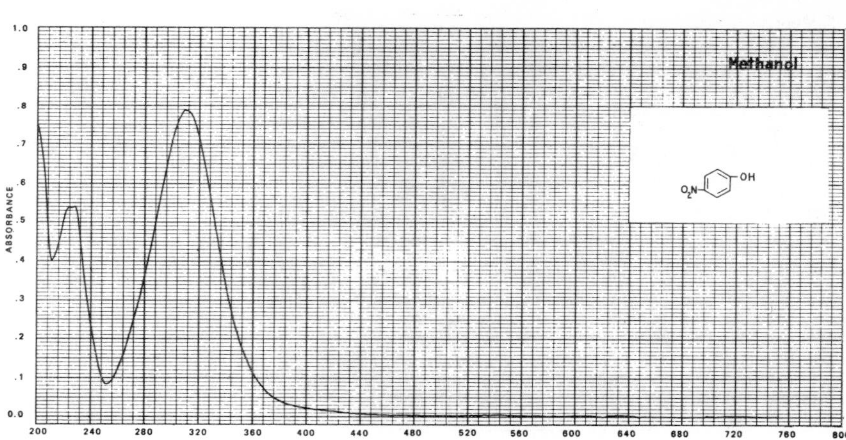

p-NITROPHENOL

1905

$C_6H_5NO_3$

Mol. Wt. 139.11

M.P. 112-113°C

Solvent: Methanol KOH

λ Max. mμ	a_m	Cell mm	Conc. g/L
390	18200	1	0.0500
300	1260	5	0.0500
290	1290	5	0.0500
224	6480	1	0.0500

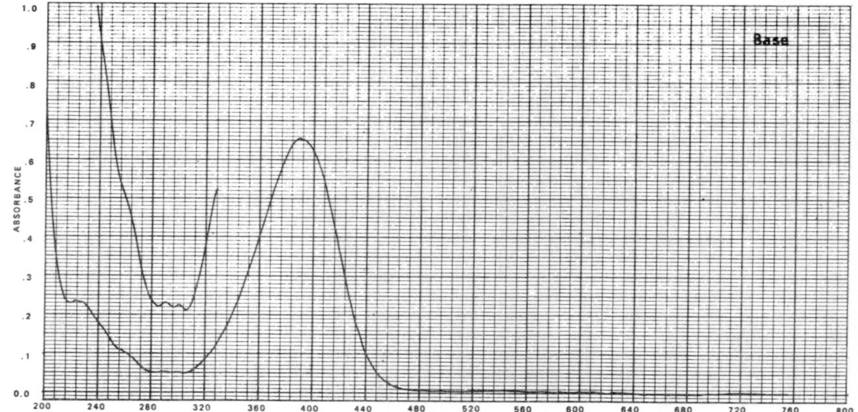

m-METHOXYPHENOL

1906

$C_7H_8O_2$

Mol. Wt. 124.13

B.P. 244°C (lit.)

Solvent: Methanol

λ Max. mμ	a_m	Cell mm	Conc. g/L
x	x	10	2.4720
280.5	1660	10	0.0989
274.5	1880	10	0.0989
x	x	10	0.0099

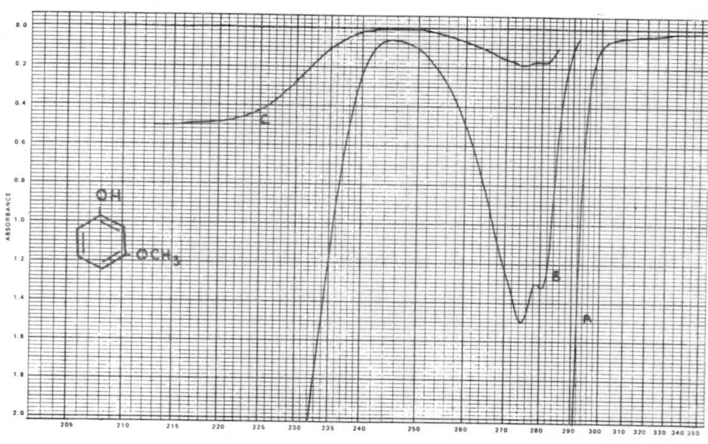

o-HYDROXYBENZYL ALCOHOL

1907

$C_7H_8O_2$

Mol. Wt. 124.14

M.P. 85-86°C

Solvent: Methanol

λ Max. mμ	^{a}m	Cell mm	Conc. g/L
274	2160	5	0.100
214.5	6460	1	0.100

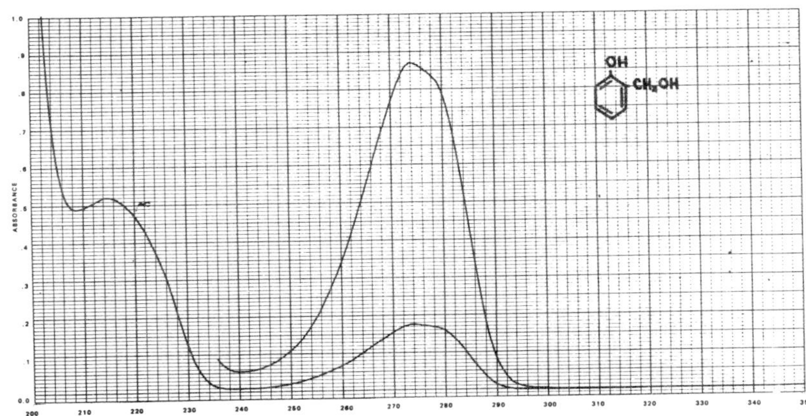

o-HYDROXYBENZYL ALCOHOL

1907

$C_7H_8O_2$

Mol. Wt. 124.14

M.P. 85-86°C

Solvent: Methanol KOH

λ Max. mμ	^{a}m	Cell mm	Conc. g/L
291	2280	2	0.100
239	5700	2	0.100

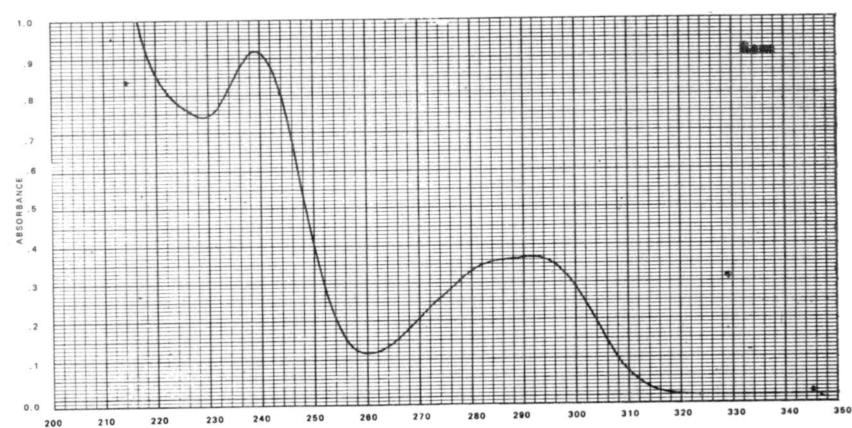

λ Max. mμ	^{a}m	Cell mm	Conc. g/L

4,4'-ISOPROPYLIDENEDIPHENOL 1908

$C_{15}H_{16}O_2$
Mol. Wt. 228.29
Solvent: Methanol

λ Max. mμ	a_m	Cell mm	Conc. g/L
278.5	6300	2	0.100
227	26900	2	0.0200

4,4'-ISOPROPYLIDENEDIPHENOL 1908

$C_{15}H_{16}O_2$
Mol. Wt. 228.29
Solvent: Methanol KOH

λ Max. mμ	a_m	Cell mm	Conc. g/L
287.5	6450	2	0.100
241.5	24900	2	0.0200

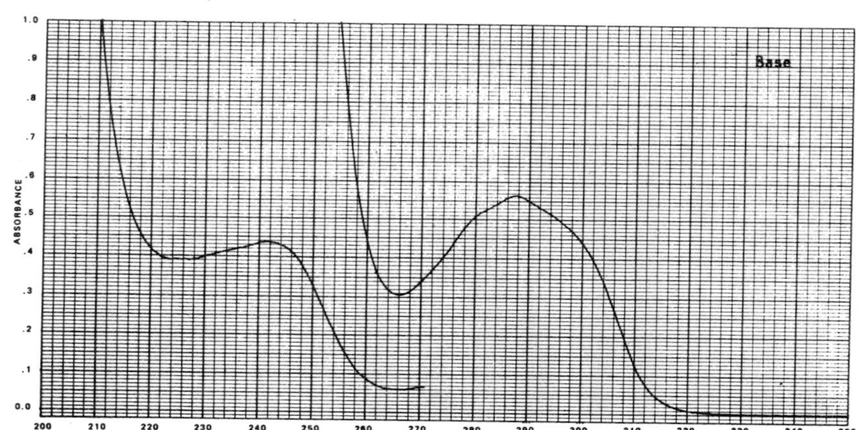

p,p'-BIPHENOL 1909

$C_{12}H_{10}O_2$
Mol. Wt. 186.21
Solvent: Methanol

λ Max. mμ	a_m	Cell mm	Conc. g/L
261.5	18400	1	0.100

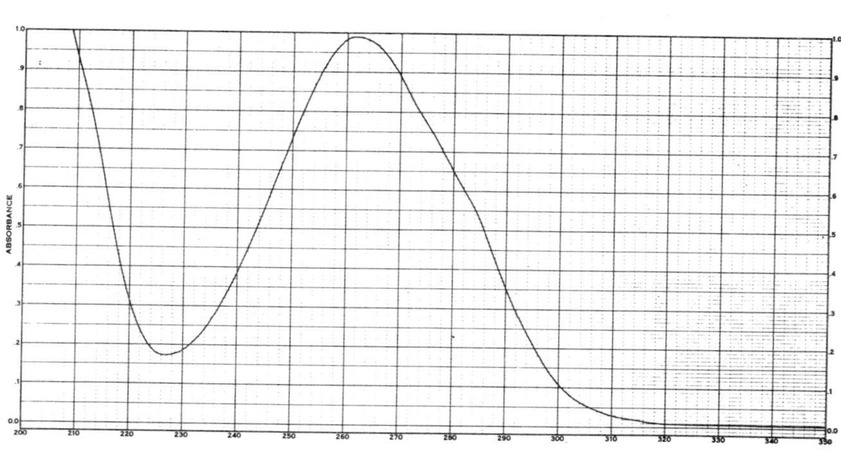

p,p'-BIPHENOL

1909

$C_{12}H_{10}O_2$
Mol. Wt. 186.21
Solvent: Methanol KOH

λ Max. mμ	a_m	Cell mm	Conc. g/L
287	21700	0.5	0.100

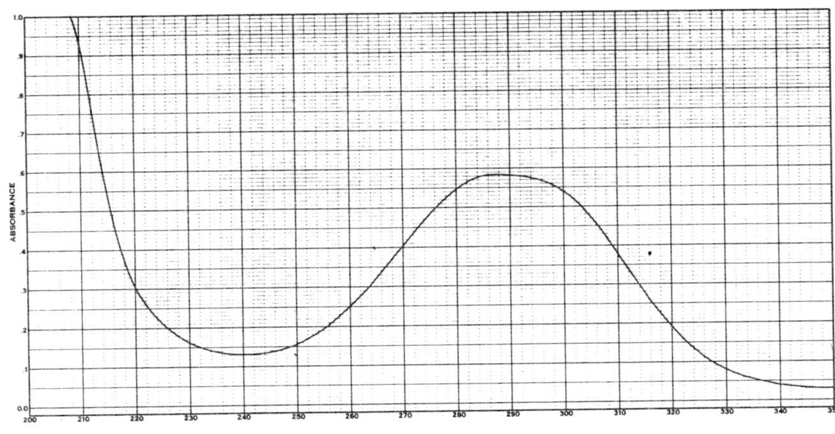

PYROCATECHOL

1910

$C_6H_6O_2$
Mol. Wt. 110.11
M.P. 175°C (lit.)
Solvent: Methanol

λ Max. mμ	a_m	Cell mm	Conc. g/L
x	x	10	2.060
277.5	2650	10	0.0618
x	x	10	0.0124

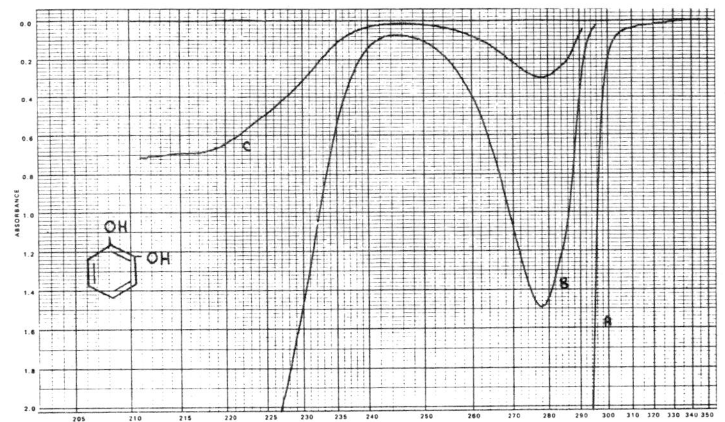

RESORCINOL

1911

$C_6H_6O_2$
Mol. Wt. 110.11
M.P. 110°C (lit.)
Solvent: Methanol

λ Max. mμ	a_m	Cell mm	Conc. g/L
x	x	10	2.32
282	1800	10	0.0928
275.5	2110	10	0.0928
x	x	10	0.0093

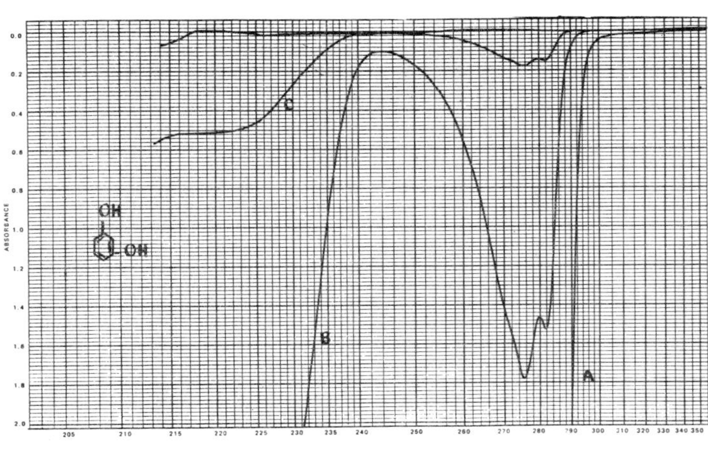

HYDROQUINONE

1912

$C_6H_6O_2$
Mol. Wt. 110.11
Solvent: Methanol

λ Max. mμ	a_m	Cell mm	Conc. g/L
293.5	2810	2	0.100
224.5	5180	2	0.100

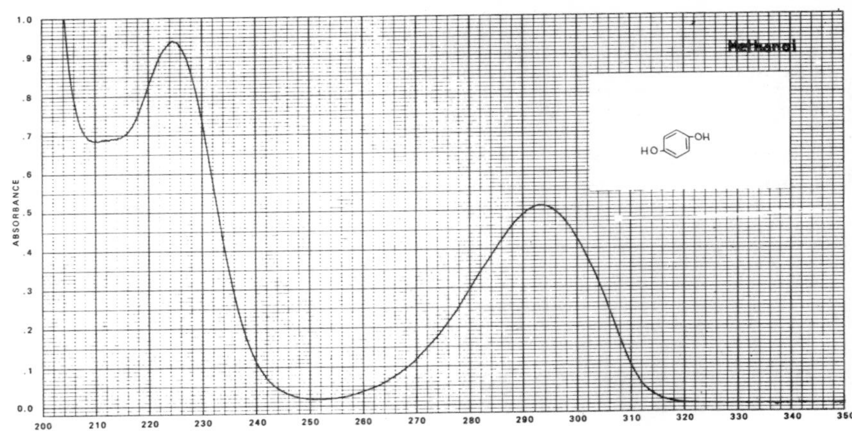

2,3-XYLENOL

1913

$C_8H_{10}O$
Mol. Wt. 122.17
M.P. 75°C B.P. 218°C
Solvent: Methanol

λ Max. mμ	a_m	Cell mm	Conc. g/L
273	1610	5	0.100
x	x	1	0.100

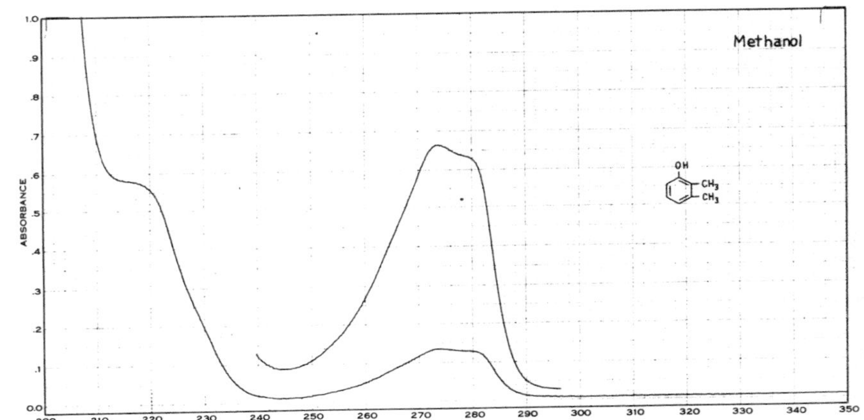

2,3-XYLENOL

1913

$C_8H_{10}O$
Mol. Wt. 122.17
M.P. 75°C B.P. 218°C
Solvent: Methanol KOH

λ Max. mμ	a_m	Cell mm	Conc. g/L
280	1780	5	0.100
239	3180	1	0.100

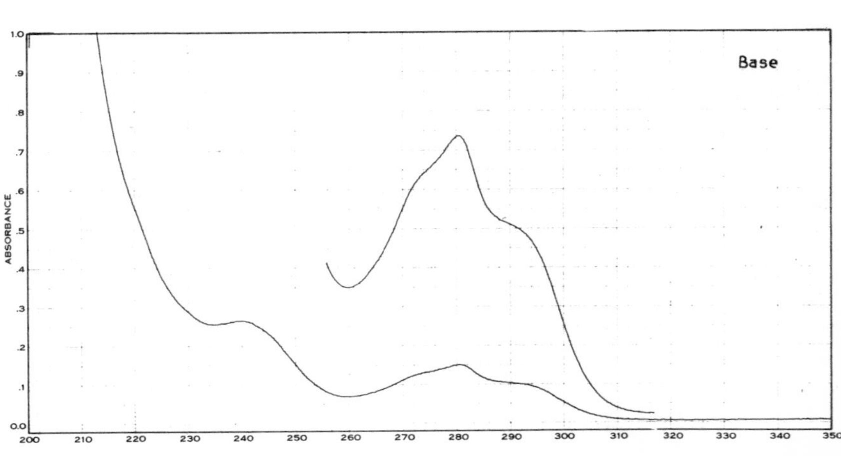

3,4-XYLENOL 1914

$C_8H_{10}O$
Mol. Wt. 122.17
M.P. 65°C B.P. 228-229°C (lit.)
Solvent: Methanol

λ Max. mμ	a_m	Cell mm	Conc. g/L
279	1890	1	0.500
217.5	6230	1	0.100

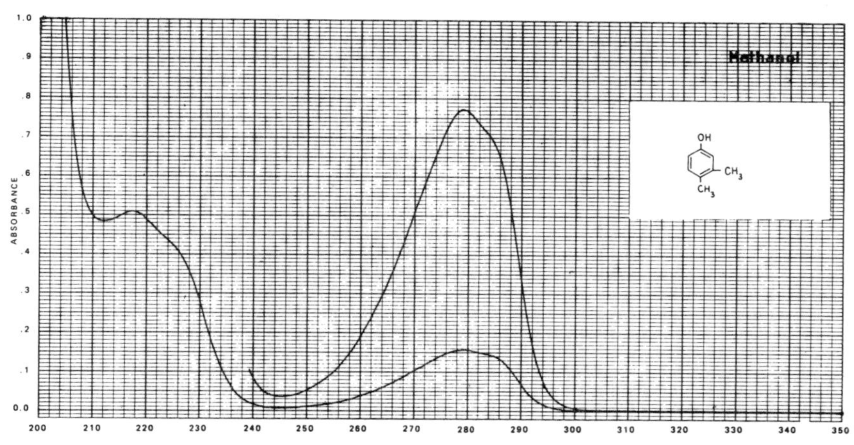

3,4-XYLENOL 1914

$C_8H_{10}O$
Mol. Wt. 122.17
M.P. 65°C B.P. 228-229°C (lit.)
Solvent: Methanol KOH

λ Max. mμ	a_m	Cell mm	Conc. g/L
287	1760	2	0.100
238	5160	2	0.100
x	x	1	0.100

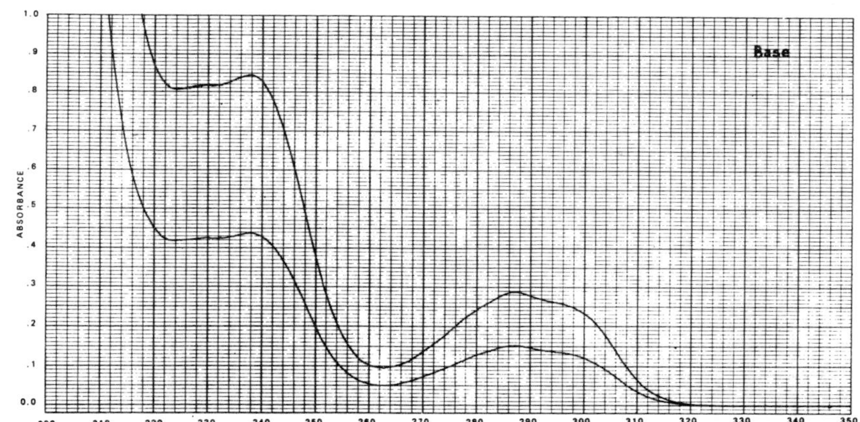

3,5-XYLENOL 1915

$C_8H_{10}O$
Mol. Wt. 122.16
M.P. 68°C
Solvent: Methanol

λ Max. mμ	a_m	Cell mm	Conc. g/L
282	1470	10	0.05
276	1460	10	0.05
203	28200	10	0.002

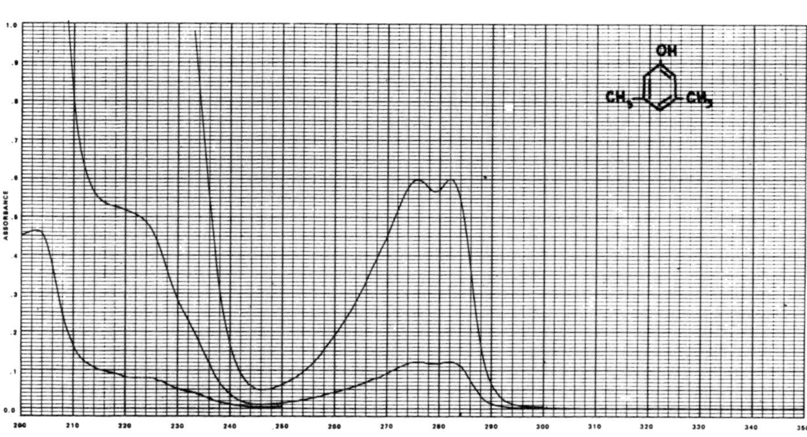

2,6-XYLENOL

1916

$C_8H_{10}O$
Mol. Wt. 122.17
M.P. 40-43°C
Solvent: Methanol

λ Max. mμ	a_m	Cell mm	Conc. g/L
272	1480	5	0.100
x	x	1	0.100

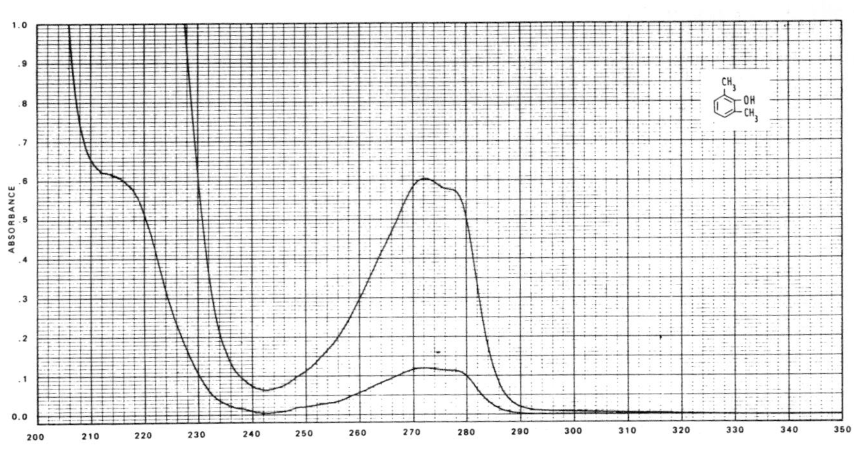

2,6-XYLENOL

1916

$C_8H_{10}O$
Mol. Wt. 122.17
M.P. 40-43°C
Solvent: Methanol KOH

λ Max. mμ	a_m	Cell mm	Conc. g/L
278	1560	5	0.100
240.5	1800	5	0.100

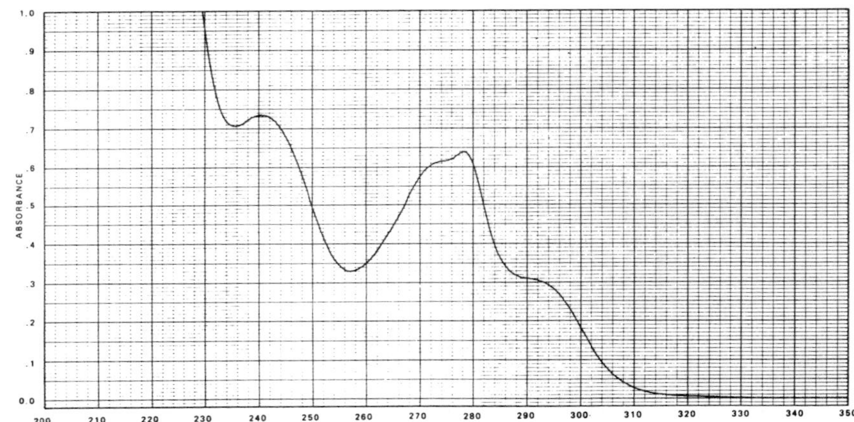

THYMOL

1917

$C_{10}H_{14}O$
Mol. Wt. 150.22
M.P. 49-51°C
Solvent: Methanol

λ Max. mμ	a_m	Cell mm	Conc. g/L
276	2320	2	0.100

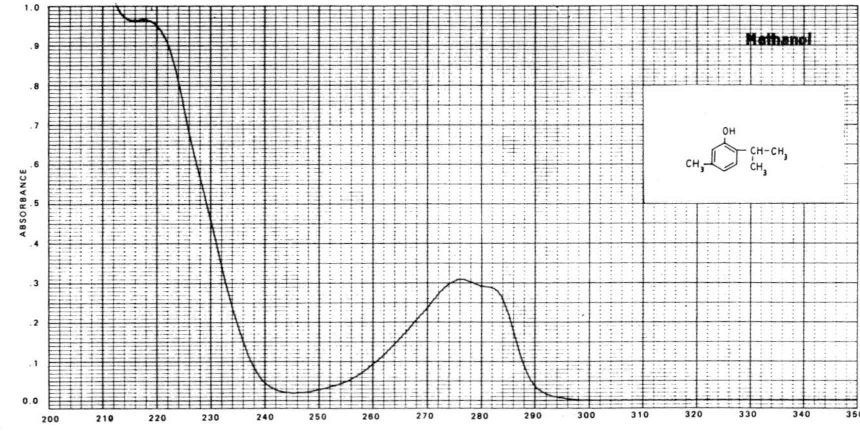

THYMOL

1917

$C_{10}H_{14}O$

Mol. Wt. 150.22

M.P. 49-51°C

Solvent: Methanol KOH

λ Max. mμ	a_m	Cell mm	Conc. g/L
283.5	2370	2	0.100
240.5	4210	2	0.100
x	x	1	0.100

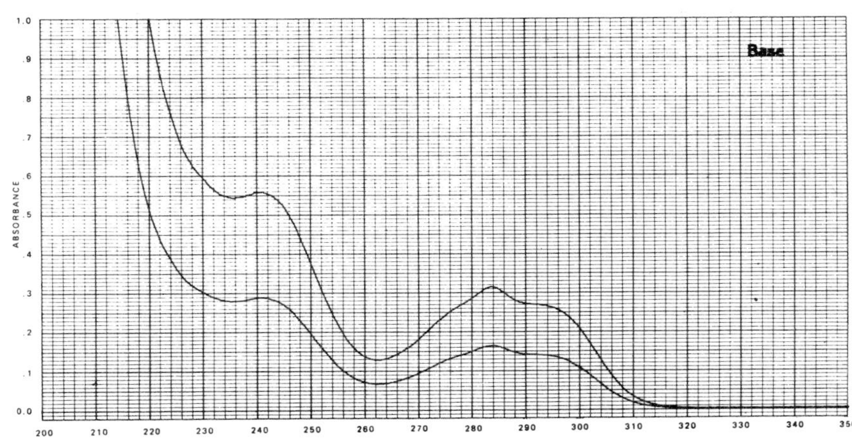

6-ALLYL-o-CRESOL

1918

$C_{10}H_{12}O$

Mol. Wt. 148.21

Solvent: Methanol

λ Max. mμ	a_m	Cell mm	Conc. g/L
x	x	10	2.3160
262.5	2710	10	0.0463
x	x	10	0.0092

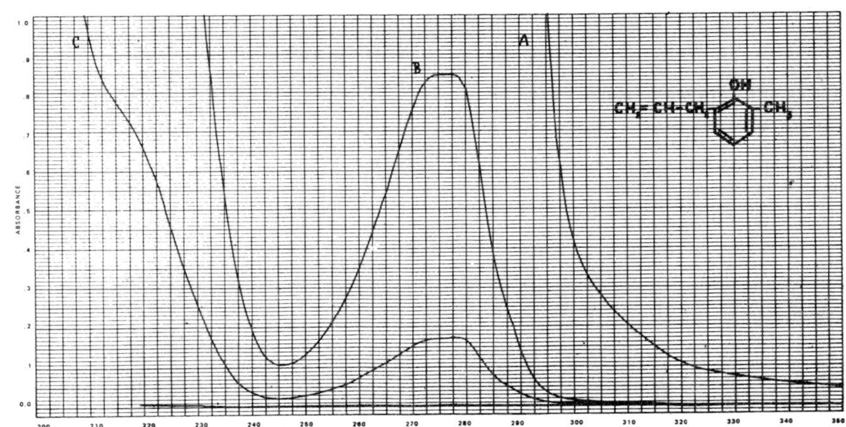

λ Max. mμ	a_m	Cell mm	Conc. g/L

2,4-DICHLOROPHENOL 1919

$C_6H_4Cl_2O$

Mol. Wt. 163.00

M.P. 44-45°C

Solvent: Methanol

λ Max. mμ	a_m	Cell mm	Conc. g/L
287	2450	2	0.100
228.5	6550	2	0.100
220.5	6580	2	0.100

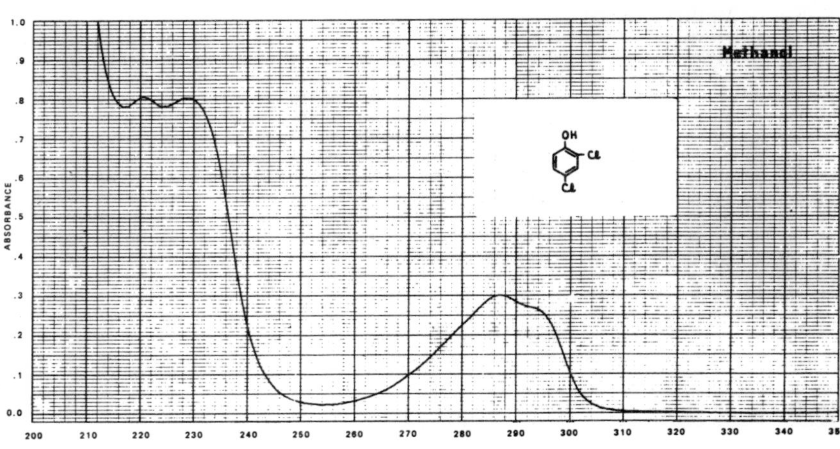

2,4-DICHLOROPHENOL 1919

$C_6H_4Cl_2O$

Mol. Wt. 163.00

M.P. 44-45°C

Solvent: Methanol KOH

λ Max. mμ	a_m	Cell mm	Conc. g/L
308	3720	1	0.100
246	10300	1	0.100

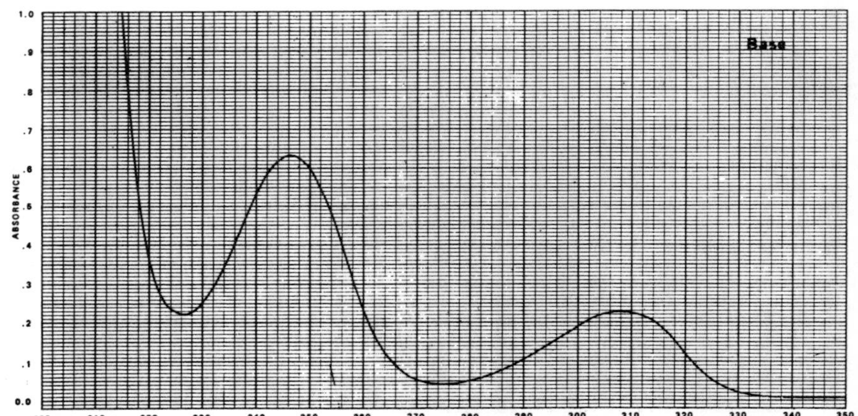

3,5-DICHLOROPHENOL 1920

$C_6H_4Cl_2O$

Mol. Wt. 163.00

M.P. 67-68°C B.P. 233°C/757mm

Solvent: Methanol

λ Max. mμ	a_m	Cell mm	Conc. g/L
286	2330	5	0.100
x	x	1	0.100

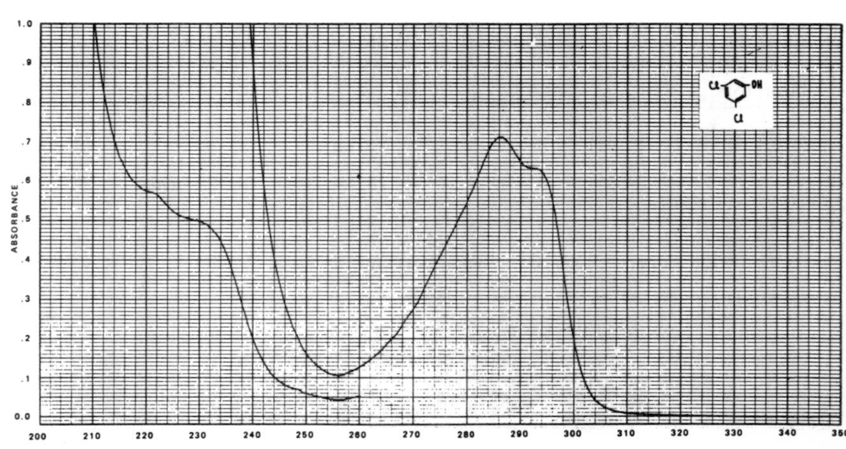

3,5-DICHLOROPHENOL

1920

$C_6H_4Cl_2O$
Mol. Wt. 163.00
M.P. 67-68°C B.P. 233°C/757mm
Solvent: Methanol KOH

λ Max. mμ	a_m	Cell mm	Conc. g/L
305	3160	5	0.100
245	13300	1	0.100

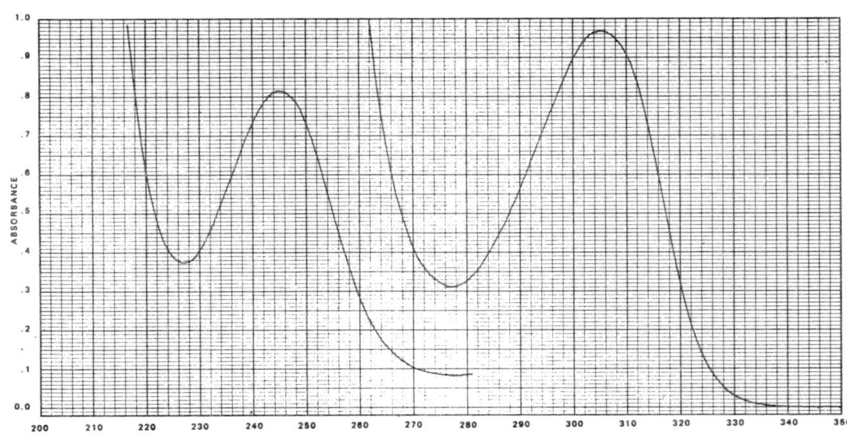

2,4-DIBROMOPHENOL

1921

$C_6H_4Br_2O$
Mol. Wt. 251.92
Solvent: Methanol

λ Max. mμ	a_m	Cell mm	Conc. g/L
288.5	2610	10	0.0800
223	9780	2	0.0800

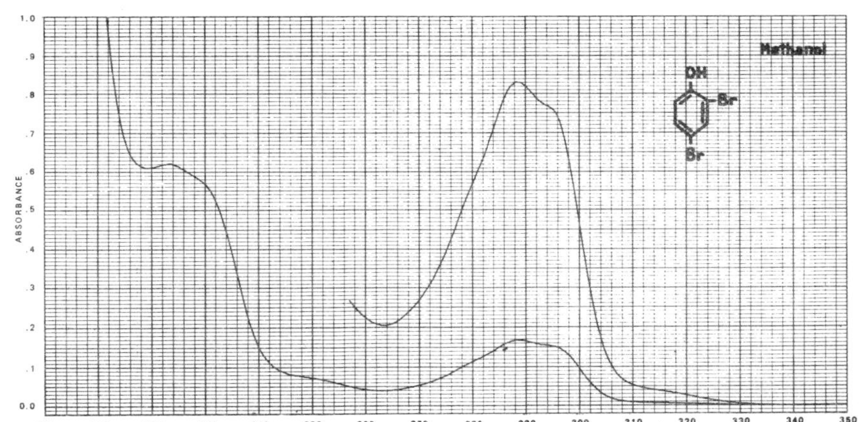

2,4-DIBROMOPHENOL

1921

$C_6H_4Br_2O$
Mol. Wt. 251.92
Solvent: Methanol KOH

λ Max. mμ	a_m	Cell mm	Conc. g/L
310.5	3780	2	0.0800
248.5	13000	2	0.0800

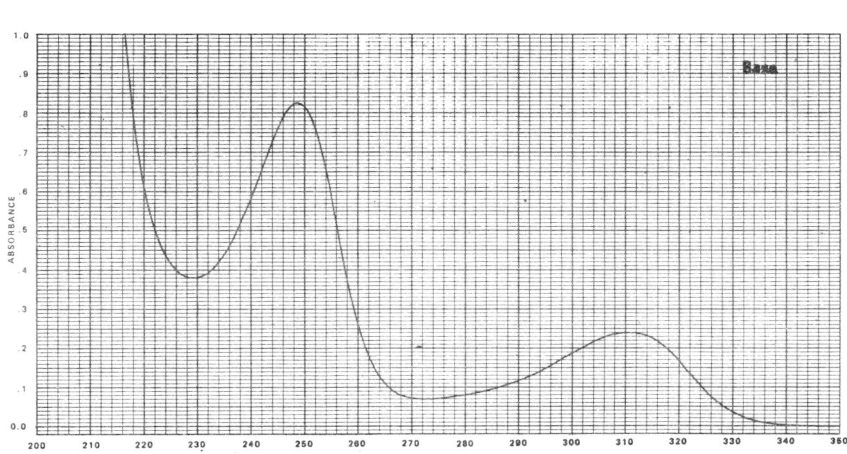

2-CHLORO-6-NITROPHENOL 1922

$C_6H_4ClNO_3$

Mol. Wt. 173.56

M.P. 70-71°C

Solvent: Methanol

λ Max. mμ	a_m	Cell mm	Conc. g/L
348	2690	5	0.100
277	5570	1	0.100
217	13400	1	0.100

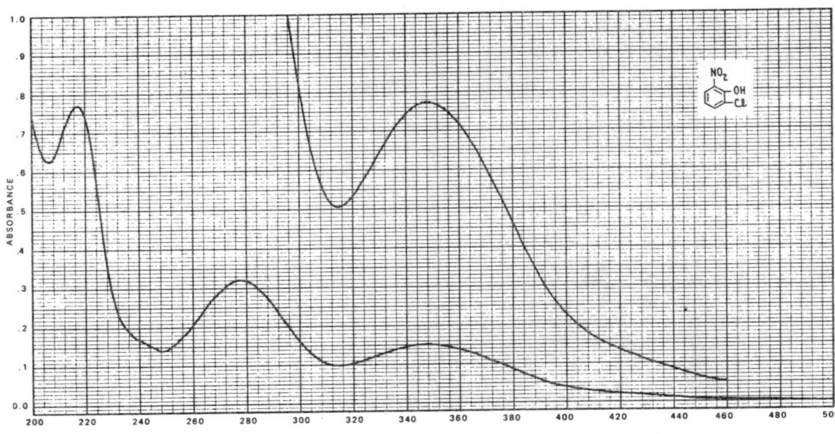

2-CHLORO-6-NITROPHENOL 1922

$C_6H_4ClNO_3$

Mol. Wt. 173.56

M.P. 70-71°C

Solvent: Methanol KOH

λ Max. mμ	a_m	Cell mm	Conc. g/L
418	4910	1	0.100
281	3390	5	0.100
234	13200	1	0.100

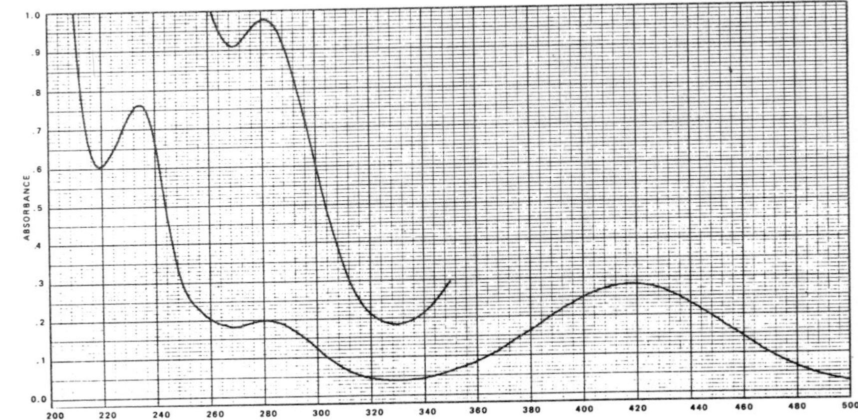

4-(METHYLTHIO)-o-CRESOL 1923

$C_8H_{10}OS$

Mol. Wt. 154.23

Solvent: Methanol

λ Max. mμ	a_m	Cell mm	Conc. g/L
285	1430	5	0.153
254	6730	1	0.153
227.5	5920	1	0.153

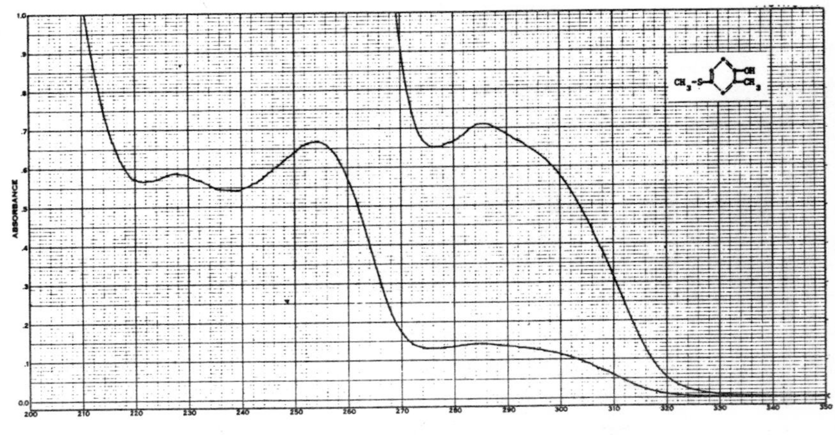

4-(METHYLTHIO)-o-CRESOL

1923

$C_8H_{10}OS$

Mol. Wt. 154.23

Solvent: Methanol KOH

λ Max. mμ	a_m	Cell mm	Conc. g/L
261.5	11300	0.5	0.153
208.5	19400	0.5	0.153

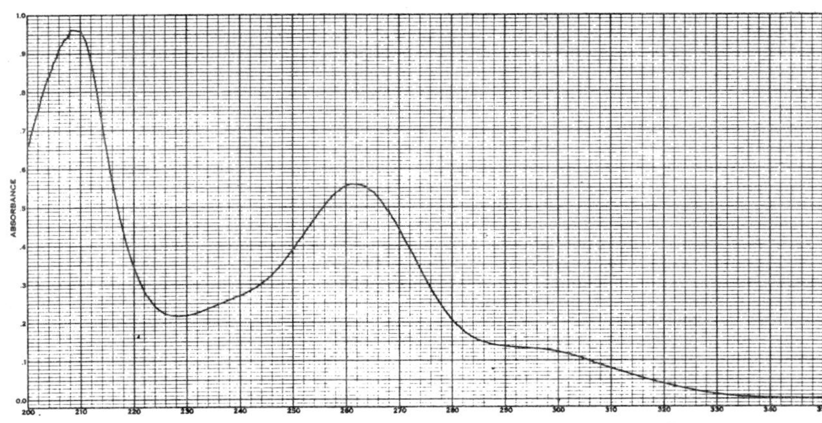

4-ALLYL-2-METHOXYPHENOL

1924

$C_{10}H_{12}O_2$

Mol. Wt. 164.21

Solvent: Methanol

λ Max. mμ	a_m	Cell mm	Conc. g/L
281	3620	2	0.100
227.5	7250	2	0.100
x	x	1	0.100

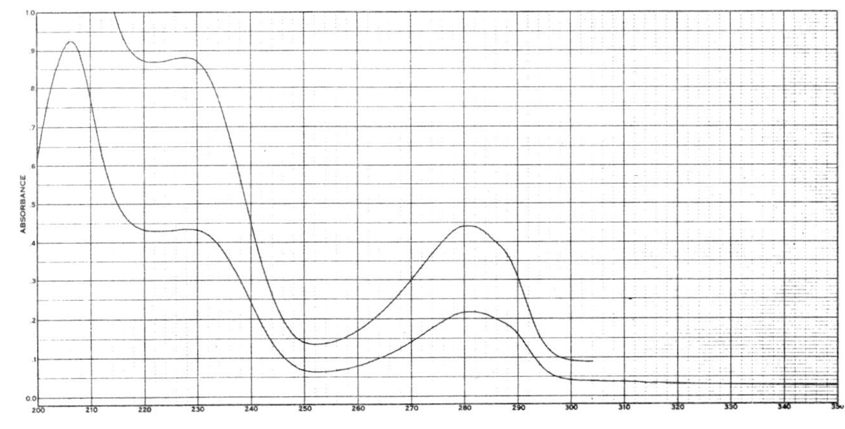

4-ALLYL-2-METHOXYPHENOL

1924

$C_{10}H_{12}O_2$

Mol. Wt. 164.21

Solvent: Methanol KOH

λ Max. mμ	a_m	Cell mm	Conc. g/L
294	4650	1	0.100
246	8650	1	0.100
x	x	0.5	0.100

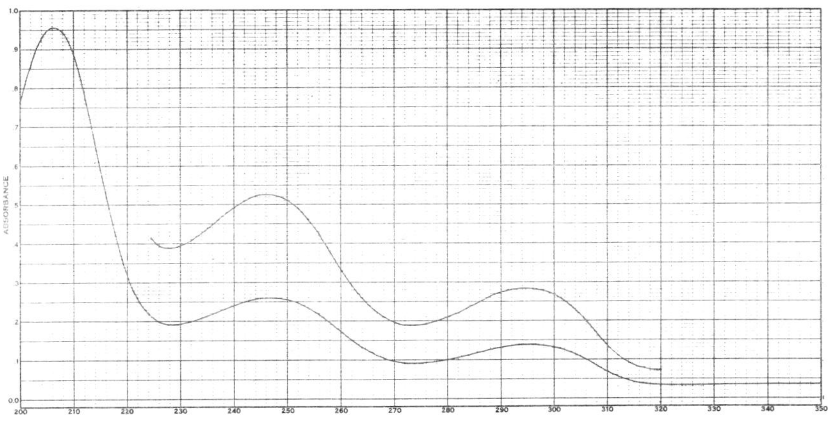

3-METHYLPYROCATECHOL 1925

$C_7H_8O_2$
Mol. Wt. 124.14
Solvent: Methanol

λ Max. mμ	a_m	Cell mm	Conc. g/L
275	21200	5	0.100
251	1620	5	0.100
x	x	1	0.100

3-METHYLPYROCATECHOL 1925

$C_7H_8O_2$
Mol. Wt. 124.14
Solvent: Methanol KOH

λ Max. mμ	a_m	Cell mm	Conc. g/L
393	1150	5	0.100
285	1990	5	0.100
246.5	7240	1	0.100

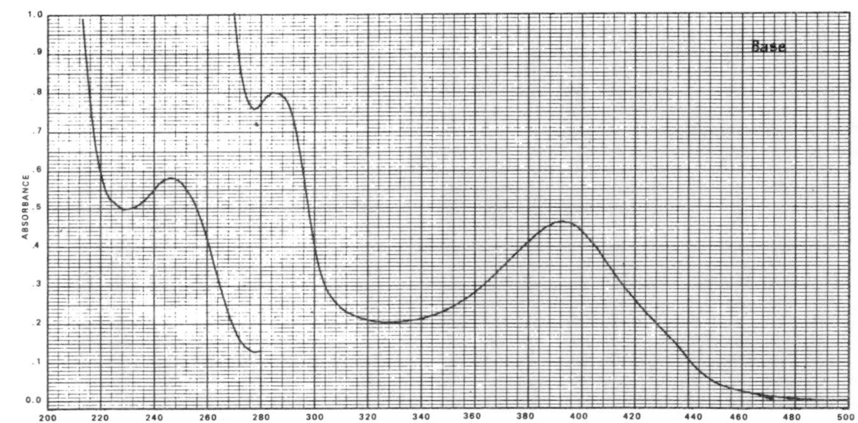

4-METHYLPYROCATECHOL 1926

$C_7H_8O_2$
Mol. Wt. 124.14
Solvent: Methanol

λ Max. mμ	a_m	Cell mm	Conc. g/L
283	3070	10	0.030
x	x	10	0.006

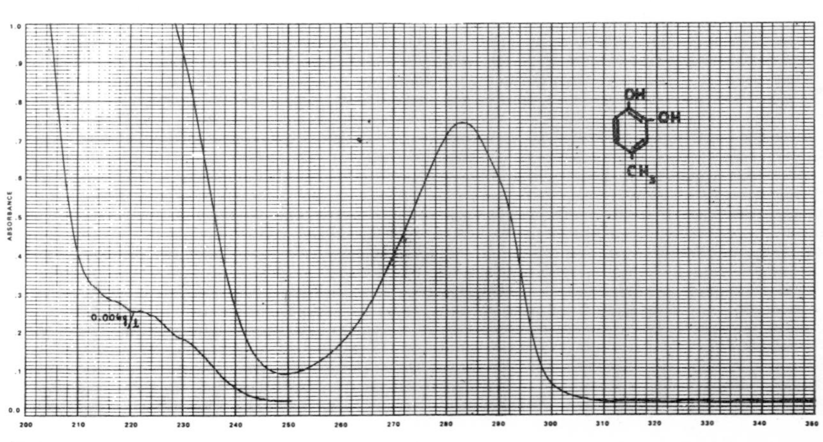

4-METHYLPYROCATECHOL

1926

$C_7H_8O_2$
Mol. Wt. 124.14
Solvent: Methanol KOH

λ Max. mμ	a_m	Cell mm	Conc. g/L
252	4410	2	0.0700

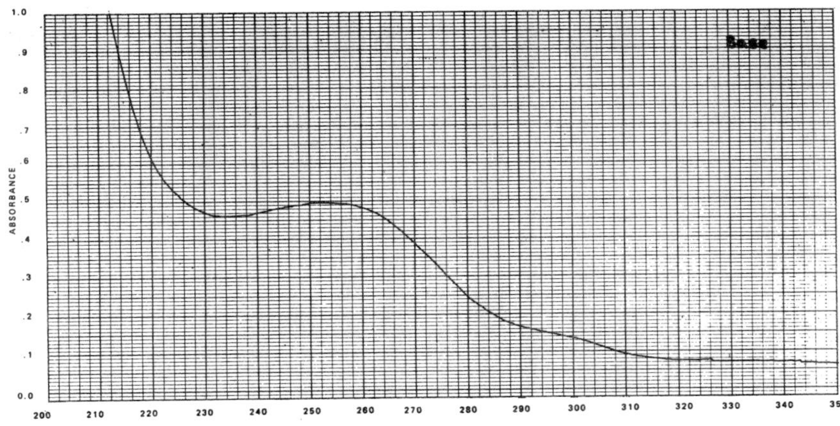

4-HEXYLRESORCINOL

1927

$C_{12}H_{10}O_2$
Mol. Wt. 194.26
B.P. 178°C/8mm (lit.)
Solvent: Methanol

λ Max. mμ	a_m	Cell mm	Conc. g/L
x	x	10	1.7040
281	2890	10	0.1022
x	x	10	0.0170

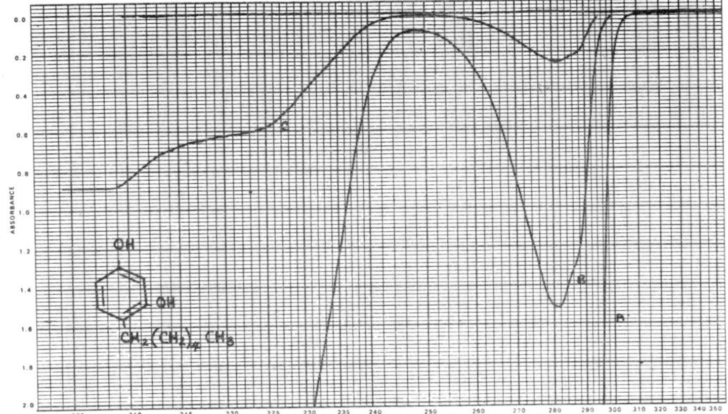

4-HEXADECYLRESORCINOL

1928

$C_{22}H_{38}O_2$
Mol. Wt. 334.55
Solvent: Methanol

λ Max. mμ	a_m	Cell mm	Conc. g/L
279.5	2920	10	0.100
x	x	1	0.100

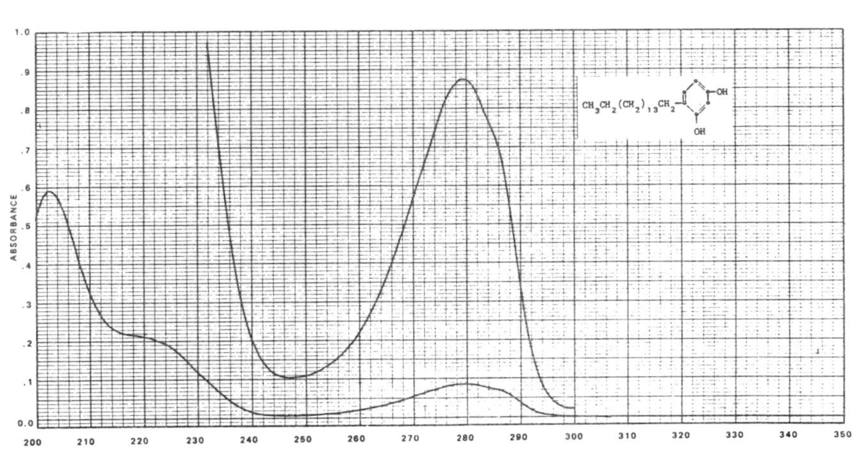

4-BENZYLRESORCINOL

1929

$C_{13}H_{12}O_2$
Mol. Wt. 200.24
Solvent: Methanol

λ Max. mμ	a_m	Cell mm	Conc. g/L
317.5	141	10	0.9960
282	3070	10	0.0498
x	x	10	0.0099

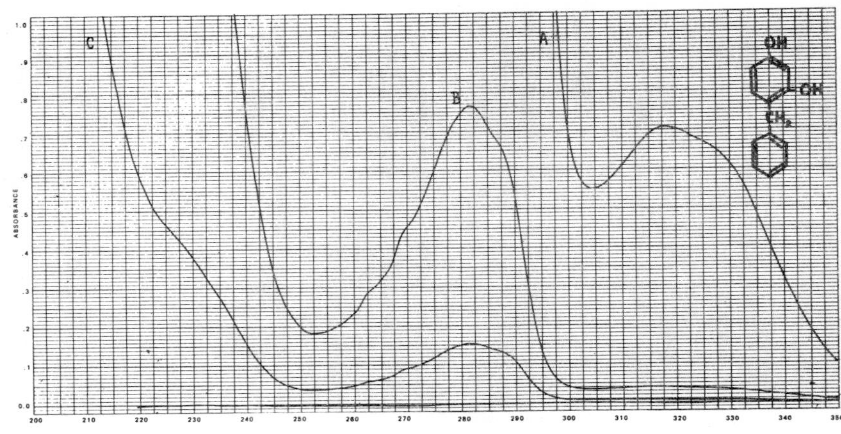

3,4-BIPHENYLDIOL

1930

$C_{12}H_{10}O_2$
Mol. Wt. 186.21
M.P. 137-138°C
Solvent: Methanol

λ Max. mμ	a_m	Cell mm	Conc. g/L
263.5	11200	1	0.100

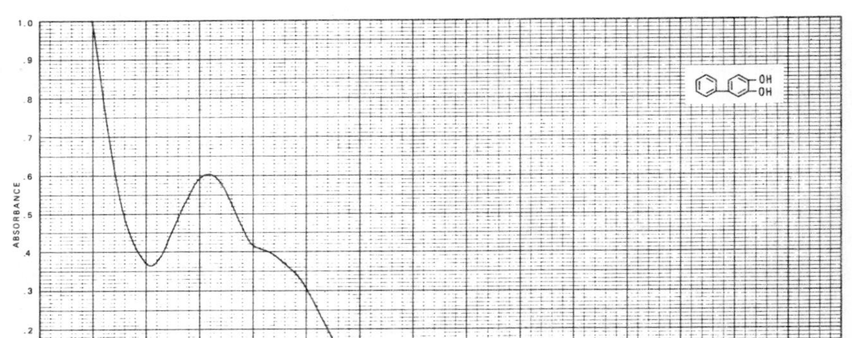

3,4-BIPHENYLDIOL

1930

$C_{12}H_{10}O_2$
Mol. Wt. 186.21
M.P. 137-138°C
Solvent: Methanol KOH

λ Max. mμ	a_m	Cell mm	Conc. g/L
417	1230	10	0.100
304	8590	2	0.100
280	8290	2	0.100

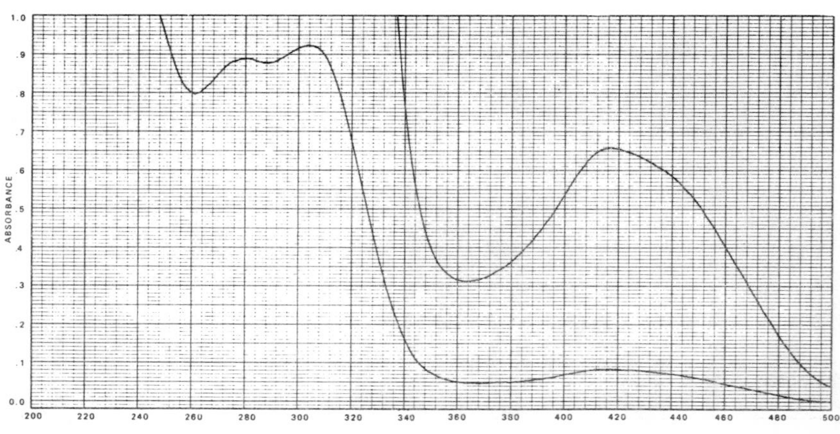

PHENYLHYDROQUINONE 1931

$C_{12}H_{10}O_2$
Mol. Wt. 186.21
M.P. 101.5-103°C
Solvent: Methanol

λ Max. mμ	a_m	Cell mm	Conc. g/L
309	5900	1	0.100

PHENYLHYDROQUINONE 1931

$C_{12}H_{10}O_2$
Mol. Wt. 186.21
M.P. 101.5-103°C
Solvent: Methanol KOH

λ Max. mμ	a_m	Cell mm	Conc. g/L
249	6240	2	0.100

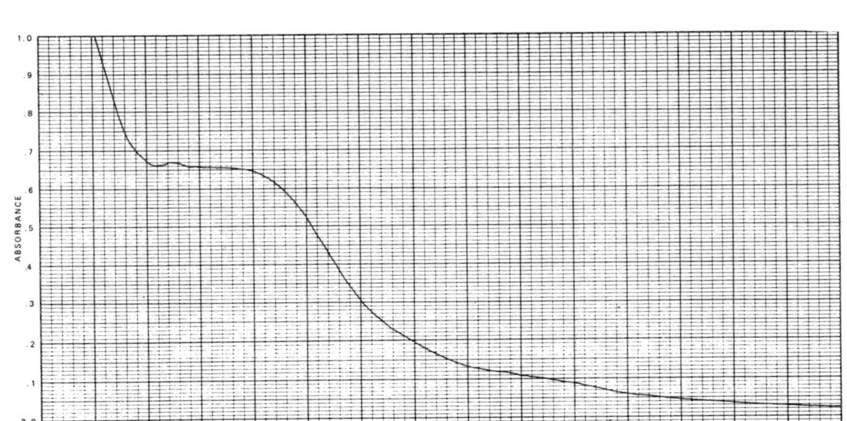

2-ALLYL-3,5-XYLENOL 1932

$C_{11}H_{14}O$
Mol. Wt. 162.23
M.P. 50.5°C

λ Max. mμ	a_m	Cell mm	Conc. g/L

Pure sample not available.

2,2′-METHYLENEBIS(6-tert-BUTYL-4-ETHYL)PHENOL

1933

$C_{25}H_{36}O_2$
Mol. Wt. 368.56
M.P. 122-125°C (lit.)
Solvent: Cyclohexane

λ Max. mμ	a_m	Cell mm	Conc. g/L
284	5450	10	0.1157
x	x	10	0.0116

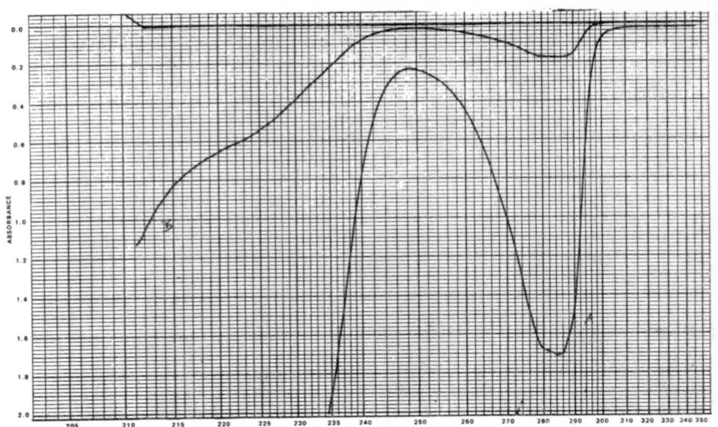

3,3′,5.5′-TETRA-tert-BUTYL-4,4′-BIPHENYLDIOL

1934

$C_{28}H_{42}O_2$
Mol. Wt. 410.64
Solvent: Cyclohexane

λ Max. mμ	a_m	Cell mm	Conc. g/L
263.5	18900	10	0.0344
x	x	10	0.0069

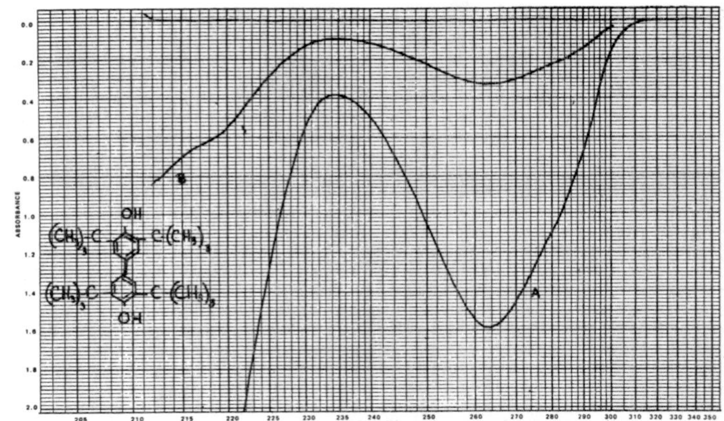

4,4′-ISOPROPYLIDENEBIS[2,6-DIBROMOPHENOL]

1935

$C_{15}H_{12}Br_4O_2$
Mol. Wt. 543.93
Solvent: Methanol

λ Max. mμ	a_m	Cell mm	Conc. g/L
x	x	10	2.0240
292.5	5950	10	0.0810
285.5	5670	10	0.0810
207	63100	10	0.0081

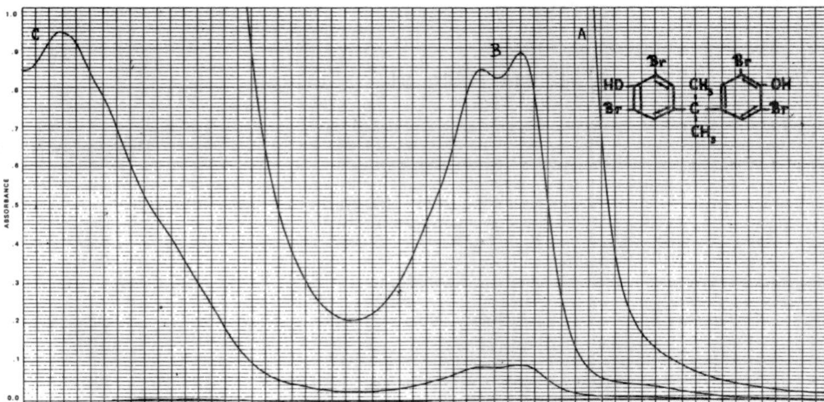

$a^2,a^{2'}$-(2-HYDROXY-5-METHYL-m-PHENYLENE)BIS[6-tert-BUTYL-2,4-XYLENOL] 1936

$C_{31}H_{40}O_3$
Mol. Wt. 460.66
Solvent: Methanol

λ Max. mμ	a_m	Cell mm	Conc. g/L
281	7340	5	0.100
x	x	1	0.100

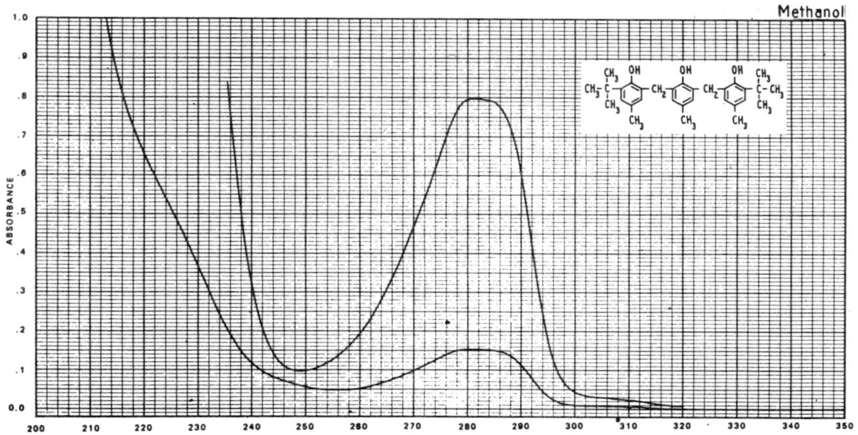

$a^2,a^{2'}$-(2-HYDROXY-5-METHYL-m-PHENYLENE)BIS[6-tert-BUTYL-2,4-XYLENOL] 1936

$C_{31}H_{40}O_3$
Mol. Wt. 460.66
Solvent: Methanol KOH

λ Max. mμ	a_m	Cell mm	Conc. g/L
303	6820	5	0.100
285	8080	5	0.100
x	x	1	0.100

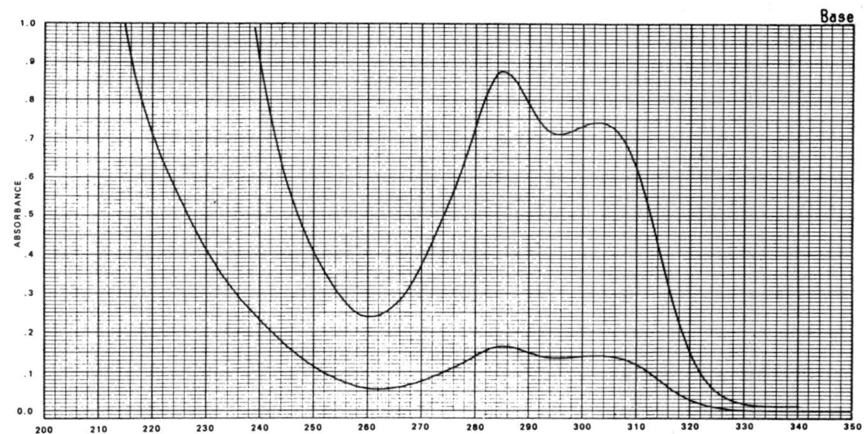

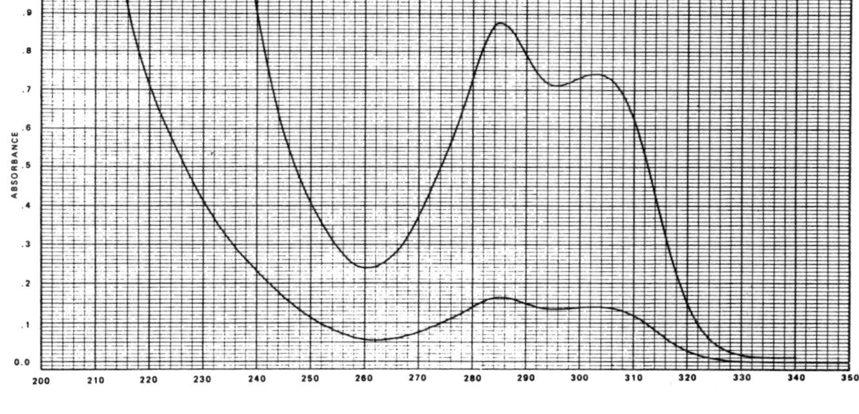

2,4,6-TRIBROMOPHENOL 1937

$C_6H_3Br_3O$
Mol. Wt. 330.83
M.P. 96°C
Solvent: Cyclohexane

λ Max. mμ	a_m	Cell mm	Conc. g/L
x	x	10	1.912
297	3180	10	0.1529
289	2900	10	0.1529
x	x	10	0.0133

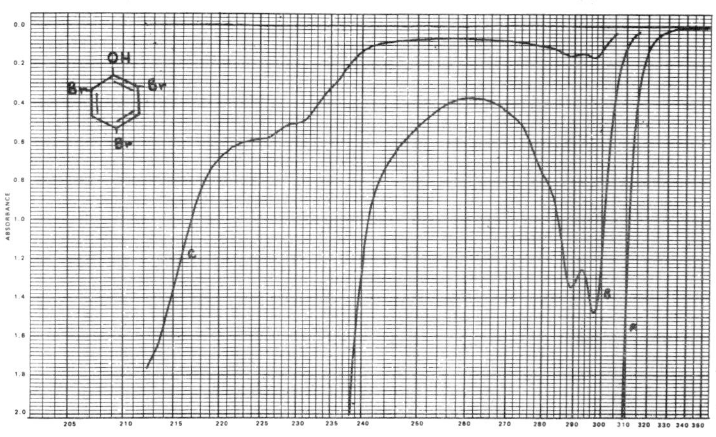

2,4,6-TRIIODOPHENOL

1938

$C_6H_3I_3O$
Mol. Wt. 471.80
M.P. 156-158°C
Solvent: Methanol

λ Max. mμ	a_m	Cell mm	Conc. g/L
295.5	3020	10	0.100
226.5	33700	1	0.100

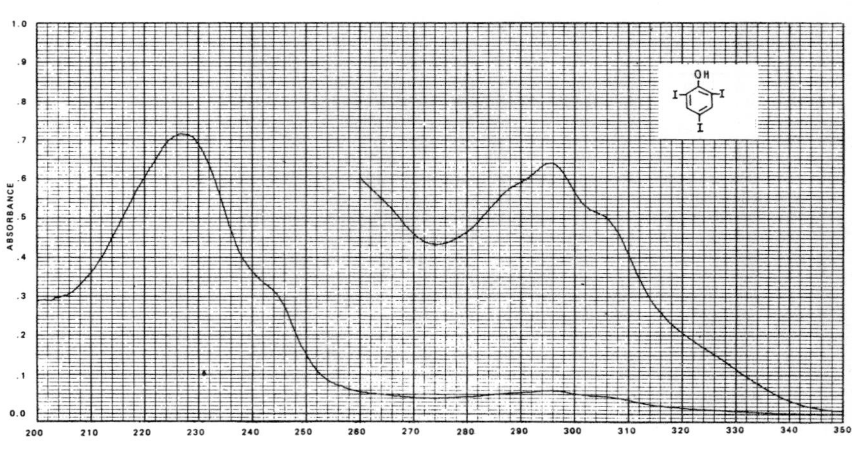

2,4,6-TRIIODOPHENOL

1938

$C_6H_3I_3O$
Mol. Wt. 471.80
M.P. 156-158°C
Solvent: Methanol KOH

λ Max. mμ	a_m	Cell mm	Conc. g/L
322	6610	5	0.100
256	11300	1	0.100
228.5	26800	1	0.100
215	25800	1	0.100

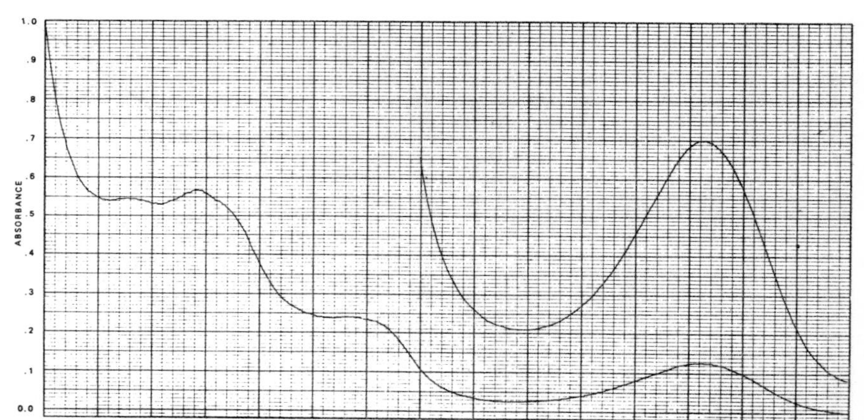

PICRIC ACID

1939

$C_6H_3N_3O_7$
Mol. Wt. 229.11
M.P. 121.8°C (lit.)
Solvent: Methanol

λ Max. mμ	a_m	Cell mm	Conc. g/L
350	6740	2	0.100

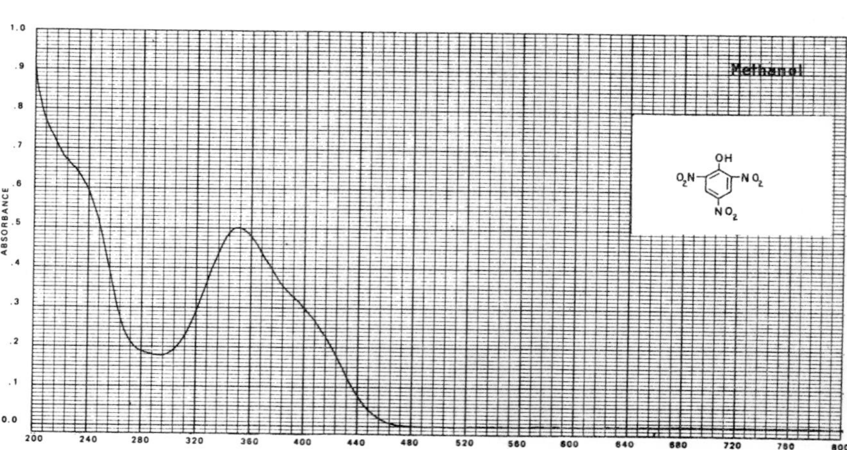

PICRIC ACID

$C_6H_3N_3O_7$

Mol. Wt. 229.11

M.P. 121.8°C (lit.)

Solvent: Methanol KOH

1939

λ Max. mμ	a_m	Cell mm	Conc. g/L
354	8020	2	0.100

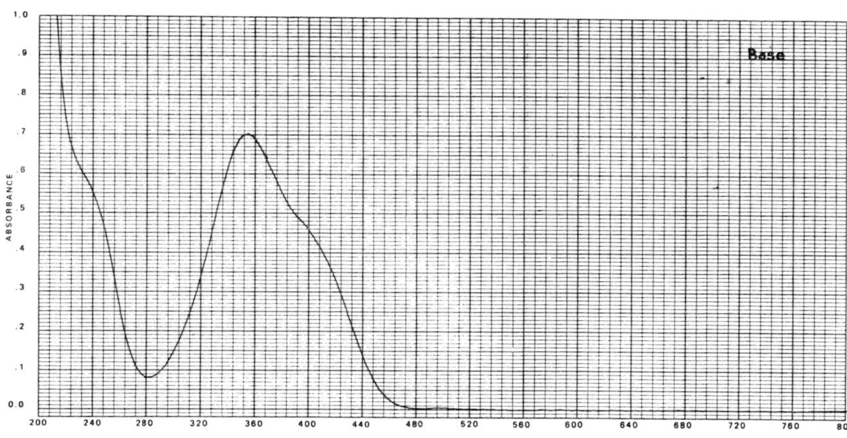

ANILINE, PICRATE

$C_6H_6N \cdot C_6H_3N_3O_7$

Mol. Wt. 322.24

M.P. 198°C

Solvent: Methanol

1940

λ Max. mμ	a_m	Cell mm	Conc. g/L
352	15200	2	0.100

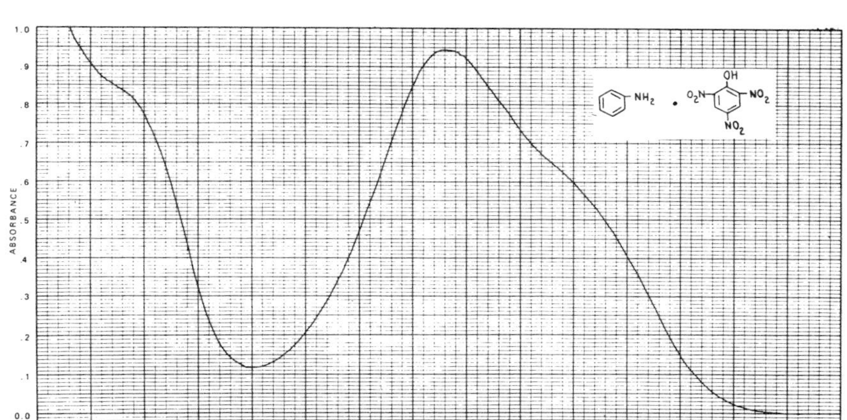

o-CHLOROANILINE, PICRATE

$C_{12}H_9ClN_4O_7$

Mol. Wt. 356.68

M.P. 134-136°C

Solvent: Methanol

1941

λ Max. mμ	a_m	Cell mm	Conc. g/L
350	13500	1	0.100
298	6060	1	0.100
236	21000	1	0.100

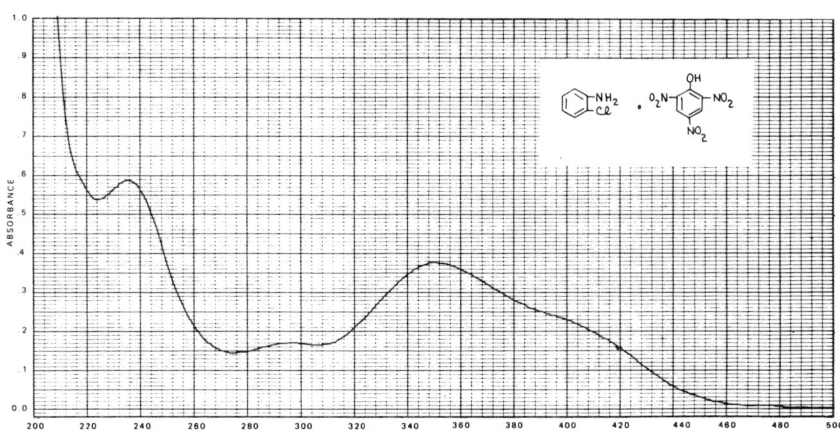

PYRIDINE, PICRATE 1942

$C_{11}H_8N_4O_7$

Mol. Wt. 308.21

M.P. 161-167°C

Solvent: Methanol

λ Max. mμ	a_m	Cell mm	Conc. g/L
352	14400	1	0.100
248	13700	1	0.100
205	17500	1	0.100

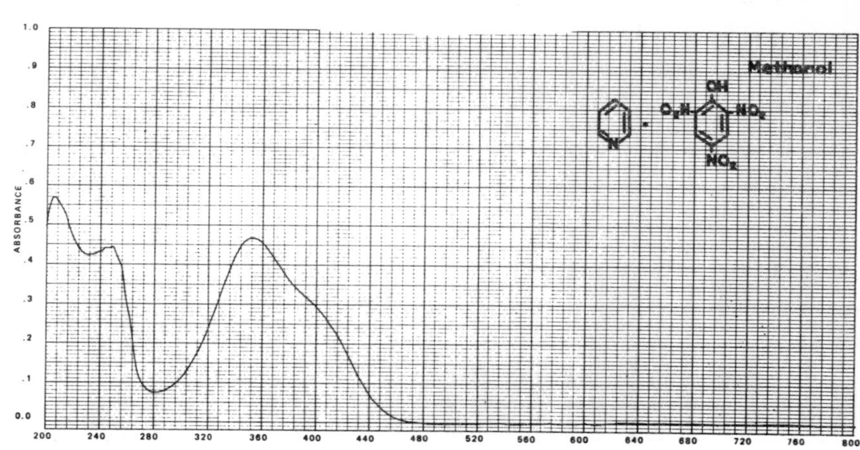

PYRIDINE, PICRATE 1942

$C_{11}H_8N_4O_7$

Mol. Wt. 308.21

M.P. 161-167°C

Solvent: Methanol HCl

λ Max. mμ	a_m	Cell mm	Conc. g/L
332	5310	5	0.100
248	17300	1	0.100
206	17200	1	0.100

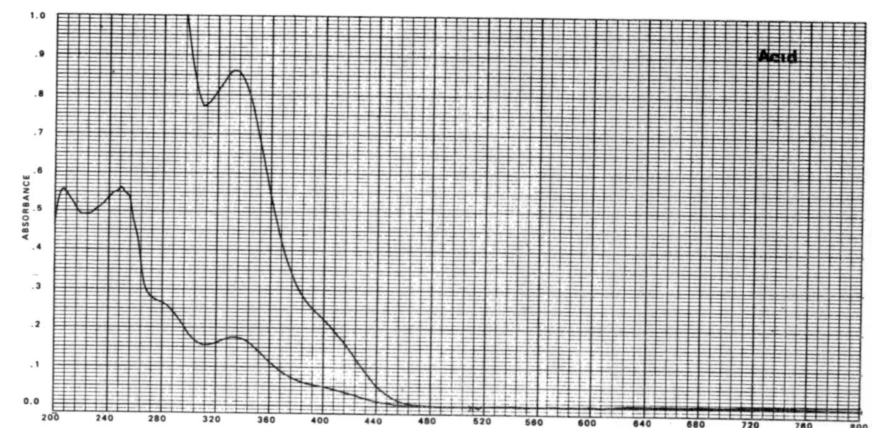

2,6-DICHLOROHYDROQUINONE 1943

$C_6H_4Cl_2O_2$

Mol. Wt. 179.00

M.P. 162-163°C

Solvent: Methanol

λ Max. mμ	a_m	Cell mm	Conc. g/L
299	1710	2	0.100
x	x	1	0.100

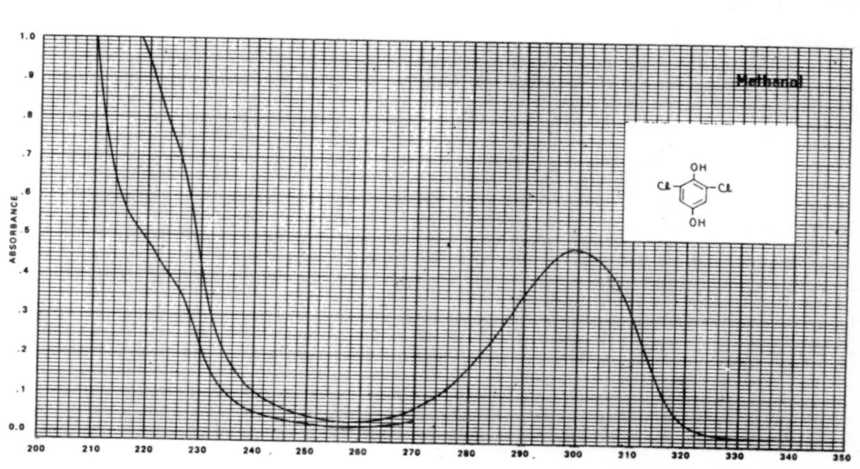

2,6-DICHLOROHYDROQUINONE 1943

$C_6H_4Cl_2O_2$
Mol. Wt. 179.00
M.P. 162-163°C
Solvent: Methanol KOH

λ Max. mμ	a_m	Cell mm	Conc. g/L
322.5	1530	2	0.100
240	2900	2	0.100
215.5	9490	1	0.100

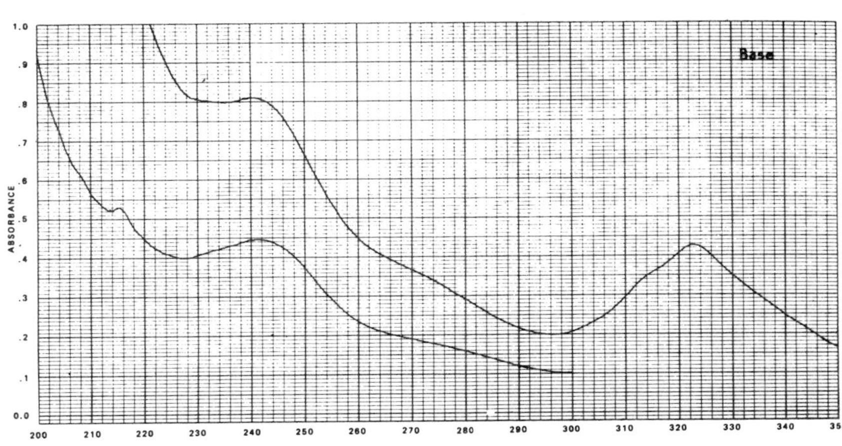

2-NITRORESORCINOL 1944

$C_6H_5NO_4$
Mol. Wt. 155.11
M.P. 82-83°C
Solvent: Methanol

λ Max. mμ	a_m	Cell mm	Conc. g/L
310	155	2	0.100
x	x	1	0.100

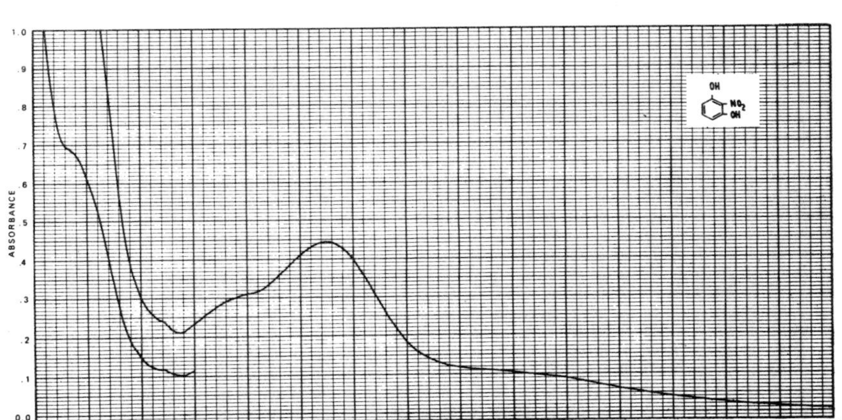

2-NITRORESORCINOL 1944

$C_6H_5NO_4$
Mol. Wt. 155.11
M.P. 82-83°C
Solvent: Methanol KOH

λ Max. mμ	a_m	Cell mm	Conc. g/L
428	1770	2	0.100
326	3890	2	0.100
282	2660	2	0.100
x	x	1	0.100

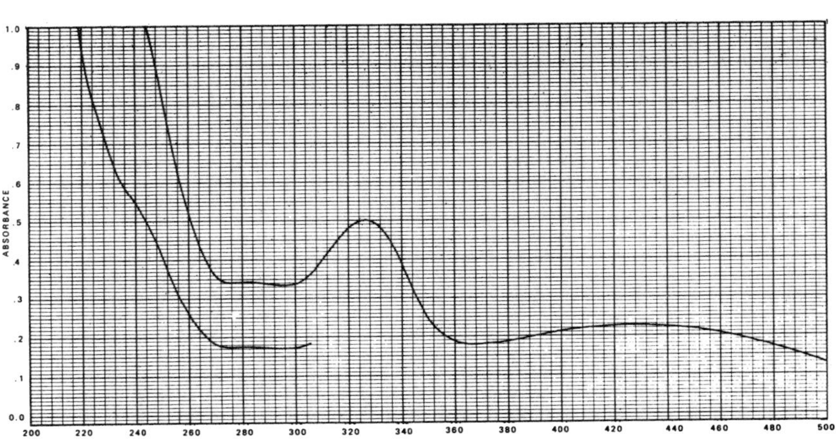

PYROGALLOL

1945

$C_6H_6O_3$

Mol. Wt. 126.11

M.R. 131-133°C (lit.)

Solvent: Methanol

λ Max. mμ	a_m	Cell mm	Conc. g/L
267	719	10	0.200
x	x	10	0.02

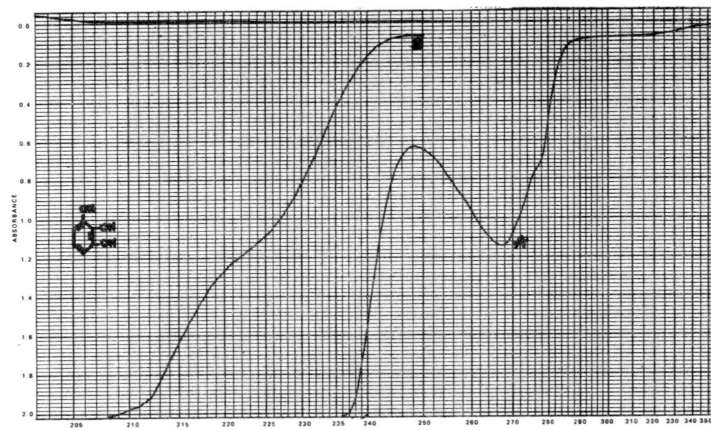

1,2,4-BENZENETRIOL

1946

$C_6H_6O_3$

Mol. Wt. 126.11

Solvent: Methanol

λ Max. mμ	a_m	Cell mm	Conc. g/L
292	7310	2	0.100

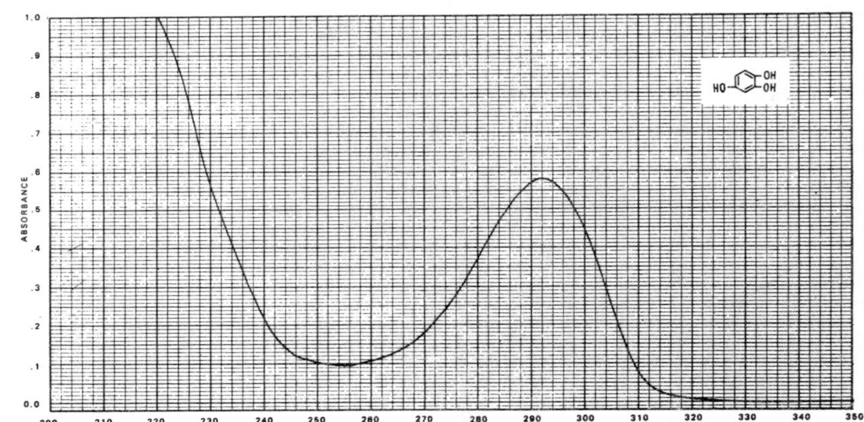

1,2,4-BENZENETRIOL

1946

$C_6H_6O_3$

Mol. Wt. 126.11

Solvent: Methanol KOH

λ Max. mμ	a_m	Cell mm	Conc. g/L
271	6120	1	0.100

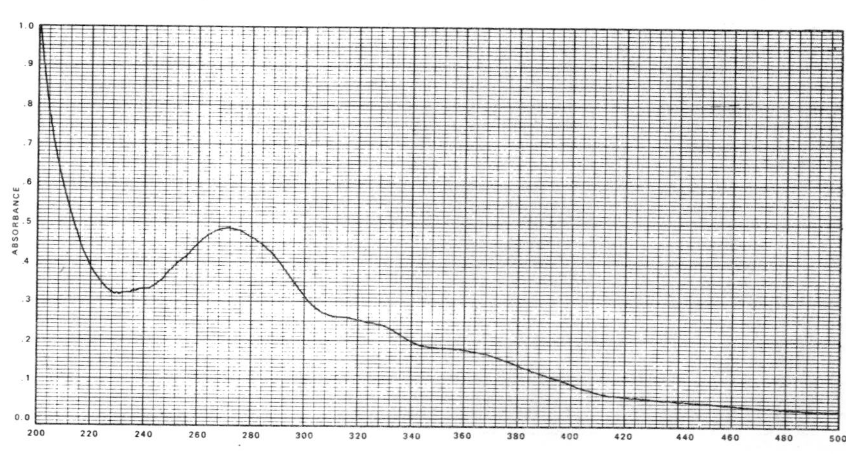

PHLOROGLUCINOL 1947

$C_6H_6O_3$
Mol. Wt. 126.11
M.P. 219°C (lit.)
Solvent: Methanol

λ Max. mμ	^am	Cell mm	Conc. g/L
272	301	20	0.100
268	354	20	0.100
x	x	1	0.100

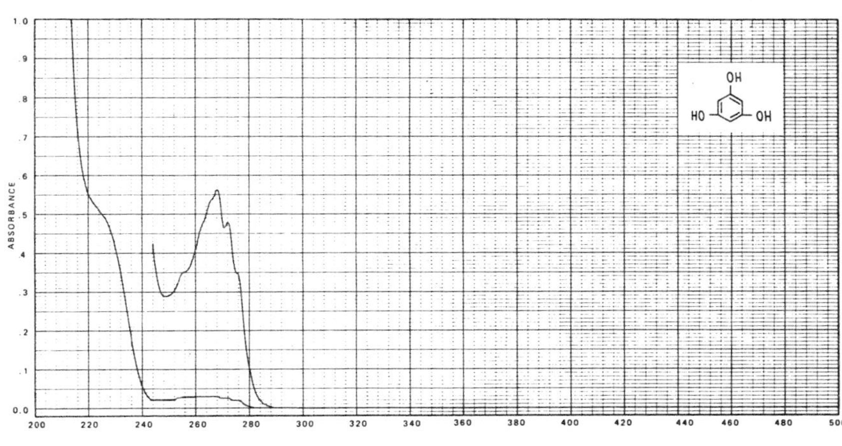

PHLOROGLUCINOL 1947

$C_6H_6O_3$
Mol. Wt. 126.11
M.P. 219°C (lit.)
Solvent: Methanol KOH

λ Max. mμ	^am	Cell mm	Conc. g/L
351	6480	1	0.0500
253	16600	1	0.0500
227	14500	1	0.0500

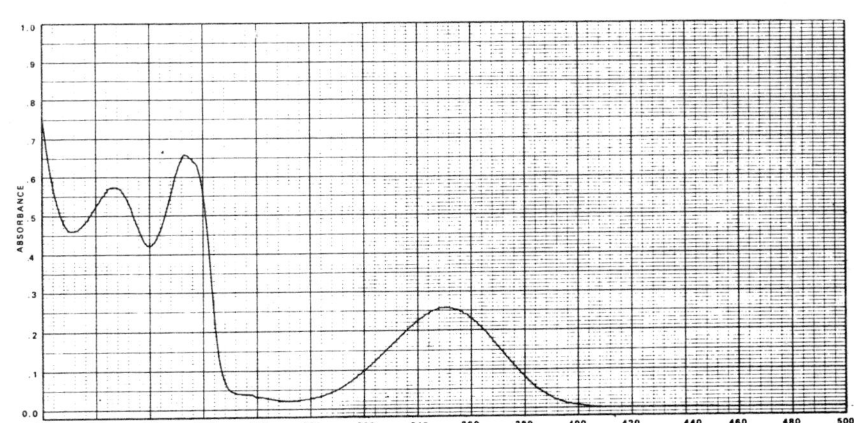

λ Max. mμ	^am	Cell mm	Conc. g/L

4-INDANOL

1948

$C_9H_{10}O$
Mol. Wt. 134.18
M.P. 39.5-40.5°C (lit.)
Solvent: Methanol

λ Max. mμ	a_m	Cell mm	Conc. g/L
277	765	10	0.100
269.5	776	10	0.100
x	x	10	0.010

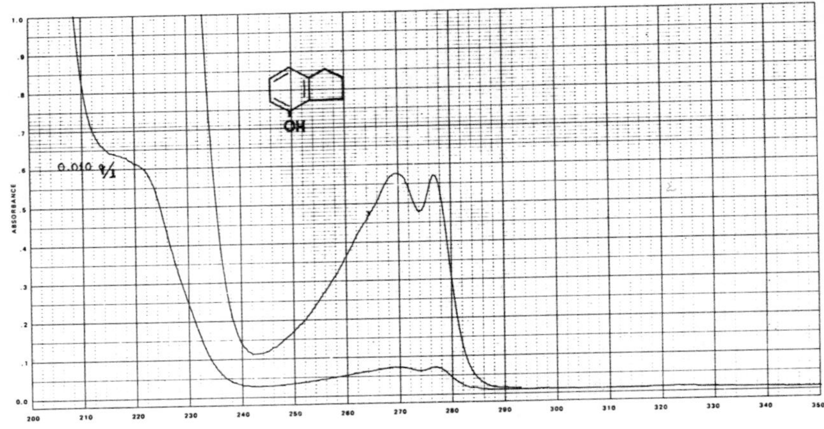

4-INDANOL

1948

$C_9H_{10}O$
Mol. Wt. 134.18
M.P. 39.5-40.5°C (lit.)
Solvent: Methanol KOH

λ Max. mμ	a_m	Cell mm	Conc. g/L
285	967	10	0.100
242.5	7220	1	0.100
x	x	1	0.0330

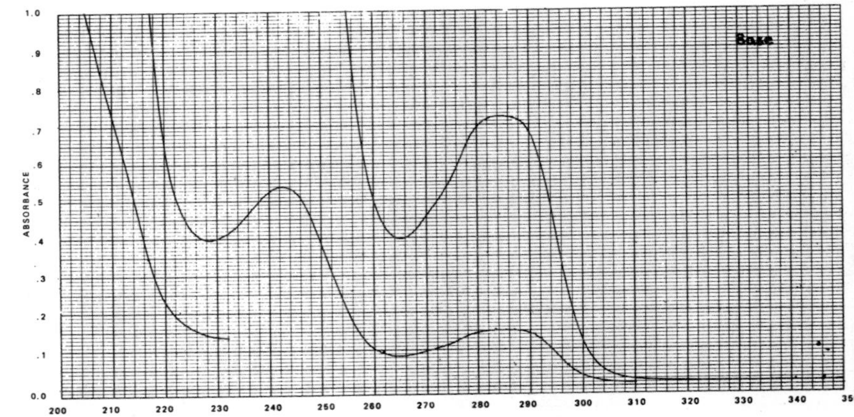

FLUOREN-2-OL

1949

$C_{13}H_{10}O$
Mol. Wt. 182.22
M.P. 169-171°C (lit.)
Solvent: Methanol

λ Max. mμ	a_m	Cell mm	Conc. g/L
314.5	5950	2	0.100
306.0	6120	2	0.100
271.0	24500	1	0.0300
205.0	44400	1	0.0300

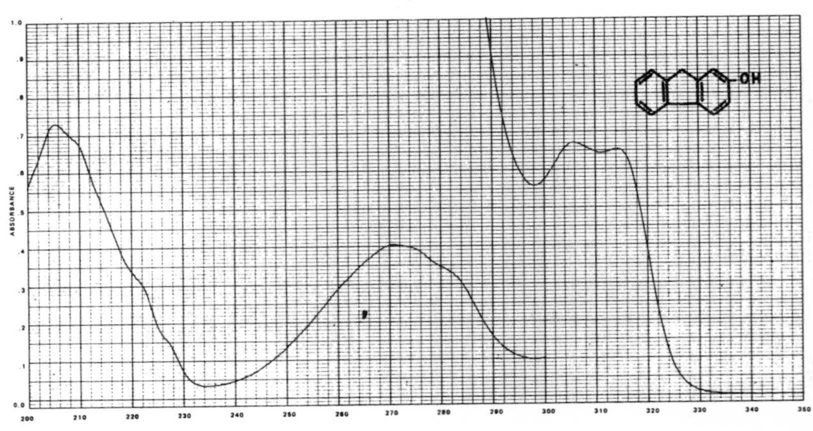

FLUOREN-2-OL

1949

$C_{13}H_{10}O$
Mol. Wt. 182.22
M.P. 169-171°C (lit.)
Solvent: Methanol KOH

λ Max. mμ	a_m	Cell mm	Conc. g/L
296	23700	2	0.0300
x	x	1	0.0150

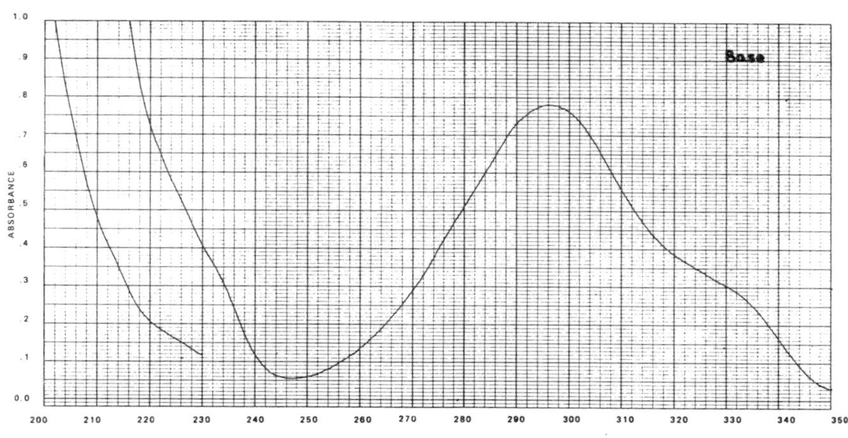

1-NAPHTHOL

1950

$C_{10}H_{8}O$
Mol. Wt. 144.16
Solvent: Methanol

2045 UV

λ Max. mμ	a_m	Cell mm	Conc. g/L
x	x	10	2.010
323	2950	10	0.0402
308.5	3840	10	0.0402
295.5	4800	10	0.0402
233	32300	10	0.00402

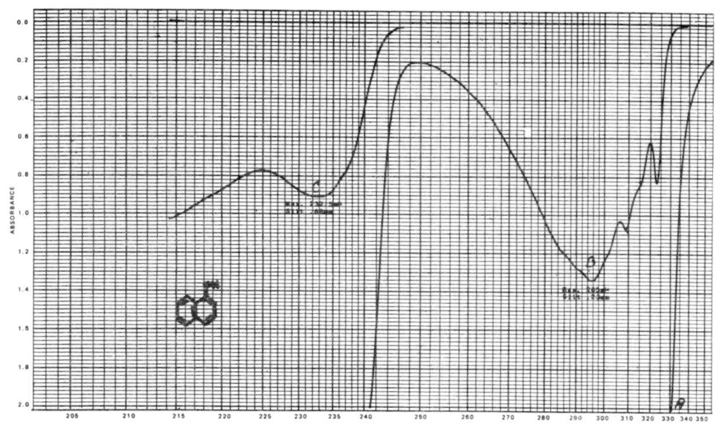

2-NAPHTHOL

1951

$C_{10}H_{8}O$
Mol. Wt. 144.17
M.P. 122-123°C
Solvent: Methanol

λ Max. mμ	a_m	Cell mm	Conc. g/L
330	1870	2	0.100
285	3030	2	0.100
273.5	4250	2	0.100
263.5	3680	2	0.100
225	75800	1	0.100

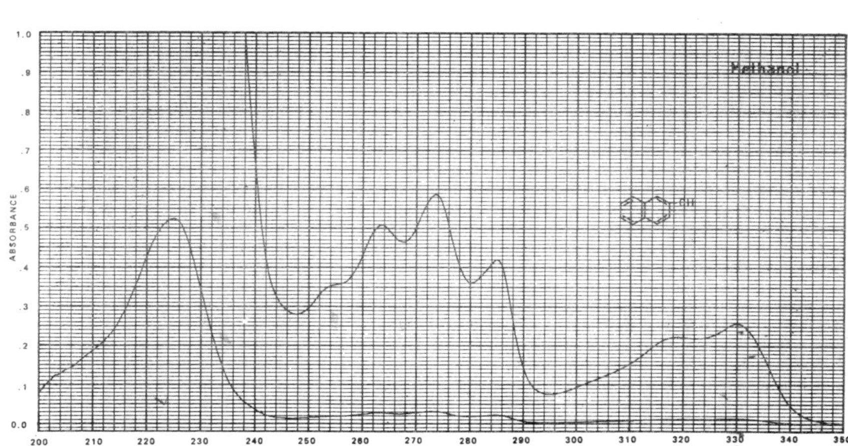

2-METHYL-1-NAPHTHOL

1952

$C_{11}H_{10}O$
Mol. Wt. 158.20
M.P. 64-66°C
Solvent: Methanol

λ Max. mμ	a_m	Cell mm	Conc. g/L
325.5	2110	20	0.020
297.5	3250	20	0.020
265	3840	20	0.020
232	31400	2	0.020
211.5	31500	2	0.020

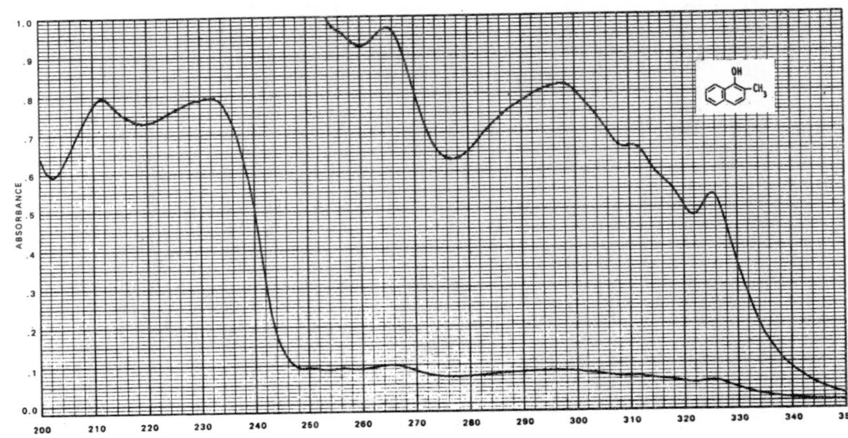

2-METHYL-1-NAPHTHOL

1952

$C_{11}H_{10}O$
Mol. Wt. 158.20
M.P. 64-66°C
Solvent: Methanol KOH

λ Max. mμ	a_m	Cell mm	Conc. g/L
336	5550	10	0.020
250.5	23800	2	0.020

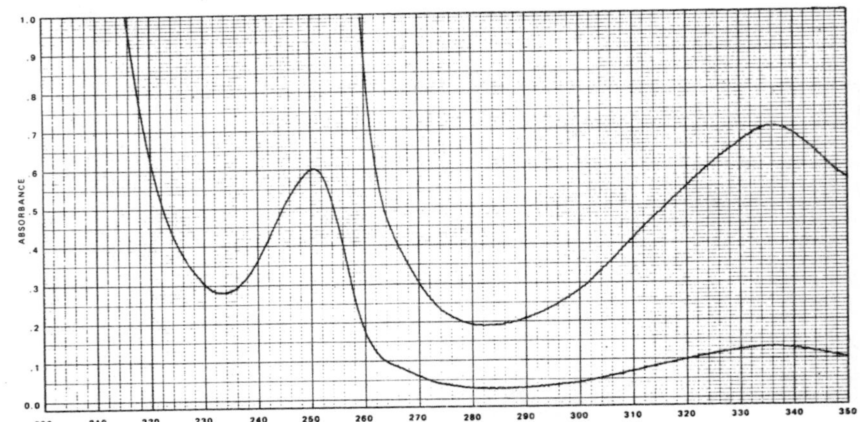

6-AMINO-1-NAPHTHOL

1953

$C_{10}H_9NO$
MOl. Wt. 159.19
Solvent: Methanol

λ Max. mμ	a_m	Cell mm	Conc. g/L
338	1460	2.5	0.100
289	4850	2.5	0.100
279	4670	2.5	0.100
249	27600	0.5	0.100

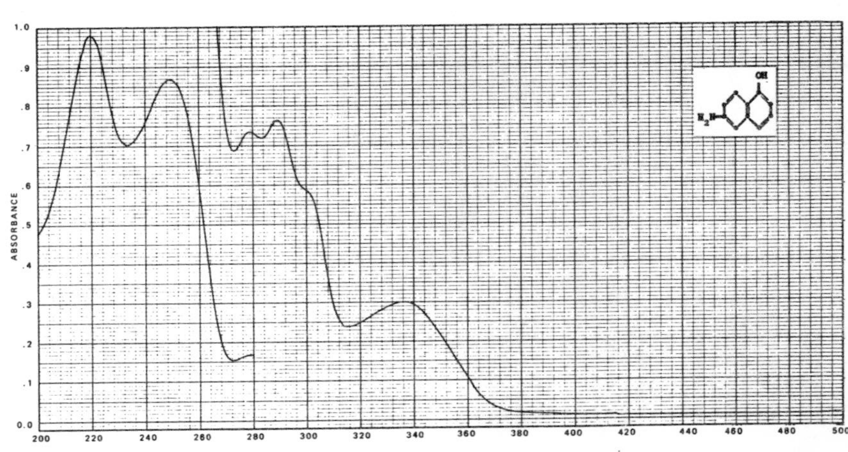

6-AMINO-1-NAPHTHOL 1953

$C_{10}H_9NO$

Mol. Wt. 159.19

Solvent: Methanol HCl

λ Max. mμ	a_m	Cell mm	Conc. g/L
322	3810	2.5	0.100
309	4200	2.5	0.100
302	4140	2.5	0.100
235	30600	0.5	0.100

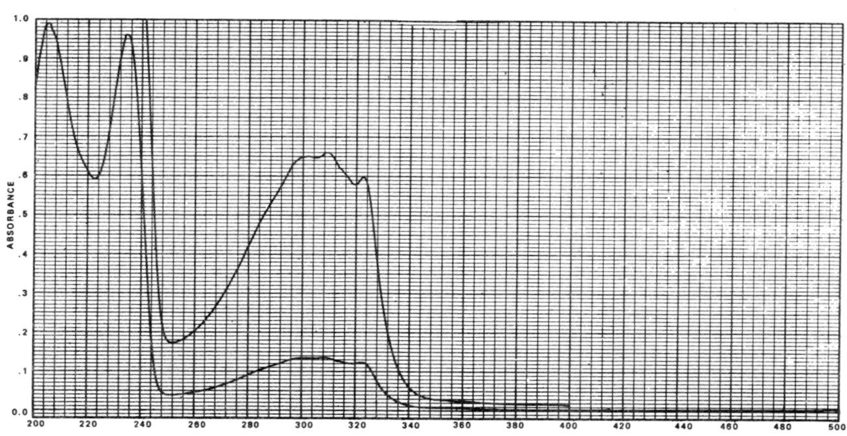

2-HYDROXY-1-NAPHTHALENEPROPIONITRILE 1954

$C_{13}H_{11}NO$

Mol. Wt. 197.23

M.P. 142°C

Solvent: Methanol

λ Max. mμ	a_m	Cell mm	Conc. g/L
335	2510	10	0.030
323	2180	10	0.030
290.5	4020	10	0.030
279	4800	10	0.030
268	3700	10	0.030
229	46300	10	0.003

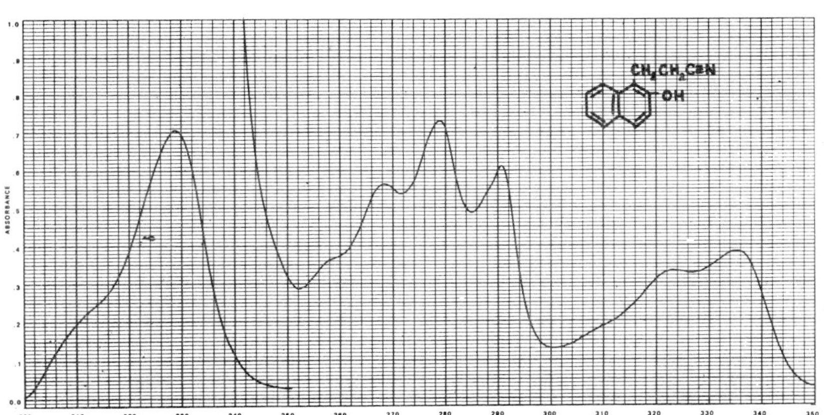

λ Max. mμ	a_m	Cell mm	Conc. g/L

1-NITROSO-2-NAPHTHOL

1955

$C_{10}H_7NO_2$
Mol. Wt. 173.17
Solvent: Methanol

λ Max. mμ	a_m	Cell mm	Conc. g/L
370	5520	1	0.100
261	14600	1	0.100
212	25600	1	0.0500

1-NITROSO-2-NAPHTHOL

1955

$C_{10}H_7NO_2$
Mol. Wt. 173.17
Solvent: Methanol KOH

λ Max. mμ	a_m	Cell mm	Conc. g/L
425	7860	1	0.100
372	6230	1	0.100
290	9070	1	0.100
262	11100	1	0.100
226	32300	1	0.0500

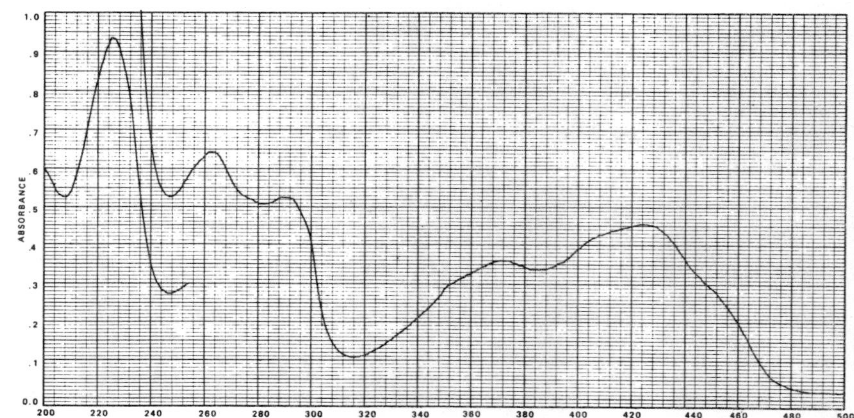

1,3-NAPHTHALENEDIOL

1956

$C_{10}H_8O_2$
Mol. Wt. 160.16
M.P. 120-125°C
Solvent: Methanol

λ Max. mμ	a_m	Cell mm	Conc. g/L
336	2570	10	0.020
286.5	4880	10	0.020
235	46900	10	0.003
214	30700	10	0.003

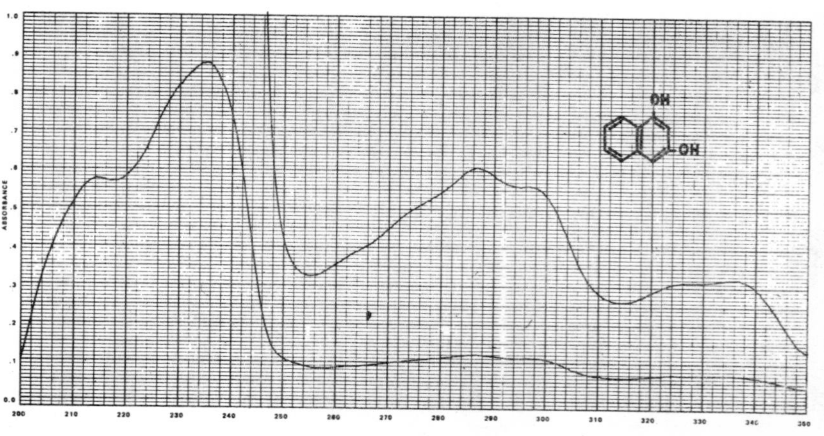

1,5-NAPHTHALENEDIOL

1957

$C_{10}H_8O_2$
Mol. Wt. 180.46
Solvent: Methanol

λ Max. mμ	a_m	Cell mm	Conc. g/L
x	x	10	2.00
330	8300	10	0.020
316	8110	10	0.020
298	9560	10	0.020
225	98200	10	0.002

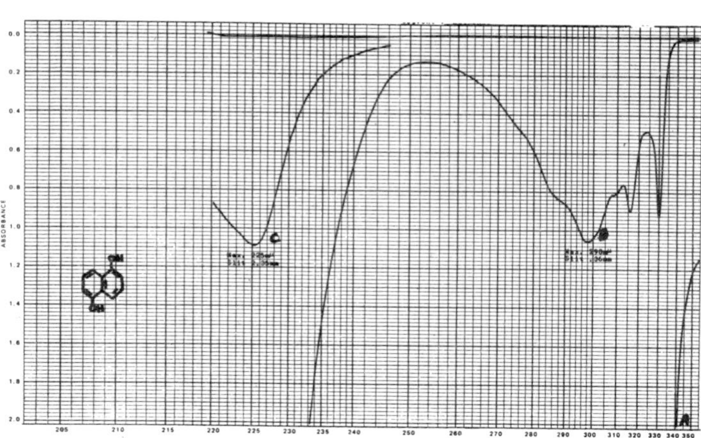

2,7-NAPHTHALENEDIOL

1958

$C_{10}H_8O_2$
Mol. Wt. 160.17
Solvent: Methanol

λ Max. mμ	a_m	Cell mm	Conc. g/L
328	3080	2	0.100
319.5	1940	2	0.100
313	2400	2	0.100
285	3360	2	0.100
231	75800	1	0.0200

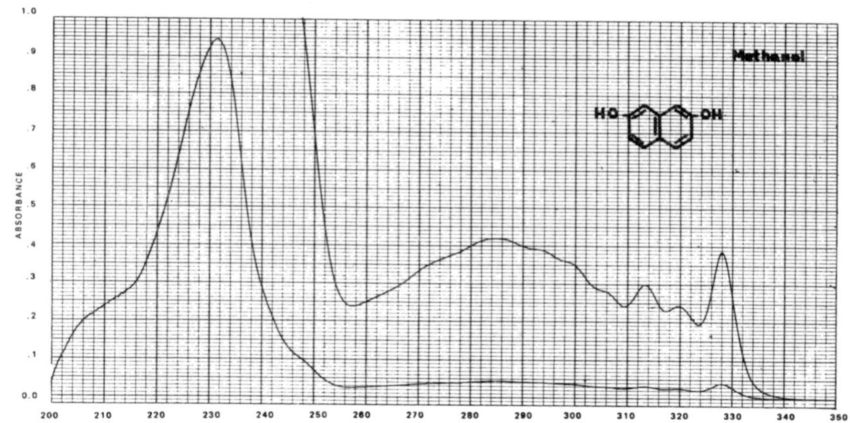

2,7-NAPHTHALENEDIOL

1958

$C_{10}H_8O_2$
Mol. Wt. 160.17
Solvent: Methanol KOH

λ Max. mμ	a_m	Cell mm	Conc. g/L
342	4020	10	0.0200
293	3600	10	0.0200
283	3610	10	0.0200
242.5	58500	1	0.0200

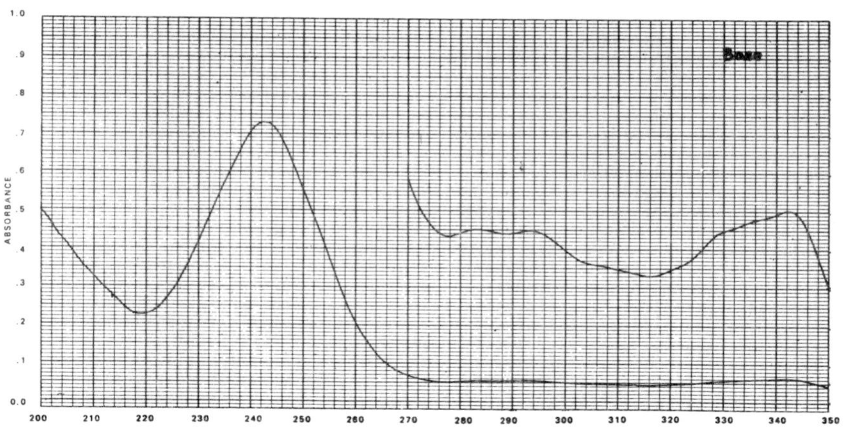

3-PYRIDINOL

1959

C_5H_5NO

Mol. Wt. 95.10

B.P. 151-153°C/3mm M.P. 126-129°C

Solvent: Methanol

λ Max. mμ	a_m	Cell mm	Conc. g/L
279	4170	10	0.016
218	5760	10	0.016

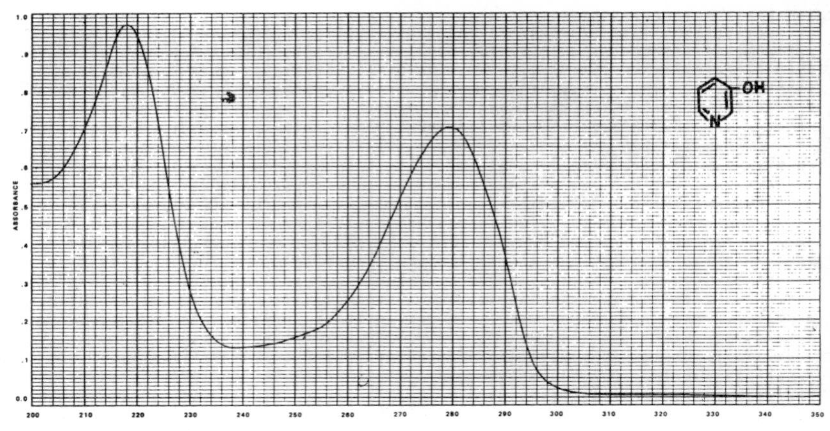

2-PYRIMIDINOL

1960

$C_4H_4N_2O$

Mol. Wt. 96.09

M.P. 170-174°C

Solvent: Methanol

λ Max. mμ	a_m	Cell mm	Conc. g/L
305	4090	1	0.050
214	11200	1	0.050

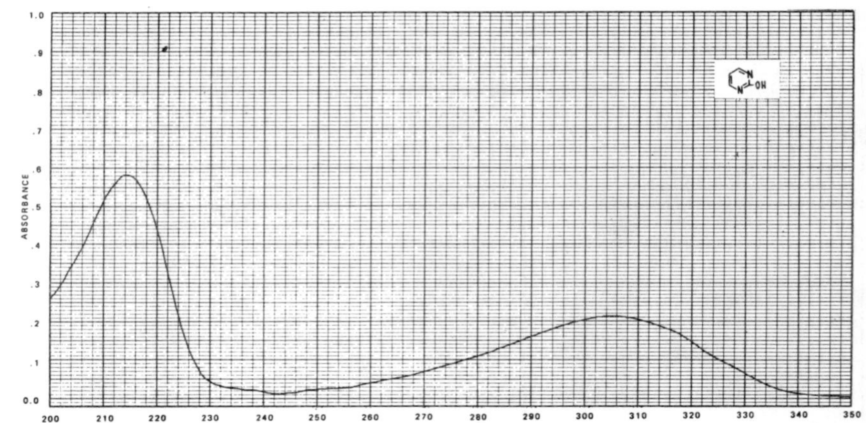

2-PYRIMIDINOL

1960

$C_4H_4N_2O$

Mol. Wt. 96.09

M.P. 170-174°C

Solvent: Methanol KOH

λ Max. mμ	a_m	Cell mm	Conc. g/L
298	4210	1	0.050
222	13000	1	0.050

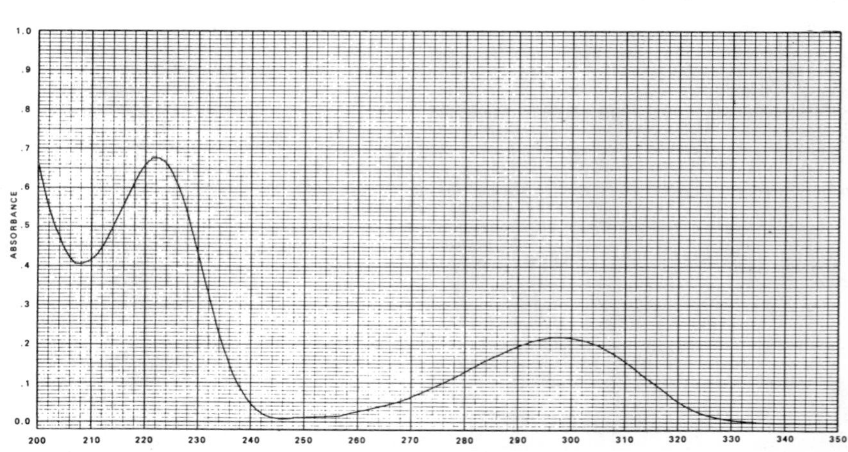

2-PYRIMIDINOL 1960

$C_4H_4N_2O$

Mol. Wt. 96.09

M.P. 170-174°C

Solvent: Methanol HCl

λ Max. mμ	a_m	Cell mm	Conc. g/L
314	5290	1	0.050
205	11200	1	0.050

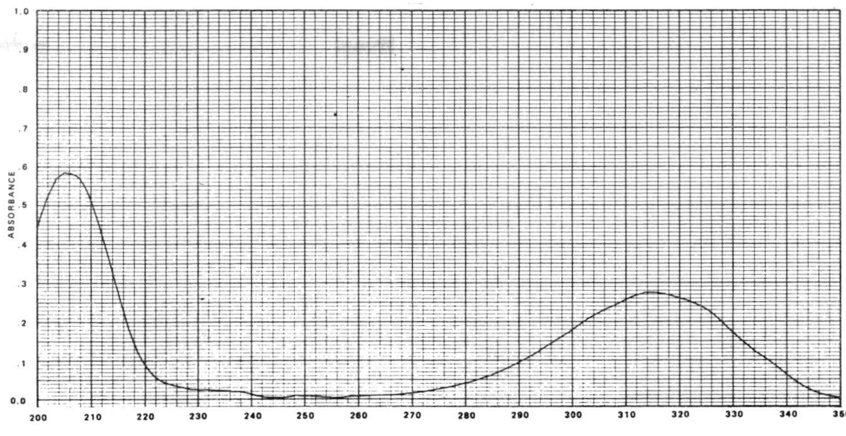

CARBOSTYRIL 1961

C_9H_7NO

Mol. Wt. 145.16

M.R. 196-197°C (lit.)

Solvent: Methanol

λ Max. mμ	a_m	Cell mm	Conc. g/L
327.5	6280	10	0.0314
268	6570	10	0.0314
229	34100	1	0.0063

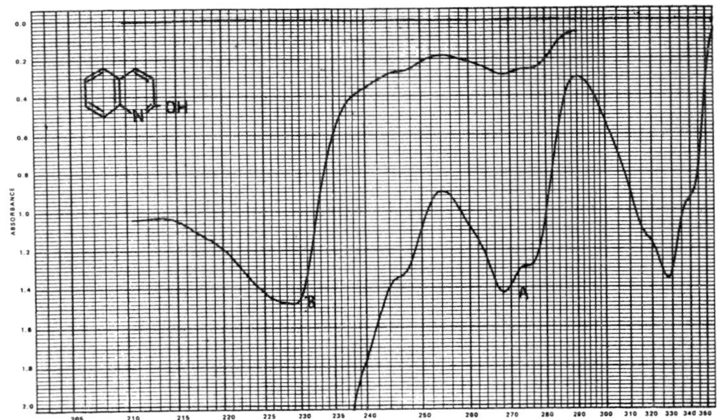

8-QUINOLINOL 1962

C_9H_7NO

Mol. Wt. 145.16

M.R. 72.9-74.2°C (lit.)

Solvent: Cyclohexane

λ Max. mμ	a_m	Cell mm	Conc. g/L
318	2300	10	0.1132
242.5	43000	10	0.0057

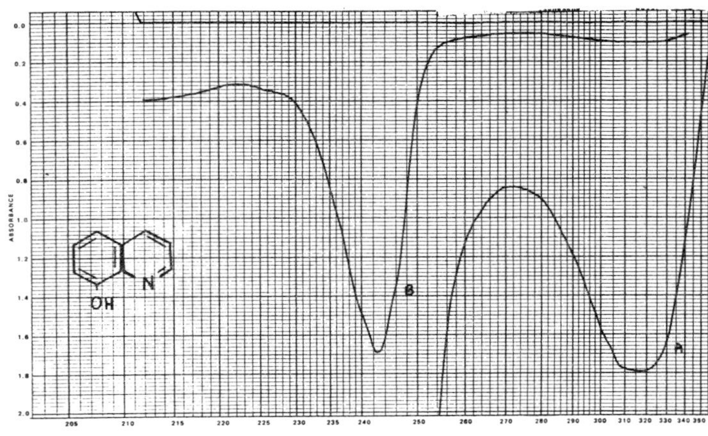

4-METHYLCARBOSTYRIL 1963

$C_{10}H_9NO$

Mol. Wt. 159.18

M.P. 221-223°C

Solvent: Methanol

λ Max. mμ	a_m	Cell mm	Conc. g/L
325	5340	10	0.02
275	4360	10	0.02
267.5	4940	10	0.02
x	x	10	0.01
229	31800	10	0.004

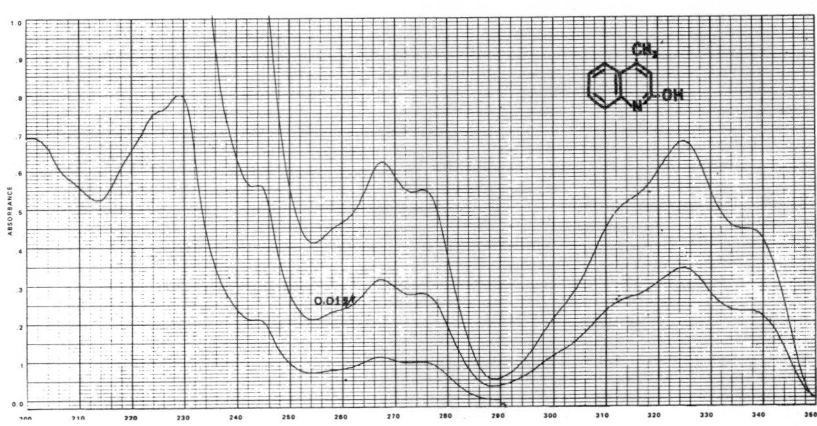

4-NITRO-1(2H)-ISOQUINOLONE 1964

$C_9H_6N_2O_3$

Mol. Wt. 190.16

M.P. 36-238°C

Solvent: Methanol

λ Max. mμ	a_m	Cell mm	Conc. g/L
343	7960	1	0.100
233	17200	1	0.100
221	21000	1	0.0500

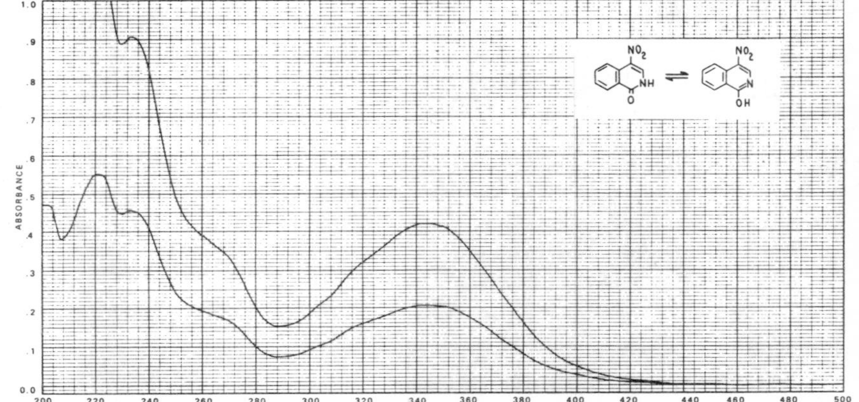

PHOSPHOROUS ACID, DIBUTYL ESTER 1965

$C_8H_{19}O_3P$

Mol. Wt. 194.21

B.P. 118-119°C/7mm

λ Max. mμ	a_m	Cell mm	Conc. g/L

The esters of phosphorus acid (compounds 1965 and 1966) do not display any maxima in the near UV.

THE KETONES

Aliphatic Compounds

The n→π^* transition of the aliphatic ketones produces a very weak maximum in the region from 268 - 287 mμ (ϵ_{max} = 15 - 150). Because these bands are of more theoretical than analytical interest, only a few selected examples are included in the Sadtler Standard UV collection and hence in this volume. Thus, for compounds 1967 through 2013, nine spectra are provided on pages 556 and 557 to indicate the type of spectra obtained from the aliphatic ketones.

Alicyclic Compounds

The λ_{max} of the alicyclic ketones varies from about 276 mμ to 291 mμ depending on ring size and substitution, i.e. Cyclobentanone - 282 mμ, Cyclohexanone - 276 mμ, 4-Methylcyclohexanone - 288 mμ (compounds 1999, 2000 and 2003).

Olefinic Compounds

The α–olefinic ketones (C=C–C(=O)–) usually display two bands in the near UV region. A weak band is observed at longer wavelength (290 - 330 mμ) and a much more intense absorption appears in the region from 220 - 251 mμ (spectra 2018 - 2030).

Aromatic Compounds

The alkyl phenones produce spectra containing two absorption bands, one near 241 mμ (ϵ_{max} = 14000) and a second band near 278 mμ (ϵ_{max} = 1000).

Compound	$\lambda_{max}(\epsilon_{max})$	$\lambda_{max}(\epsilon_{max})$	Spectrum
Acetophenone	240 (14300)	279 (1290)	2045
2'-Methyl	242 (9410)	286 (1450)	2055
4'-Methyl	250 (12300)	----------	2056
4'-Ethyl	253 (15000)	----------	2059
2'-Chloro	237 (6000)	283 (829)	2064
3'-Chloro	239 (10600)	286 (1090)	2065

The Benzophenones

The bands of the benzophenones absorb at longer wavelengths than those of the acetophenones. The 240 mμ band is shifted to 252 mμ and the 279 mμ band appears at 331 mμ. Additional bathochromic shifts result from substitution of the aromatic rings.

A table containing the data for benzophenone and two substituted derivatives is given below (all methanol solutions).

Compound	$\lambda_{max}(\epsilon_{max})$	$\lambda_{max}(\epsilon_{max})$	Spectrum
Benzophenone	252 (18600)	331 (167)	2098
4-Methylbenzophenone	259 (18300)	328 (285)	2100
4-Bromobenzophenone	261 (20900)	----------	2102

ACETONE

C_3H_6O

Mol. Wt. 58.08

Solvent: Methanol

1967

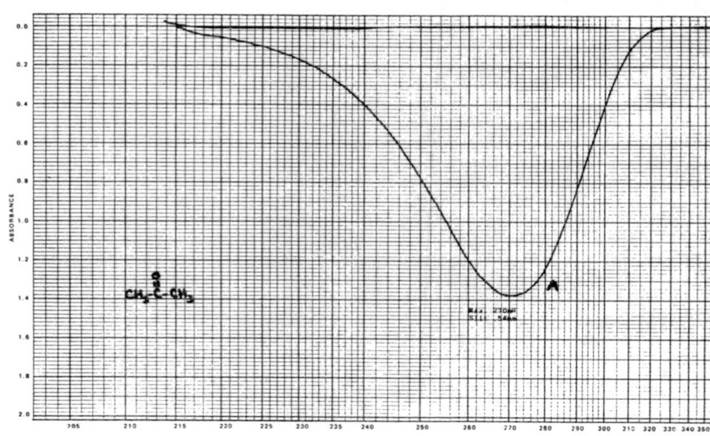

λ Max. mμ	a_m	Cell mm	Conc. g/L
270.5	16.0	10	5.00

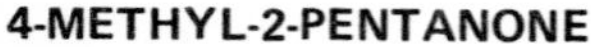

4-METHYL-2-PENTANONE

$C_6H_{12}O$

Mol. Wt. 100.16

B.P. 114.8°C (lit.)

Solvent: Cyclohexane

1971

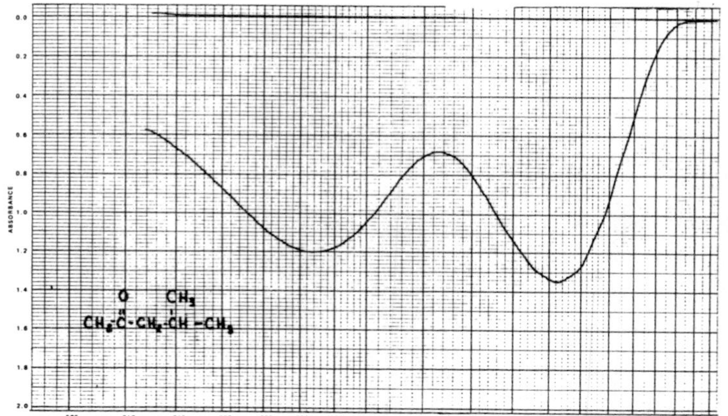

λ Max. mμ	a_m	Cell mm	Conc. g/L
282.5	145	10	0.930
232	129	10	0.930

3-OCTANONE

$C_8H_{16}O$

Mol. Wt. 128.22

B.P. 159°C (lit.)

Solvent: Cyclohexane

1975

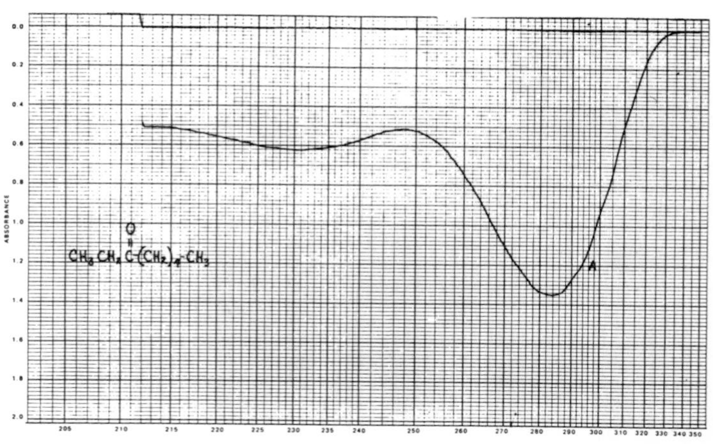

λ Max. mμ	a_m	Cell mm	Conc. g/L
284	20.9	10	8.2880
231	9.59	10	8.2880

2,6-DIMETHYL-4-HEPTANONE

1979

$C_9H_{18}O$

Mol. Wt. 142.23

B.P. 168.1°C (lit.)

Solvent: Cyclohexane

λ Max. mμ	a_m	Cell mm	Conc. g/L
287	23.3	10	7.828
233	14.3	10	7.828

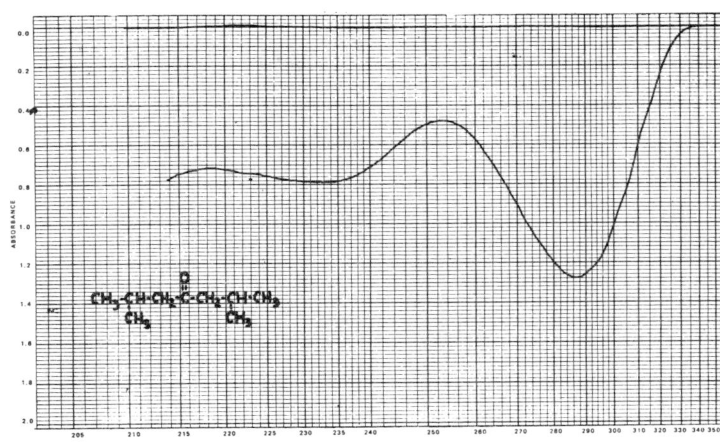

2,5-HEXANEDIONE

1995

$C_6H_{10}O_2$

Mol. Wt. 114.14

B.P. 192.2°C

Solvent: Methanol

λ Max. mμ	a_m	Cell mm	Conc. g/L
268	19.3	10	0.4496
223	133	10	0.4496

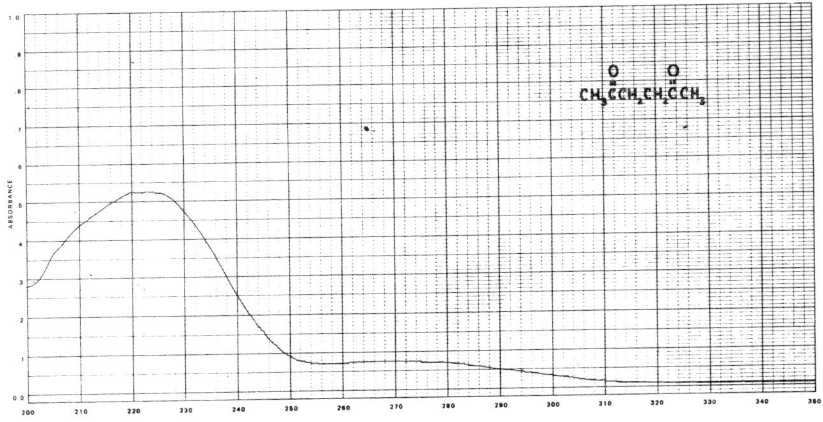

DICYCLOPROPYL KETONE

1996

$C_7H_{10}O$

Mol. Wt. 110.16

B.P. 160-162°C (lit.)

Solvent: Cyclohexane

λ Max. mμ	a_m	Cell mm	Conc. g/L
275	21.5	10	8.10
229	3.81	10	8.10

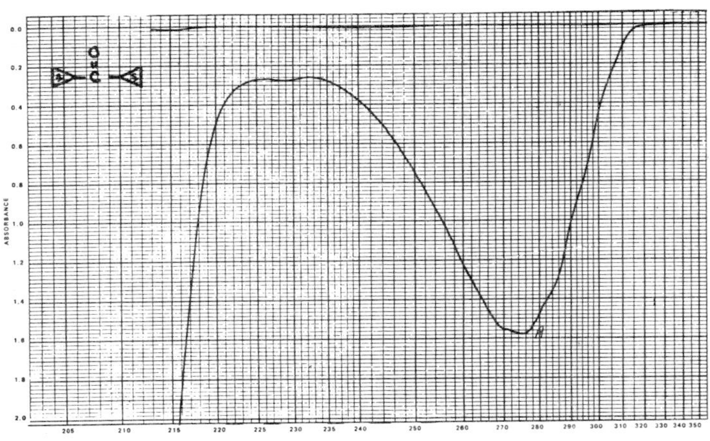

CYCLOPENTANONE

1999

C_5H_8O

Mol. Wt. 84.12

B.P. 129-131°C

Solvent: Methanol

λ Max. mμ	a_m	Cell mm	Conc. g/L
282	18.0	20	0.520
259	16.2	20	0.520
x	x	1	0.520

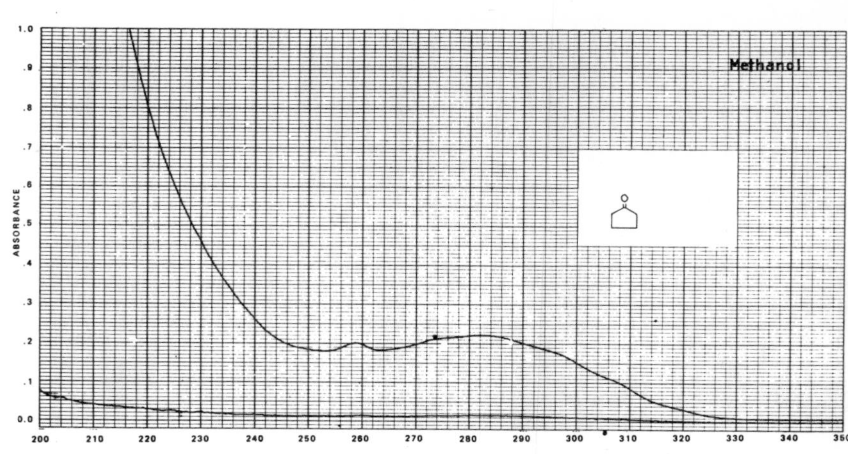

CYCLOHEXANONE

2000

$C_6H_{10}O$

Mol. Wt. 98.15

B.P. 154-156°C

Solvent: Methanol

λ Max. mμ	a_m	Cell mm	Conc. g/L
279.5	27.0	20	0.500
276	26.0	20	0.500
x	x	10	0.500
x	x	1	0.500

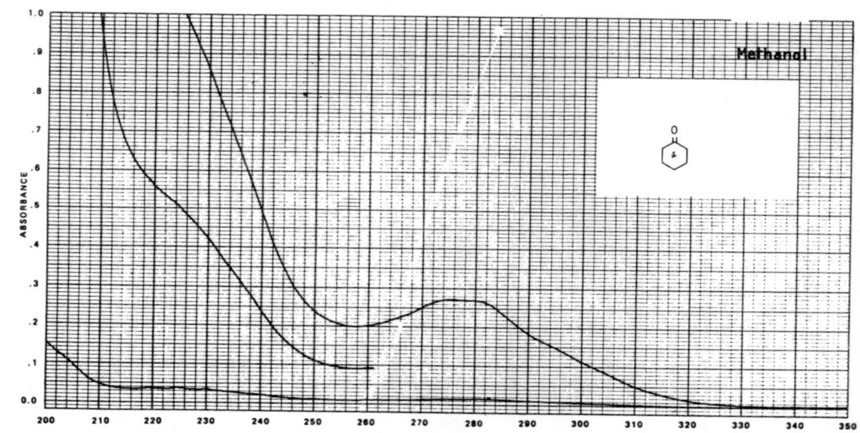

4-METHYLCYCLOHEXANONE

2003

$C_7H_{12}O$

Mol. Wt. 112.17

Solvent: Cyclohexane

λ Max. mμ	a_m	Cell mm	Conc. g/L
291	18.2	10	4.564
221	40.1	10	2.282

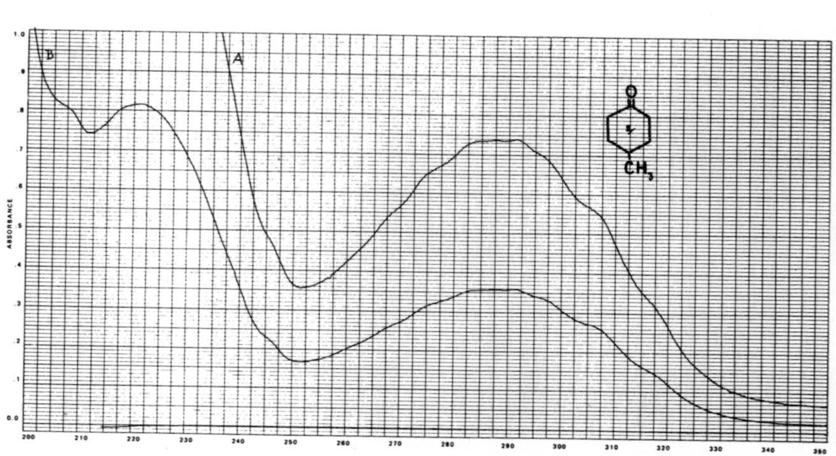

1-PHENETHYL-4-PIPERIDONE — 2014

$C_{13}H_{17}NO$
Mol. Wt. 203.29
M.P. 57-60°C
Solvent: Methanol

λ Max. mμ	^{a}m	Cell mm	Conc. g/L
266.5	234	20	0.242
262	275	20	0.242
256.8	335	20	0.242
251	327	20	0.242
245.5	310	20	0.242

1-BENZYL-4-PIPERIDONE — 2015

$C_{12}H_{15}NO$
Mol. Wt. 189.26
Solvent: Methanol

λ Max. mμ	^{a}m	Cell mm	Conc. g/L
264	336	10	0.2216
258	410	10	0.2216
252	420	10	0.2216
247	419	10	0.2216
206.5	10200	10	0.0111

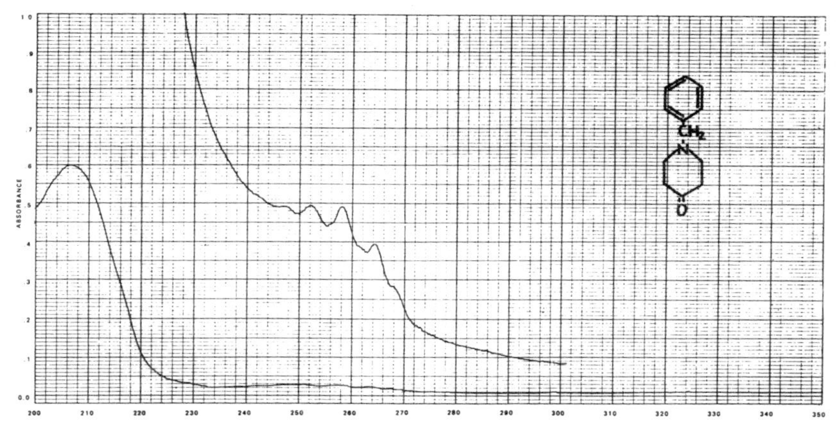

TETRAHYDROTHIOPYRAN-4-ONE — 2016

C_5H_8OS
Mol. Wt. 116.18
M.P. 59-61°C

λ Max. mμ	^{a}m	Cell mm	Conc. g/L

Pure sample not available.

3-BUTEN-2-ONE

C_4H_6O

Mol. Wt. 70.09

Solvent: Methanol

2017

λ Max. mμ	a_m	Cell mm	Conc. g/L
x	x	20	0.100

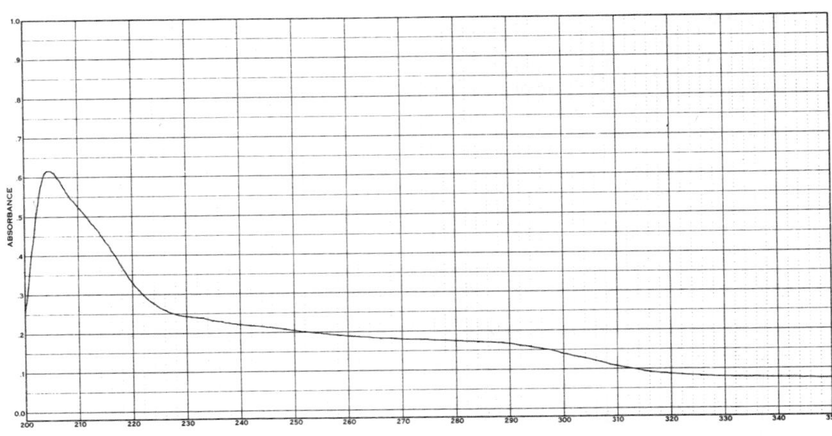

3-PENTEN-2-ONE

C_5H_8O

Mol. Wt. 84.12

Solvent: Methanol

2018

λ Max. mμ	a_m	Cell mm	Conc. g/L
271.5	533	5	0.100
222.5	1620	5	0.100

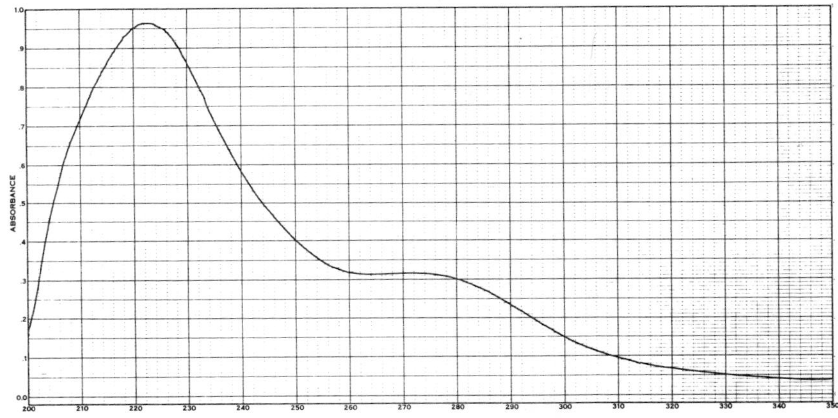

5-HEXEN-2-ONE

$C_6H_{10}O$

Mol. Wt. 98.15

B.P. 128-129°C

2019

λ Max. mμ	a_m	Cell mm	Conc. g/L

Pure sample not available.

4-METHYL-3-PENTEN-2-ONE

2020

$C_6H_{10}O$

Mol. Wt. 98.14

B.P. 129.2-129.4°C

Solvent: Methanol

λ Max. mμ	a_m	Cell mm	Conc. g/L
237	11500	10	0.0052

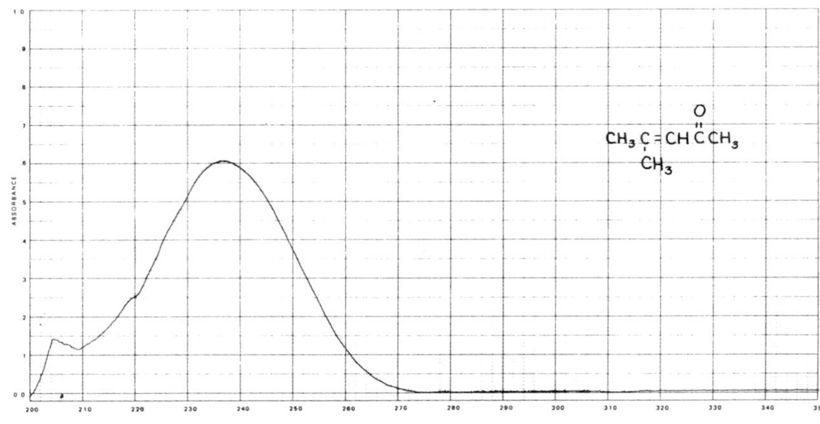

5-ETHYL-3-HEPTEN-2-ONE

2021

$C_9H_{16}O$

Mol. Wt. 140.23

Solvent: Methanol

λ Max. mμ	a_m	Cell mm	Conc. g/L
223	10900	1	0.100

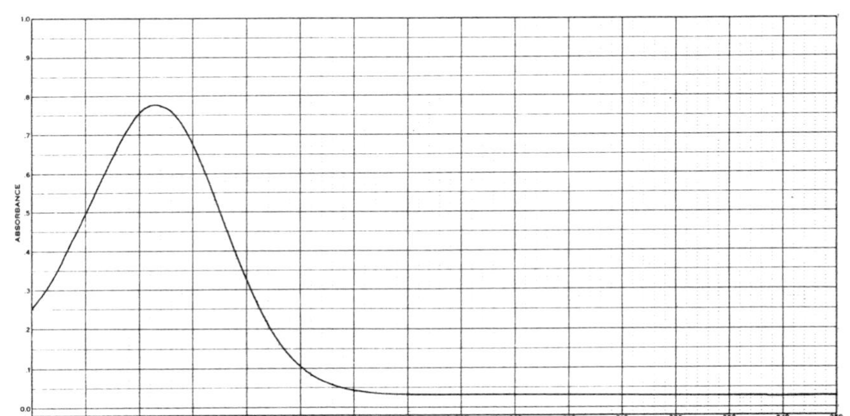

1-CYCLOHEXEN-1-YL METHYL KETONE

2022

$C_8H_{12}O$

Mol. Wt. 124.18

Solvent: Methanol

λ Max. mμ	a_m	Cell mm	Conc. g/L
308	1450	40	0.100
232	13200	0.5	0.100

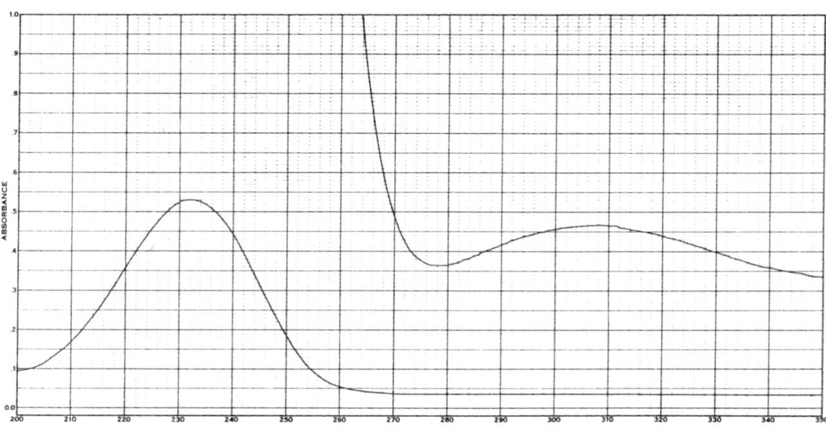

FUROIN 2023

$C_{10}H_8O_4$
Mol. Wt. 192.17
Solvent: Methanol

λ Max. mμ	a_m	Cell mm	Conc. g/L
276	14700	10	0.0112
217	10000	10	0.0112

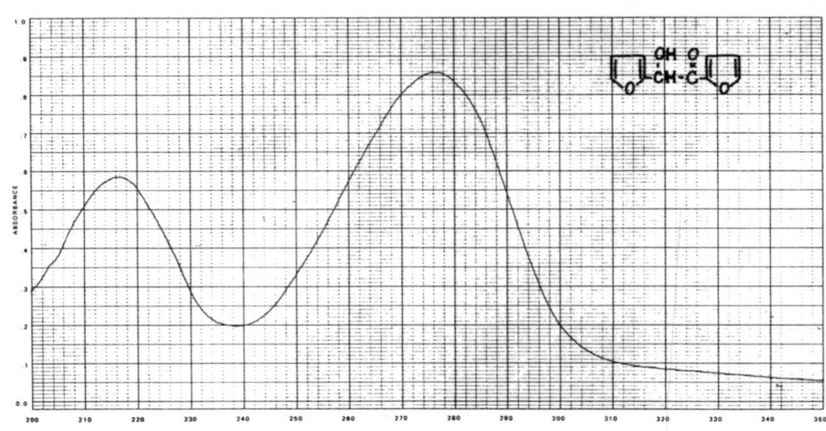

3-CHLORO-2-CYCLOPENTEN-1-ONE 2024

C_5H_5ClO
Mol. Wt. 116.55
B.P. 35°C/0.7mm

λ Max. mμ	a_m	Cell mm	Conc. g/L

Pure sample not available.

2-CYCLOHEXEN-1-ONE 2025

C_6H_8O
Mol. Wt. 96.13
Solvent: Methanol

λ Max. mμ	a_m	Cell mm	Conc. g/L
x	x	10	0.100
225	8230	1	0.100

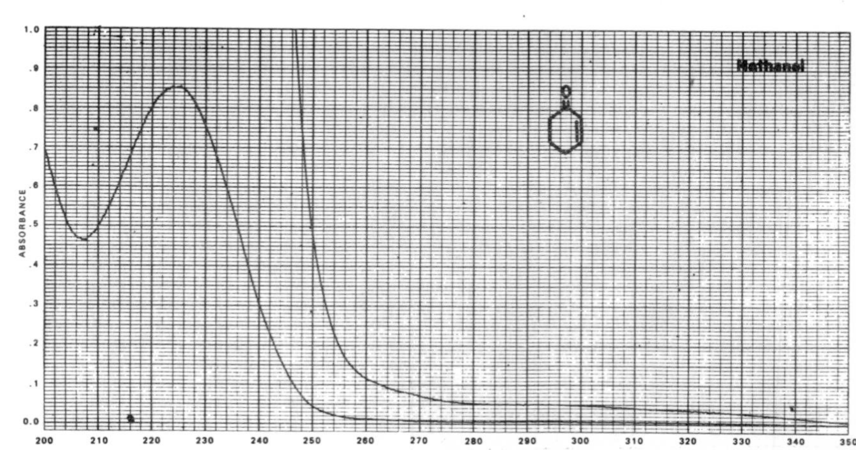

3-CHLORO-2-CYCLOHEXEN-1-ONE

2026

C_6H_7ClO
Mol. Wt. 130.58
B.P. 63°C/4mm
Solvent: Methanol

λ Max. mμ	a_m	Cell mm	Conc. g/L
310	2090	4	0.100
245	7820	1	0.100

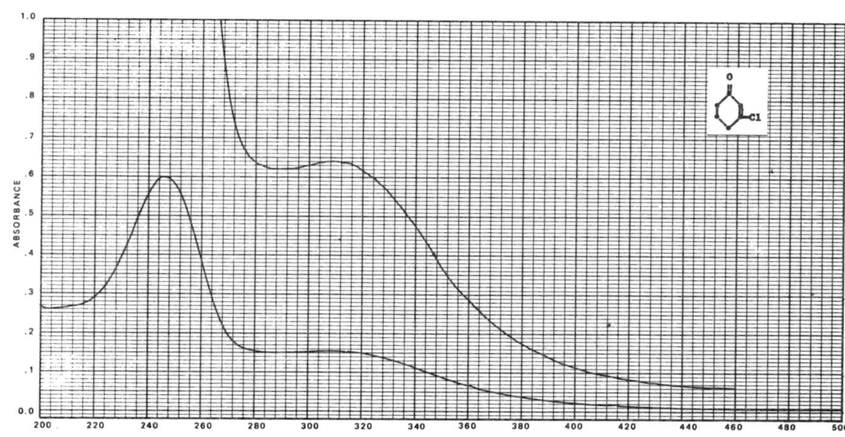

3,5-DIMETHYL-2-CYCLOHEXEN-1-ONE

2027

$C_8H_{12}O$
Mol. Wt. 124.18
Solvent: Methanol

λ Max. mμ	a_m	Cell mm	Conc. g/L
x	x	10	2.236
x	x	10	0.2236
237.5	12900	10	0.0089

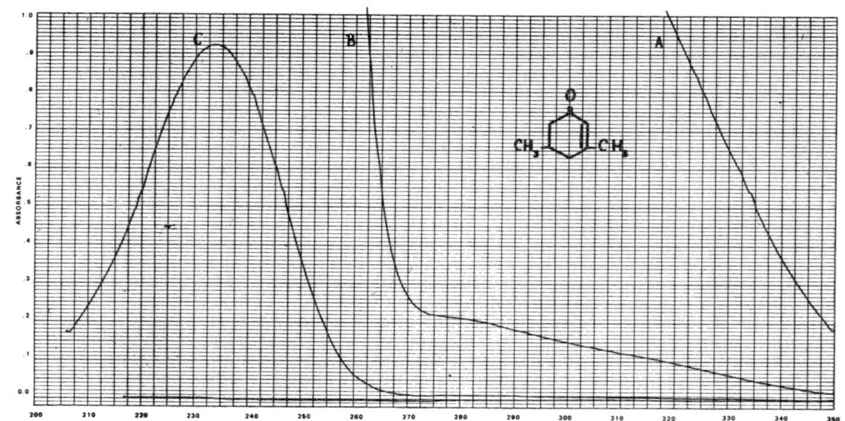

3-CHLORO-2-METHYL-2-CYCLOHEXEN-1-ONE

2028

C_7H_9ClO
Mol. Wt. 144.60
B.P. 62°C/2mm

λ Max. mμ	a_m	Cell mm	Conc. g/L

Pure sample not available.

3-CHLORO-5,5-DIMETHYL-2-CYCLOHEXEN-1-ONE

$C_8H_{11}ClO$

Mol. Wt. 158.63

Solvent: Methanol

λ Max. mμ	a_m	Cell mm	Conc. g/L
251	11600	1	0.100

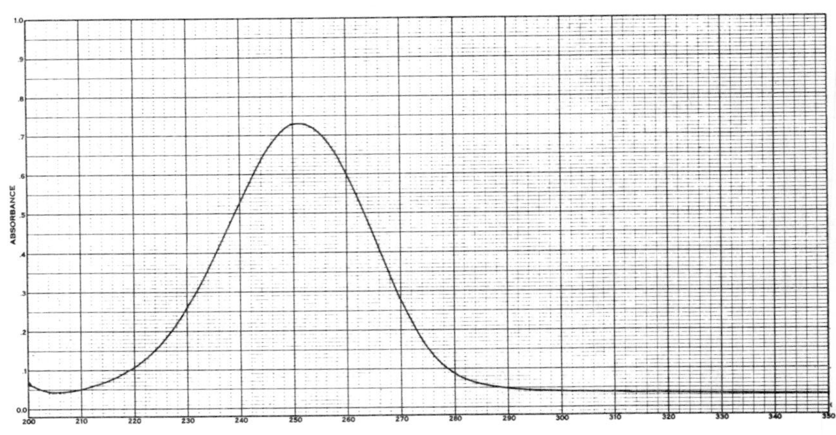

2030

p-TOLUQUINONE

$C_7H_6O_2$

Mol. Wt. 122.13

M.P. 66.5-68°C

Solvent: Methanol

λ Max. mμ	a_m	Cell mm	Conc. g/L
298	733	1	1.00
245	16700	1	0.0560

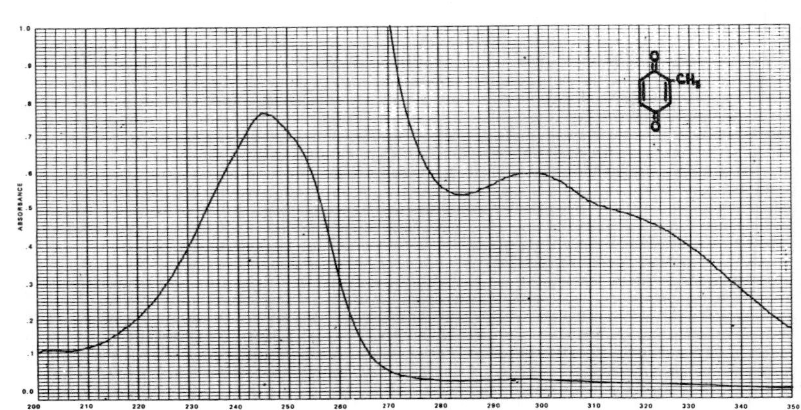

2030

p-TOLUQUINONE

$C_7H_6O_2$

Mol. Wt. 122.13

M.P. 66.5-68°C

Solvent: Methanol KOH

λ Max. mμ	a_m	Cell mm	Conc. g/L
257	11600	1	0.0800

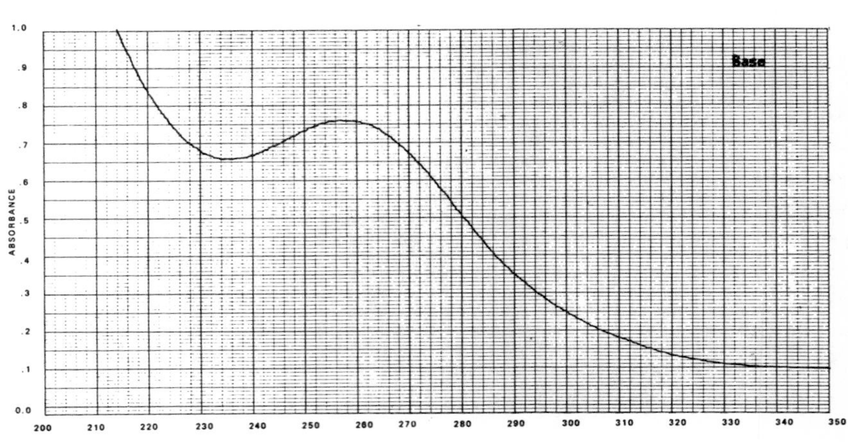

2,5-DI-tert-PENTYL-p-BENZOQUINONE 2031

$C_{16}H_{24}O_2$
Mol. Wt. 248.37
M.P. 134-135°C
Solvent: Methanol

λ Max. mμ	a_m	Cell mm	Conc. g/L
296.5	584	10	0.100
256	16700	1	0.100

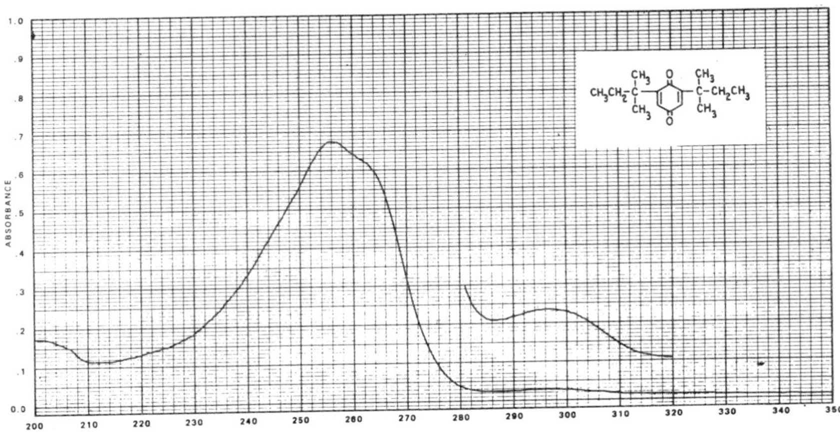

TETRAMETHYL-p-BENZOQUINONE 2032

$C_{10}H_{12}O_2$
Mol. Wt. 164.21
M.P. 109.5-110°C
Solvent: Methanol

λ Max. mμ	a_m	Cell mm	Conc. g/L
266	21200	1	0.0500
259	20700	1	0.0500

λ Max. mμ	a_m	Cell mm	Conc. g/L

PHENYL-p-BENZOQUINONE 2033

$C_{12}H_8O_2$

Mol. Wt. 184.20

M.P. 112-114°C

Solvent: Methanol

λ Max. mμ	a_m	Cell mm	Conc. g/L
309	5690	1	0.100
253.5	8580	1	0.100
219	16200	1	0.100

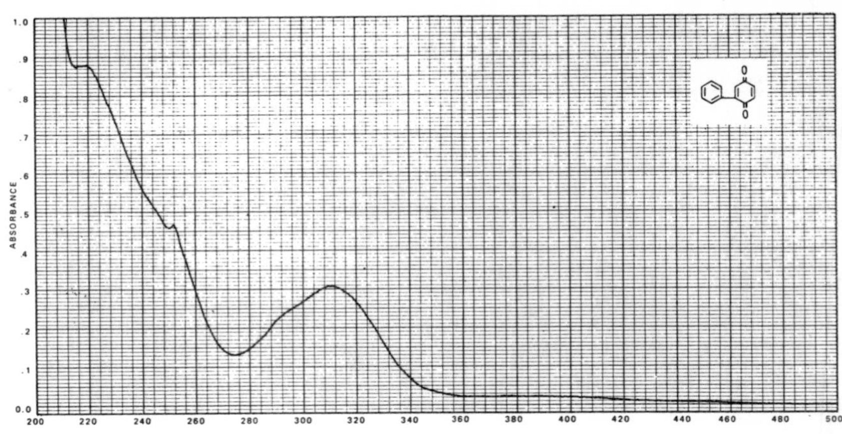

PHENYL-p-BENZOQUINONE 2033

$C_{12}H_8O_2$

Mol. Wt. 184.20

M.P. 112-114°C

Solvent: Methanol KOH

λ Max. mμ	a_m	Cell mm	Conc. g/L
296	5280	2	0.100
254	7610	2	0.100

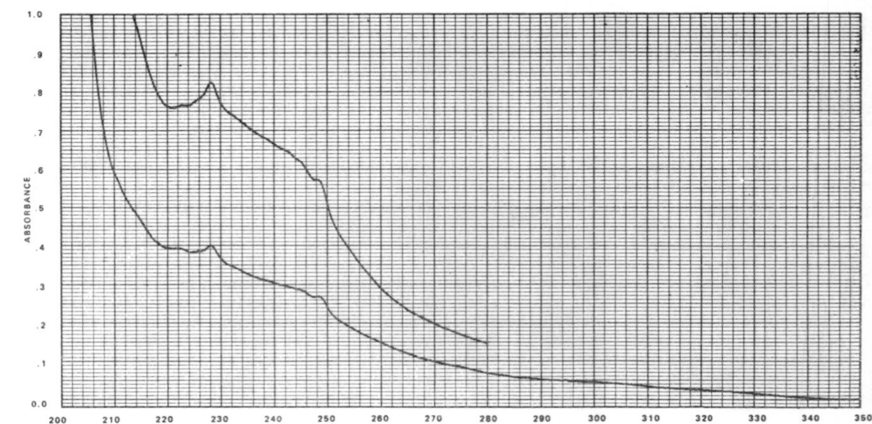

1-PHENYL-2-BUTANONE 2034

$C_{10}H_{12}O$

Mol. Wt. 148.21

Solvent: Cyclohexane

λ Max. mμ	a_m	Cell mm	Conc. g/L
x	x	10	1.94
286	196	10	0.778
279	195	10	0.778
266	851	10	0.778
260	278	10	0.778
238.5	810	10	0.194
x	x	10	0.0388

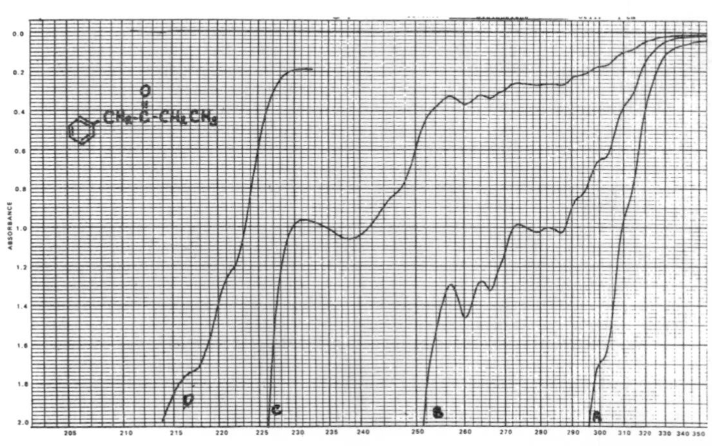

3-METHYL-1-PHENYL-2-BUTANONE

2035

$C_{11}H_{14}O$

Mol. Wt. 162.23

B.P. 115-116°C/14.5mm (lit.)

Solvent: Cyclohexane

λ Max. mμ	a_m	Cell mm	Conc. g/L
281	324	10	0.8816
258	515	10	0.4408
x	x	10	0.0441

4-PHENYL-2-BUTANONE

2036

$C_{10}H_{12}O$

Mol. Wt. 148.21

B.P. 235°C

Solvent: Methanol

λ Max. mμ	a_m	Cell mm	Conc. g/L
268	198	10	0.5060
264	199	10	0.5060
261	230	10	0.5060
258.5	232	10	0.5060
254.5	193	10	0.5060
253	195	10	0.5060
248	146	10	0.5060
236.5	90.8	10	0.5060
209	8350	10	0.0101

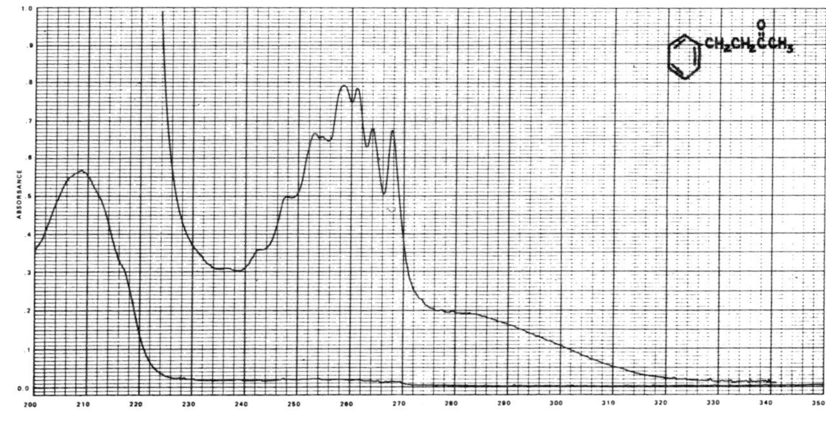

3,4-DIBROMO-4-PHENYL-2-BUTANONE

2037

$C_{10}H_{10}Br_2O$

Mol. Wt. 306.02

Solvent: Methanol

λ Max. mμ	a_m	Cell mm	Conc. g/L
x	x	10	2.008
228	5660	10	0.020

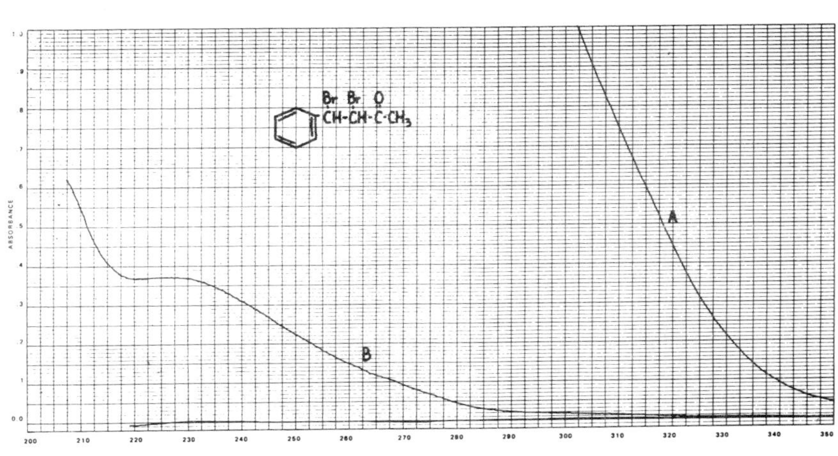

4-(p-HYDROXYPHENYL)-2-BUTANONE 2038

$C_{10}H_{12}O_2$
Mol. Wt. 162.19
Solvent: Methanol

λ Max. mμ	a_m	Cell mm	Conc. g/L
279	3780	1	0.100
224	15900	1	0.100

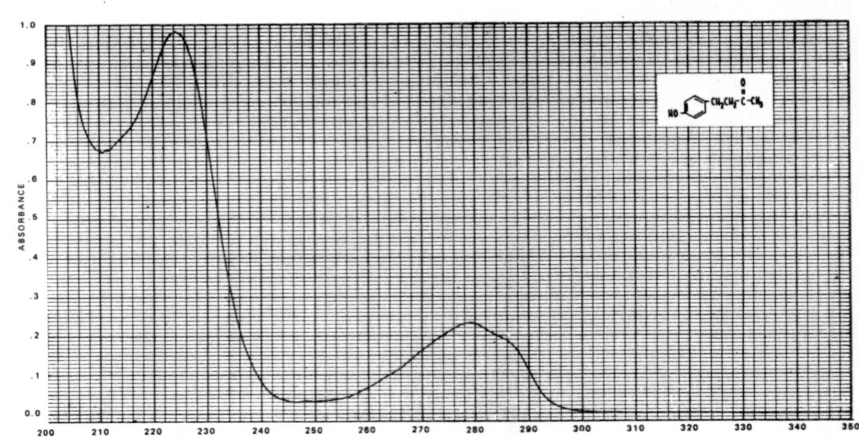

4-(p-HYDROXYPHENYL)-2-BUTANONE 2038

$C_{10}H_{12}O_2$
Mol. Wt. 162.19
Solvent: Methanol KOH

λ Max. mμ	a_m	Cell mm	Conc. g/L
288	3800	1	0.100
239.5	13600	1	0.100
229	13500	1	0.100

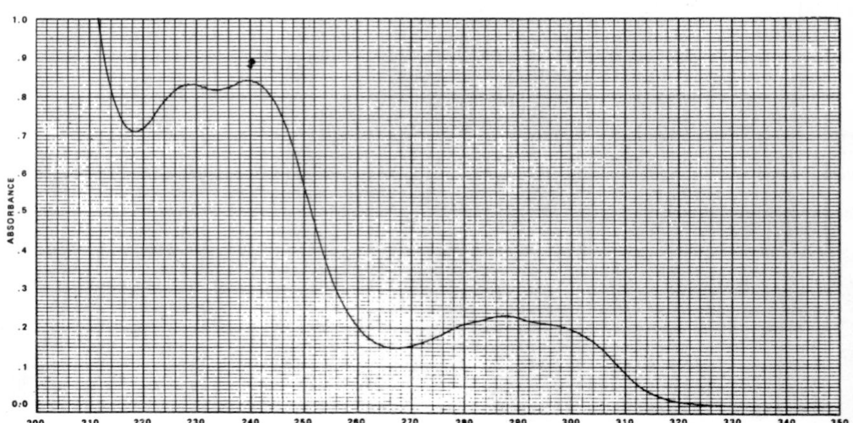

1-[3,4-(METHYLENEDIOXY)PHENYL]-2-PROPANONE 2039

$C_{10}H_{10}O_3$
Mol. Wt. 178.19
Solvent: Methanol

λ Max. mμ	a_m	Cell mm	Conc. g/L
287.5	3660	1	0.3560
234.5	3820	1	0.3560

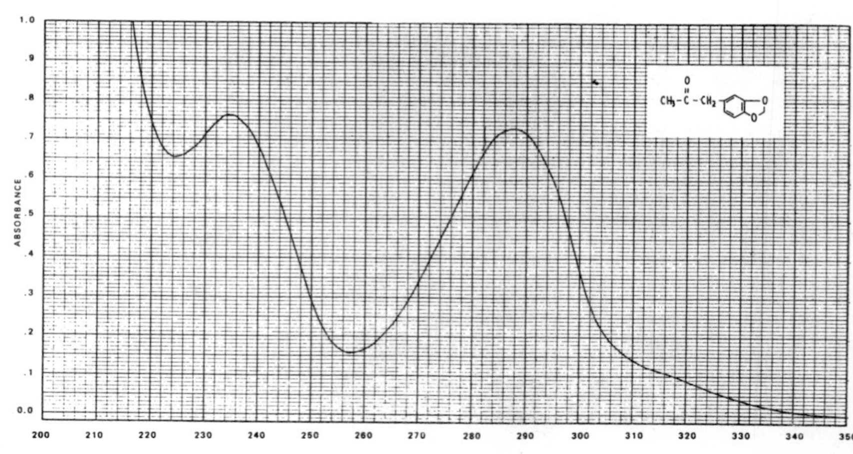

1,3-DIPHENYL-2-PROPANONE 2040

$C_{15}H_{14}O$

Mol. Wt. 210.28

M.P. 33.5°C

Solvent: Methanol

λ Max. mμ	a_m	Cell mm	Conc. g/L
258.5	802.0	2	1.00
253	767.0	2	1.00
x	x	1	0.0800

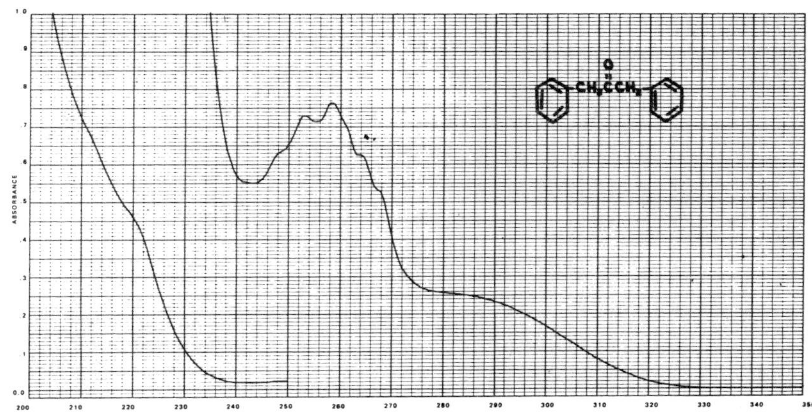

1-PHENYL-1-HEPTEN-3-ONE 2041

$C_{13}H_{16}O$

Mol. Wt. 188.27

M.P. 34-36°C

Solvent: Methanol

λ Max. mμ	a_m	Cell mm	Conc. g/L
279.5	2050	0.5	0.100
218.5	10200	1	0.100
213.5	4930	1	0.100

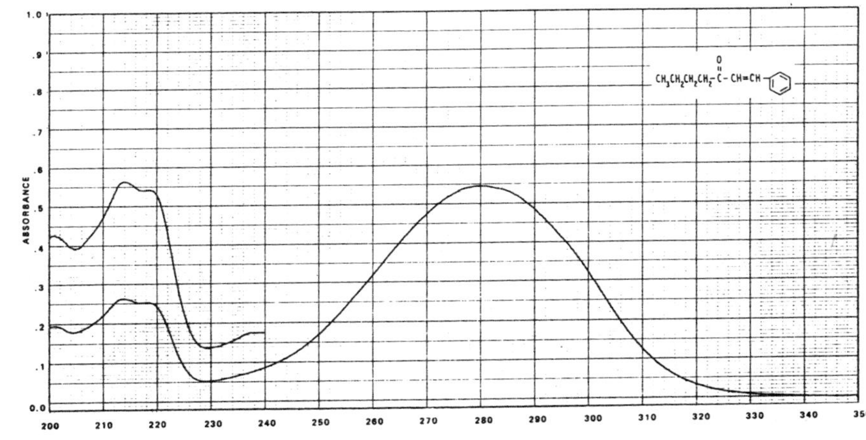

4,4-DIPHENYL-3-BUTEN-2-ONE 2042

$C_{16}H_{14}O$

Mol. Wt. 222.29

M.P. 33°C

λ Max. mμ	a_m	Cell mm	Conc. g/L

Pure sample not available.

2043

1,5-DIPHENYL-1,4-PENTADIEN-3-ONE

$C_{17}H_{14}O$
Mol. Wt. 234.28
M.P. 111-112°C
Solvent: Methanol

λ Max. mμ	a_m	Cell mm	Conc. g/L
327	25600	10	0.005
229.5	12400	10	0.005

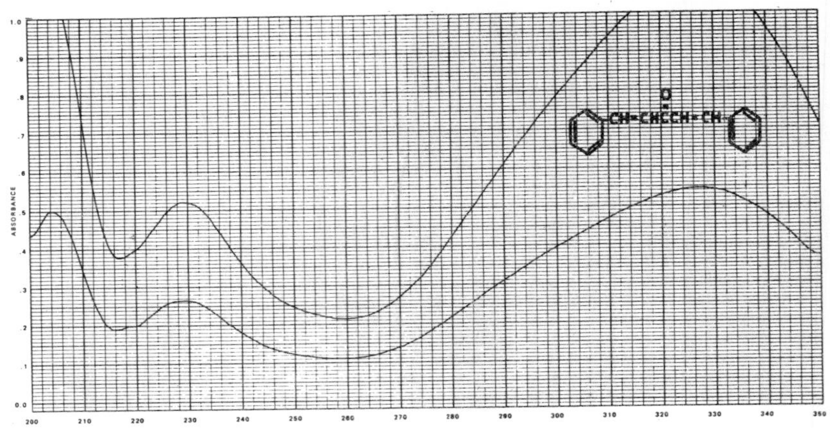

2044

4-PHENYL-3-BUTYN-2-ONE

$C_{10}H_8O$
Mol. Wt. 144.17
B.P. 75-76°C/0.8mm
Solvent: Methanol

λ Max. mμ	a_m	Cell mm	Conc. g/L
271	14700	0.5	0.100
234	6520	0.5	0.100
213	11300	0.5	0.100

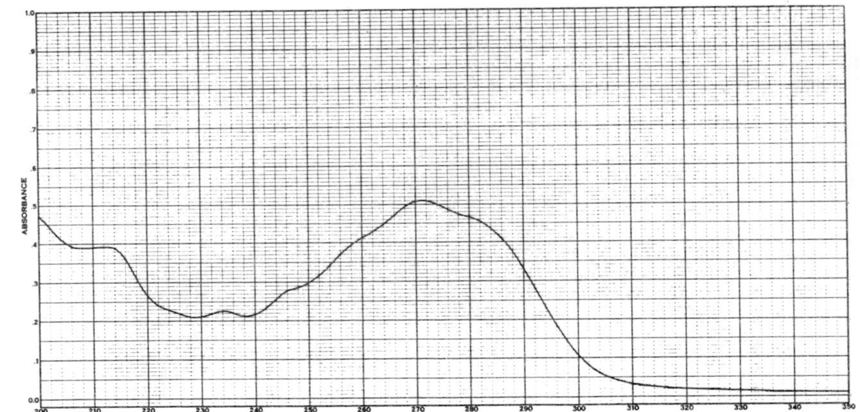

2045

ACETOPHENONE

C_8H_8O
Mol. Wt. 120.15
B.P. 202°C (lit.)
Solvent: Methanol

λ Max. mμ	a_m	Cell mm	Conc. g/L
278.5	1290	5	0.177
240	14300	1	0.0354

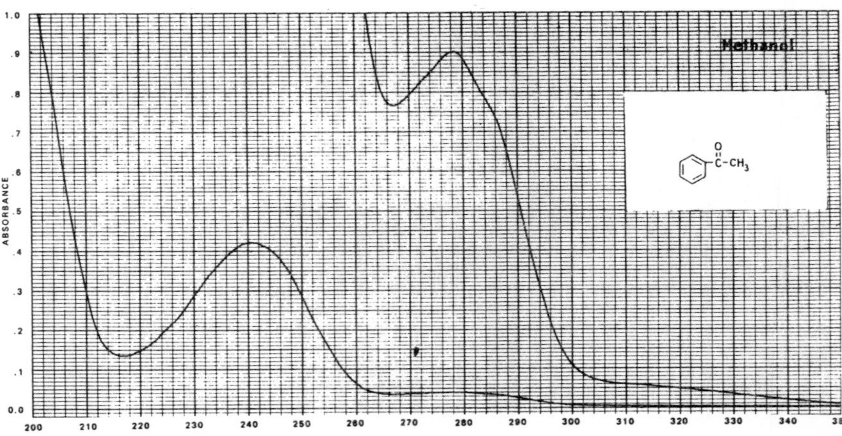

PROPIOPHENONE

$C_9H_{10}O$

Mol. Wt. 134.18

Solvent: Methanol

2046

λ Max. mμ	a_m	Cell mm	Conc. g/L
278	1190	2	0.345
240	1470	2	0.0345

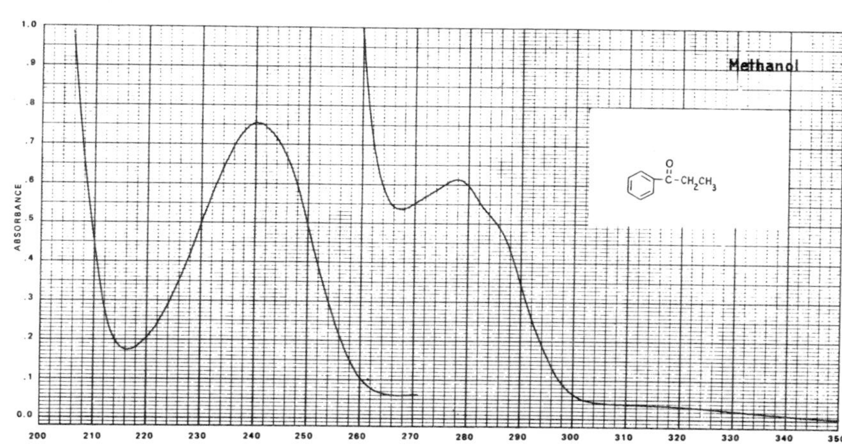

BUTYROPHENONE

$C_{10}H_{12}O$

Mol. Wt. 148.21

M.P. 11.5-13°C (lit.)

Solvent: Methanol

2047

λ Max. mμ	a_m	Cell mm	Conc. g/L
x	x	10	1.720
278	950	10	0.1720
240.5	2750	10	0.0720

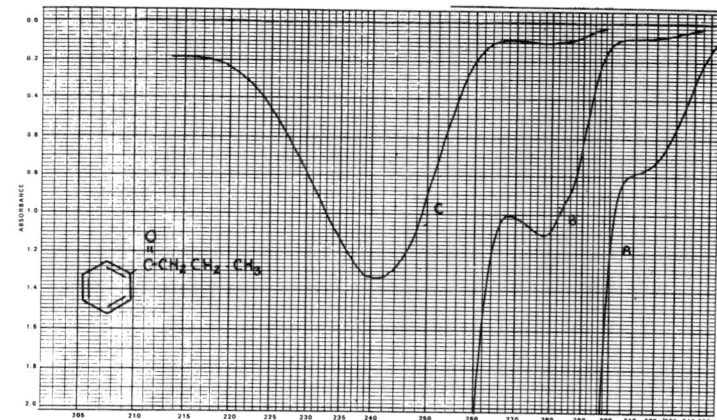

ISOBUTYROPHENONE

$C_{10}H_{12}O$

Mol. Wt. 148.21

B.P. 91.5-93.5°C/7mm

Solvent: Methanol

2048

λ Max. mμ	a_m	Cell mm	Conc. g/L
313	93.0	20	0.305
277.5	1110	2	0.305
241	13800	1	0.0610

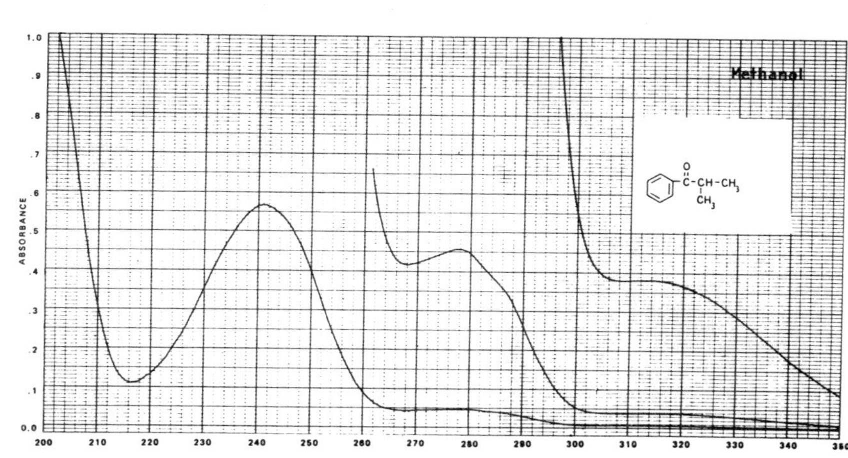

HEPTANOPHENONE

2049

$C_{13}H_{18}O$

Mol. Wt. 190.29

Solvent: Methanol

λ Max. mμ	a_m	Cell mm	Conc. g/L
276.5	1050	10	0.100
240.5	12300	1	0.100
x	x	1	0.100

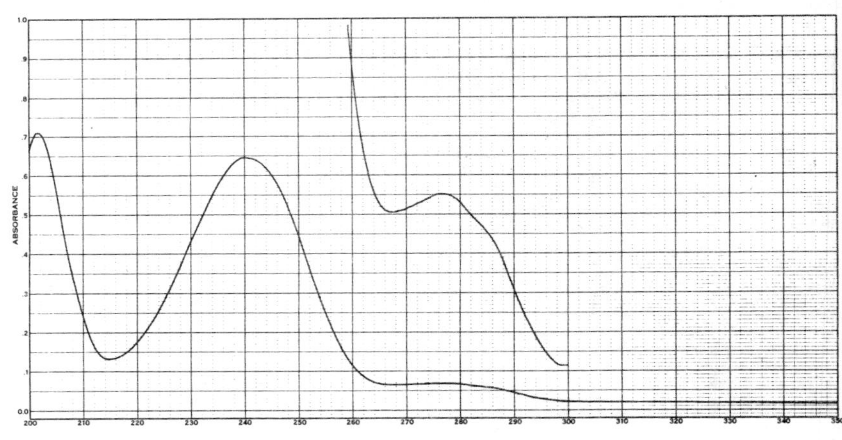

MYRISTOPHENONE

2050

$C_{20}H_{32}O$

Mol. Wt. 288.48

M.P. 53-55°C

Solvent: Methanol

λ Max. mμ	a_m	Cell mm	Conc. g/L
277	983	10	0.263
240	13700	1	0.132

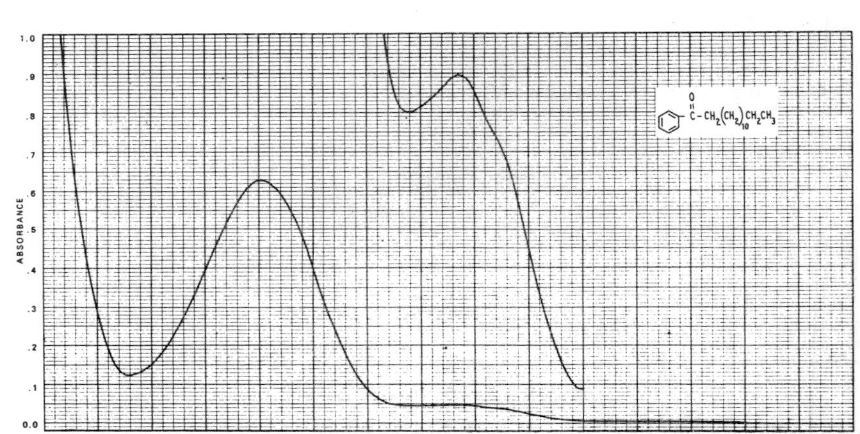

2-CHLOROACETOPHENONE

2051

C_8H_7ClO

Mol. Wt. 154.60

M.P. 59°C B.P. 247°C (lit.)

Solvent: Methanol

λ Max. mμ	a_m	Cell mm	Conc. g/L
x	x	10	0.2340
245	13700	10	0.0187

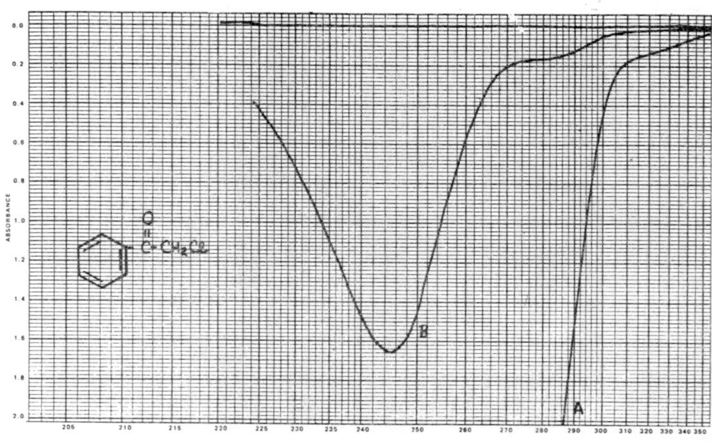

2052

3-CHLOROPROPIOPHENONE

C_9H_9ClO

Mol. Wt. 168.62

M.P. 49-50°C

Solvent: Methanol

λ Max. mμ	a_m	Cell mm	Conc. g/L
x	x	5	0.119
241	13500	1	0.119

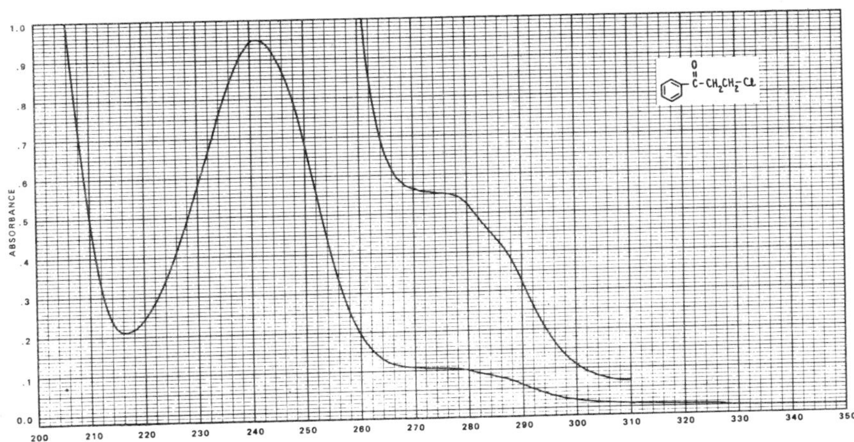

2053

2-BROMOACETOPHENONE

C_8H_7BrO

Mol. Wt. 199.06

M.P. 49°C (lit.)

Solvent: Methanol

λ Max. mμ	a_m	Cell mm	Conc. g/L
x	x	10	2.120
249	2890	10	0.1060
x	x	10	0.0212

λ Max. mμ	a_m	Cell mm	Conc. g/L

BENZOYLACETONITRILE 2054

C_9H_7NO

Mol. Wt. 145.16

M.P. 80-81.5°C

Solvent: Methanol

λ Max. mμ	a_m	Cell mm	Conc. g/L
280.5	1950	5	0.100
244	12300	1	0.100

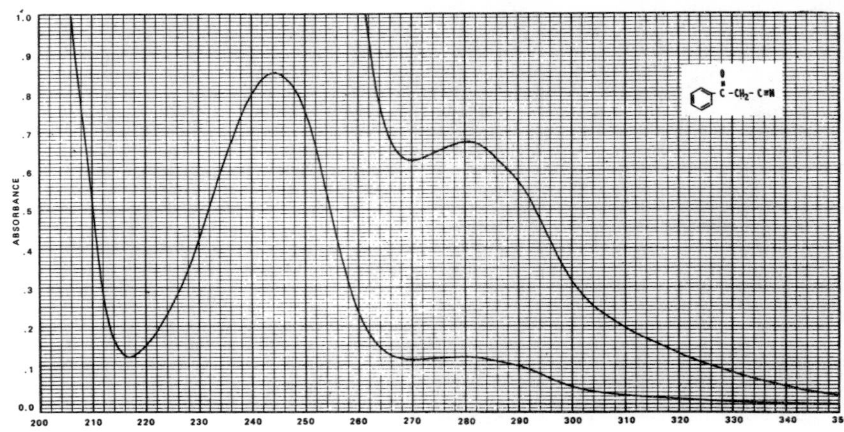

BENZOYLACETONITRILE 2054

C_9H_7NO

Mol. Wt. 145.16

M.P. 80-81.5°C

Solvent: Methanol KOH

λ Max. mμ	a_m	Cell mm	Conc. g/L
302	9870	1	0.100
226	11000	1	0.100

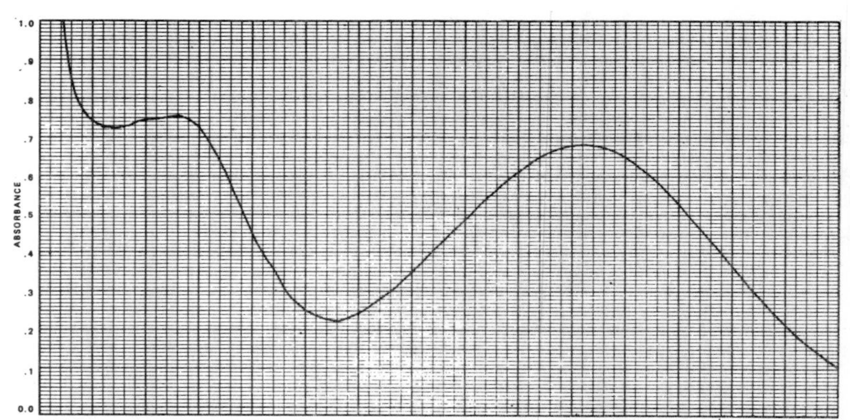

2'-METHYLACETOPHENONE 2055

$C_9H_{10}O$

Mol. Wt. 134.18

B.P. 214°C

Solvent: Methanol

λ Max. mμ	a_m	Cell mm	Conc. g/L
285.5	1450	5	0.108
241.5	9410	1	0.108

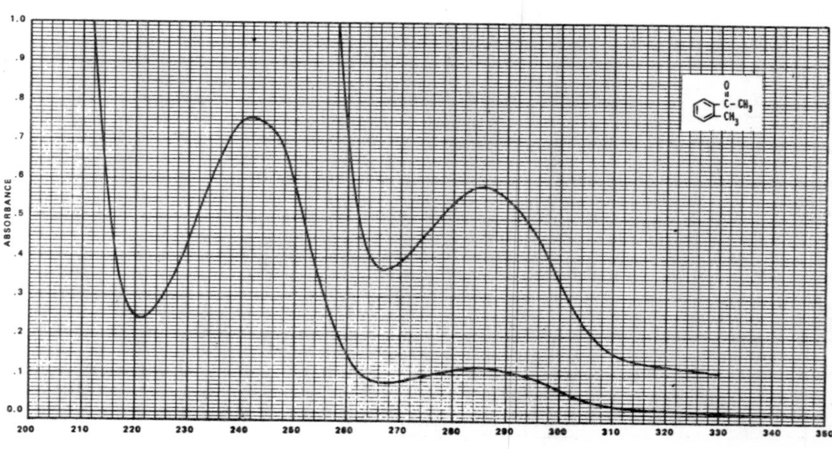

4'-METHYLACETOPHENONE

2056

$C_9H_{10}O$
Mol. Wt. 134.18
B.P. 222°C (lit.)
Solvent: Methanol

λ Max. mμ	a_m	Cell mm	Conc. g/L
x	x	1	0.310
252	12300	2	0.0310
x	x	1	0.0310

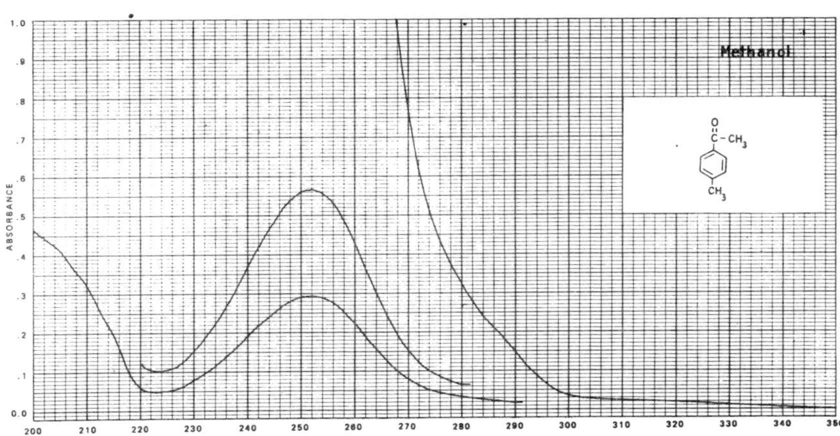

2',5'-DIMETHYLACETOPHENONE

2057

$C_{10}H_{12}O$
Mol. Wt. 148.21
B.P. 114-116°C/17mm
Solvent: Methanol

λ Max. mμ	a_m	Cell mm	Conc. g/L
294	1580	5	0.108
248	8670	1	0.054
210	24700	1	0.054

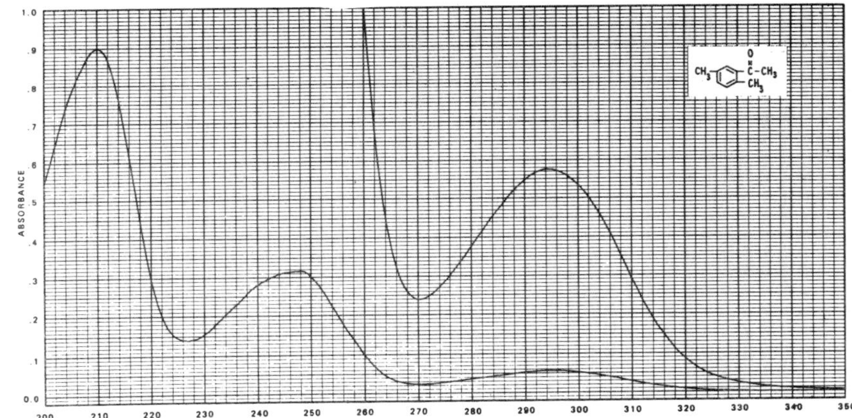

2',3',5',6'-TETRAMETHYLACETOPHENONE

2058

$C_{12}H_{16}O$
Mol. Wt. 176.26
M.P. 70-73°C
Solvent: Methanol

λ Max. mμ	a_m	Cell mm	Conc. g/L
276.5	932	10	0.100
x	x	1	0.100

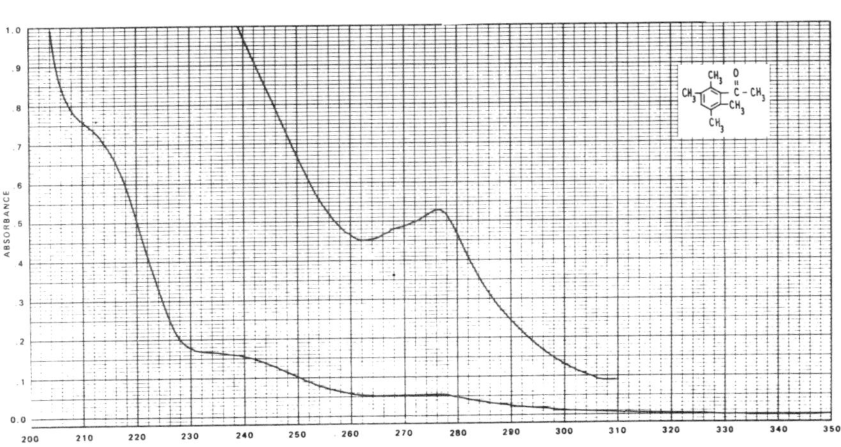

4′-ETHYLACETOPHENONE 2059

$C_{10}H_{12}O$
Mol. Wt. 148.21
B.P. 113-115°C/11mm
Solvent: Methanol

λ Max. mμ	a_m	Cell mm	Conc. g/L
252.5	15000	1	0.0832

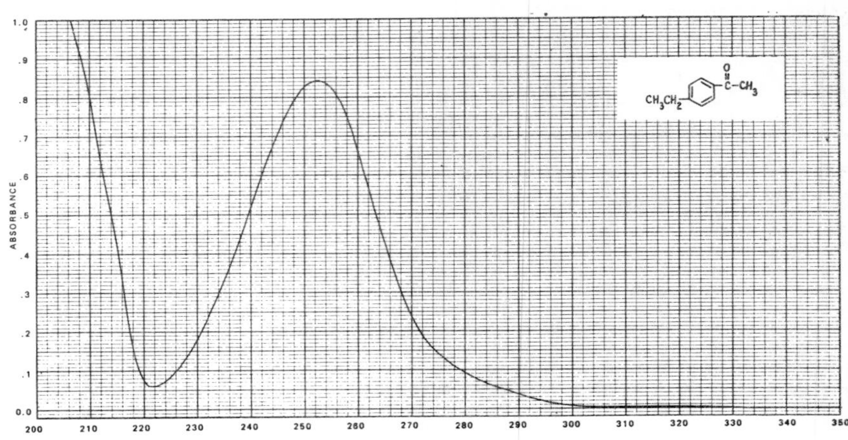

4-METHYLVALEROPHENONE 2060

$C_{12}H_{16}O$
Mol. Wt. 176.26
Solvent: Methanol

λ Max. mμ	a_m	Cell mm	Conc. g/L
251	12100	1	0.100

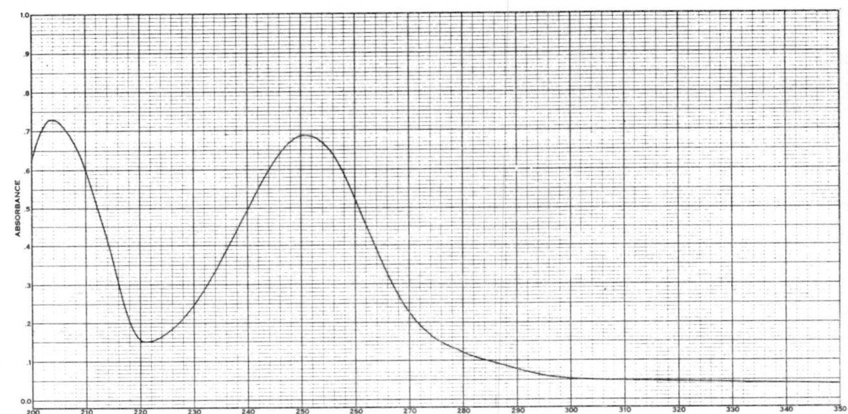

2′,4′-DIMETHYLPIVALOPHENONE 2061

$C_{13}H_{18}O$
Mol. Wt. 190.29
Solvent: Methanol

λ Max. mμ	a_m	Cell mm	Conc. g/L
245	3100	5	0.100
x	x	1	0.100

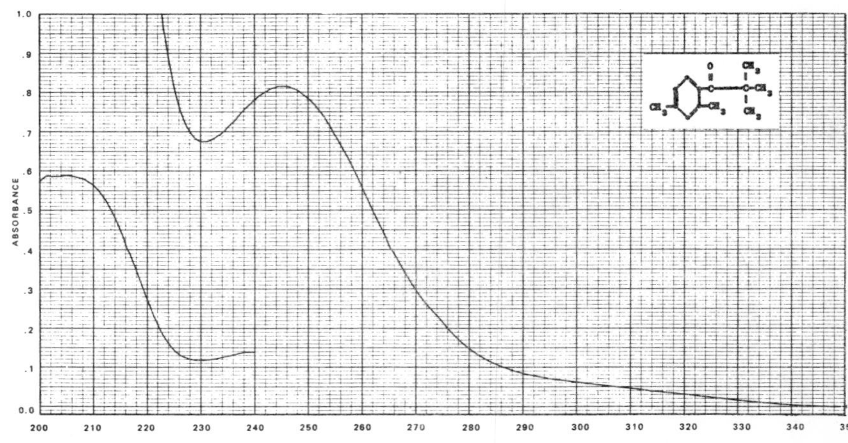

2-BROMO-4'-METHYLACETOPHENONE

2062

C_9H_9BrO

Mol. Wt. 213.08

M.P. 45-49°C

Solvent: Methanol

λ Max. mμ	a_m	Cell mm	Conc. g/L
260	13200	1	0.100
x	x	1	0.100

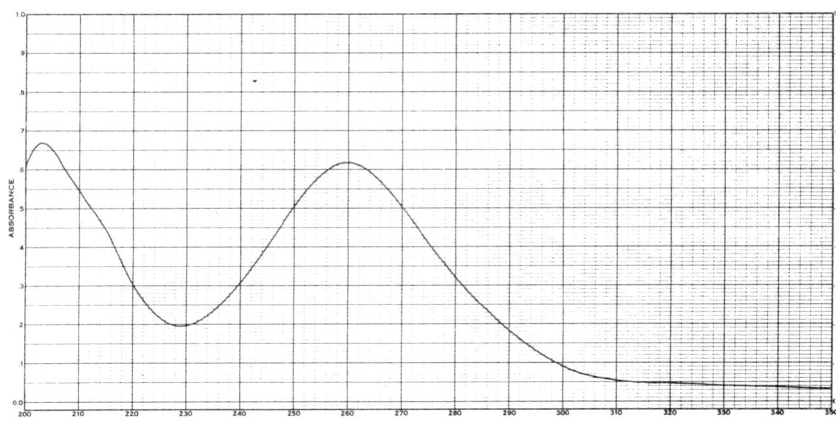

2',4'-DIFLUOROACETOPHENONE

2063

$C_8H_6F_2O$

Mol. Wt. 156.13

B.P. 60-61°C/7mm

Solvent: Methanol

λ Max. mμ	a_m	Cell mm	Conc. g/L
267.5	1530	5	0.107
231	10200	1	0.107

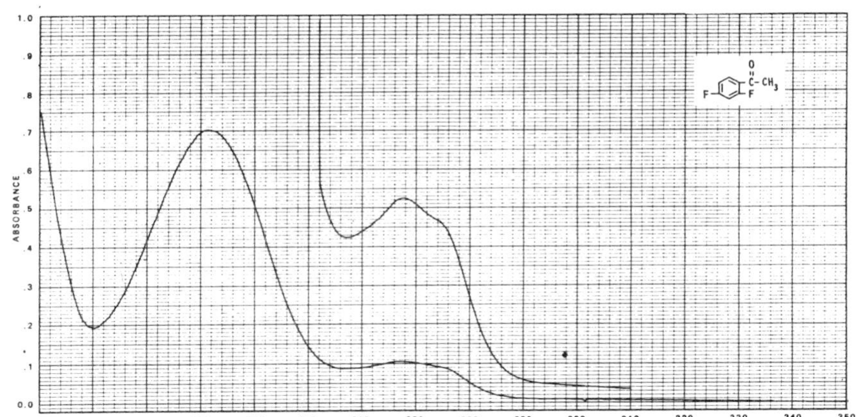

2'-CHLOROACETOPHENONE

2064

C_8H_7ClO

Mol. Wt. 154.60

B.P. 104-106°C/12mm

Solvent: Methanol

λ Max. mμ	a_m	Cell mm	Conc. g/L
283	829	10	0.125
236.5	6000	1	0.125

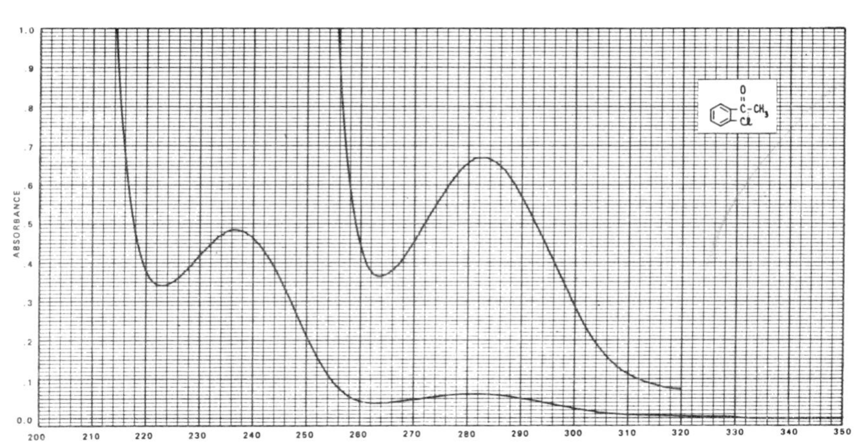

3′-CHLOROACETOPHENONE 2065

C_8H_7ClO

Mol. Wt. 154.60

B.P. 233-235°C

Solvent: Methanol

λ Max. mμ	a_m	Cell mm	Conc. g/L
285.5	1090	10	0.073
239	10600	1	0.073

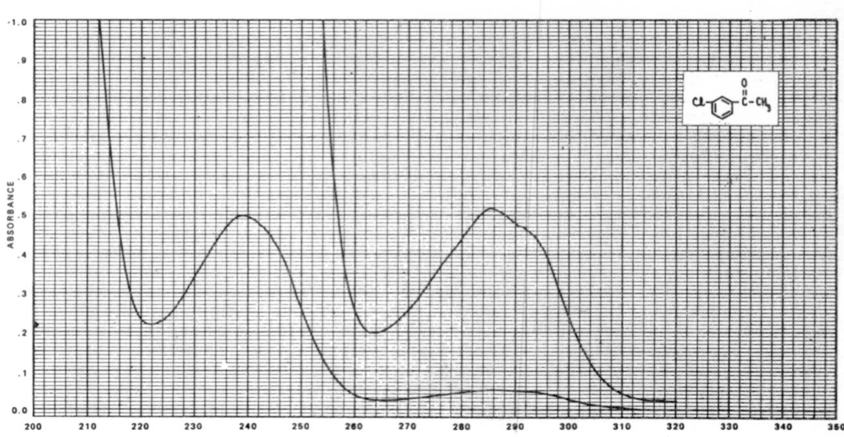

4′-CHLOROVALEROPHENONE 2066

$C_{11}H_{13}ClO$

Mol. Wt. 196.68

Solvent: Methanol

λ Max. mμ	a_m	Cell mm	Conc. g/L
247	14900	1	0.110

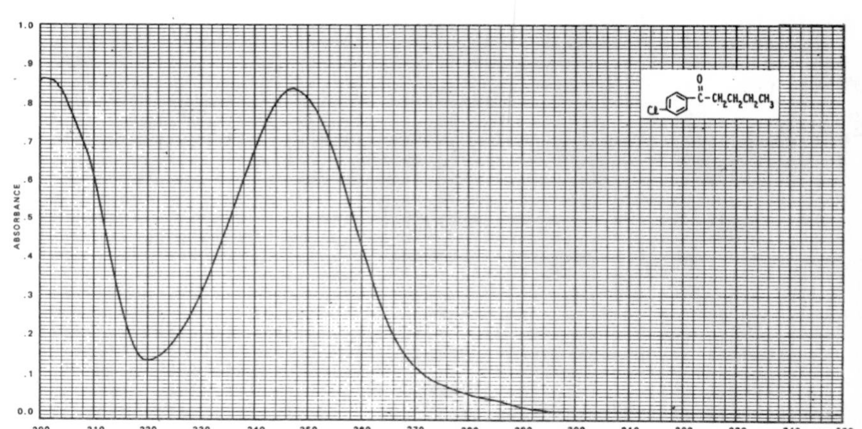

2′,5′-DICHLOROACETOPHENONE 2067

$C_8H_6Cl_2O$

Mol. Wt. 189.04

M.P. 11-13°C

Solvent: Methanol

λ Max. mμ	a_m	Cell mm	Conc. g/L
292	885	5	0.261
215	23700	1	0.052

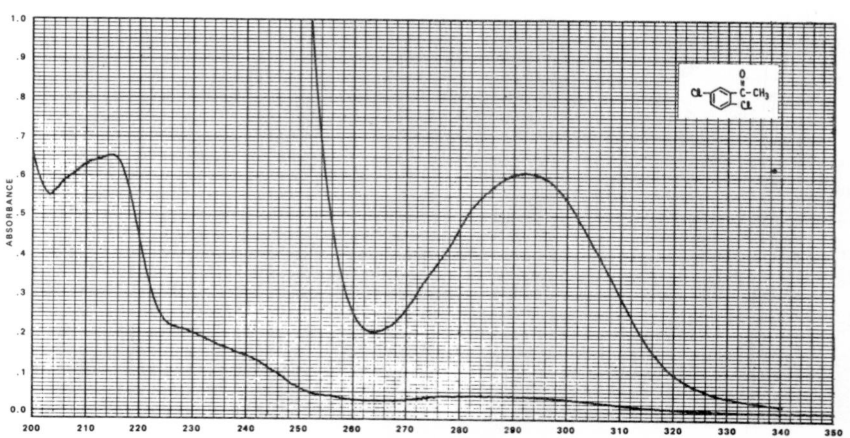

3'-BROMOACETOPHENONE 2068

C_8H_7BrO

Mol. Wt. 199.05

M.P. 13-15°C

Solvent: Methanol

λ Max. mμ	a_m	Cell mm	Conc. g/L
287	1280	10	0.106
240.5	9970	1	0.106

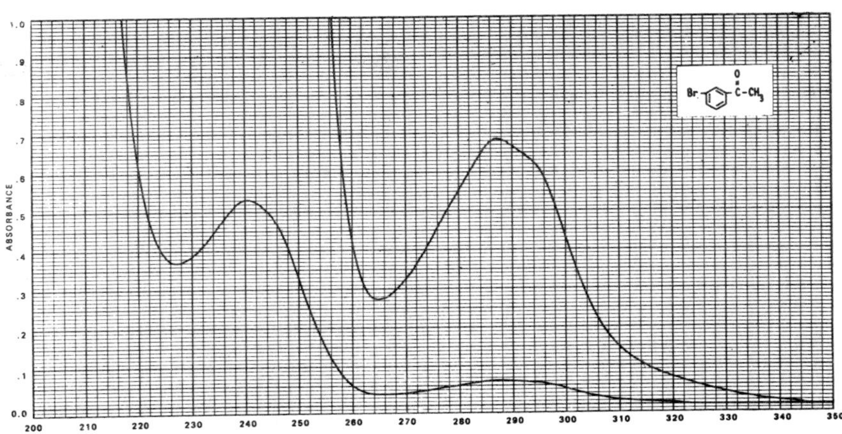

3'-IODOACETOPHENONE 2069

C_8H_7IO

Mol. Wt. 246.05

M.P. 26-29°C

Solvent: Methanol

λ Max. mμ	a_m	Cell mm	Conc. g/L
288.5	1900	10	0.1125
217.5	21600	1	0.1125

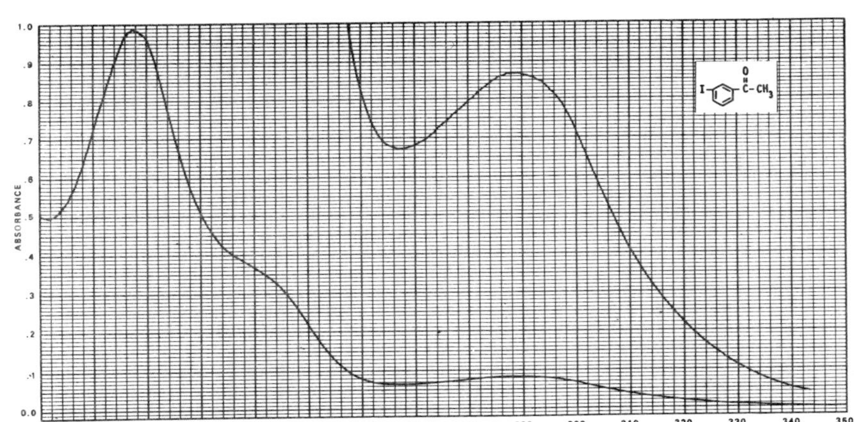

λ Max. mμ	a_m	Cell mm	Conc. g/L

4'-AMINOBUTYROPHENONE 2070

$C_{10}H_{13}NO$
Mol. Wt. 163.22
Solvent: Methanol

λ Max. mμ	a_m	Cell mm	Conc. g/L
316	20200	1	0.060
231	6330	2	0.100

4'-AMINOBUTYROPHENONE 2070

$C_{10}H_{13}NO$
Mol. Wt. 163.22
Solvent: Methanol HCl

λ Max. mμ	a_m	Cell mm	Conc. g/L
316.5	1040	5	0.100
281	1020	5	0.100
276	1060	5	0.100
237	10800	2	0.060

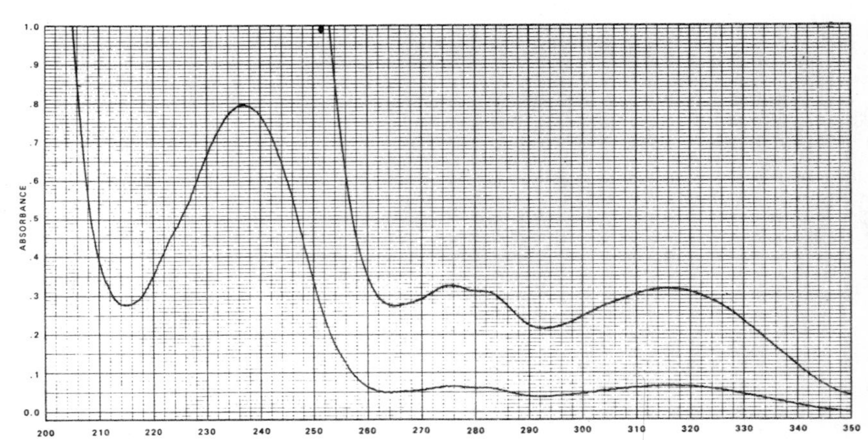

4'-AMINOVALEROPHENONE 2071

$C_{11}H_{15}NO$
Mol. Wt. 177.25
M.P. 72-74°C
Solvent: Methanol

λ Max. mμ	a_m	Cell mm	Conc. g/L
314	20800	1	0.0700
233	6580	1	0.0700

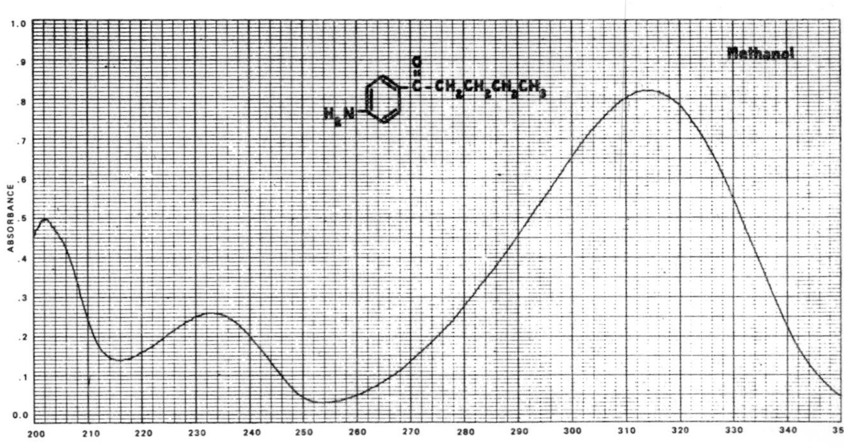

4'-AMINOVALEROPHENONE

2071

$C_{11}H_{15}NO$
Mol. Wt. 177.25
M.P. 72-74°C
Solvent: Methanol HCl

λ Max. mμ	a_m	Cell mm	Conc. g/L
315	2950	2	0.0700
236.5	9900	2	0.0700

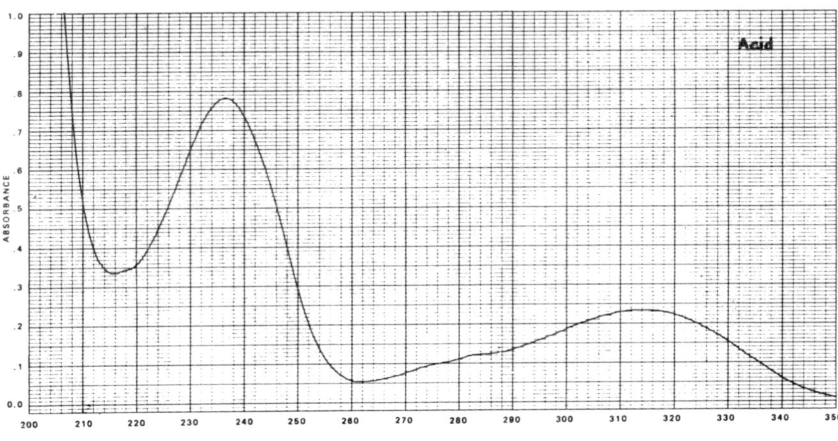

2'-NITROACETOPHENONE

2072

$C_8H_7NO_3$
Mol. Wt. 165.15
B.P. 158.5-159°C (lit.)
Solvent: Methanol

λ Max. mμ	a_m	Cell mm	Conc. g/L
255	5220	2	0.0920
x	x	1	0.0920

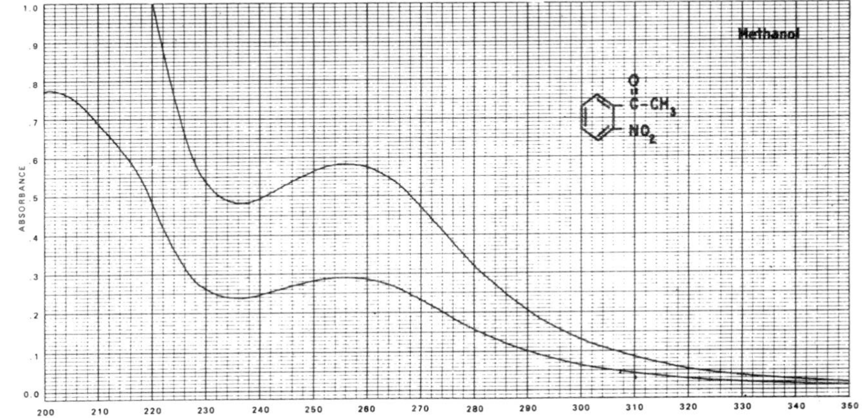

3'-NITROACETOPHENONE

2073

$C_8H_7NO_3$
Mol. Wt. 165.15
M.P. 77-79°C
Solvent: Methanol

λ Max. mμ	a_m	Cell mm	Conc. g/L
226	23300	1	0.0500

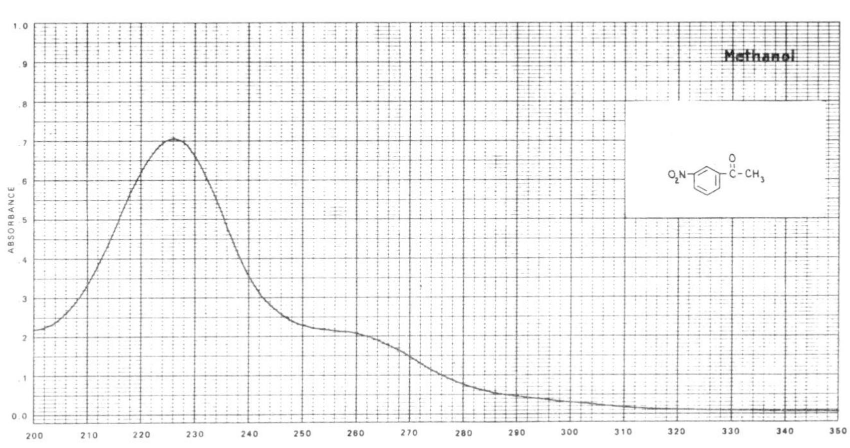

4'-(METHYLTHIO)ACETOPHENONE

2074

$C_9H_{10}OS$

Mol. Wt. 166.24

Solvent: Methanol

λ Max. mμ	a_m	Cell mm	Conc. g/L
305	15100	1	0.100
229	5340	1	0.100
x	x	1	0.100

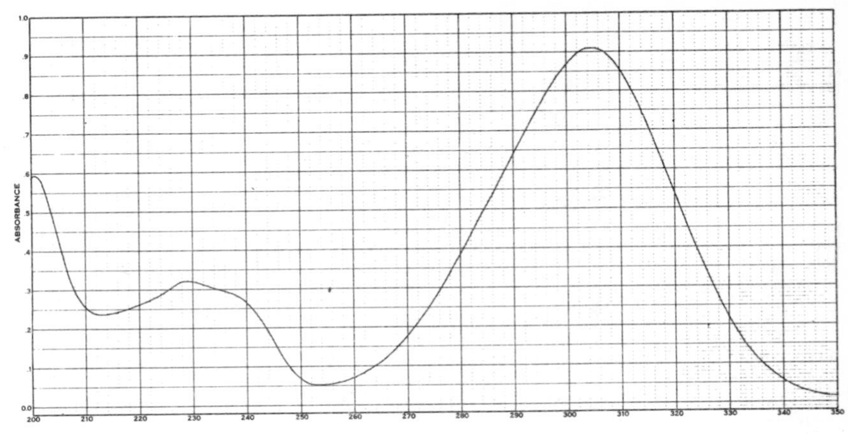

4'-METHOXYACETOPHENONE

2075

$C_9H_{10}O_2$

Mol. Wt. 150.18

M.P. 36°C

Solvent: Methanol

λ Max. mμ	a_m	Cell mm	Conc. g/L
270	16100	1	0.0800
217	11600	1	0.0800

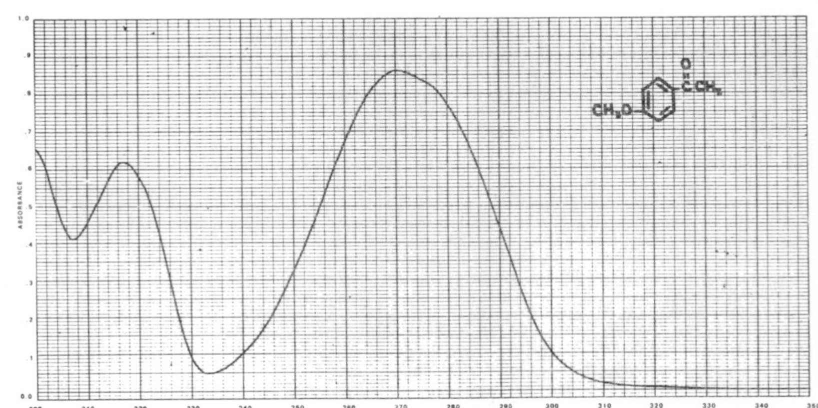

4'-ETHOXYACETOPHENONE

2076

$C_{10}H_{12}O_2$

Mol. Wt. 164.21

M.P. 33-36°C

Solvent: Methanol

λ Max. mμ	a_m	Cell mm	Conc. g/L
271.5	16300	1	0.068
217.5	11600	1	0.068

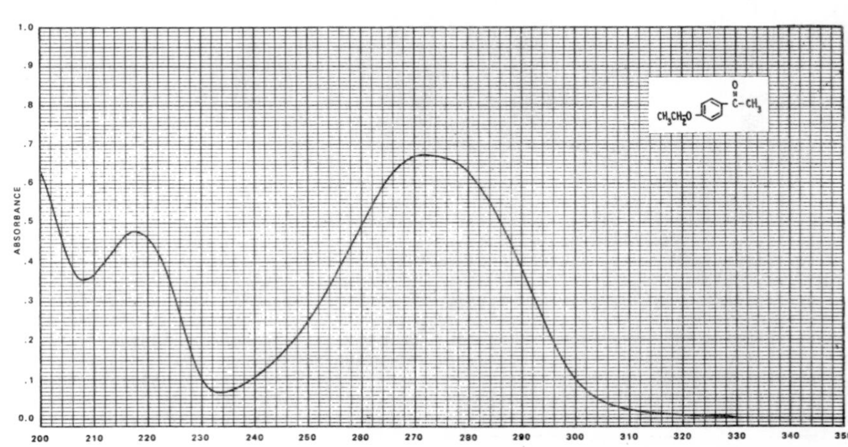

4'-METHOXYBUTYROPHENONE

2077

$C_{11}H_{14}O_2$

Mol. Wt. 178.23

Solvent: Methanol

λ Max. mμ	a_m	Cell mm	Conc. g/L
270	15600	10	0.0101
217	10600	10	0.0101

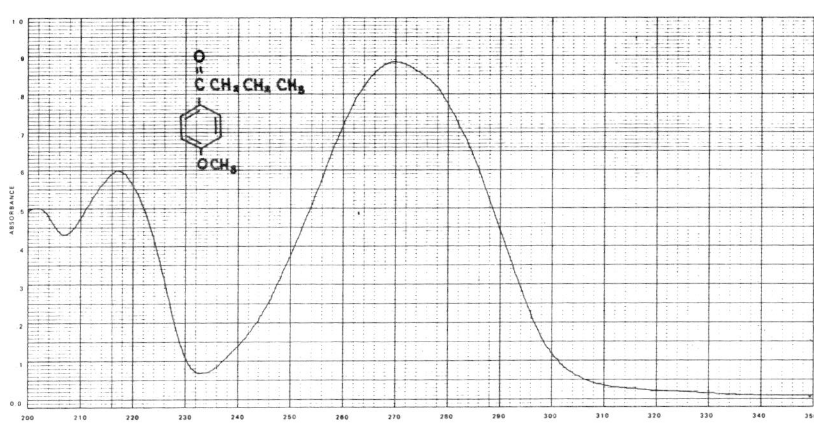

4'-HYDROXY-2'-METHYLACETOPHENONE

2078

$C_9H_{10}O_2$

MOl. Wt. 150.17

M.P. 123°C

Solvent: Methanol

λ Max. mμ	a_m	Cell mm	Conc. g/L
272	14300	10	0.010
221.5	9420	10	0.010
205	14800	10	0.010

λ Max. mμ	a_m	Cell mm	Conc. g/L

5'-CHLORO-2'-HYDROXYACETOPHENONE **2079**

$C_8H_7ClO_2$

Mol. Wt. 170.60

Solvent: Methanol

λ Max. mμ	a_m	Cell mm	Conc. g/L
336	4470	1	0.100
247	8480	1	0.100
218	30300	0.5	0.100

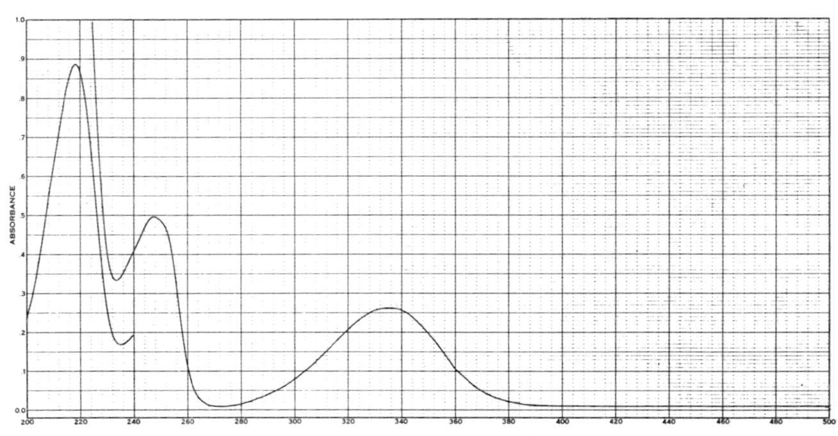

5'-CHLORO-2'-HYDROXYACETOPHENONE **2079**

$C_8H_7ClO_2$

Mol. Wt. 170.60

Solvent: Methanol KOH

λ Max. mμ	a_m	Cell mm	Conc. g/L
372	6590	1	0.100
255	9200	1	0.100
230	22100	0.5	0.100
x	x	0.5	0.100

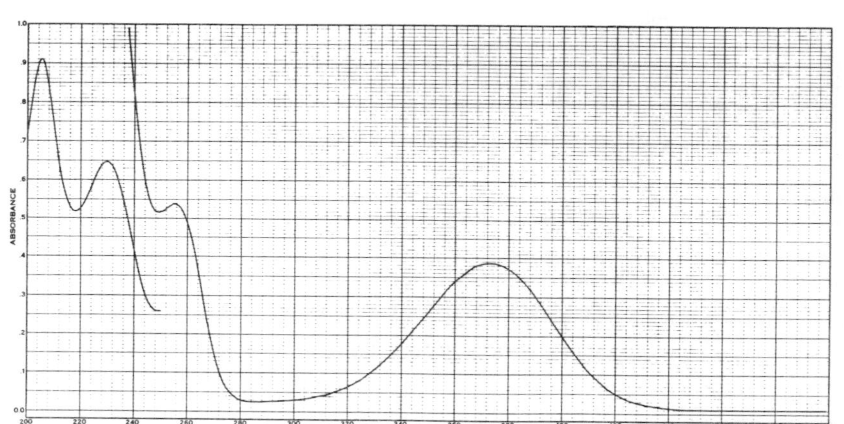

2',5'-DIHYDROXYACETOPHENONE **2080**

$C_8H_8O_3$

Mol. Wt. 152.15

Solvent: Methanol

λ Max. mμ	a_m	Cell mm	Conc. g/L
255	7000	10	0.016
227	15900	10	0.008

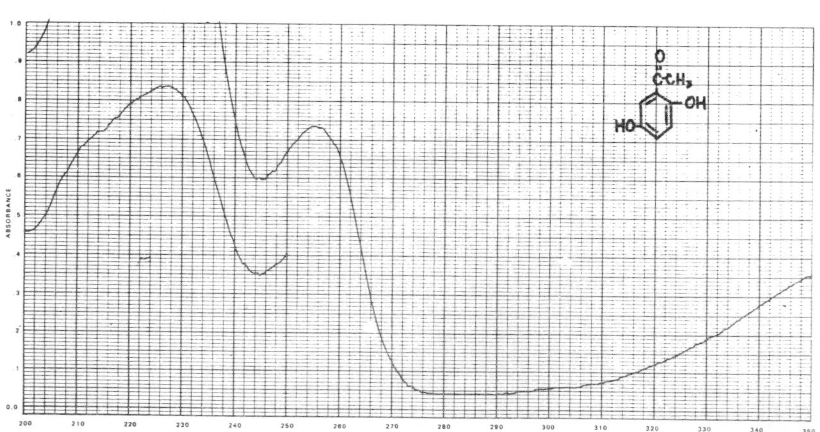

2',5'-DIHYDROXYACETOPHENONE

2080

$C_8H_8O_3$

Mol. Wt. 152.15

Solvent: Methanol KOH

λ Max. mμ	a_m	Cell mm	Conc. g/L
240.5	18200	1	0.0603

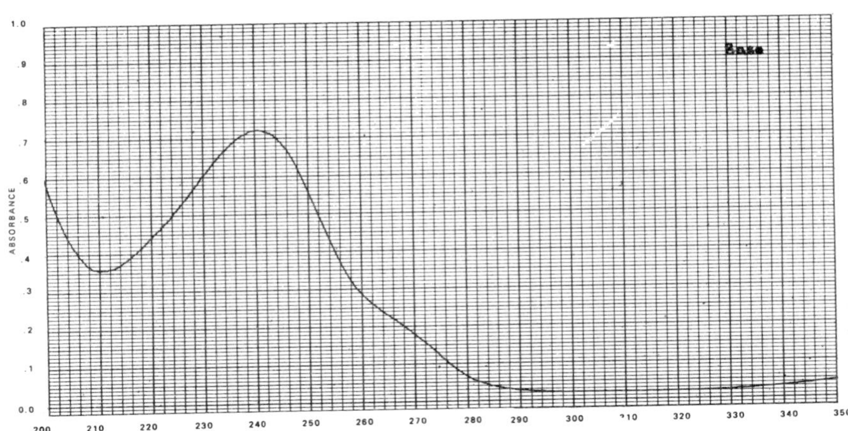

m-DIACETYLBENZENE

2081

$C_{10}H_{10}O_2$

Mol. Wt. 162.19

M.P. 31-32°C

Solvent: Methanol

λ Max. mμ	a_m	Cell mm	Conc. g/L
297	688	10	0.100
289	793	10	0.100
223	31000	1	0.0500

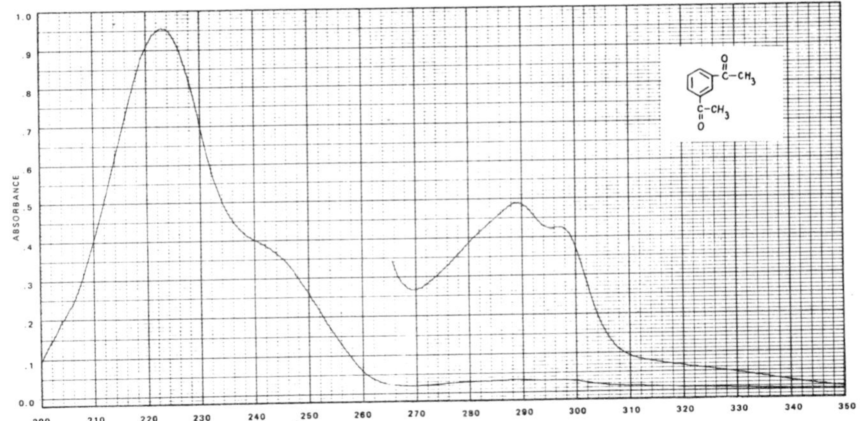

p-DIACETYLBENZENE

2082

$C_{10}H_{10}O_2$

Mol. Wt. 162.19

Solvent: Methanol

λ Max. mμ	a_m	Cell mm	Conc. g/L
295	1720	10	0.06
256	21100	10	0.006
203	14100	10	0.006

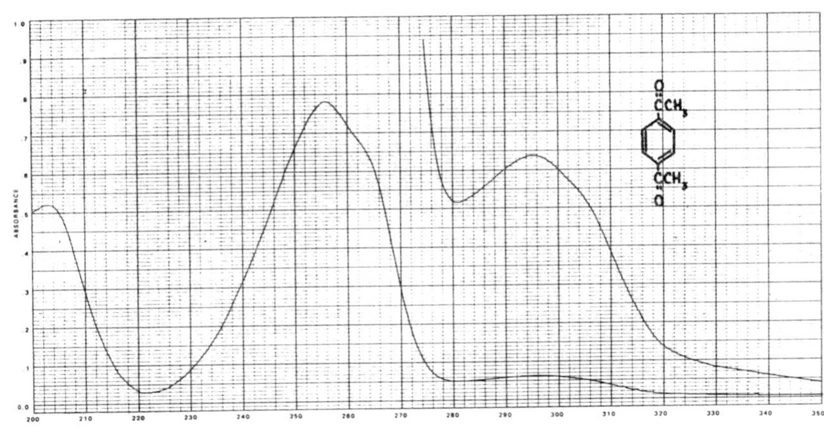

CYCLOPENTYL PHENYL KETONE

2083

$C_{12}H_{14}O$
Mol. Wt. 174.24
B.P. 166.5-167.5°C/2mm (lit.)
Solvent: Methanol

λ Max. mμ	a_m	Cell mm	Conc. g/L
277.5	990	10	0.100
241.5	1290	1	0.100
x	x	1	0.100

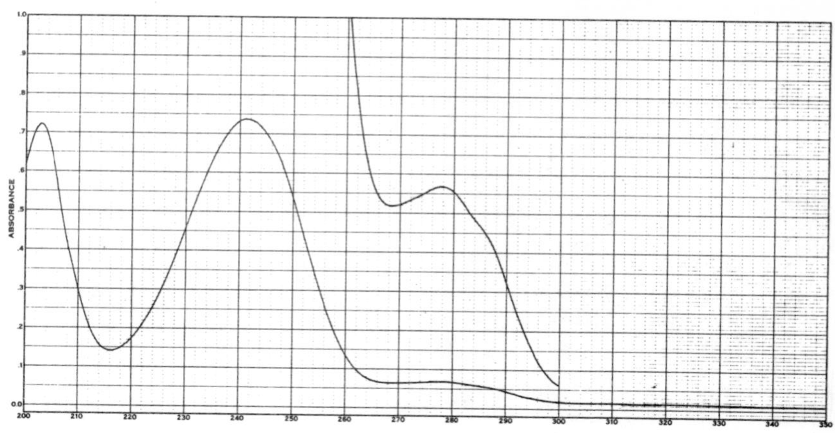

CYCLOHEXYL PHENYL KETONE

2084

$C_{13}H_{16}O$
Mol. Wt. 188.27
M.P. 55-57°C
Solvent: Methanol

λ Max. mμ	a_m	Cell mm	Conc. g/L
278	971	1	0.100
241.5	12100	1	0.100

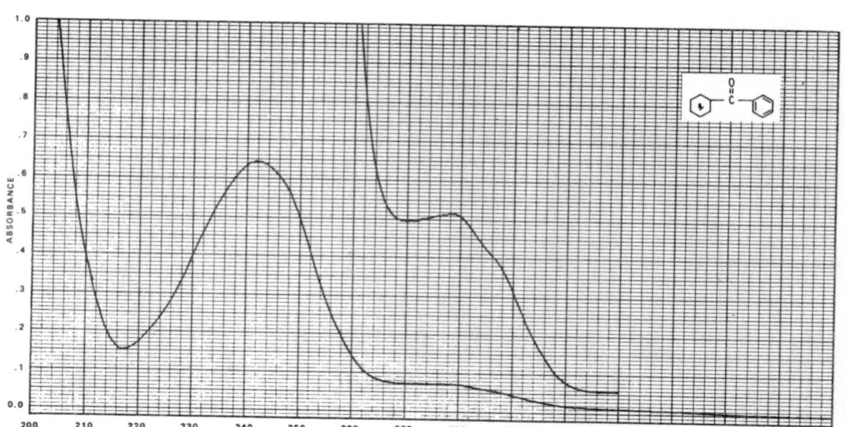

2-PHENYLACETOPHENONE

2085

$C_{14}H_{12}O$
Mol. Wt. 196.24
M.P. 55-56°C
Solvent: Methanol

λ Max. mμ	a_m	Cell mm	Conc. g/L
280	1170	10	0.100
272	1470	10	0.100
265.5	1370	10	0.100
227	16100	10	0.010

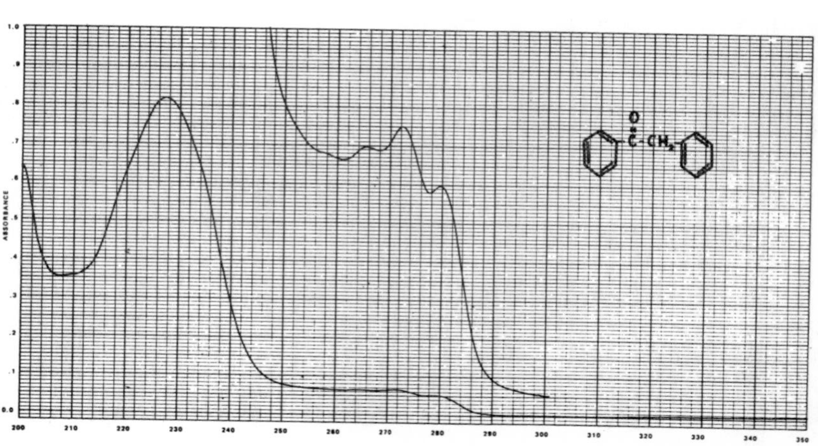

2-(p-CHLOROPHENYL)ACETOPHENONE

2086

$C_{14}H_{11}ClO$
Mol. Wt. 230.70
M.P. 134-136°C
Solvent: Methanol

λ Max. mμ	a_m	Cell mm	Conc. g/L
240	13600	1	0.100
218	11500	1	0.100

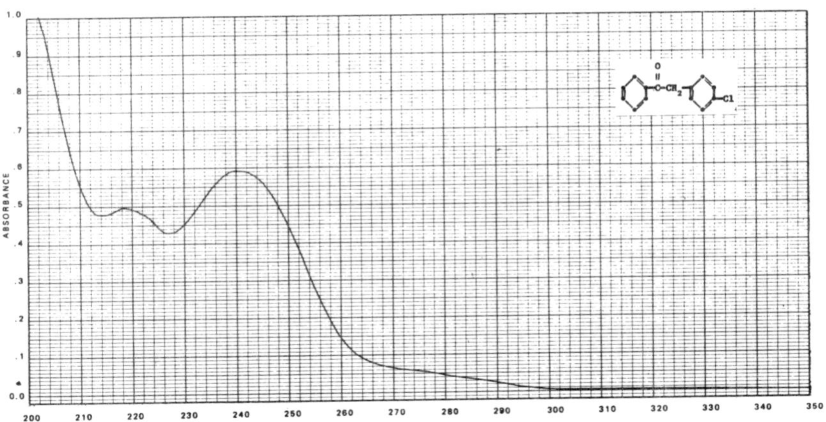

2-BROMO-2-PHENYLACETOPHENONE

2087

$C_{14}H_{11}BrO$
Mol. Wt. 275.15
M.P. 55-57°C
Solvent: Methanol

λ Max. mμ	a_m	Cell mm	Conc. g/L
250	12700	2	0.100

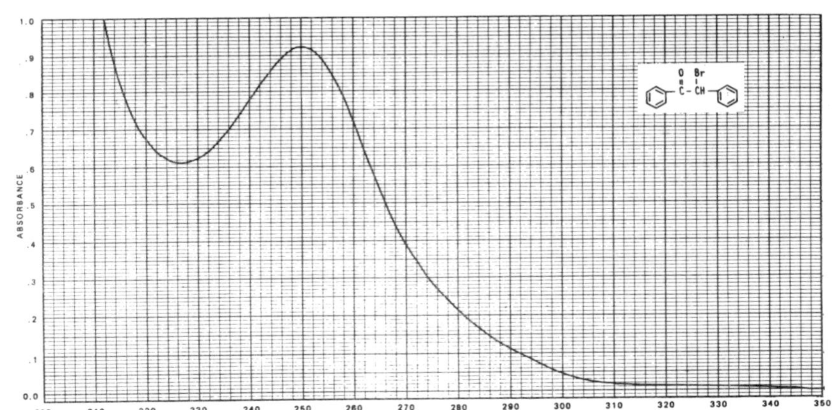

3-PHENYLPROPIOPHENONE

2088

$C_{15}H_{14}O$
Mol. Wt. 210.28
M.P. 69-71°C
Solvent: Methanol

λ Max. mμ	a_m	Cell mm	Conc. g/L
241	7760	2.0	0.100
x	x	1.0	0.100

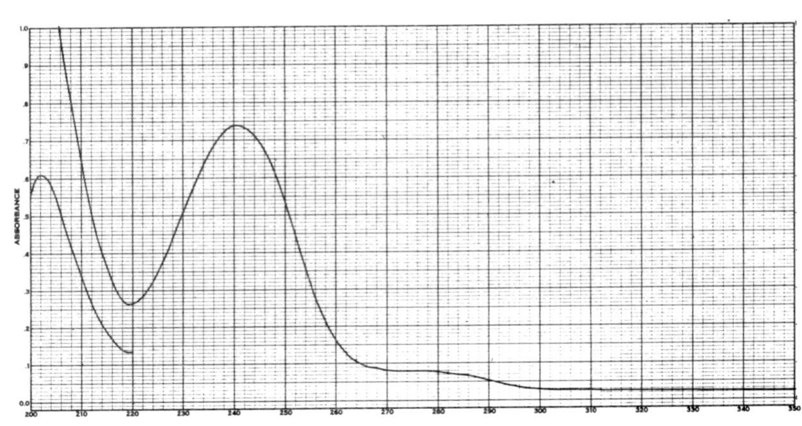

2-PHENOXYACETOPHENONE 2089

$C_{14}H_{12}O_2$
Mol. Wt. 212.25
M.P. 71-72°C (lit.)
Solvent: Methanol

λ Max. mμ	a_m	Cell mm	Conc. g/L
276	2420	5	0.100
243	13600	1	0.100

2-PHENOXYPROPIOPHENONE 2090

$C_{15}H_{14}O_2$
Mol. Wt. 226.28
M.P. 76°C (lit.)
Solvent: Methanol

λ Max. mμ	a_m	Cell mm	Conc. g/L
245	12400	1	0.100

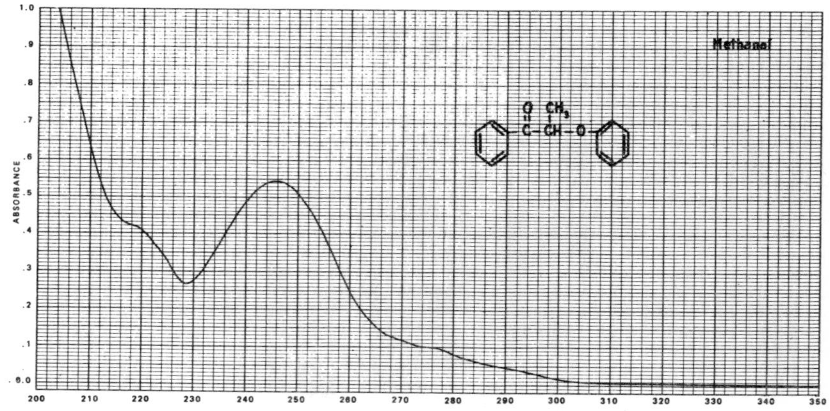

3-(2-FURYL)ACRYLOPHENONE 2091

$C_{13}H_{10}O_2$
Mol. Wt. 198.22
B.P. 178-181°C/8mm
Solvent: Methanol

λ Max. mμ	a_m	Cell mm	Conc. g/L
340	24800	1	0.0469
259	7610	2	0.0469
254	7610	2	0.0469

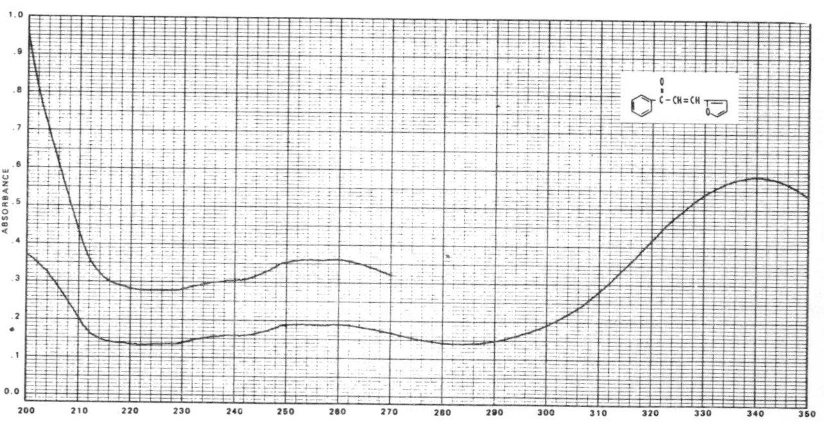

CHALCONE

$C_{15}H_{12}O$

Mol. Wt. 208.26

M.P. 62°C (lit.)

Solvent: Methanol

2092

λ Max. mμ	a_m	Cell mm	Conc. g/L
308	21600	1	0.0500
226	11800	1	0.0500

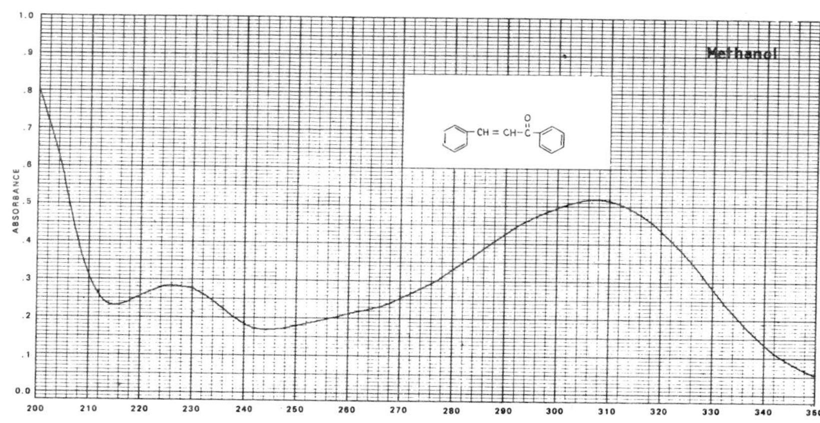

4'-METHYLCHALCONE

$C_{16}H_{14}O$

Mol. Wt. 222.29

Solvent: Methanol

2093

λ Max. mμ	a_m	Cell mm	Conc. g/L
310	25300	1	0.0800
226	10700	1	0.0800
219	10400	1	0.0800

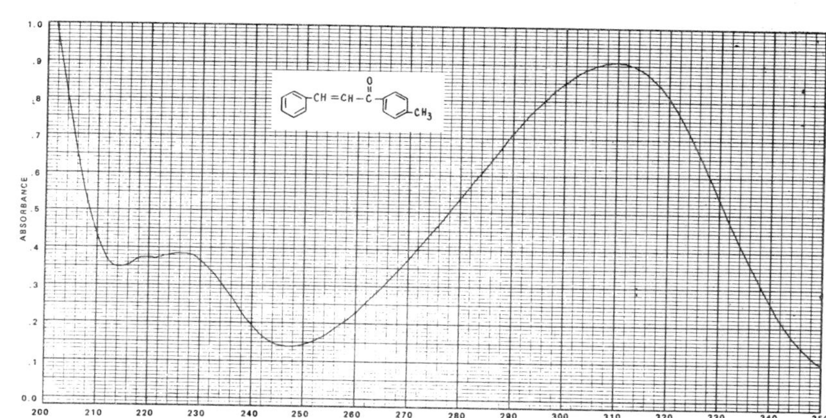

4'-BROMOCHALCONE

$C_{15}H_{11}BrO$

Mol. Wt. 287.16

M.P. 103-105°C

Solvent: methanol

2094

λ Max. mμ	a_m	Cell mm	Conc. g/L
310	20100	1	0.100
223	12400	1	0.100

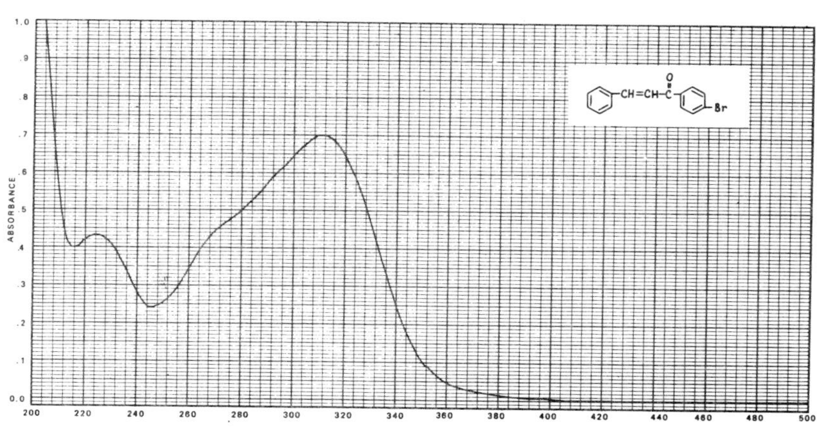

3-NITROCHALCONE

2095

$C_{15}H_{11}NO_3$
Mol. Wt. 253.26
Solvent: Methanol

λ Max. mμ	a_m	Cell mm	Conc. g/L
422	736	20	0.100
397	802	20	0.100
260	17700	1	0.100

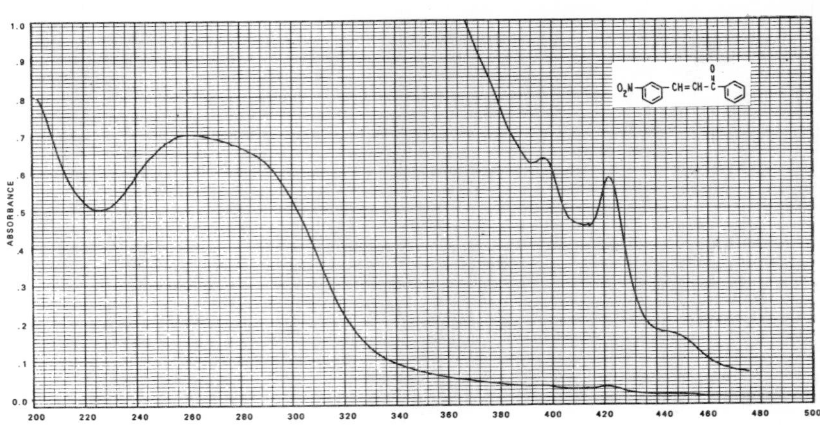

cis-4′-METHOXYCHALCONE

2096

$C_{16}H_{14}O_2$
Mol. Wt. 238.29
M.P. 104-106°C
Solvent: Methanol

λ Max. mμ	a_m	Cell mm	Conc. g/L
317	26900	0.5	0.100
227	11900	0.5	0.100

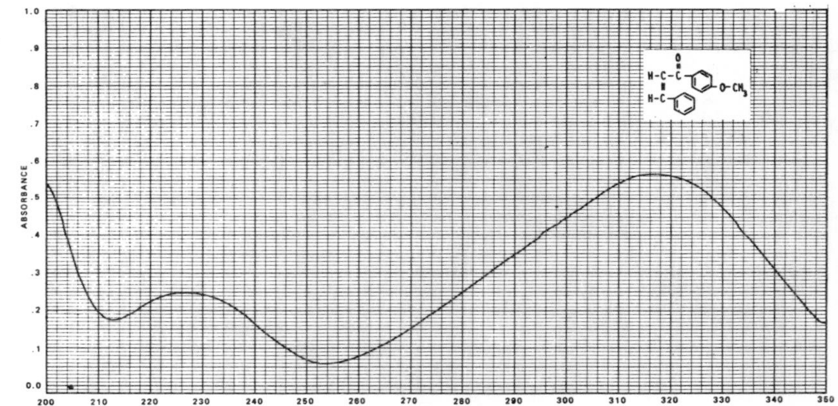

1,2-DIBENZOYLETHYLENE

2097

$C_{16}H_{12}O_2$
Mol. Wt. 236.25
Solvent: Cyclohexane

λ Max. mμ	a_m	Cell mm	Conc. g/L
x	x	10	2.00
266	23600	10	0.010

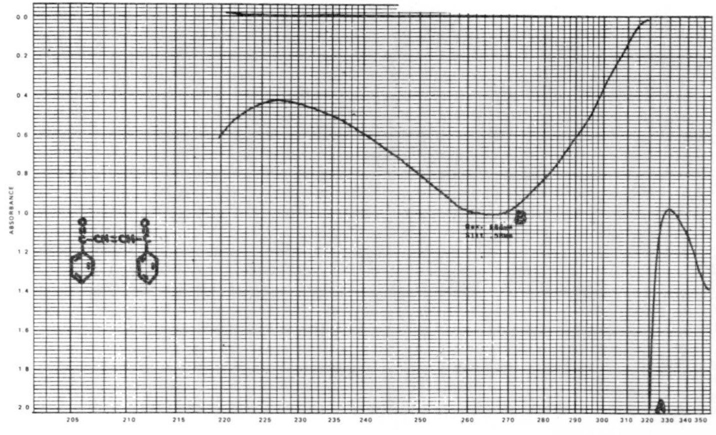

BENZOPHENONE 2098

$C_{13}H_{10}O$

Mol. Wt. 182.22

M.P. 47°C (lit.)

Solvent: Methanol

λ Max. mμ	a_m	Cell mm	Conc. g/L
330.5	167	20	0.100
252	18600	1	0.0500

2-METHYLBENZOPHENONE 2099

$C_{14}H_{12}O$

Mol. Wt. 196.25

Solvent: Methanol

λ Max. mμ	a_m	Cell mm	Conc. g/L
251	15600	1	0.097

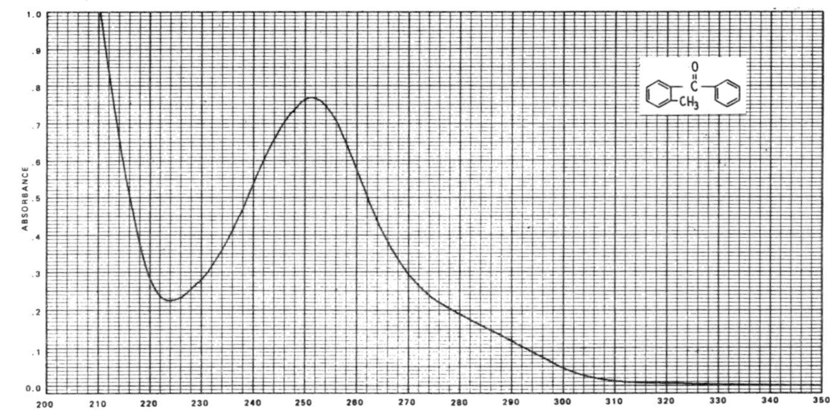

4-METHYLBENZOPHENONE 2100

$C_{14}H_{12}O$

Mol. Wt. 196.25

M.P. 55-57°C

Solvent: Methanol

λ Max. mμ	a_m	Cell mm	Conc. g/L
328	285	20	0.100
259	18300	1	0.100

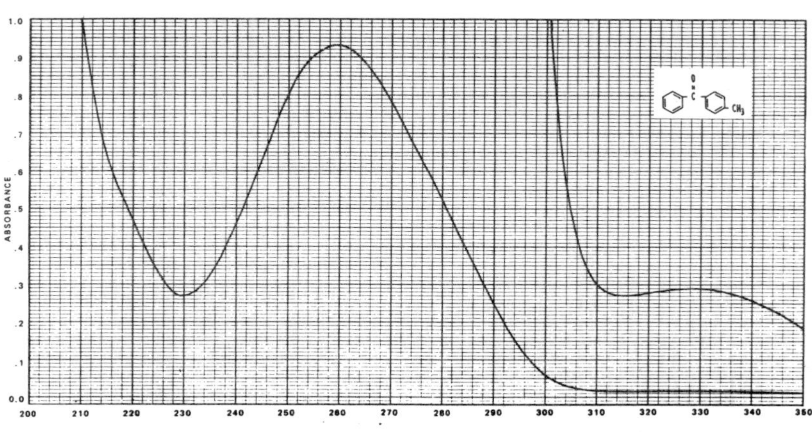

4,4′-DIMETHYLBENZOPHENONE

2101

$C_{15}H_{14}O$
Mol. Wt. 210.26
M.P. 95°C
Solvent: Methanol

λ Max. mμ	a_m	Cell mm	Conc. g/L
264	22100	10	0.008

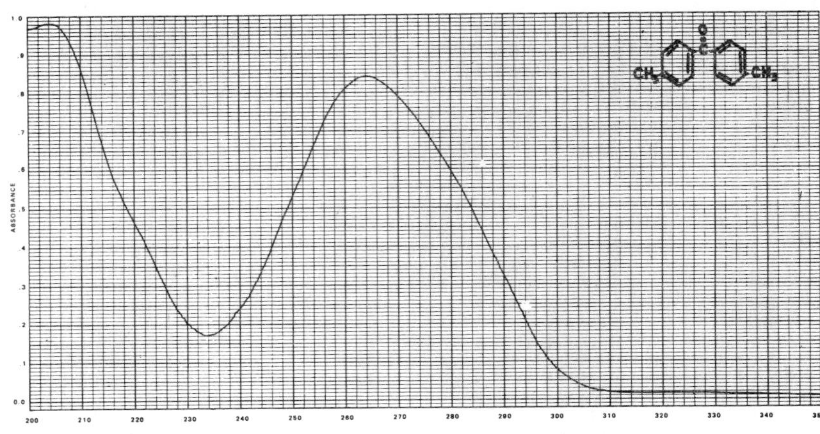

4-BROMOBENZOPHENONE

2102

$C_{13}H_9BrO$
Mol. Wt. 261.13
Solvent: Methanol

λ Max. mμ	a_m	Cell mm	Conc. g/L
261	20900	10	0.01

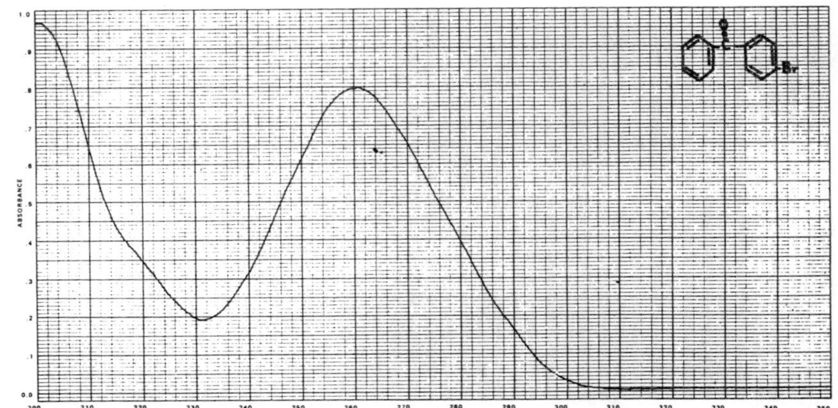

3-AMINOBENZOPHENONE

2103

$C_{13}H_{11}NO$
Mol. Wt. 197.24
Solvent: Methanol

λ Max. mμ	a_m	Cell mm	Conc. g/L
332	1630	10	0.100
237.5	23900	1	0.050

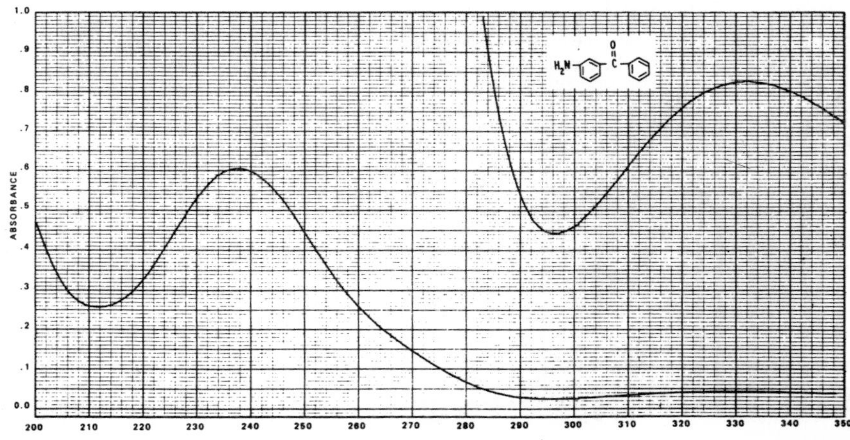

2103

3-AMINOBENZOPHENONE

$C_{13}H_{11}NO$
Mol. Wt. 197.24
Solvent: Methanol HCl

λ Max. mμ	a_m	Cell mm	Conc. g/L
243	14800	1	0.100

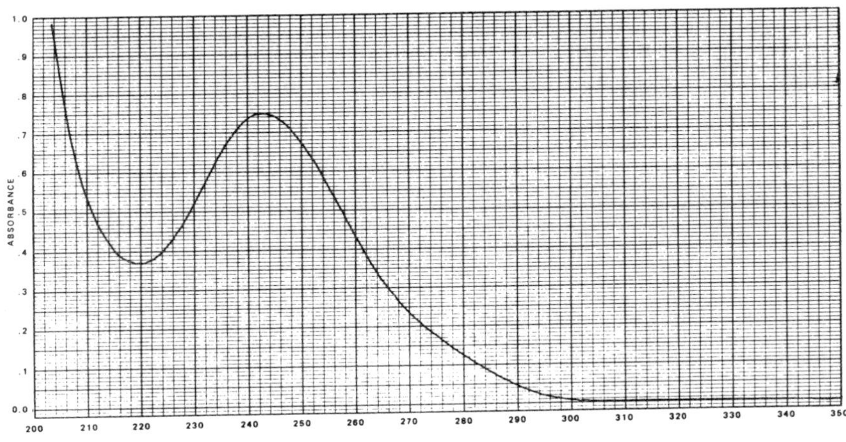

2104

4,4′-BIS(DIETHYLAMINO)BENZOPHENONE

$C_{21}H_{28}N_2O$
Mol. Wt. 324.47
M.P. 94.5-95°C
Solvent: Methanol

λ Max. mμ	a_m	Cell mm	Conc. g/L
378	36700	1	0.0800
248	13500	1	0.0800

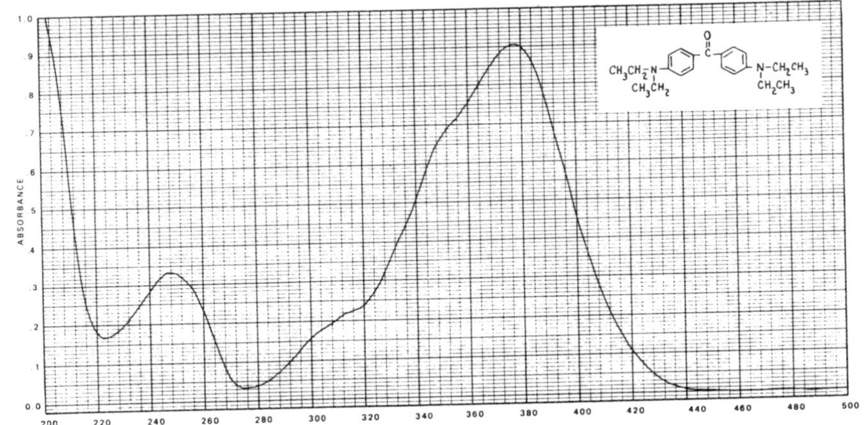

2104

4,4′-BIS(DIETHYLAMINO)BENZOPHENONE

$C_{21}H_{28}N_2O$
Mol. Wt. 324.47
M.P. 94.5-95°C
Solvent: Methanol HCl

λ Max. mμ	a_m	Cell mm	Conc. g/L
370	13000	2	0.100
244	13800	2	0.100

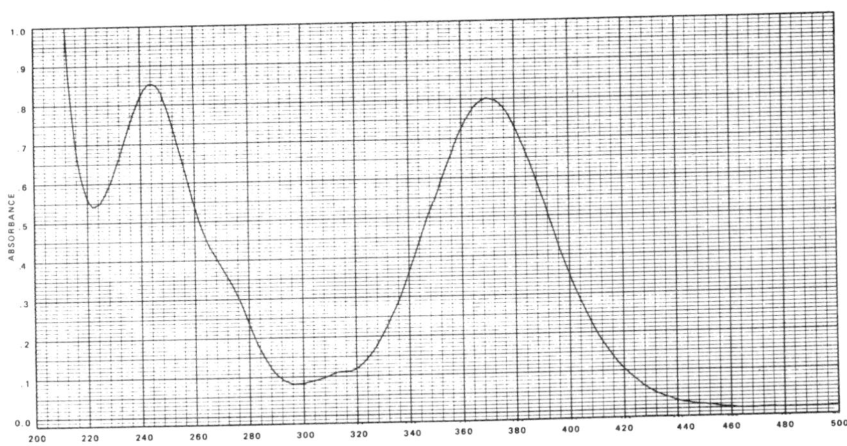

2105

2-HYDROXY-4'-METHYLBENZOPHENONE

$C_{14}H_{12}O_2$
Mol. Wt. 212.24
M.P. 40-41°C
Solvent: Methanol

λ Max. mμ	a_m	Cell mm	Conc. g/L
335	4880	10	0.010
265	13800	10	0.010

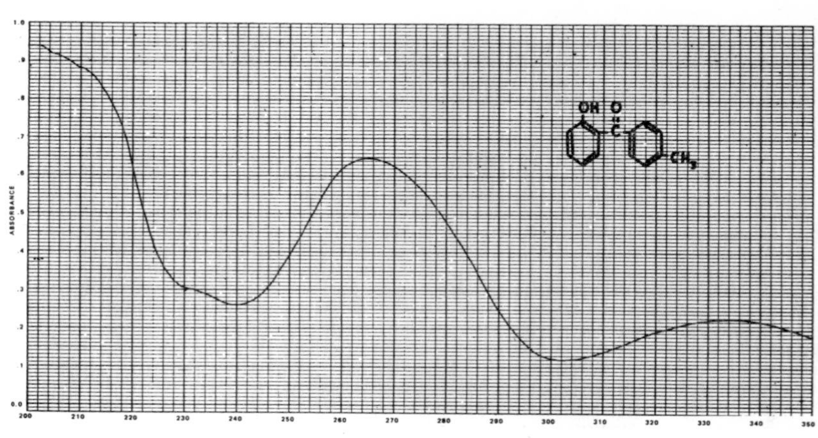

2106

m-DIBENZOYLBENZENE

$C_{20}H_{14}O_2$
Mol. Wt. 286.33
Solvent: Methanol

λ Max. mμ	a_m	Cell mm	Conc. g/L
252.5	33400	1	0.0500

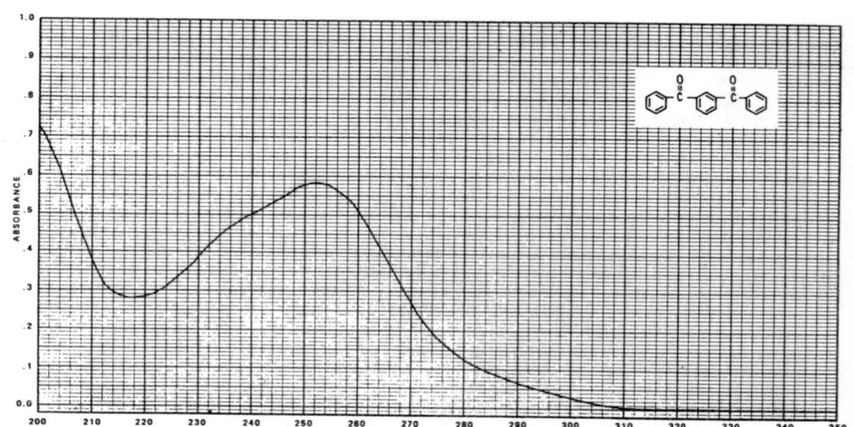

2107

p-DIBENZOYLBENZENE

$C_{20}H_{14}O_2$
Mol. Wt. 286.33
M.P. 158-159°C
Solvent: Methanol

λ Max. mμ	a_m	Cell mm	Conc. g/L
344	530	20	0.100
263	32400	1	0.0670

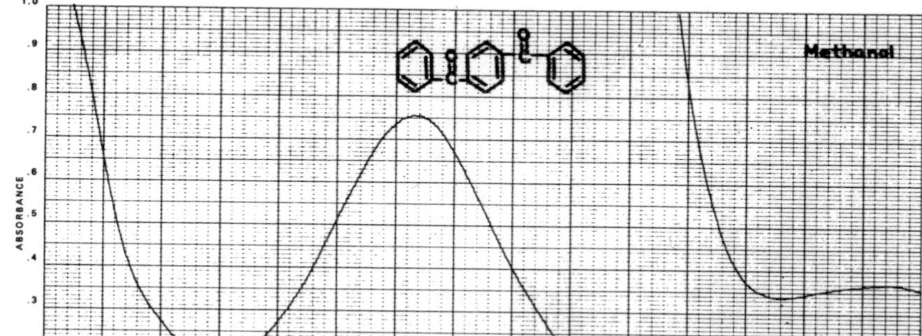

5-INDANYL METHYL KETONE

2108

$C_{11}H_{12}O$
Mol. Wt. 160.22
B.P. 132-136°C/7mm
Solvent: Methanol

λ Max. mμ	a_m	Cell mm	Conc. g/L
258	1240	1	0.5815
208	1990	1	0.5815

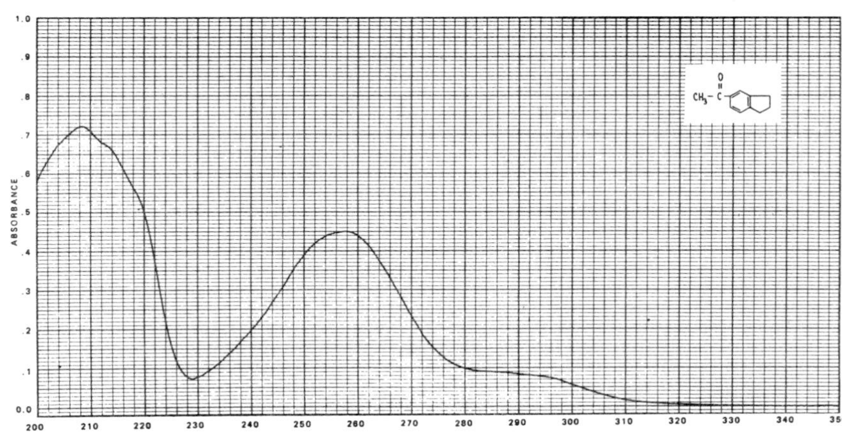

1,4-BENZODIOXAN-6-YL METHYL KETONE

2109

$C_{10}H_{10}O_3$
Mol. Wt. 178.19
Solvent: Methanol

λ Max. mμ	a_m	Cell mm	Conc. g/L
305	5650	1	0.100
272	10200	1	0.100
230	16100	1	0.100
209.5	15600	1	0.100

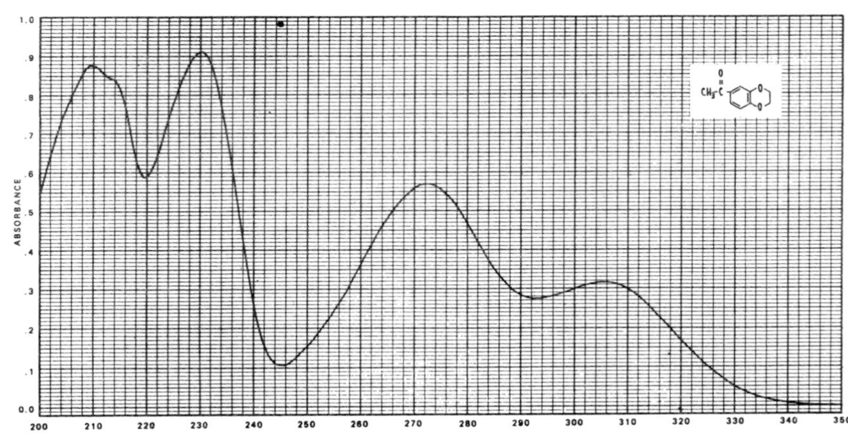

λ Max. mμ	a_m	Cell mm	Conc. g/L

METHYL 2-PYRIDYL KETONE

2110

C_7H_7NO

Mol. Wt. 121.14

Solvent: Methanol

λ Max. mμ	a_m	Cell mm	Conc. g/L
267.5	4130	1	0.130
228.5	7760	1	0.130

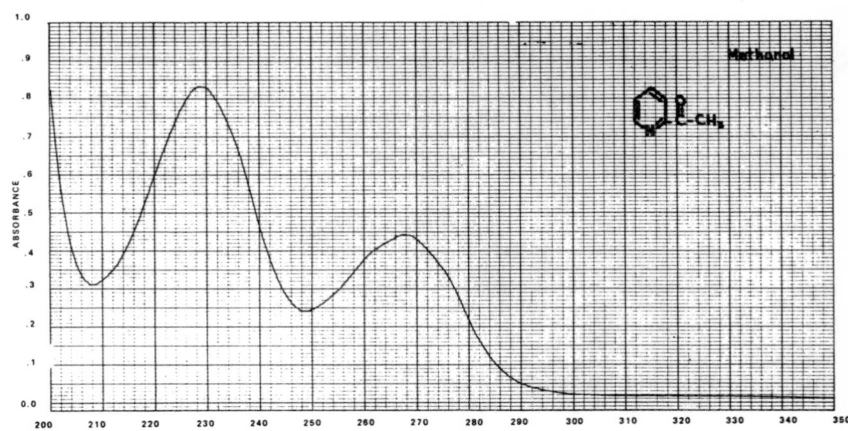

METHYL 2-PYRIDYL KETONE

2110

C_7H_7NO

Mol. Wt. 121.14

Solvent: Methanol HCl

λ Max. mμ	a_m	Cell mm	Conc. g/L
260.5	6090	1	0.130

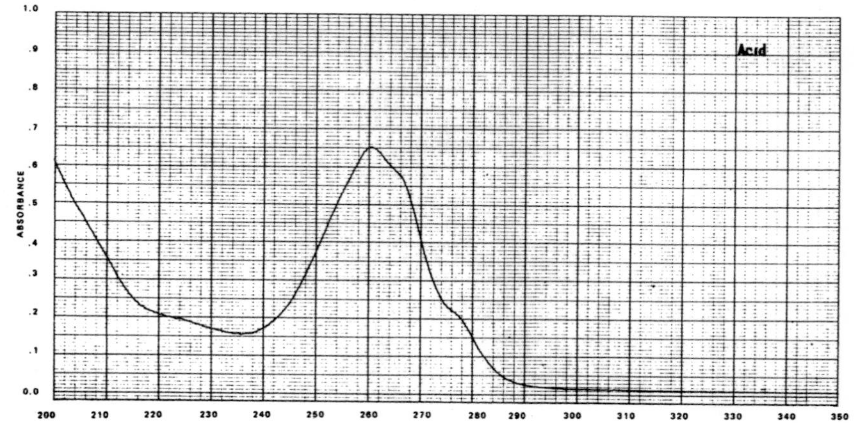

METHYL 6-METHYL-2-PYRIDYL KETONE

2111

C_8H_9NO

Mol. Wt. 135.17

Solvent: Methanol

λ Max. mμ	a_m	Cell mm	Conc. g/L
274	4440	2	0.100
231	5580	2	0.100

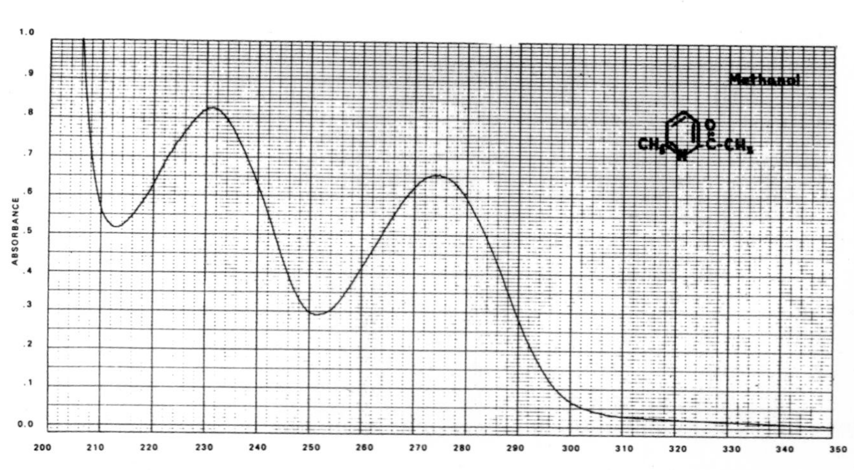

METHYL 6-METHYL-2-PYRIDYL KETONE

2111

C_8H_9NO
Mol. Wt. 135.17
Solvent: Methanol HCl

λ Max. mμ	a_m	Cell mm	Conc. g/L
270.5	7300	1	0.100

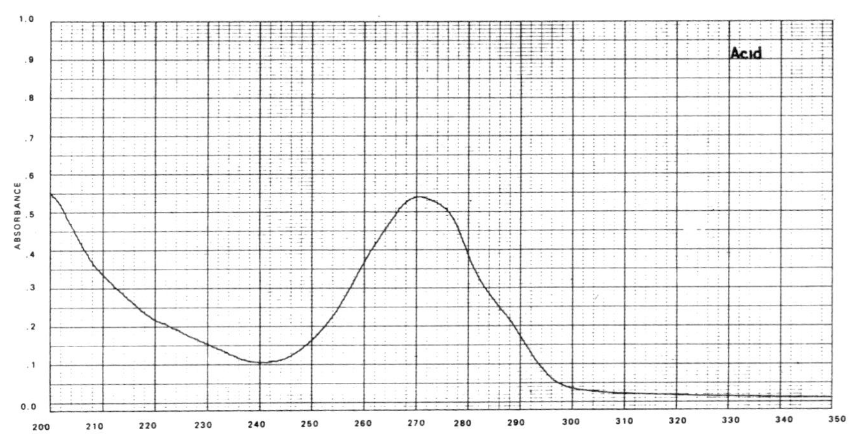

PHENYL 3-PYRIDYL KETONE

2112

$C_{12}H_9NO$
Mol. Wt. 183.21
Solvent: Methanol

λ Max. mμ	a_m	Cell mm	Conc. g/L
334	124	10	0.968
253	11400	10	0.010

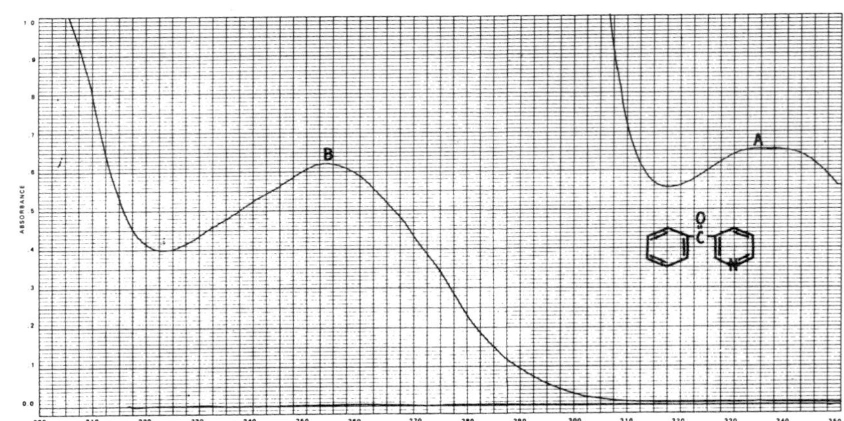

2'-ACETONAPHTHONE

2113

$C_{12}H_{10}O$
Mol. Wt. 170.21
Solvent: Methanol

λ Max. mμ	a_m	Cell mm	Conc. g/L
338.5	1680	5	0.100
290	8480	1	0.100
281.5	9530	1	0.100
246	50300	1	0.0200
207.5	21600	2	0.0200

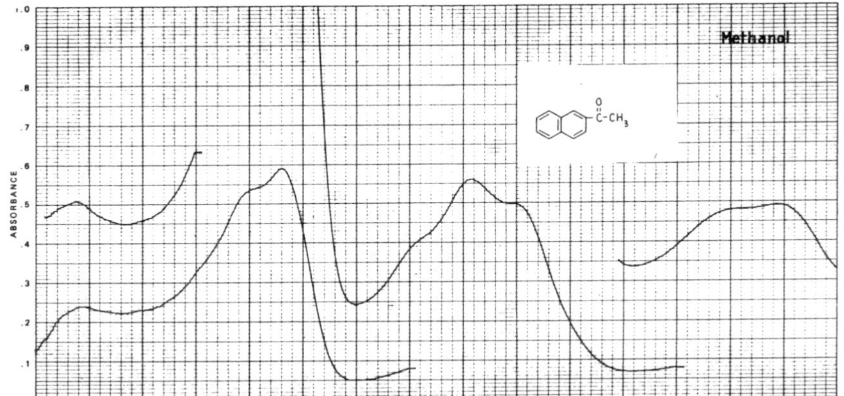

3,4-DIHYDRO-1(2H)-NAPHTHALENONE

2114

$C_{10}H_{10}O$
Mol. Wt. 146.19
Solvent: Methanol

λ Max. mμ	a_m	Cell mm	Conc. g/L
291	3490	2	0.100
245.5	15300	0.5	0.100
x	x	0.5	0.100

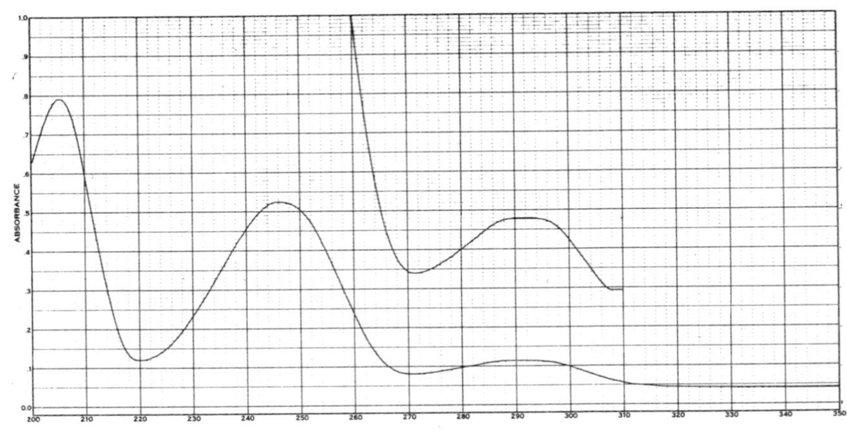

3,4-DIHYDRO-7-ETHYL-1(2H)-NAPHTHALENONE

2115

$C_{12}H_{14}O$
Mol. Wt. 174.24
B.P. 142-144°C/6mm
Solvent: Methanol

λ Max. mμ	a_m	Cell mm	Conc. g/L
301.5	2240	5	0.114
249.5	12500	1	0.114

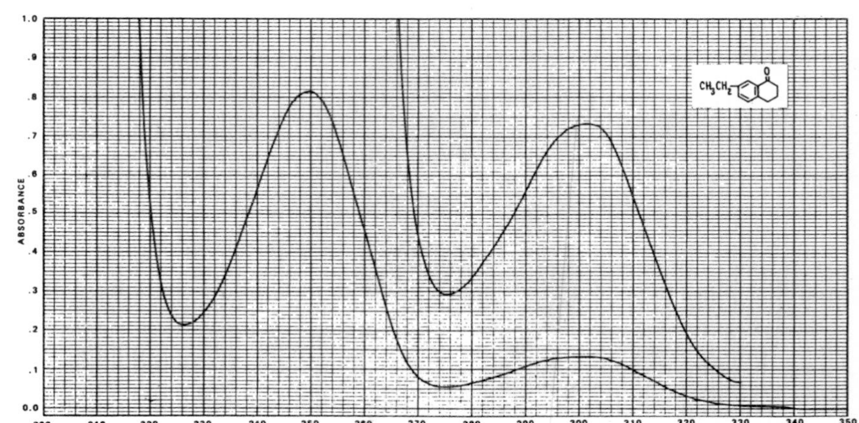

3,4-DIHYDRO-7-METHOXY-2(1H)-NAPHTHALENONE

2116

$C_{11}H_{12}O_2$
Mol. Wt. 176.22
Solvent: Methanol

λ Max. mμ	a_m	Cell mm	Conc. g/L
279.5	2520	5	0.1050
221	9370	5	0.1050

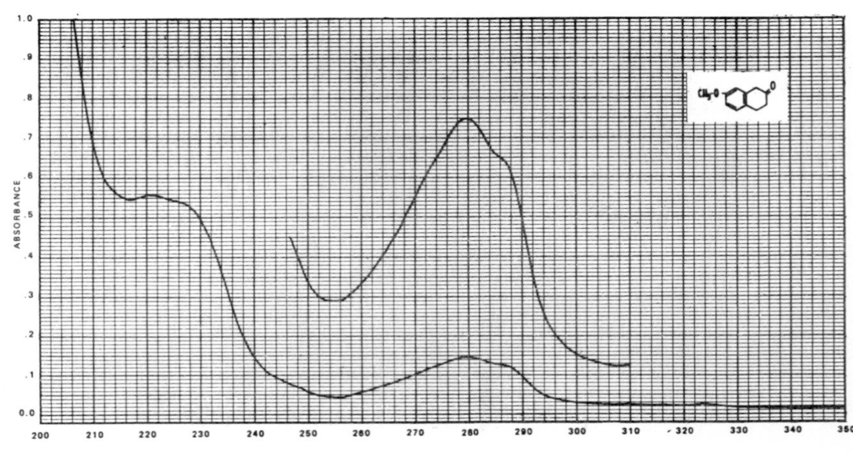

6-METHYL-4-CHROMANONE 2117

$C_{10}H_{10}O_2$
Mol. Wt. 162.19
M.P. 33-35°C
Solvent: Methanol

λ Max. mμ	a_m	Cell mm	Conc. g/L
253	8210	1	0.0640
317	21000	1	0.0640
331	3230	5	0.0640

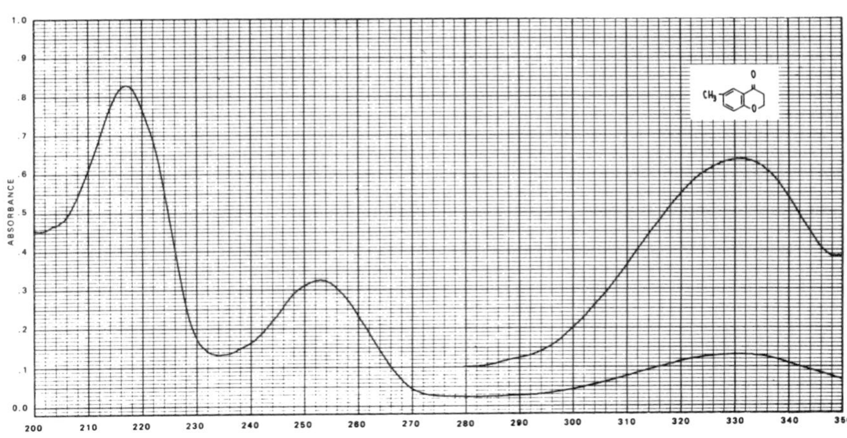

6-CHLORO-4-CHROMANONE 2118

$C_9H_7ClO_2$
Mol. Wt. 182.61
Solvent: Methanol

λ Max. mμ	a_m	Cell mm	Conc. g/L
330	3140	5	0.100
245	8110	0.5	0.100
218	25000	0.5	0.100

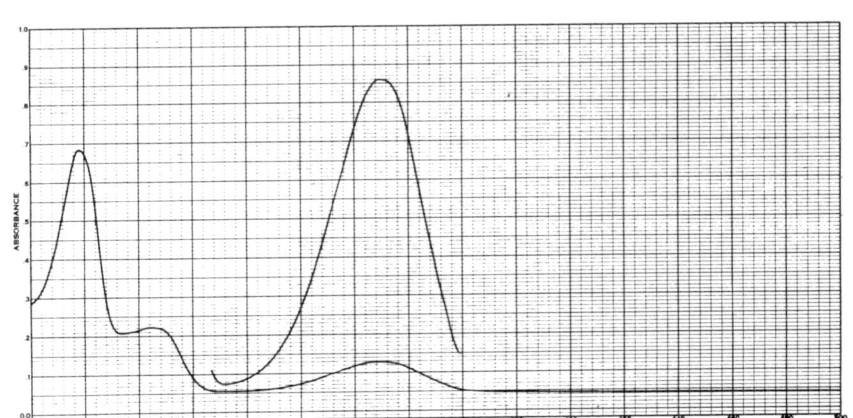

2-METHYL-1,4-NAPHTHOQUINONE 2119

$C_{11}H_8O_2$
Mol. Wt. 172.17
M.P. 107°C
Solvent: Cyclohexane

λ Max. mμ	a_m	Cell mm	Conc. g/L
329	2520	10	0.067
263.5	18000	10	0.013
253	20900	10	0.013
249	21100	10	0.013
242	20400	10	0.013
224.5	8080	10	0.013

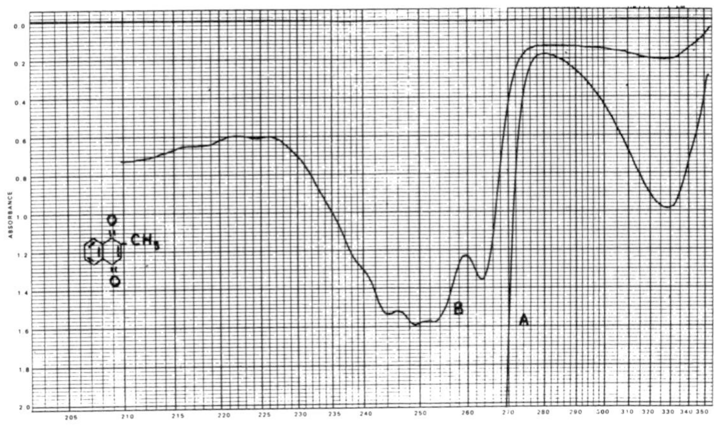

2-tert-BUTYL-1,4-NAPHTHOQUINONE 2120

$C_{14}H_{14}O_2$

Mol. Wt. 214.25

M.P. 73-76°C

Solvent: Methanol

λ Max. mμ	a_m	Cell mm	Conc. g/L
331	2730	10	0.05
264	14200	10	0.01
248	18600	10	0.01

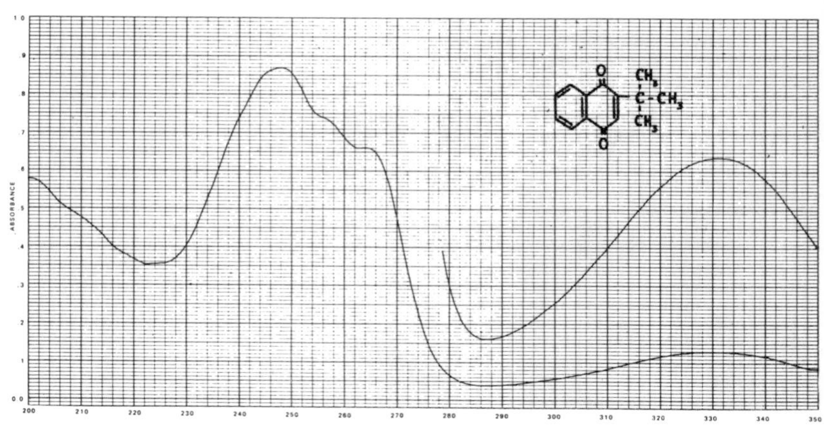

2-CYCLOHEXYL-1,4-NAPHTHOQUINONE 2121

$C_{16}H_{16}O_2$

Mol. Wt. 240.30

Solvent: Methanol

λ Max. mμ	a_m	Cell mm	Conc. g/L
332	2720	10	0.05
264	2900	10	0.05
251	3380	10	0.05
246	3450	10	0.05
210	2160	10	0.05

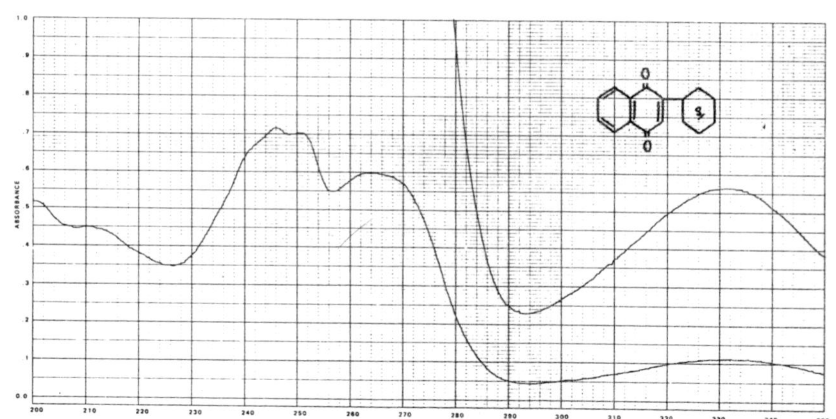

FLUOREN-9-ONE 2122

$C_{13}H_8O$

Mol. Wt. 180.19

Solvent: Methanol

λ Max. mμ	a_m	Cell mm	Conc. g/L
320	1160	10	0.202
305	1680	10	0.202
292	3190	10	0.081
255	9950	10	0.024
247	6160	10	0.024

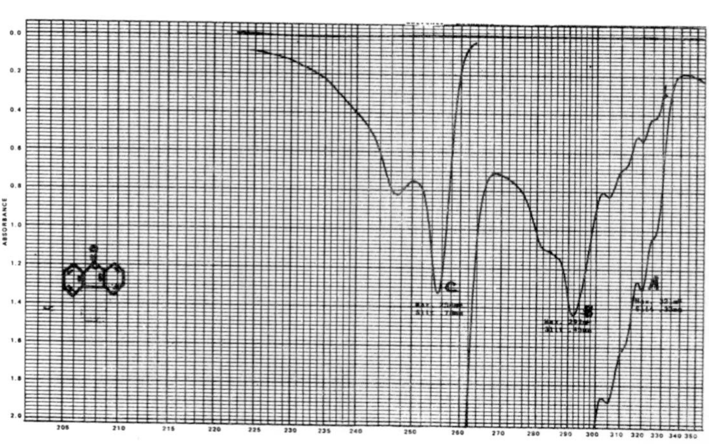

2-FLUOROFLUOREN-9-ONE

2123

$C_{13}H_7FO$

Mol. Wt. 198.20

Solvent: Methanol

λ Max. mμ	a_m	Cell mm	Conc. g/L
292.0	3770	5	0.0680
256.0	91700	1	0.0136
248.0	61800	1	0.0136
204	25800	1	0.0136

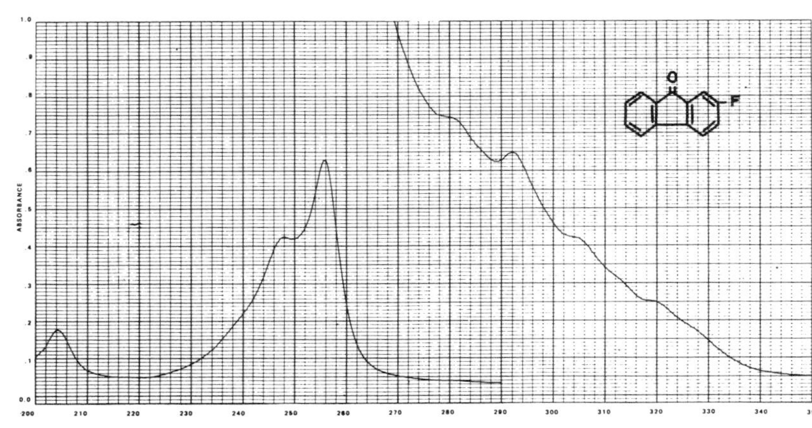

ANTHRONE

2124

$C_{14}H_{10}O$

Mol. Wt. 194.24

M.P. 154-155°C

Solvent: Dioxane

λ Max. mμ	a_m	Cell mm	Conc. g/L
307	5750	2	0.100
263	29800	1	0.0500

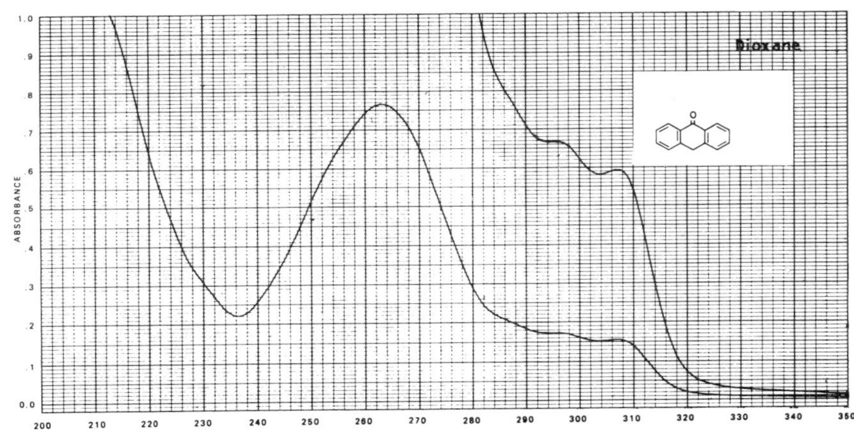

5H-DIBENZO[a,d] CYCLOHEPTEN-5-ONE

2125

$C_{15}H_{10}O$

Mol. Wt. 206.24

M.P. 88-89°C

Solvent: Methanol

λ Max. mμ	a_m	Cell mm	Conc. g/L
306.5	12300	1	0.0500
254.5	37500	1	0.0500

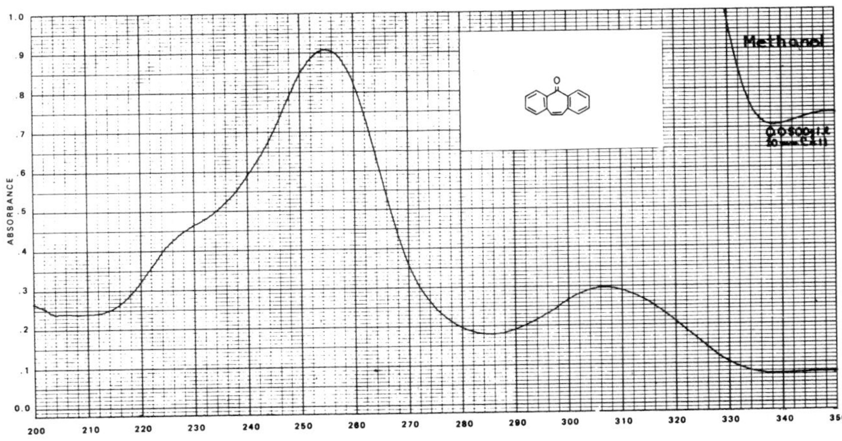

2-METHYLANTHRAQUINONE

2126

$C_{15}H_{10}O_2$
Mol. Wt. 222.23
M.R. 174-176°C (lit.)
Solvent: Methanol

λ Max. mμ	a_m	Cell mm	Conc. g/L
x	x	10	0.200
325	5000	10	0.04
273	17200	10	0.004
254.5	50600	10	0.004

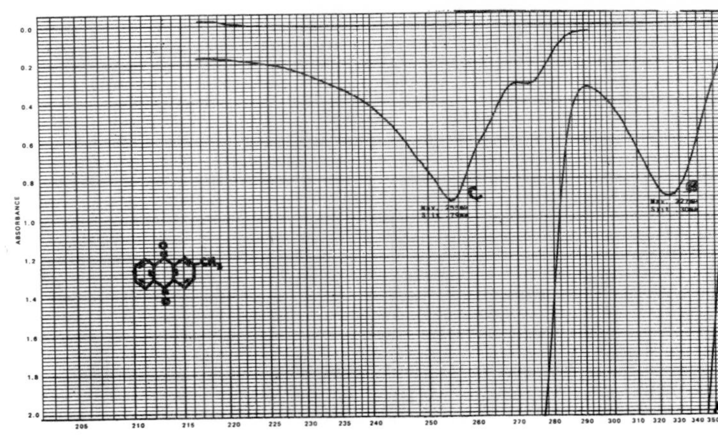

1,4-DIMETHYLANTHRAQUINONE

2127

$C_{16}H_{12}O_2$
Mol. Wt. 236.27
M.P. 133-135°C
Solvent: Methanol

λ Max. mμ	a_m	Cell mm	Conc. g/L
253	26100	1	0.0500

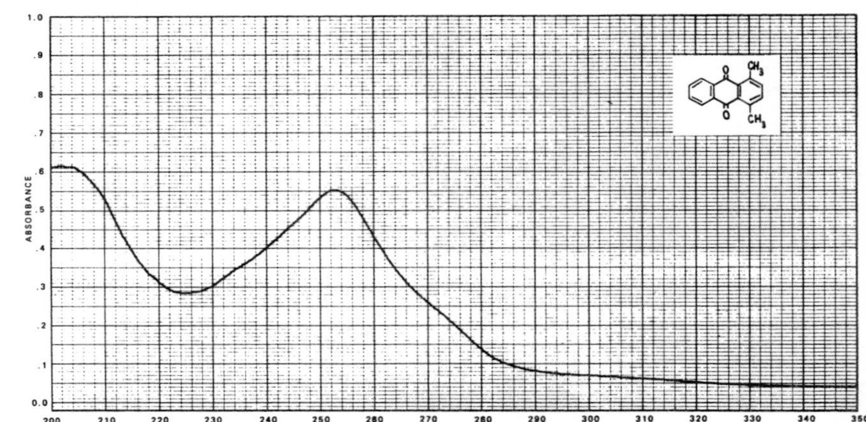

2,3-DIMETHYLANTHRAQUINONE

2128

$C_{16}H_{12}O_2$
Mol. Wt. 236.27
Solvent: Methanol

λ Max. mμ	a_m	Cell mm	Conc. g/L
329.5	2470	2	0.100
258	15400	1	0.100
x	x	1	0.100

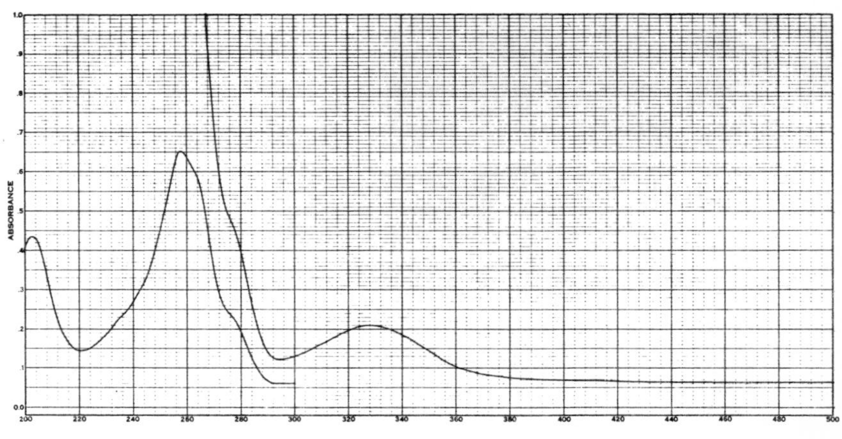

3β-HYDROXYANDROST-5-EN-17-ONE 2129

$C_{19}H_{28}O_2$
Mol. Wt. 288.43
M.P. 140-141°C (Lit.)

λ Max. mμ	a_m	Cell mm	Conc. g/L

Pure sample not available.

CHOLEST-4-EN-3-ONE 2130

$C_{27}N_{44}O$
Mol. Wt. 384.65
M.P. 77-79°C
Solvent: Methanol

λ Max. mμ	a_m	Cell mm	Conc. g/L
303	885	10	1.00
241	16300	2	0.100

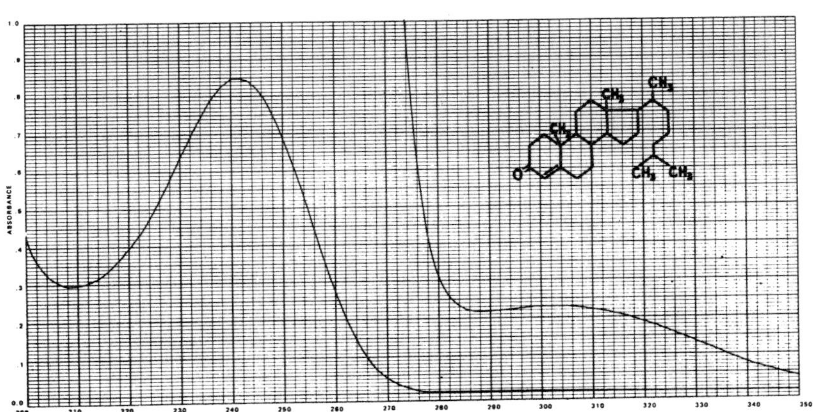

λ Max. mμ	a_m	Cell mm	Conc. g/L

NOTES

α-DIKETONES

Non-Aromatic Compounds

The non-aromatic α-diketones such as biacetyl are reported to exhibit a weak $n \rightarrow \pi^*$ band with fine structure near 450 mμ (ϵ = 20) in non-polar solvents.

In methanol solution a band or shoulder is seen about 268 mμ with diminished structural character (spectra 2131, 2132 and 2133).

Aromatic Compounds

The major band of benzil absorbs at slightly longer wavelength but with comparable intensity to that of benzophenone; Benzil -- 259 mμ (20500), Benzophenone -- 252 mμ (18600).

The UV spectra of the α-diketones do not show any significant changes upon the addition of either acid or base.

THE β-DIKETONES

The enol character of the β-diketones produces a shift to longer wavelength of both the $\pi \rightarrow \pi^*$ band of the ethylenic linkage (190 mμ) and the $n \rightarrow \pi^*$ band of the carbonyl group (275 mμ), resulting in UV spectra with one major band near 236 mμ and another in the region from 270 - 380 mμ (spectra 2141, 2144 and 2145).

Upon the addition of base, the major band undergoes a bathochromic shift to longer wavelength of about 30 mμ with a twofold increase in intensity (spectra 2145 and 2146).

2,3-PENTANEDIONE

2131

$C_5H_8O_2$
Mol. Wt. 100.12
B.P. 107-109°C
Solvent: Methanol

λ Max. mμ	a_m	Cell mm	Conc. g/L
268	401	20	0.100
x	x	20	0.100

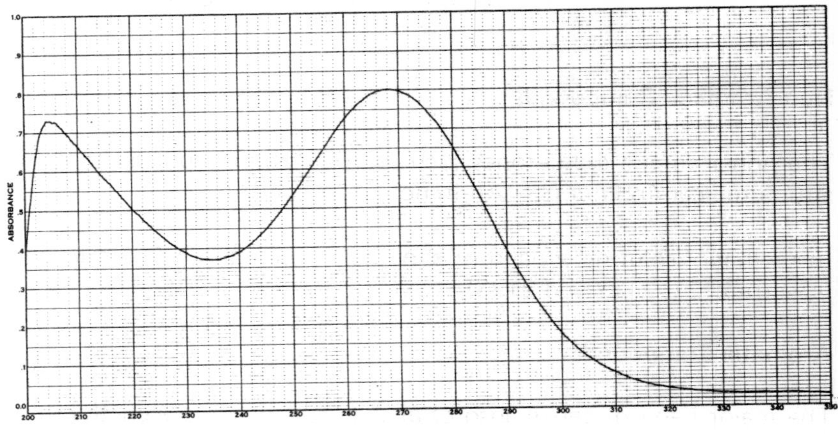

D-2,3-BORNANEDIONE

2132

$C_{10}H_{14}O_2$
Mol. Wt. 166.22
Solvent: Methanol

λ Max. mμ	a_m	Cell mm	Conc. g/L
x	x	10	0.100
x	x	40	0.100

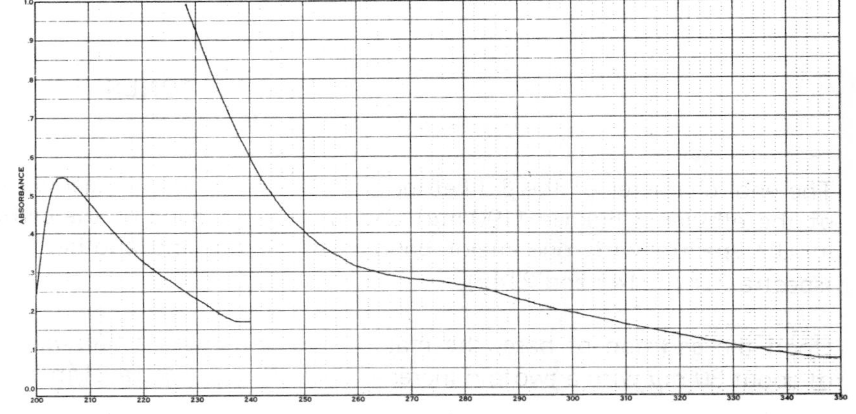

FURIL

2133

$C_{10}H_6O_4$
Mol. Wt. 190.15
Solvent: Methanol

λ Max. mμ	a_m	Cell mm	Conc. g/L
268.5	9530	1	0.100
212	1570	1	0.100
209.5	15700	1	0.100

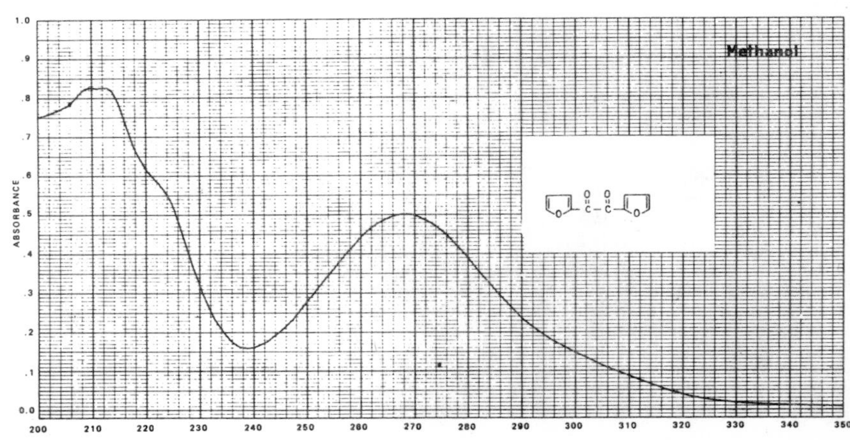

BENZIL

2134

$C_{14}H_{10}O_2$
Mol. Wt. 210.23
Solvent: Methanol

λ Max. mμ	a_m	Cell mm	Conc. g/L
259	20500	1	0.0500

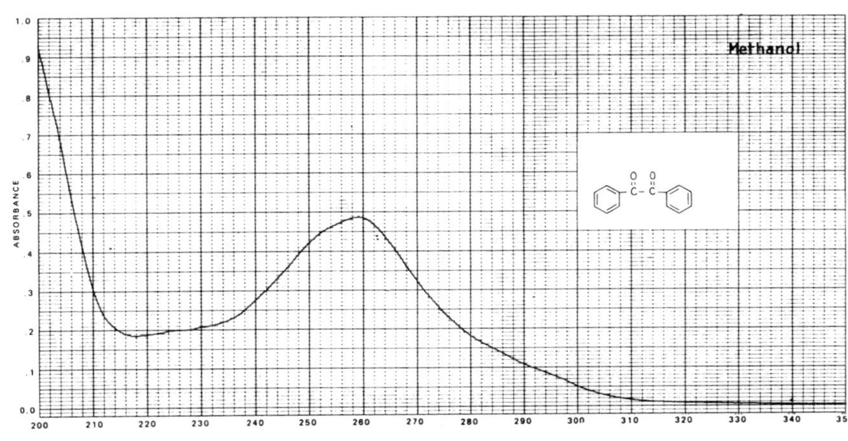

p-ANISIL

2135

$C_{16}H_{14}O_4$
Mol. Wt. 270.29
M.P. 131-132°C
Solvent: Methanol

λ Max. mμ	a_m	Cell mm	Conc. g/L
298	31400	1	0.0500
221	18500	1	0.0500

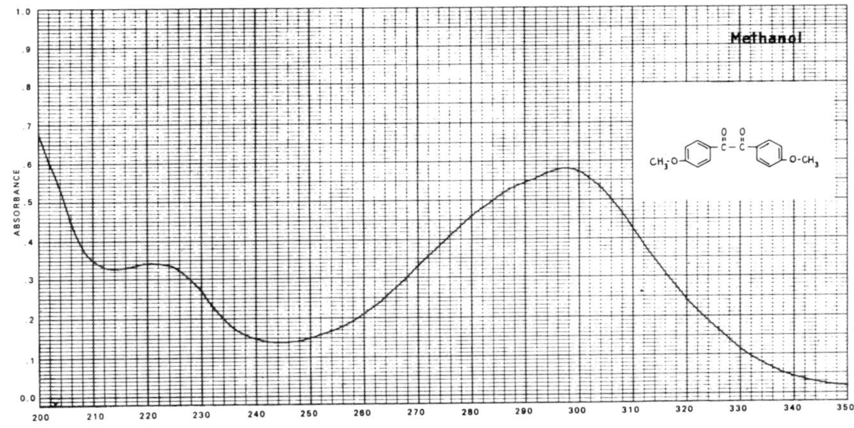

ACENAPHTHENEQUINONE

2136

$C_{12}H_6O_2$
Mol. Wt. 182.18
Solvent: Methanol

λ Max. mμ	a_m	Cell mm	Conc. g/L
337	2800	10	0.02
310.5	5820	10	0.02
301	6050	10	0.02
225	48000	10	0.003
219	46200	10	0.003

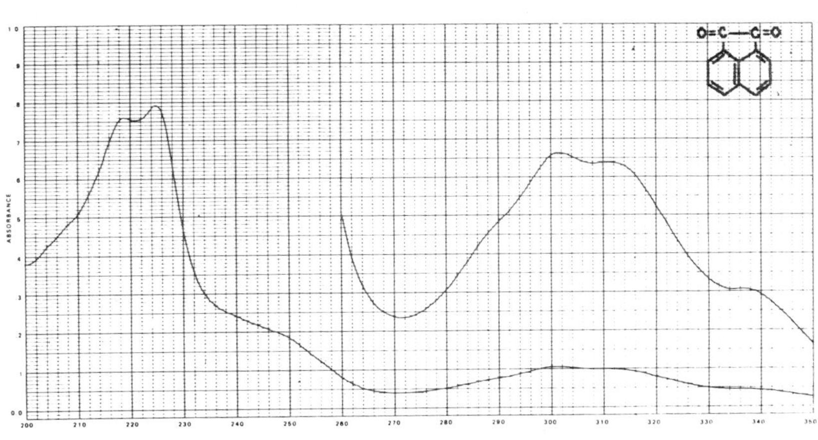

3-ETHYL-2,4-PENTANEDIONE 2137

$C_7H_{12}O_2$
Mol. Wt. 128.17

λ Max. mμ	a_m	Cell mm	Conc. g/L

Pure sample not available.

3,5-HEPTANEDIONE 2138

$C_7H_{12}O_2$
Mol. Wt. 128.17
B.P. 46-48°C/6mm

λ Max. mμ	a_m	Cell mm	Conc. g/L

Pure sample not available.

4,6-NONANEDIONE 2139

$C_9H_{16}O_2$
Mol. Wt. 156.23
B.P. 79-80°C/8mm

λ Max. mμ	a_m	Cell mm	Conc. g/L

Pure sample not available.

3-ISOBUTYL-2,4-PENTANEDIONE 2140

$C_9H_{16}O_2$
Mol. Wt. 156.23

λ Max. mμ	a_m	Cell mm	Conc. g/L

Pure sample not available.

1-(2-FURYL)-1,3-BUTANEDIONE 2141

$C_8H_8O_3$
Mol. Wt. 152.15
Solvent: Methanol

λ Max. mμ	a_m	Cell mm	Conc. g/L
321	876	5	0.100
236	1880	5	0.100

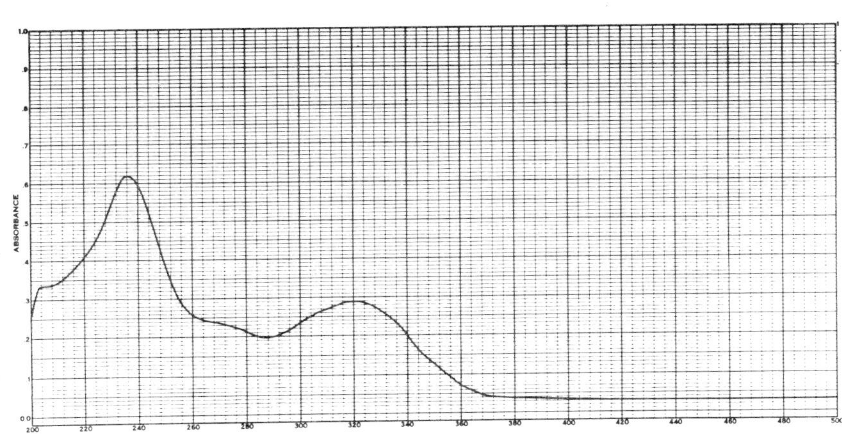

2,2,4,4-TETRAMETHYL-1,3-CYCLOBUTANEDIONE 2142

$C_8H_{12}O_2$
Mol. Wt. 140.18
Solvent: Methanol

λ Max. mμ	a_m	Cell mm	Conc. g/L
341.5	21.2	20	0.50
303	33.1	20	0.50
282	25.5	20	0.50
226	163	10	0.50

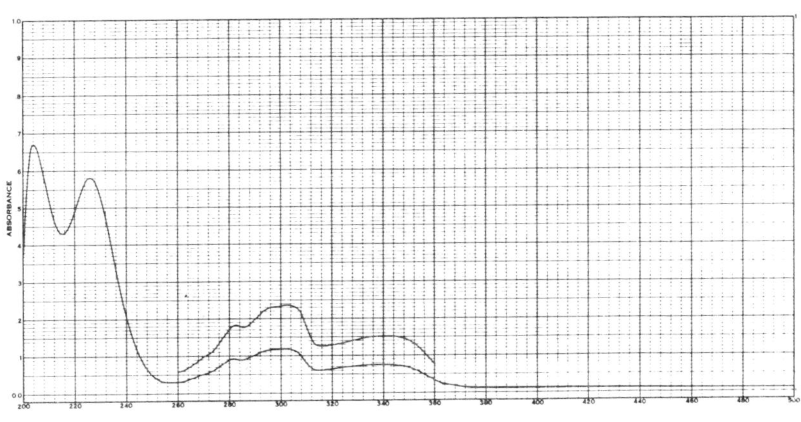

2-ACETYLCYCLOPENTANONE

2143

$C_7H_{10}O_2$

Mol. Wt. 126.16

Solvent: Cyclohexane

λ Max. mμ	a_m	Cell mm	Conc. g/L
283.5	7600	0.5	0.25

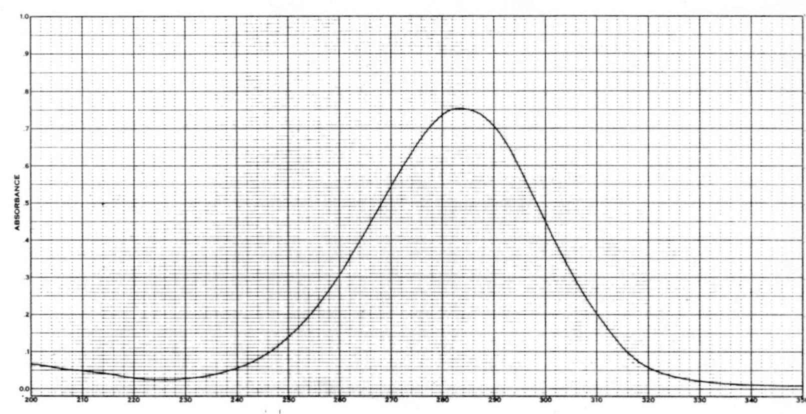

5,5-DIMETHYL-1,3-CYCLOHEXANEDIONE

2144

$C_8H_{12}O_2$

Mol. Wt. 140.18

M.R. 146-148°C (lit.)

Solvent: Methanol

λ Max. mμ	a_m	Cell mm	Conc. g/L
x	x	10	2.00
256	14000	10	0.016

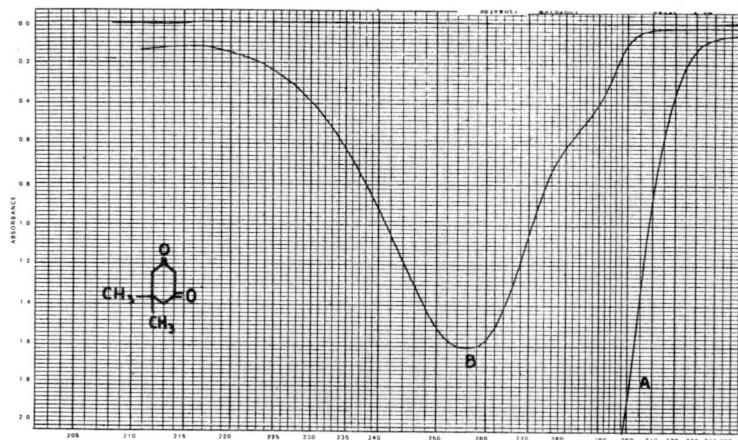

2-ACETYL-1,3-CYCLOHEXANEDIONE

2145

$C_8H_{10}O_3$

Mol. Wt. 154.17

Solvent: Methanol

λ Max. mμ	a_m	Cell mm	Conc. g/L
272.5	9580	1	0.1228
232	10500	1	0.1228

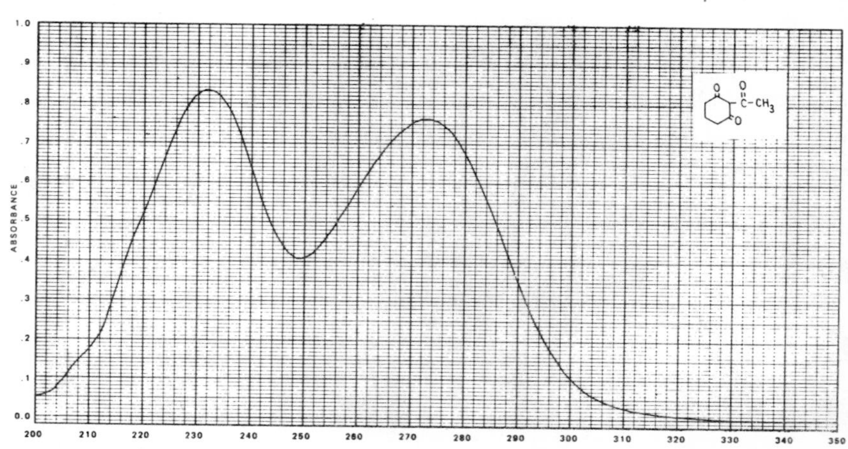

2-ACETYL-1,3-CYCLOHEXANEDIONE

2145

$C_8H_{10}O_3$
Mol. Wt. 154.17
Solvent: Methanol KOH

λ Max. mμ	a_m	Cell mm	Conc. g/L
265.5	19400	1	0.0614

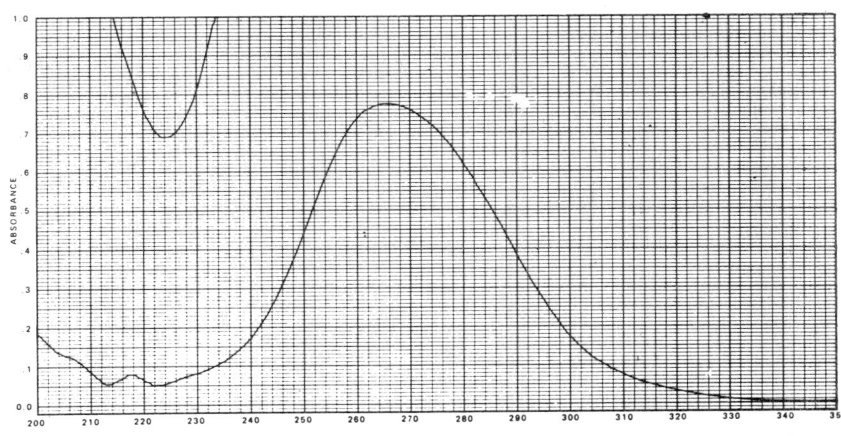

1-PHENYL-2,4-PENTANEDIONE

2146

$C_{11}H_{12}O_2$
Mol. Wt. 176.22
B.P. 142-145°C
Solvent: Methanol

λ Max. mμ	a_m	Cell mm	Conc. g/L
275	9270	1	0.0928

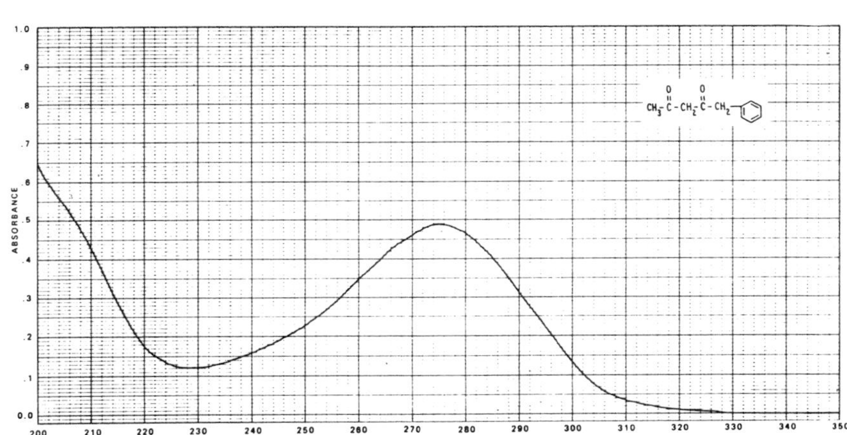

1-PHENYL-2,4-PENTANEDIONE

2146

$C_{11}H_{12}O_2$
Mol. Wt. 176.22
B.P. 142-145°C
Solvent: Methanol KOH

λ Max. mμ	a_m	Cell mm	Conc. g/L
296.5	21900	1	0.046

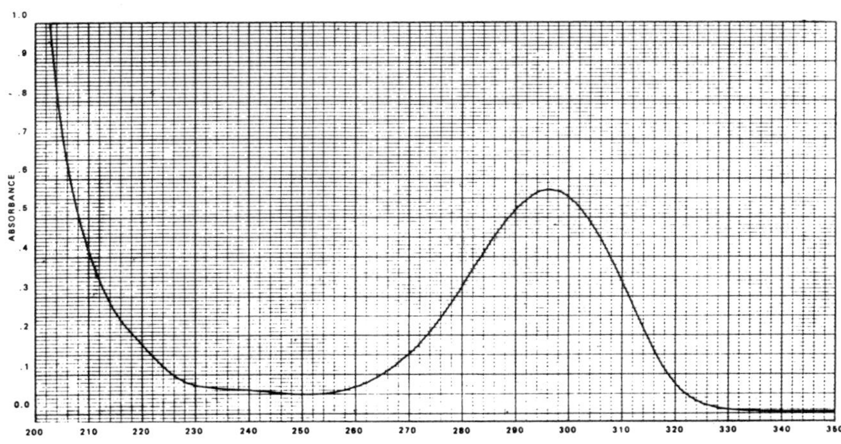

1-PHENYL-1,3-BUTANEDIONE

2147

$C_{10}H_{10}O_2$
Mol. Wt. 162.19
M.P. 56-58°C
Solvent: Methanol

λ Max. mμ	a_m	Cell mm	Conc. g/L
308	17400	1	0.0500
247	6940	2	0.100
230	5000	2	0.100

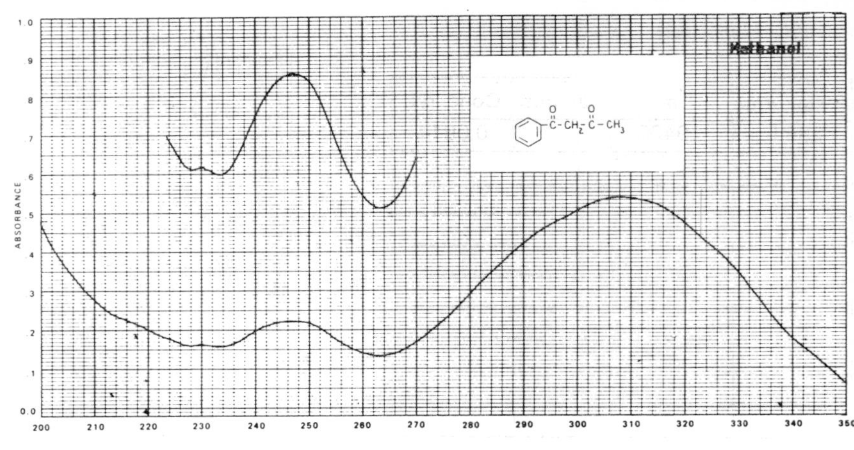

1,5-DIPHENYL-1,3,5-PENTANETRIONE

2148

$C_{17}H_{14}O_3$
Mol. Wt. 266.30
Solvent: Methanol

λ Max. mμ	a_m	Cell mm	Conc. g/L
379	36100	0.5	0.100
241	16900	0.5	0.100

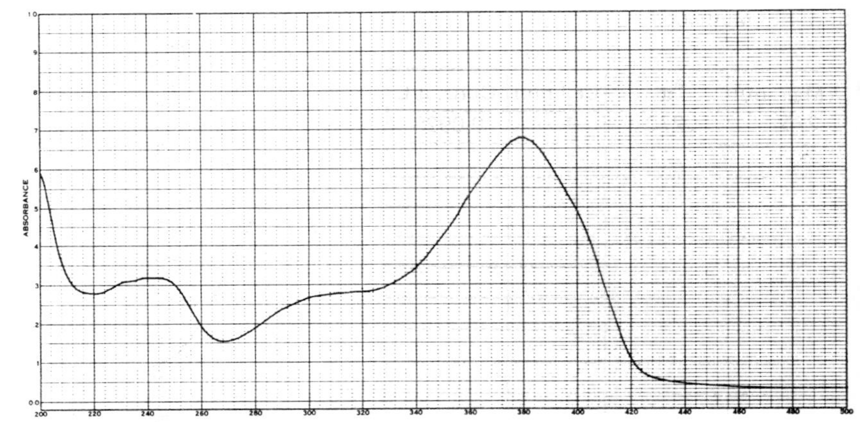

5-CHLORO-1,3-INDANDIONE

2149

$C_9H_5ClO_2$
Mol. Wt. 180.59
Solvent: Methanol

λ Max. mμ	a_m	Cell mm	Conc. g/L
524	793	10	0.100
341	784	10	0.100
256	7280	1	0.100
229	16600	1	0.100

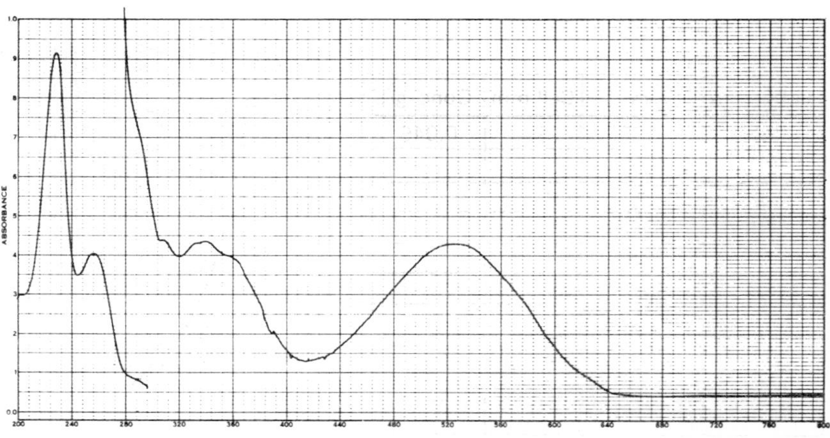

2,2-DIHYDROXY-1,3-INDANDIONE **2150**

$C_9H_4O_3 \cdot H_2O$

Mol. Wt. 178.15

M.P. 239-240°C (dec.) (lit.)

Solvent: Methanol

λ Max. mμ	a_m	Cell mm	Conc. g/L
303	319	10	0.100
288	809	10	0.100
279	907	10	0.100
248	11500	1	0.100
228	46200	1	0.0300

2,2-DIHYDROXY-1,3-INDANDIONE **2150**

$C_9H_4O_3 \cdot H_2O$

Mol. Wt. 178.15

M.P. 239-240°C (dec.) (lit.)

Solvent: Methanol KOH

λ Max. mμ	a_m	Cell mm	Conc. g/L
x	x	10	0.100
224.5	45300	1	0.0300

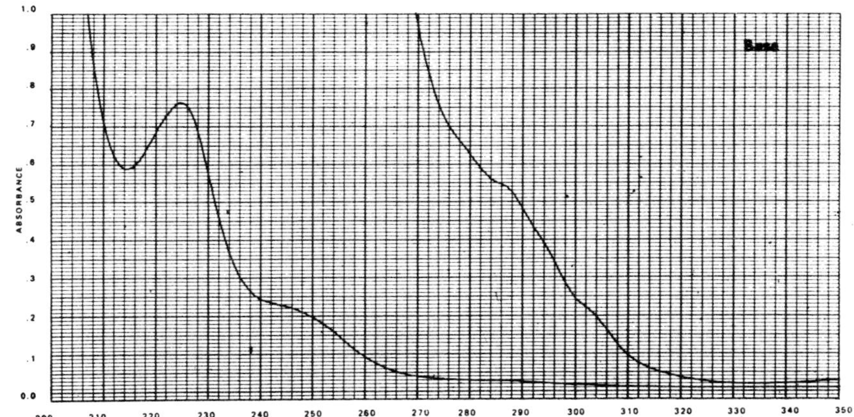

λ Max. mμ	a_m	Cell mm	Conc. g/L

NOTES

Aliphatic Compounds

The alkyl and alicyclic aldehydes display a very weak absorption band for the carbonyl $n \rightarrow \pi^*$ transition near 280 mμ. Spectrum 2153 (Heptanal) shows this band with ϵ_{max} = 60. Acetaldehyde is reported to show its absorption at 285 mμ (ϵ_{max} = 12) in methanol solution.

Olefinic Compounds

The conjugated alkenals (spectra 2156 and 2157) display a relatively intense $\pi \rightarrow \pi^*$ absorption near 220 mμ (ϵ_{max} = 12000) in addition to the weaker $n \rightarrow \pi^*$ transition at longer wavelength.

Aromatic Compounds

The near UV spectrum of benzaldehyde (spectrum 2163) contains many more maxima than almost any other monosubstituted benzene compound. Three major bands are observed at about 241, 279 and 338 mμ with superimposed fine structure producing more than ten distinct maxima or shoulders. Most of this fine structure is lost when benzaldehyde is examined in methanol solution.

In general, the substituted benzaldehydes, as shown in the table below, may not clearly display the very weak 339 mμ band of the parent compound when examined in methanol solution.

Compound	$\lambda_{max}(\epsilon_{max})$	$\lambda_{max}(\epsilon_{max})$	$\lambda_{max}(\epsilon_{max})$	Spectrum
Benzaldehyde	244 (6100)	279 (600)	321 (14)	Lit.
—, 2-Methyl	249 (4550)	280 (872)	----------	2164
—, 3-Methyl	249 (10100)	289 (1330)	----------	2165
—, 2-Chloro	246 (11000)	294 (1780)	----------	2166
—, 3-Chloro	243 (7160)	290 (854)	----------	2167
—, 2-Bromo	249 (7610)	297 (1170)	----------	2168
—, 4-Bromo	246 (10900)	----------	----------	2169

Upon the addition of acid, the UV spectra of the aldehydes may change markedly due to reactions of the aldehyde group with solvents such as the alcohols.

BUTYRALDEHYDE

2151

C_4H_8O
Mol. Wt. 72.11
B.P. 73-75°C

λ Max. mμ	a_m	Cell mm	Conc. g/L

Pure sample not available.

ISOBUTYRALDEHYDE

2152

C_4H_8O
Mol. Wt. 72.11
B.P. 63-65°C

λ Max. mμ	a_m	Cell mm	Conc. g/L

Pure sample not available.

HEPTANAL

2153

$C_7H_{14}O$
Mol. Wt. 114.19
B.P. 40-42°C/10mm
Solvent: Cyclohexane

λ Max. mμ	a_m	Cell mm	Conc. g/L
280	59.5	20	0.5

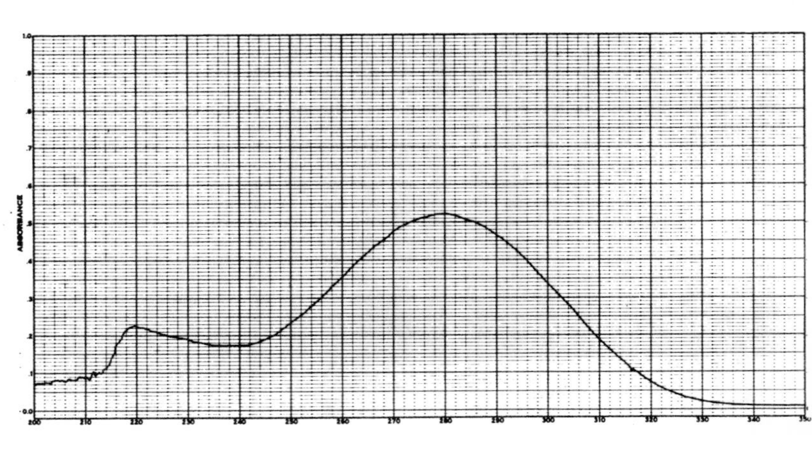

DECANAL

2154

$C_{10}H_{20}O$
Mol. Wt. 156.20

λ Max. mμ	a_m	Cell mm	Conc. g/L

Pure sample not available.

CYCLOHEXANECARBOXALDEHYDE

2155

$C_7H_{12}O$
Mol. Wt. 112.17
B.P. 161-163°C

λ Max. mμ	a_m	Cell mm	Conc. g/L

Pure sample not available.

2-HEXENAL

2156

$C_6H_{10}O$
Mol. Wt. 98.15
Solvent: Methanol

λ Max. mμ	a_m	Cell mm	Conc. g/L
303	591	10	0.100
219.5	12600	0.5	0.100

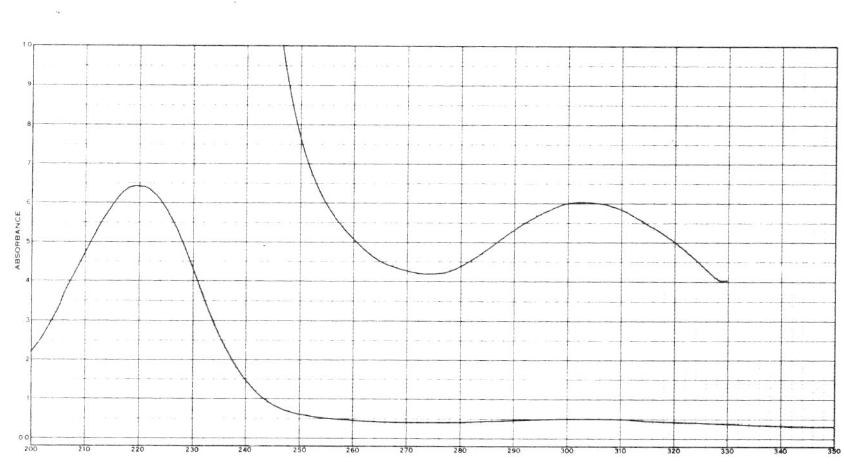

2-ETHYL-2-HEXENAL

2157

$C_8H_{14}O$
Mol. Wt. 126.20
B.P. 175°C
Solvent: Cyclohexane

λ Max. mμ	a_m	Cell mm	Conc. g/L
277	616	10	0.125
222.5	11300	0.5	0.125

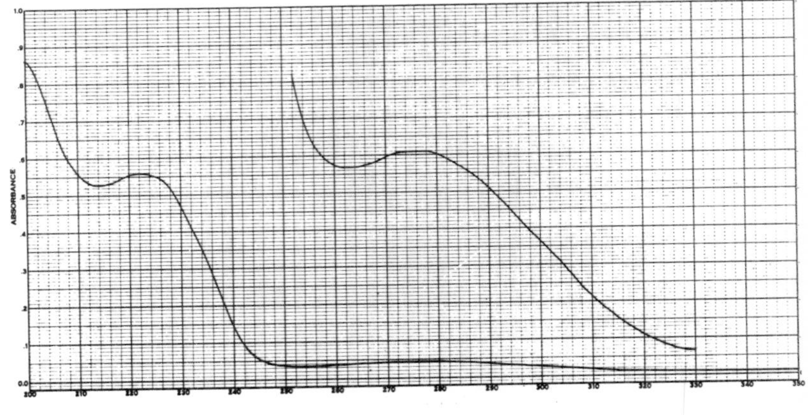

3-CYCLOHEXENE-1-CARBOXALDEHYDE

2158

$C_7H_{10}O$
Mol. Wt. 110.16
B.P. 164.5°C
Solvent: Methanol

λ Max. mμ	a_m	Cell mm	Conc. g/L
279	238	5	0.50

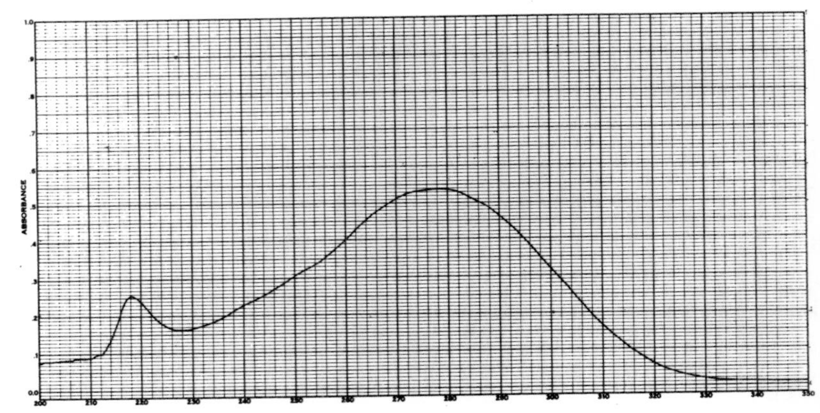

HYDROCINNAMALDEHYDE

2159

$C_9H_{10}O$
Mol. Wt. 134.18
Solvent: Methanol

λ Max. mμ	a_m	Cell mm	Conc. g/L
285	74.5	10	0.306
267.5	227	10	0.306
264	225	10	0.306
261	272	10	0.306
258	276	10	0.306
253	254	10	0.306
247.5	235	10	0.306
242	206	10	0.306
208	9460	10	0.010

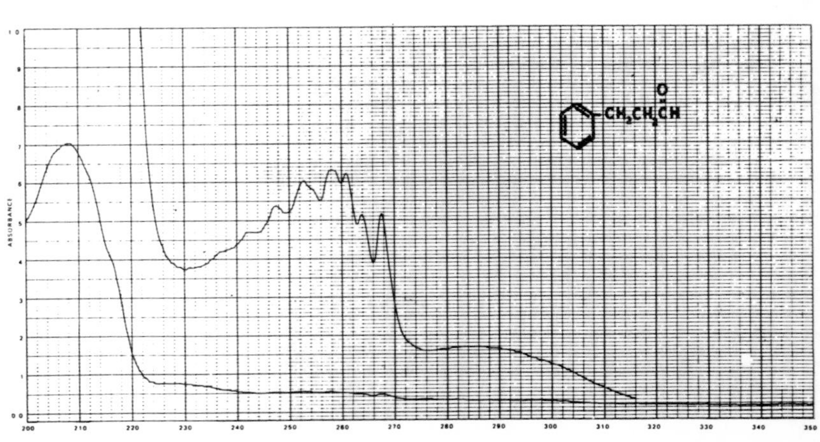

α-METHYLCINNAMALDEHYDE

2160

$C_{10}H_{10}O$

Mol. Wt. 146.19

B.P. 113-117°C/8mm

Solvent: Methanol

λ Max. mμ	a_m	Cell mm	Conc. g/L
281.5	23200	1	0.0453
219	9590	1	0.0453

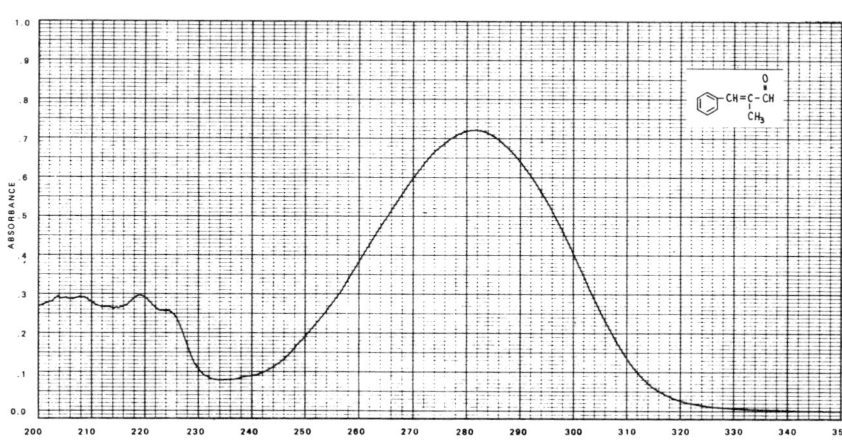

α-METHYLCINNAMALDEHYDE

2160

$C_{10}H_{10}O$

Mol. Wt. 146.19

B.P. 113-117°C/8mm

Solvent: Methanol HCl

λ Max. mμ	a_m	Cell mm	Conc. g/L
282	14200	1	0.0453
253	9330	1	0.0453
225	7970	1	0.0453

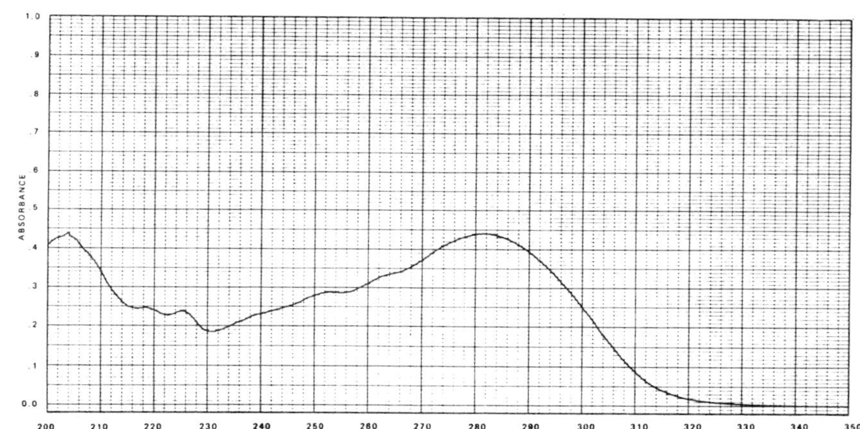

α-BUTYLCINNAMALDEHYDE

2161

$C_{13}H_{16}O$

Mol. Wt. 188.27

Solvent: Methanol

λ Max. mμ	a_m	Cell mm	Conc. g/L
283	22800	10	0.007
220	10500	10	0.007

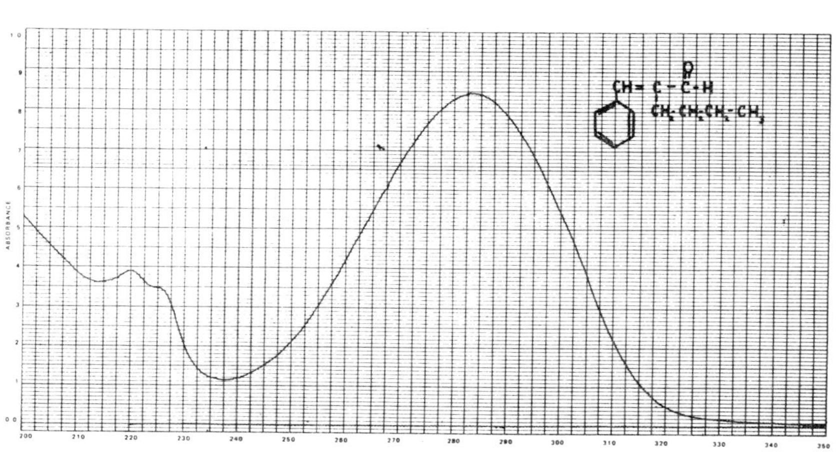

p-NITROCINNAMALDEHYDE

2162

$C_9H_7NO_3$

Mol. Wt. 177.16

M.P. 142-144°C

λ Max. mμ	a_m	Cell mm	Conc. g/L

Pure sample not available.

BENZALDEHYDE

2163

C_7H_6O

Mol. Wt. 100.12

B.P. 179°C (lit.)

Solvent: Cyclohexane

λ Max. mμ	a_m	Cell mm	Conc. g/L
352	22.2	10	5.13
338	27.3	10	5.13
327	26.3	10	5.13
317	24.2	10	5.13
305	19.4	10	5.13
288	974	10	0.103
278.5	1150	10	0.103
241	15200	10	0.010
214.5	2603	10	0.010

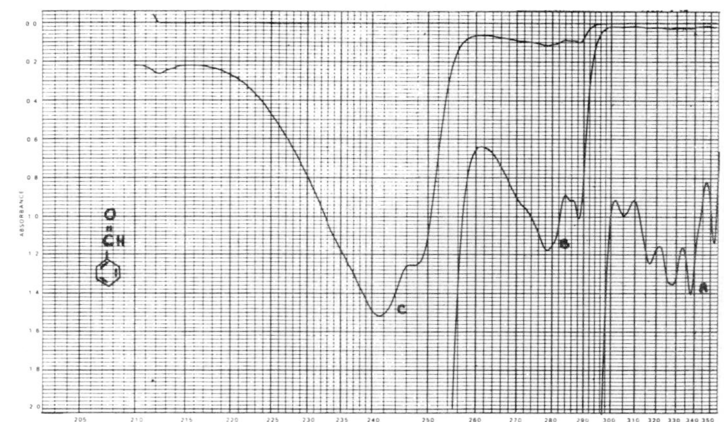

o-TOLUALDEHYDE

2164

C_8H_8O

Mol. Wt. 120.15

B.P. 85-87°C/14mm

Solvent: Methanol

λ Max. mμ	a_m	Cell mm	Conc. g/L
280	872	5	0.149
249	4550	1	0.149

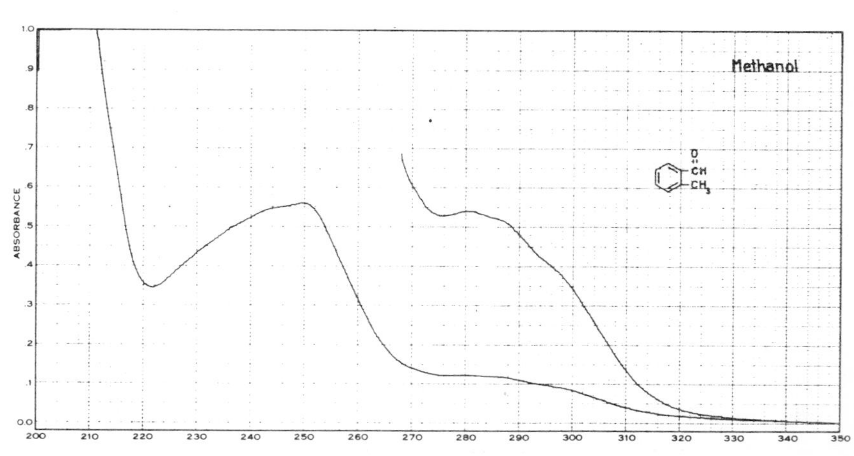

m-TOLUALDEHYDE

C_8H_8O

Mol. Wt. 120.15

B.P. 80-82°C/11mm

Solvent: Methanol

2165

λ Max. mμ	a_m	Cell mm	Conc. g/L
289	1330	5	0.100
249	10100	1	0.100
x	x	0.5	0.100

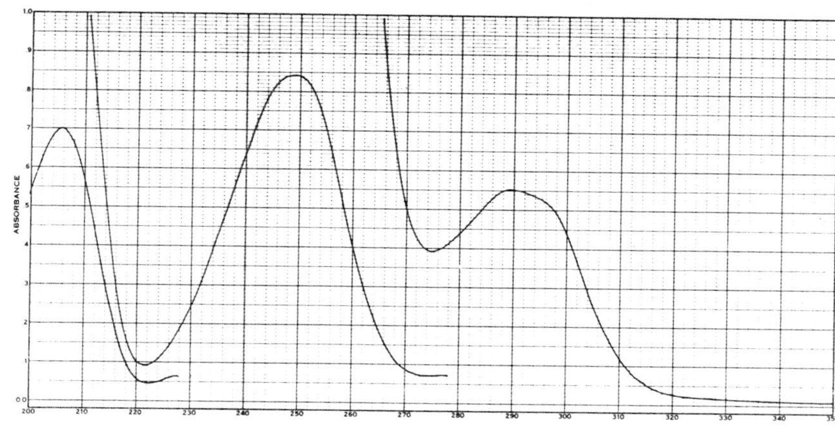

o-CHLOROBENZALDEHYDE

C_7H_5ClO

Mol. Wt. 140.57

Solvent: Cyclohexane

2166

λ Max. mμ	a_m	Cell mm	Conc. g/L
304	1390	10	0.123
302	1380	10	0.123
293.5	1780	10	0.123
246	11000	10	0.019

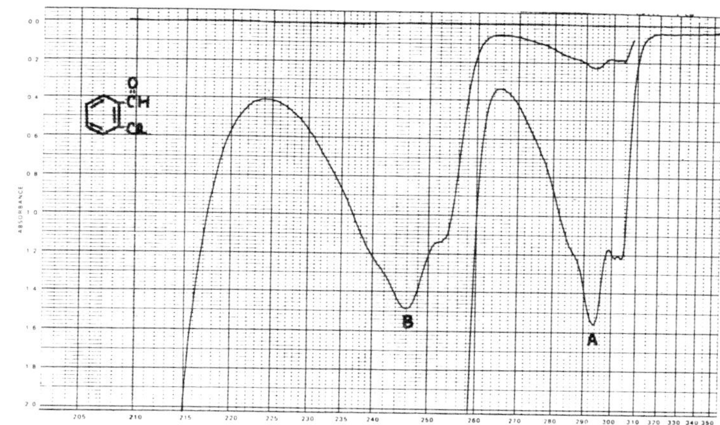

m-CHLOROBENZALDEHYDE

C_7H_5ClO

Mol. Wt. 140.57

B.P. 213-214°C

Solvent: Methanol

2167

λ Max. mμ	a_m	Cell mm	Conc. g/L
289.5	854	10	0.1142
243	7160	1	0.1142

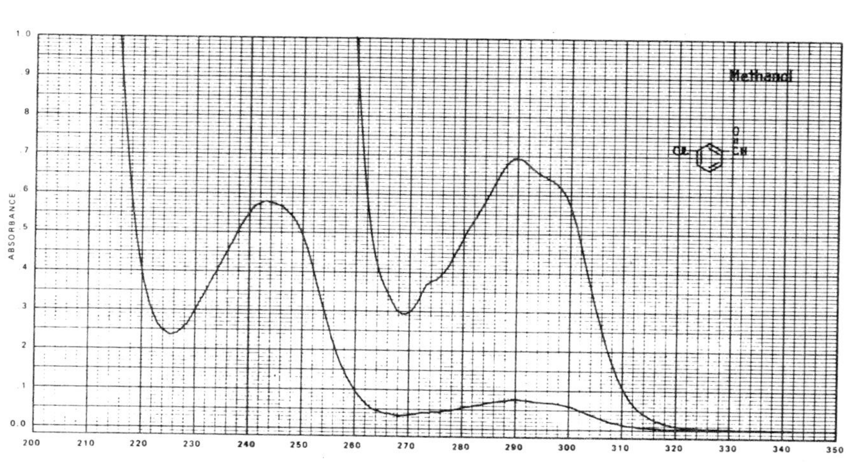

o-BROMOBENZALDEHYDE

2168

C_7H_5BrO

Mol. Wt. 185.03

Solvent: Methanol

λ Max. mμ	a_m	Cell mm	Conc. g/L
297	1170	10	0.100
248.5	7610	2	0.100
x	x	0.5	0.100

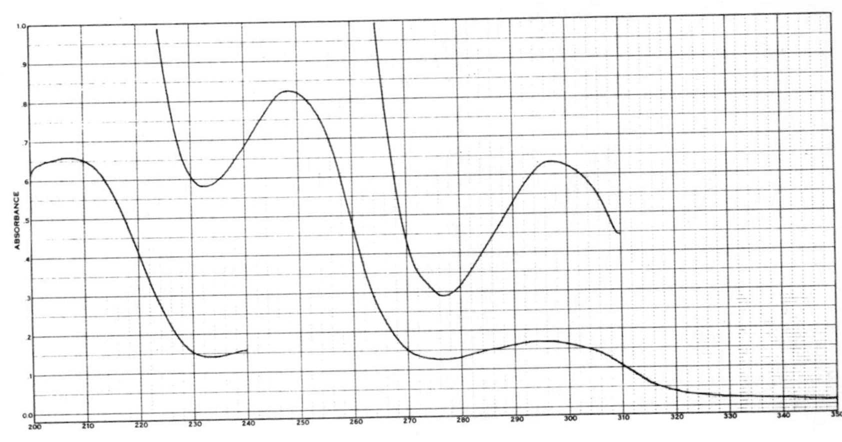

p-BROMOBENZALDEHYDE

2169

C_7H_5BrO

Mol. Wt. 185.03

Solvent: Methanol

λ Max. mμ	a_m	Cell mm	Conc. g/L
245.5	10900	10	0.012

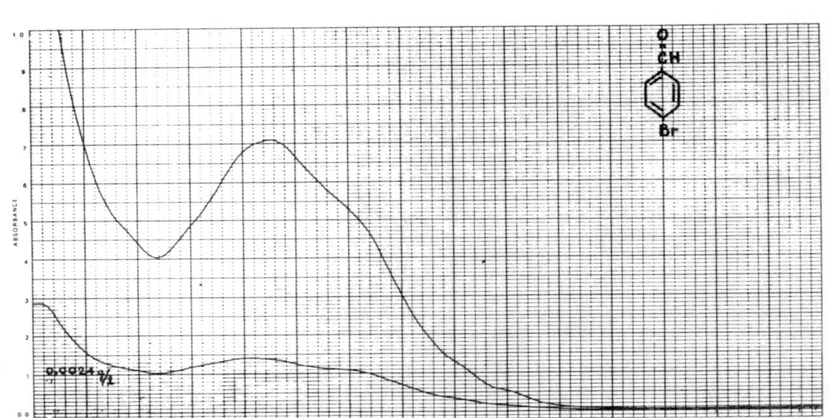

p-DIMETHYLAMINOBENZALDEHYDE

2170

$C_9H_{11}NO$

Mol. Wt. 149.19

M.P. 74°C (lit.)

Solvent: Methanol

λ Max. mμ	a_m	Cell mm	Conc. g/L
339.5	26300	10	0.003
243	7010	10	0.010

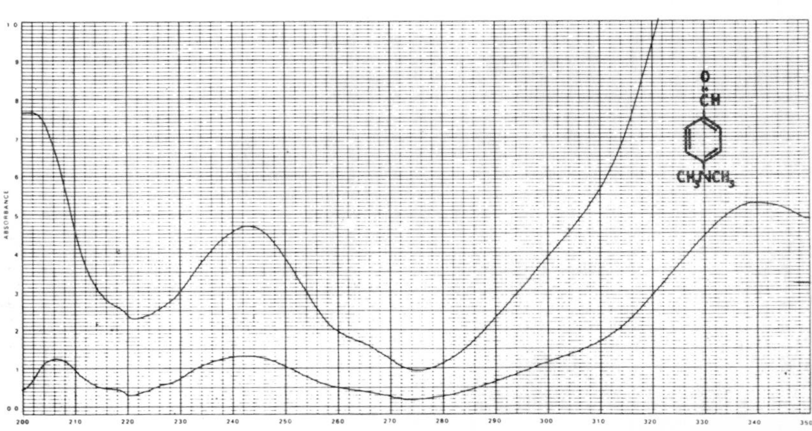

m-NITROBENZALDEHYDE

2171

$C_7H_5NO_3$

Mol. Wt. 151.12

M.P. 58°C B.P. 164°C/23mm

Solvent: Water

λ Max. mμ	a_m	Cell mm	Conc. g/L
232.5	20900	1	0.0500

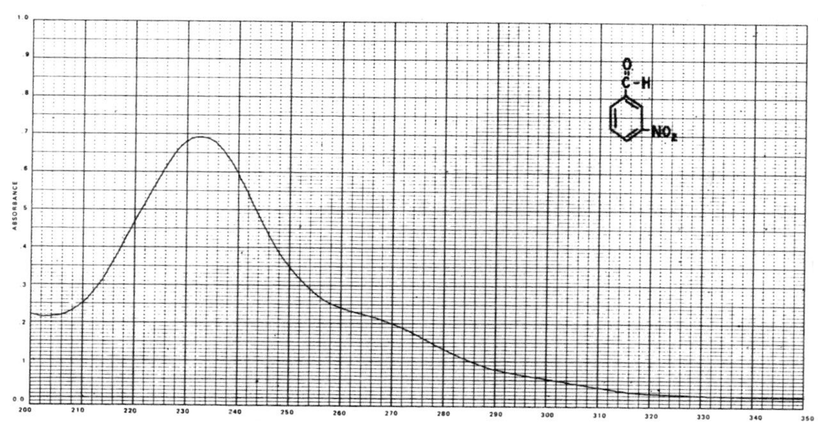

p-NITROBENZALDEHYDE

2172

$C_7H_5NO_3$

Mol. Wt. 151.12

M.P. 42-44°C (lit.)

Solvent: Methanol

λ Max. mμ	a_m	Cell mm	Conc. g/L
265	10600	1	0.100

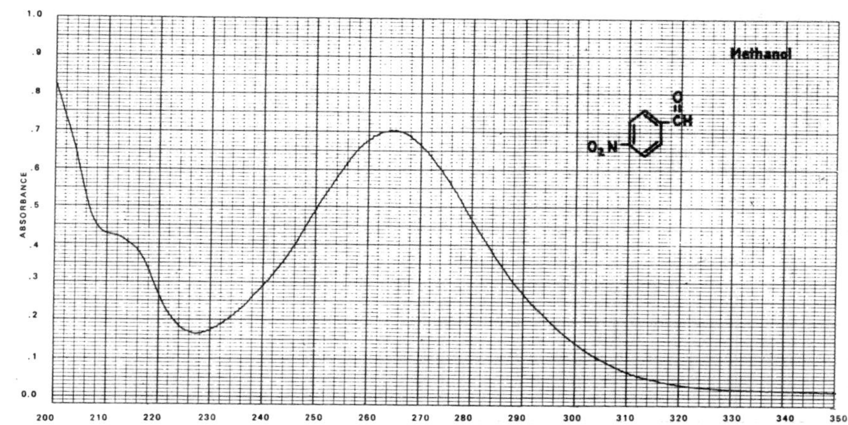

p-PROPOXYBENZALDEHYDE

2173

$C_{10}H_{12}O_2$

Mol. Wt. 164.21

B.P. 129-130°C/9mm

Solvent: Methanol

λ Max. mμ	a_m	Cell mm	Conc. g/L
276.5	10500	1	0.100
214	7620	1	0.100

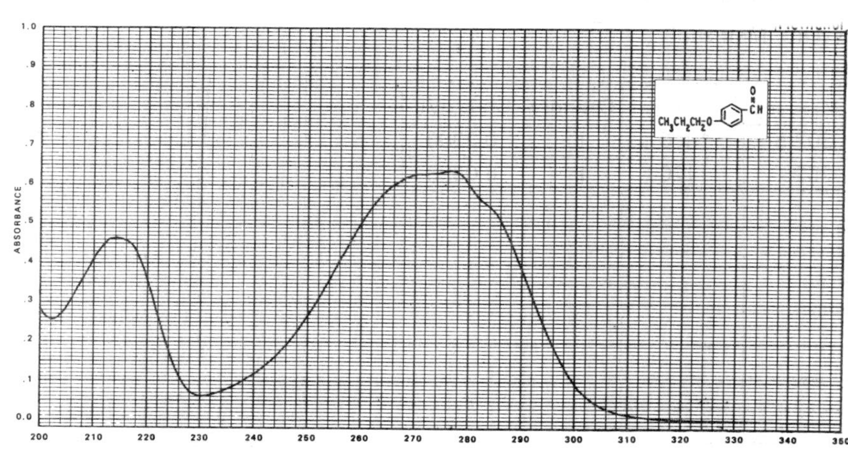

p-(PENTYLOXY)BENZALDEHYDE

2174

$C_{12}H_{16}O_2$
Mol. Wt. 192.26
M.P. 154-155°C
Solvent: Methanol

λ Max. mμ	a_m	Cell mm	Conc. g/L
283.5	16800	1	0.08750
220.5	11800	1	0.08750

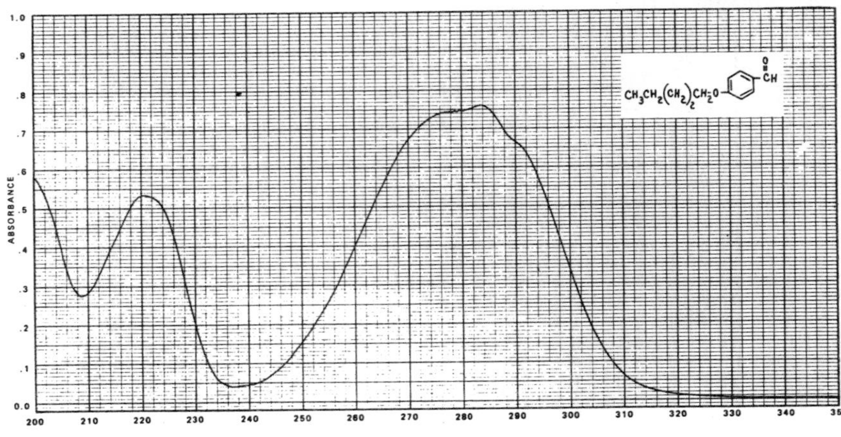

p-(ALLYLOXY)BENZALDEHYDE

2175

$C_{10}H_{10}O_2$
Mol. Wt. 162.19
B.P. 142°C/10mm (lit.)
Solvent: Methanol

λ Max. mμ	a_m	Cell mm	Conc. g/L
282	17600	1	0.0360
276	17800	1	0.0360
220	12700	1	0.0360

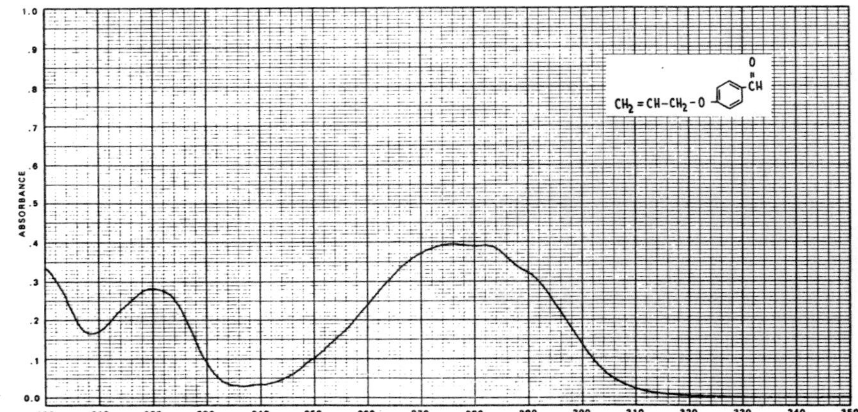

2,5-DIMETHYLBENZALDEHYDE

2176

$C_9H_{10}O$
Mol. Wt. 134.18
B.P. 104.5-106.5°C/14mm
Solvent: Methanol

λ Max. mμ	a_m	Cell mm	Conc. g/L
302.5	1810	1	0.2900
252	11200	1	0.0900

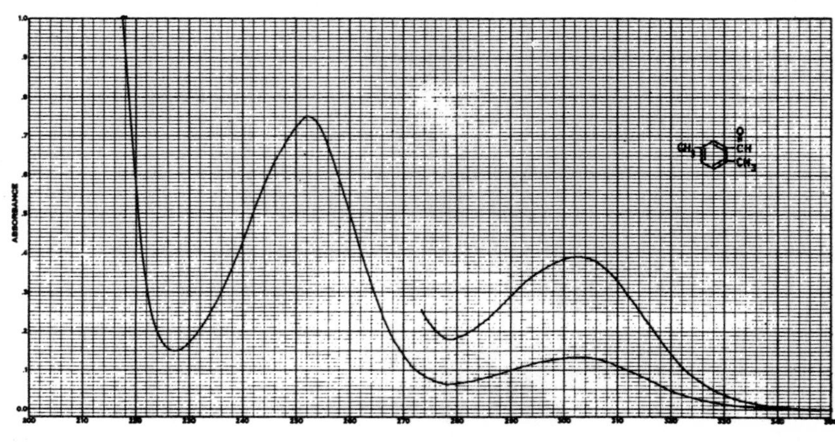

2,5-DIMETHYLBENZALDEHYDE

2176

$C_9H_{10}O$

Mol. Wt. 134.18

B.P. 104.5-106.5°C/14mm

Solvent: Methanol HCl

λ Max. mμ	a_m	Cell mm	Conc. g/L
297	277	5	0.2900
275.5	794	2	0.2900
253	1690	2	0.2900
x	x	1	0.2900

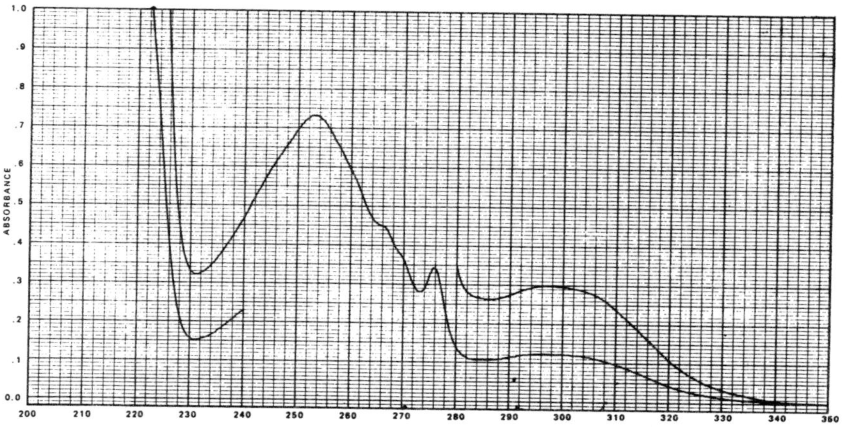

3,4-DICHLOROBENZALDEHYDE

2177

$C_7H_4Cl_2O$

Mol. Wt. 175.02

M.P. 42-44°C (lit.)

Solvent: Methanol

λ Max. mμ	a_m	Cell mm	Conc. g/L
x	x	10	2.284
289.5	483	10	0.457
280	609	10	0.457
271.5	507	10	0.457
x	x	10	0.046
x	x	10	0.005

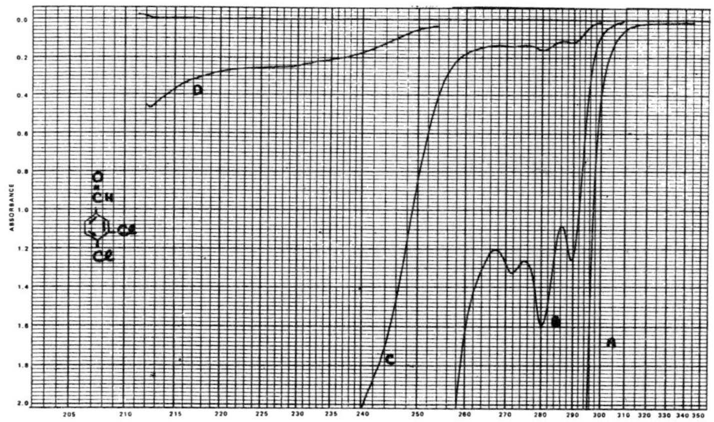

λ Max. mμ	a_m	Cell mm	Conc. g/L

6-HYDROXY-m-ANISALDEHYDE

2178

$C_8H_8O_3$
Mol. Wt. 152.15
B.P. 103°C/2.5mm
Solvent: Methanol

λ Max. mμ	a_m	Cell mm	Conc. g/L
358	4830	5	0.0500
257	8920	1	0.0500
228	21800	1	0.0500

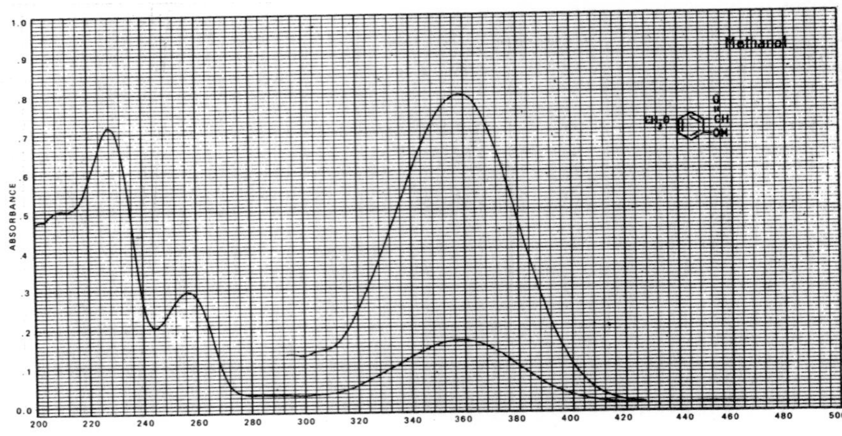

6-HYDROXY-m-ANISALDEHYDE

2178

$C_8H_8O_3$
Mol. Wt. 152.15
B.P. 103°C/2.5mm
Solvent: Methanol KOH

λ Max. mμ	a_m	Cell mm	Conc. g/L
406	8160	1	0.0500
262	9130	1	0.0500
223	21400	1	0.0500

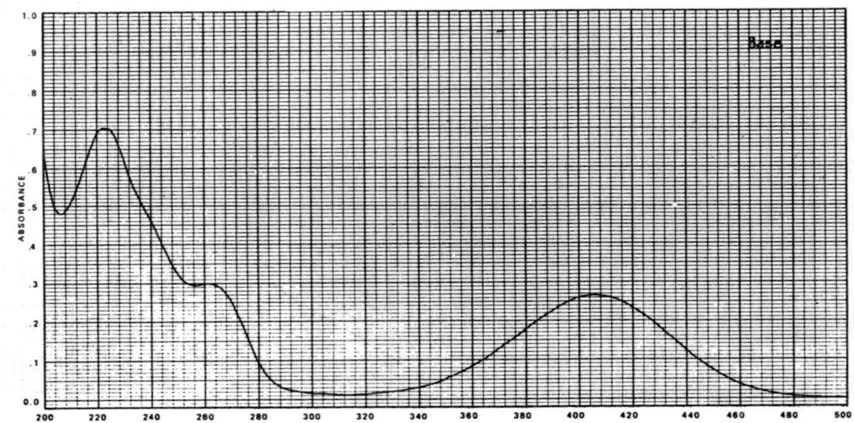

5-INDANCARBOXALDEHYDE

2179

$C_{10}H_{10}O$
Mol. Wt. 146.19
Solvent: Methanol

λ Max. mμ	a_m	Cell mm	Conc. g/L
261	11300	1.0	0.100
212.8	13700	1.0	0.100

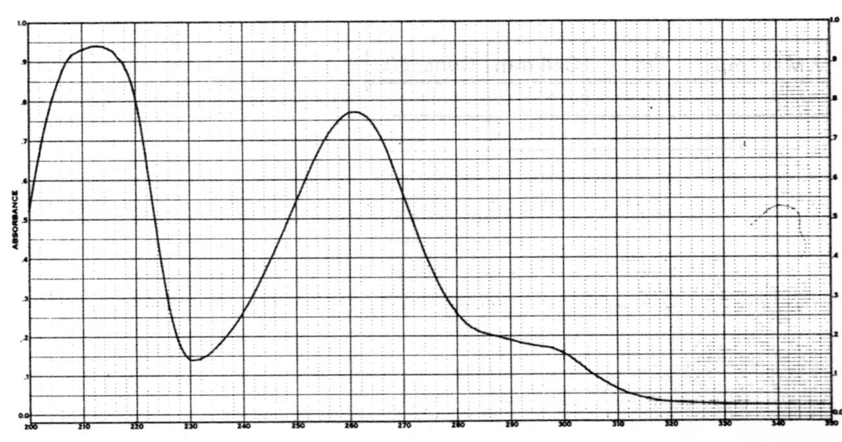

FLUORENE-2-CARBOXALDEHYDE

2180

$C_{14}H_{10}O$

Mol. Wt. 194.22

M.P. 85-86°C

Solvent: Methanol

λ Max. mμ	a_m	Cell mm	Conc. g/L
315	27800	1	0.0500

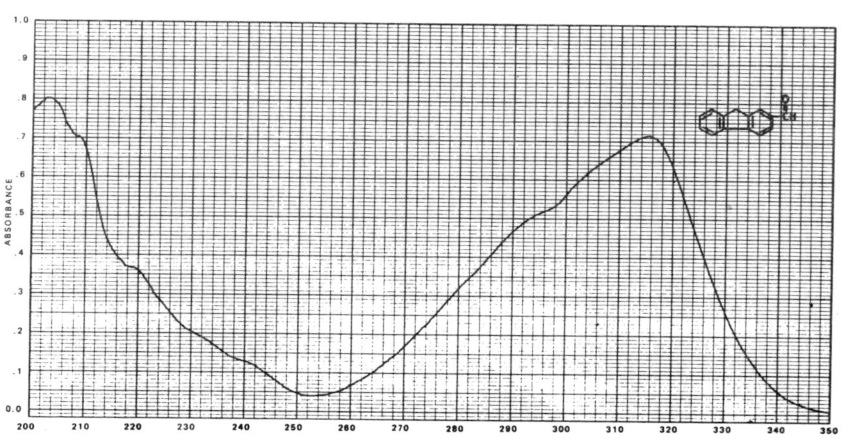

FLUORENE-2-CARBOXALDEHYDE

2180

$C_{14}H_{10}O$

Mol. Wt. 194.22

M.P. 85-86°C

Solvent: Methanol HCl

λ Max. mμ	a_m	Cell mm	Conc. g/L
315	7480	1	0.100
300.5	14600	1	0.100
289	10800	1	0.100
266.5	18400	1	0.100
220	14800	1	0.100

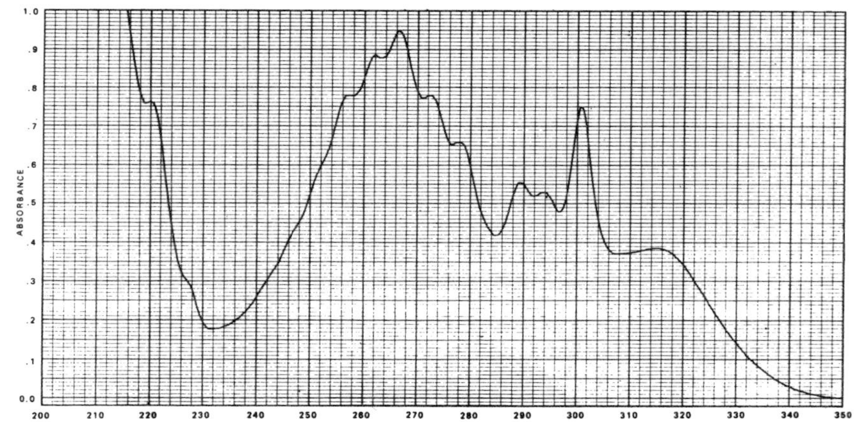

3-PYRENECARBOXALDEHYDE

2181

$C_{17}H_{10}O$

Mol. Wt. 230.27

M.P. 124°C

Solvent: Methanol

λ Max. mμ	a_m	Cell mm	Conc. g/L
394	15600	1	0.0500
363	28100	1	0.0500
287	39100	1	0.0500
242	42000	1	0.0500
232	54100	1	0.0500

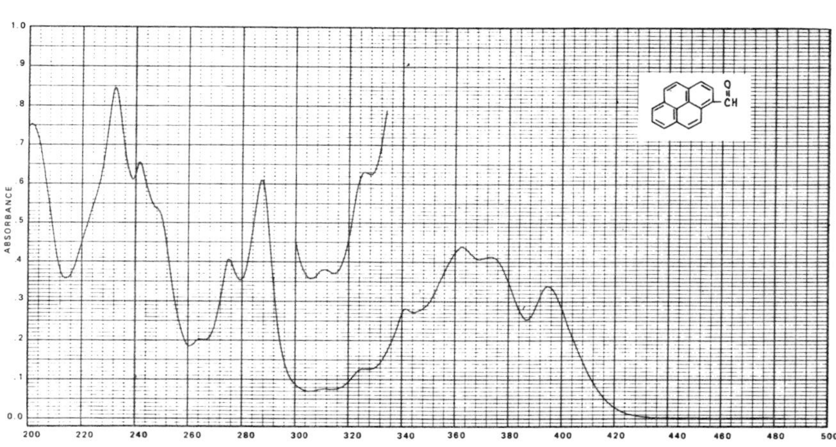

PYRROLE-2-CARBOXALDEHYDE

2182

C_5H_5NO

Mol. Wt. 95.10

Solvent: Methanol

λ Max. mμ	a_m	Cell mm	Conc. g/L
288	16700	0.5	0.100

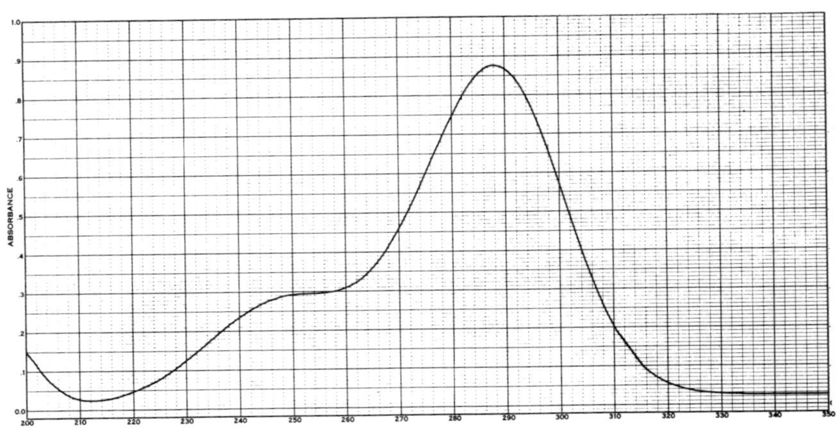

3-QUINOLINECARBOXALDEHYDE

2183

$C_{10}H_7NO$

Mol. Wt. 151.17

Solvent: Methanol

λ Max. mμ	a_m	Cell mm	Conc. g/L
315	2620	2	0.100
301	3620	2	0.100
284	4610	2	0.100
245	16300	0.5	0.100
231	22400	0.5	0.100
227	25500	0.5	0.100
x	x	0.5	0.100

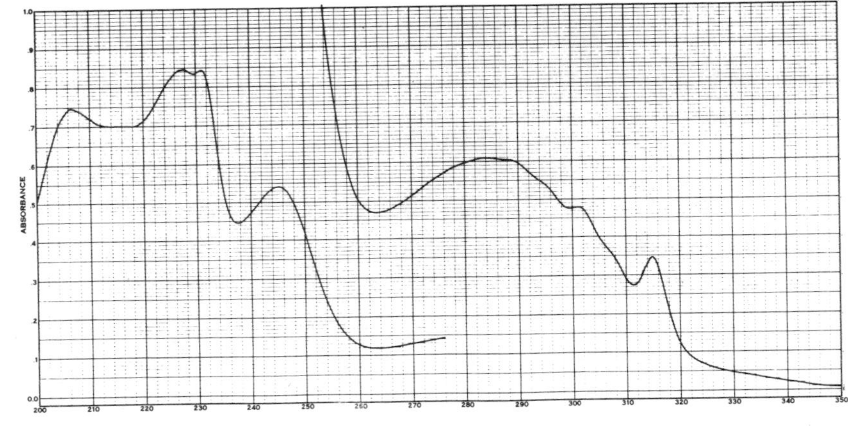

3-QUINOLINECARBOXALDEHYDE

2183

$C_{10}H_7NO$

Mol. Wt. 151.17

Solvent: Methanol HCl

λ Max. mμ	a_m	Cell mm	Conc. g/L
314	2310	4	0.100
236	13200	1	0.100
x	x	1	0.100

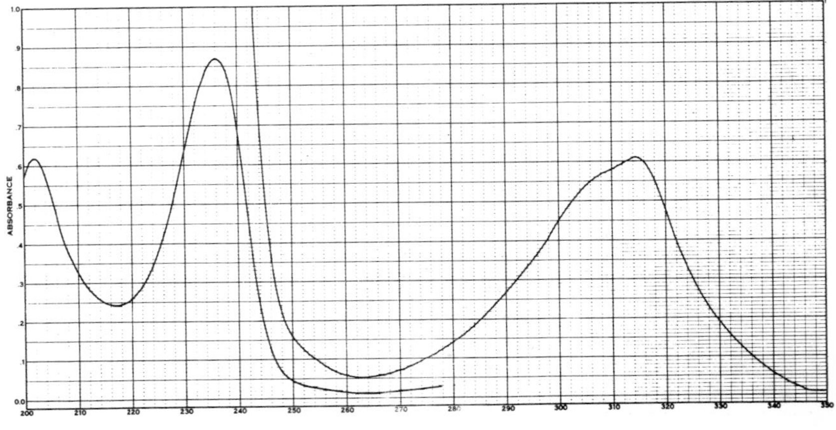

5-METHYL-2-THIOPHENECARBOXALDEHYDE 2184

C_6H_6OS
Mol. Wt. 126.18
Solvent: Methanol

λ Max. mμ	a_m	Cell mm	Conc. g/L
294	10800	1	0.105
262	9440	1	0.105

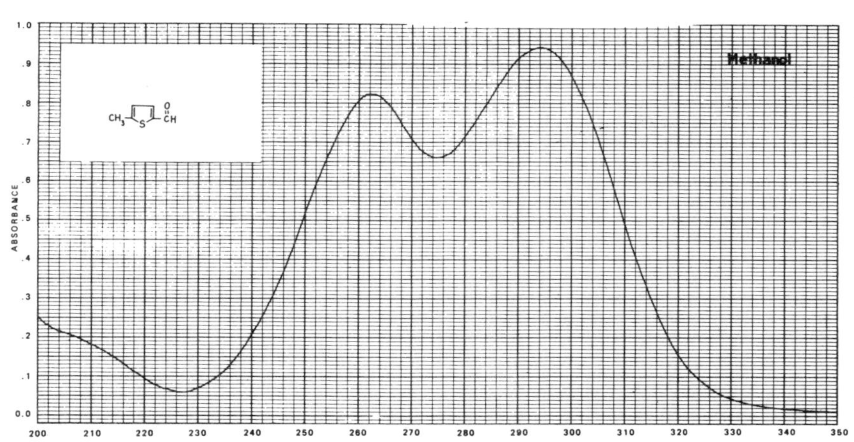

5-METHYL-2-THIOPHENECARBOXALDEHYDE 2184

C_6H_6OS
Mol. Wt. 12618
Solvent: Methanol HCl

λ Max. mμ	a_m	Cell mm	Conc. g/L
294	4220	1	0.105
242.5	5960	1	0.105

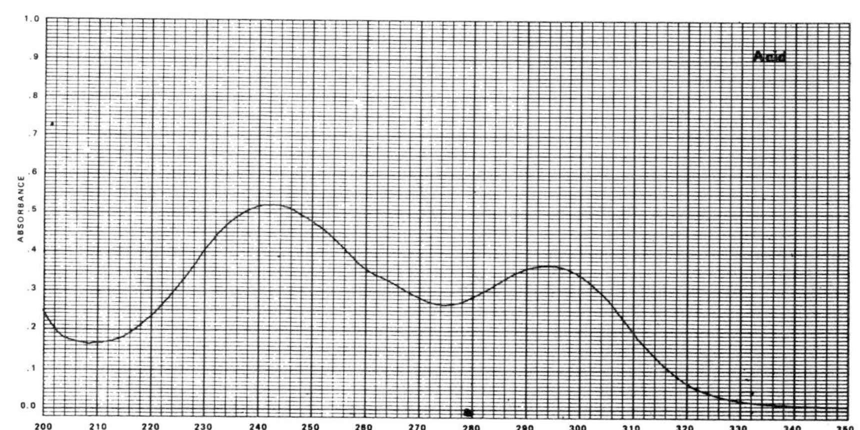
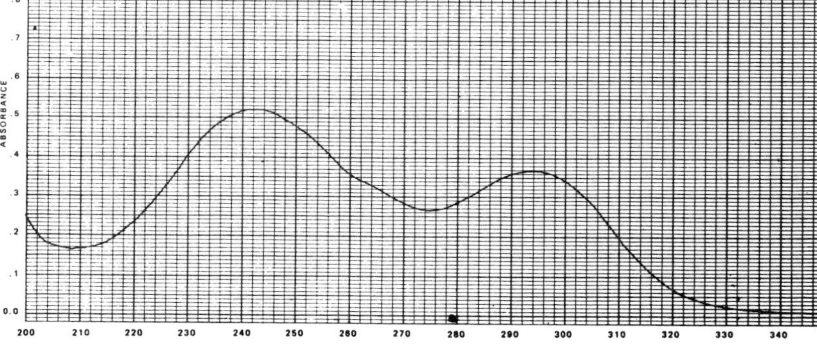

5-NITROFURFURAL 2185

$C_5H_3NO_4$
Mol. Wt. 141.08
M.P. 36°C
Solvent: Methanol

λ Max. mμ	a_m	Cell mm	Conc. g/L
309	12400	10	0.01
227	4330	10	0.01

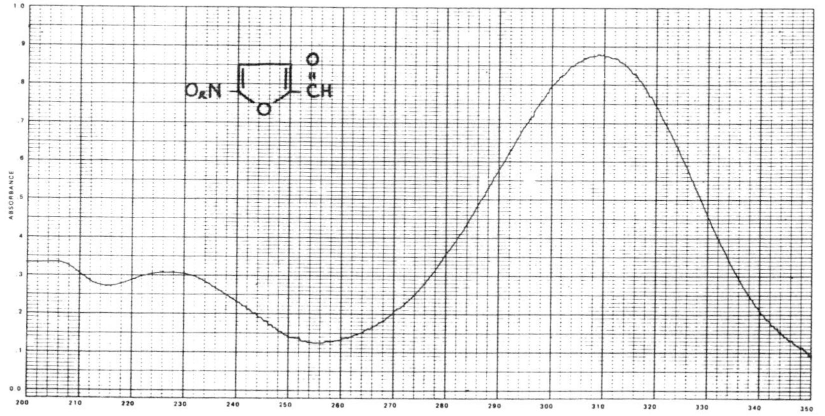

PIPERONAL 2186

$C_8H_6O_3$

Mol. Wt. 150.14

M.P. 35-37°C

Solvent: Methanol

λ Max. mμ	a_m	Cell mm	Conc. g/L
312	8630	1	0.0800
272	7060	1	0.0800
230.5	16600	1	0.0800

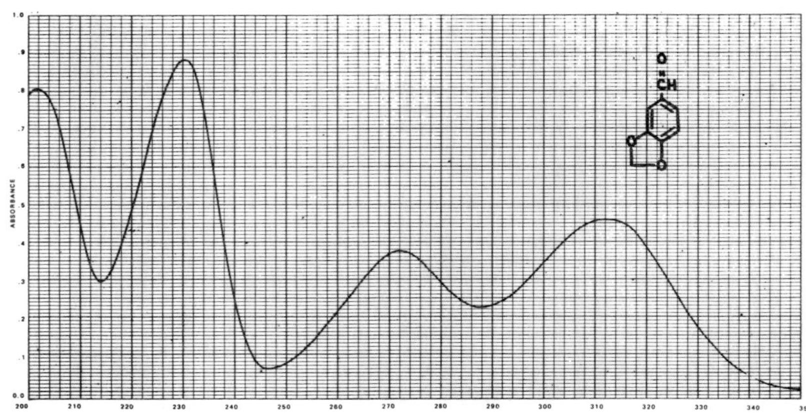

λ Max. mμ	a_m	Cell mm	Conc. g/L

λ Max. mμ	a_m	Cell mm	Conc. g/L

THE ACID HALIDES

Aliphatic Compounds

The n→π* transition of the acid chlorides appears as a very weak maximum (ϵ_{max} = 50 - 150) near 236 mμ. Due to the low intensity of these maxima, coupled with their high degree of reactivity to moisture and solvents such as the alcohols, no UV spectra of the aliphatic acid halides are included in either the Sadtler Standard collection or this volume. As a result, there are no spectra in this section for compounds 2187 through 2207.

Olefinic Compounds

The conjugated alkenyl chlorides such as fumaroyl chloride (spectrum 2209) and 1-cyclohexene-1-carbonyl chloride (spectrum 2210) display a π→π* transition in the region from 220 mμ to 240 mμ similar to those of the corresponding aldehydes (spectrum 2156).

Aromatic Compounds

The benzoyl halides produce near ultraviolet spectra consisting of two major bands at about 240 mμ and 280 mμ. The precise wavelengths are dependent upon the halide atom that is present as indicated by the listing given below.

Compound	$\lambda_{max}(\epsilon_{max})$	$\lambda_{max}(\epsilon_{max})$	Solvent	Spectrum
Benzoyl fluoride	231 (13200)	276 (1270)	Methanol	2219
Benzoyl chloride	241 (15000)	281 (1390)	Cyclohexane	2220
Benzoyl bromide	246 (29400)	282 (3250)	Cyclohexane	2221

SORBOYL CHLORIDE 2208

C_6H_7ClO

Mol. Wt. 130.58

Solvent: Methanol

λ Max. mμ	a_m	Cell mm	Conc. g/L
274.5	16600	0.5	0.100

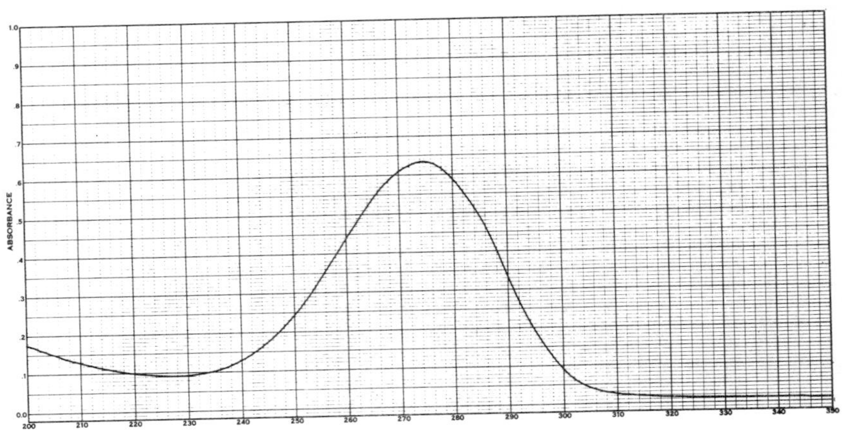

FUMAROYL CHLORIDE 2209

$C_4H_2Cl_2O_2$

Mol. Wt. 152.97

B.P. 159-161°C

Solvent: Cyclohexane

λ Max. mμ	a_m	Cell mm	Conc. g/L
222.5	16490	0.5	0.1

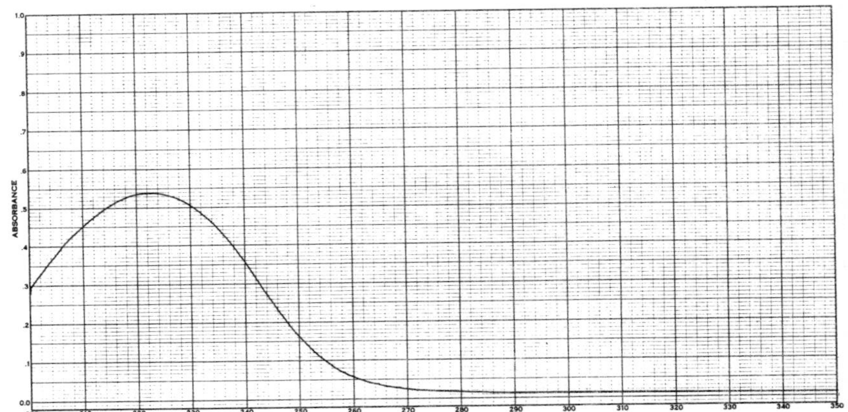

1-CYCLOHEXENE-1-CARBONYL CHLORIDE 2210

C_7H_9ClO

Mol. Wt. 144.60

Solvent: Methanol

λ Max. mμ	a_m	Cell mm	Conc. g/L
234.5	11200	1	0.100

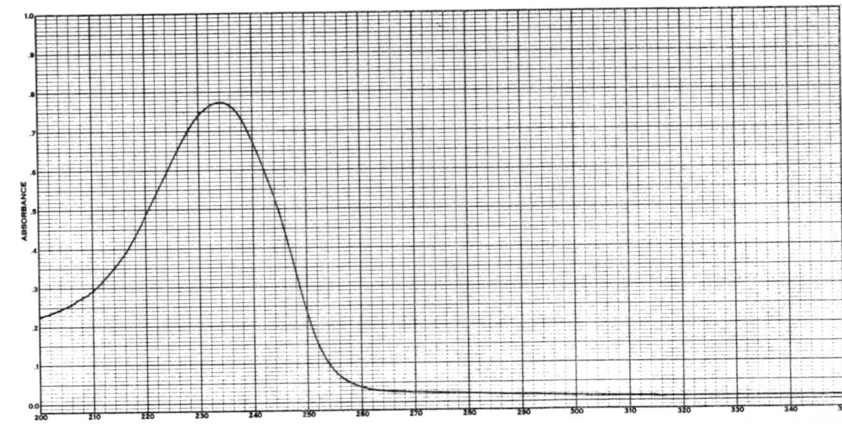

3-CYCLOHEXENE-1-CARBONYL CHLORIDE

2211

C_7H_9ClO

Mol. Wt. 144.60

λ Max. mμ	a_m	Cell mm	Conc. g/L

Pure sample not available.

HYDROCINNAMOYL CHLORIDE

2212

C_9H_9ClO

Mol. Wt. 168.62

M.P. -7° to -5°C

Solvent: Cyclohexane

λ Max. mμ	a_m	Cell mm	Conc. g/L
308	99	20	0.100
265	314	20	0.100
259.5	417	20	0.100
252	493	20	0.100
248	475	20	0.100
243	453	20	0.100
219.5	2390	5	0.100

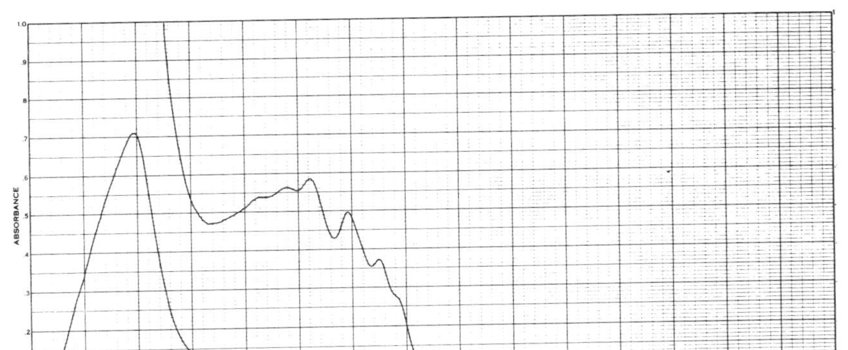

CHLOROPHENYL ACETYL CHLORIDE

2213

$C_8H_6Cl_2O$

Mol. Wt. 189.04

B.P. 120°C/23mm

Solvent: Methanol

λ Max. mμ	a_m	Cell mm	Conc. g/L
266.5	577	20	0.100
259.0	621	20	0.100
220.0	8260	2	0.100
x	x	1	0.100

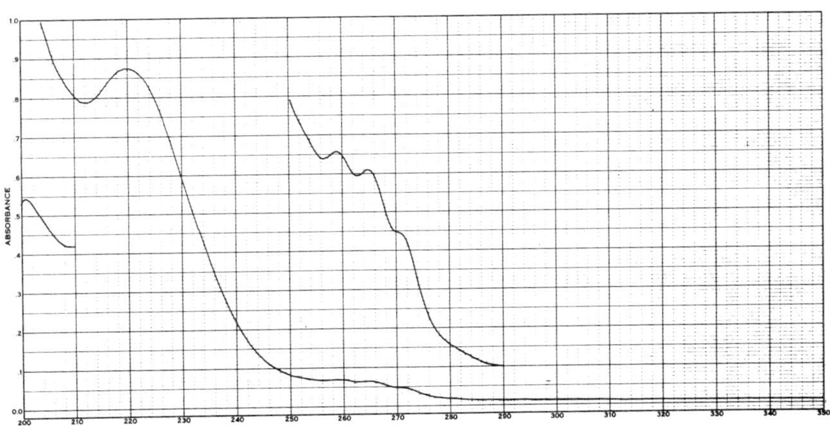

BROMODIPHENYLACETYL BROMIDE

2214

$C_{14}H_{10}Br_2O$

Mol. Wt. 354.05

λ Max. mμ	a_m	Cell mm	Conc. g/L

Pure sample not available.

PHENOXYACETYL CHLORIDE

2215

$C_8H_7ClO_2$

Mol. Wt. 170.60

B.P. 96-98°C/10mm

Solvent: Cyclohexane

λ Max. mμ	a_m	Cell mm	Conc. g/L
275	1420	5	0.100
268	1720	5	0.100
262.5	1350	5	0.100
221	2650	5	0.100

2-PHENOXYPROPIONYL CHLORIDE

2216

$C_9H_9ClO_2$

Mol. Wt. 184.62

B.P. 92-94°C/5mm

Solvent: Methanol

λ Max. mμ	a_m	Cell mm	Conc. g/L
269	1770	10	0.100
x	x	1	0.100

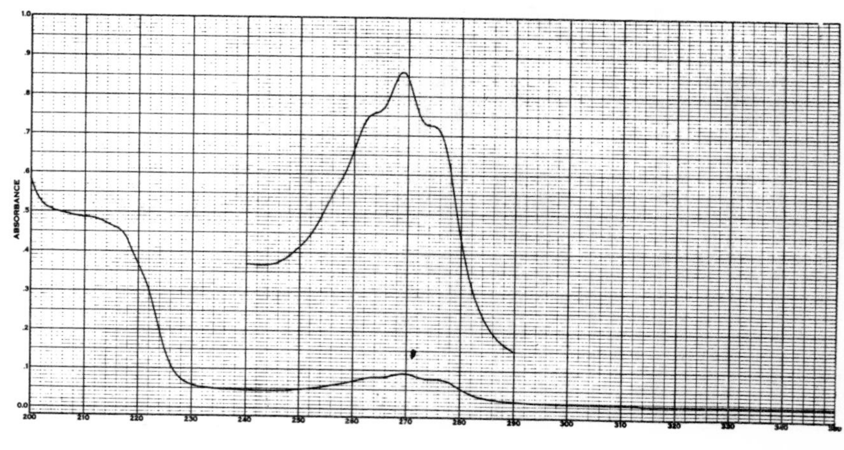

p-CHLOROPHENYLACETYL CHLORIDE

2217

$C_8H_6Cl_2O$
Mol. Wt. 189.04
Solvent: Cyclohexane

λ Max. mμ	a_m	Cell mm	Conc. g/L
276	231	20	0.100
267.5	311	20	0.100
260.5	373	20	0.100
255	302	20	0.100
229	3630	5	0.100

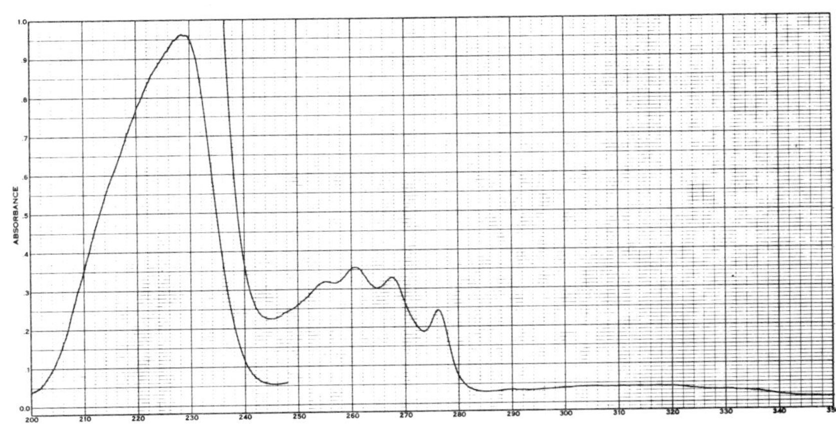

4-(p-BROMOPHENYL)BUTYRYL CHLORIDE

2218

$C_{10}H_{10}BrClO$
Mol. Wt. 261.55

λ Max. mμ	a_m	Cell mm	Conc. g/L

Pure sample not available.

BENZOYL FLUORIDE

2219

C_7H_5FO
Mol. Wt. 124.12
B.P. 159-161°C
Solvent: Methanol

λ Max. mμ	a_m	Cell mm	Conc. g/L
276	1270	5	0.100
231	13200	0.5	0.100

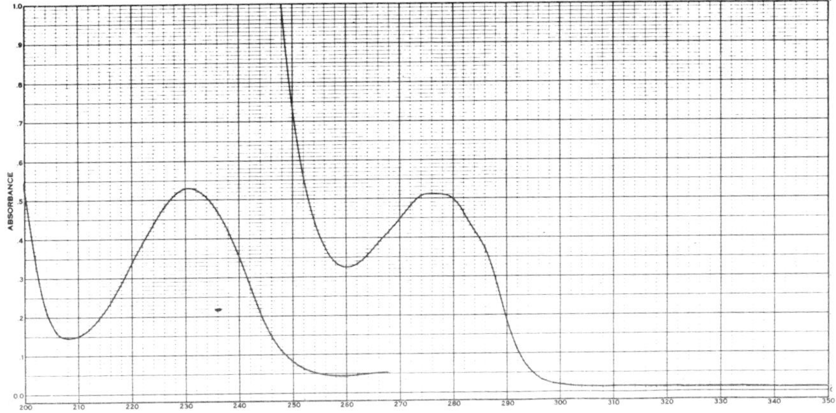

BENZOYL CHLORIDE

2220

C_7H_5ClO

Mol. Wt. 140.57

B.P. 198°C (lit.)

Solvent: Cyclohexane

λ Max. mμ	a_m	Cell mm	Conc. g/L
x	x	10	2.752
280.5	1390	10	0.138
241	15000	10	0.014

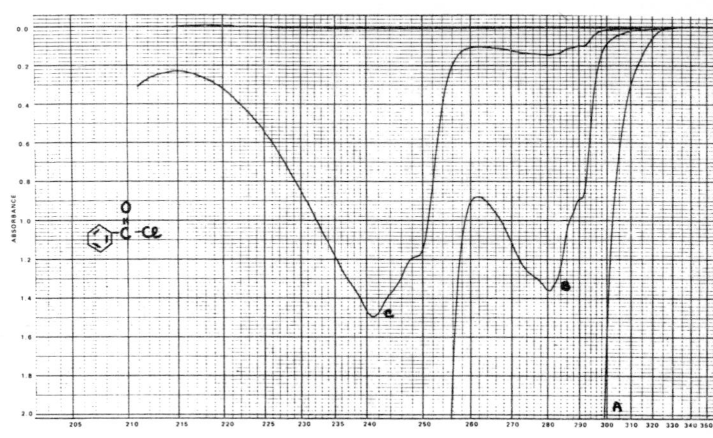

BENZOYL BROMIDE

2221

C_7H_5BrO

Mol. Wt. 185.03

M.P. 218-219°C

Solvent: Cyclohexane

λ Max. mμ	a_m	Cell mm	Conc. g/L
282	3250	4	0.100
245.5	29400	0.5	0.100
x	x	0.5	0.100

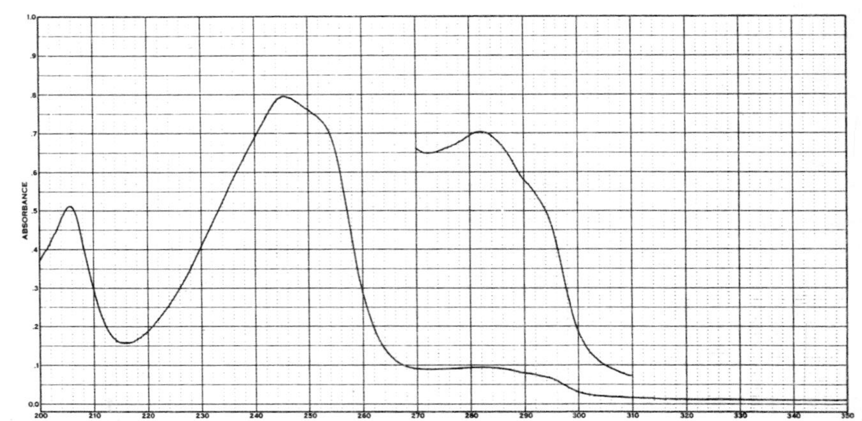

o-TOLUOYL CHLORIDE

2222

C_8H_7ClO

Mol. Wt. 154.60

B.P. 88-89°C/11 mm

Solvent: Cyclohexane

λ Max. mμ	a_m	Cell mm	Conc. g/L
290.5	3010	4	0.100
244	18700	0.5	0.100
x	x	0.5	0.100

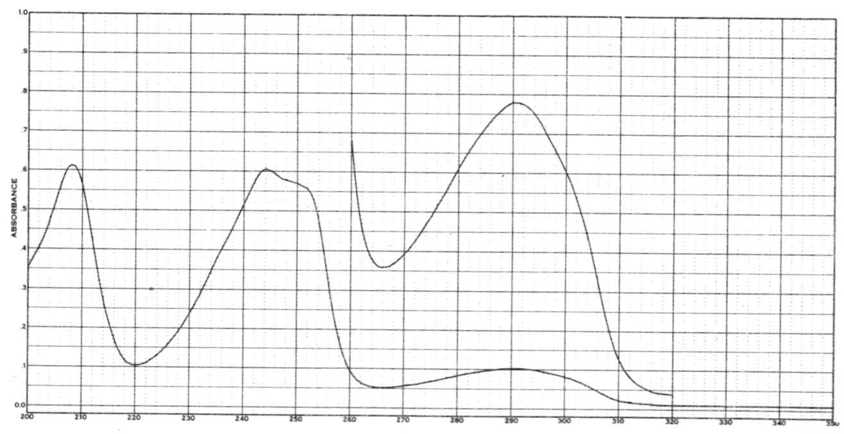

p-TOLUOYL CHLORIDE 2223

C_8H_7ClO

Mol. Wt. 154.60

Solvent: Methanol

λ Max. mμ	a_m	Cell mm	Conc. g/L
283.5	804	10	0.100
272.5	1160	10	0.100
244	15800	0.5	0.100
x	x	0.5	0.100

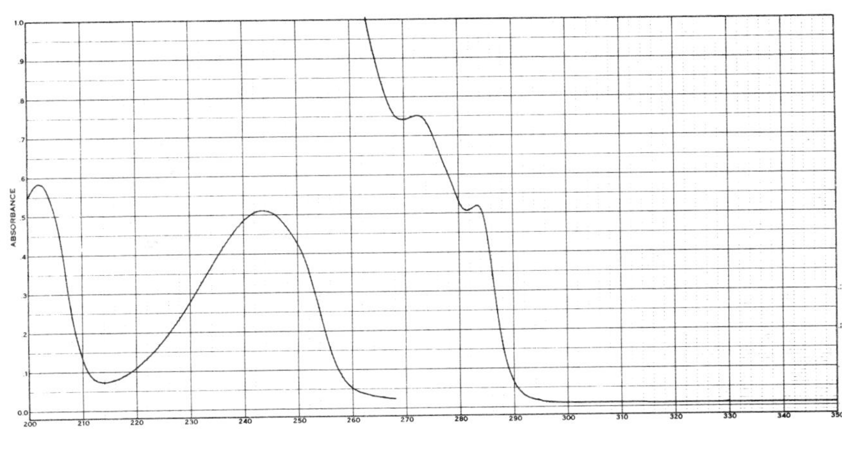

p-tert-BUTYL BENZOYL CHLORIDE 2224

$C_{11}H_{13}ClO$

Mol. Wt. 196.68

B.P. 135°C/20mm

Solvent: Cyclohexane

λ Max. mμ	a_m	Cell mm	Conc. g/L
255	24000	0.5	0.100
x	x	0.5	0.100

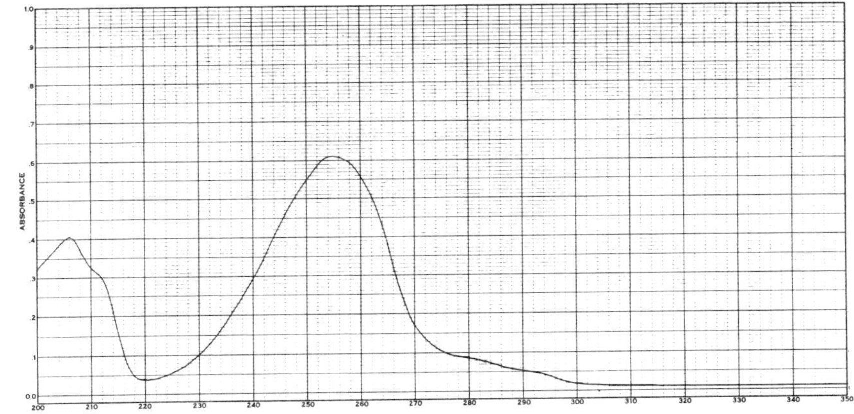

***a,a,a*-TRIFLUORO-o-TOLUOYL CHLORIDE** 2225

$C_8H_4ClF_3O$

Mol. Wt. 208.57

Solvent: Dioxane

λ Max. mμ	a_m	Cell mm	Conc. g/L
272	1980	10	0.100
236	8320	1	0.100

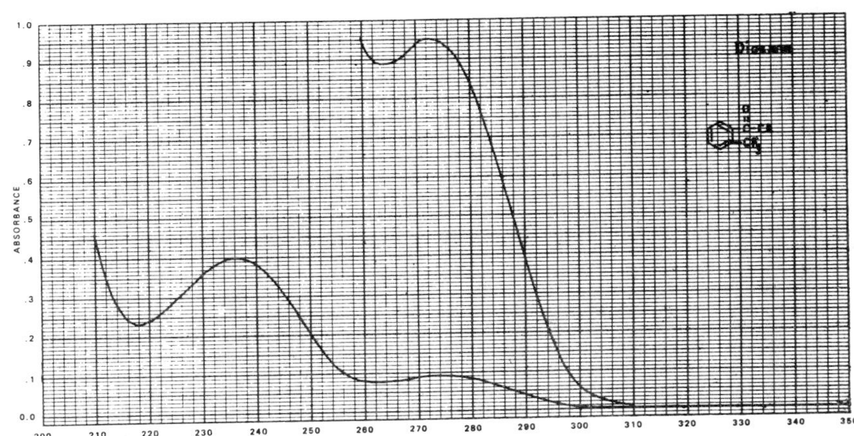

α,α,α-TRIFLUORO-p-TOLUOYL CHLORIDE

2226

$C_8H_4ClF_3O$

Mol. Wt. 208.57

B.P. 199-200°C/750mm (Lit.)

λ Max. mμ	a_m	Cell mm	Conc. g/L

Pure sample not available.

o-FLUOROBENZOYL CHLORIDE

2227

C_7H_4ClFO

Mol. Wt. 158.56

Solvent: Methanol

λ Max. mμ	a_m	Cell mm	Conc. g/L
285.5	2380	4	0.100
236	13800	1	0.100
x	x	1	0.100

m-FLUOROBENZOYL CHLORIDE

2228

C_7H_4ClFO

Mol. Wt. 158.56

B.P. 189°C

Solvent: Methanol

λ Max. mμ	a_m	Cell mm	Conc. g/L
291.5	2830	4	0.100
248	15700	0.5	0.100
240	17800	0.5	0.100
x	x	0.5	0.100

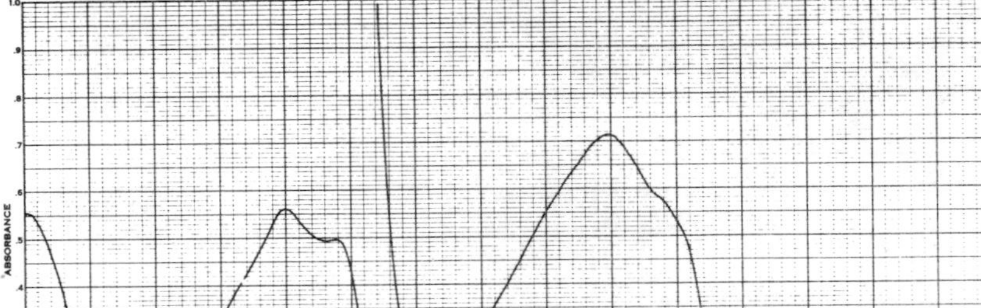

o-CHLOROBENZOYL CHLORIDE

2229

$C_7H_4Cl_2O$

Mol. Wt. 175.02

M.P. -5 to -4°C B.P. 235-238°C

Solvent: Cyclohexane

λ Max. mμ	a_m	Cell mm	Conc. g/L
292	3190	4	0.100
242.5	16800	0.5	0.100
211	31800	0.5	0.100

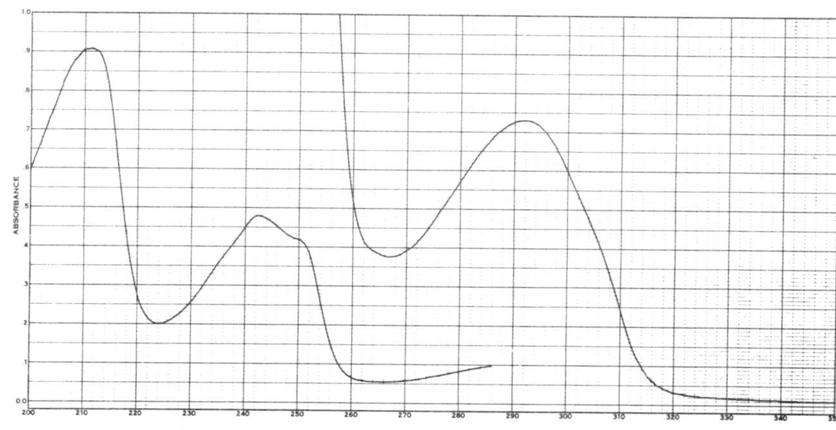

m-CHLOROBENZOYL CHLORIDE

2230

$C_7H_4Cl_2O$

Mol. Wt. 175.02

Solvent: Cyclohexane

λ Max. mμ	a_m	Cell mm	Conc. g/L
x	x	10	2.480
302	1220	10	0.198
293	1500	10	0.198
250.5	10900	10	0.020
242.5	11500	10	0.020

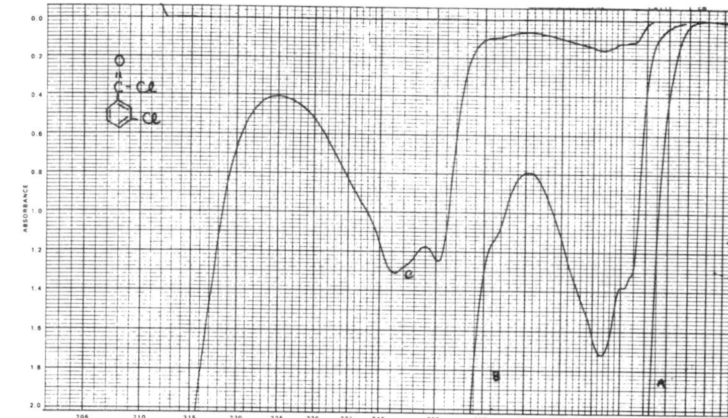

p-CHLOROBENZOYL CHLORIDE

2231

847

$C_7H_4Cl_2O$

Mol. Wt. 175.02

F.P. 10-12.0°C (lit.)

Solvent: Cyclohexane

λ Max. mμ	a_m	Cell mm	Conc. g/L
256	20000	10	0.014

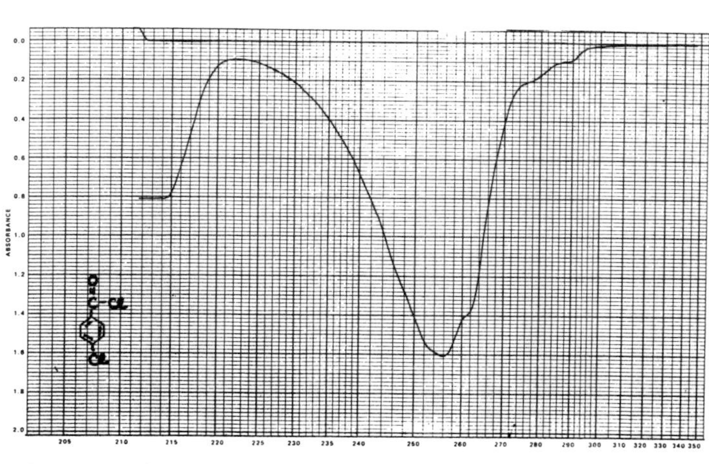

o-BROMOBENZOYL CHLORIDE 2232

C_7H_4BrClO

Mol. Wt. 219.47

B.P. 120-125°C/15mm

Solvent: Methanol

λ Max. mμ	a_m	Cell mm	Conc. g/L
294.5	3200	4	0.100
253	11600	0.5	0.100
245	12900	0.5	0.100
213	31700	0.5	0.100

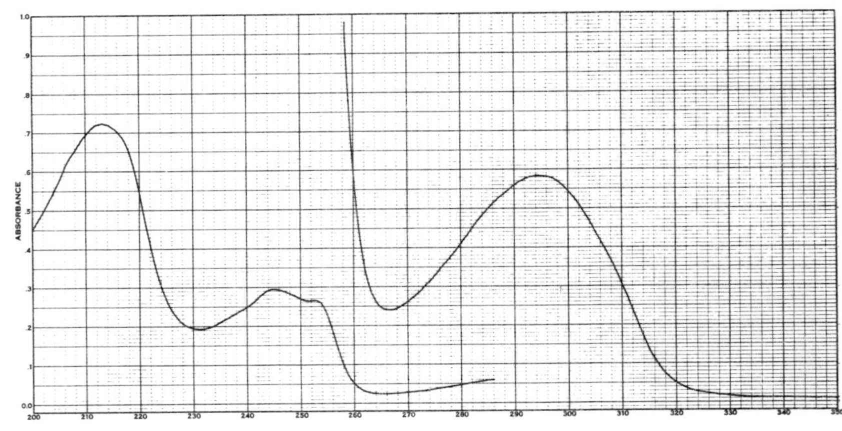

m-BROMOBENZOYL CHLORIDE 2233

C_7H_4BrClO

Mol. Wt. 219.47

Solvent: Methanol

λ Max. mμ	a_m	Cell mm	Conc. g/L
296	2940	5	0.100
252	20100	0.5	0.100
244	20700	0.5	0.100
217	38100	0.5	0.100
214	38300	0.5	0.100

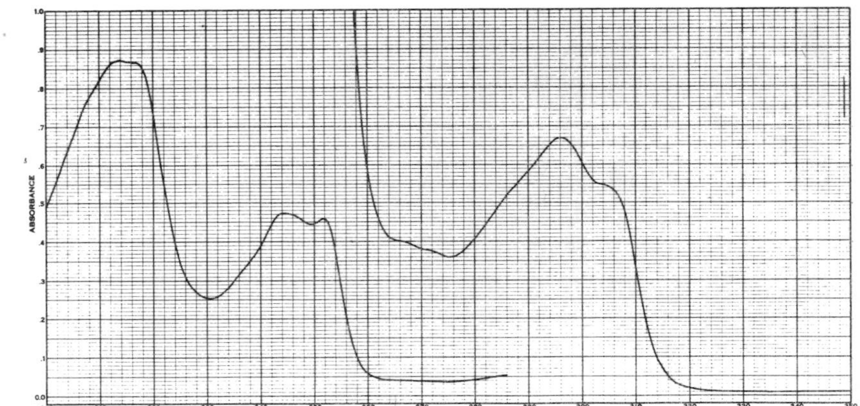

m-BROMOBENZOYL BROMIDE 2234

$C_7H_4Br_2O$

Mol. Wt. 263.93

B.P. 124-126°C/10mm

λ Max. mμ	a_m	Cell mm	Conc. g/L

Pure sample not available.

o-NITROBENZOYL CHLORIDE 2235

$C_7H_4ClNO_3$

Mol. Wt. 185.57

Solvent: Cyclohexane

λ Max. mμ	a_m	Cell mm	Conc. g/L
247	9190	2	0.100
x	x	0.5	0.100

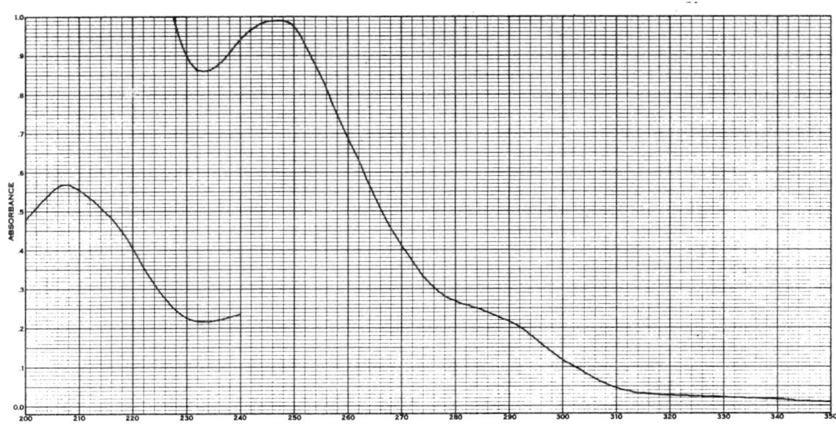

m-NITROBENZOYL CHLORIDE 2236

$C_7H_4ClNO_3$

Mol. Wt. 185.57

Solvent: Cyclohexane

λ Max. mμ	a_m	Cell mm	Conc. g/L
296	904	10	0.100
285.5	1340	10	0.100
221.5	27500	0.5	0.100

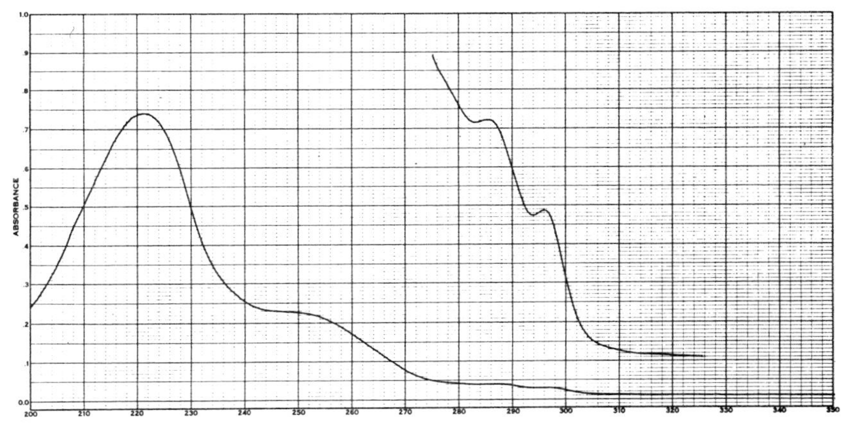

o-PHTHALOYL CHLORIDE 2237

$C_8H_4Cl_2O_2$

Mol. Wt. 203.03

M.P. 10-13°C   B.P. 131-135°C/1mm

Solvent: Cyclohexane

λ Max. mμ	a_m	Cell mm	Conc. g/L
285.5	3200	5	0.100
244.5	13500	1	0.100
211	27300	0.5	0.100

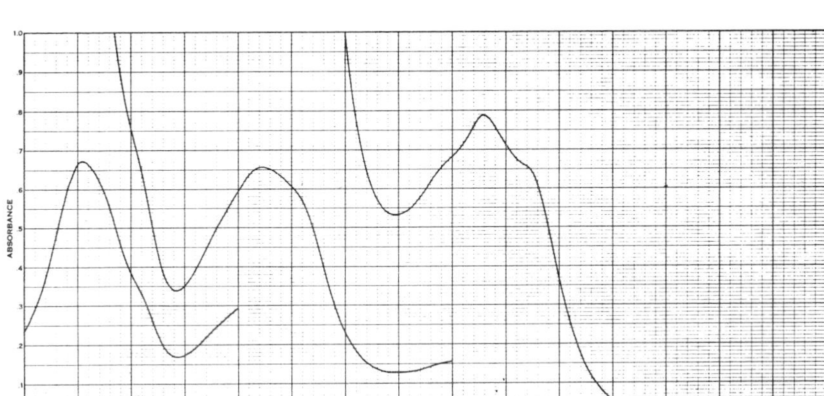

2238

2,3-DIMETHYLBENZOYL CHLORIDE

C_9H_9ClO

Mol. Wt. 168.62

Solvent: Methanol

λ Max. mμ	a_m	Cell mm	Conc. g/L
294	2260	5	0.100
247.5	13900	1	0.100
x	x	0.5	0.100

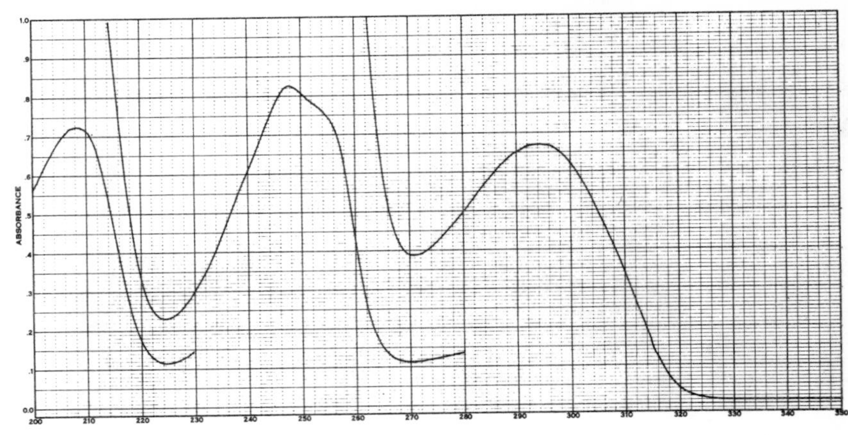

2239

3,4-DIMETHYLBENZOYL CHLORIDE

C_9H_9ClO

Mol. Wt. 168.62

Solvent: Methanol

λ Max. mμ	a_m	Cell mm	Conc. g/L
286	3590	4	0.100
255.5	27000	0.5	0.100
x	x	0.5	0.100

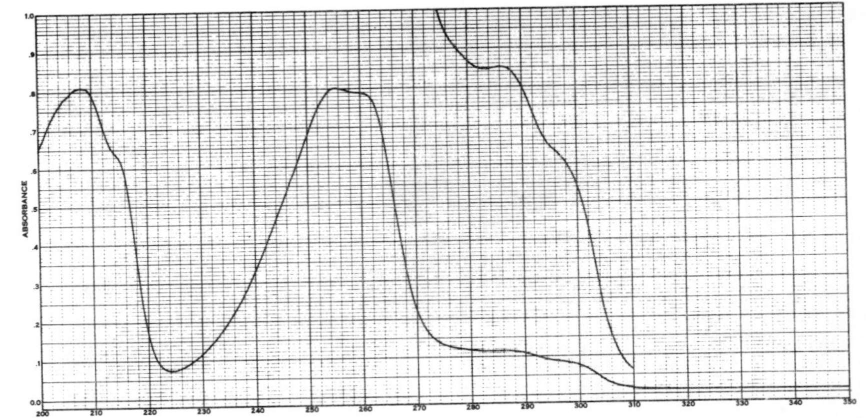

2240

3,5-DIMETHYLBENZOYL CHLORIDE

C_9H_9ClO

Mol. Wt. 168.62

B.P. 101-103°C/8mm

λ Max. mμ	a_m	Cell mm	Conc. g/L

Pure sample not available.

3-NITRO-p-TOLUOYL CHLORIDE 2241

$C_8H_6ClNO_3$
Mol. Wt. 199.59
Solvent: Methanol

λ Max. mμ	a_m	Cell mm	Conc. g/L
237	36000	0.5	0.100
x	x	0.5	0.100

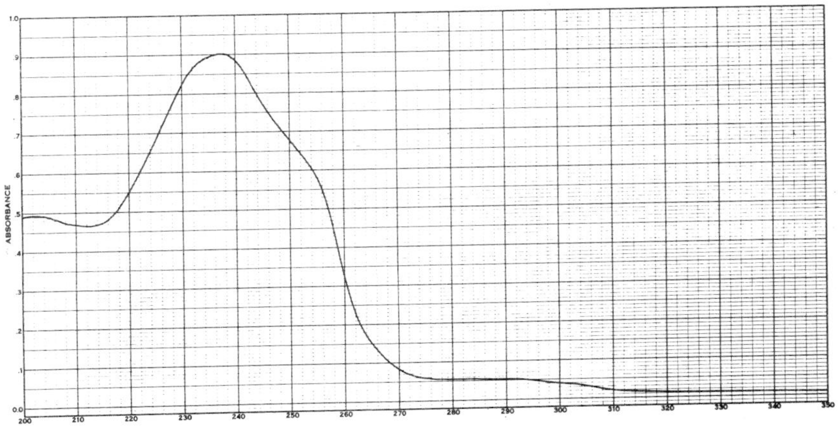

2-CHLORO-4-NITROBENZOYL CHLORIDE 2242

$C_7H_3Cl_2NO_3$
Mol. Wt. 220.01

λ Max. mμ	a_m	Cell mm	Conc. g/L

Pure sample not available.

2-CHLORO-5-NITROBENZOYL CHLORIDE 2243

$C_7H_3Cl_2NO_3$
Mol. Wt. 220.01

λ Max. mμ	a_m	Cell mm	Conc. g/L

Pure sample not available.

3,5-DIMETHOXYBENZOYL CHLORIDE 2244

$C_9H_9ClO_3$

Mol. Wt. 200.62

λ Max. mμ	a_m	Cell mm	Conc. g/L

Pure sample not available.

1-NAPHTHOYL CHLORIDE 2245

$C_{11}H_7ClO$

Mol. Wt. 190.63

M.P. 17-19°C

Solvent: Cyclohexane

λ Max. mμ	a_m	Cell mm	Conc. g/L
320	6790	0.5	0.100
242.5	16000	0.5	0.100
240.5	15900	0.5	0.100
210	31500	0.5	0.100

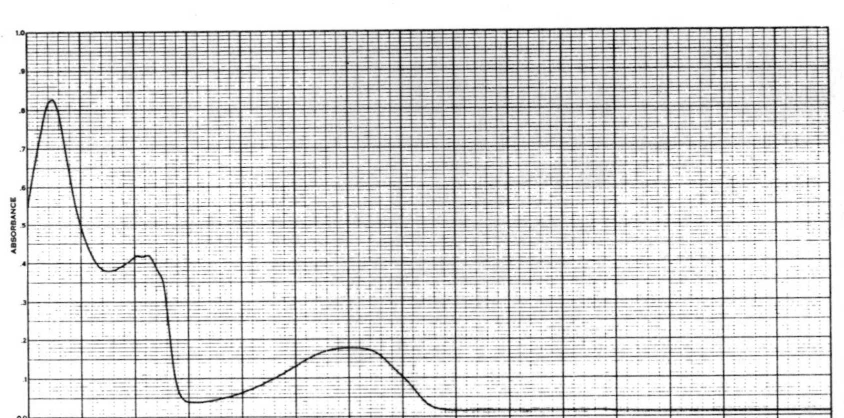

2-FUROYL CHLORIDE 2246

$C_5H_3ClO_2$

Mol. Wt. 130.53

B.P. 173-176°C (lit.)

Solvent: Cyclohexane

λ Max. mμ	a_m	Cell mm	Conc. g/L
x	x	10	2.700
272	13600	10	0.014
266.5	14300	10	0.014
232.5	2050	10	0.014
225	2330	10	0.014

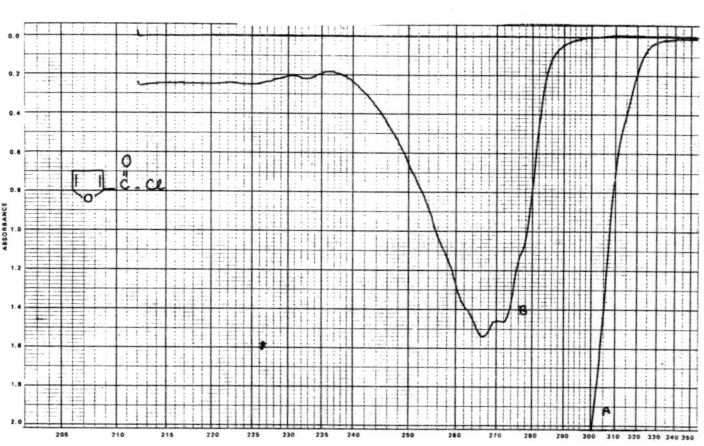

THE CARBOXYLIC ACID ANHYDRIDES

Aliphatic Compounds

The aliphatic acid anhydrides do not display any maxima in the near UV region (220 mμ - 350 mμ) and as a consequence there are no spectra in this section for compounds 2247 through 2257.

Olefinic Compounds

The unsaturated cyclic anhydrides such as compounds 2258, 2263, 2264, 2265, 2266 and 2267 do not produce any maxima above 220 mμ although a shoulder may be observed near 250 mμ. This shoulder, upon the addition of base, increases in intensity and may become a maximum at shorter wavelength (near 230 mμ).

Aromatic Compounds

Benzoic anhydride produces a spectrogram consisting of two major bands. The more intense band is observed at 228 mμ (ϵ_{max} = 21200) and the second band appears at about 270 mμ (ϵ_{max} = 2020) with a minor maximum or shoulder at 277 mμ.

The phthalic anhydrides (compounds 2271 and 2272) produce UV spectra similar in appearance to that of benzoic anhydride with appropriate shifts in wavelength and band intensity appropriate to the substituents that are present.

Compound	$\lambda_{max}(\epsilon_{max})$	$\lambda_{max}(\epsilon_{max})$	Solvent	Spectrum
4-Methylphthalic anhydride	233 (8830)	276 (1100)	Methanol	2271
4-Fluorophthalic anhydride	225 (8260)	272 (845)	Methanol	2272

The UV spectra of the anhydrides change upon the addition of base to the samples resulting in a hypsochromic shift to lower wavelength of about 15 mμ (compound 2267).

METHYLENESUCCINIC ANHYDRIDE

$C_5H_4O_3$
Mol. Wt. 112.09

Solvent: Methanol

2258

λ Max. mμ	a_m	Cell mm	Conc. g/L
x	x	20	0.100

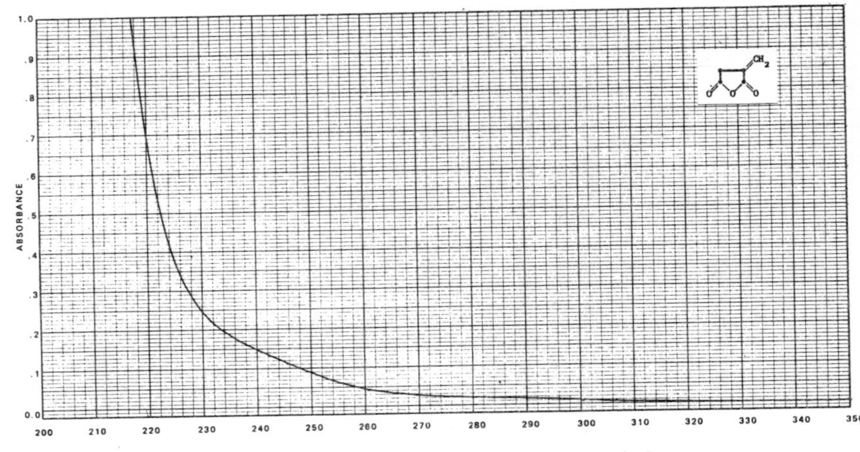

2258

METHYLENESUCCINIC ANHYDRIDE

$C_5H_4O_3$
Mol. Wt. 112.09

Solvent: Methanol KOH

λ Max. mμ	a_m	Cell mm	Conc. g/L
x	x	10	0.100

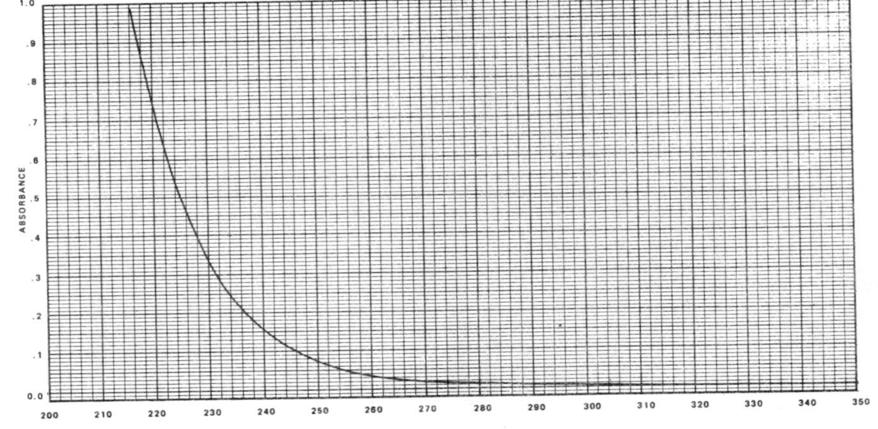

2259

λ Max. mμ	a_m	Cell mm	Conc. g/L

The alicyclic anhydrides (compounds 2259 through 2262) do not display any maxima in the near UV.

MALEIC ANHYDRIDE

$C_4H_2O_3$
Mol. Wt. 98.06
M.P. 52.4-52.6°C (lit.) B.P. 199-200°C (lit.)
Solvent: Methanol

λ Max. mμ	a_m	Cell mm	Conc. g/L
x	x	10	2.096
x	x	10	0.210
x	x	10	0.021

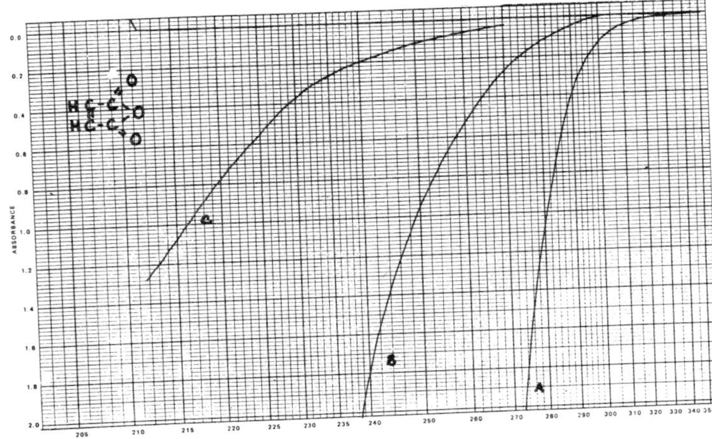

2264

CITRACONIC ANHYDRIDE

$C_5H_4O_3$
Mol. Wt. 112.09
Solvent: Methanol

λ Max. mμ	a_m	Cell mm	Conc. g/L
206	9730	1	0.1024

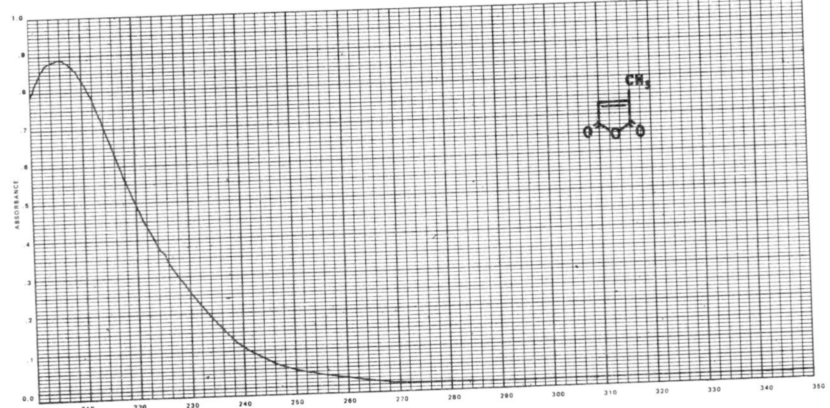

λ Max. mμ	a_m	Cell mm	Conc. g/L

DIMETHYLMALEIC ANHYDRIDE 2265

$C_6H_6O_3$
Mol. Wt. 126.11
M.P. 88-89°C
Solvent: Methanol

λ Max. mμ	a_m	Cell mm	Conc. g/L
207	8070	1	0.100

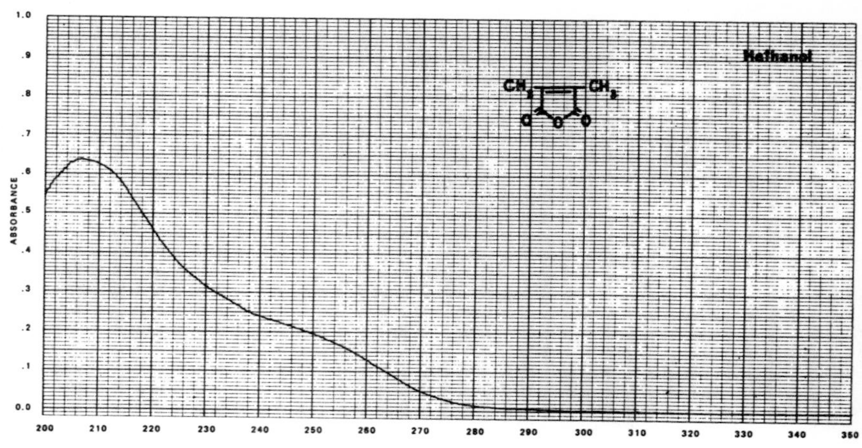

DIMETHYLMALEIC ANHYDRIDE 2265

$C_6H_6O_3$
Mol. Wt. 126.11
M.P. 88-89°C
Solvent: Methanol KOH

λ Max. mμ	a_m	Cell mm	Conc. g/L
234	6340	1	0.100

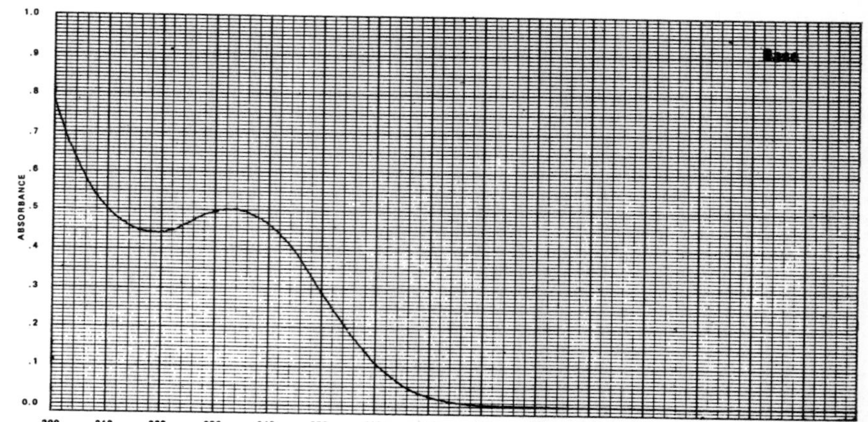

BROMOMALEIC ANHYDRIDE 2266

C_4HBrO_3
Mol. Wt. 176.96
Solvent: Methanol

λ Max. mμ	a_m	Cell mm	Conc. g/L
218	11000	1	0.100

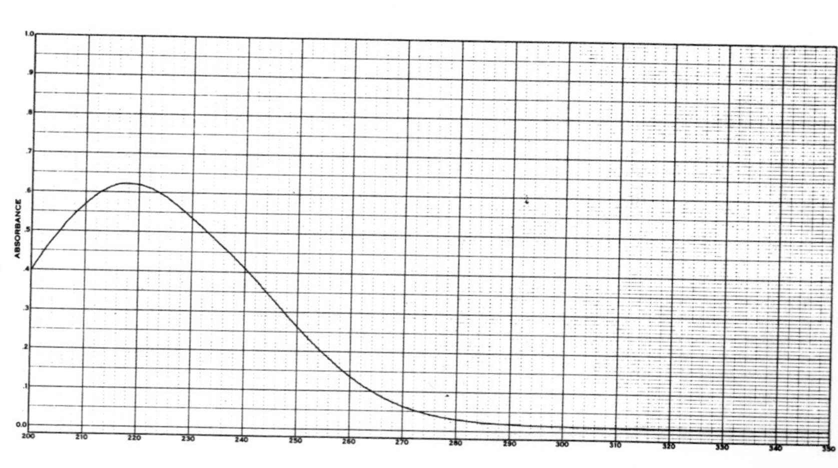

1-CYCLOHEXENE-1,2-DICARBOXYLIC ANHYDRIDE

2267

$C_8H_8O_3$

Mol. Wt. 152.15

Solvent: Methanol

λ Max. mμ	a_m	Cell mm	Conc. g/L
x	x	5	0.100
205.5	8540	1	0.100

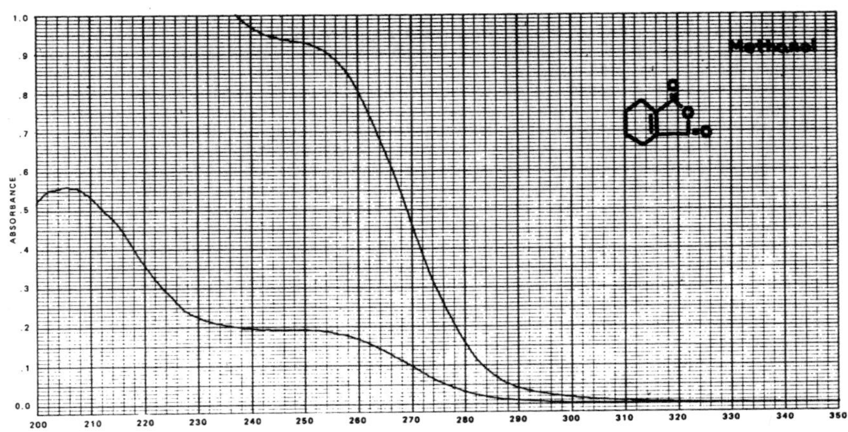

4-CYCLOHEXENE-1,2-DICARBOXYLIC ACID, ANHYDRIDE

2268

$C_8H_8O_3$

Mol. Wt. 152.15

λ Max. mμ	a_m	Cell mm	Conc. g/L

Pure sample not available.

CINNAMIC ANHYDRIDE

2269

$C_{18}H_{14}O_3$

Mol. Wt. 278.31

M.P. 134-136°C

Solvent: Methanol

λ Max. mμ	a_m	Cell mm	Conc. g/L
280	37300	1	0.0500
213	25000	1	0.0500
203	27800	1	0.0500

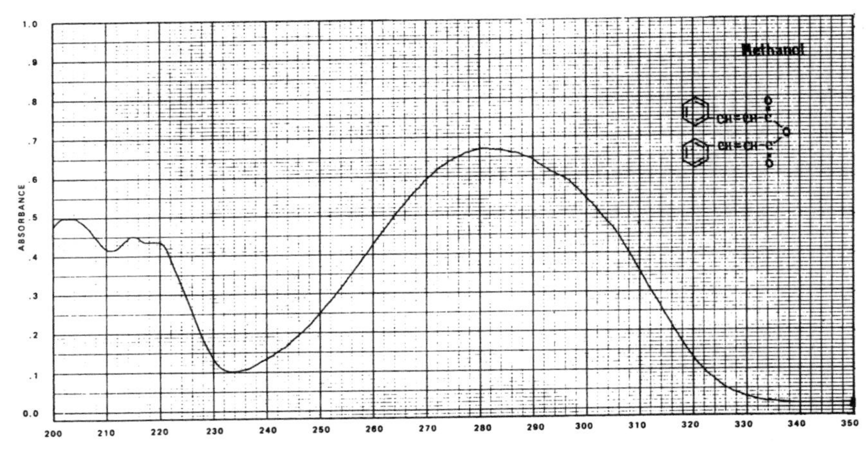

BENZOIC ANHYDRIDE 2270

$C_{14}H_{10}O_3$

Mol. Wt. 226.22

M.P. 42°C (lit.)

Solvent: Methanol

λ Max. mμ	a_m	Cell mm	Conc. g/L
x	x	10	0.400
276.5	1770	10	0.160
270	2020	10	0.160
227.5	21200	10	0.016

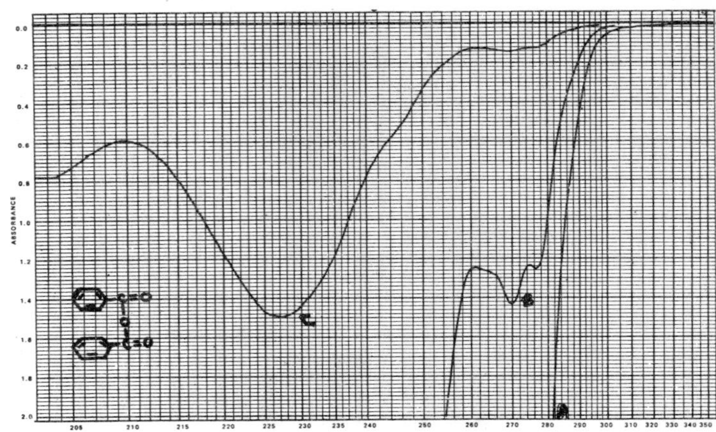

4-METHYLPHTHALIC ANHYDRIDE 2271

$C_9H_6O_3$

Mol. Wt. 162.15

M.P. 90-92°C

Solvent: Methanol

λ Max. mμ	a_m	Cell mm	Conc. g/L
276	1100	10	0.115
232.5	8830	1	0.115

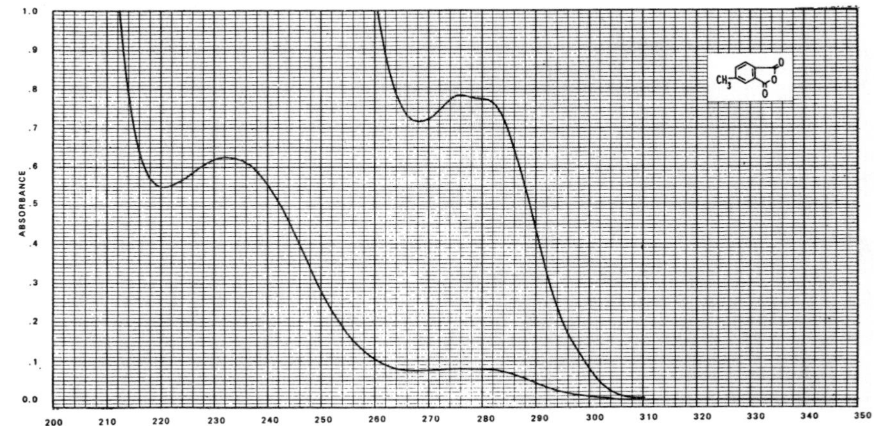

4-FLUOROPHTHALIC ANHYDRIDE 2272

$C_8H_3FO_3$

Mol. Wt. 166.11

M.P. 78-79°C

Solvent: Methanol

λ Max. mμ	a_m	Cell mm	Conc. g/L
272	845	10	0.100
225	8260	1	0.100

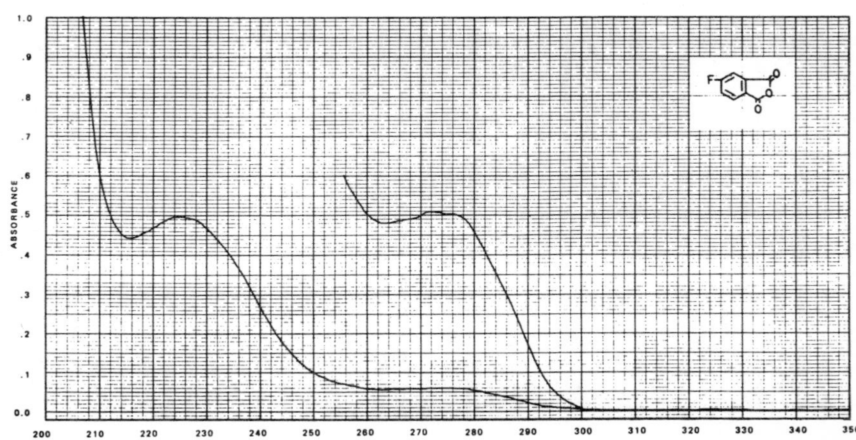

1,2,4,5-BENZENETETRACARBOXYLIC 1,2:4,5-DIANHYDRIDE 2273

$C_{10}H_2O_6$
Mol. Wt. 281.13
Solvent: Methanol

λ Max. mμ	a_m	Cell mm	Conc. g/L
291.5	1900	10	0.100
210	24300	10	0.005

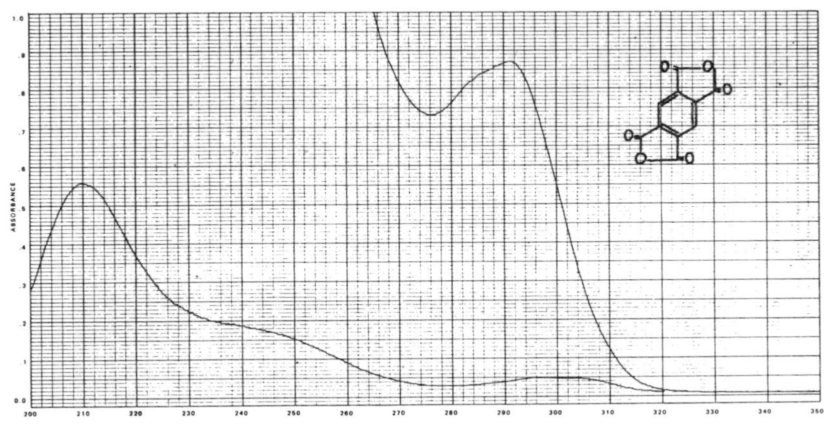

NAPHTHALIC ANHYDRIDE 2274

$C_{12}H_6O_3$
Mol. Wt. 198.18
M.P. 272-273°C
Solvent: Methanol

λ Max. mμ	a_m	Cell mm	Conc. g/L
338	5710	5	0.0500
322.5	6180	5	0.0500
309	6370	5	0.0500
301	6290	5	0.0500
225	35400	1	0.0500

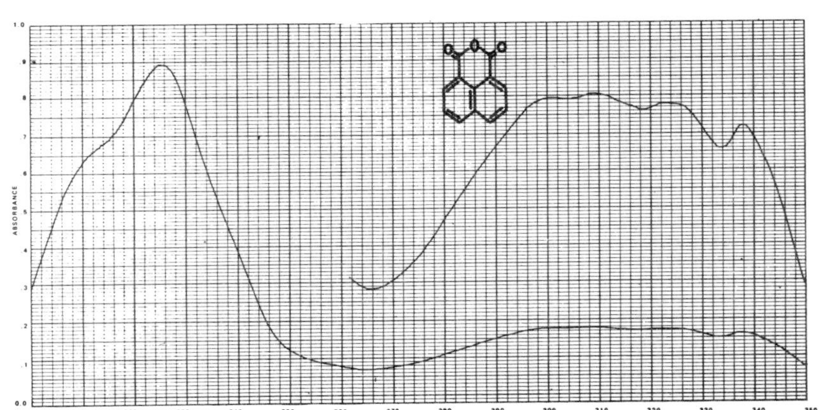

NAPHTHALIC ANHYDRIDE 2274

$C_{12}H_6O_3$
Mol. Wt. 198.18
M.P. 272-273°C
Solvent: Methanol KOH

λ Max. mμ	a_m	Cell mm	Conc. g/L
295.5	7300	5	0.0500
224.5	43300	1	0.0300

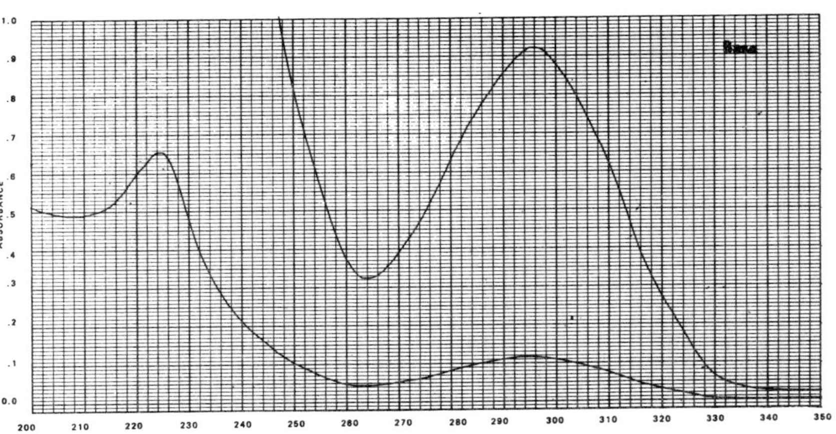

NOTES

THE AMIDES

Aliphatic Compounds

The primary, secondary and tertiary amides do not produce any maxima in the near ultraviolet region and thus there are no spectra in this section for compounds 2275 - 2285, 2295 - 2303 or 2347 - 2360.

The Acrylamides

The acrylamides which contain the conjugated $H_2C{=}CH{-}C({=}O){-}$ group, display an absorbance band of moderate intensity near 226 mμ (spectra 2304, 2305 and 2306).

Aromatic Compounds

The benzamides (compounds 2288 - 2293) give rise to one major maxima in the near UV near 225 mμ which undergoes hypsochromic and bathochromic shifts of up to 10 mμ depending upon the substituents that are present. Two weaker maxima or shoulders may be observed at about 270 mμ in the near UV for the benzamides.

The anilides, in which case the phenyl group is bonded to the nitrogen atom, display their major band near 242 mμ with one or more weak maxima or shoulders near 280 mμ.

The table shown below lists the wavelength and intensity data for a selected listing of aromatic amides that were examined in methanol solution.

Compound	$\lambda_{max}(\epsilon_{max})$	$\lambda_{max}(\epsilon_{max})$	Spectrum
Benzamide	225 (11000)	268 (691)	2288
Benzamide–, 4-nitro-	216 * (5810)	260 (11300)	2292
Benzamide–, 2-bromo-	224 * (6800)	267 (406)	2291
Benzamide–, 3-methyl-	229 (10500)	276 (949)	2289
Benzamide–, 2-hydroxy-	235 (7120)	302 (3810)	2293
Diphenylacetamide	234 (10500)	----------	2368
Diphenylformamide	238 (13300)	----------	2367
Acetanilide	241 (15400)	282 (630)	Lit.
Acetanilide–, 3-methyl-	243 (14700)	----------	2322
Acetanilide–, 3-fluoro-	241 (15300)	272 (2220)	2326

* Shoulder

The spectra of the amides do not undergo any significant changes upon the addition of either acid or base.

2-PHENYLBUTYRAMIDE

2286

$C_{10}H_{13}NO$
Mol. Wt. 163.22
M.P. 83-85°C
Solvent: Methanol

λ Max. mμ	a_m	Cell mm	Conc. g/L
264	158	10	0.500
257.5	209	10	0.500
252	173	10	0.500
247	140	10	0.500
x	x	1	0.100

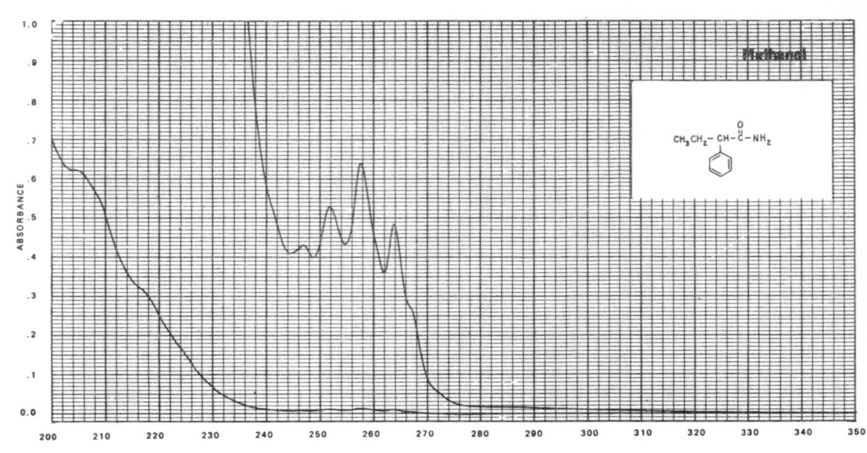

1-NAPHTHALENEACETAMIDE

2287

$C_{12}H_{11}NO$
Mol. Wt. 185.23
M.P. 183-184°C
Solvent: Methanol

λ Max. mμ	a_m	Cell mm	Conc. g/L
291	5150	5	0.0200
288	5150	5	0.0200
281.5	7320	5	0.0200
270.5	6280	5	0.0200
223.5	75800	1	0.0200

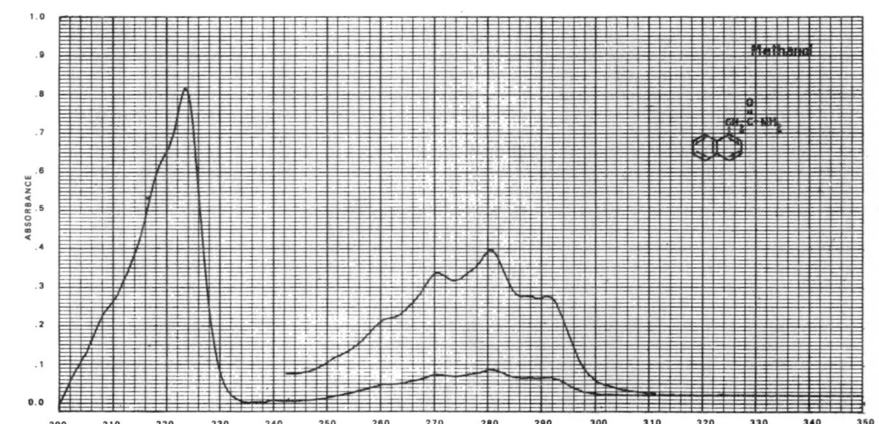

BENZAMIDE

2288

C_7H_7NO
Mol. Wt. 121.14
M.P. 130°C
Solvent: Methanol

λ Max. mμ	a_m	Cell mm	Conc. g/L
267.5	691	10	0.100
224.5	11000	1	0.100

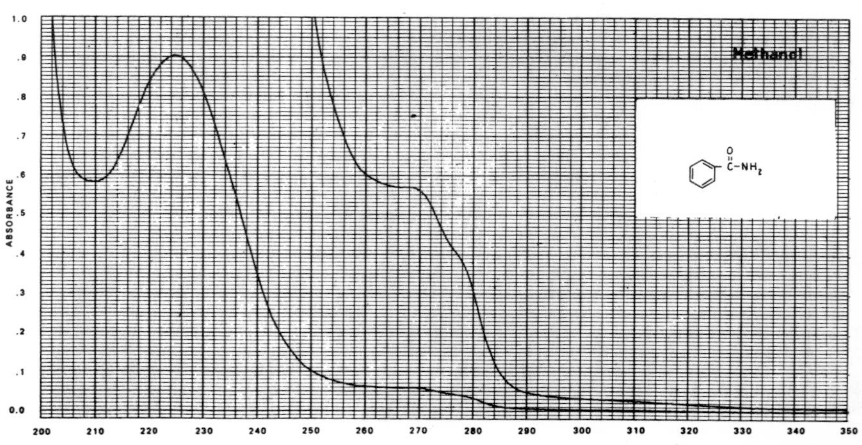

m-TOLUAMIDE

2289

C_8H_9NO

Mol. Wt. 135.16

M.R. 94-95°C (lit.)

Solvent: Methanol

λ Max. mμ	a_m	Cell mm	Conc. g/L
x	x	10	2.00
276	949	10	0.200
229	10500	10	0.020

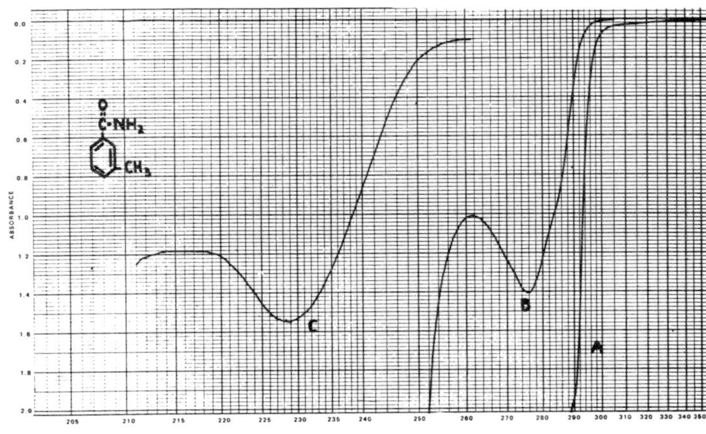

p-TOLUAMIDE

2290

C_8H_9NO

Mol. Wt. 135.16

Solvent: Methanol

λ Max. mμ	a_m	Cell mm	Conc. g/L
x	x	10	2.000
234.5	14400	10	0.010

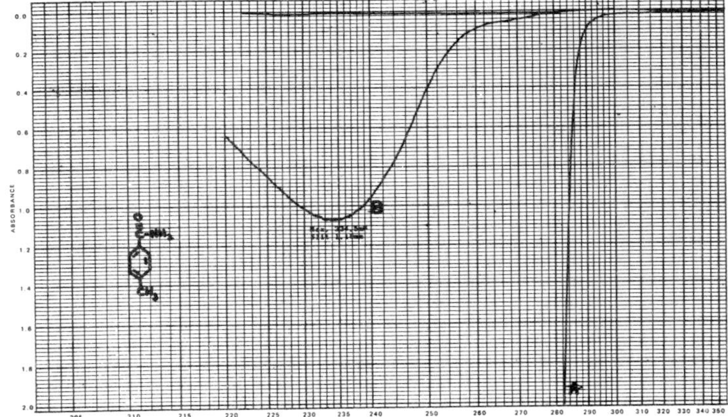

o-BROMOBENZAMIDE

2291

C_7H_6BrNO

Mol. Wt. 200.04

M.P. 160-161°C

Solvent: Methanol

λ Max. mμ	a_m	Cell mm	Conc. g/L
266.5	406	5	0.0500
x	x	1	0.0500

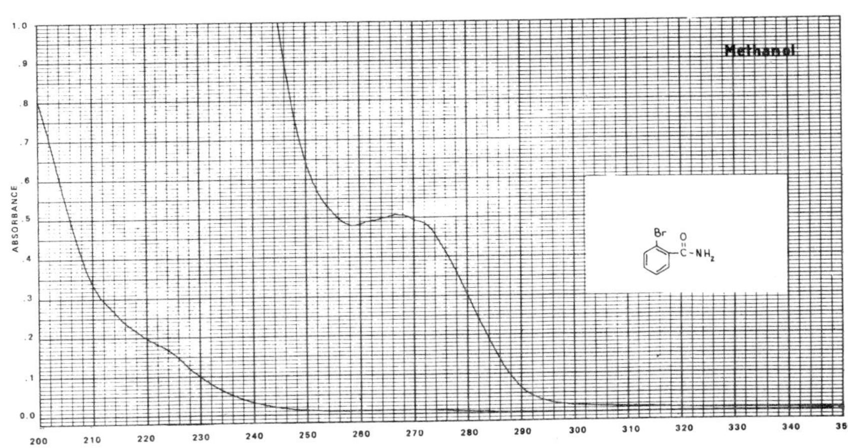

p-NITROBENZAMIDE 2292

$C_7H_6N_2O_3$
Mol. Wt. 166.13
M.P. 199-200°C
Solvent: Methanol

λ Max. mμ	a_m	Cell mm	Conc. g/L
260	11300	10	0.010

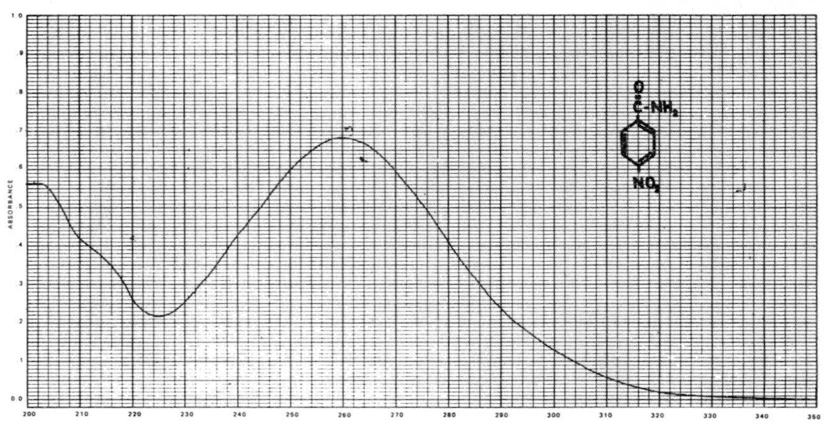

SALICYLAMIDE 2293

$C_7H_7NO_2$
Mol. Wt. 137.14
M.P. 139°C
Solvent: Methanol

λ Max. mμ	a_m	Cell mm	Conc. g/L
302	3810	2	0.0528
234.5	7120	2	0.0528

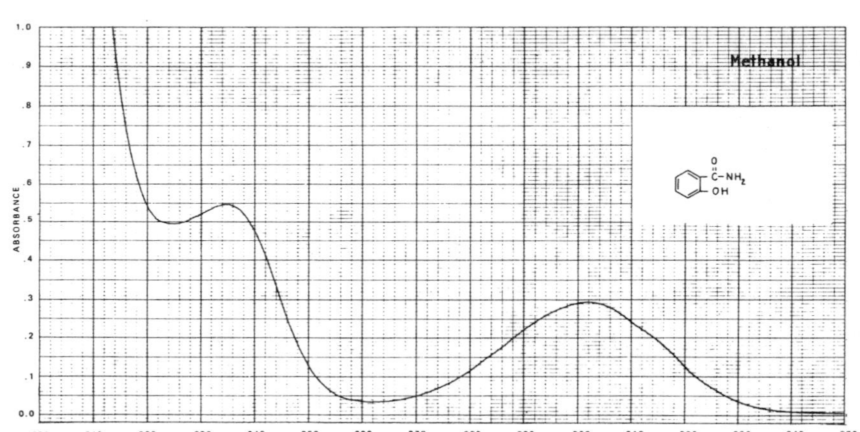

SALICYLAMIDE 2293

$C_7H_7NO_2$
Mol. Wt. 137.14
M.P. 139°C
Solvent: Methanol KOH

λ Max. mμ	a_m	Cell mm	Conc. g/L
329	5690	2	0.0528
242.5	7050	2	0.0528
214	33000	2	0.0106

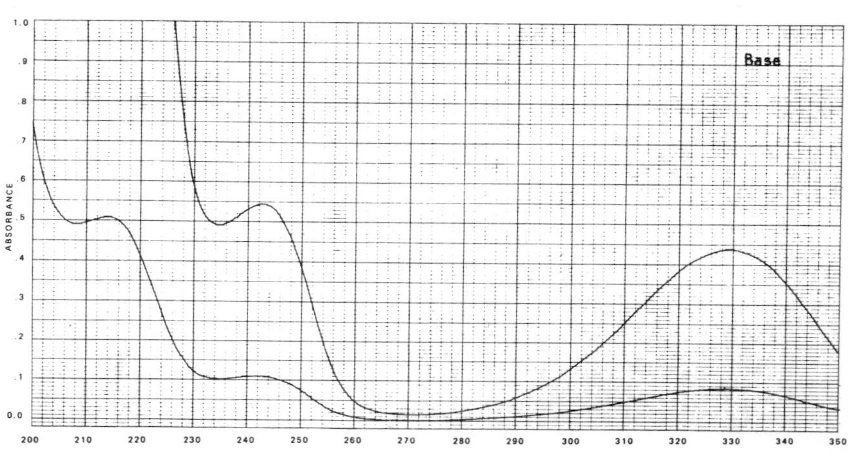

2-FURAMIDE

$C_5H_5NO_2$

Mol. Wt. 111.10

M.P. 144.5-145°C

Solvent: Methanol

2294

λ Max. mμ	a_m	Cell mm	Conc. g/L
247.5	13200	1	0.0500
213	6510	1	0.0500

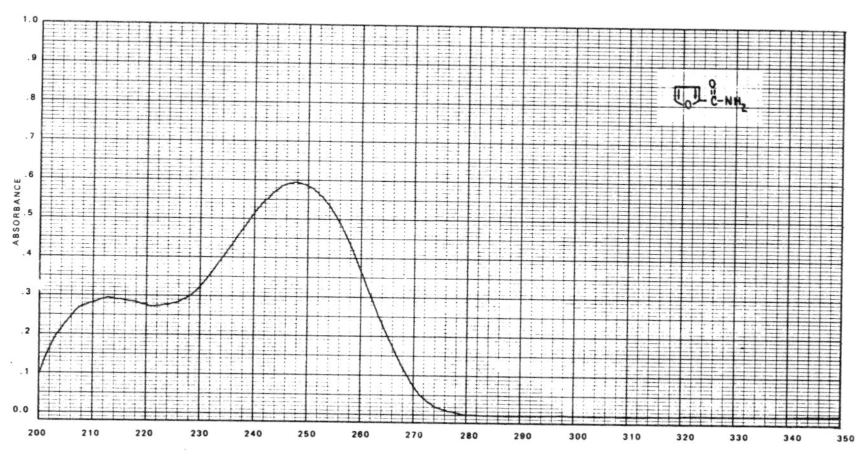

2295

λ Max. mμ	a_m	Cell mm	Conc. g/L

The alkyl secondary amides (compounds 2295 through 2303) do not display any maxima in the near UV.

N-tert-BUTYLACRYLAMIDE

$C_7H_{13}NO$

Mol. Wt. 127.18

M.P. 128-130°C

Solvent: Methanol

2304

λ Max. mμ	a_m	Cell mm	Conc. g/L
226	4900	10	0.010
203	8340	10	0.010

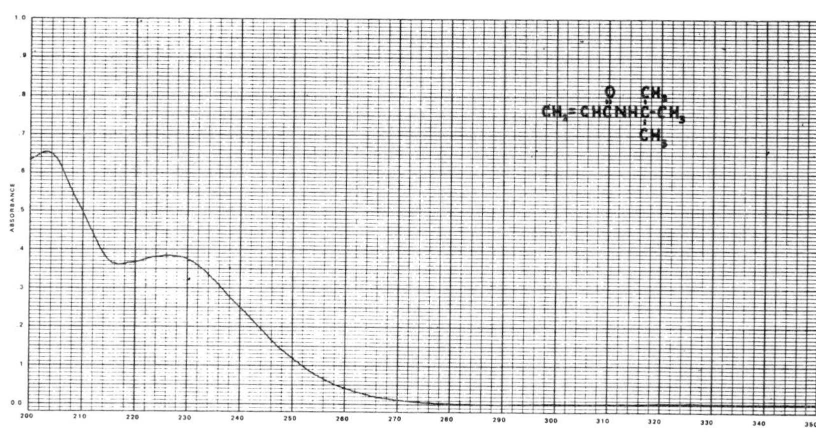

N-(1,1,3,3-TETRAMETHYLBUTYL)ACRYLAMIDE 2305

$C_{11}H_{21}NO$

Mol. Wt. 183.30

Solvent: Methanol

λ Max. mμ	a_m	Cell mm	Conc. g/L
226.5	7190	2	0.100
x	x	1	0.100

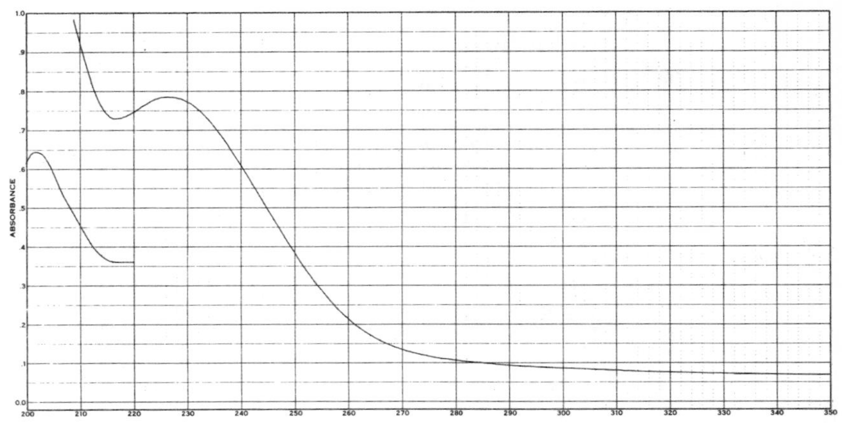

N-ALLYLACRYLAMIDE 2306

C_6H_9NO

Mol. Wt. 111.14

Solvent: Methanol

λ Max. mμ	a_m	Cell mm	Conc. g/L
222.1	4930	2	0.100
x	x	1	0.100

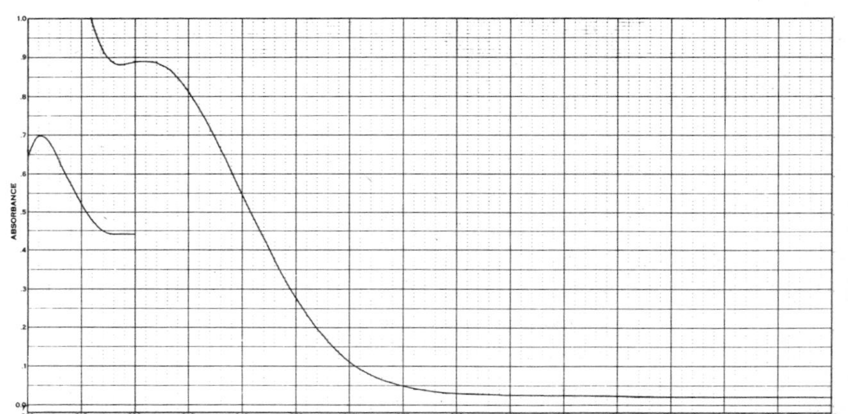

N-(α-METHYLBENZYL)FORMAMIDE 2307

$C_9H_{11}NO$

Mol. Wt. 149.19

M.P. 45°C

Solvent: Methanol

λ Max. mμ	a_m	Cell mm	Conc. g/L
263.5	157	10	0.500
257.5	206	10	0.500
251.5	176	10	0.500
247	143	10	0.500
x	x	1	0.100

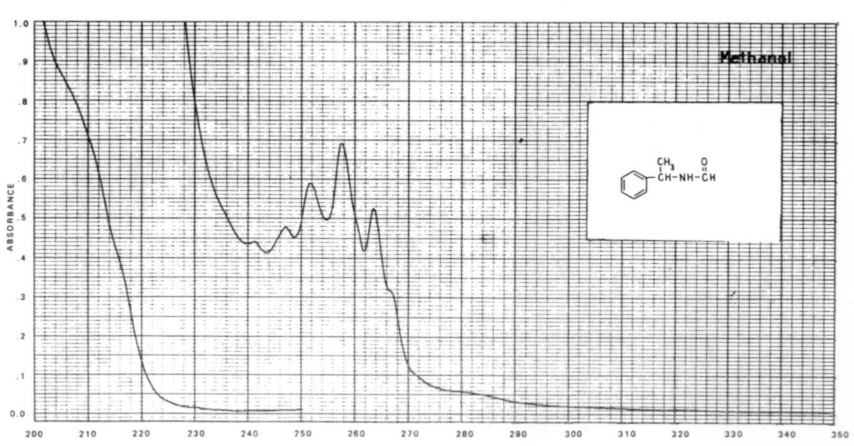

N-(α-BENZYLPHENETHYL)FORMAMIDE

2308

$C_{16}H_{17}NO$

Mol. Wt. 239.32

Solvent: Methanol

λ Max. mμ	a_m	Cell mm	Conc. g/L
264.5	706	10	0.100
258.5	862	10	0.100
252.5	859	10	0.100
247.5	830	10	0.100
x	x	1	0.100

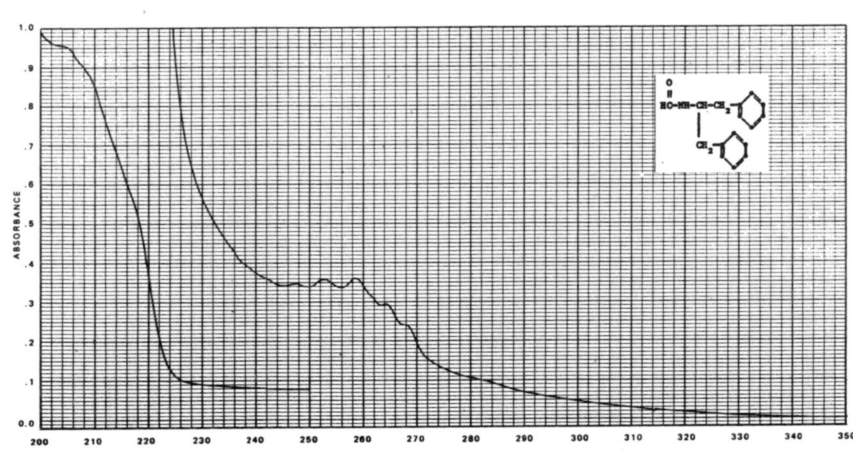

N-PHENETHYLACETAMIDE

2309

$C_{10}H_{13}NO$

Mol. Wt. 163.22

Solvent: Dioxane

λ Max. mμ	a_m	Cell mm	Conc. g/L
268	107	20	0.428
264	117	20	0.428
258.5	150	20	0.428
253.5	127	20	0.428
x	x	1	0.428

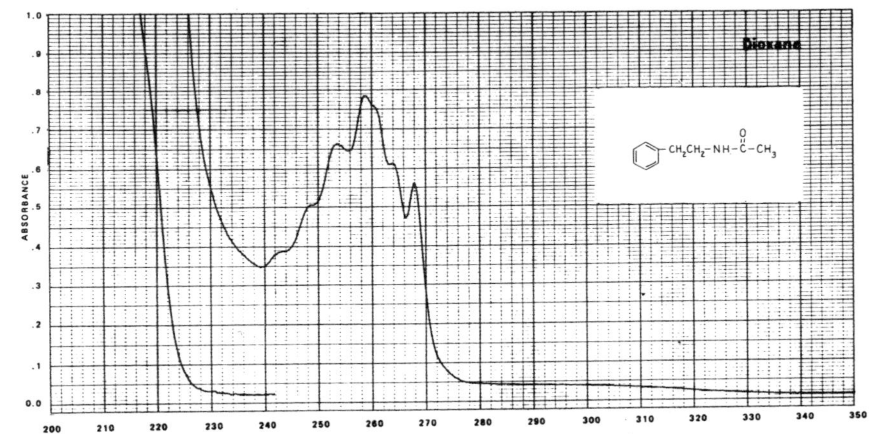

N-(α-METHYLBENZYL)ACETAMIDE

2310

$C_{10}H_{13}NO$

Mol. Wt. 163.22

M.P. 76°C

Solvent: Methanol

λ Max. mμ	a_m	Cell mm	Conc. g/L
263.5	144	10	0.500
257	193	10	0.500
251.5	183	10	0.500
246.5	136	10	0.500
x	x	2	0.100

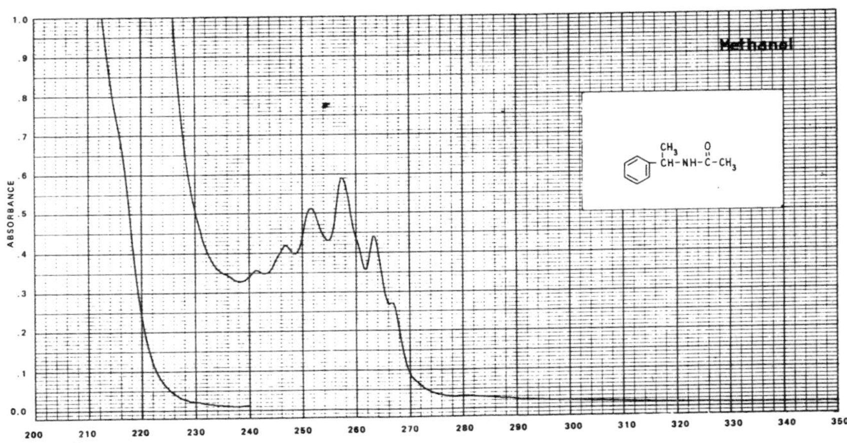

N-PHENETHYL-2,2,2-TRIFLUOROACETAMIDE 2311

$C_{10}H_{10}F_3NO$
Mol. Wt. 217.19
M.P. 55.5-56.5°C
Solvent: Methanol

λ Max. mμ	a_m	Cell mm	Conc. g/L
267	118	10	1.00
263	160	10	1.00
257	207	10	1.00
252	179	10	1.00
246.5	152	10	1.00
241	144	10	1.00

N-METHYL-2-PHENYLACETAMIDE 2312

$C_9H_{11}NO$
Mol. Wt. 149.20
M.P. 56-59°C
Solvent: Methanol

λ Max. mμ	a_m	Cell mm	Conc. g/L
267	68.5	10	0.600
264	150	10	0.600
258	192	10	0.600
252	152	10	0.600
247	111	10	0.600
242	86.5	10	0.600

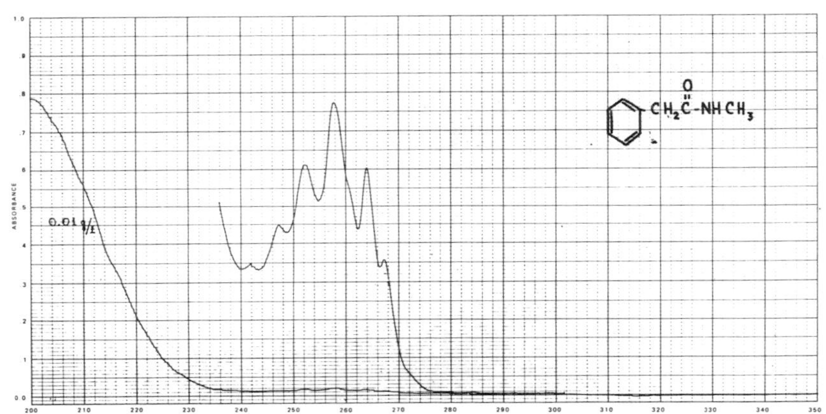

N-BENZYL-3-CHLOROPROPIONAMIDE 2313

$C_{10}H_{12}ClNO$
Mol. Wt. 197.67
Solvent: Methanol

λ Max. mμ	a_m	Cell mm	Conc. g/L
x	x	10	2.224
267	106	10	0.667
263.5	161	10	0.667
257.5	207	10	0.667
252	174	10	0.667
247.5	134	10	0.667
242	104	10	0.667
x	x	10	0.067

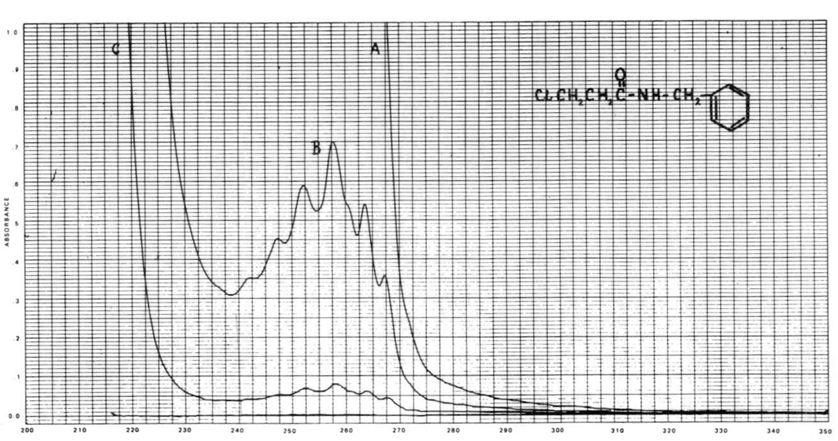

N-BENZYL-2-PHENYLACETAMIDE

2314

$C_{15}H_{15}NO$
Mol. Wt. 225.29
Solvent: Methanol

λ Max. mμ	a_m	Cell mm	Conc. g/L
263.5	188	40	0.100
258	243	40	0.100
252	208	40	0.100
x	x	2	0.100

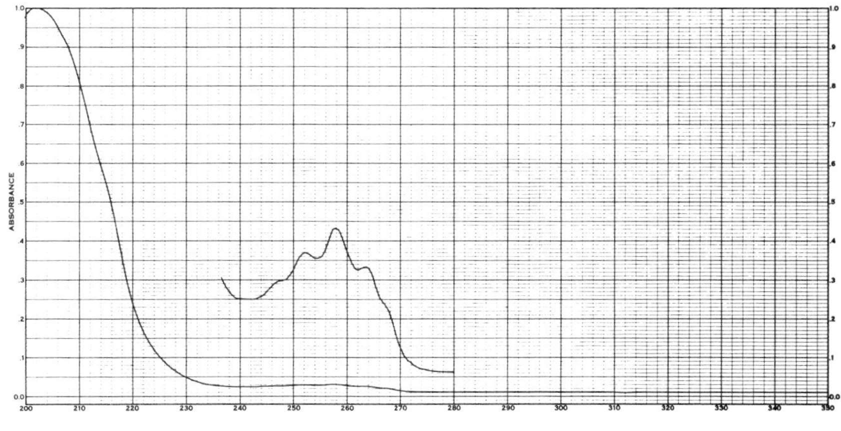

PROPIONANILIDE

2315

$C_9H_{11}NO$
Mol. Wt. 149.19
M.P. 105-107°C
Solvent: Methanol

λ Max. mμ	a_m	Cell mm	Conc. g/L
242	15700	1	0.0800

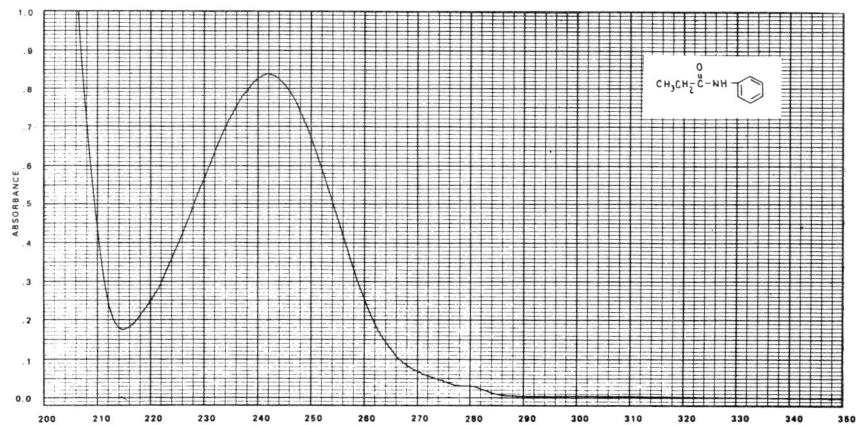

BUTYRANILIDE

2316

$C_{10}H_{13}NO$
Mol. Wt. 163.22
M.P. 93-95°C
Solvent: Methanol

λ Max. mμ	a_m	Cell mm	Conc. g/L
241.5	15600	1	0.100

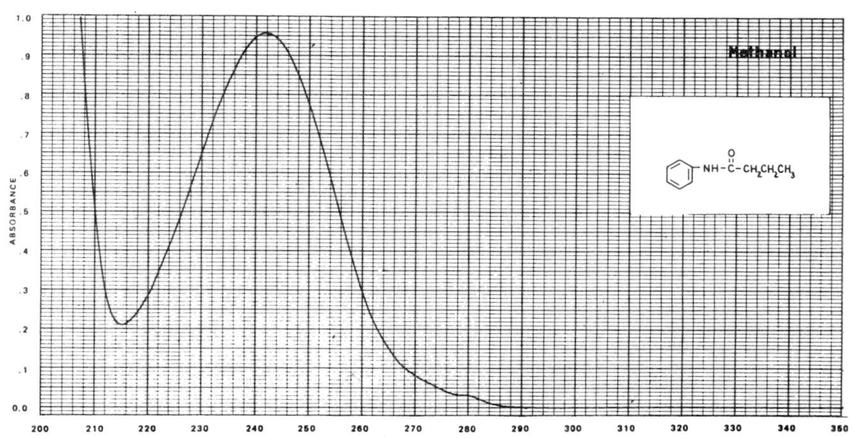

ISOBUTYRANILIDE

2317

$C_{10}H_{13}NO$

Mol. Wt. 163.22

M.P. 104°C

Solvent: Methanol

λ Max. mμ	a_m	Cell mm	Conc. g/L
279.5	666	10	0.100
241.5	13400	1	0.100

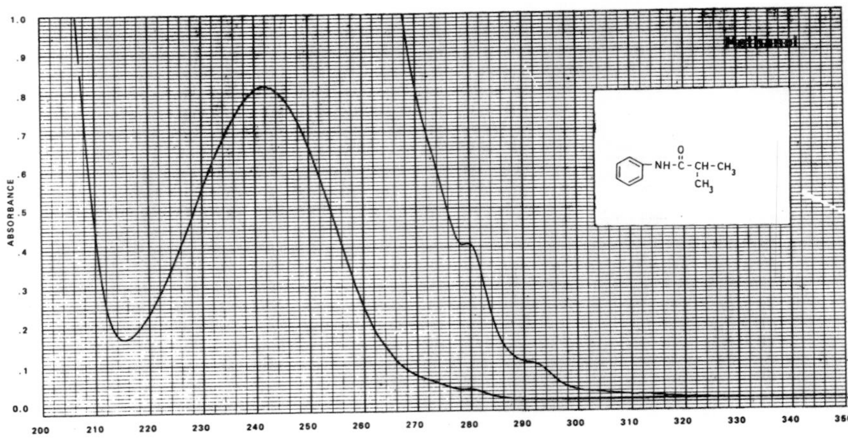

2-CHLOROACETANILIDE

2318

C_8H_8ClNO

Mol. Wt. 169.62

M.P. 134-135°C

Solvent: Methanol

λ Max. mμ	a_m	Cell mm	Conc. g/L
244	12000	10	0.010

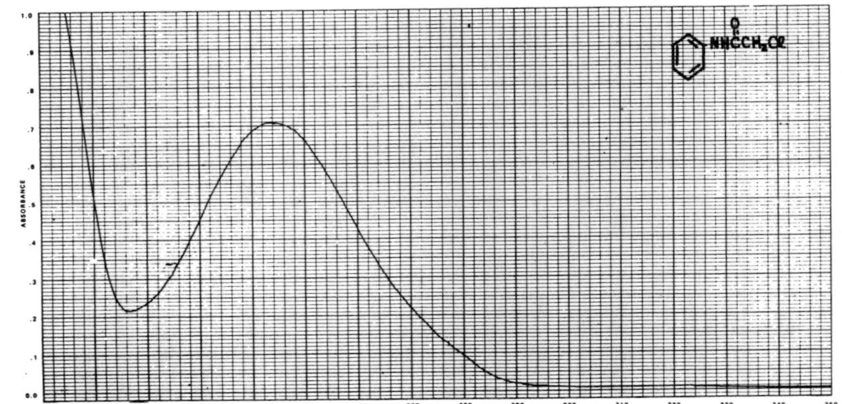

ACETOACETANILIDE

2319

$C_{10}H_{11}NO_2$

Mol. Wt. 177.21

M.P. 85°C (lit.)

Solvent: Methanol

λ Max. mμ	a_m	Cell mm	Conc. g/L
x	x	10	0.376
x	x	10	0.038
244	13200	10	0.019

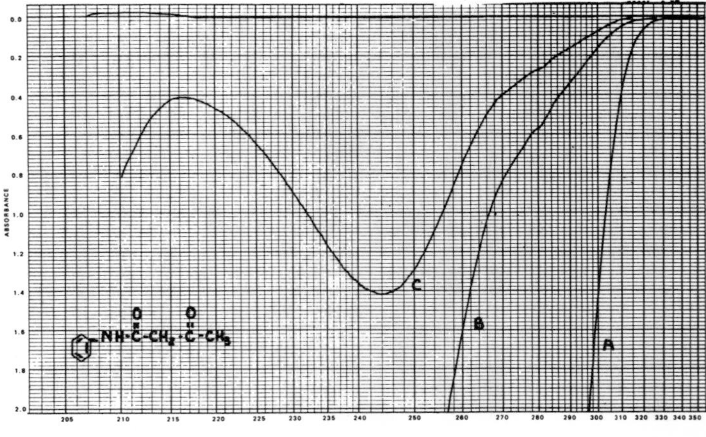

MALONANILIDE

2320

$C_{15}H_{14}N_2O_2$

Mol. Wt. 254.28

M.P. 229-230.5°C (lit.)

Solvent: Methanol

λ Max. mμ	a_m	Cell mm	Conc. g/L
x	x	10	0.412
245	34300	10	0.012

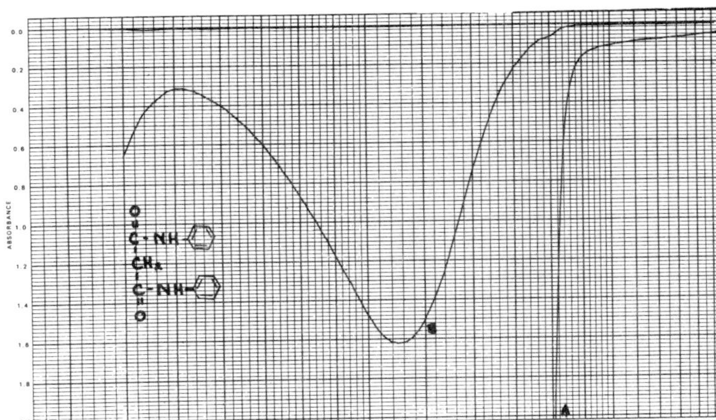

o-ACETOTOLUIDIDE

2321

$C_9H_{11}NO$

Mol. Wt. 149.20

M.R. 110-111°C (lit.)

Solvent: Methanol

λ Max. mμ	a_m	Cell mm	Conc. g/L
x	x	10	2.000
227.5	7340	10	0.020

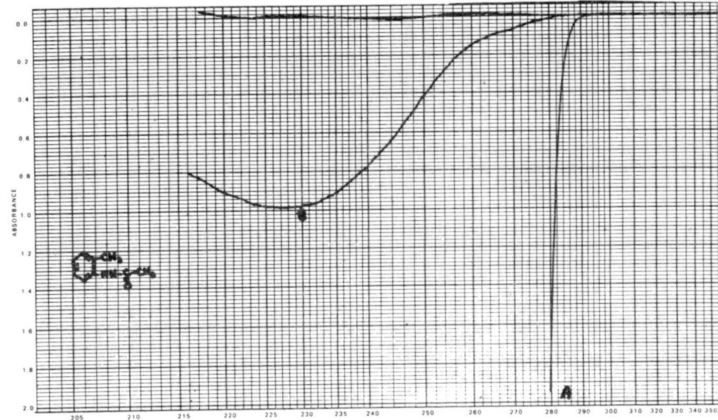

m-ACETOTOLUIDIDE

2322

$C_9H_{11}NO$

Mol. Wt. 149.19

M.R. 65-66°C (lit.)

Solvent: Methanol

λ Max. mμ	a_m	Cell mm	Conc. g/L
x	x	10	2.000
243	14700	10	0.010

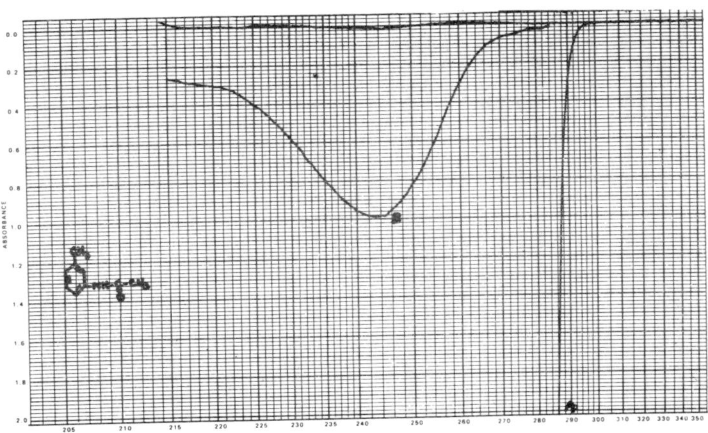

p-ACETOTOLUIDIDE

2323

$C_9H_{11}NO$

Mol. Wt. 150.20

M.R. 148-149°C (lit.)

Solvent: Methanol

λ Max. mμ	a_m	Cell mm	Conc. g/L
x	x	10	2.000
244	17700	10	0.010

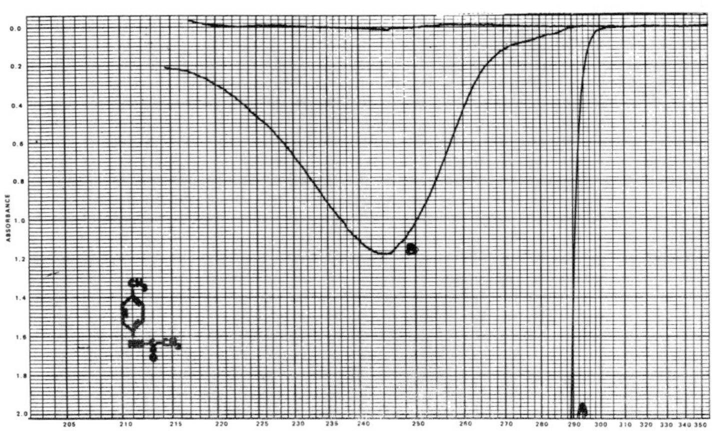

p-ETHYLACETANILIDE

2324

$C_{10}H_{13}NO$

Mol. Wt. 163.21

M.P. 90.1-90.7°C

Solvent: Methanol

λ Max. mμ	a_m	Cell mm	Conc. g/L
245	15500	10	0.010

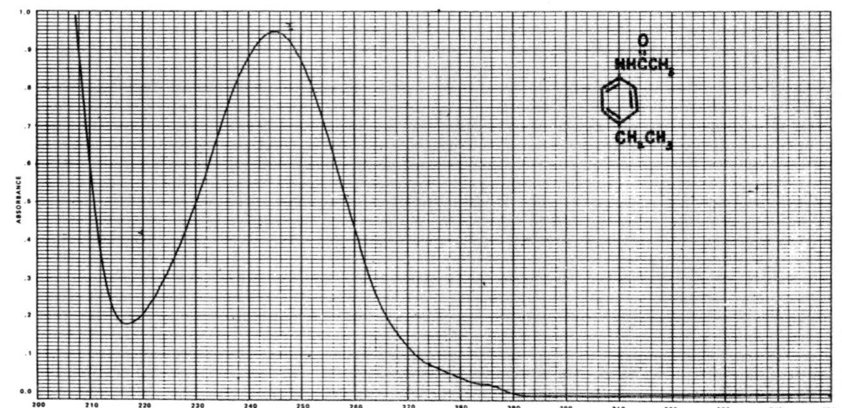

p-tert-BUTYLACETANILIDE

2325

$C_{12}H_{17}NO$

Mol. Wt. 191.26

Solvent: Methanol

λ Max. mμ	a_m	Cell mm	Conc. g/L
245.5	16800	10	0.010

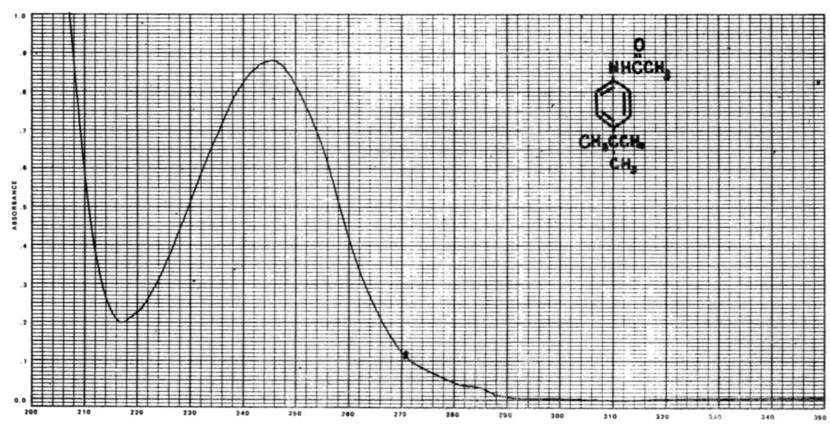

3'-FLUOROACETANILIDE

2326

C_8H_8FNO

Mol. Wt. 153.16

M.P. 88°C

Solvent: Methanol

λ Max. mμ	a_m	Cell mm	Conc. g/L
278.5	1760	5	0.0800
272.5	2220	5	0.0800
240.5	15300	1	0.0800

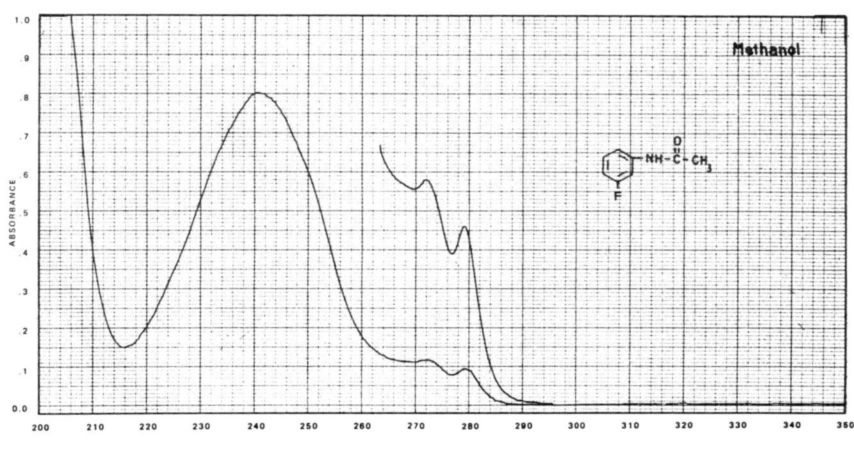

4'-FLUOROACETANILIDE

2327

C_8H_8FNO

Mol. Wt. 153.16

M.P. 152-153°C

Solvent: Methanol

λ Max. mμ	a_m	Cell mm	Conc. g/L
276	1170	10	0.100
239	12200	1	0.100

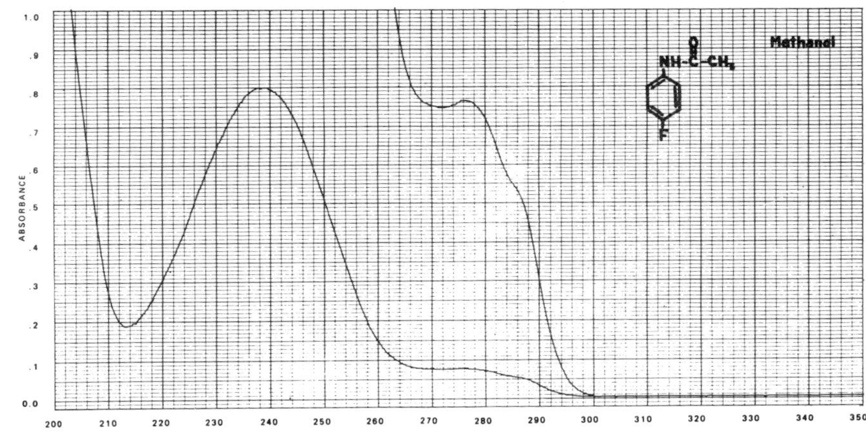

o-CHLOROACETANILIDE

2328

C_8H_8ClNO

Mol. Wt. 169.61

M.P. 87-88°C (lit.)

Solvent: Methanol

λ Max. mμ	a_m	Cell mm	Conc. g/L
x	x	10	0.464
250.5	15300	10	0.014

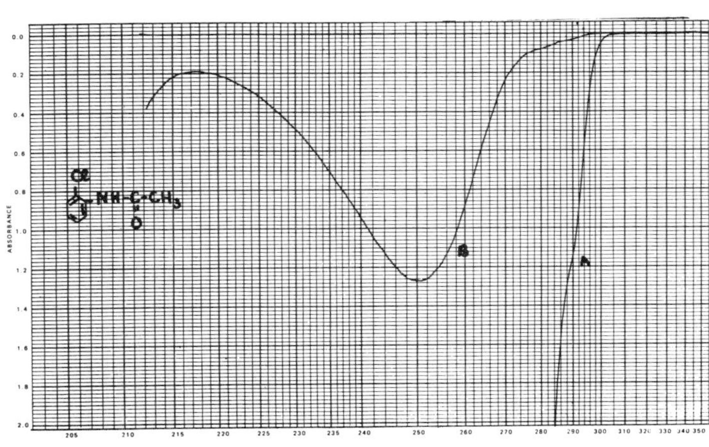

3′-CHLOROACETANILIDE 2329

C_8H_8ClNO

Mol. Wt. 169.61

Solvent: Methanol

λ Max. mμ	a_m	Cell mm	Conc. g/L
285	814	10	0.100
277	1640	10	0.100
244	16200	1	0.0500
210	33700	1	0.0500

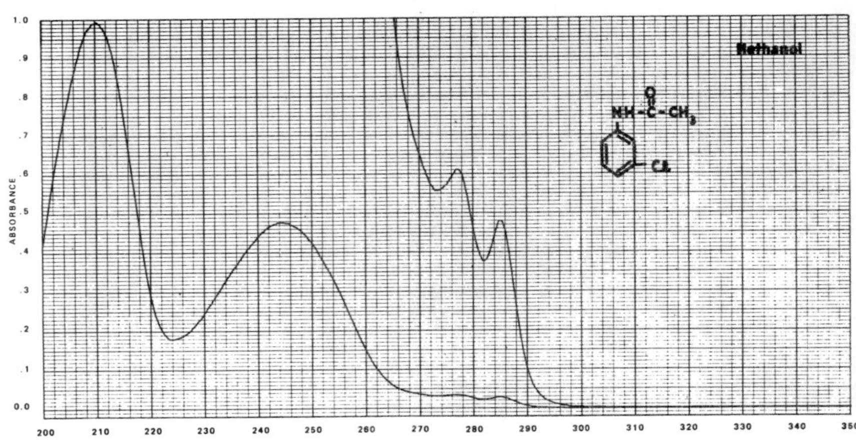

4′-CHLOROACETANILIDE 2330

C_8H_8ClNO

Mol. Wt. 169.61

M.P. 177-179°C

Solvent: Methanol

λ Max. mμ	a_m	Cell mm	Conc. g/L
247.5	19200	1	0.0800

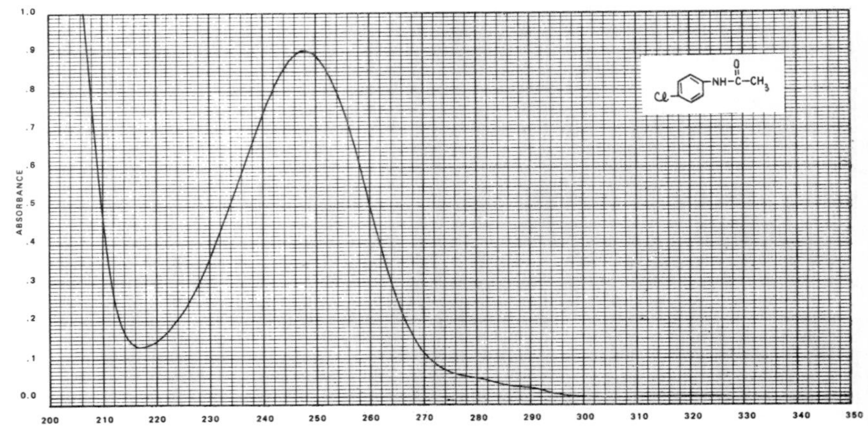

4′-BROMOACETANILIDE 2331

C_8H_8BrNO

Mol. Wt. 214.07

M.P. 165-167°C (lit.)

Solvent: Methanol

λ Max. mμ	a_m	Cell mm	Conc. g/L
250	20000	1	0.100

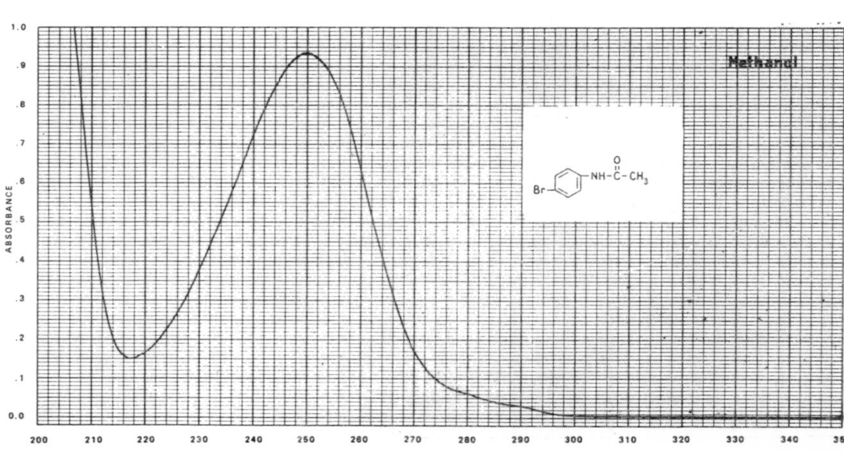

4'-FORMYLACETANILIDE, OXIME

2332

$C_9H_{10}N_2O_2$

Mol. Wt. 178.19

Solvent: Methanol

λ Max. mμ	a_m	Cell mm	Conc. g/L
281	21800	1	0.0500

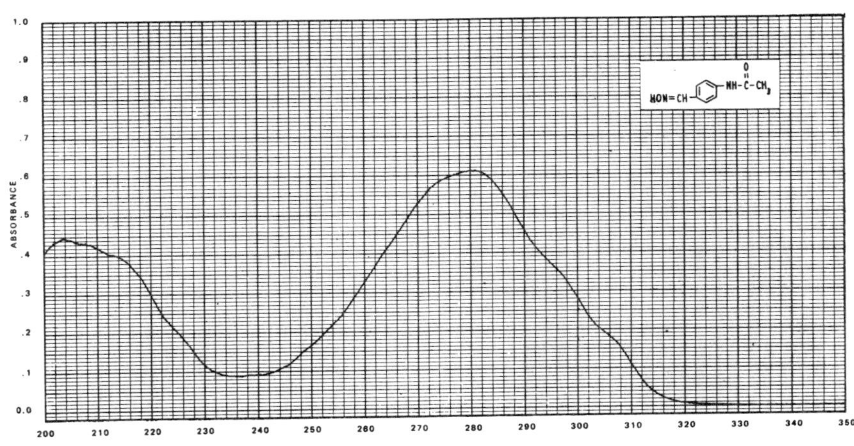

4'-FORMYLACETANILIDE, OXIME

2332

$C_9H_{10}N_2O_2$

Mol. Wt. 178.19

Solvent: Methanol KOH

λ Max. mμ	a_m	Cell mm	Conc. g/L
282.5	21000	1	0.0500

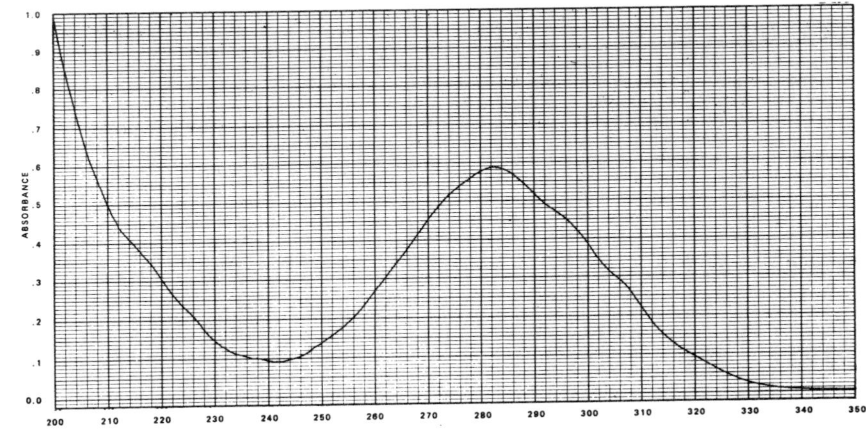

2'-NITROACETANILIDE

2333

$C_8H_8N_2O_3$

Mol. Wt. 180.16

M.P. 90-91°C

Solvent: Methanol

λ Max. mμ	a_m	Cell mm	Conc. g/L
338	2400	5	0.100
231	17500	1	0.100

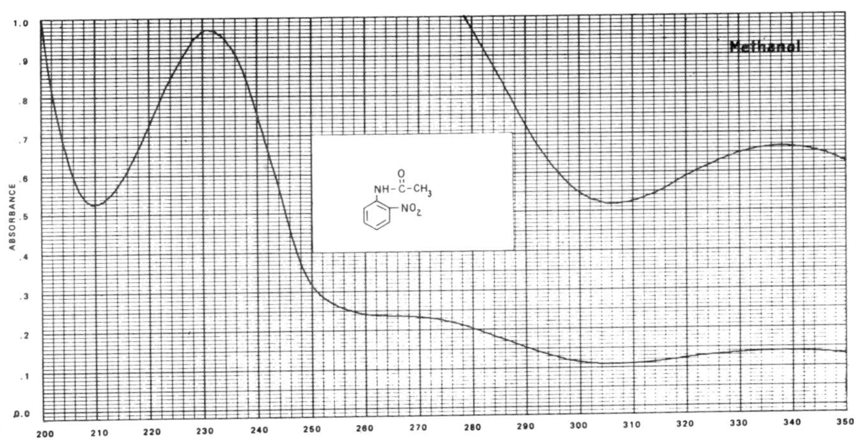

2'-HYDROXYACETANILIDE

2334

$C_8H_9NO_2$
Mol. Wt. 151.17
M.P. 200-203°C (lit.)
Solvent: Methanol

λ Max. mμ	a_m	Cell mm	Conc. g/L
283	7410	1	0.100
242	14300	1	0.100
207	42300	1	0.0200

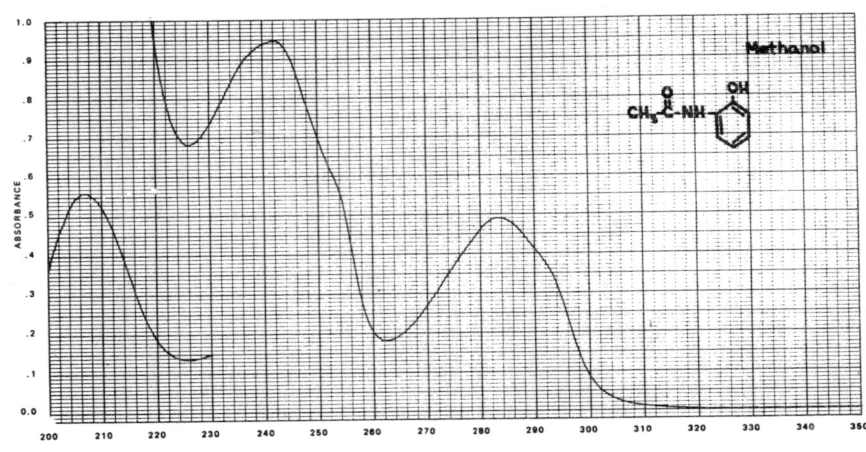

2'-HYDROXYACETANILIDE

2334

$C_8H_9NO_2$
Mol. Wt. 151.17
M.P. 200-203°C (lit.)
Solvent: Methanol KOH

λ Max. mμ	a_m	Cell mm	Conc. g/L
306	10200	1	0.100
250.5	13600	1	0.100
219	31600	1	0.0200

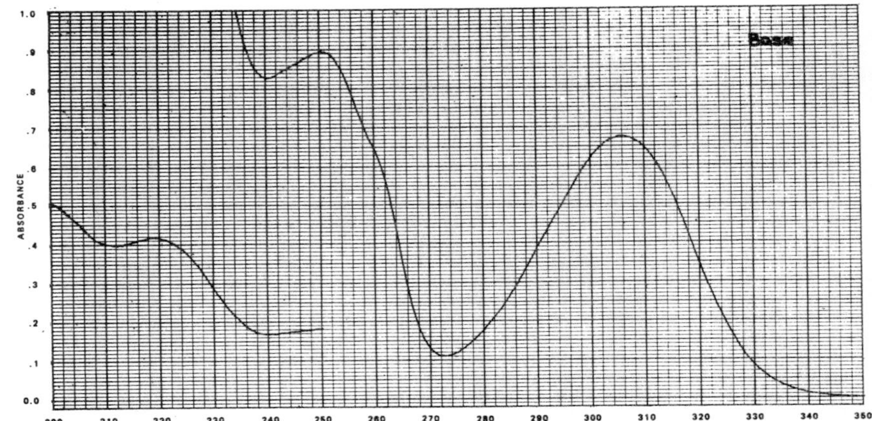

3'-HYDROXYACETANILIDE

2335

$C_8H_9NO_2$
Mol. Wt. 151.17
Solvent: Methanol

λ Max. mμ	a_m	Cell mm	Conc. g/L
290	2900	10	0.030
283	3220	10	0.030
245	11200	10	0.010
212	30200	10	0.005

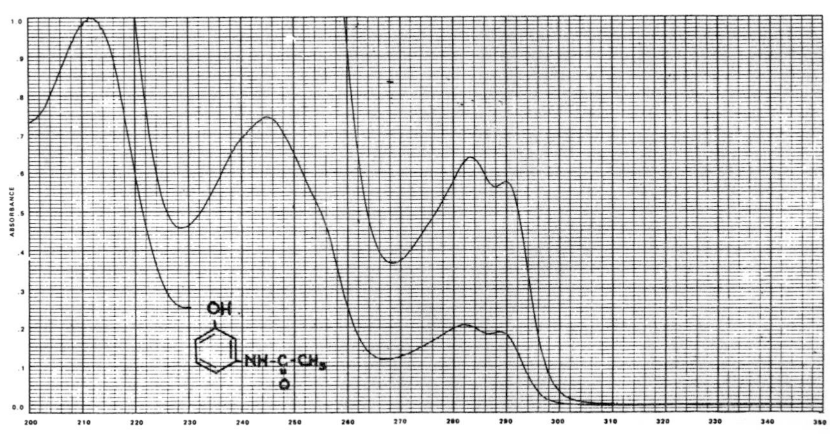

4′-HYDROXYACETANILIDE

2336

$C_8H_9NO_2$
Mol. Wt. 151.17
Solvent: Methanol

λ Max. mμ	a_m	Cell mm	Conc. g/L
x	x	10	2.000
x	x	10	0.100
248	14800	10	0.010

p-ACETANISIDIDE

2337

$C_9H_{11}NO_2$
Mol. Wt. 165.19
M.P. 129-131°C (lit.)
Solvent: Methanol

λ Max. mμ	a_m	Cell mm	Conc. g/L
248	14900	1	0.100

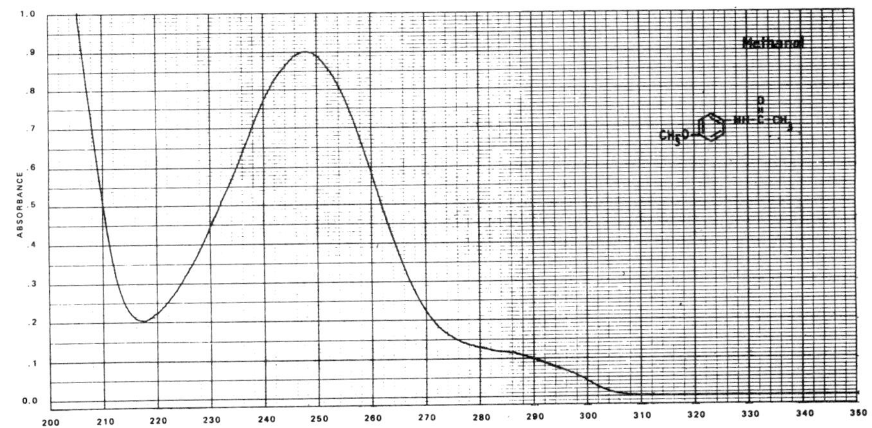

2′,4′-ACETOXYLIDIDE

2338

$C_{10}H_{13}NO$
Mol. Wt. 163.22
Solvent: Methanol

λ Max. mμ	a_m	Cell mm	Conc. g/L
228	6710	2	0.100

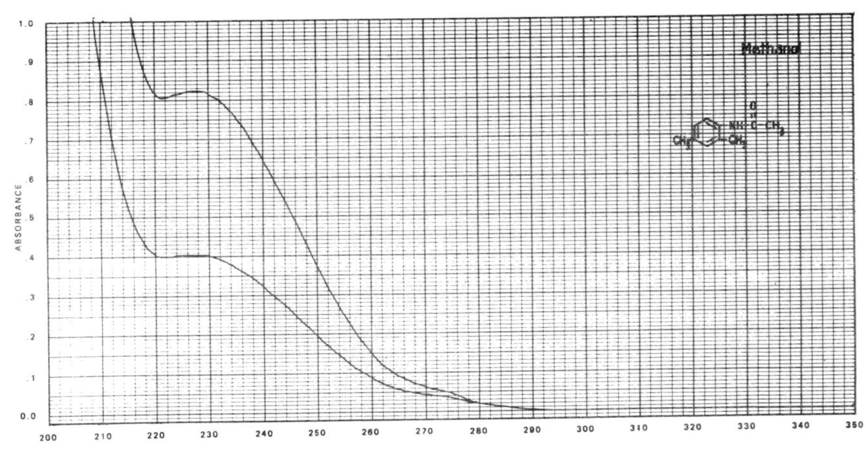

2',5'-ACETOXYLIDIDE 2339

$C_{10}H_{13}NO$

Mol. Wt. 163.22

Solvent: Methanol

λ Max. mμ	a_m	Cell mm	Conc. g/L
274	825	10	0.100
x	x	1	0.100

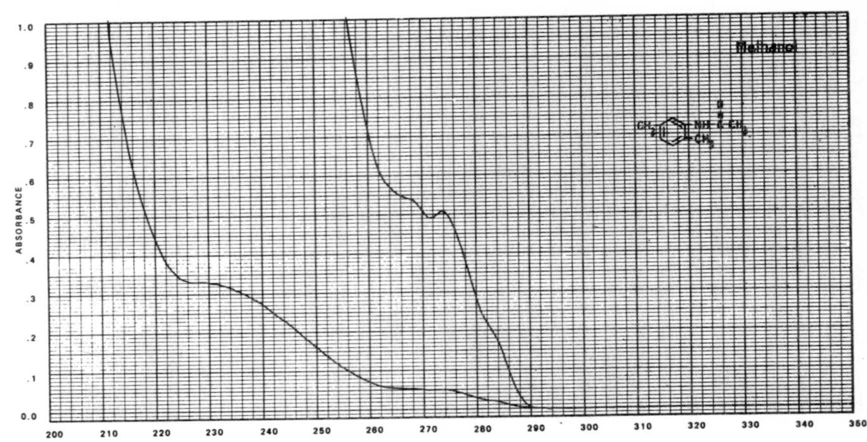

N-(2-NAPHTHYL)ACETAMIDE 2340

$C_{12}H_{11}NO$

Mol. Wt. 185.23

M.P. 131-132°C

Solvent: Methanol

λ Max. mμ	a_m	Cell mm	Conc. g/L
330	778	20	0.100
314.5	817	20	0.100
282	7919	2	0.100
273	6980	2	0.100
241.5	51100	1	0.0200

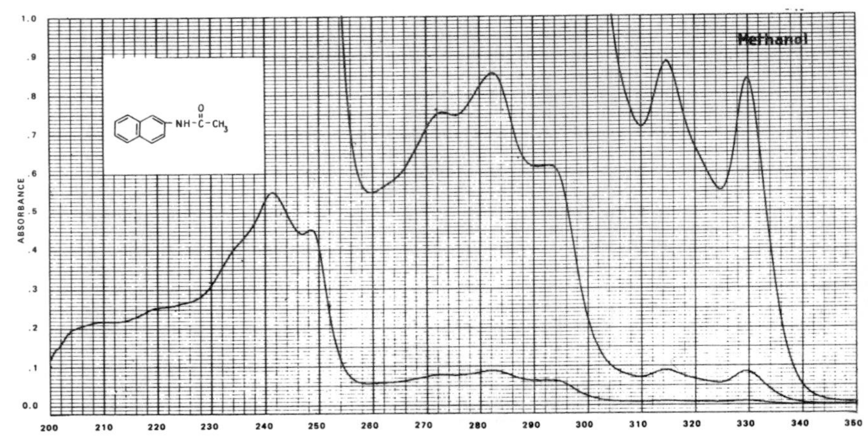

2-ACETAMIDOPYRIDINE 2341

$C_7H_8N_2O$

Mol. Wt. 136.16

Solvent: Methanol

λ Max. mμ	a_m	Cell mm	Conc. g/L
275	6710	1	0.100
234.5	12800	1	0.100

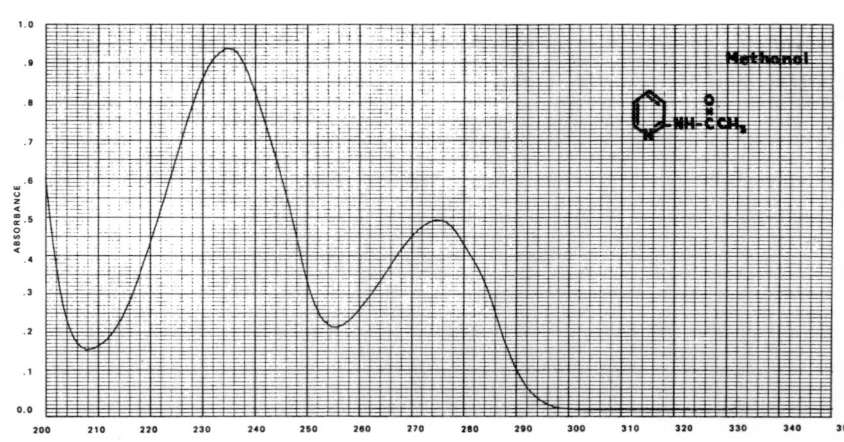

2-ACETAMIDOPYRIDINE

2341

$C_7H_8N_2O$

Mol. Wt. 136.16

Solvent: Methanol HCl

λ Max. mμ	a_m	Cell mm	Conc. g/L
293	11300	1	0.100
231.5	12200	1	0.100

N-METHYLBENZAMIDE

2342

C_8H_9NO

Mol. Wt. 135.17

M.P. 79-82°C

Solvent: Methanol

λ Max. mμ	a_m	Cell mm	Conc. g/L
225	11100	1	0.100

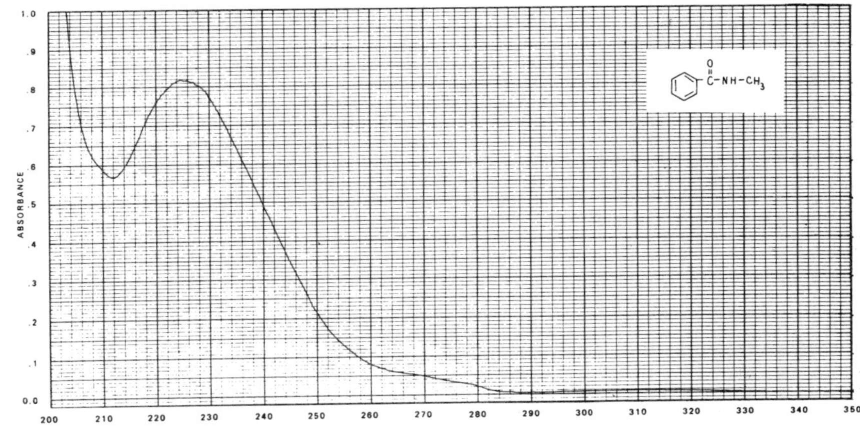

BENZANILIDE

2343

$C_{13}H_{11}NO$

Mol. Wt. 197.24

M.P. 163.08°C

Solvent: Methanol

λ Max. mμ	a_m	Cell mm	Conc. g/L
263	15500	1	0.100

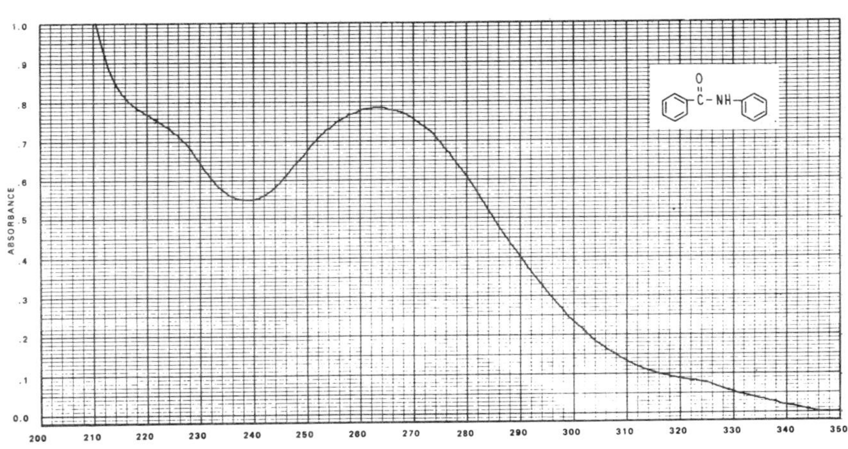

o-BENZOTOLUIDIDE 2344

$C_{14}H_{13}NO$
Mol. Wt. 211.26
M.P. 143°C
Solvent: Methanol

λ Max. mμ	a_m	Cell mm	Conc. g/L
224	13900	1	0.0800

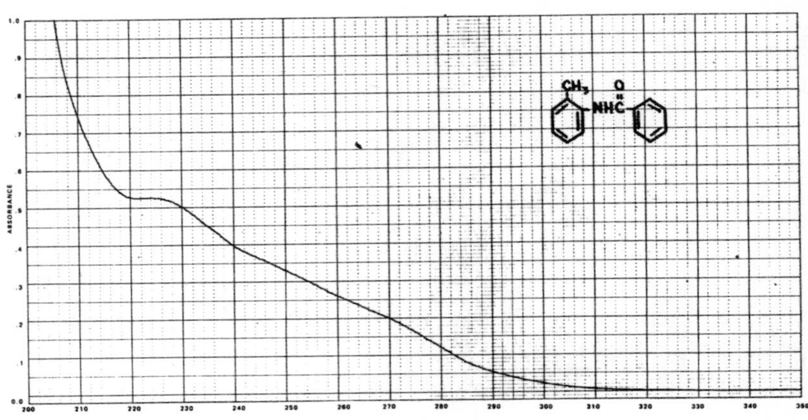

p-BENZOTOLUIDIDE 2345

$C_{14}H_{13}NO$
Mol. Wt. 211.27
M.P. 158°C
Solvent: Methanol

λ Max. mμ	a_m	Cell mm	Conc. g/L
269.5	13500	1	0.100

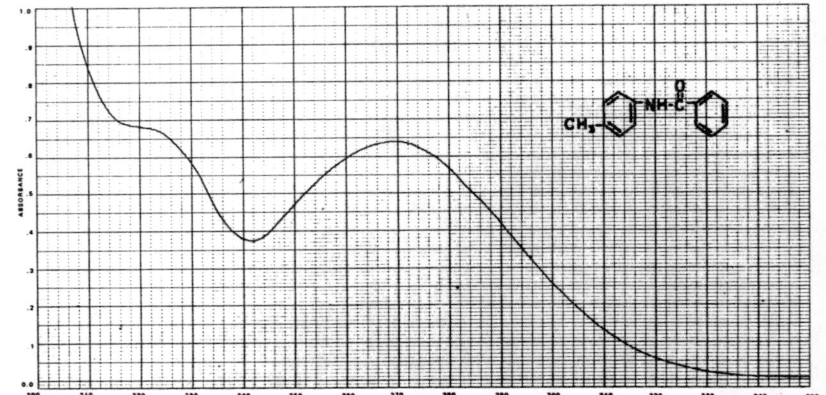

N-BENZYLNICOTINAMIDE 2346

$C_{13}H_{12}N_2O$
Mol. Wt. 212.26
Solvent: Methanol

λ Max. mμ	a_m	Cell mm	Conc. g/L
x	x	10	2.064
261	4370	10	0.021
256	4540	10	0.021

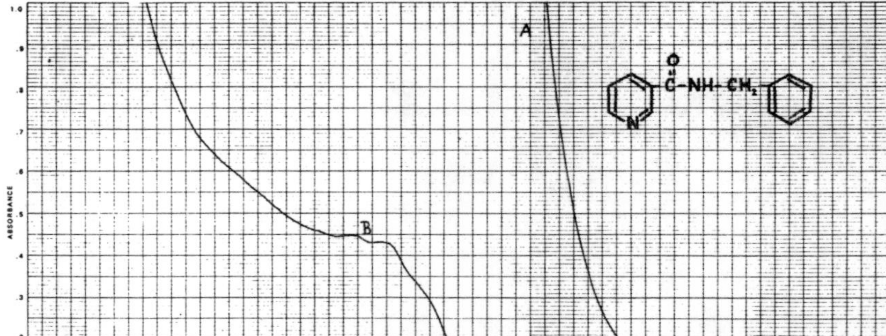

2347

λ Max. mμ	a_m	Cell mm	Conc. g/L

The alkyl tertiary amides (compounds 2347 - 2360) do not display any maxima in the near UV.

2361

N-ETHYLFORMANILIDE

$C_9H_{11}NO$

Mol. Wt. 149.19

B.P. 130-131°C/14mm

Solvent: Methanol

λ Max. mμ	a_m	Cell mm	Conc. g/L
226	8760	1	0.128

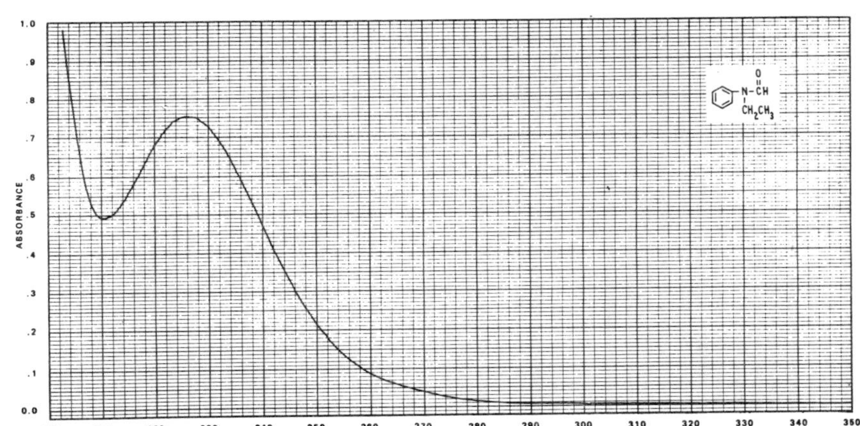

2362

N-ETHYL-p-FORMOTOLUIDIDE

$C_{10}H_{13}NO$

Mol. Wt. 163.22

B.P. 128-134°C/9mm

Solvent: Methanol

λ Max. mμ	a_m	Cell mm	Conc. g/L
231.5	10300	1	0.116

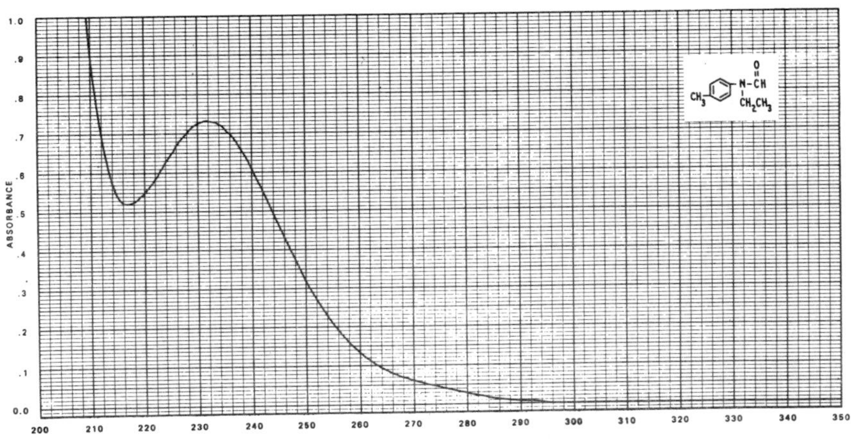

N-METHYLACETANILIDE

2363

$C_9H_{11}NO$
Mol. Wt. 149.19
M.P. 100-102°C
Solvent: Methanol

λ Max. mμ	a_m	Cell mm	Conc. g/L
223.5	5870	2	0.100

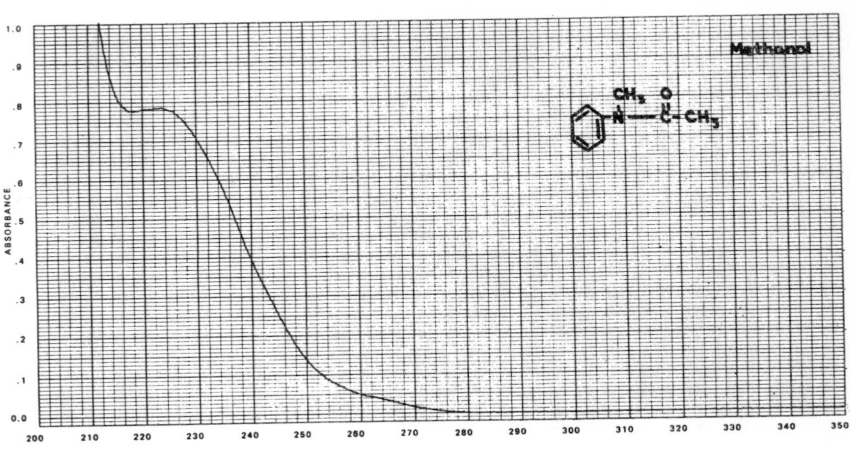

N-ETHYLACETANILIDE

2364

$C_{10}H_{13}NO$
Mol. Wt. 163.22
M.P. 53-54°C
Solvent: Methanol

λ Max. mμ	a_m	Cell mm	Conc. g/L
x	x	1	0.0500

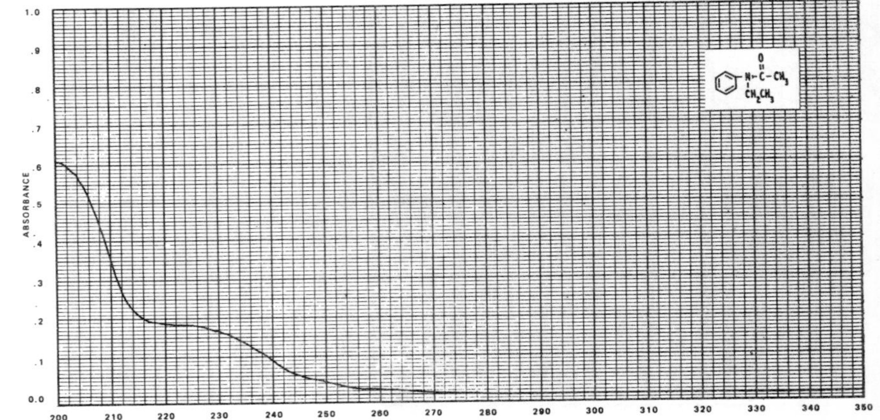

N-PROPYLACETANILIDE

2365

$C_{11}H_{15}NO$
Mol. Wt. 177.25
M.P. 48-50°C
Solvent: Methanol

λ Max. mμ	a_m	Cell mm	Conc. g/L
223	6170	2	0.100

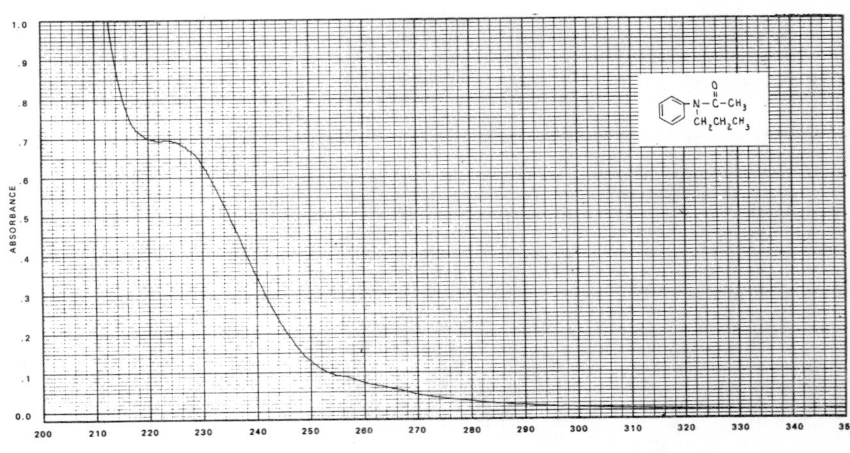

N-BUTYLACETANILIDE

2366

$C_{12}H_{17}NO$

Mol. Wt. 191.27

B.R. 140-142°C/9mm (lit.)

Solvent: Cyclohexane

λ Max. mμ	a_m	Cell mm	Conc. g/L
x	x	10	2.640
238.5	5408	10	0.053

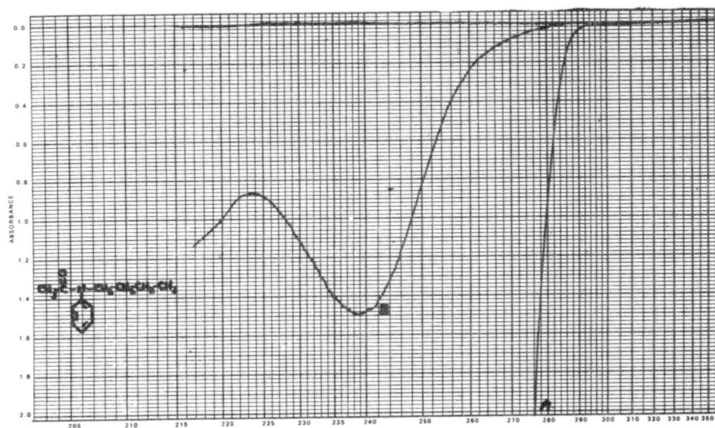

DIPHENYLFORMAMIDE

2367

$C_{13}H_{11}NO$

Mol. Wt. 197.24

M.P. 69-71°C

Solvent: Methanol

λ Max. mμ	a_m	Cell mm	Conc. g/L
238	13300	1	0.100

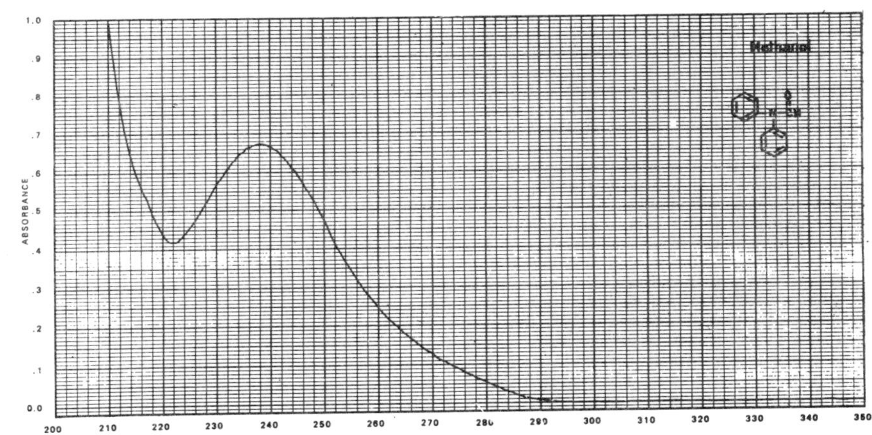

N,N-DIPHENYLACETAMIDE

2368

$C_{14}H_{13}NO$

Mol. Wt. 211.27

M.P. 99°C

Solvent: Methanol

λ Max. mμ	a_m	Cell mm	Conc. g/L
234	10500	1	0.100

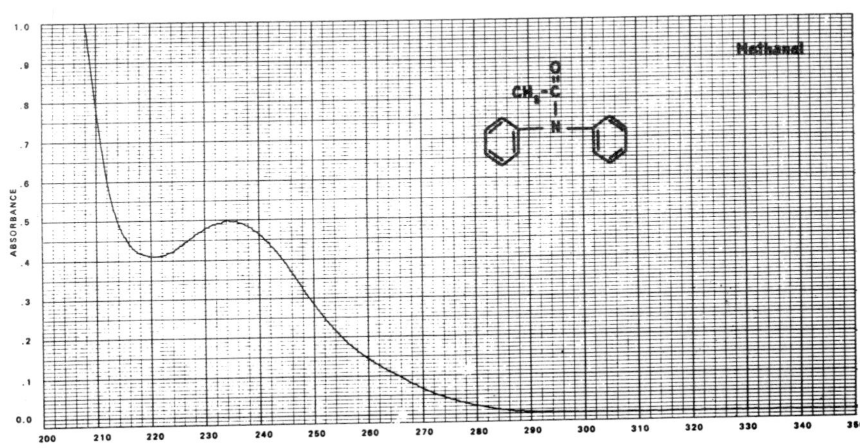

1-BENZOYLPIPERIDINE

2369

$C_{12}H_{15}NO$

Mol. Wt. 189.26

M.P. 47-49°C

Solvent: Methanol

λ Max. mμ	a_m	Cell mm	Conc. g/L
x	x	1	0.100

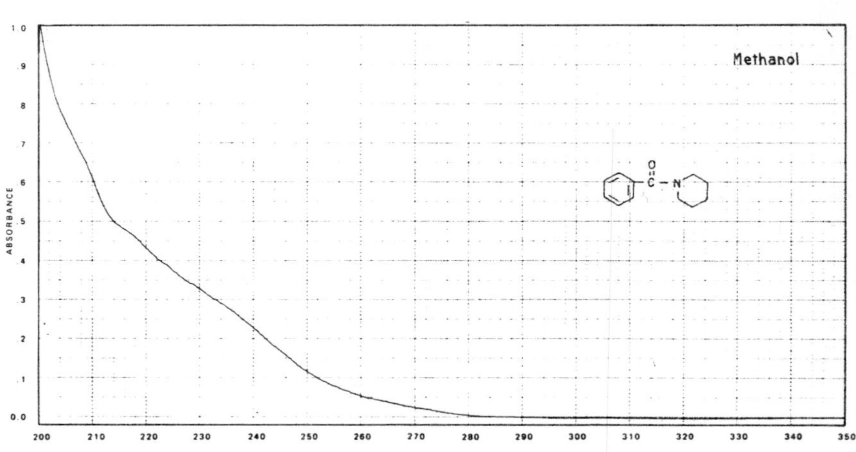

N,N,N′,N′-TETRAETHYLPHTHALAMIDE

2370

$C_{16}H_{24}N_2O_2$

Mol. Wt. 276.38

M.P. 37-39.5°C

Solvent: Methanol

λ Max. mμ	a_m	Cell mm	Conc. g/L
x	x	1	0.210

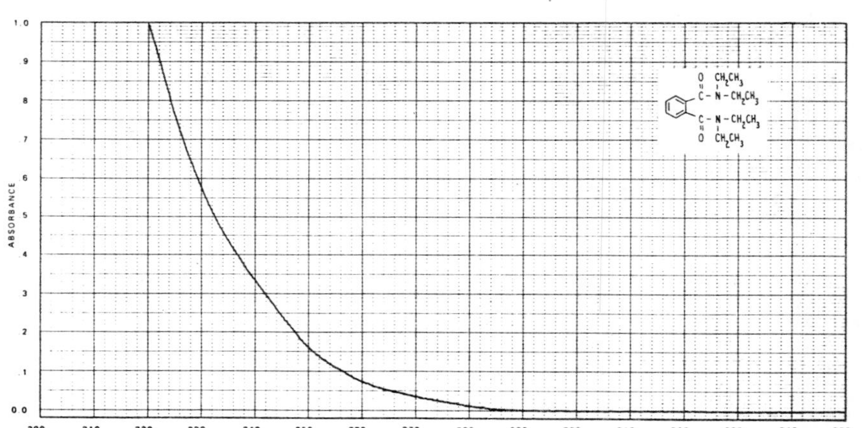

3,4-DIHYDRO-1(2H)-QUINOLINECARBOXALDEHYDE

2371

$C_{10}H_{11}NO$

Mol. Wt. 161.21

B.P. 165-168°C/14mm

Solvent: Methanol

λ Max. mμ	a_m	Cell mm	Conc. g/L
237	10900	1	0.1050

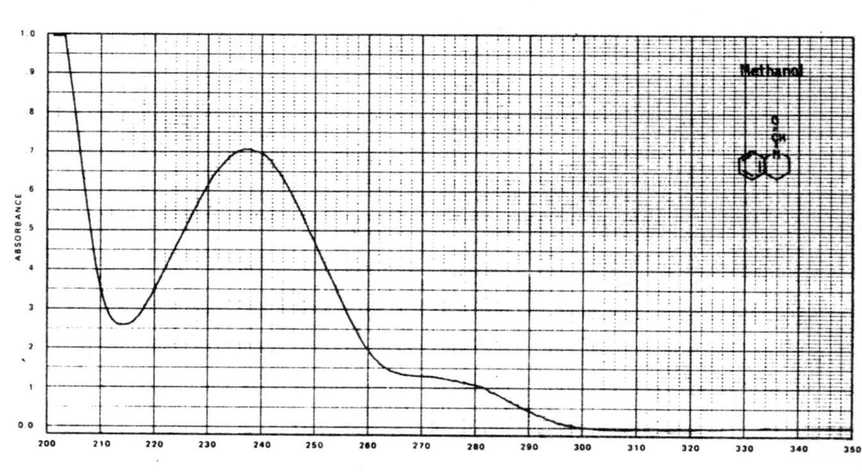

1-ACETYL-1,2,3,4-TETRAHYDROQUINOLINE 2372

$C_{11}H_{13}NO$
Mol. Wt. 175.23
Solvent: Methanol

λ Max. mμ	a_m	Cell mm	Conc. g/L
242.5	10700	1	0.100

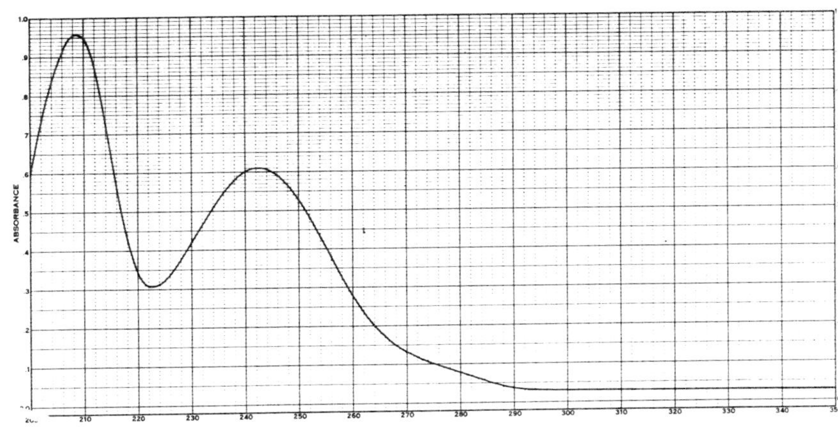

9-ACETYLCARBAZOLE 2373

$C_{14}H_{11}NO$
Mol. Wt. 209.25
M.P. 68-69°C
Solvent: Methanol

λ Max. mμ	a_m	Cell mm	Conc. g/L
310.5	65500	1	0.100
299	59201	1	0.100
284.5	10800	1	0.100
261	16400	1	0.100
230	4100	1	0.0500

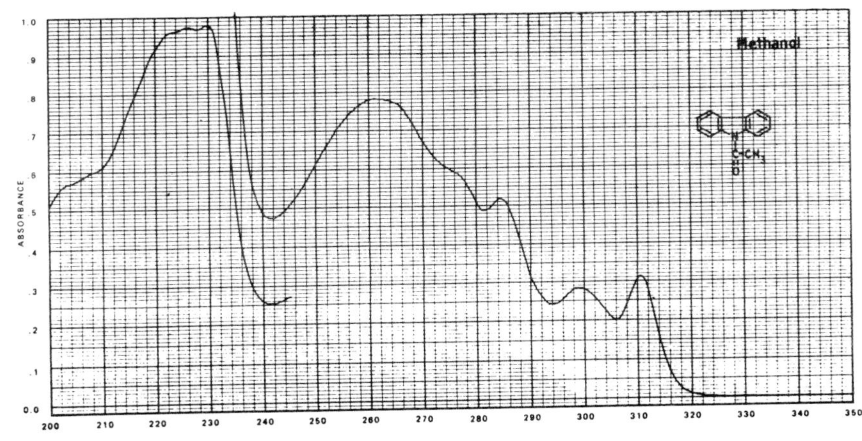

1-PHENYL-2-PYRROLIDINONE 2374

$C_{10}H_{11}NO$
Mol. Wt. 161.21
Solvent: Methanol

λ Max. mμ	a_m	Cell mm	Conc. g/L
246.5	11900	1	0.100

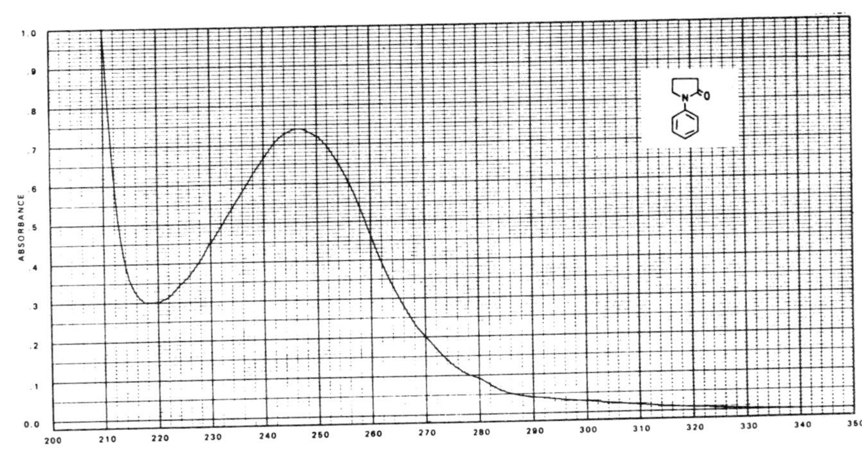

NOTES

THE IMIDES

Aliphatic and Alicyclic Compounds

With the exception of succinimide, the aliphatic and alicyclic imides do not display any maxima in the near UV region.

Succinimide shows one weak absorption near 238 mμ (ϵ_{max} = 87) in aqueous solution but three maxima in acetonitrile at 216, 221 and 244 with ϵ_{max} = 75 - 125 (Lit.).

The Maleimides

Maleimide produces two major maxima, the more intense absorption band at 216 mμ (ϵ_{max} = 14700) shows some unresolved fine structure while the band at 274 mμ (ϵ_{max} = 718) does not (spectrum 2379).

The N-ethyl derivative of maleimide displays a 217 mμ band similar to that of the parent compound but the longer wavelength absorption undergoes a bathochromic shift and is observed at 295 mμ (ϵ_{max} = 577) in spectrum 2384. No maxima are observed in the near UV for the maleimides after the addition of base to their methanol solutions.

The Phthalimides

The phthalimides produce near UV maxima that are somewhat similar in appearance to those of the maleimides.

Two major bands are seen in the spectrum of phthalimide at about 216 mμ (ϵ_{max} = 30500) and 290 mμ (1390) in addition to two poorly resolved maxima near 229 and 238 mμ.

Upon the addition of base, the major bands of phthalimide undergo a change in shape and a slight (5 - 10 mμ) shift to longer wavelength (compound 2380, page 682).

SUCCINIMIDE 2375

$C_4H_5NO_2$
Mol. Wt. 99.09
M.P. 124-126°C
B.P. 228°C (Lit.)

λ Max. mμ	a_m	Cell mm	Conc. g/L

Pure sample not available.

2-METHYLSUCCINIMIDE 2376

$C_5H_7NO_2$
Mol. Wt. 113.12
M.P. 68-70°C

λ Max. mμ	a_m	Cell mm	Conc. g/L

Pure sample not available.

GLUTARIMIDE 2377

$C_5H_7NO_2$
Mol. Wt. 113.12
Solvent: Methanol

λ Max. mμ	a_m	Cell mm	Conc. g/L
x	x	0.50	0.5

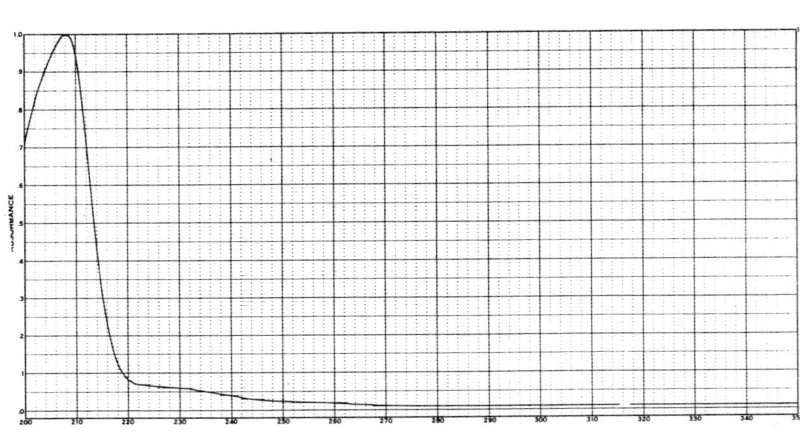

3-AZASPIRO[5.5] UNDECANE-2,4-DIONE

2378

$C_{10}H_{15}NO_2$
Mol. Wt. 181.24
Solvent: Methanol

λ Max. mμ	a_m	Cell mm	Conc. g/L
x	x	0.5	0.50

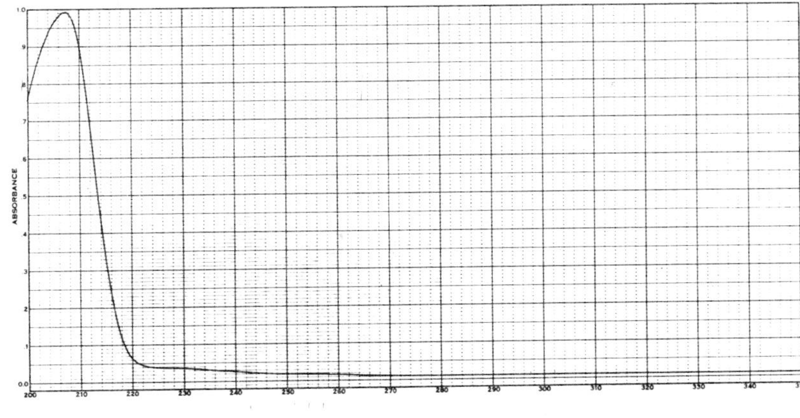

MALEIMIDE

2379

$C_4H_3NO_2$
Mol. Wt. 97.07
M.P. 93.5-94.5°C
Solvent: Methanol

λ Max. mμ	a_m	Cell mm	Conc. g/L
274	718	10	0.100
216	14700	10	0.006

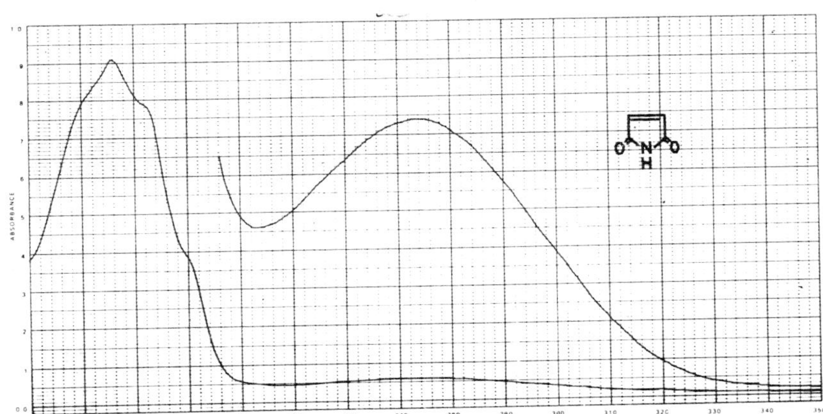

λ Max. mμ	a_m	Cell mm	Conc. g/L

PHTHALIMIDE

2380

$C_8H_5NO_2$
Mol. Wt. 147.14
M.P. 231°C
Solvent: Methanol

λ Max. mμ	a_m	Cell mm	Conc. g/L
290.5	1390	10	0.100
237	8960	5	0.0250
229	12900	1	0.0250
215.5	30500	1	0.0250

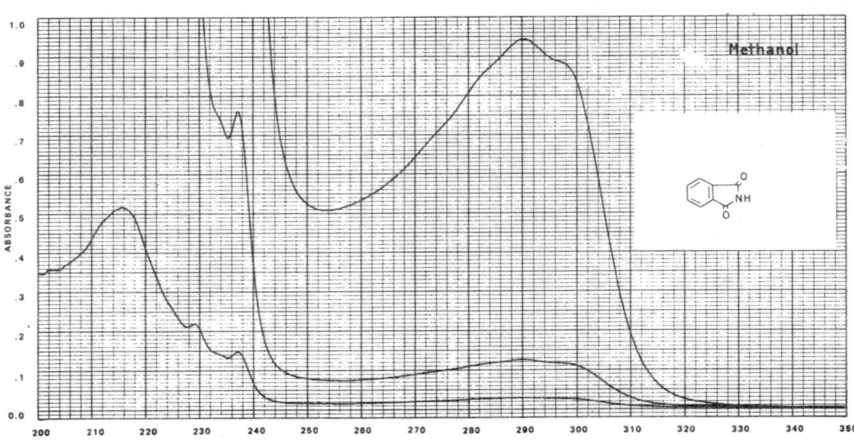

PHTHALIMIDE

2380

$C_8H_5NO_2$
Mol. Wt. 147.14
M.P. 231°C
Solvent: Methanol KOH

λ Max. mμ	a_m	Cell mm	Conc. g/L
299.5	1500	5	0.100
290.5	1470	5	0.100
221	24100	2	0.0250

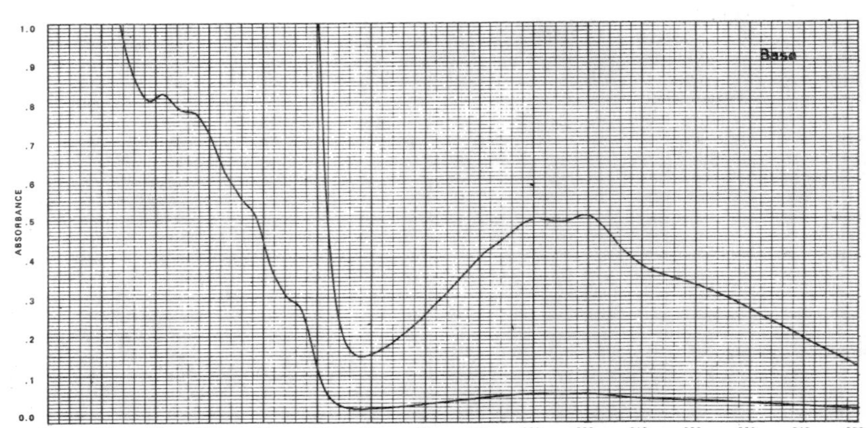

4-NITROPHTHALIMIDE

2381

$C_8H_4N_2O_4$
Mol. Wt. 192.13
M.P. 199-201°C
Solvent: Methanol

λ Max. mμ	a_m	Cell mm	Conc. g/L
229	12900	10	0.010
205	15300	10	0.010

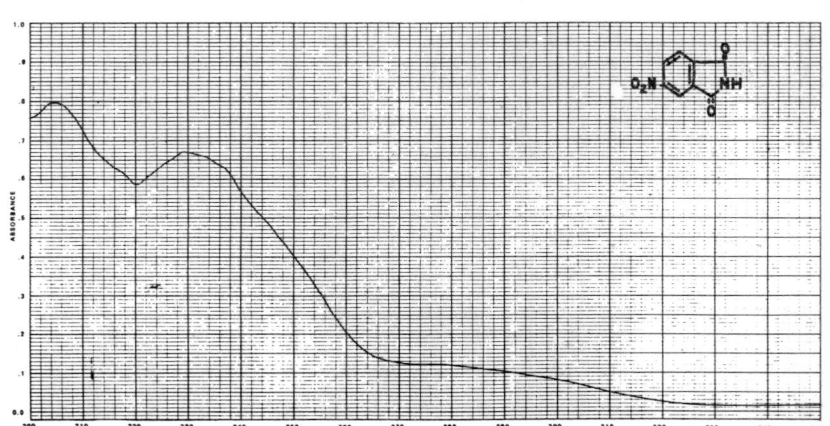

N-PENTYLSUCCINIMIDE

2382

$C_9H_{15}NO_2$
Mol. Wt. 169.23
B.P. 138-140°C/9mm

λ Max. mμ	a_m	Cell mm	Conc. g/L

Pure sample not available.

1-ACETYLHEXAHYDRO-2H-AZEPIN-2-ONE

2383

$C_8H_{13}NO_2$
Mol. Wt. 155.20
B.P. 132-133°C/19mm

λ Max. mμ	a_m	Cell mm	Conc. g/L

Pure sample not available.

λ Max. mμ	a_m	Cell mm	Conc. g/L

N-ETHYLMALEIMIDE 2384

$C_6H_7NO_2$
Mol. Wt. 125.13
Solvent: Methanol

λ Max. mμ	a_m	Cell mm	Conc. g/L
294.5	577	10	0.200
216.5	13100	1	0.0800

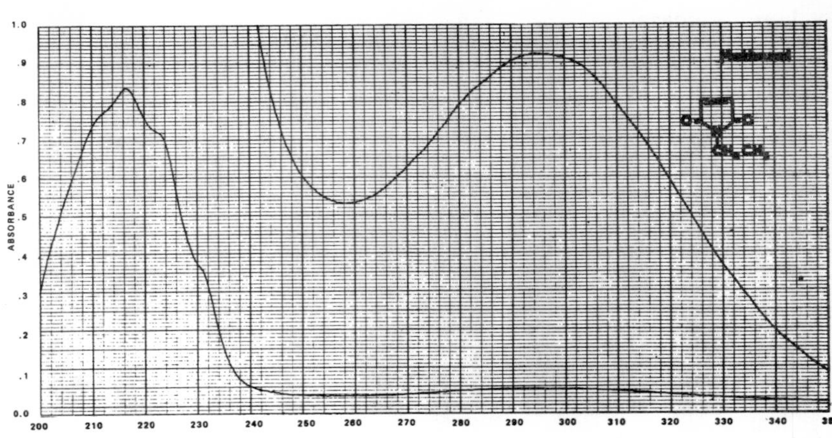

N-ETHYLMALEIMIDE 2384

$C_6H_7NO_2$
Mol. Wt. 125.13
Solvent: Methanol KOH

λ Max. mμ	a_m	Cell mm	Conc. g/L
x	x	1	0.200

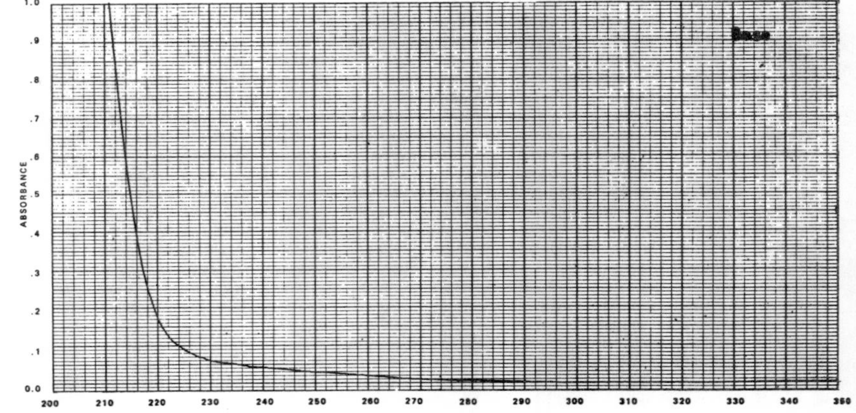

N-PHENETHYLMALEIMIDE 2385

$C_{12}H_{11}NO_2$
Mol. Wt. 201.23
M.P. 102°C
Solvent: Methanol

λ Max. mμ	a_m	Cell mm	Conc. g/L
295	526	20	0.100
266.5	543	20	0.100
263.5	599	20	0.100
257.5	695	20	0.100
x	x	1	0.100

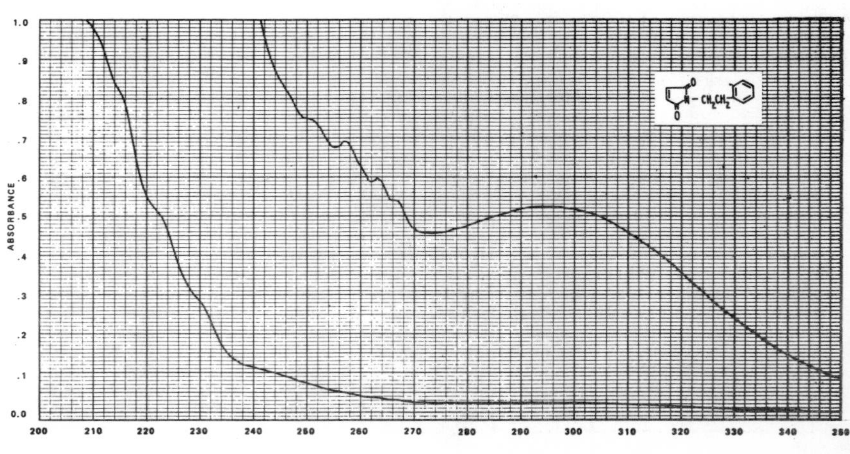

N-BENZYLMALEIMIDE 2386

$C_{11}H_9NO_2$
Mol. Wt. 187.20
M.P. 70°C
Solvent: Methanol

λ Max. mμ	a_m	Cell mm	Conc. g/L
x	x	1	0.100

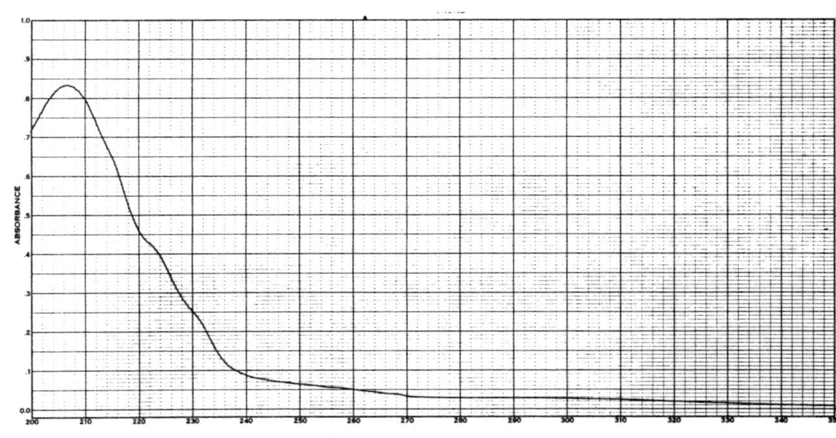

N-(o-CHLOROPHENYL)MALEIMIDE 2387

$C_{10}H_6ClNO_2$
Mol. Wt. 207.62
M.P. 74°C
Solvent: Methanol

λ Max. mμ	a_m	Cell mm	Conc. g/L
272	1250	10	0.100
265	1330	10	0.100
259	1310	10	0.100
x	x	1	0.100

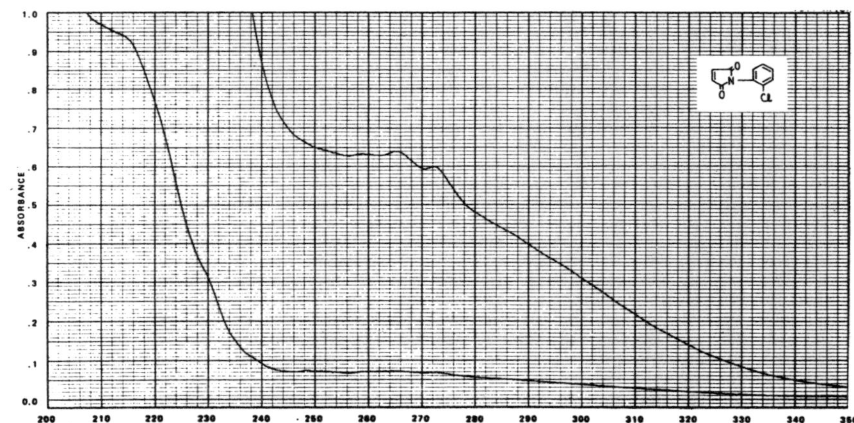

N-(o-CHLOROPHENYL)MALEIMIDE 2387

$C_{10}H_6ClNO_2$
Mol. Wt. 207.62
M.P. 74°C
Solvent: Methanol KOH

λ Max. mμ	a_m	Cell mm	Conc. g/L
284	479	20	0.100
243	10200	2	0.100

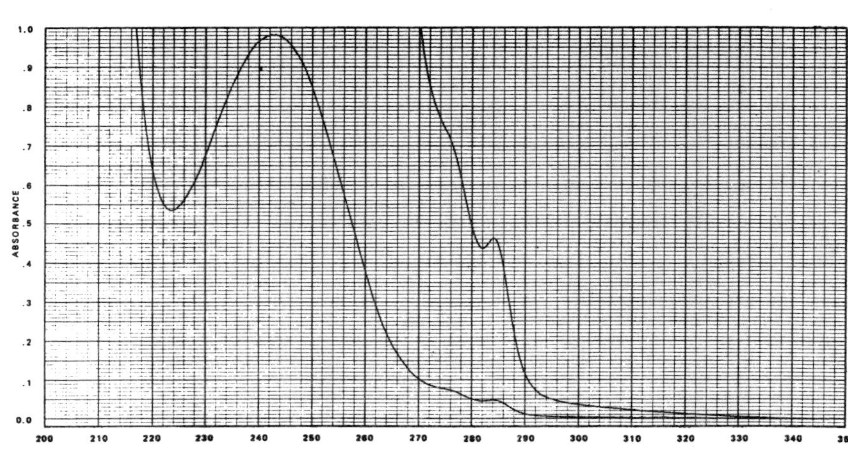

N-(p-BROMOPHENYL)MALEIMIDE 2388

$C_{10}H_6BrNO_2$
Mol. Wt. 252.07
M.P. 112°C
Solvent: Methanol

λ Max. mμ	a_m	Cell mm	Conc. g/L
254	9180	2	0.100
226	10800	2	0.100

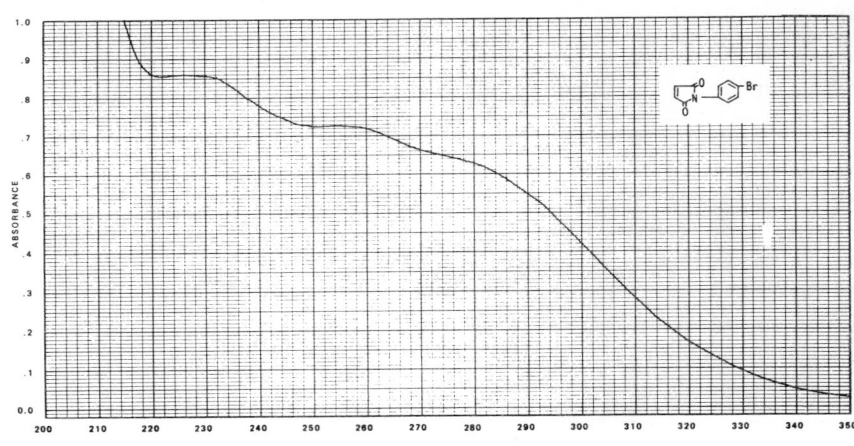

N-(p-BROMOPHENYL)MALEIMIDE 2388

$C_{10}H_6BrNO_2$
Mol. Wt. 252.07
M.P. 112°C
Solvent: Methanol KOH

λ Max. mμ	a_m	Cell mm	Conc. g/L
251	17900	1	0.100

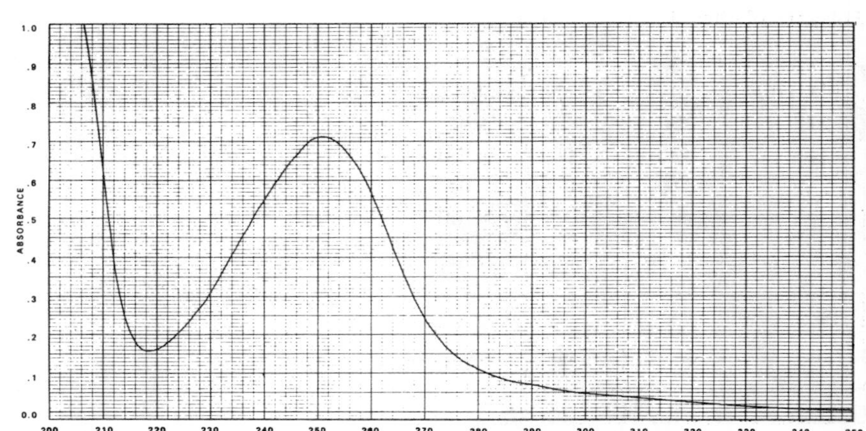

N-(p-IODOPHENYL)MALEIMIDE 2389

$C_{10}H_6INO_2$
Mol. Wt. 299.06
M.P. 150°C
Solvent: Methanol

λ Max. mμ	a_m	Cell mm	Conc. g/L
259	11800	1	0.100

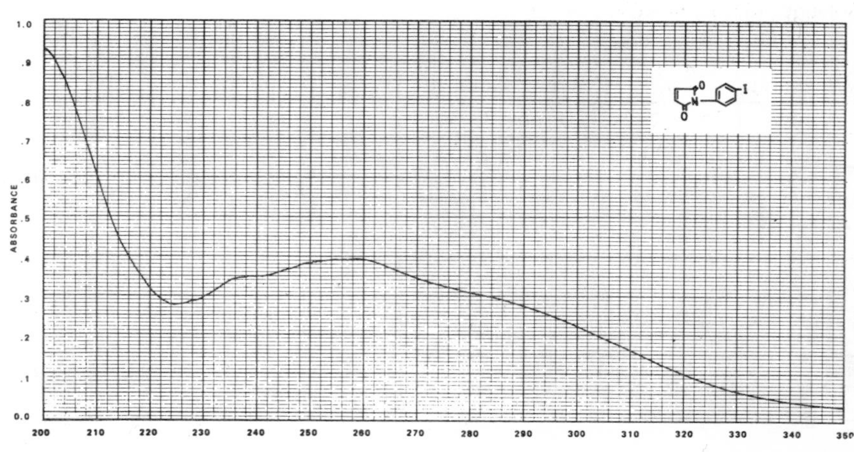

N-(p-IODOPHENYL)MALEIMIDE 2389

$C_{10}H_6INO_2$
Mol. Wt. 299.06
M.P. 150°C
Solvent: Methanol KOH

λ Max. mμ	a_m	Cell mm	Conc. g/L
254.5	20200	1	0.100

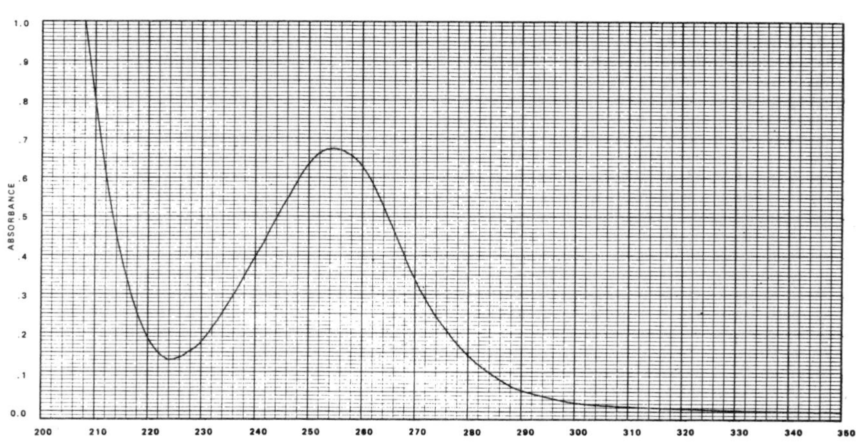

N,N′-(m-PHENYLENE)DIMALEIMIDE 2390

$C_{14}H_8N_2O_4$
Mol. Wt. 268.23
Solvent: Methanol

λ Max. mμ	a_m	Cell mm	Conc. g/L
233	12800	2	0.100

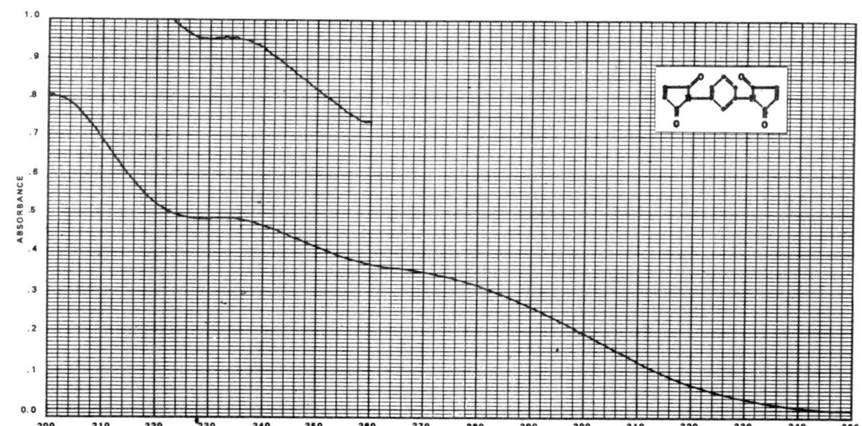

λ Max. mμ	a_m	Cell mm	Conc. g/L

N-METHYLPHTHALIMIDE 2391

$C_9H_7NO_2$

Mol. Wt. 161.16

M.P. 132-135°C

Solvent: Methanol

λ Max. mμ	a_m	Cell mm	Conc. g/L
292.5	930	10	0.100
240	11500	5	0.020
231	16100	1	0.020
218	42800	1	0.020

N-METHYLPHTHALIMIDE 2391

$C_9H_7NO_2$

Mol. Wt. 161.16

M.P. 132-135°C

Solvent: Methanol KOH

λ Max. mμ	a_m	Cell mm	Conc. g/L
293	1070	10	0.100
239	2400	5	0.100
x	x	1	0.020

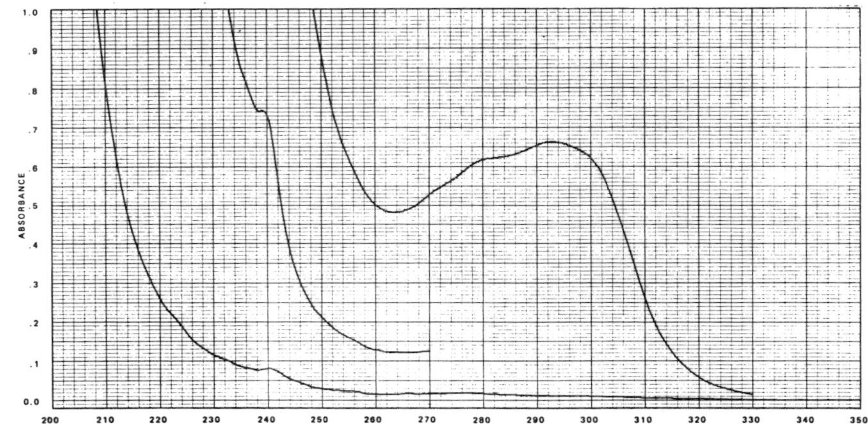

N-(2-CHLOROETHYL)PHTHALIMIDE 2392

$C_{10}H_8ClNO_2$

Mol. Wt. 209.63

Solvent: Methanol

λ Max. mμ	a_m	Cell mm	Conc. g/L
293	1780	10	0.100
240	10600	1	0.0400
231	14500	1	0.0400
218	44200	1	0.0400

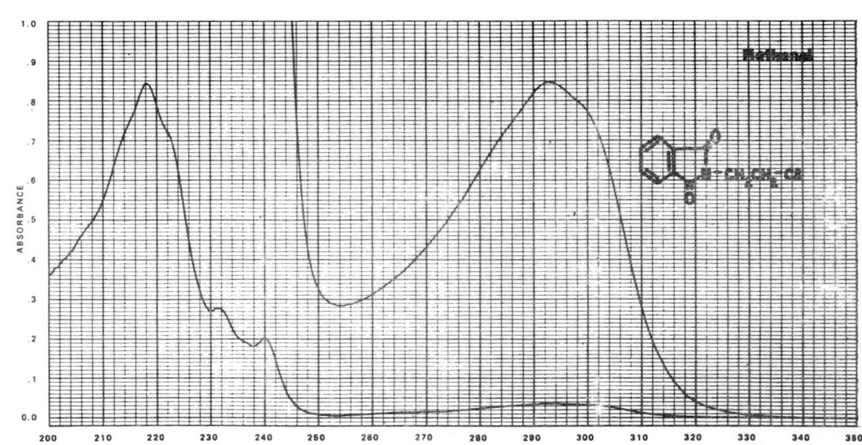

N-(BROMOMETHYL)PHTHALIMIDE

2393

$C_9H_6BrNO_2$

Mol. Wt. 240.06

M.P. 149-150°C (lit.)

Solvent: Methanol

λ Max. mμ	a_m	Cell mm	Conc. g/L
x	x	10	2.044
293	2081	10	0.164
238.5	12000	10	0.016
217.5	15400	10	0.016

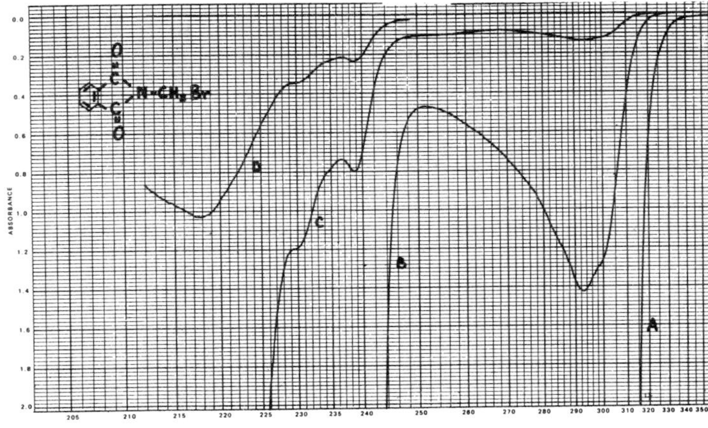

N-(2,3-EPOXYPROPYL)PHTHALIMIDE

2394

$C_{11}H_9NO_3$

Mol. Wt. 203.20

M.P. 98-100°C

Solvent: Methanol

λ Max. mμ	a_m	Cell mm	Conc. g/L
293	1760	10	0.100
240.5	9410	1	0.100
232	12900	1	0.100
219	39200	1	0.0500

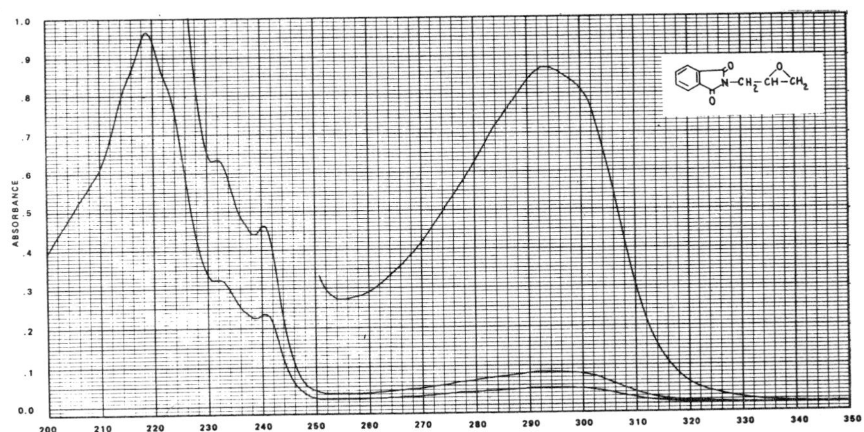

N-VINYLPHTHALIMIDE

2395

$C_{10}H_7NO_2$

Mol. Wt. 173.17

M.P. 82-86°C

Solvent: Methanol

λ Max. mμ	a_m	Cell mm	Conc. g/L
234	18500	1	0.050
227.5	19500	1	0.050
221	19600	1	0.050
209.5	18900	1	0.050

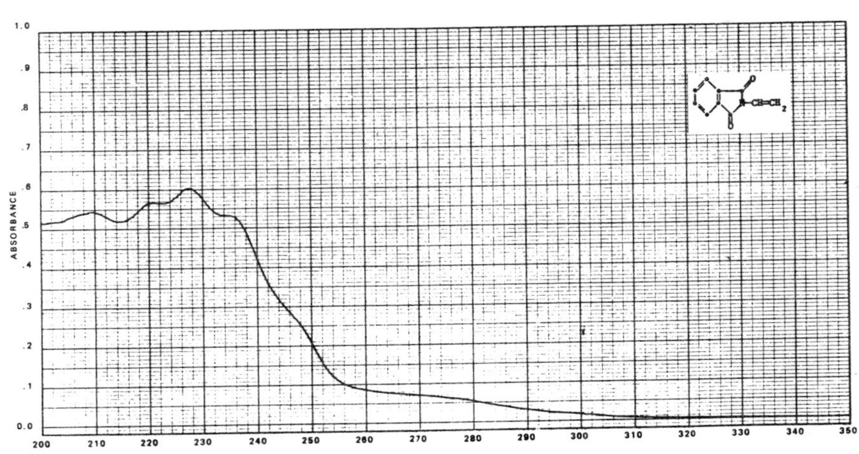

N-BENZYLPHTHALIMIDE

2396

$C_{15}H_{11}NO_2$
Mol. Wt. 237.26
Solvent: Methanol

λ Max. mμ	a_m	Cell mm	Conc. g/L
293	2130	10	0.100
267.5	1110	10	0.100
263.5	1090	10	0.100
257	1130	10	0.100
219.5	51600	2	0.0200

N-o-TOLYLPHTHALIMIDE

2397

$C_{15}H_{11}NO_2$
Mol. Wt. 237.26
M.P. 182°C
Solvent: Methanol

λ Max. mμ	a_m	Cell mm	Conc. g/L
293.5	1870	10	0.100
269	1640	10	0.100
219	42300	1	0.0500

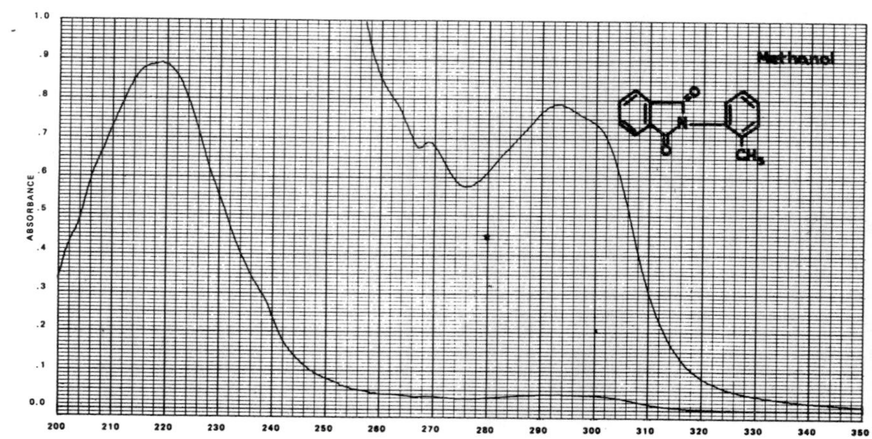

N-(p-METHOXYPHENYL)PHTHALIMIDE

2398

$C_{15}H_{11}NO_3$
Mol. Wt. 253.26
M.P. 162°C
Solvent: Methanol

λ Max. mμ	a_m	Cell mm	Conc. g/L
214.5	33900	1	0.0700

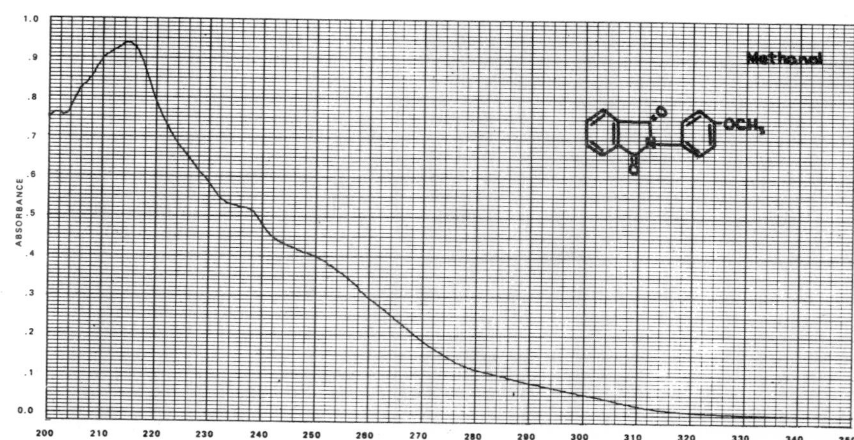

N,N'-HEXAMETHYLENEDIPHTHALIMIDE 2399

$C_{22}H_{20}N_2O_4$
Mol. Wt. 376.42
M.P. 183-184°C
Solvent: Methanol

λ Max. mμ	a_m	Cell mm	Conc. g/L
293	1430	20	0.100
241	8280	1	0.100
232.5	11100	1	0.100
220	32100	1	0.100

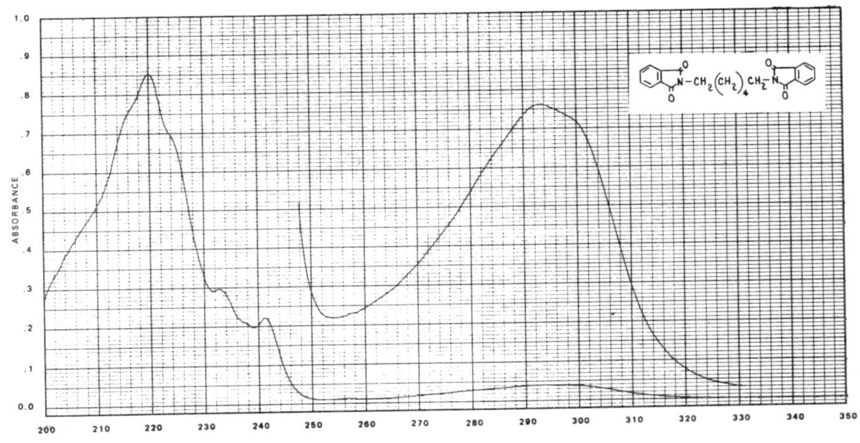

N,N'-[(BENZYLIMINO)DIMETHYLENE] DIPHTHALIMIDE 2400

$C_{25}H_{19}N_3O_4$
Mol. Wt. 425.45
M.P. 187-188°C
Solvent: Methanol

λ Max. mμ	a_m	Cell mm	Conc. g/L
291.5	3230	1	1.00
237	20300	1	0.0500
228	32300	1	0.0500
215.5	76900	1	0.0500

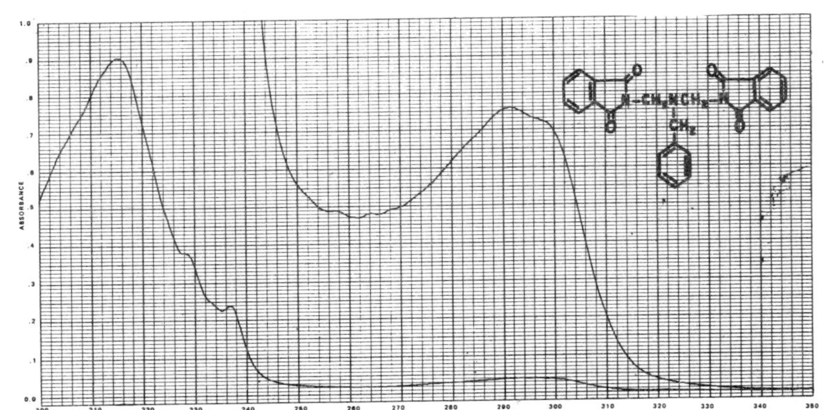

N,N'-[(BENZYLIMINO)DIMETHYLENE] DIPHTHALIMIDE 2400

$C_{25}H_{19}N_3O_4$
Mol. Wt. 425.45
M.P. 187-188°C
Solvent: Methanol KOH

λ Max. mμ	a_m	Cell mm	Conc. g/L
299	3500	1	1.00
290	3450	1	1.00

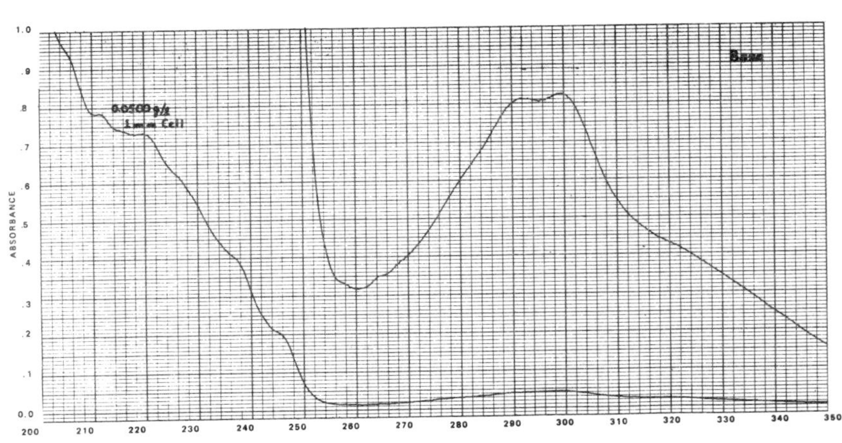

1,2,4,5,-BENZENETETRACARBOXYLIC ACID, 1,2:4,5-DIIMIDE

2401

$C_{10}H_4N_2O_4$
Mol. Wt. 216.15
Solvent: Methanol

λ Max. mμ	a_m	Cell mm	Conc. g/L
305	2080	5	0.100
x	x	1	0.050

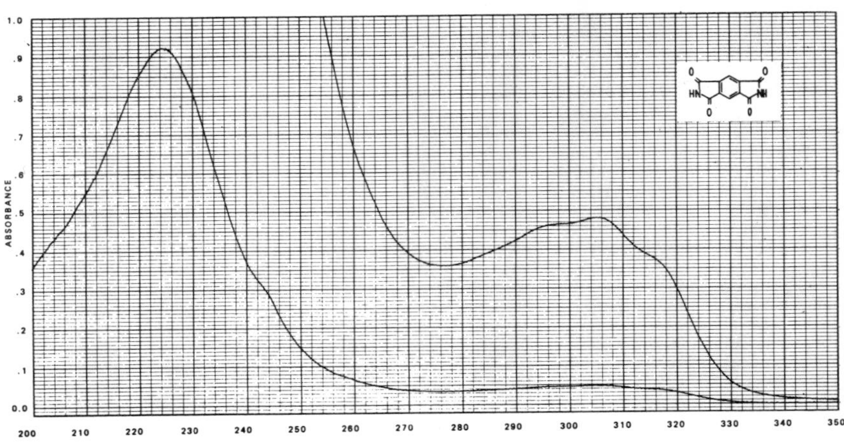

N-AMINOPHTHALIMIDE

2402

$C_8H_6N_2O_2$
Mol. Wt. 162.15
M.P. 203-205°C
Solvent: Methanol

λ Max. mμ	a_m	Cell mm	Conc. g/L
293	2600	5	0.100
262	1530	5	0.100
212	3850	1	0.0200

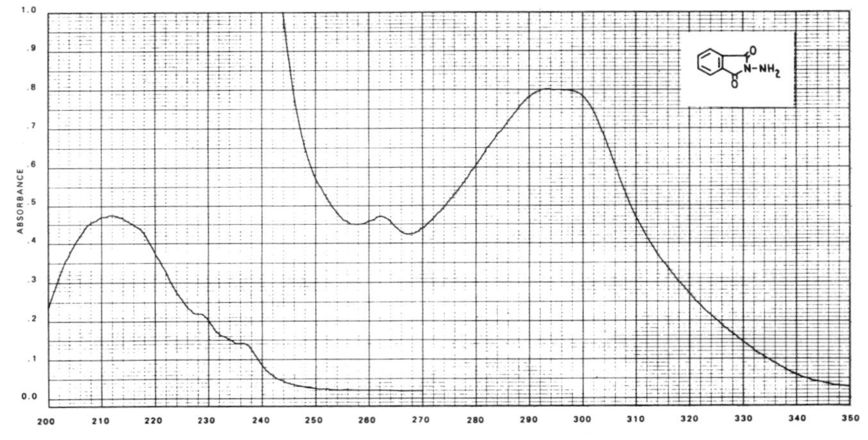

N-AMINOPHTHALIMIDE

2402

$C_8H_6N_2O_2$
Mol. Wt. 162.15
M.P. 203-205°C
Solvent: Methanol KOH

λ Max. mμ	a_m	Cell mm	Conc. g/L
301	2440	5	0.100
212	3990	1	0.0200
207	3880	1	0.0200

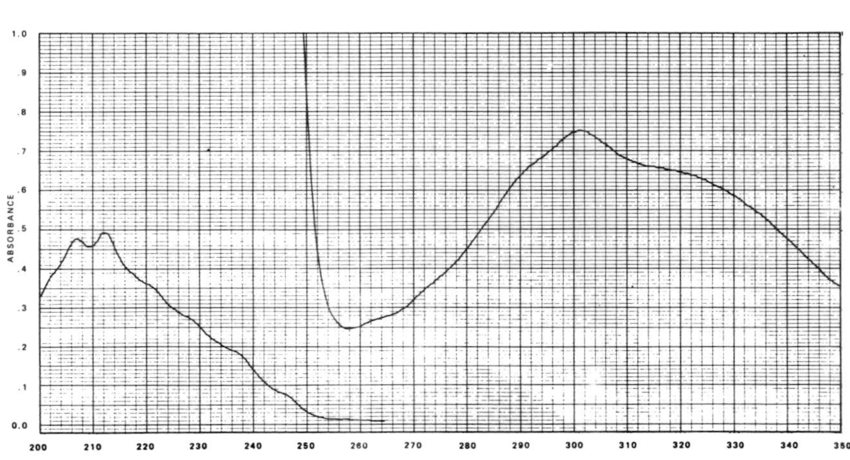

THE HYDRAZIDES

Aliphatic Compounds

The alkyl hydrazides do not display any maxima in the near UV region and as a consequence there are no spectra in this section for compounds 2403 or 2404.

Aromatic Compounds

The ultraviolet spectra of the hydrazides are found to be similar to those of the parent carboxylic acids (see page 719) differing primarily in that they do not contain the three maxima near 272 mμ that are often observed for the benzoic acids.

Two such acid-hydrazide comparisons are given below (methanol solutions).

Compound	$\lambda_{max}(\epsilon_{max})$	$\lambda_{max}(\epsilon_{max})$	Spectrum
4-Bromobenzoic acid	241 (16100)	282 (568)	2574
—, Hydrazide	238 (14400)	- - - - - - - - - -	2406
2-Nitrobenzoic acid	250 * (3680)	- - - - - - - - - -	2581
—, Hydrazide	248 (5580)	- - - - - - - - - -	2407

* Shoulder

(p-AMINOPHENYL)ACETIC ACID, HYDRAZIDE

2405

$C_8H_{11}N_3O$

Mol. Wt. 165.20

M.P. 160°C

Solvent: Methanol

λ Max. mμ	a_m	Cell mm	Conc. g/L
290.5	1480	10	0.100
240	10900	1	0.100
x	x	2	0.0200

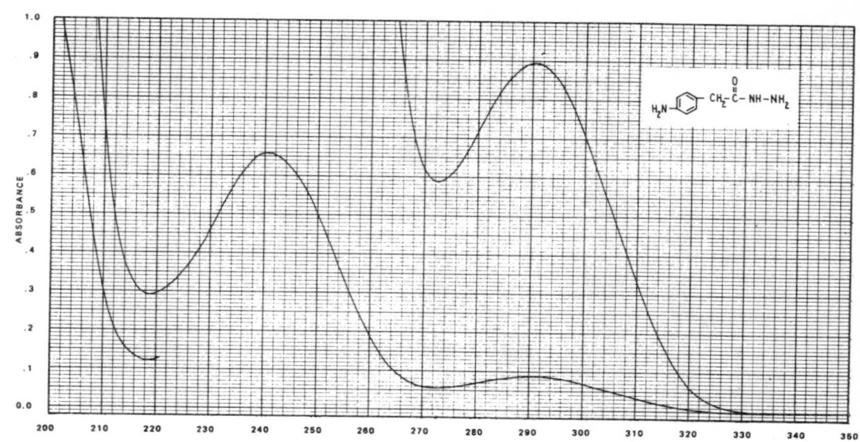

(p-AMINOPHENYL)ACETIC ACID, HYDRAZIDE

2405

$C_8H_{11}N_3O$

Mol. Wt. 165.20

M.P. 160°C

Solvent: Methanol HCl

λ Max. mμ	a_m	Cell mm	Conc. g/L
264	809	10	0.100
259	1130	10	0.100
251.5	1220	10	0.100
205.5	43800	1	0.0200

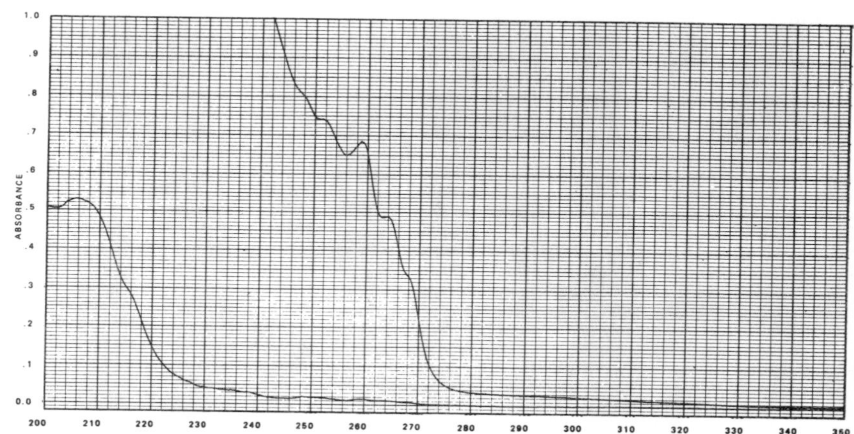

p-BROMOBENZOIC ACID, HYDRAZIDE

2406

$C_7H_7BrN_2O$

Mol. Wt. 215.06

Solvent: Methanol

λ Max. mμ	a_m	Cell mm	Conc. g/L
238	14400	10	0.010

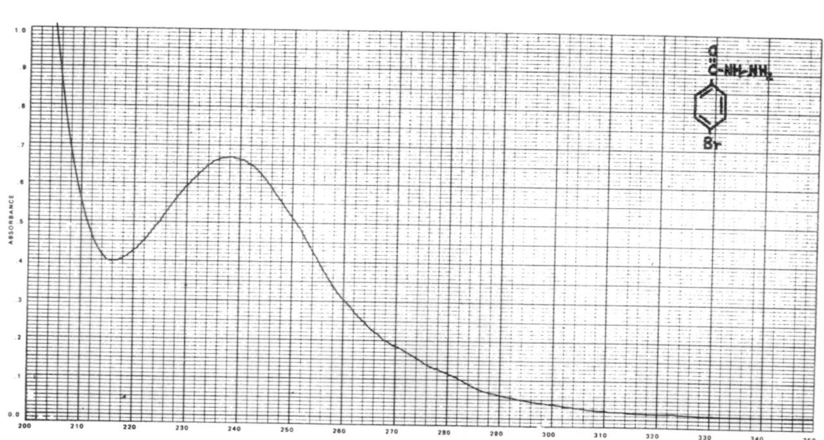

2407

o-NITROBENZOIC ACID, HYDRAZIDE

$C_7H_7N_3O_3$

Mol. Wt. 181.15

Solvent: Methanol

λ Max. mμ	a_m	Cell mm	Conc. g/L
248	5580	1	0.100
205.5	12600	1	0.100

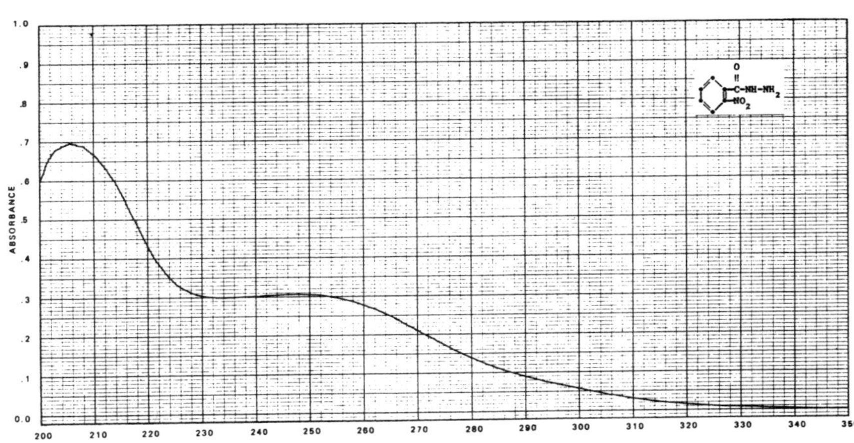

2408

PICOLINIC ACID, HYDRAZIDE

$C_6H_7N_3O$

Mol. Wt. 137.14

M.P. 98-100°C

Solvent: Methanol

λ Max. mμ	a_m	Cell mm	Conc. g/L
265	5490	1	0.100
217	8780	1	0.100

2408

PICOLINIC ACID, HYDRAZIDE

$C_6H_7N_3O$

Mol. Wt. 137.14

M.P. 98-100°C

Solvent: Methanol HCl

λ Max. mμ	a_m	Cell mm	Conc. g/L
265	4550	1	0.100
220.5	9050	1	0.100

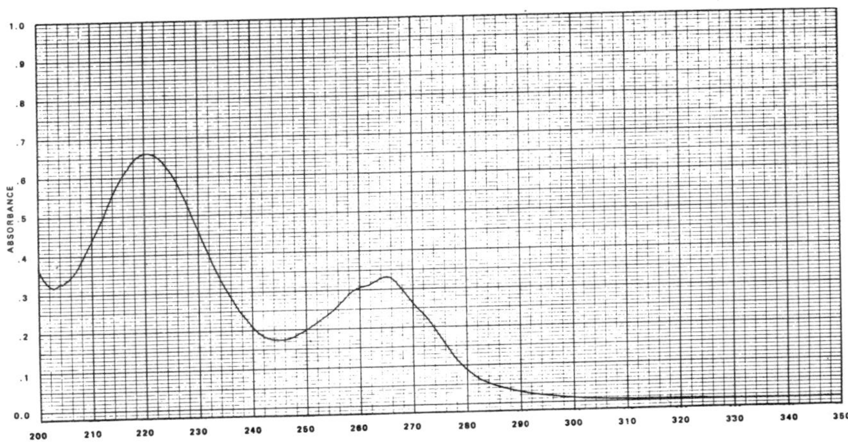

NICOTINIC ACID, HYDRAZIDE

2409

$C_6H_7N_3O$

Mol. Wt. 137.14

M.P. 160-163^oC

Solvent: Methanol

λ Max. mμ	a_m	Cell mm	Conc. g/L
262	5230	1	0.100
211	8120	1	0.100

ABSORBANCE

Methanol

NICOTINIC ACID, HYDRAZIDE

2409

$C_6H_7N_3O$

Mol. Wt. 137.14

M.P. 160-163^oC

Solvent: Methanol KOH

λ Max. mμ	a_m	Cell mm	Conc. g/L
269	4680	2	0.100
244	5000	2	0.100
x	x	1	0.100

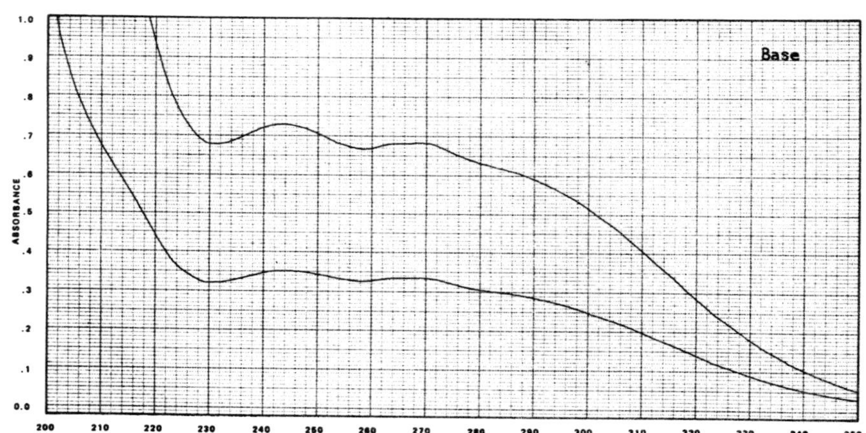

NICOTINIC ACID, HYDRAZIDE

2409

$C_6H_7N_3O$

Mol. Wt. 137.14

M.P. 160-163^oC

Solvent: Methanol HCl

λ Max. mμ	a_m	Cell mm	Conc. g/L
261.5	5360	2	0.100
x	x	1	0.100

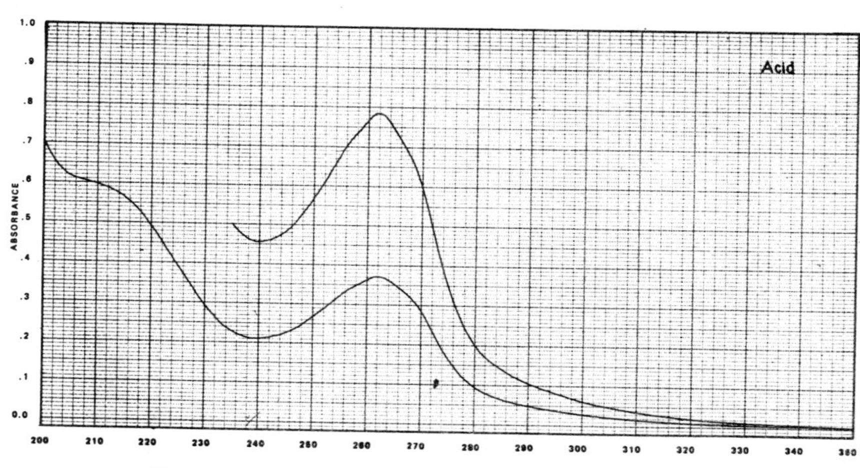

p-CHLOROBENZOIC ACID, 2,2-DIMETHYLHYDRAZIDE

2410

$C_9H_{11}ClN_2O$

Mol. Wt. 198.65

M.P. 132-134°C

Solvent: Methanol

λ Max. mμ	a_m	Cell mm	Conc. g/L
232	12500	1	0.100

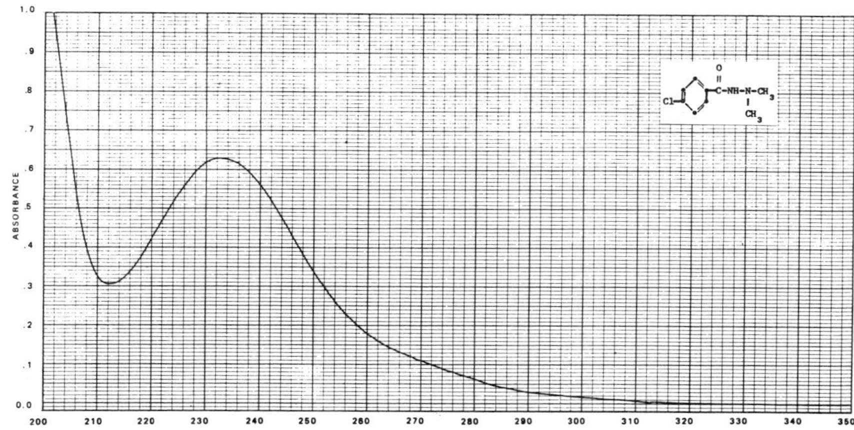

BENZOIC ACID, CYCLOHEXYLIDENEHYDRAZIDE

2411

$C_{13}H_{16}N_2O$

Mol. Wt. 216.29

M.P. 163-165°C

Solvent: Methanol

λ Max. mμ	a_m	Cell mm	Conc. g/L
257	11900	1	0.100
227	11100	1	0.100

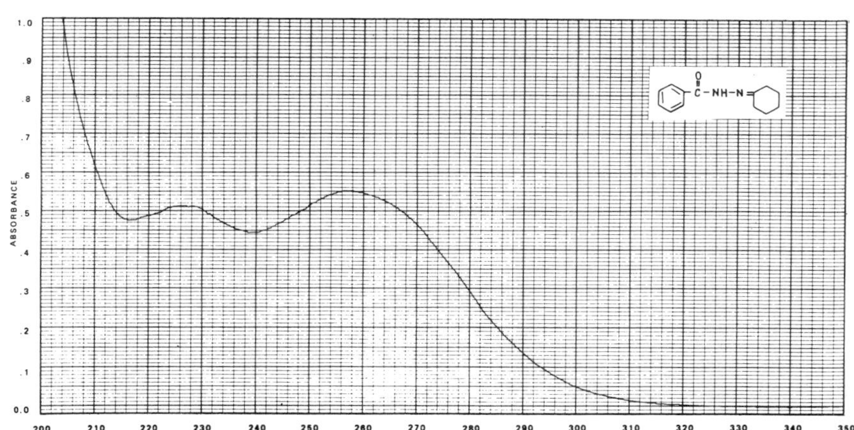

BENZOIC ACID, CYCLOHEXYLIDENEHYDRAZIDE

2411

$C_{13}H_{16}N_2O$

Mol. Wt. 216.29

M.P. 163-165°C

Solvent: Methanol HCl

λ Max. mμ	a_m	Cell mm	Conc. g/L
229.5	11200	1	0.100

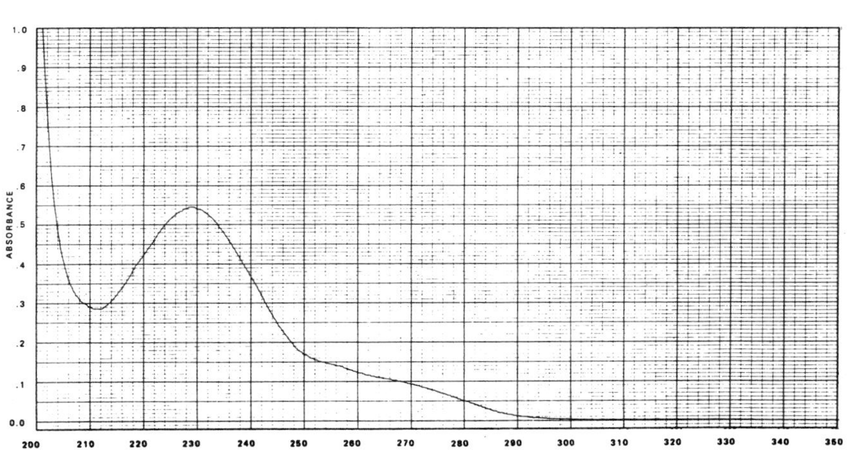

5-PHENYL-3-PYRAZOLIDINONE 2412

$C_9H_{10}N_2O$
Mol. Wt. 162.19
M.P. 104-105°C

λ Max. mμ	a_m	Cell mm	Conc. g/L

Pure sample not available.

1,2-DIBUTYRYLHYDRAZINE 2413

$C_8H_{16}N_2O_2$
Mol. Wt. 172.23
M.P. 163-164°C

λ Max. mμ	a_m	Cell mm	Conc. g/L

Pure sample not available.

1,2-DIBENZOYL-1,2-DIMETHYLHYDRAZINE 2414

$C_{16}H_{16}N_2O$
Mol. Wt. 252.32
Solvent: Methanol

λ Max. mμ	a_m	Cell mm	Conc. g/L
x	x	20	0.100
x	x	0.5	0.100

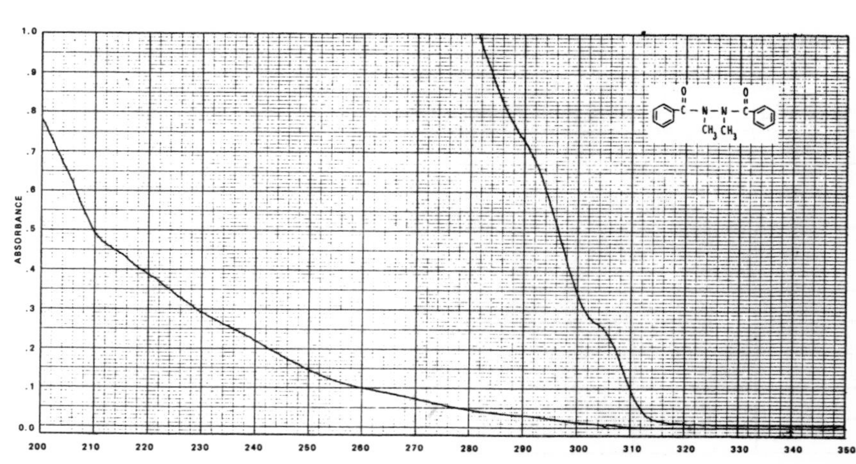

THE UREAS

Aliphatic and Alicyclic Compounds

The aliphatic and alicyclic ureas do not display any maxima in the near ultraviolet region and thus there are no spectra in this text for compounds 2415 through 2421.

Aromatic Compounds

The aromatic urea compounds produce spectra in the near UV containing one major band near 242 mμ. A weak inflection or maxima may be observed in the region 270 - 290 mμ.

The data for several of these compounds is listed below (methanol solutions).

Urea	$\lambda_{max}(\epsilon_{max})$	$\lambda_{max}(\epsilon_{max})$	Spectrum
—, 1,1-Dimethyl-2-phenyl	239 (17400)	- - - - - - - - - -	2435
—, p-Tolyl	239 (17800)	279 (1040)	2423
—, 1,1-Diphenyl	240 (10900)	- - - - - - - - - -	2427
—, 4-Methoxyphenyl	241 (15900)	289 (1710)	2425
—, 1,3-Dimethyl-1,3-diphenyl	243 (9270)	- - - - - - - - - -	2440
—, 1,1-Diphenyl-3-methyl	245 (10900)	- - - - - - - - - -	2436
—, 4-Bromophenyl	246 (22400)	- - - - - - - - - -	2424

The spectra of the aromatic ureas do not show any significant changes upon the addition of either acid or base.

THE HYDANTOINS

Hydantoin, and its alkyl derivatives, do not display any maxima in the near UV (220 - 350 mμ). The aromatic hydantoins display two distinct sets of spectra depending upon whether the phenyl group is bonded to the position 5 carbon or the position 1 or 3 nitrogen atoms.

The spectra of the 5-phenyl hydantoins display a maximum or shoulder near 215 mμ and a weak band with superimposed fine structure at about 260 mμ. The benzyl hydantoins give rise to similar spectra (compound 2445).

The 1-phenyl and 3-phenyl hydantoins produce spectra with a major band near 240 mμ with weak inflections in the 270 - 280 mμ region (compound 2450).

THE URACILS

The C=C—C(=O) conjugated chromophore of the uracils produces a moderately strong absorption band in the region from 260 - 295 mμ depending on the type of substituents present at positions 5 or 6 of the double bond.

Upon the addition of base, these bands show a bathochromic shift of about 25 - 30 mμ.

BENZYLUREA

2422

$C_8H_{10}N_2O$
Mol. Wt. 150.18
Solvent: Methanol

λ Max. mμ	a_m	Cell mm	Conc. g/L
266.5	140	20	0.100
263	182	20	0.100
257	234	20	0.100
251.5	210	20	0.100
246	181	20	0.100

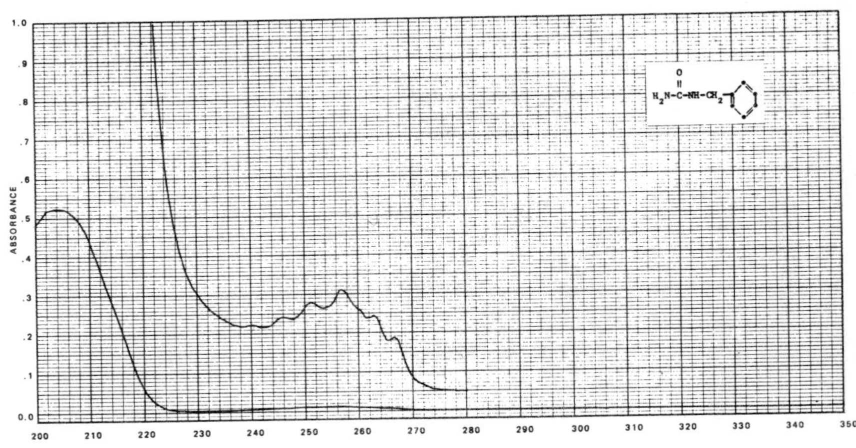

p-TOLYLUREA

2423

$C_8H_{10}N_2O$
Mol. Wt. 150.18
M.P. 185°C
Solvent: Methanol

λ Max. mμ	a_m	Cell mm	Conc. g/L
279	1040	10	0.100
239	17800	1	0.0500

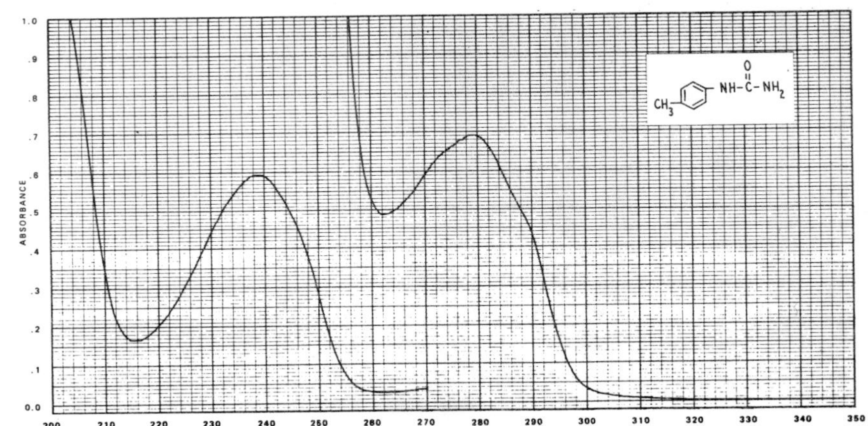

(p-BROMOPHENYL)UREA

2424

$C_7H_7BrNO_2$
Mol. Wt. 217.05
Solvent: Methanol

λ Max. mμ	a_m	Cell mm	Conc. g/L
245.5	22400	1	0.050

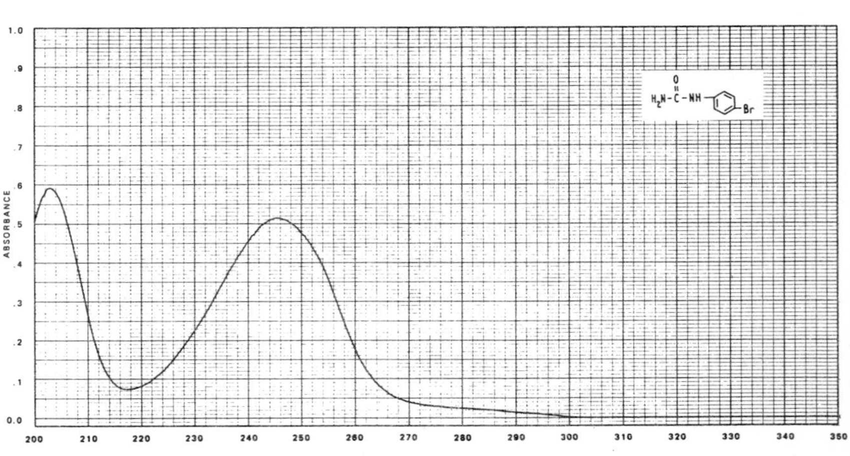

(p-METHOXYPHENYL) UREA

2425

$C_8H_{10}N_2O_2$
Mol. Wt. 166.18
M.P. 169-171°C
Solvent: Methanol

λ Max. mμ	a_m	Cell mm	Conc. g/L
289	1710	5	0.100
241	15900	1	0.100

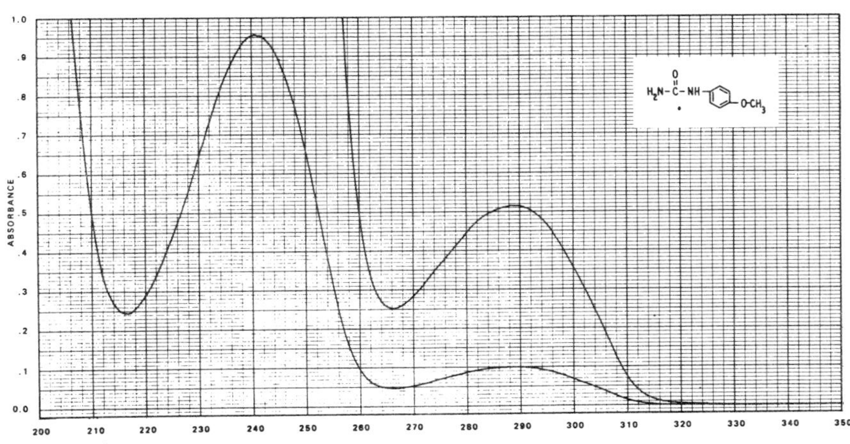

1,1-DIMETHYLUREA

2426

$C_3H_8N_2O$
Mol. Wt. 88.11
M.P. 181.5-182°C

λ Max. mμ	a_m	Cell mm	Conc. g/L

This compound does not display any maxima in the near UV.

1,1-DIPHENYLUREA

2427

$C_{13}H_{12}N_2O$
Mol. Wt. 212.25
M.P. 188°C (dec.)
Solvent: Methanol

λ Max. mμ	a_m	Cell mm	Conc. g/L
240	10900	1	0.0500

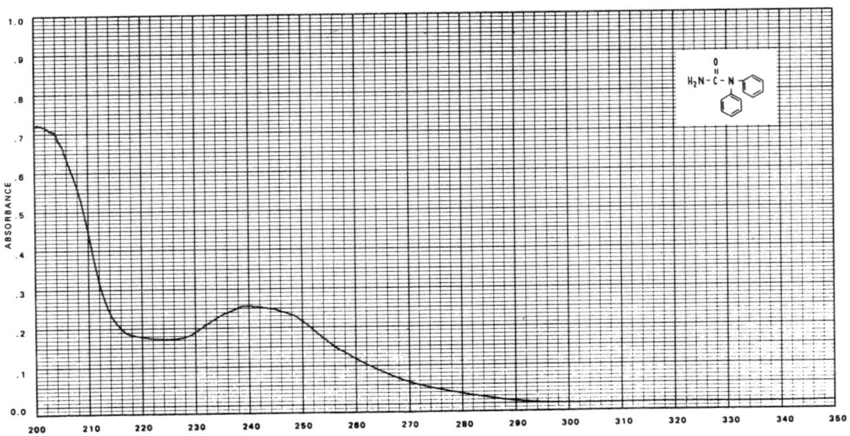

λ Max. mμ	a_m	Cell mm	Conc. g/L

Alkyl and alicyclic ureas (compounds 2428 through 2431) do not display any maxima in the near UV.

1,3-DIBENZYLUREA 2432

$C_{15}H_{16}N_2O$
Mol. Wt. 240.31
M.P. 167-170°C
Solvent: Methanol

λ Max. mμ	a_m	Cell mm	Conc. g/L
302	66	20	0.100
267.5	372	20	0.100
263.5	461	20	0.100
258	567	20	0.100
252.5	503	20	0.100

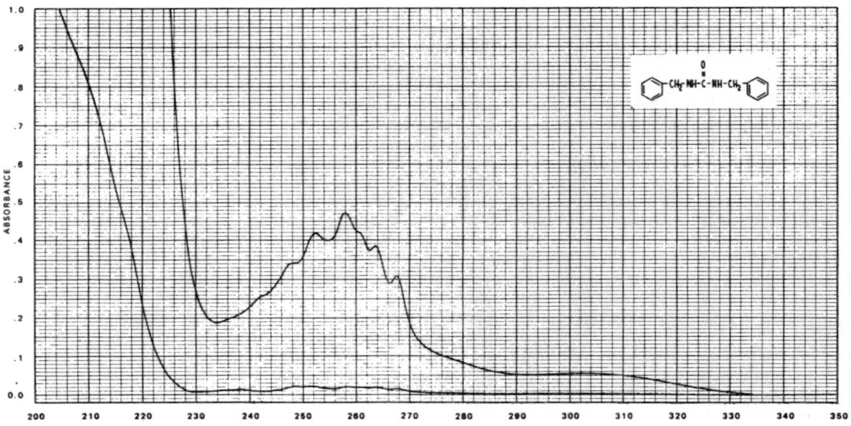

1-BUTYL-2-IMIDAZOLIDINONE 2433

$C_7H_{14}N_2O$
Mol. Wt. 142.20
M.P. 36-39°C
B.P. 102°C/0.3mm

λ Max. mμ	a_m	Cell mm	Conc. g/L

This compound does not display any maxima in the near UV.

1-ALLYL-2-IMIDAZOLIDINONE 2434

$C_6H_{10}N_2O$
Mol. Wt. 126.16
M.P. 56.5-58°C
B.P. 95°C/0.25mm

λ Max. mμ	a_m	Cell mm	Conc. g/L

Pure sample not available.

1,1-DIMETHYL-3-PHENYLUREA 2435

$C_9H_{12}N_2O$
Mol. Wt. 164.21
M.P. 131-132°C
Solvent: Methanol

λ Max. mμ	a_m	Cell mm	Conc. g/L
239	17400	1	0.0500

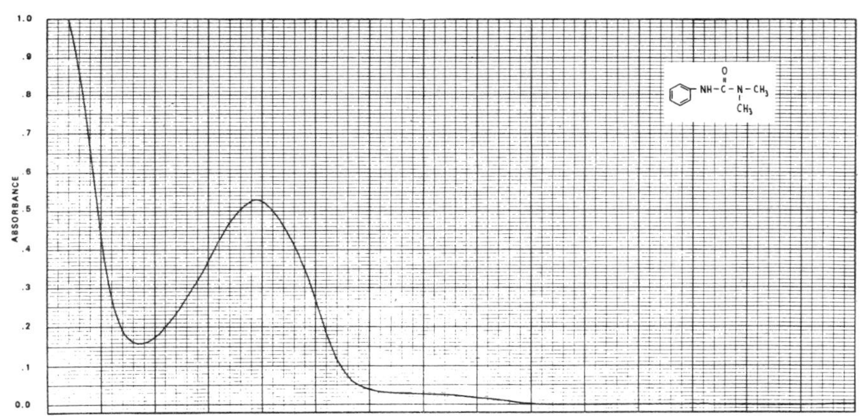

1,1-DIPHENYL-3-METHYLUREA 2436

$C_{14}H_{14}N_2O$
Mol. Wt. 226.28
M.P. 170-174°C
Solvent: Methanol

λ Max. mμ	a_m	Cell mm	Conc. g/L
245	10900	1	0.100

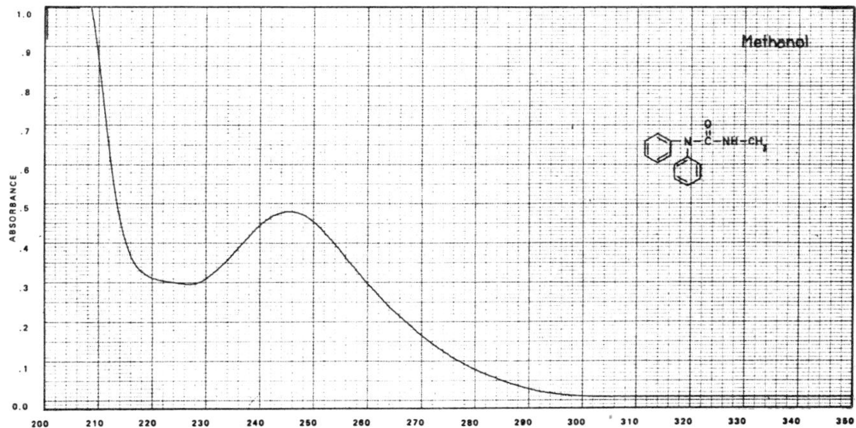

2437

λ Max. mμ	a_m	Cell mm	Conc. g/L

Alkyl ureas (compounds 2437 and 2438) do not display any maxima in the near UV.

1,1′-CARBONYLDIPIPERIDINE 2439

$C_{11}H_{20}N_2O$
Mol. Wt. 196.29
M.P. 44-47°C
B.P. 296-298°C

λ Max. mμ	a_m	Cell mm	Conc. g/L

Pure sample not available.

N,N′-DIMETHYLCARBANILIDE 2440

$C_{15}H_{16}N_2O$
Mol. Wt. 240.31
M.P. 120-122°C
Solvent: Methanol

λ Max. mμ	a_m	Cell mm	Conc. g/L
243	9270	2	0.100

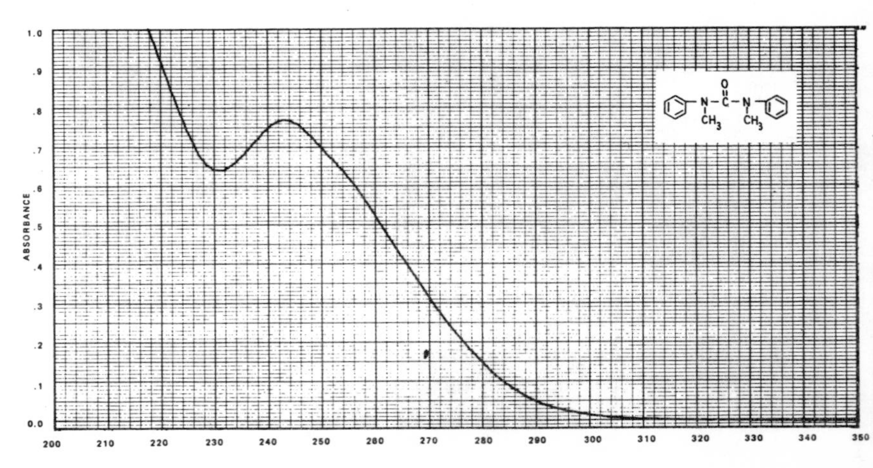

1-PHENYL-2-BENZIMIDAZOLINONE **2441**

$C_{13}H_{10}N_2O$
Mol. Wt. 210.24
M.P. 203.5-204°C
Solvent: Methanol

λ Max. mμ	a_m	Cell mm	Conc. g/L
282	5060	2	0.100
251	4230	1	0.100

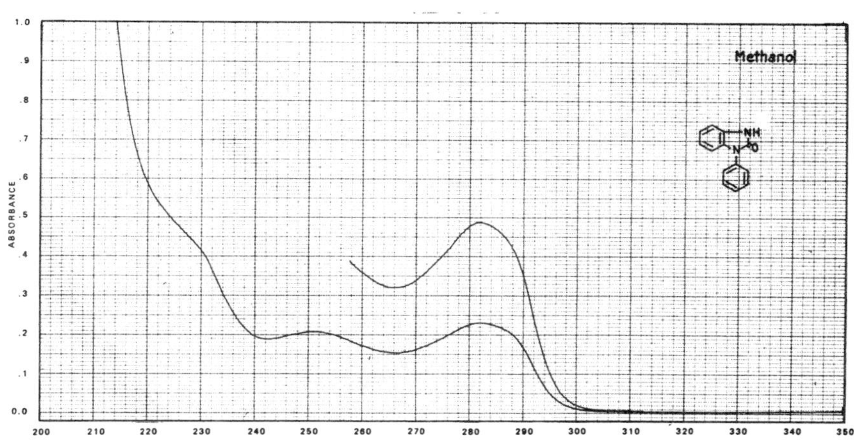

5,5-DIMETHYLTETRAHYDRO-2(1H)-PYRIMIDINONE **2442**

$C_6H_{12}N_2O$
Mol. Wt. 128.18
M.P. 255-257°C

λ Max. mμ	a_m	Cell mm	Conc. g/L

Compound 2442 does not display any maxima in the near UV.

2443

λ Max. mμ	a_m	Cell mm	Conc. g/L

Hydantoin and 5-Methylhydantoin (compounds 2443 and 2444) do not display any maxima in the near UV.

3-BENZYL-5,5-DIMETHYLHYDANTOIN

2445

$C_{12}H_{14}N_2O_2$

Mol. Wt. 218.26

M.P. 105-106°C

Solvent: Methanol

λ Max. mμ	a_m	Cell mm	Conc. g/L
266.5	477	20	0.100
263	764	20	0.100
257	981	20	0.100
251	853	20	0.100
246	797	20	0.100

5-PHENYLHYDANTOIN

2446

$C_9H_8N_2O_2$

Mol. Wt. 176.18

Solvent: Methanol

λ Max. mμ	a_m	Cell mm	Conc. g/L
263.5	178	40	0.100
257	2480	40	0.100
215.5	3270	5	0.100

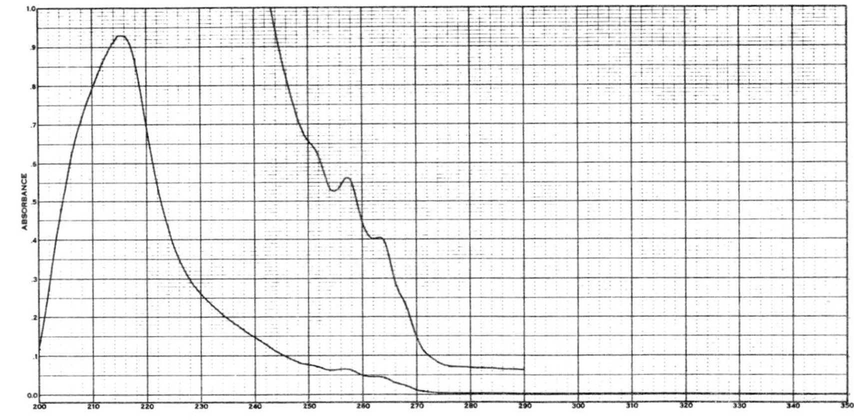

5-METHYL-5-PHENYLHYDANTOIN

2447

$C_{10}H_{10}N_2O_2$

Mol. Wt. 190.20

M.P. 244°C (lit.)

Solvent: Methanol

λ Max. mμ	a_m	Cell mm	Conc. g/L
263.5	226	20	0.100
257	340	20	0.100
x	x	1	0.100

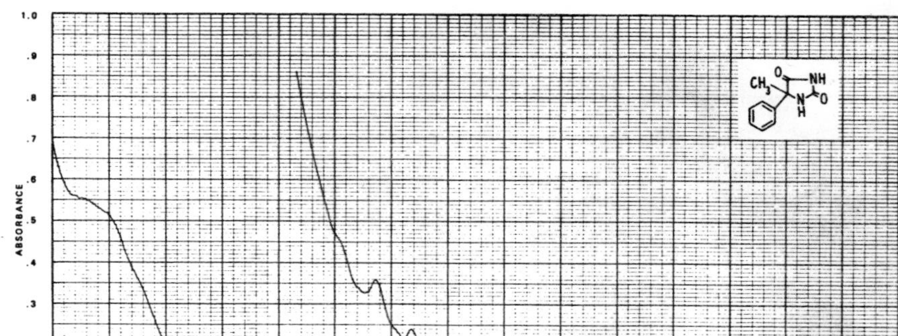

3-METHYL-5-PHENYLHYDANTOIN

2448

$C_{10}H_{10}N_2O_2$
Mol. Wt. 190.20
Solvent: Methanol

λ Max. mμ	a_m	Cell mm	Conc. g/L
263	216	20	0.100
257	268	20	0.100
x	x	1	0.100

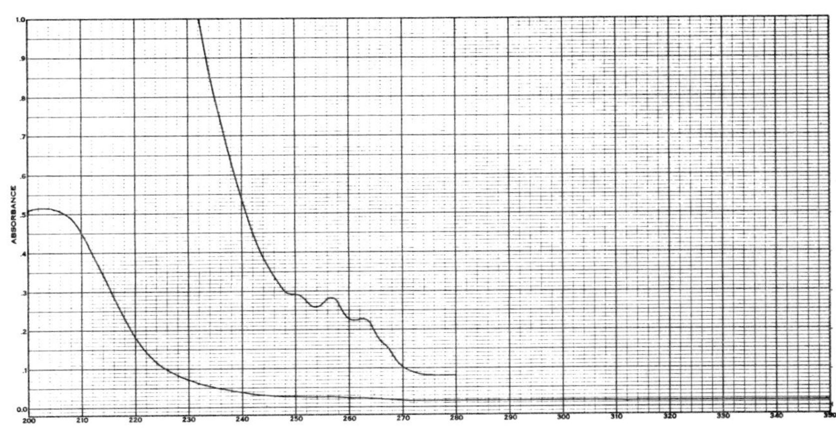

3-ETHYL-5-PHENYLHYDANTOIN

2449

$C_{11}H_{12}N_2O_2$
Mol. Wt. 204.23
M.P. 91-93°C
Solvent: Methanol

λ Max. mμ	a_m	Cell mm	Conc. g/L
316.5	712	2	1.00
263.5	312	2	1.00
257.5	351	2	1.00
251.5	347	2	1.00

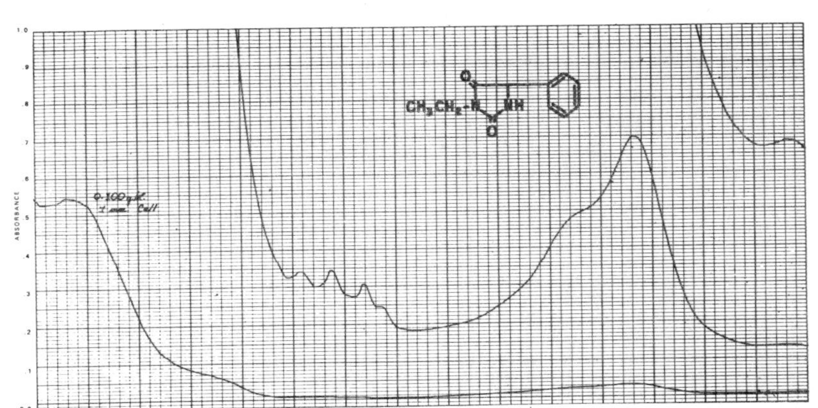

1,3-DIPHENYLHYDANTOIN

2450

$C_{15}H_{12}N_2O_2$
Mol. Wt. 252.28
Solvent: Methanol

λ Max. mμ	a_m	Cell mm	Conc. g/L
239	18000	1	0.100

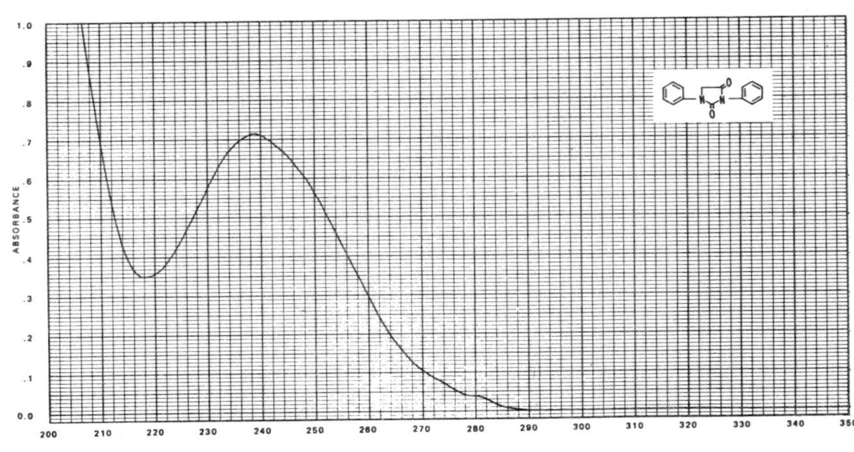

ALLANTOIN 2451

$C_4H_6N_4O_3$
Mol. Wt. 158.10
M.P. 240°C (Dec.)

λ Max. mμ	a_m	Cell mm	Conc. g/L

Compound does not display any maxima in the near UV.

1,3-DIMETHYLURACIL 2452

$C_6H_8N_2O_2$
Mol. Wt. 140.15
Solvent: Methanol

λ Max. mμ	a_m	Cell mm	Conc. g/L
316	981	10	0.010
264.5	9820	10	0.010

THYMINE 2453

$C_5H_6N_2O_2$
Mol. Wt. 126.12
M.P. 335-337°C
Solvent: Methanol

λ Max. mμ	a_m	Cell mm	Conc. g/L
262.5	7860	1	0.100
206.5	9400	1	0.100

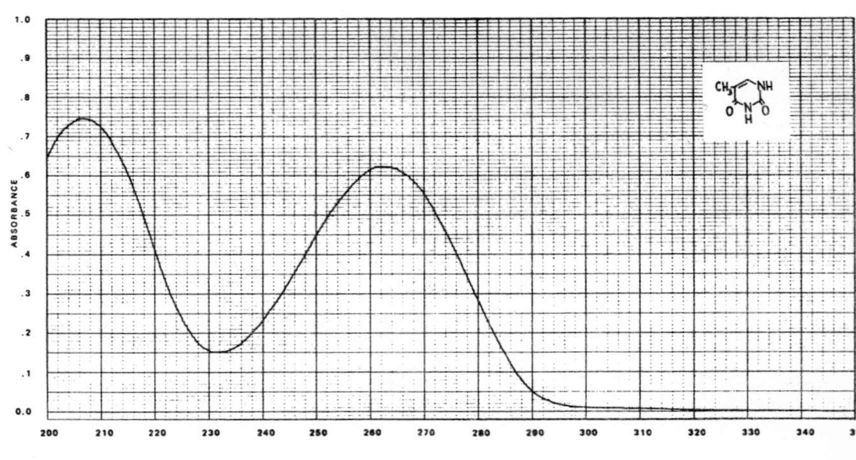

THYMINE

$C_5H_6N_2O_2$
Mol. Wt. 126.12
M.P. 335-337°C
Solvent: Methanol KOH

λ Max. mμ	a_m	Cell mm	Conc. g/L
292.5	8900	1	0.100

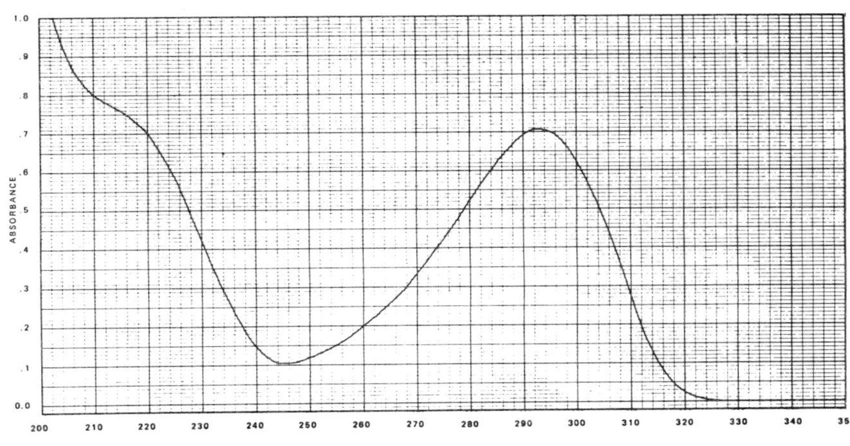

6-METHYLURACIL

$C_5H_6N_2O_2$
Mol. Wt. 126.11
Solvent: Methanol

λ Max. mμ	a_m	Cell mm	Conc. g/L
x	x	10	1.640
259.5	10900	10	0.016

λ Max. mμ	a_m	Cell mm	Conc. g/L

5,6-DIMETHYLURACIL

2455

$C_6H_8N_2O_2$

Mol. Wt. 140.15

Solvent: Methanol

λ Max. mμ	a_m	Cell mm	Conc. g/L
265	8660	1	0.100
207	8470	1	0.100

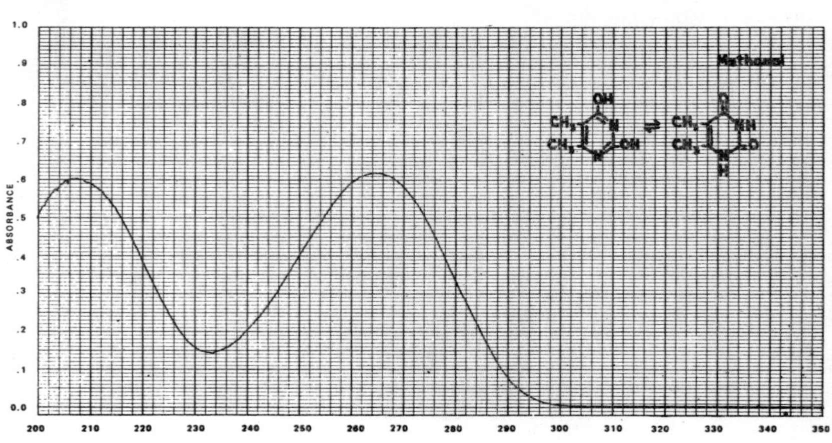

5,6-DIMETHYLURACIL

2455

$C_6H_8N_2O_2$

Mol. Wt. 140.15

Solvent: Methanol KOH

λ Max. mμ	a_m	Cell mm	Conc. g/L
291	8300	1	0.100

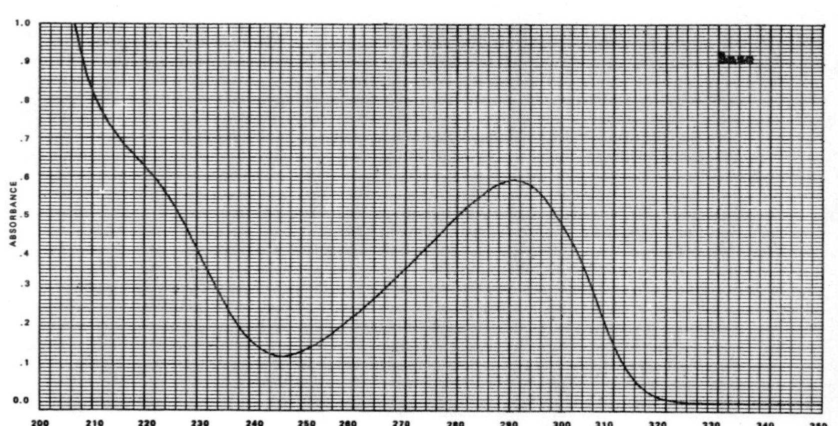

5-BROMOURACIL

2456

$C_4H_3BrN_2O_2$

Mol. Wt. 190.99

M.P. 305-310°C (dec.)

Solvent: Methanol

λ Max. mμ	a_m	Cell mm	Conc. g/L
272	7050	1	0.100
207	9550	1	0.100

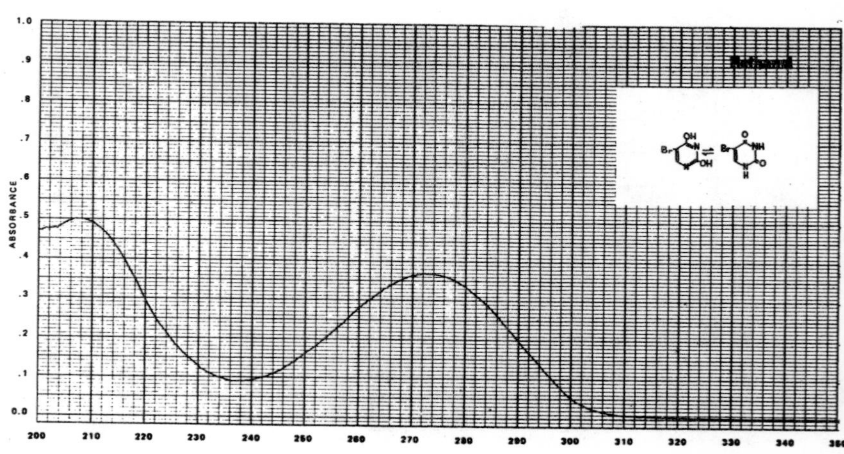

5-BROMOURACIL 2456

$C_4H_3BrN_2O_2$
Mol. Wt. 190.99
M.P. 305-310°C (dec.)
Solvent: Methanol KOH

λ Max. mμ	a_m	Cell mm	Conc. g/L
300	9550	1	0.100
217.5	9360	1	0.100

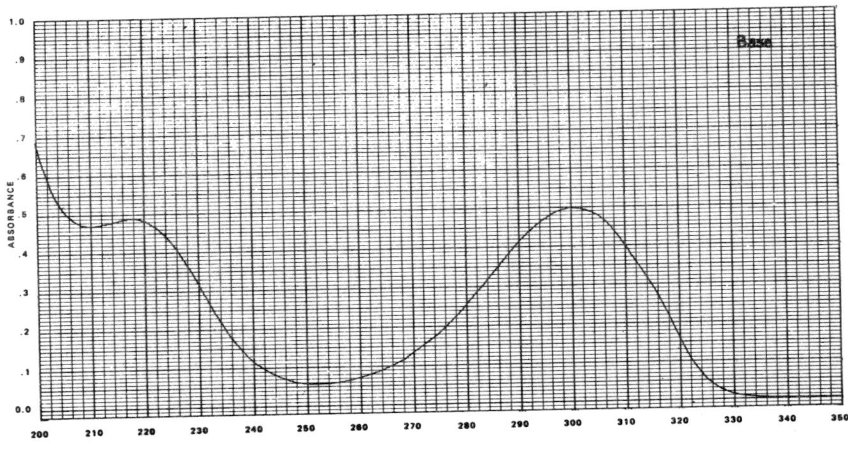

5-IODOURACIL 2457

$C_4H_3IN_2O_2$
Mol. Wt. 237.99
Solvent: Methanol

λ Max. mμ	a_m	Cell mm	Conc. g/L
279	6270	2	0.100
213	10200	2	0.100

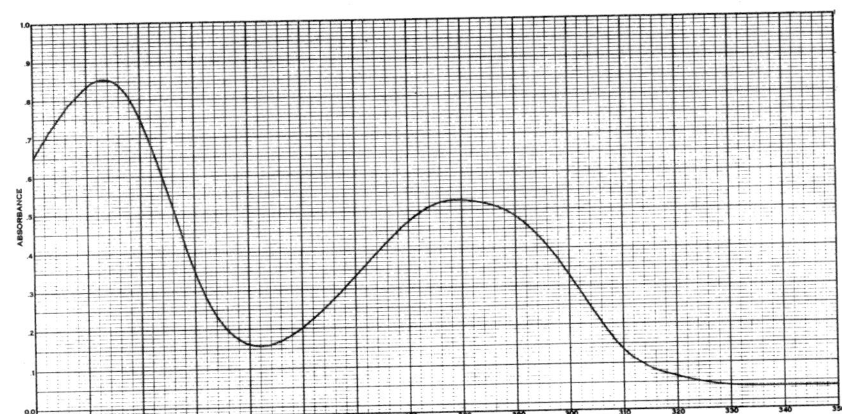

λ Max. mμ	a_m	Cell mm	Conc. g/L

5-NITROURACIL

2458

$C_4H_3N_3O_4$

Mol. Wt. 157.09

Solvent: Methanol

λ Max. mμ	a_m	Cell mm	Conc. g/L
295	8750	1	0.100
235	6980	1	0.100

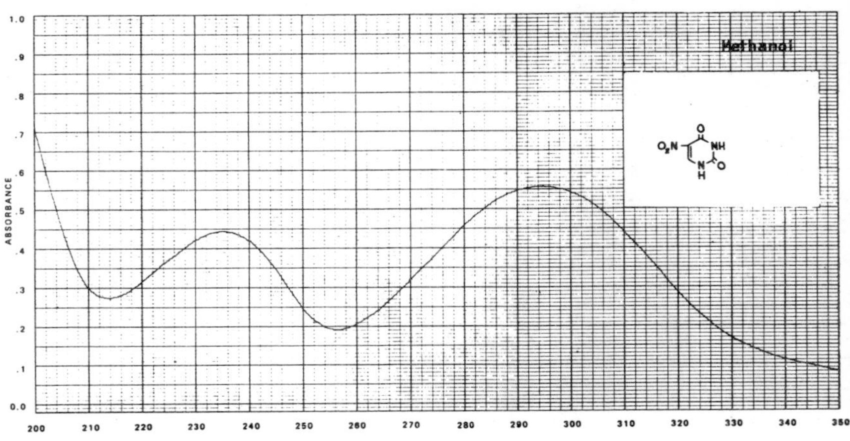

5-NITROURACIL

2458

$C_4H_3N_3O_4$

Mol. Wt. 157.09

Solvent: Methanol KOH

λ Max. mμ	a_m	Cell mm	Conc. g/L
338	16400	1	0.0800
258	5850	1	0.0800
232	5700	1	0.0800

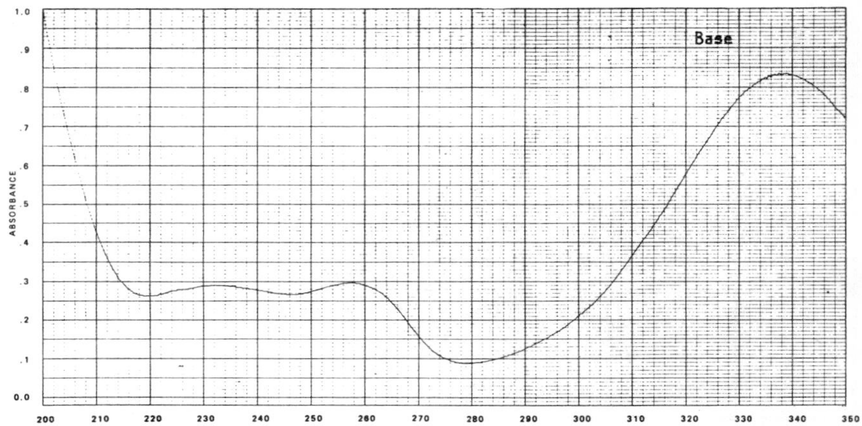

5-(1-METHYLBUTYL)BARBITURIC ACID

2459

$C_9H_{14}N_2O_3$

Mol. Wt. 198.23

M.P. 165-168°C

Solvent: Methanol

λ Max. mμ	a_m	Cell mm	Conc. g/L
269	20900	10	0.005
228.5	5010	10	0.020

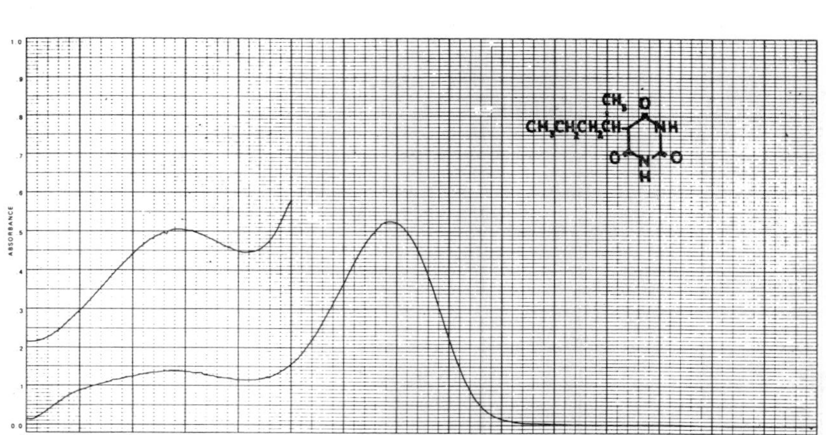

5,5-DIETHYLBARBITURIC ACID 2460

$C_8H_{10}N_2O_3$
Mol. Wt. 182.18
Solvent: Methanol

λ Max. mμ	a_m	Cell mm	Conc. g/L
x	x	10	2.240
x	x	10	0.224
x	x	10	0.022

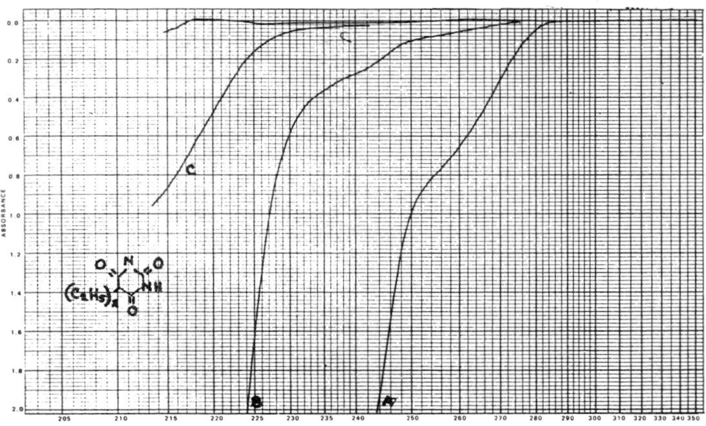

5,5-DIALLYLBARBITURIC ACID 2461

$C_{10}H_{12}N_2O_3$
Mol. Wt. 208.22
M.P. 174°C

λ Max. mμ	a_m	Cell mm	Conc. g/L

Pure sample not available.

5,5-DIBENZYLBARBITURIC ACID 2462

$C_{18}H_{16}N_2O_3$
Mol. Wt. 308.34
M.P. 221-225°C

λ Max. mμ	a_m	Cell mm	Conc. g/L

Pure sample not available.

5-BENZYLIDENEBARBITURIC ACID

2463

$C_{11}H_8N_2O_3$

Mol. Wt. 216.20

M.P. 256°C

Solvent: Methanol

λ Max. mμ	a_m	Cell mm	Conc. g/L
324	8460	2	0.100
255.5	4540	2	0.100

5-BENZYLIDENEBARBITURIC ACID

2463

$C_{11}H_8N_2O_3$

Mol. Wt. 216.20

M.P. 256°C

Solvent: Methanol KOH

λ Max. mμ	a_m	Cell mm	Conc. g/L
258	18800	1	0.100

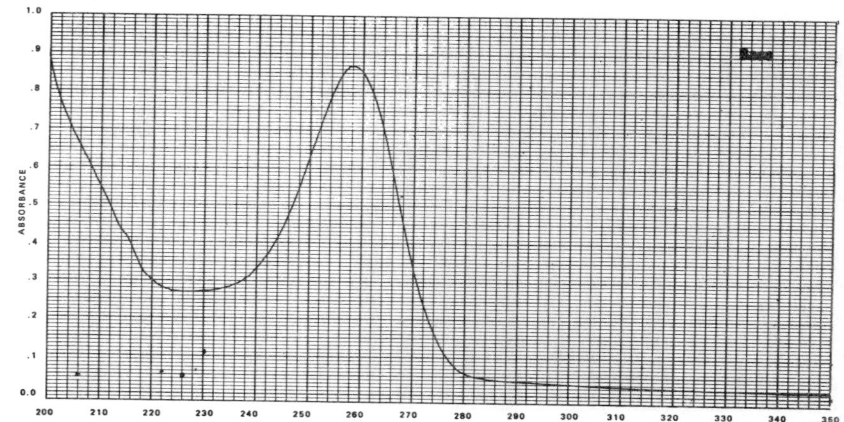

5-ALLYL-5-PHENYLBARBITURIC ACID

2464

$C_{13}H_{12}N_2O_3$

Mol. Wt. 244.25

Solvent: Methanol

λ Max. mμ	a_m	Cell mm	Conc. g/L
x	x	2	0.100

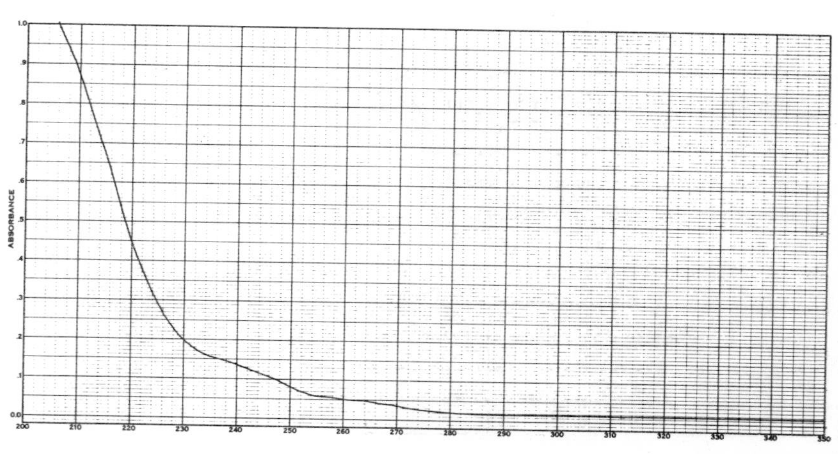

1,3,5-TRIS(2-HYDROXYETHYL)-s-TRIAZINE-2,4,6(1H,3H,5H)-TRIONE

2465

$C_9H_{15}N_3O_6$
Mol. Wt. 261.24

λ Max. mμ	a_m	Cell mm	Conc. g/L

Pure sample not available.

1,3-DIPHENYL-5-ETHYL-s-TRIAZINE-2,4,6(1H,3H,5H)-TRIONE

2466

$C_{17}H_{15}N_3O_3$
Mol. Wt. 309.33
M.P. 155-156°C
Solvent: Methanol

λ Max. mμ	a_m	Cell mm	Conc. g/L
264.5	294	20	0.100
259	439	20	0.100
255	478	20	0.100
249.5	396	20	0.100
x	x	1	0.100

λ Max. mμ	a_m	Cell mm	Conc. g/L

1,4-DIPHENYLSEMICARBAZIDE

2467

$C_{13}H_{13}N_3O$

Mol. Wt. 227.27

M.P. 175-178°C

Solvent: Methanol

λ Max. mμ	a_m	Cell mm	Conc. g/L
238	27500	1	0.0500

1,4-DIPHENYLSEMICARBAZIDE

2467

$C_{13}H_{13}N_3O$

Mol. Wt. 227.27

M.P. 175-178°C

Solvent: Methanol KOH

λ Max. mμ	a_m	Cell mm	Conc. g/L
235	18800	2	0.0500

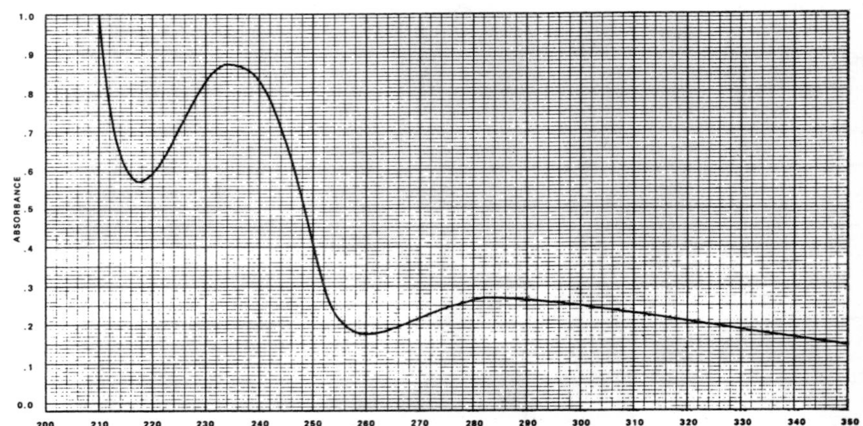

4,4-DIPHENYLSEMICARBAZIDE

2468

$C_{13}H_{13}N_3O$

Mol. Wt. 227.27

M.P. 155-156°C

Solvent: Methanol

λ Max. mμ	a_m	Cell mm	Conc. g/L
243.5	12800	1	0.100

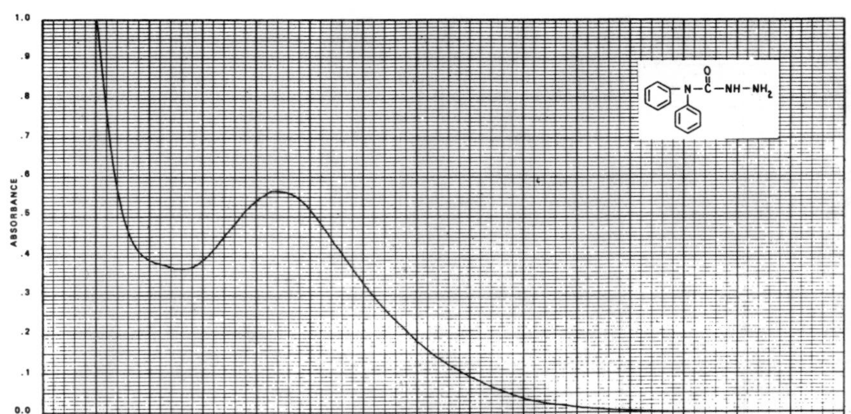

3-METHYL-2-BUTANONE, SEMICARBAZONE 2469

$C_6H_{13}N_3O$

Mol. Wt. 143.19

λ Max. mμ	a_m	Cell mm	Conc. g/L

Pure sample not available.

2-HEPTANONE, SEMICARBAZONE 2470

$C_8H_{17}N_3O$

Mol. Wt. 171.25

M.P. 120-122°C

λ Max. mμ	a_m	Cell mm	Conc. g/L

Pure sample not available.

λ Max. mμ	a_m	Cell mm	Conc. g/L

NOTES

THE CARBOXYLIC ACIDS

Aliphatic Compounds

The aliphatic, alicyclic and non-conjugated olefinic carboxylic acids do not display any maxima in the near UV. As a consequence, there are no spectra in this section for compounds 2471 through 2511.

Olefinic Compounds

The acrylic acids (compounds 2517 - 2535) normally show a maximum or shoulder in the region from 207 - 225 mμ depending on the substituent and its position on the olefinic double bond.

The ultraviolet spectra of these compounds show a significant change in band position and intensity upon the addition of base to the sample.

Aromatic Compounds

The aromatic carboxylic acids which possess an acid group that is isolated from the phenyl group by one or more carbon atoms, give rise to spectra which display one major absorption band at 258 mμ with associated benzenoid fine structure.

Due to the presence of insulating carbon atom(s), the spectra show little or no change upon the addition of base to the sample (see compound 2541, page 729).

Benzoic acid (compound 2566) and many of its derivatives produce ultraviolet spectra containing two major bands; a relatively strong band near 228 mμ and a weaker band at 272 mμ with superimposed fine structure.

A table of several benzoic acids is presented below (methanol solutions).

Compound	$\lambda_{max} (\epsilon_{max})$	$\lambda_{max} (\epsilon_{max})$	Spectrum
Benzoic acid	228 (11900)	272 (893)	2566
—, 4-Methyl	236 (13500)	272 * (871)	2567
—, 2-Fluoro	224 (5140)	275 (1540)	2569
—, 4-Fluoro	229 (10400)	262 (559)	2570
—, 4-Chloro	237 (15200)	270 * (783)	2571
—, 2-Bromo	225 * (6840)	280 (940)	2572
—, 4-Bromo	225 (9610)	281 (955)	2573
—, 4-Iodo	252 (16500)	- - - - - - - - - -	2577

* Shoulder

The spectra of the benzoic acids usually show marked hypsochromic shifts upon the addition of base to their methanol solutions.

AMINO ACIDS

The amino acids do not display any maxima in the near UV (220 - 350 mμ) unless conjugated or a chromophore is present in its molecular structure.

2-THIOPHENEACETIC ACID 2512

$C_6H_6O_2S$

Mol. Wt. 142.18

Solvent: Methanol

λ Max. mμ	a_m	Cell mm	Conc. g/L
231.5	7140	1	0.100

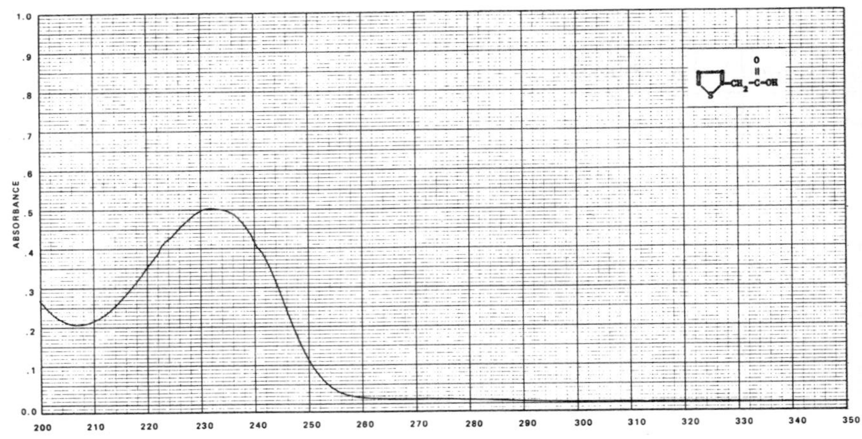

2513

λ Max. mμ	a_m	Cell mm	Conc. g/L

The alicyclic and allyl carboxylic acids (compounds 2513 through 2516) do not display any maxima in the near UV.

CROTONIC ACID 2517

$C_4H_6O_2$

Mol. Wt. 86.09

M.P. 171°C (lit.)

Solvent: Methanol

λ Max. mμ	a_m	Cell mm	Conc. g/L
x	x	10	0.400
x	x	10	0.004

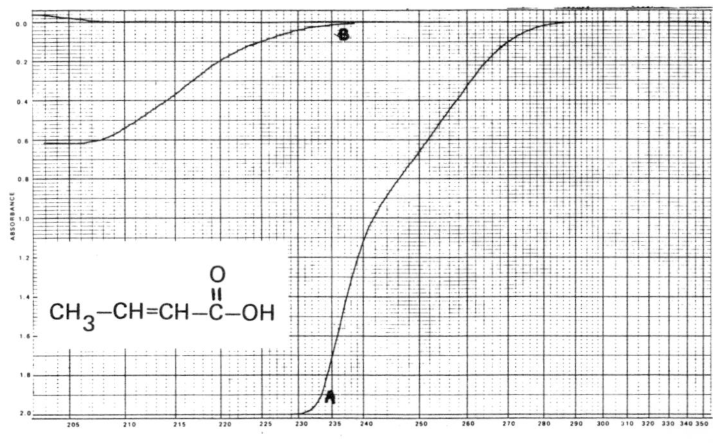

4-PENTENOIC ACID **2518**

$C_5H_8O_2$

Mol. Wt. 110.12

λ Max. mμ	a_m	Cell mm	Conc. g/L

4-Pentenoic acid does not display any maxima in the near UV.

3-METHYLCROTONIC ACID **2519**

$C_5H_8O_2$

Mol. Wt. 100.12

Solvent: Methanol

λ Max. mμ	a_m	Cell mm	Conc. g/L
215.3	19500	0.5	0.100

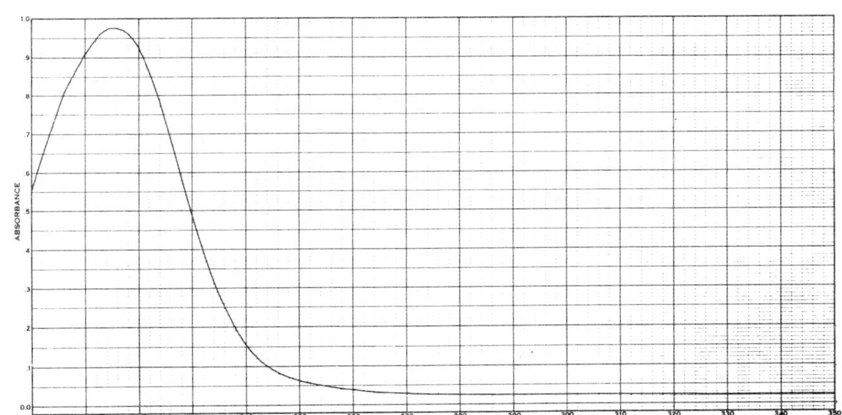

3-METHYLCROTONIC ACID **2519**

$C_5H_8O_2$

Mol. Wt. 100.12

Solvent: Methanol KOH

λ Max. mμ	a_m	Cell mm	Conc. g/L
x	x	0.5	0.100

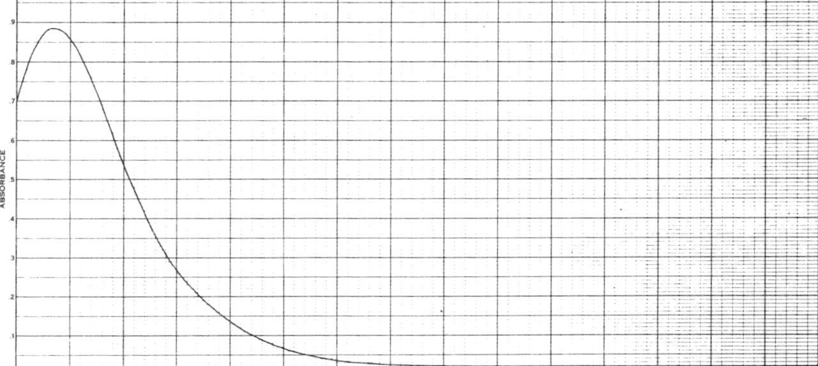

trans-2-HEXENOIC ACID

2520

$C_6H_{10}O_2$
Mol. Wt. 114.15
Solvent: Methanol

λ Max. mμ	a_m	Cell mm	Conc. g/L
212	10800	1	0.100

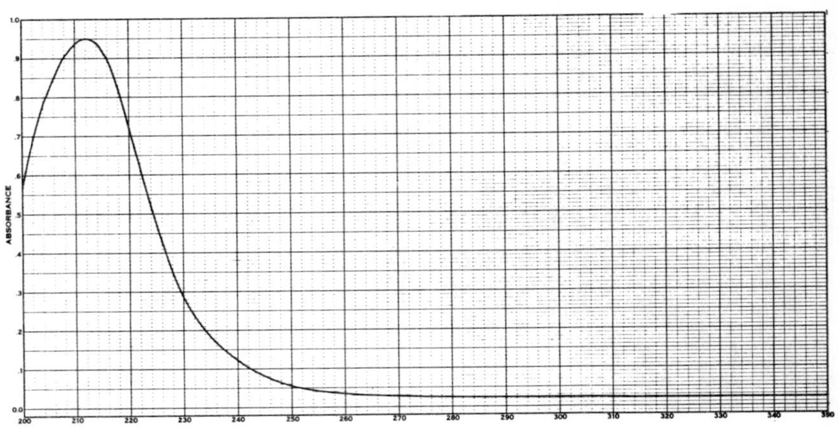

trans-2-HEXENOIC ACID

2520

$C_6H_{10}O_2$
Mol. Wt. 114.15
Solvent: Methanol KOH

λ Max. mμ	a_m	Cell mm	Conc. g/L
x	x	0.5	0.100

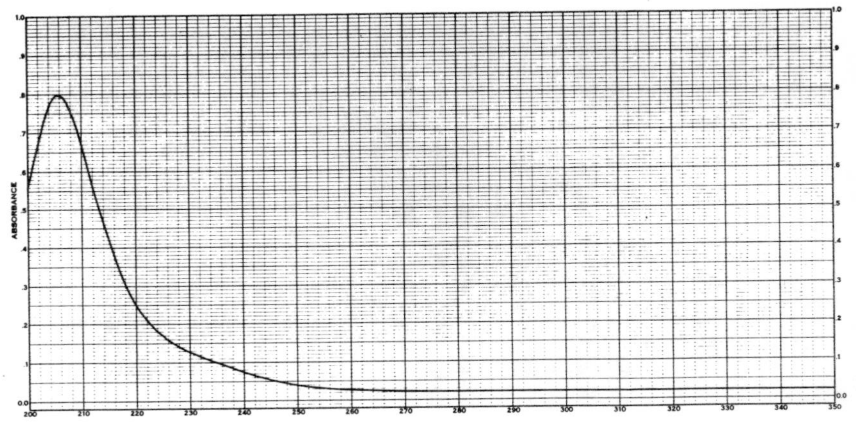

3-HEPTENOIC ACID

2521

$C_7H_{12}O_2$
Mol. Wt. 128.17

λ Max. mμ	a_m	Cell mm	Conc. g/L

3-Heptenoic acid does not display any maxima in the near UV.

4-METHYL-2-HEPTENOIC ACID 2522

$C_8H_{14}O_2$
Mol. Wt. 142.20
Solvent: Methanol

λ Max. mμ	a_m	Cell mm	Conc. g/L
x	x	1	0.100

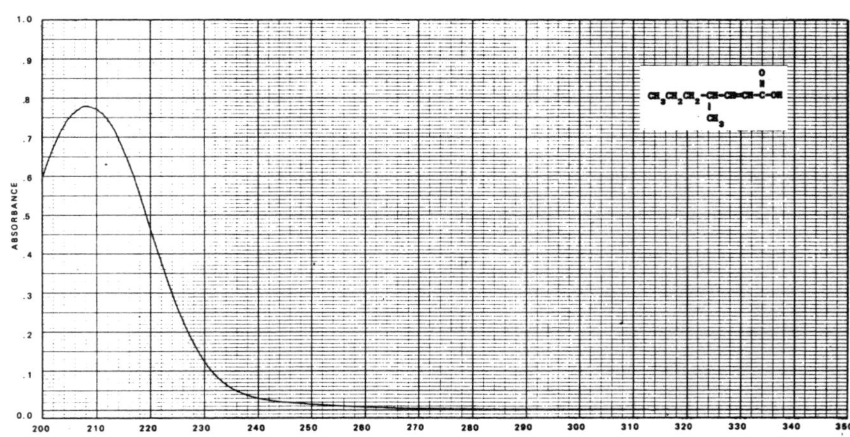

2-ETHYL-2-HEXENOIC ACID 2523

$C_8H_{14}O_2$
Mol. Wt. 142.20
B.P. 233.8-240.8°C
Solvent: Methanol

λ Max. mμ	a_m	Cell mm	Conc. g/L
x	x	20	0.100

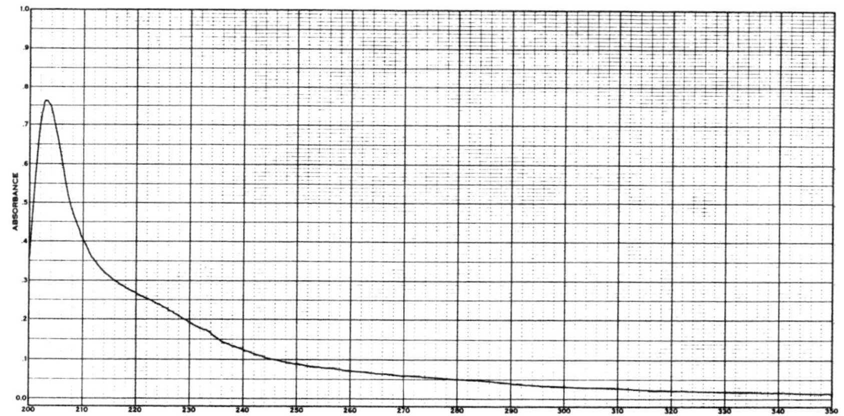

2-ETHYL-2-HEXENOIC ACID 2523

$C_8H_{14}O_2$
Mol. Wt. 142.20
B.P. 233.8-240.8°C
Solvent: Methanol KOH

λ Max. mμ	a_m	Cell mm	Conc. g/L
212	2330	5	0.100

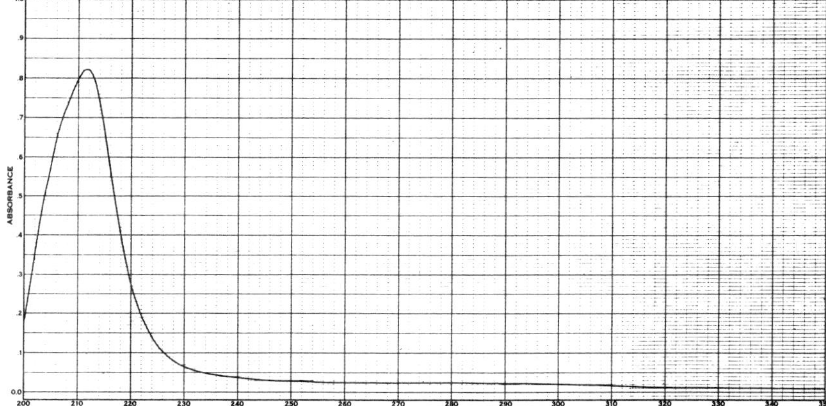

2524

2-DECENOIC ACID

$C_{10}H_{18}O_2$
Mol. Wt. 170.25
Solvent: Methanol

λ Max. mμ	a_m	Cell mm	Conc. g/L
x	x	1	0.100

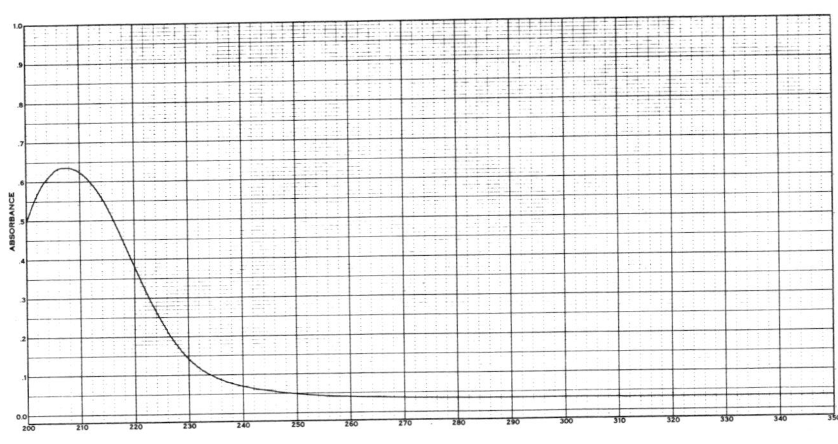

2524

2-DECENOIC ACID

$C_{10}H_{18}O_2$
Mol. Wt. 170.25
Solvent: Methanol KOH

λ Max. mμ	a_m	Cell mm	Conc. g/L
x	x	1	0.100

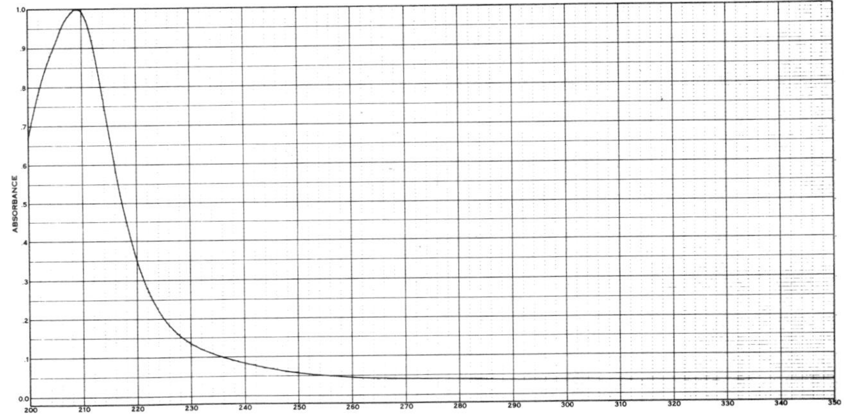

2525

λ Max. mμ	a_m	Cell mm	Conc. g/L

The non-conjugated olefinic carboxylic acids (compounds 2525 through 2529) do not display any maxima in the near UV.

SORBIC ACID

2530

$C_6H_8O_2$
Mol. Wt. 112.13
B.P. 120°C/10mm (lit.)
Solvent: Methanol

λ Max. mμ	a_m	Cell mm	Conc. g/L
x	x	10	0.233
253	25000	10	0.007

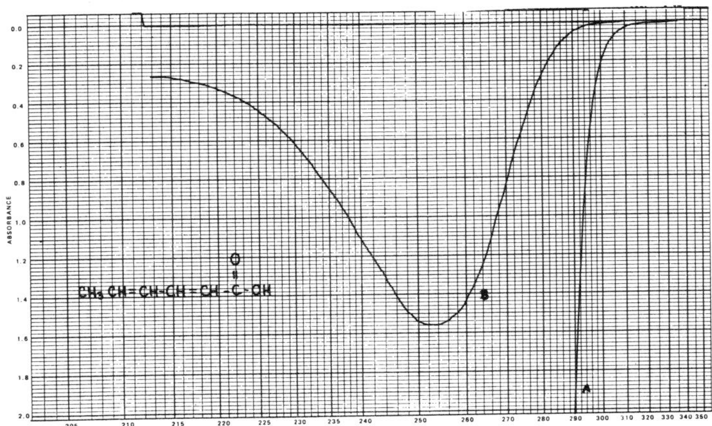

cis-3-CHLOROACRYLIC ACID

2531

$C_3H_3ClO_2$
Mol. Wt. 106.51
M.P. 61-62°C
Solvent: Methanol

λ Max. mμ	a_m	Cell mm	Conc. g/L
225	7490	1	0.100

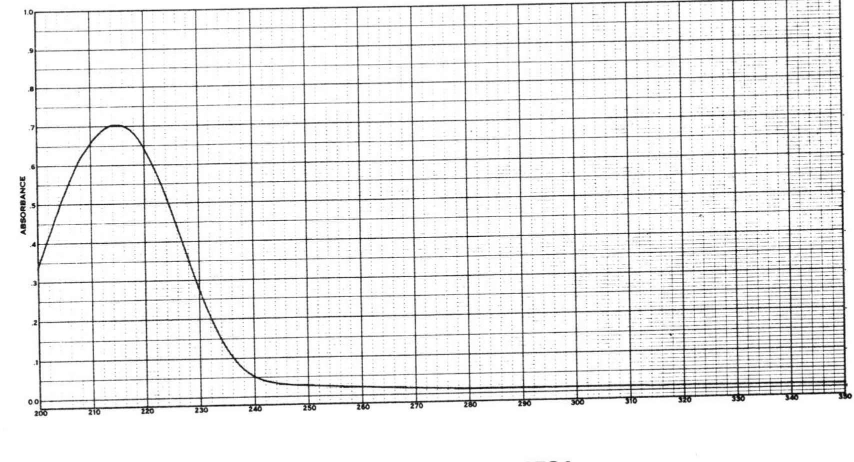

cis-3-CHLOROACRYLIC ACID

2531

$C_3H_3ClO_2$
Mol. Wt. 106.51
M.P. 61-62°C
Solvent: Methanol KOH

λ Max. mμ	a_m	Cell mm	Conc. g/L
x	x	1	0.100

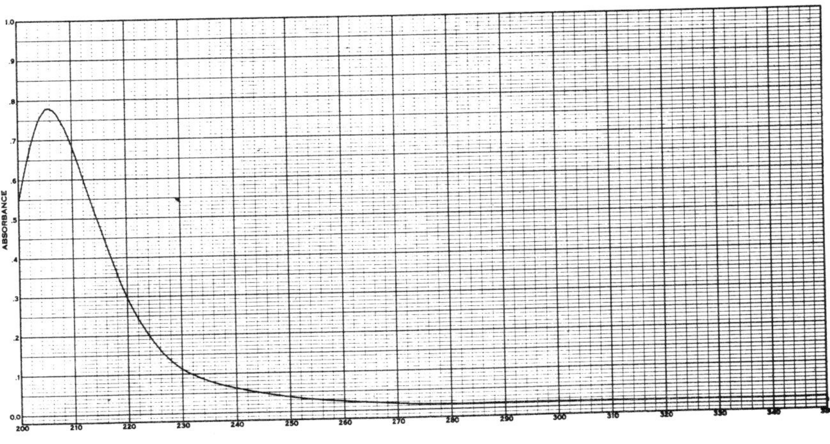

RICINOLEIC ACID 2532

$C_{18}H_{34}O_3$
Mol. Wt. 298.47
M.P. -7 to -1°C

λ Max. mμ	a_m	Cell mm	Conc. g/L

Ricinoleic acid does not display any maxima in the near UV.

FUMARIC ACID 2533

$C_4H_4O_4$
Mol. Wt. 116.07
M.P. 288.7°C (lit.)
Solvent: Methanol

λ Max. mμ	a_m	Cell mm	Conc. g/L
207	14400	1	0.0500

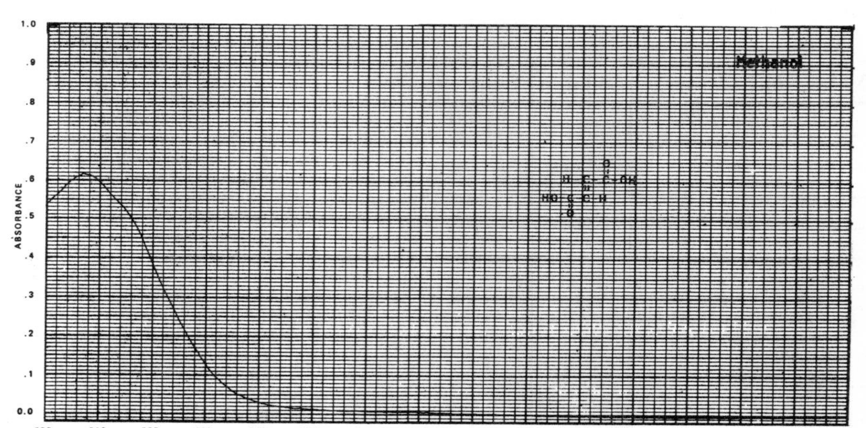

MESACONIC ACID 2534

$C_5H_6O_4$
Mol. Wt. 130.10
M.P. 200-202°C
Solvent: Methanol

λ Max. mμ	a_m	Cell mm	Conc. g/L
220	12500	1	0.100

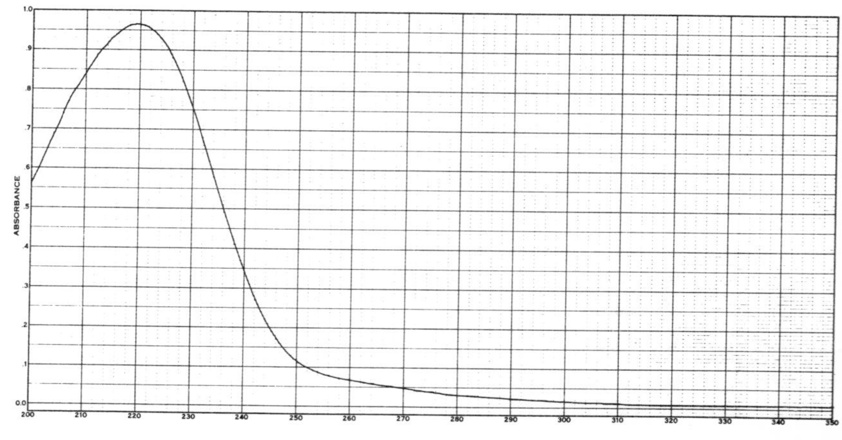

MESACONIC ACID 2534

$C_5H_6O_4$

Mol. Wt. 130.10

M.P. 200-202°C

Solvent: Methanol KOH

λ Max. mμ	a_m	Cell mm	Conc. g/L
x	x	5	0.100

CYCLOHEXENE-1-CARBOXYLIC ACID 2535

$C_7H_{10}O_2$

Mol. Wt. 126.16

Solvent: Methanol

λ Max. mμ	a_m	Cell mm	Conc. g/L
218	9880	1	0.08350

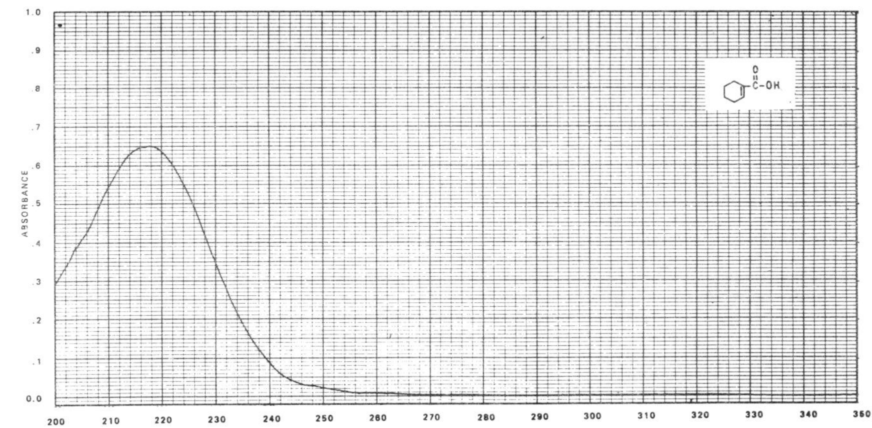

CYCLOHEXENE-1-CARBOXYLIC ACID 2535

$C_7H_{10}O_2$

Mol. Wt. 126.16

Solvent: Methanol KOH

λ Max. mμ	a_m	Cell mm	Conc. g/L
x	x	1	0.08350

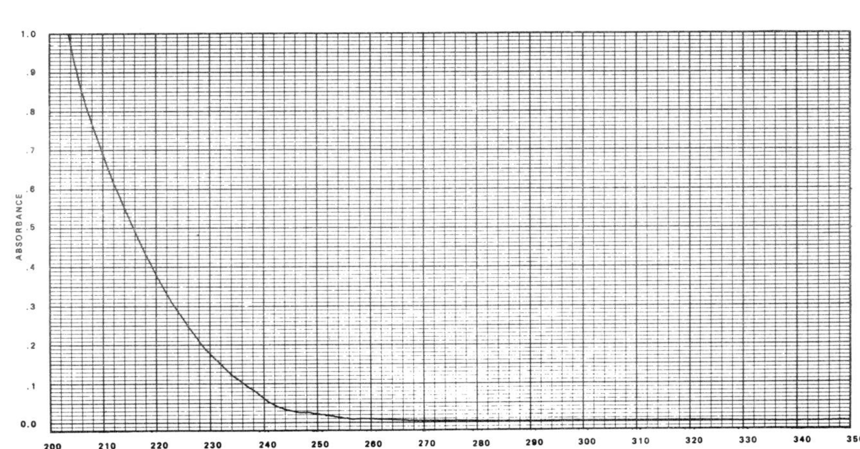

λ Max. mμ	a_m	Cell mm	Conc. g/L

The non-conjugated cycloalkenyl carboxylic acids (compounds 2536 through 2538) do not display any maxima in the near UV.

2539

PHENYLACETIC ACID

$C_8H_8O_2$

Mol. Wt. 136.14

Solvent: Methanol

λ Max. mμ	a_m	Cell mm	Conc. g/L
264	134	10	1.00
258	174	10	1.00
252	142	10	1.00
247	109	10	1.00
x	x	10	0.500

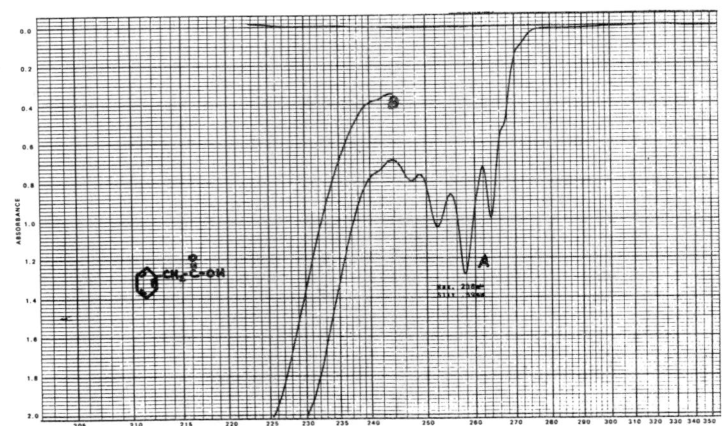

2540

HYDROCINNAMIC ACID

$C_9H_{10}O_2$

Mol. Wt. 150.17

Solvent: Methanol

λ Max. mμ	a_m	Cell mm	Conc. g/L
x	x	10	2.00
266.5	261	10	0.800
263	215	10	0.800
260	282	10	0.800
257.5	289	10	0.800
250	229	10	0.800

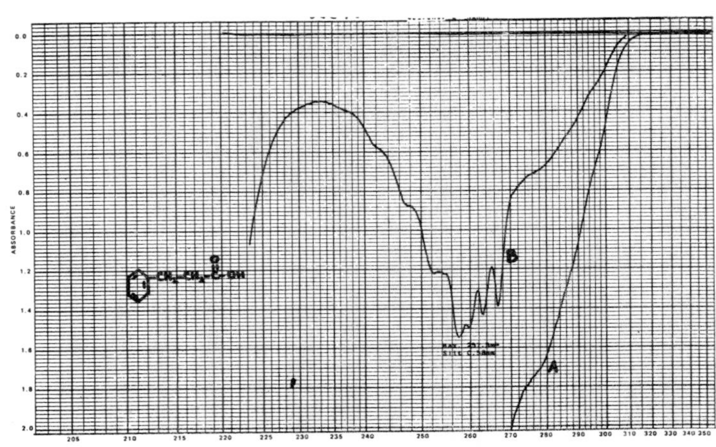

HYDRATROPIC ACID

2541

$C_9H_{10}O_2$
Mol. Wt. 150.18
B.P. 135-136°C/9mm
Solvent: Methanol

λ Max. mμ	a_m	Cell mm	Conc. g/L
264	142	10	0.4610
258	195	10	0.4610
252	171	10	0.4610
247	146	10	0.4610
x	x	1	0.09210

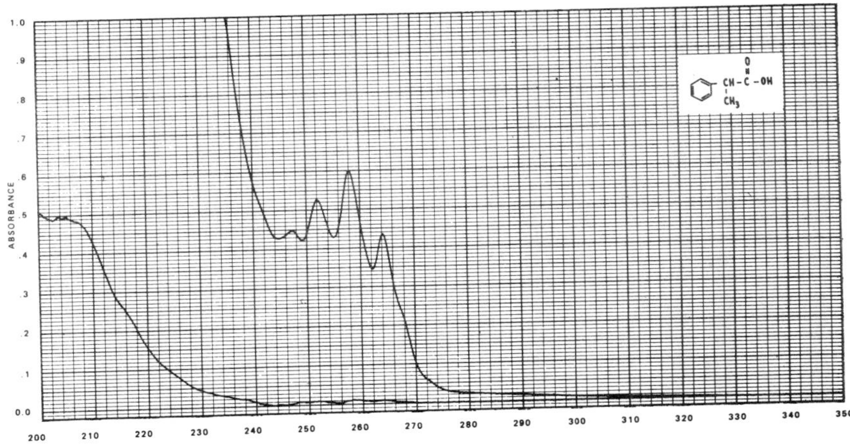

2,5-DIPHENYLHEXANEDIOIC ACID

2542

$C_{18}H_{18}O_4$
Mol. Wt. 298.34
M.P. 238°C
Solvent: Methanol

λ Max. mμ	a_m	Cell mm	Conc. g/L
264	307	5	1.00
257.5	400	5	1.00
252	328	5	1.00
247	276	5	1.00
206	16300	1	0.100

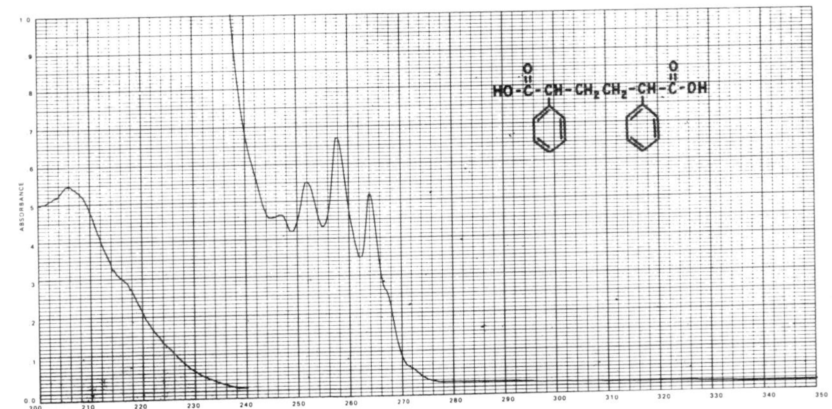

3-PHENYL-3-PROPYLGLUTARIC ACID

2543

$C_{14}H_{18}O_4$
Mol. Wt. 250.30
Solvent: Methanol

λ Max. mμ	a_m	Cell mm	Conc. g/L
274	828	10	0.100
267	826	10	0.100
263.5	836	10	0.100
257	833	10	0.100
251	808	10	0.100

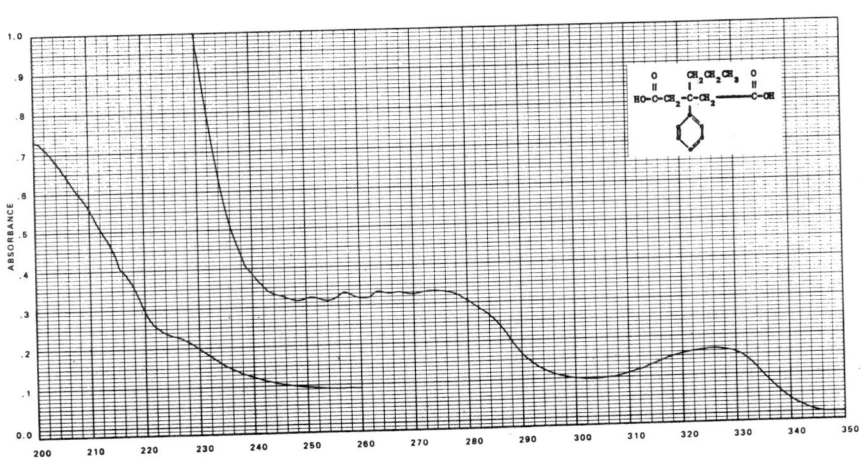

α-BENZYLHYDROCINNAMIC ACID

2544

$C_{16}H_{16}O_2$
Mol. Wt. 240.30
M.P. 88-89°C
Solvent: Methanol

λ Max. mμ	a_m	Cell mm	Conc. g/L
268	246	20	0.2250
264.5	335	20	0.2250
259	427	20	0.2250
253	352	20	0.2250
248	267	20	0.2250

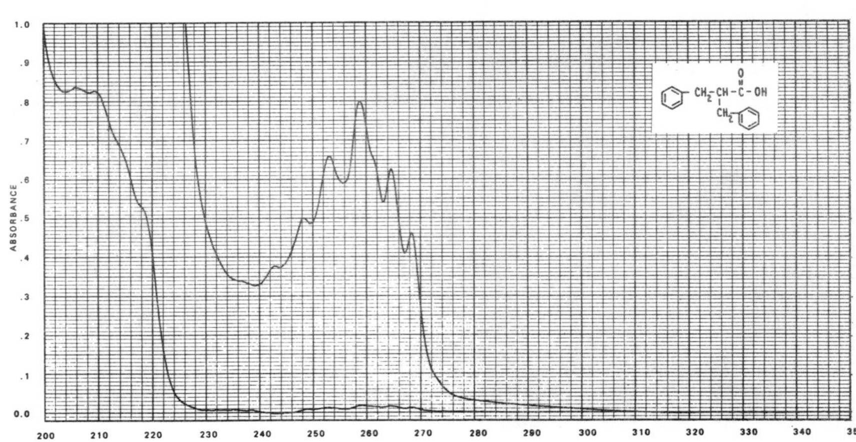

2,2-DIPHENYLVALERIC ACID

2545

$C_{17}H_{18}O_2$
Mol. Wt. 254.33
Solvent: Methanol

λ Max. mμ	a_m	Cell mm	Conc. g/L
259	486	20	0.100
252.5	465	20	0.100
x	x	1	0.100

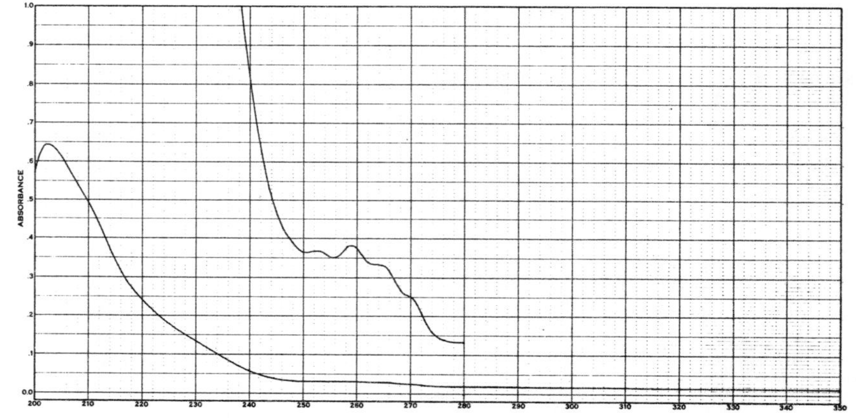

DIPHENYLACETIC ACID

2546

$C_{14}H_{12}O_2$
Mol. Wt. 212.24
Solvent: Methanol

λ Max. mμ	a_m	Cell mm	Conc. g/L
268	235	10	0.442
265	355	10	0.442
258	449	10	0.442
253	381	10	0.442
248	310	10	0.442
x	x	10	0.044

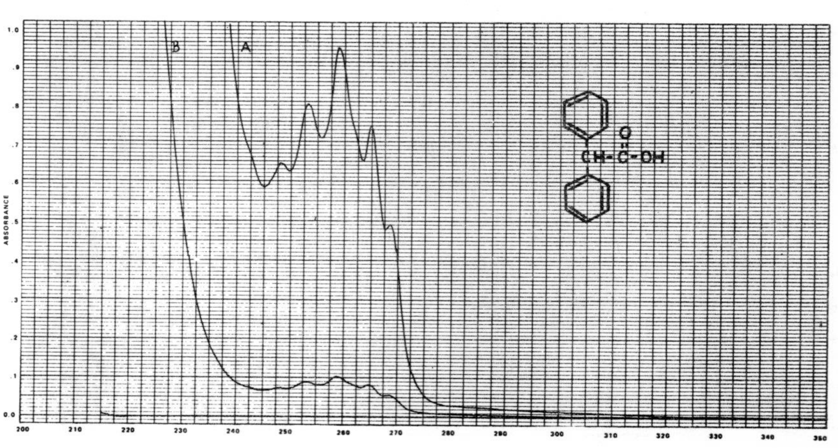

TRIPHENYLACETIC ACID 2547

$C_{20}H_{16}O_2$
Mol. Wt. 288.35
Solvent: Methanol

λ Max. mμ	a_m	Cell mm	Conc. g/L
259.5	1100	20	0.100
x	x	0.5	0.100

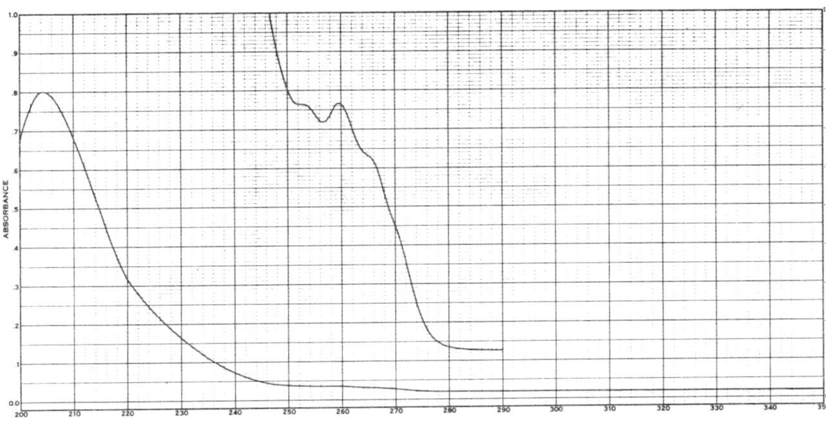

(PHENYLIMINO)DIACETIC ACID 2548

$C_{10}H_{11}NO_4$
Mol. Wt. 209.20
Solvent: Methanol

λ Max. mμ	a_m	Cell mm	Conc. g/L
292.5	2360	5	0.100
244	15600	1	0.0500

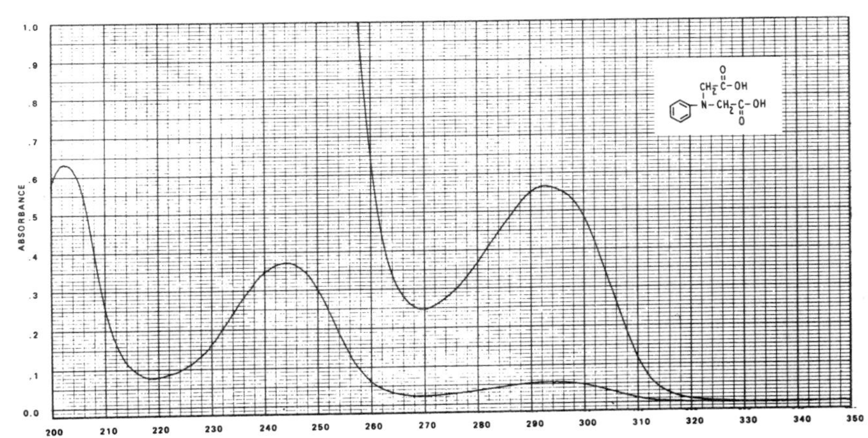

(PHENYLIMINO)DIACETIC ACID 2548

$C_{10}H_{11}NO_4$
Mol. Wt. 209.20
Solvent: Methanol KOH

λ Max. mμ	a_m	Cell mm	Conc. g/L
301.5	2520	5	0.100
254.5	17600	1	0.100

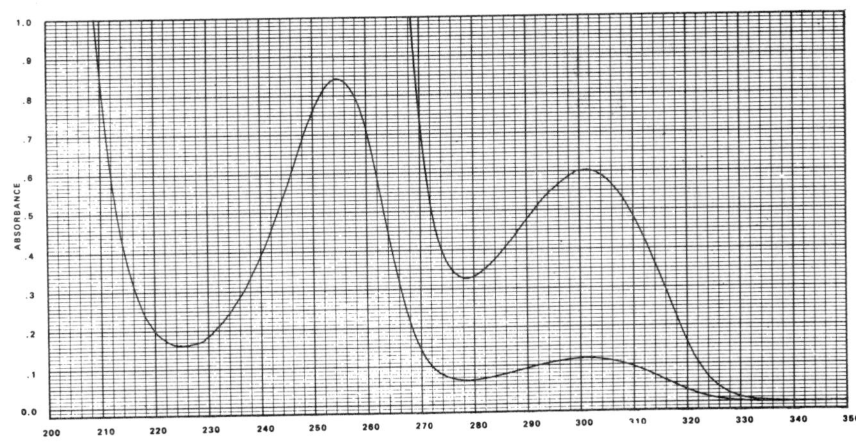

STYRYLACETIC ACID

2549

$C_{10}H_{10}O_2$
Mol. Wt. 162.19
M.P. 84-86°C
Solvent: Methanol

λ Max. mμ	a_m	Cell mm	Conc. g/L
292	403	20	0.100
283	608	20	0.100
250	16400	1	0.0500
204	22200	1	0.0500

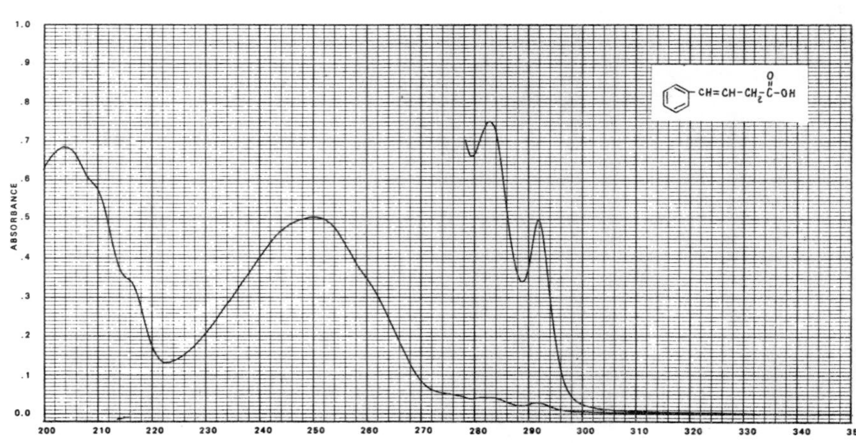

CINNAMIC ACID

2550

$C_9H_8O_2$
Mol. Wt. 148.15
Solvent: Methanol

λ Max. mμ	a_m	Cell mm	Conc. g/L
x	x	10	2.00
x	x	10	0.200
272	22500	10	0.010

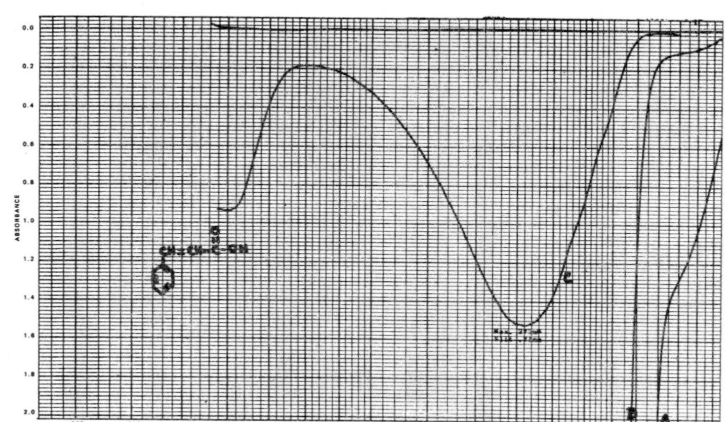

α-ETHYLCINNAMIC ACID

2551

$C_{11}H_{12}O_2$
Mol. Wt. 174.21
Solvent: Methanol

λ Max. mμ	a_m	Cell mm	Conc. g/L
x	x	10	2.000
263	16000	10	0.008
204.5	16000	10	0.008

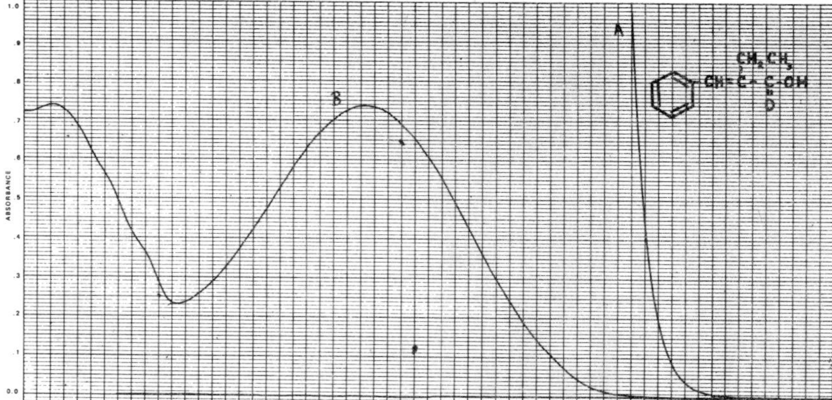

DL-α-METHOXYPHENYLACETIC ACID

$C_9H_{10}O_3$
Mol. Wt. 166.18
M.P. 70-72°C
Solvent: Methanol

λ Max. mμ	a_m	Cell mm	Conc. g/L
264	173	10	0.500
258	219	10	0.500
251.5	191	10	0.500
205	7960	1	0.100

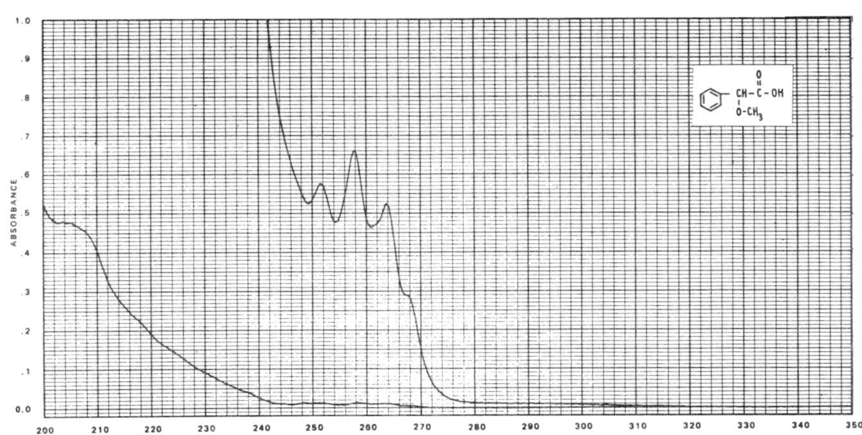

PHENOXYACETIC ACID

$C_8H_8O_3$
Mol. Wt. 152.15
M.P. 98-99°C
Solvent: Methanol

λ Max. mμ	a_m	Cell mm	Conc. g/L
275.5	1190	2	0.500
269	1430	2	0.500
263.5	1050	2	0.500
218	7060	2	0.100

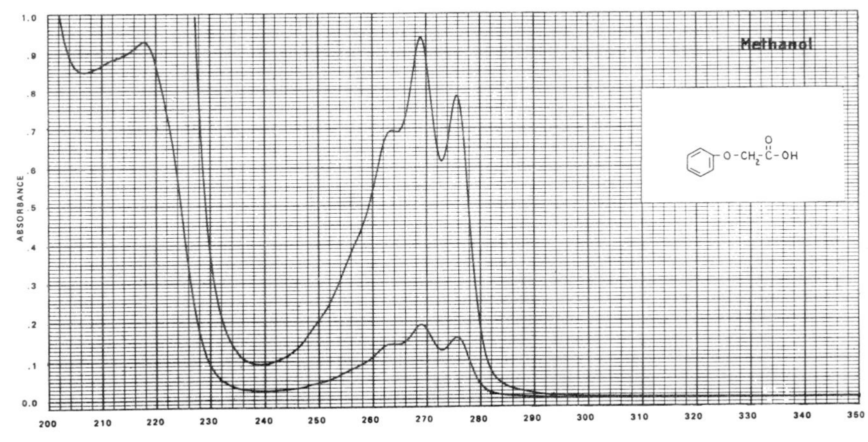

11-PHENOXYUNDECANOIC ACID

$C_{17}H_{20}O_3$
Mol. Wt. 278.39
Solvent: Methanol

λ Max. mμ	a_m	Cell mm	Conc. g/L
278.5	1070	20	0.100
272	1320	20	0.100
219	6370	4	0.100

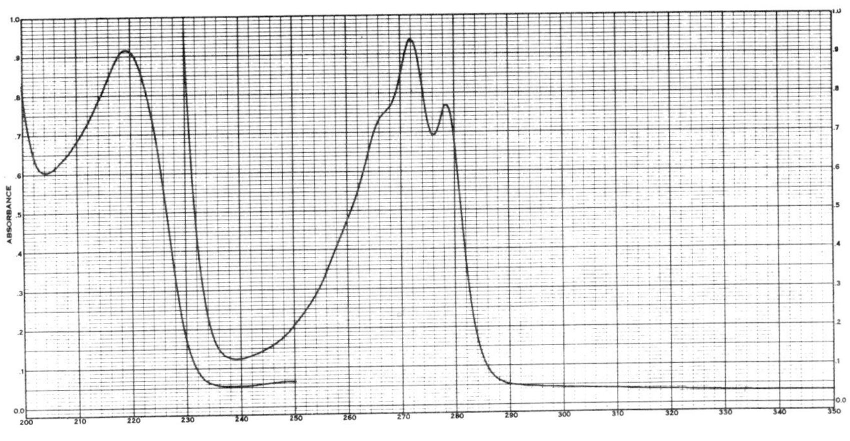

D(–)MANDELIC ACID 2555

$C_8H_8O_3$
Mol. Wt. 152.15
M.P. 132-135°C

λ Max. mμ	a_m	Cell mm	Conc. g/L

Pure sample not available.

BENZILIC ACID 2556

$C_{14}H_{12}O_3$
Mol. Wt. 228.25
M.P. 146-149°C
Solvent: Methanol

λ Max. mμ	a_m	Cell mm	Conc. g/L
264	480	20	0.100
258	617	20	0.100
251.5	590	20	0.100
x	x	1	0.100

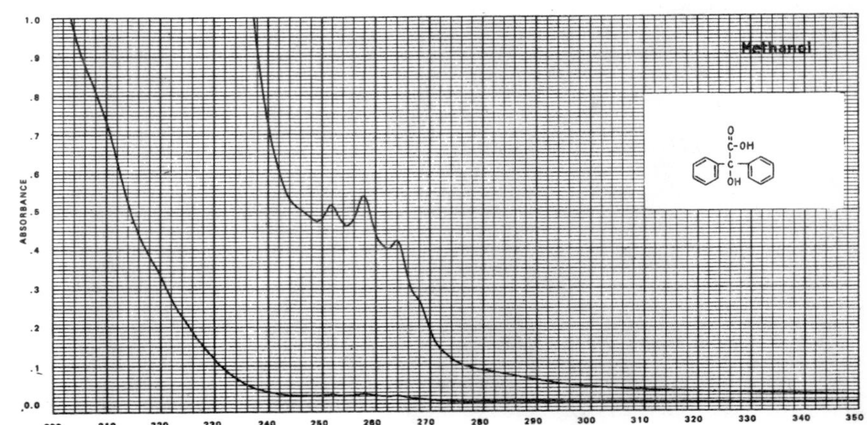

p-TOLYLACETIC ACID 2557

$C_9H_{10}O_2$
Mol. Wt. 150.17
M.R. 88-91°C (lit.)
Solvent: Methanol

λ Max. mμ	a_m	Cell mm	Conc. g/L
x	x	10	2.00
271	291	10	0.800
263	313	10	0.800
257.5	252	10	0.800
x	x	10	0.008

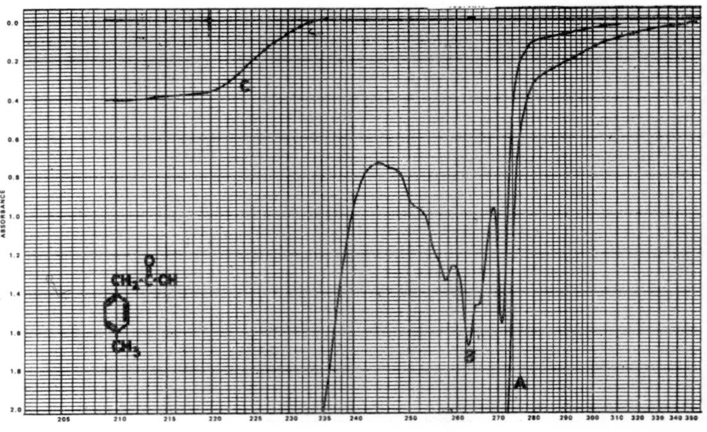

(o-FLUOROPHENYL)ACETIC ACID

2558

$C_8H_7FO_2$
Mol. Wt. 154.14
Solvent: Methanol

λ Max. mμ	a_m	Cell mm	Conc. g/L
268	771	10	0.100
262	832	10	0.100
205	7290	1	0.100

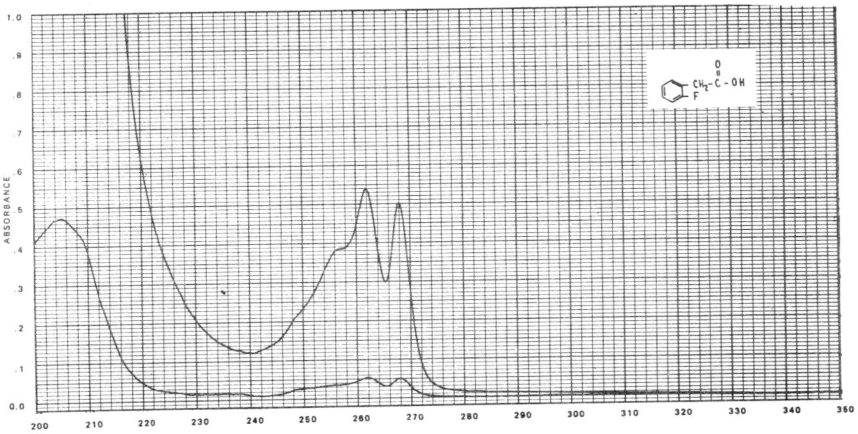

(m-FLUOROPHENYL)ACETIC ACID

2559

$C_8H_7FO_2$
Mol. Wt. 154.14

λ Max. mμ	a_m	Cell mm	Conc. g/L

Pure sample not available.

λ Max. mμ	a_m	Cell mm	Conc. g/L

4-(o-AMINOPHENYL)BUTYRIC ACID, HYDROCHLORIDE

2560

$C_{10}H_{13}NO_2 \cdot HCl$
Mol. Wt. 215.68
Solvent: Methanol

λ Max. mμ	a_m	Cell mm	Conc. g/L
278.5	265	20	0.100
261.5	286	20	0.100
226	1180	10	0.100

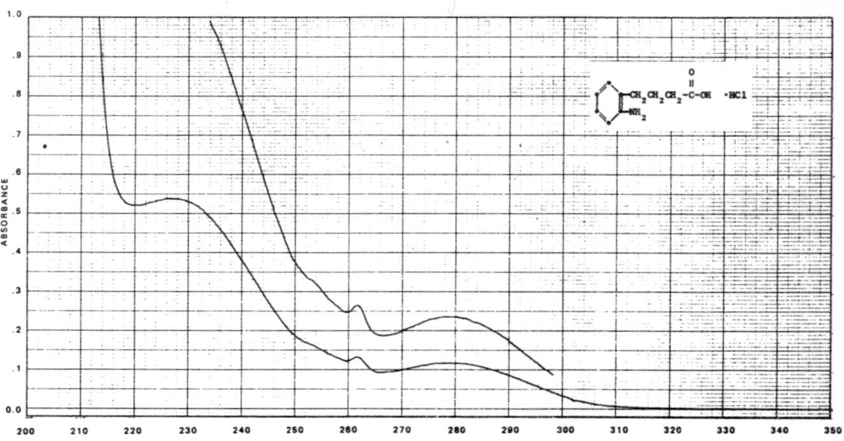

4-(o-AMINOPHENYL)BUTYRIC ACID, HYDROCHLORIDE

2560

$C_{10}H_{13}NO_2 \cdot HCl$
Mol. Wt. 215.68
Solvent: Methanol KOH

λ Max. mμ	a_m	Cell mm	Conc. g/L
280	2050	10	0.100
230	7190	2	0.100

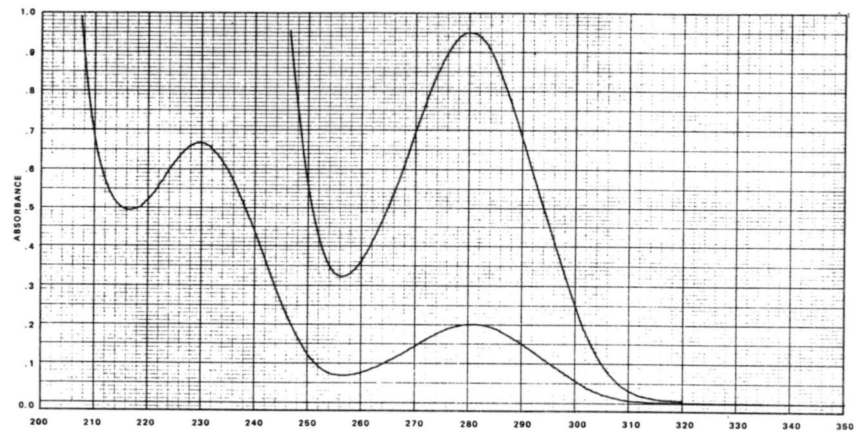
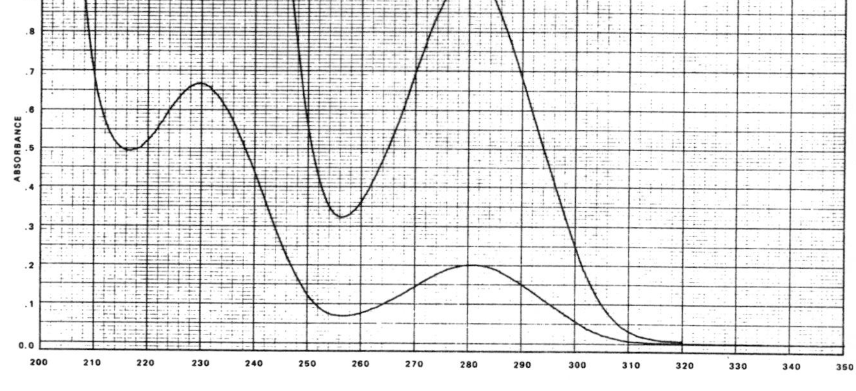

(p-NITROPHENYL)ACETIC ACID

2561

$C_8H_7NO_4$
Mol. Wt. 181.14
Solvent: Methanol

λ Max. mμ	a_m	Cell mm	Conc. g/L
x	x	10	0.200
270	9240	10	0.020

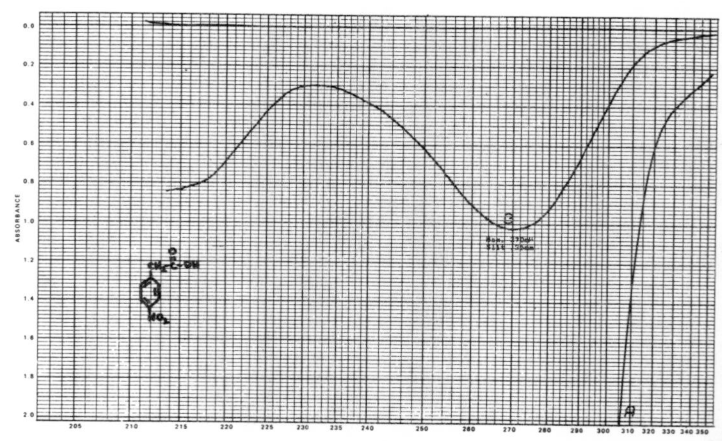

2-(p-CHLOROPHENOXY)-2-METHYLPROPIONIC ACID

2562

$C_{10}H_{11}ClO_3$

Mol. Wt. 214.65

Solvent: Methanol

λ Max. mμ	a_m	Cell mm	Conc. g/L
287	733	20	0.100
279	1030	20	0.100
226	10700	1	0.100

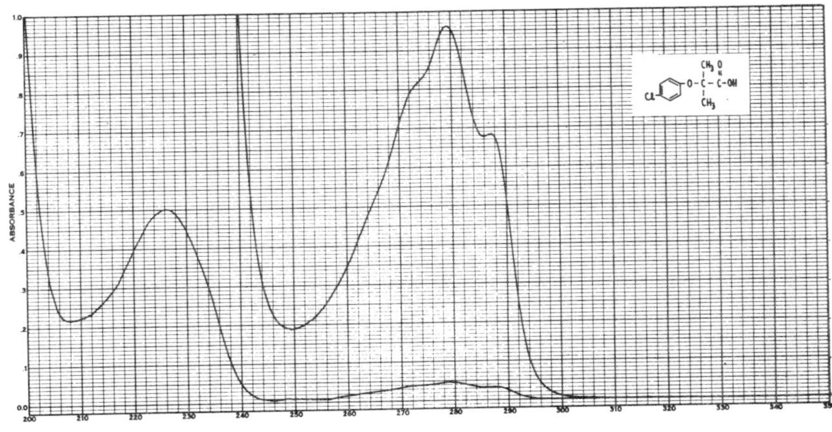

(4-ETHOXYPHENYL)ACETIC ACID

2563

$C_{10}H_{12}O_3$

Mol. Wt. 180.21

M.P. 91.5°C

Solvent: Methanol

λ Max. mμ	a_m	Cell mm	Conc. g/L
283.5	1480	10	0.04
276.5	1730	10	0.04
226	11000	10	0.01

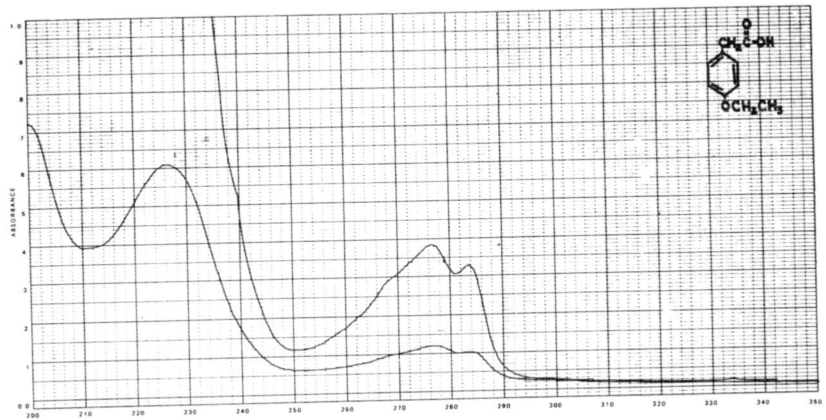

p-METHYLCINNAMIC ACID

2564

$C_{10}H_{10}O_2$

Mol. Wt. 162.19

M.P. 197-199°C (lit.)

Solvent: Methanol

λ Max. mμ	a_m	Cell mm	Conc. g/L
283.5	23200	1	0.0600
225	13100	1	0.0600
220	15000	1	0.0600
207	13200	1	0.0600

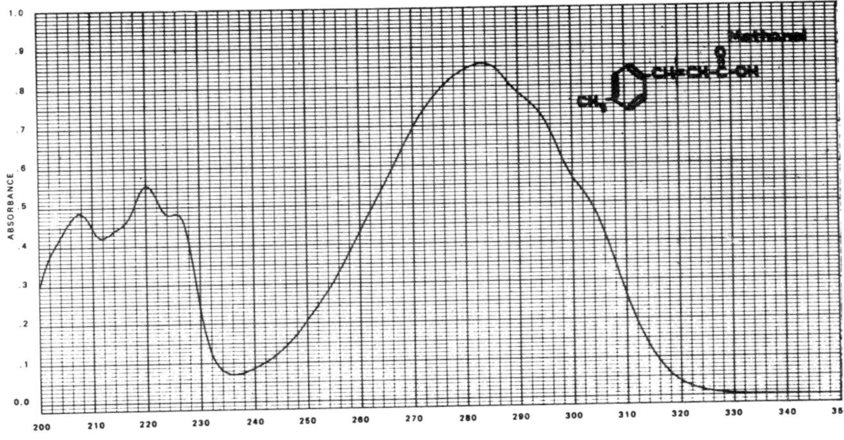

(p-PHENYLENEDIOXY)DIACETIC ACID

2565

$C_{10}H_{10}O_6$

Mol. Wt. 226.19

Solvent: Methanol

λ Max. mμ	a_m	Cell mm	Conc. g/L
286	1440	10	0.10
225	5880	10	0.01

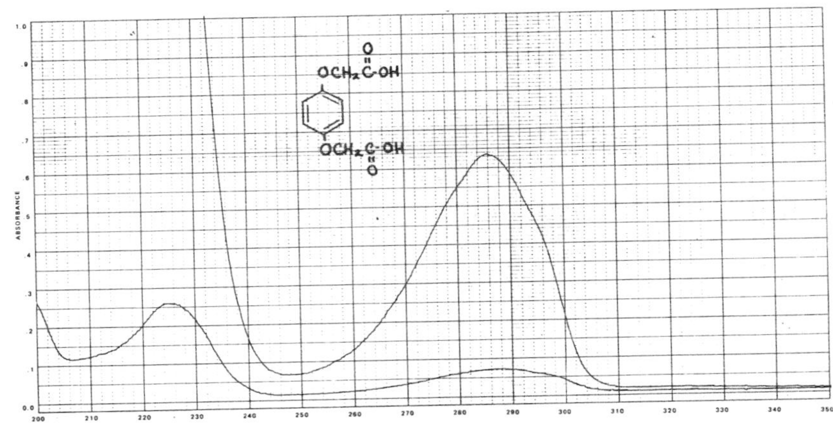

BENZOIC ACID

2566

$C_7H_6O_2$

Mol. Wt. 122.12

M.P. 121°C (lit.)

Solvent: Methanol

λ Max. mμ	a_m	Cell mm	Conc. g/L
279	729	10	0.100
271.5	893	10	0.100
227.5	11900	1	0.100

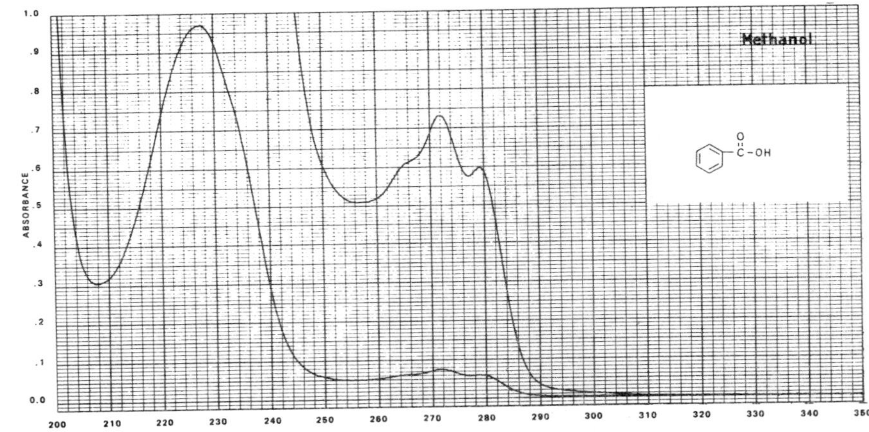

BENZOIC ACID

2566

$C_7H_6O_2$

Mol. Wt. 122.12

M.P. 121°C (lit.)

Solvent: Methanol KOH

λ Max. mμ	a_m	Cell mm	Conc. g/L
276	426	10	0.100
268.5	598	10	0.100
261.5	639	10	0.100
222	8890	1	0.100

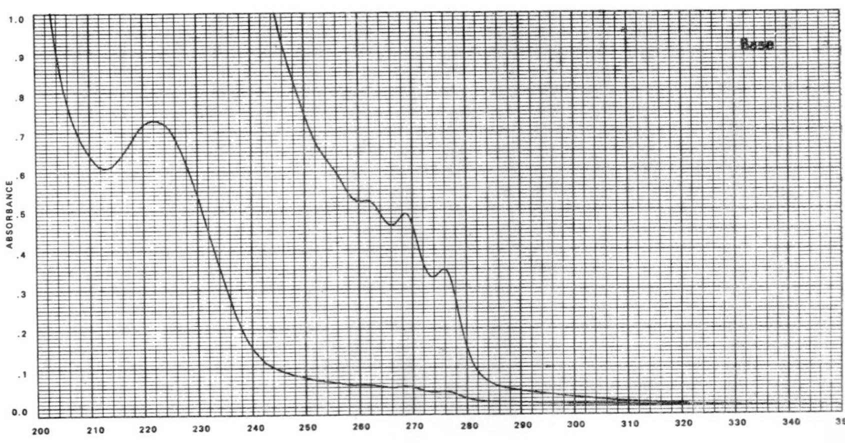

p-TOLUIC ACID

2567

$C_8H_8O_2$

Mol. Wt. 136.15

M.P. 178-180°C (lit.)

Solvent: Methanol

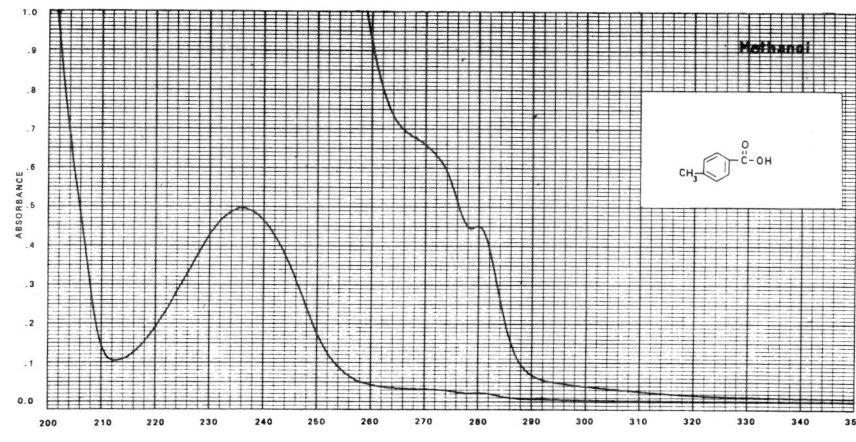

λ Max. mμ	a_m	Cell mm	Conc. g/L
280	614	10	0.100
236	13500	1	0.0500

p-TOLUIC ACID

2567

$C_8H_8O_2$

Mol. Wt. 136.15

M.P. 178-180°C (lit.)

Solvent: Methanol KOH

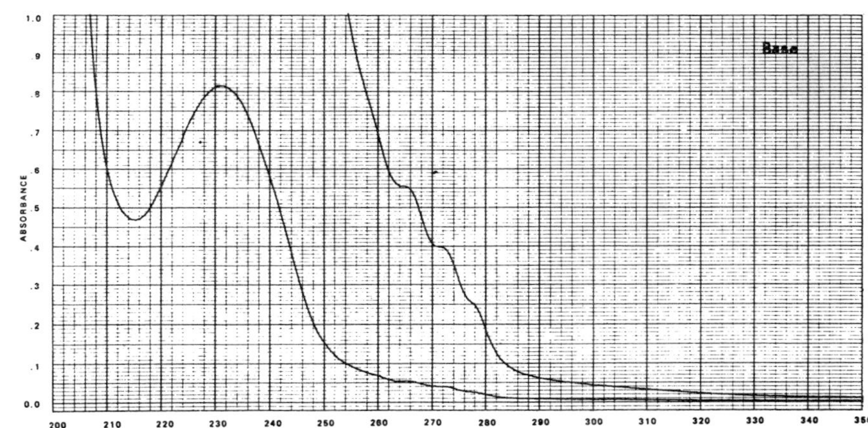

λ Max. mμ	a_m	Cell mm	Conc. g/L
264.5	754	10	0.100
231	11100	1	0.100

λ Max. mμ	a_m	Cell mm	Conc. g/L

2568

a,a,a-TRIFLUORO-o-TOLUIC ACID

$C_8H_5F_3O_2$
Mol. Wt. 190.12
M.P. 108-109°C (lit.)
Solvent: Methanol

λ Max. mμ	a_m	Cell mm	Conc. g/L
268.5	1080	10	0.100
x	x	1	0.100

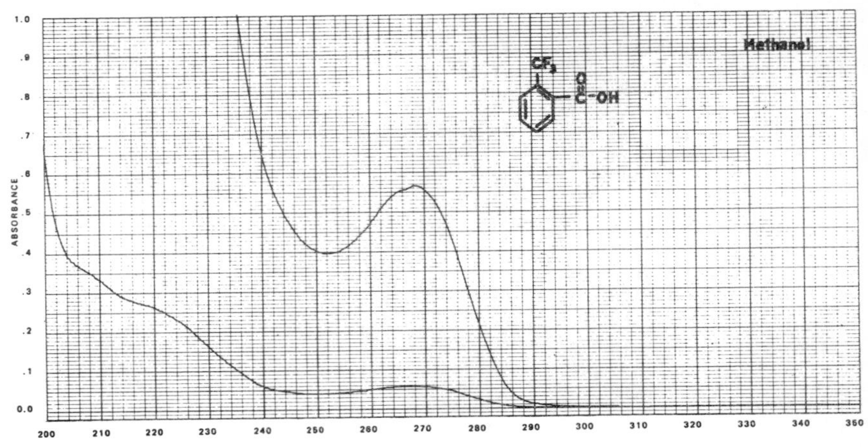

2568

a,a,a-TRIFLUORO-o-TOLUIC ACID

$C_8H_5F_3O_2$
Mol. Wt. 190.12
M.P. 108-109°C (lit.)
Solvent: Methanol KOH

λ Max. mμ	a_m	Cell mm	Conc. g/L
272.5	1100	10	0.100
266	1210	10	0.100
x	x	1	0.100

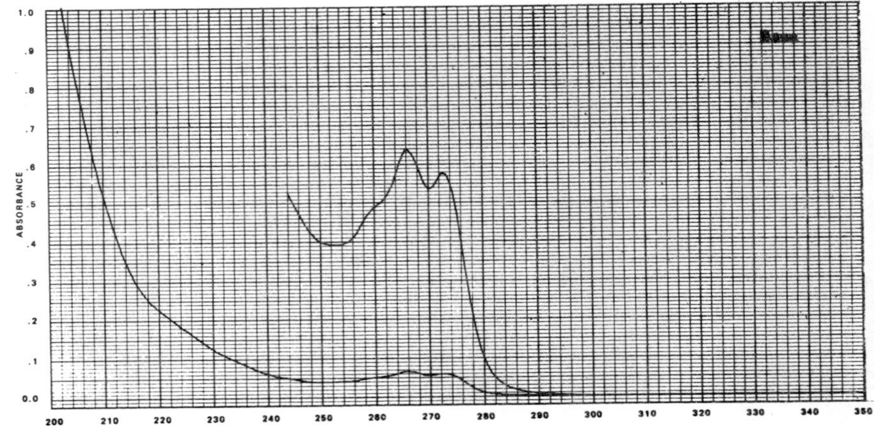

2569

o-FLUOROBENZOIC ACID

$C_7H_5FO_2$
Mol. Wt. 140.11
M.P. 124-126°C
Solvent: Methanol

λ Max. mμ	a_m	Cell mm	Conc. g/L
274.5	1540	5	0.100
223.5	5140	1	0.100

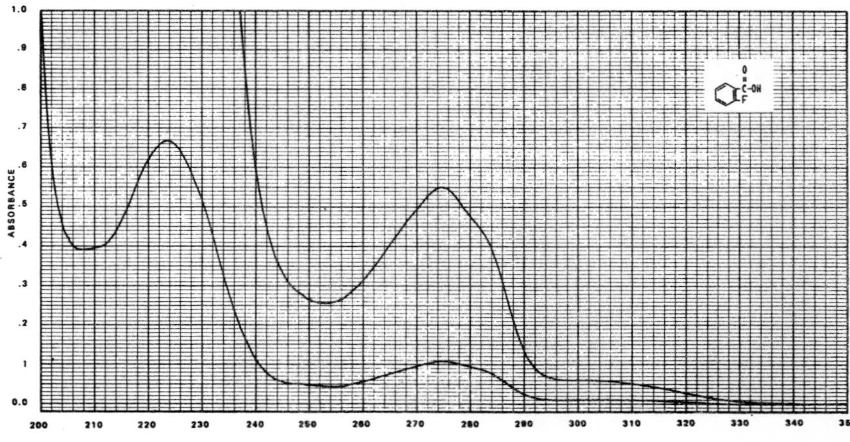

o-FLUOROBENZOIC ACID

2569

$C_7H_5FO_2$
Mol. Wt. 140.11
M.P. 124-126°C
Solvent: Methanol KOH

λ Max. mμ	a_m	Cell mm	Conc. g/L
295	151	10	0.100
268.5	1060	10	0.100
x	x	1	0.100

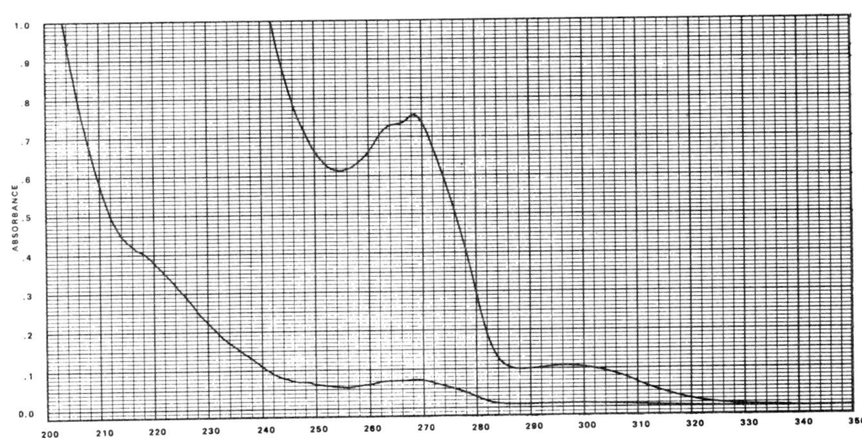

p-FLUOROBENZOIC ACID

2570

$C_7H_5FO_2$
Mol. Wt. 140.12
M.P. 184-186°C
Solvent: Methanol

λ Max. mμ	a_m	Cell mm	Conc. g/L
269.5	383	20	0.100
262.5	559	20	0.100
228.5	10400	1	0.100

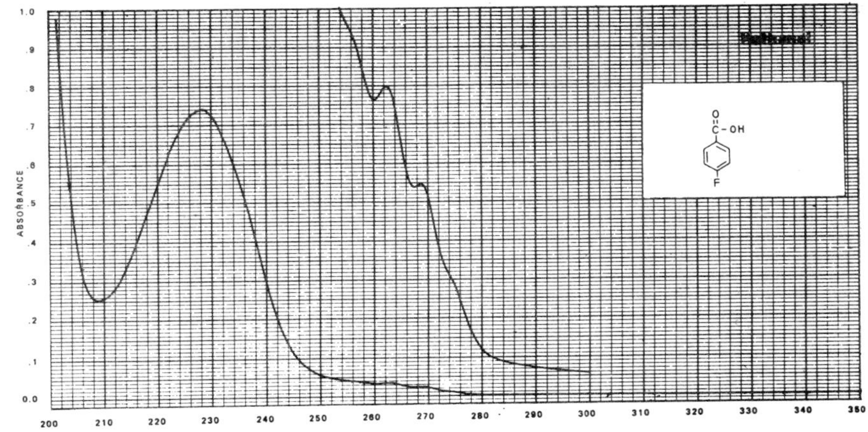

p-FLUOROBENZOIC ACID

2570

$C_7H_5FO_2$
Mol. Wt. 140.12
M.P. 184-186°C
Solvent: Methanol KOH

λ Max. mμ	a_m	Cell mm	Conc. g/L
268	334	20	0.100
262.5	516	20	0.100
x	x	1	0.100

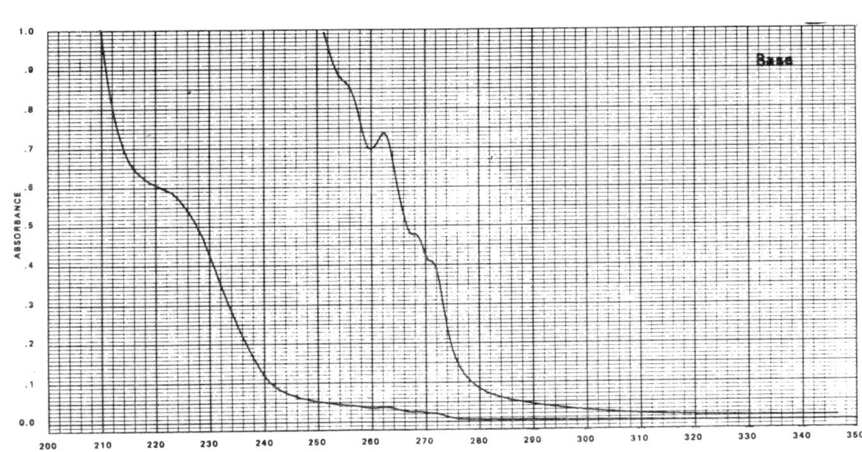

p-CHLOROBENZOIC ACID

2571

$C_7H_5ClO_2$

Mol. Wt. 156.57

M.P. 241°C (lit.)

Solvent: Methanol

λ Max. mμ	a_m	Cell mm	Conc. g/L
280	582	20	0.100
236.5	15200	1	0.100

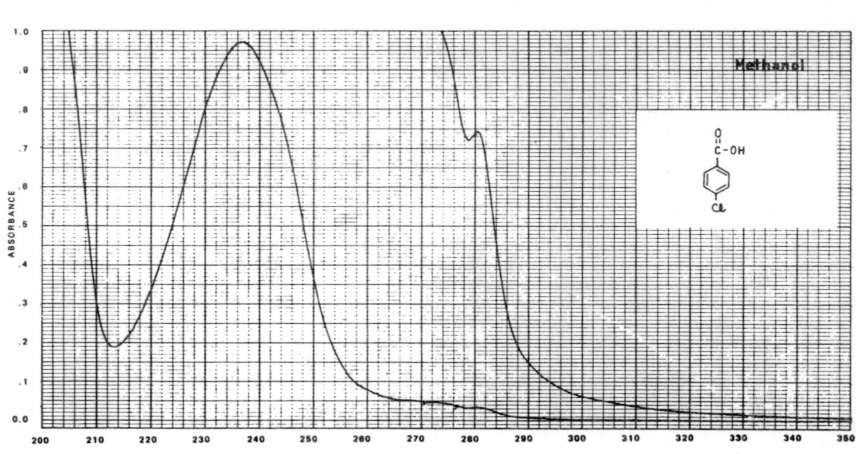

p-CHLOROBENZOIC ACID

2571

$C_7H_5ClO_2$

Mol. Wt. 156.57

M.P. 241.5°C (lit.)

Solvent: Methanol KOH

λ Max. mμ	a_m	Cell mm	Conc. g/L
266.5	827	10	0.100
231	13000	1	0.100

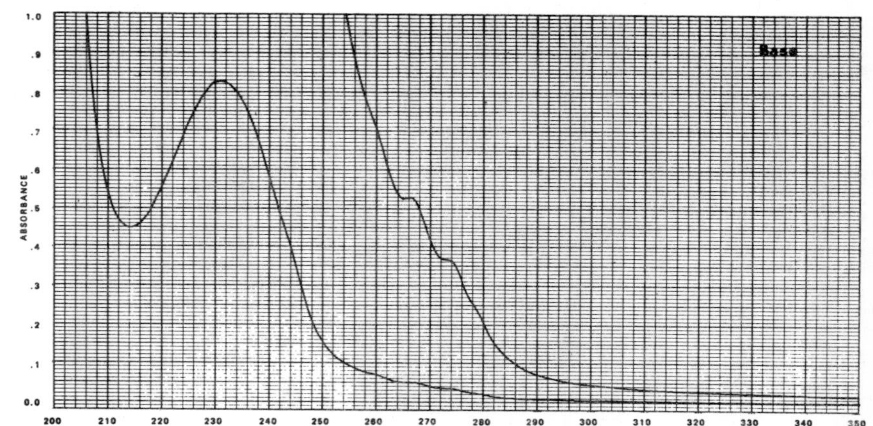

o-BROMOBENZOIC ACID

2572

$C_7H_5BrO_2$

Mol. Wt. 201.03

M.R. 147-150°C (lit.)

Solvent: Methanol

λ Max. mμ	a_m	Cell mm	Conc. g/L
x	x	10	2.00
280	940	10	0.400
x	x	10	0.02

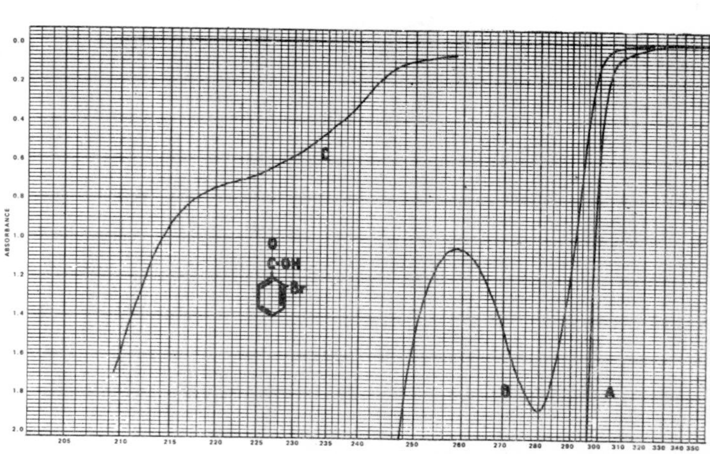

m-BROMOBENZOIC ACID

2573

$C_7H_5BrO_2$
Mol. Wt. 201.03
M.P. 152-154°C
Solvent: Methanol

λ Max. mμ	a_m	Cell mm	Conc. g/L
288	835	20	0.0920
281	955	20	0.0920
225	9610	1	0.0460
204	39200	1	0.0460

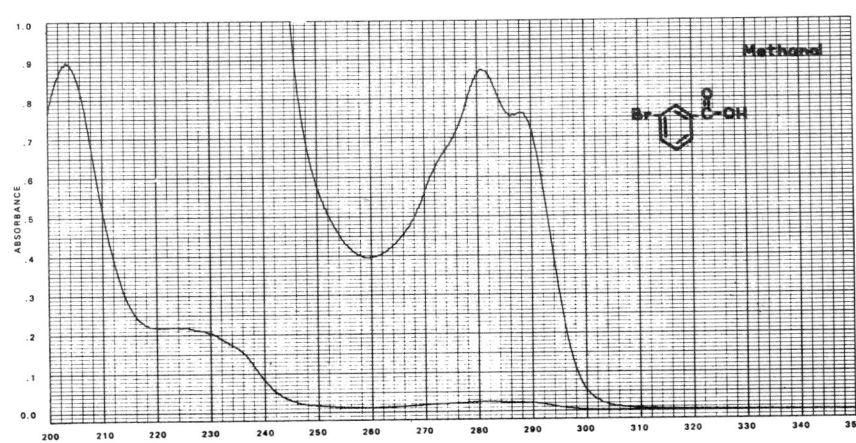

m-BROMOBENZOIC ACID

2573

$C_7H_5BrO_2$
Mol. Wt. 201.03
M.P. 152-154°C
Solvent: Methanol KOH

λ Max. mμ	a_m	Cell mm	Conc. g/L
284	415	20	0.0920
276	533	20	0.0920
268.5	479	20	0.0920
x	x	1	0.0460

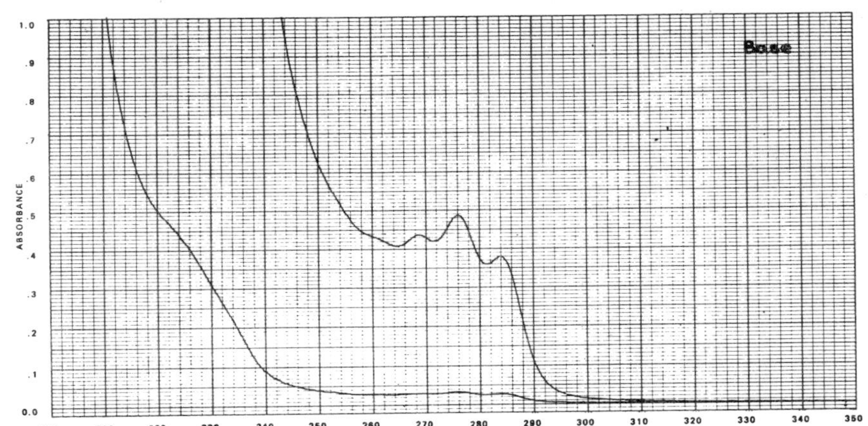

p-BROMOBENZOIC ACID

2574

$C_7H_5BrO_2$
Mol. Wt. 201.03
M.R. 251-253°C (lit.)
Solvent: Methanol

λ Max. mμ	a_m	Cell mm	Conc. g/L
x	x	10	2.00
282	568	10	0.200
241	16100	10	0.020

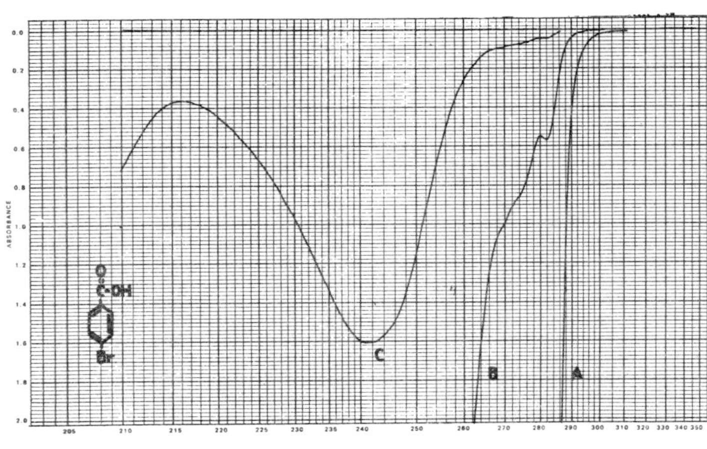

o-IODOBENZOIC ACID

2575

$C_7H_5IO_2$

Mol. Wt. 248.02

M.P. 160-162°C (lit.)

Solvent: Methanol

λ Max. mμ	a_m	Cell mm	Conc. g/L
285.5	1450	10	0.100
x	x	1	0.100

o-IODOBENZOIC ACID

2575

$C_7H_5IO_2$

Mol. Wt. 248.02

M.P. 160-162°C (lit.)

Solvent: Methanol KOH

λ Max. mμ	a_m	Cell mm	Conc. g/L
x	x	1	0.100

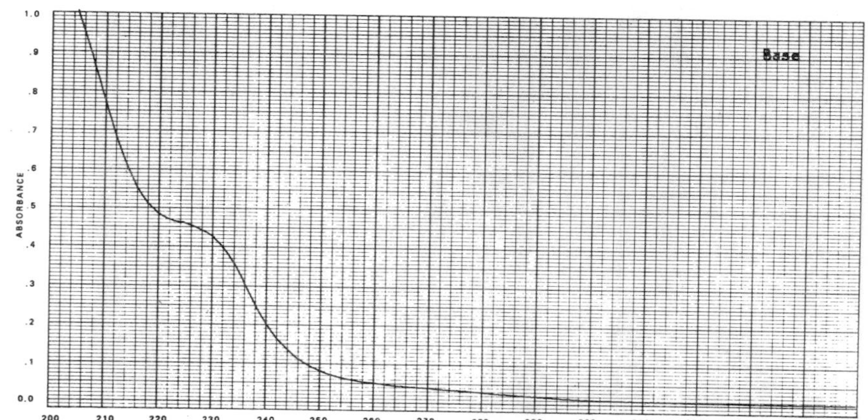

m-IODOBENZOIC ACID

2576

$C_7H_5IO_2$

Mol. Wt. 248.02

M.P. 187-188°C

Solvent: Methanol

λ Max. mμ	a_m	Cell mm	Conc. g/L
216.5	24400	1	0.100

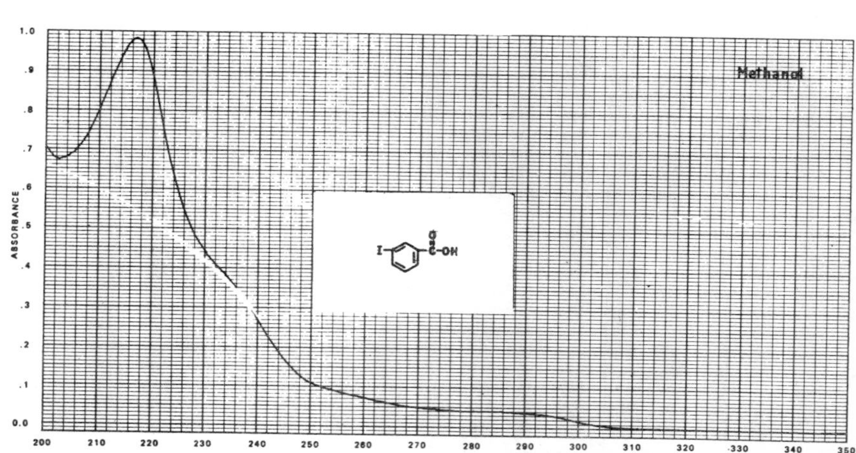

2577

p-IODOBENZOIC ACID

$C_7H_5IO_2$

Mol. Wt. 248.02

M.P. 265-270°C

Solvent: Methanol

λ Max. mμ	a_m	Cell mm	Conc. g/L
252	16500	1	0.100

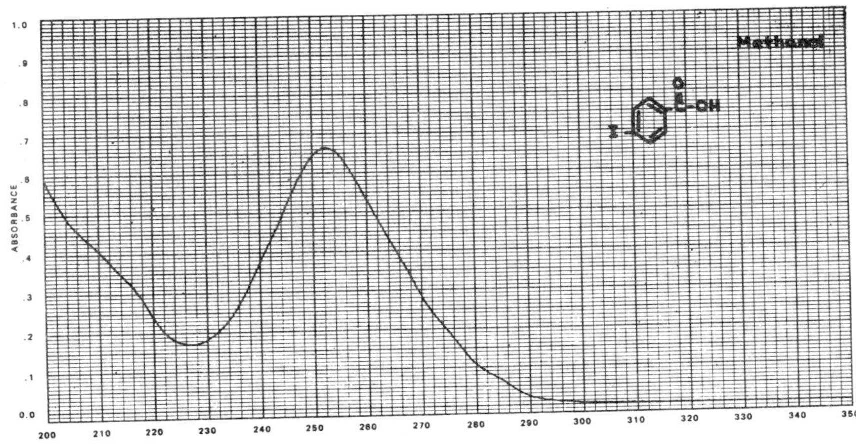

2577

p-IODOBENZOIC ACID

$C_7H_5IO_2$

Mol. Wt. 248.02

M.P. 265-270°C

Solvent: Methanol KOH

λ Max. mμ	a_m	Cell mm	Conc. g/L
245	16200	1	0.100

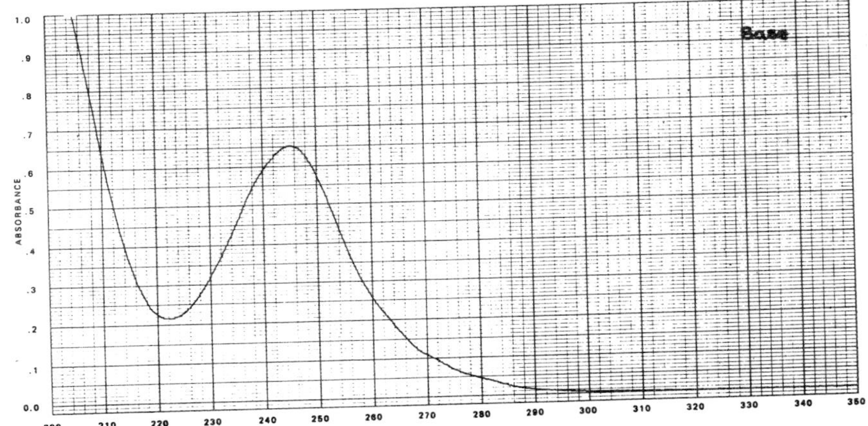

λ Max. mμ	a_m	Cell mm	Conc. g/L

p-AMINOBENZOIC ACID 2578

$C_7H_7NO_2$
Mol. Wt. 137.14
M.P. 187-188°C
Solvent: Methanol

λ Max. mμ	a_m	Cell mm	Conc. g/L
289	18200	1	0.0500
219	8560	1	0.0500

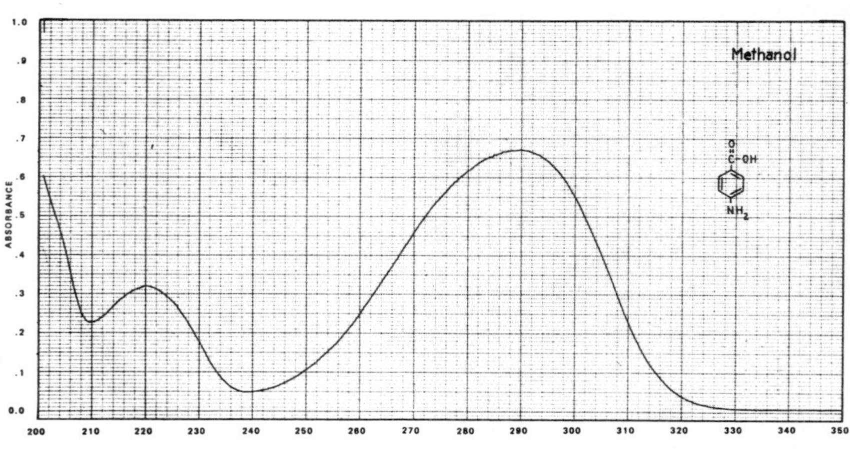

p-AMINOBENZOIC ACID 2578

$C_7H_7NO_2$
Mol. Wt. 137.14
M.P. 187-188°C
Solvent: Methanol KOH

λ Max. mμ	a_m	Cell mm	Conc. g/L
268	14800	1	0.0500

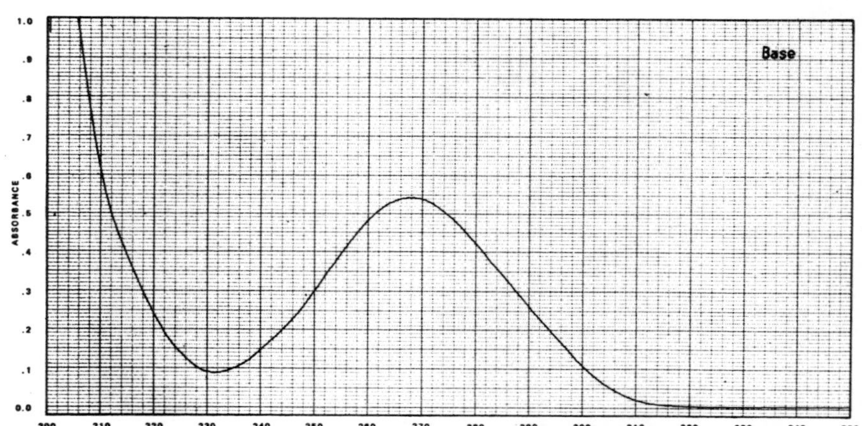

N-PHENYLANTHRANILIC ACID 2579

$C_{13}H_{11}NO_2$
Mol. Wt. 213.24
M.P. 185-188°C
Solvent: Methanol

λ Max. mμ	a_m	Cell mm	Conc. g/L
349	7110	1	0.060
284	15400	1	0.060
219	24800	1	0.060

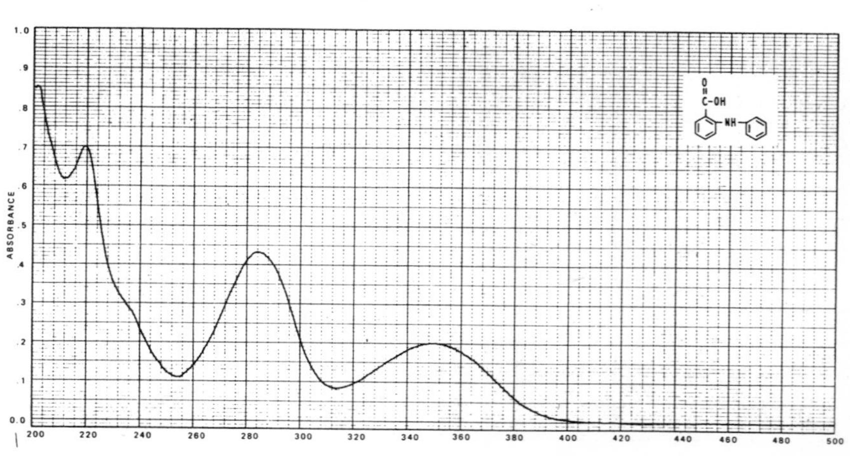

N-PHENYLANTHRANILIC ACID 2579

$C_{13}H_{11}NO_2$
Mol. Wt. 213.24
M.P. 185-188°C
Solvent: Methanol KOH

λ Max. mμ	a_m	Cell mm	Conc. g/L
333	6040	1	0.060
292	18200	1	0.060

m-CYANOBENZOIC ACID 2580

$C_8H_5NO_2$
Mol. Wt. 147.13
M.P. 222-224°C
Solvent: Methanol

λ Max. mμ	a_m	Cell mm	Conc. g/L
287	552	20	0.100
279	600	20	0.100
225	16700	1	0.100

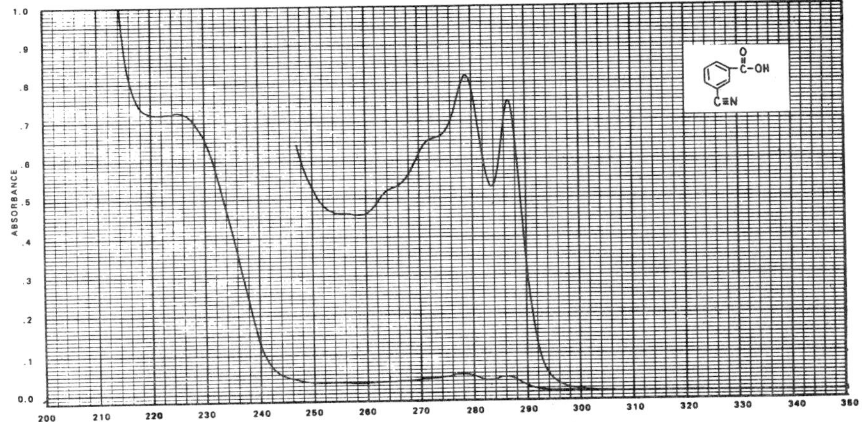

m-CYANOBENZOIC ACID 2580

$C_8H_5NO_2$
Mol. Wt. 147.13
M.P. 222-224°C
Solvent: Methanol KOH

λ Max. mμ	a_m	Cell mm	Conc. g/L
285.5	700	10	0.100
278	733	10	0.100
270.5	594	10	0.100
x	x	1	0.100

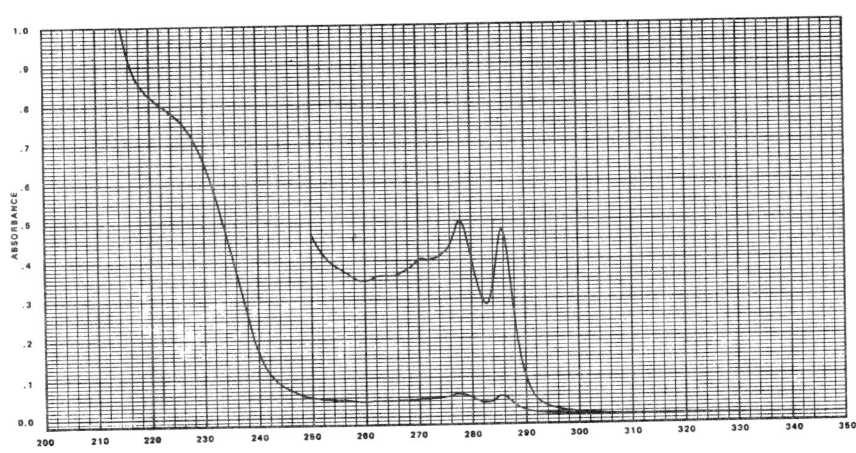

o-NITROBENZOIC ACID 2581

$C_7H_5NO_4$

Mol. Wt. 167.12

M.P. 147-148°C

Solvent: Methanol

λ Max. mμ	a_m	Cell mm	Conc. g/L
x	x	1	0.100

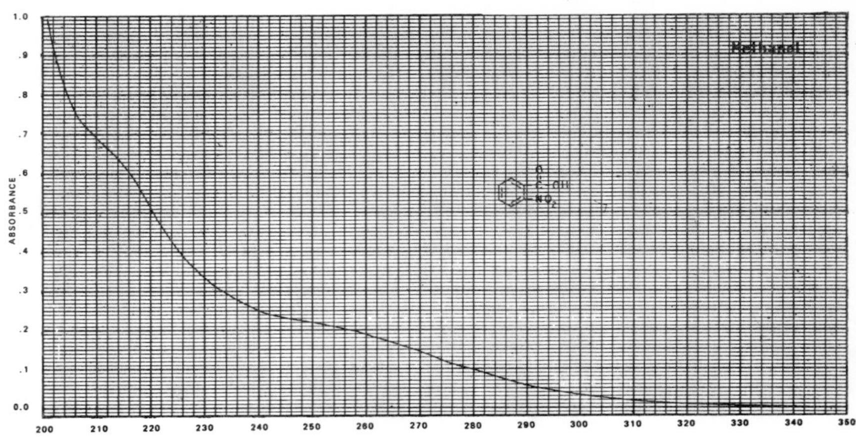

o-NITROBENZOIC ACID 2581

$C_7H_5NO_4$

Mol. Wt. 167.12

M.P. 147-148°C

Solvent: Methanol KOH

λ Max. mμ	a_m	Cell mm	Conc. g/L
x	x	1	0.100

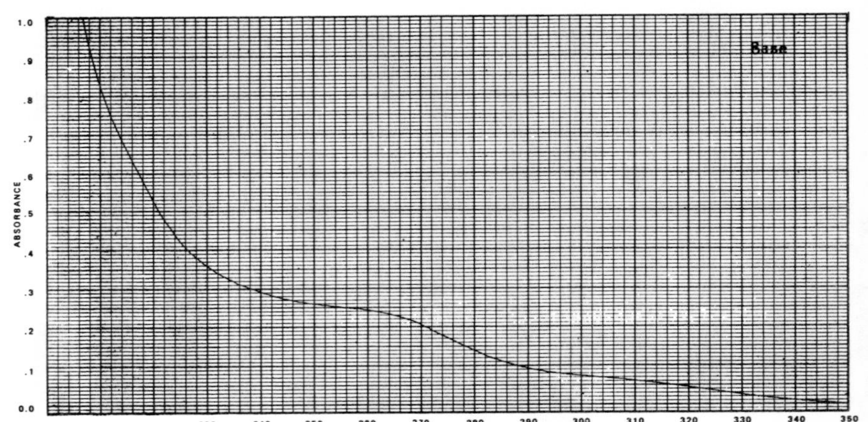

p-NITROBENZOIC ACID 2582

$C_7H_5NO_4$

Mol. Wt. 167.13

Solvent: Methanol

λ Max. mμ	a_m	Cell mm	Conc. g/L
x	x	10	0.200
258.5	12000	10	0.020

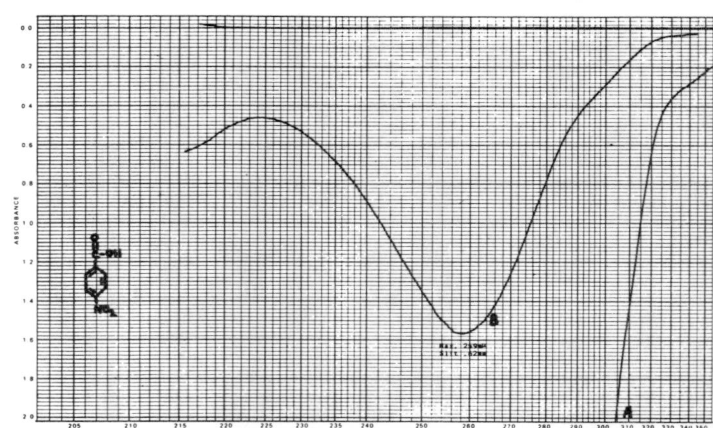

m-ANISIC ACID

2583

$C_8H_8O_3$
Mol. Wt. 152.15
M.P. 104-106°C
Solvent: Methanol

λ Max. mμ	a_m	Cell mm	Conc. g/L
294	2430	2	0.100
230	6620	2	0.100
209	28800	1	0.0500

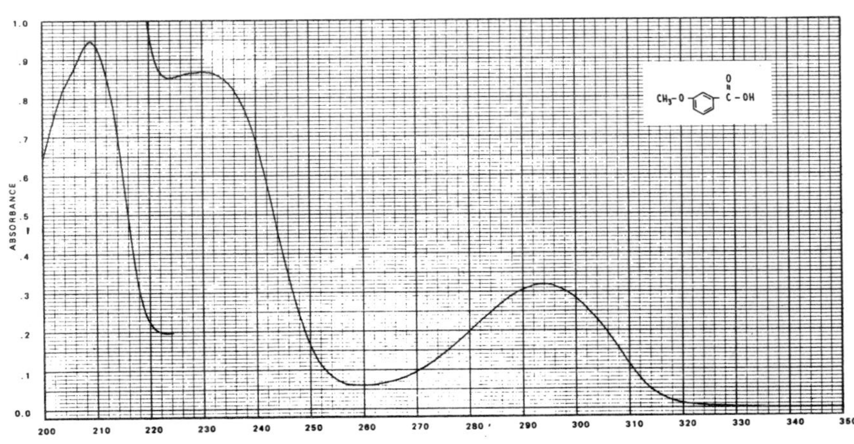

p-ANISIC ACID

2584

$C_8H_8O_3$
Mol. Wt. 152.15
M.P. 184-185°C
Solvent: Methanol

λ Max. mμ	a_m	Cell mm	Conc. g/L
253	16500	1	0.0700

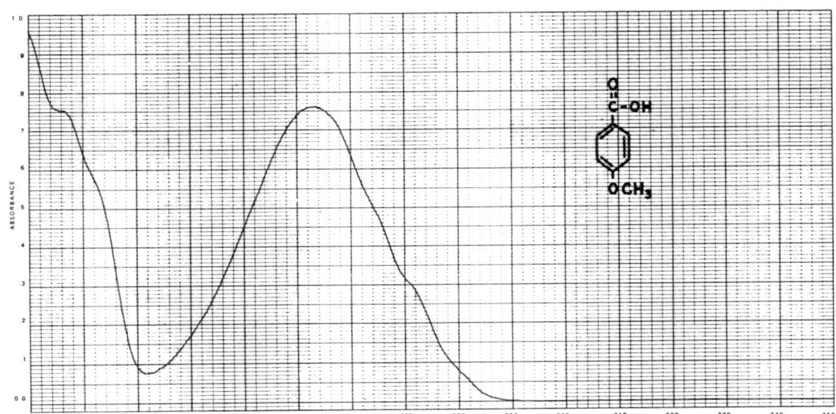

λ Max. mμ	a_m	Cell mm	Conc. g/L

o-ETHOXYBENZOIC ACID

2585

$C_9H_{10}O_3$
Mol. Wt. 166.18
M.P. 22-24°C
Solvent: Methanol

λ Max. mμ	a_m	Cell mm	Conc. g/L
294	3070	2	0.1170
232.5	7070	2	0.1170
x	x	1	0.0234

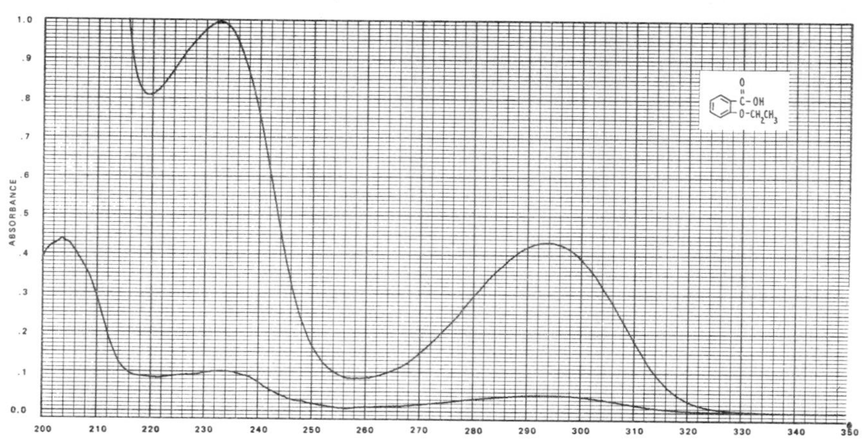

o-ETHOXYBENZOIC ACID

2585

$C_9H_{10}O_3$
Mol. Wt. 166.18
M.P. 22-24°C
Solvent: Methanol KOH

λ Max. mμ	a_m	Cell mm	Conc. g/L
280	2140	5	0.1170
x	x	1	0.1170

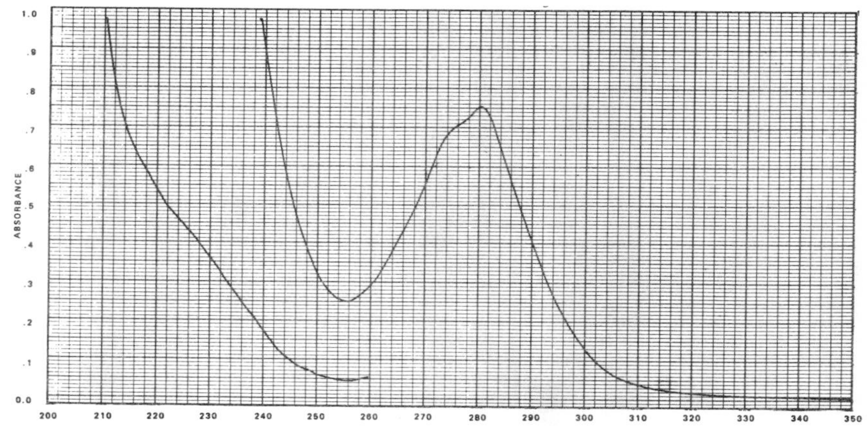

p-PROPOXYBENZOIC ACID

2586

$C_{10}H_{12}O_3$
Mol. Wt. 180.21
Solvent: Methanol

λ Max. mμ	a_m	Cell mm	Conc. g/L
254.5	17200	1	0.100

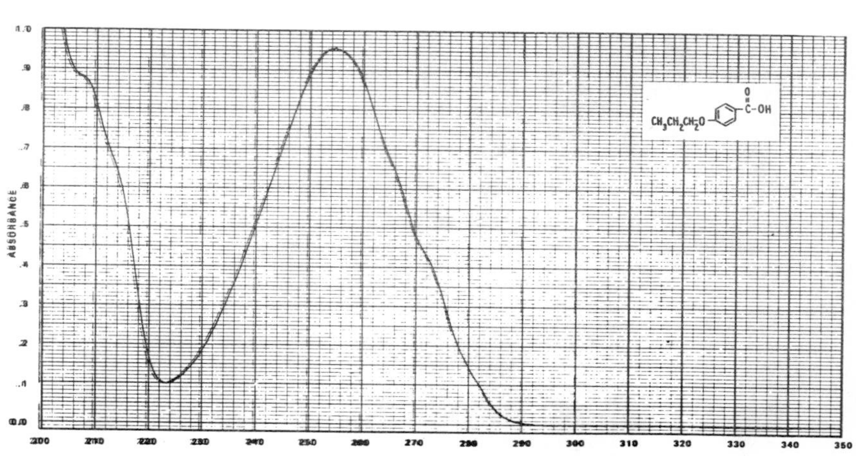

2586

p-PROPOXYBENZOIC ACID

$C_{10}H_{12}O_3$

Mol. Wt. 180.21

Solvent: Methanol KOH

λ Max. mμ	a_m	Cell mm	Conc. g/L
282	991	10	0.100
247	14900	1	0.100

2587

SALICYLIC ACID

$C_7H_6O_3$

Mol. Wt. 138.12

M.P. 159°C (lit.)

Solvent: Methanol

λ Max. mμ	a_m	Cell mm	Conc. g/L
x	x	10	2.000
302	4070	10	0.020
235	7600	10	0.020

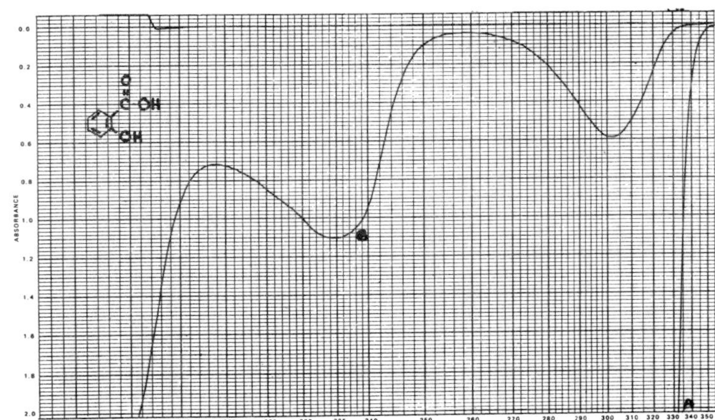

λ Max. mμ	a_m	Cell mm	Conc. g/L

p-HYDROXYBENZOIC ACID

2588

$C_7H_6O_3$
Mol. Wt. 138.12
M.P. 215-216°C
Solvent: Methanol

λ Max. mμ	a_m	Cell mm	Conc. g/L
254	15100	1	0.0500

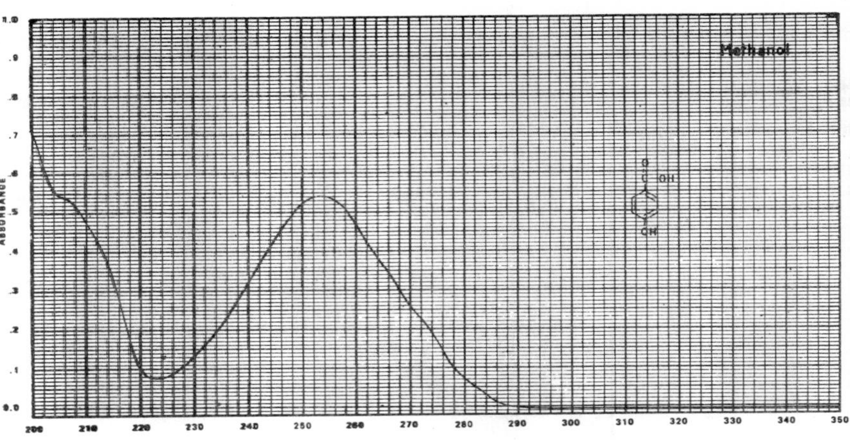

p-HYDROXYBENZOIC ACID

2588

$C_7H_6O_3$
Mol. Wt. 138.12
M.P. 215-216°C
Solvent: Methanol KOH

λ Max. mμ	a_m	Cell mm	Conc. g/L
272.5	16300	1	0.0500

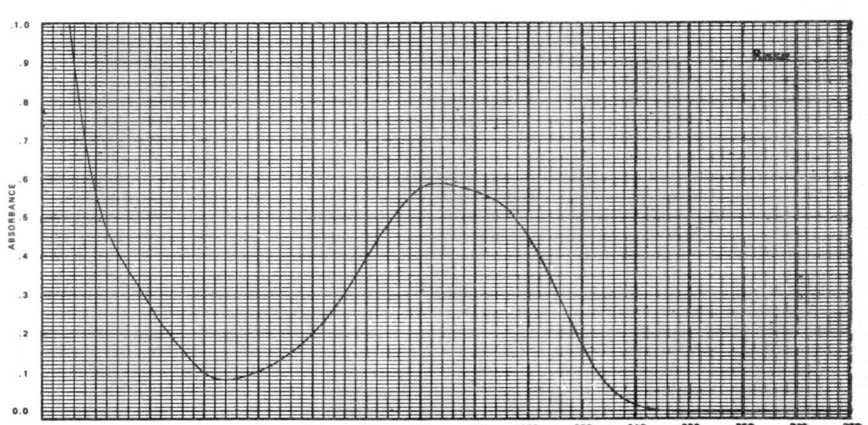

4,4'-OXYDIBENZOIC ACID

2589

$C_{14}H_{10}O_5$
Mol. Wt. 258.23
M.P. 300°C
Solvent: Methanol

λ Max. mμ	a_m	Cell mm	Conc. g/L
259.5	23200	1	0.100

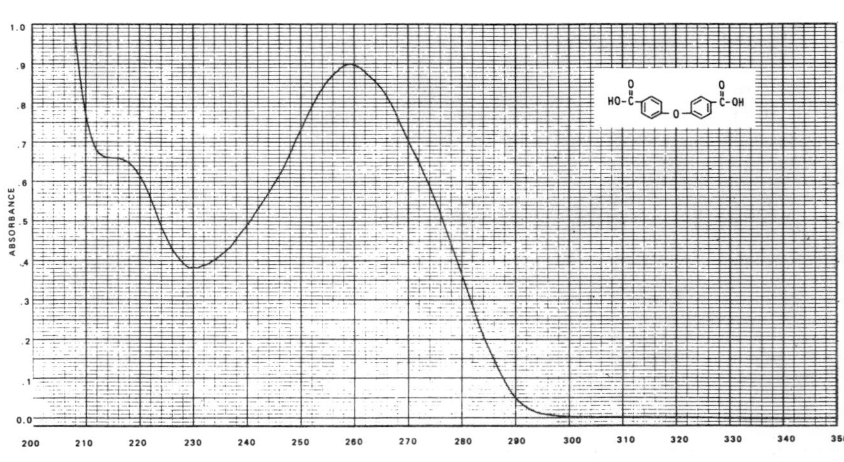

4,4'-OXYDIBENZOIC ACID

2589

$C_{14}H_{10}O_5$
Mol. Wt. 258.23
M.P. 300°C
Solvent: Methanol KOH

λ Max. mμ	a_m	Cell mm	Conc. g/L
252.5	21200	1	0.100

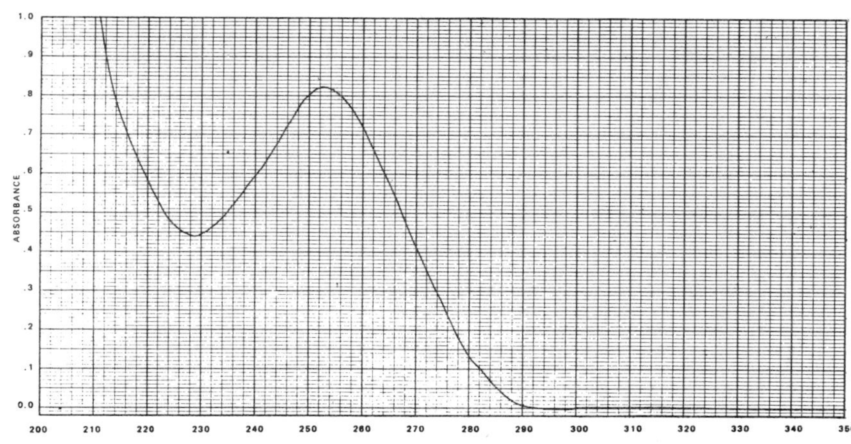

PHTHALIC ACID

2590

$C_8H_6O_4$
Mol. Wt. 166.13
M.R. 206-208°C (lit.)
Solvent: Methanol

λ Max. mμ	a_m	Cell mm	Conc. g/L
x	x	10	2.00
272	1170	10	0.200
x	x	10	0.020

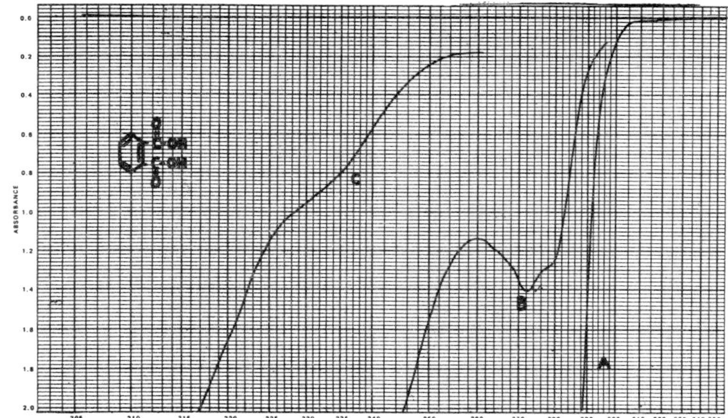

ISOPHTHALIC ACID

2591

$C_8H_6O_4$
Mol. Wt. 166.13
M.P. 340-342°C (lit.)
Solvent: Methanol

λ Max. mμ	a_m	Cell mm	Conc. g/L
287.5	840	10	0.324
279.5	872	10	0.324
x	x	10	0.032
x	x	10	0.0032

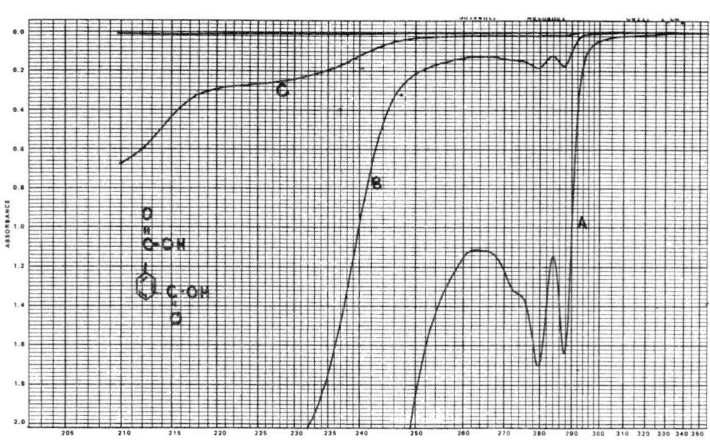

TEREPHTHALIC ACID

2592

$C_8H_6O_4$
Mol. Wt. 166.14
M.P. subl.
Solvent: Dioxane

λ Max. mμ	a_m	Cell mm	Conc. g/L
285.5	1960	10	0.0800
240.5	17500	1	0.0800

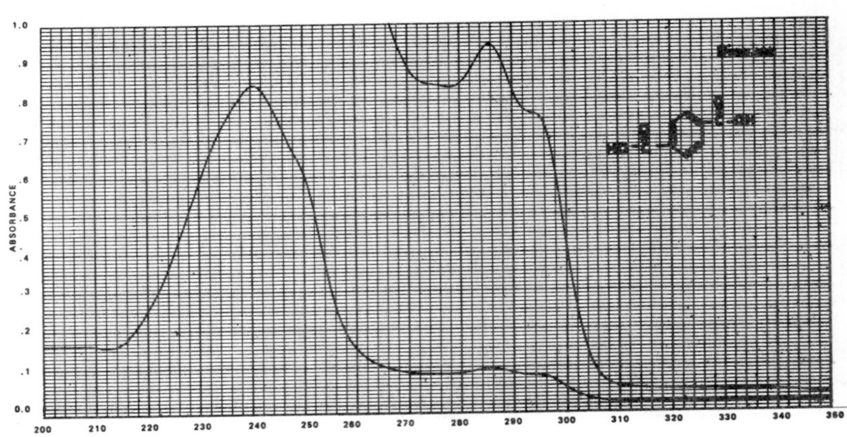

TEREPHTHALIC ACID

2592

$C_8H_6O_4$
Mol. Wt. 166.14
M.P. subl.
Solvent: Dioxane KOH

λ Max. mμ	a_m	Cell mm	Conc. g/L
286	1440	10	0.0800
240	6060	2	0.0800

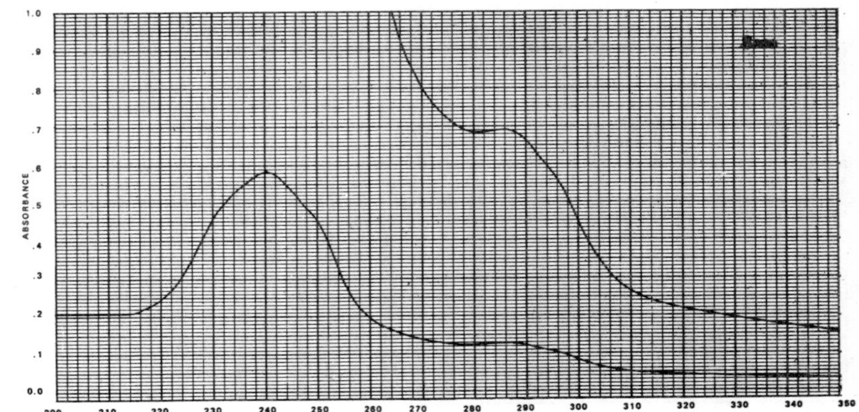

2,6-DIMETHYLBENZOIC ACID

2593

$C_9H_{10}O_2$
Mol. Wt. 150.18
M.P. 115-117°C
Solvent: Methanol

λ Max. mμ	a_m	Cell mm	Conc. g/L
273	553	20	0.100
268	541	20	0.100

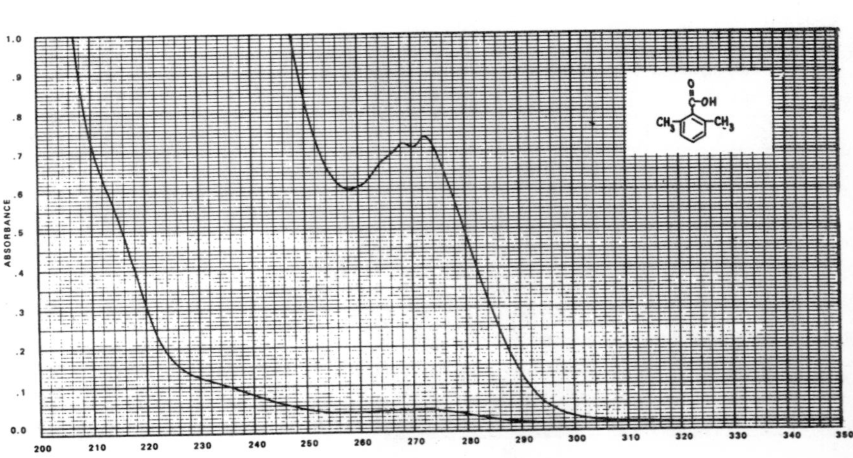

2,6-DIMETHYLBENZOIC ACID

2593

$C_9H_{10}O_2$

Mol. Wt. 150.18

M.P. 115-117°C

Solvent: Methanol KOH

λ Max. mμ	a_m	Cell mm	Conc. g/L
263	308	20	0.100
x	x	1	0.100

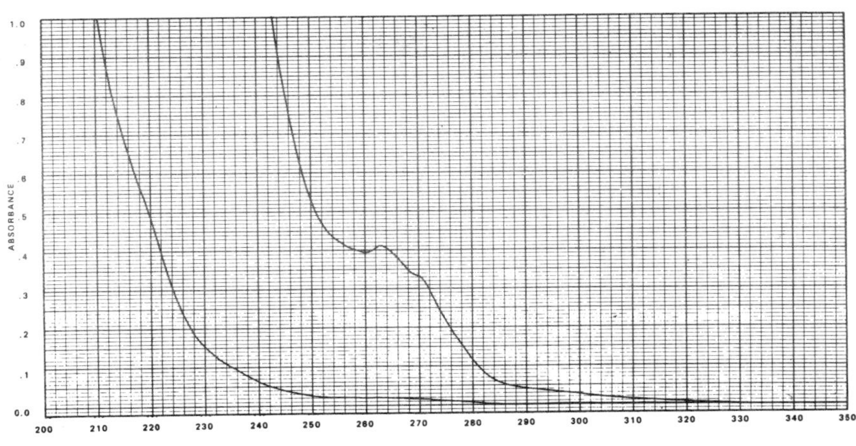

2,4-DINITROBENZOIC ACID

2594

$C_7H_4N_2O_6$

Mol. Wt. 212.13

M.P. 179-181°C

Solvent: Methanol

λ Max. mμ	a_m	Cell mm	Conc. g/L
236	12400	10	0.010
206.5	14000	10	0.010

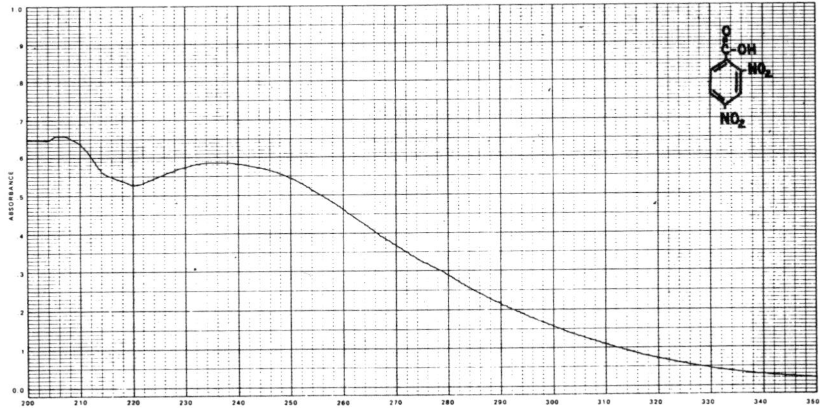

λ Max. mμ	a_m	Cell mm	Conc. g/L

6-AMINO-m-ANISIC ACID

2595

$C_8H_9NO_3$

Mol. Wt. 167.17

Solvent: Methanol

λ Max. mμ	a_m	Cell mm	Conc. g/L
353	3150	5	0.100
246	4470	1	0.100
216	16200	1	0.100

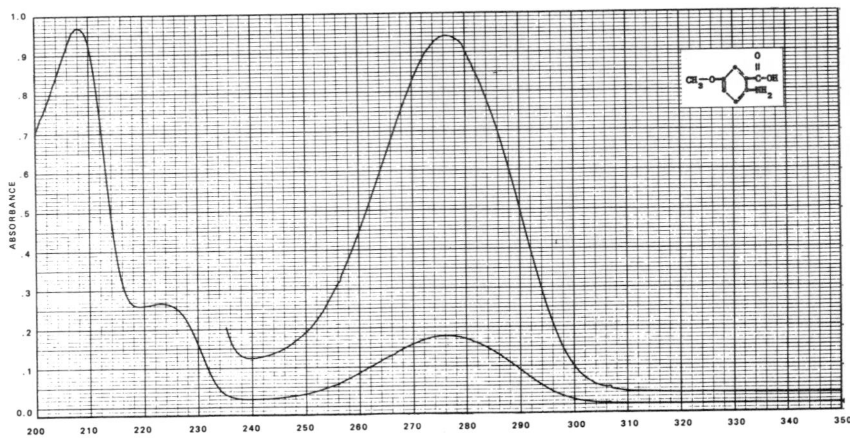

6-AMINO-m-ANISIC ACID

2595

$C_8H_9NO_3$

Mol. Wt. 167.17

Solvent: Methanol KOH

λ Max. mμ	a_m	Cell mm	Conc. g/L
328	2670	2	0.100
242	5440	2	0.100

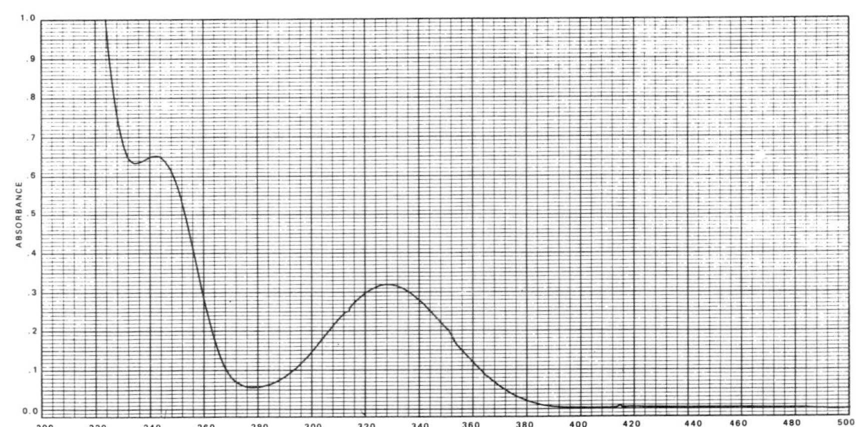

6-AMINO-m-ANISIC ACID

2595

$C_8H_9NO_3$

Mol. Wt. 167.17

Solvent: Methanol HCl

λ Max. mμ	a_m	Cell mm	Conc. g/L
294	2100	2	0.100
228	5800	2	0.100

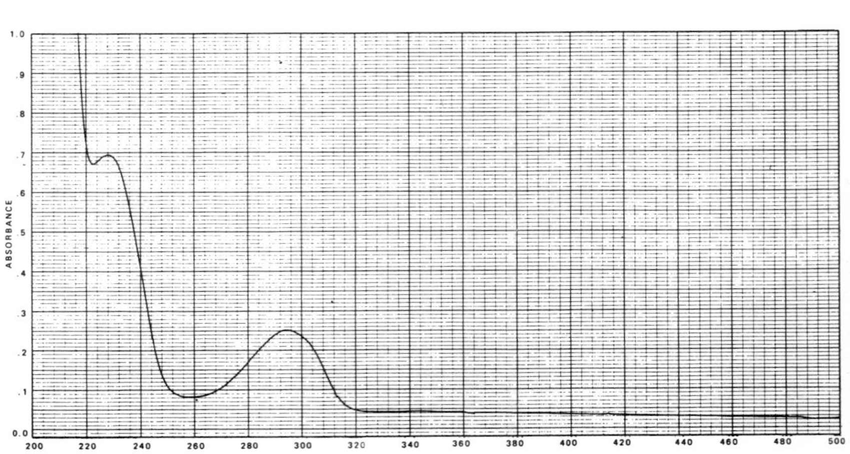

2,4-CRESOTIC ACID

2596

$C_8H_8O_3$

Mol. Wt. 152.14

M.P. 177°C (lit.)

Solvent: Methanol

λ Max. mμ	a_m	Cell mm	Conc. g/L
x	x	10	2.000
306	4250	10	0.060
240.5	8980	10	0.020

3-NITROSALICYLIC ACID

2597

$C_7H_5NO_5$

Mol. Wt. 183.13

M.P. 146-148°C

Solvent: Methanol

λ Max. mμ	a_m	Cell mm	Conc. g/L
329	4210	10	0.030
225.5	14300	10	0.010

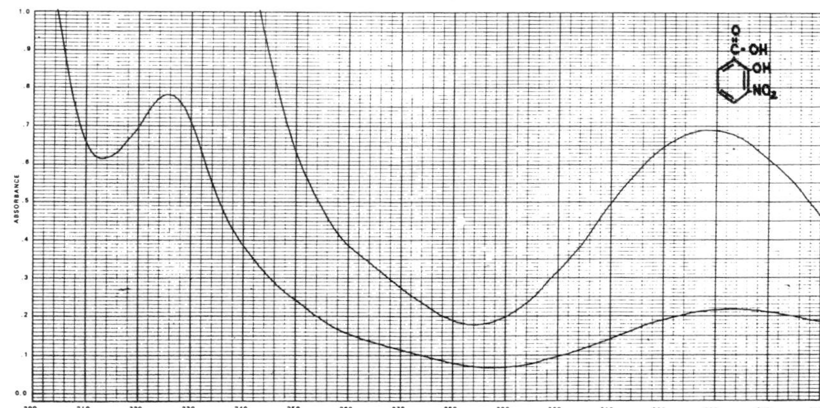

λ Max. mμ	a_m	Cell mm	Conc. g/L

VANILLIC ACID 2598

$C_8H_8O_4$
Mol. Wt. 168.15
M.P. 210-212°C
Solvent: Methanol

λ Max. mμ	a_m	Cell mm	Conc. g/L
290	6210	2	0.100
259	11900	2	0.0200
217	22900	2	0.0200

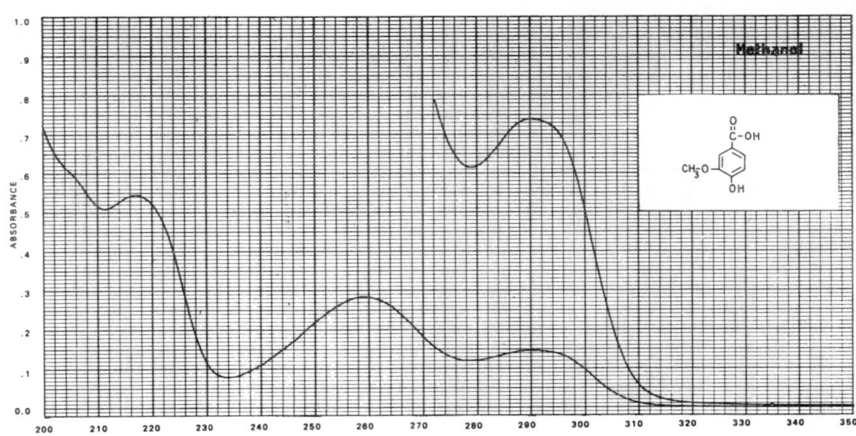

VANILLIC ACID 2598

$C_8H_8O_4$
Mol. Wt. 168.15
M.P. 210-212°C
Solvent: Methanol KOH

λ Max. mμ	a_m	Cell mm	Conc. g/L
296.5	14100	1	0.100

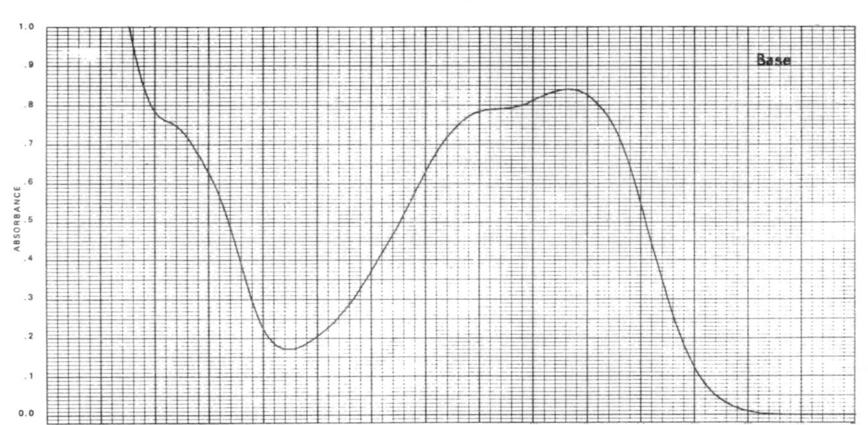

β-RESORCYLIC ACID 2599

$C_7H_6O_4$
Mol. Wt. 154.12
Solvent: Methanol

λ Max. mμ	a_m	Cell mm	Conc. g/L
295	5650	5	0.0500
256	12900	1	0.0500
209	27100	1	0.0500

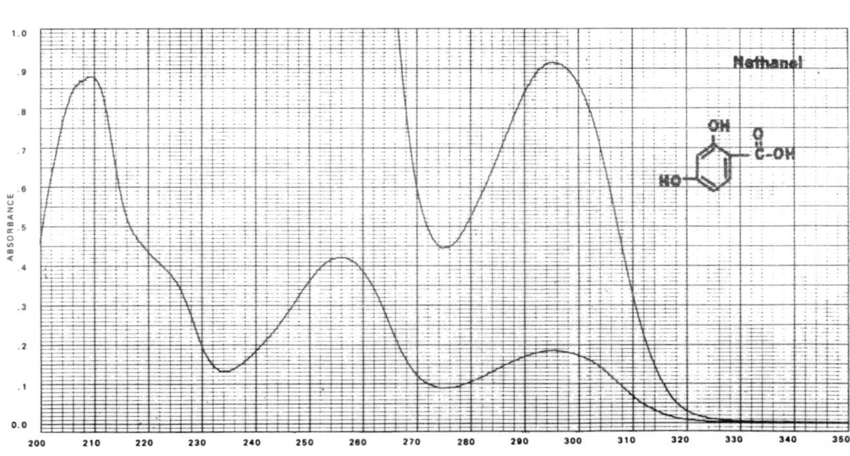

β-RESORCYLIC ACID **2599**

$C_7H_6O_4$

Mol. Wt. 154.12

Solvent: Methanol KOH

λ Max. mμ	a_m	Cell mm	Conc. g/L
298	10900	2	0.0500
269.5	13900	2	0.0500
230.5	10400	2	0.0500
x	x	1	0.0500

PROTOCATECHUIC ACID **2600**

$C_7H_6O_4$

Mol. Wt. 154.12

Solvent: Methanol

λ Max. mμ	a_m	Cell mm	Conc. g/L
281.5	2760	5	0.100
219	5550	1	0.100

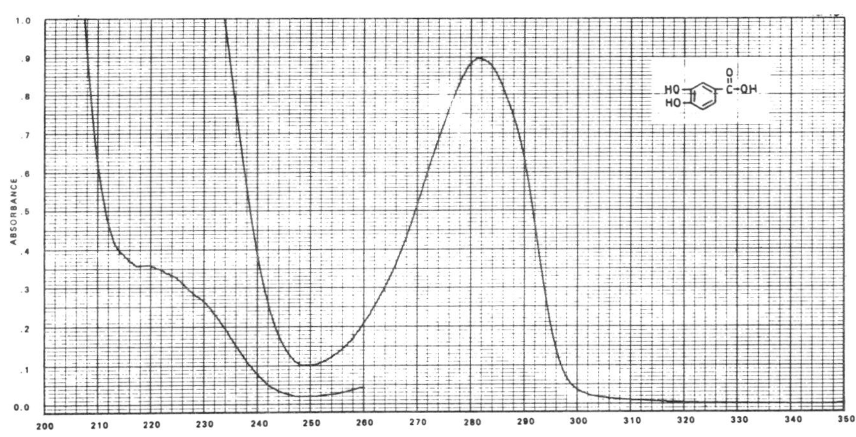

PROTOCATECHUIC ACID **2600**

$C_7H_6O_4$

Mol. Wt. 154.12

Solvent: Methanol KOH

λ Max. mμ	a_m	Cell mm	Conc. g/L
421	670	20	0.100
x	x	1	0.100

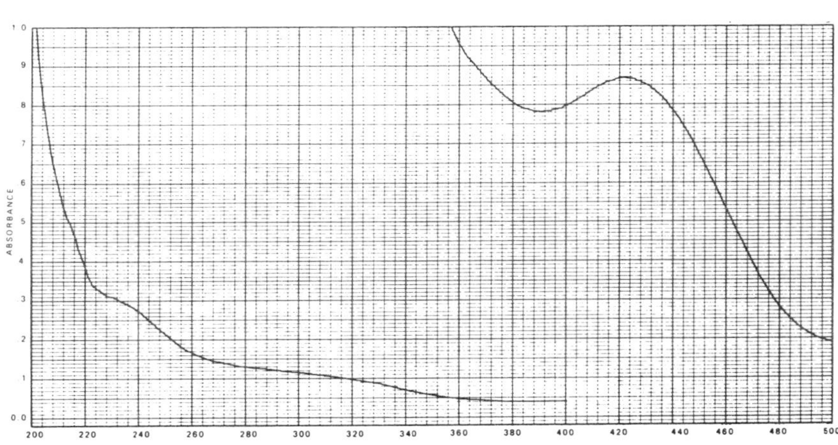

4-NITROPHTHALIC ACID 2601

$C_8H_5NO_6$
Mol. Wt. 211.13
M.P. 164-165°C
Solvent: Methanol

λ Max. mμ	a_m	Cell mm	Conc. g/L
259	8590	1	0.100
214	15600	1	0.100

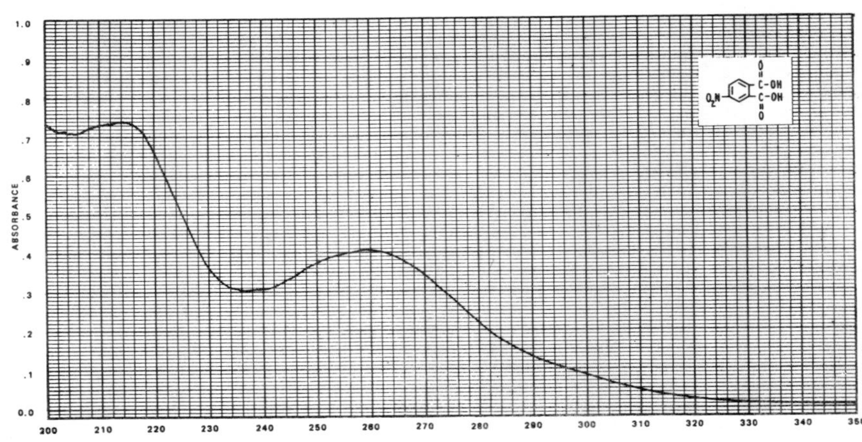

5-NITROISOPHTHALIC ACID 2602

$C_8H_5NO_6$
Mol. Wt. 211.14
M.P. 255°C (dec.) (lit.)
Solvent: Methanol

λ Max. mμ	a_m	Cell mm	Conc. g/L
251	6550	1	0.0800
220	25500	1	0.0800

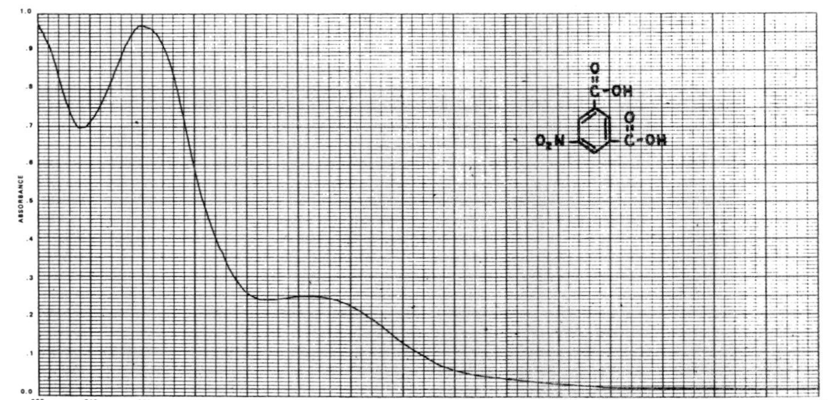

5-NITROISOPHTHALIC ACID 2602

$C_8H_5NO_6$
Mol. Wt. 211.14
M.P. 255°C (dec.) (lit.)
Solvent: Methanol KOH

λ Max. mμ	a_m	Cell mm	Conc. g/L
260	6700	1	0.0800

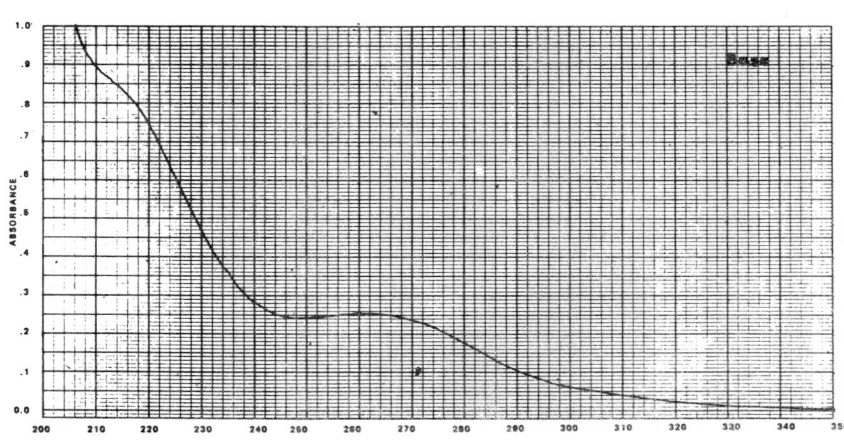

1,3,5-BENZENETRICARBOXYLIC ACID

2603

$C_9H_6O_6$
Mol. Wt. 210.15
Solvent: Methanol

λ Max. mμ	a_m	Cell mm	Conc. g/L
x	x	10	2.312
281	610	10	0.231
210.5	69300	10	0.002

3-FUROIC ACID

2604

$C_5H_4O_3$
Mol. Wt. 112.09
M.P. 120-122°C
Solvent: Methanol

λ Max. mμ	a_m	Cell mm	Conc. g/L
232	2790	2	0.100

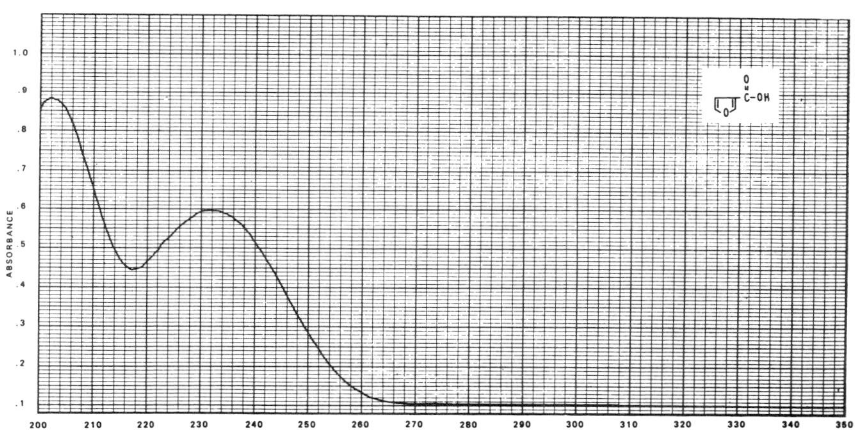

3-FUROIC ACID

2604

$C_5H_4O_3$
Mol. Wt. 112.09
M.P. 120-122°C
Solvent: Methanol KOH

λ Max. mμ	a_m	Cell mm	Conc. g/L
202	5380	2	0.100

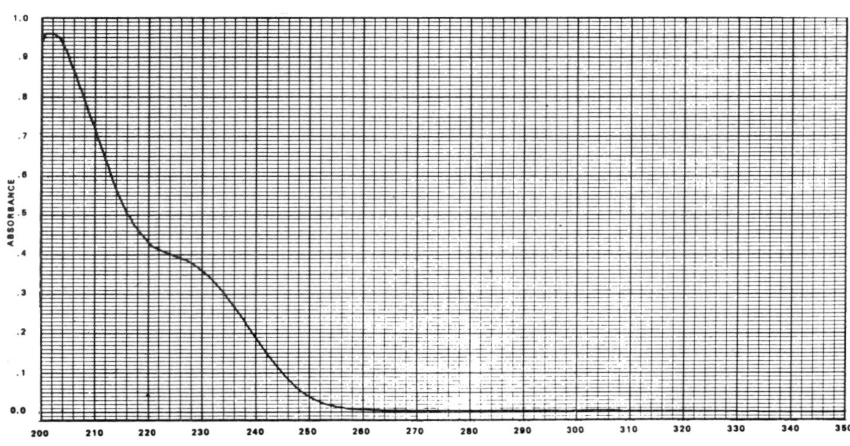

2-FURANACRYLIC ACID

2605

$C_7H_6O_3$

Mol. Wt. 138.12

M.P. 141°C

Solvent: Methanol

λ Max. mμ	a_m	Cell mm	Conc. g/L
297	21100	10	0.006

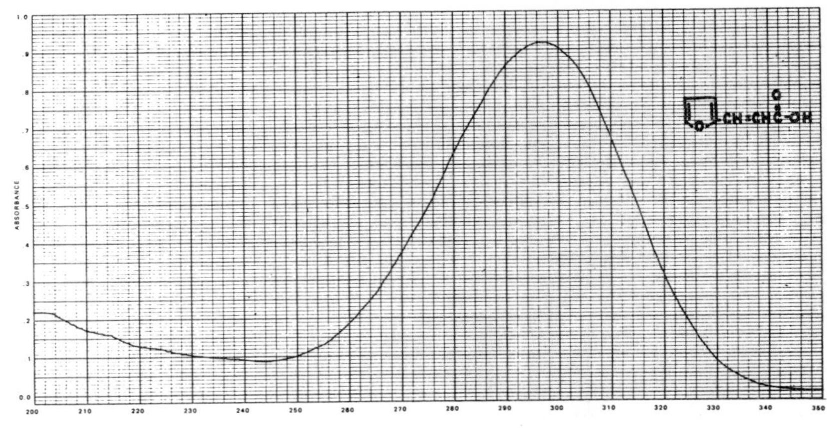

NICOTINIC ACID, HYDROCHLORIDE

2606

$C_6H_5NO_2 \cdot HCl$

Mol. Wt. 159.57

M.P. 271-273°C

Solvent: Methanol

λ Max. mμ	a_m	Cell mm	Conc. g/L
261	3620	2	0.100
215	6380	2	0.100

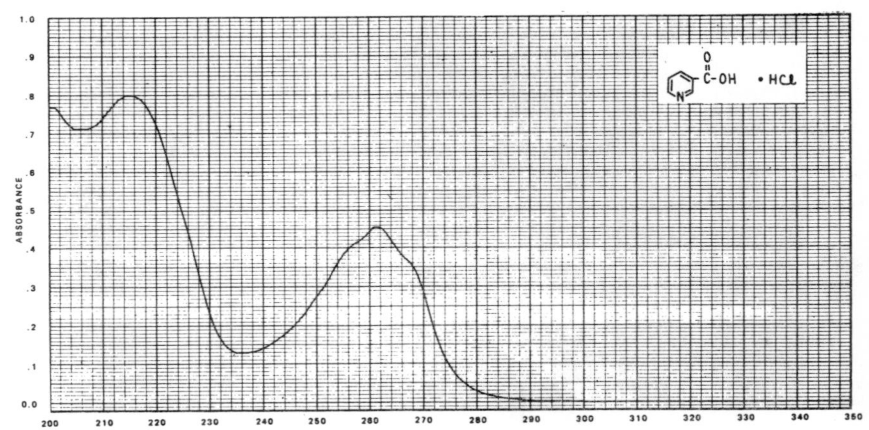

NICOTINIC ACID, HYDROCHLORIDE

2606

$C_6H_5NO_2 \cdot HCl$

Mol. Wt. 159.57

M.P. 271-273°C

Solvent: Methanol KOH

λ Max. mμ	a_m	Cell mm	Conc. g/L
262.5	2860	5	0.100
257	2630	5	0.100
x	x	1	0.100

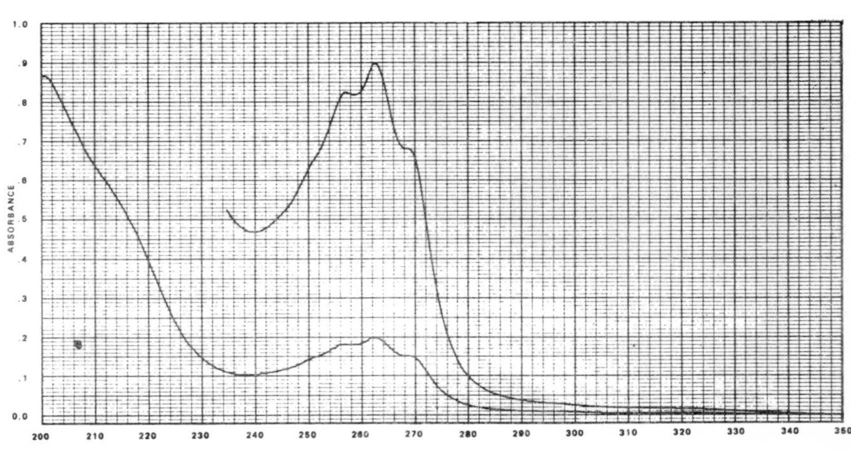

3-INDOLEACETIC ACID

$C_{10}H_9NO_2$
Mol. Wt. 175.19
Solvent: Methanol

λ Max. mμ	a_m	Cell mm	Conc. g/L
289.5	5170	2	0.100
280	6120	2	0.100
273	5870	2	0.100
220	34300	2	0.0200

PIPERONYLIC ACID

2608

$C_8H_6O_4$
Mol. Wt. 166.14
M.P. 228°C (lit.)
Solvent: Dioxane

λ Max. mμ	a_m	Cell mm	Conc. g/L
296	6370	1	0.0600
261	7260	1	0.0600
220	23500	1	0.0600

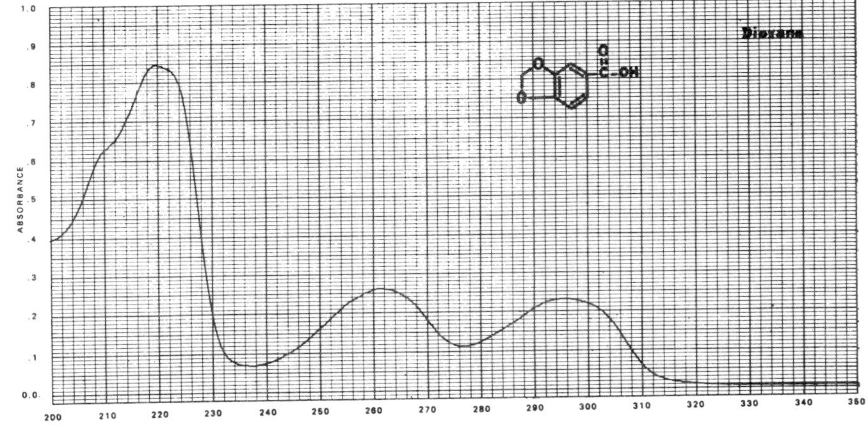

PIPERONYLIC ACID

2608

$C_8H_6O_4$
Mol. Wt. 166.14
M.P. 228°C (lit.)
Solvent: Dioxane KOH

λ Max. mμ	a_m	Cell mm	Conc. g/L
292	2410	1	0.200
255	2720	1	0.200

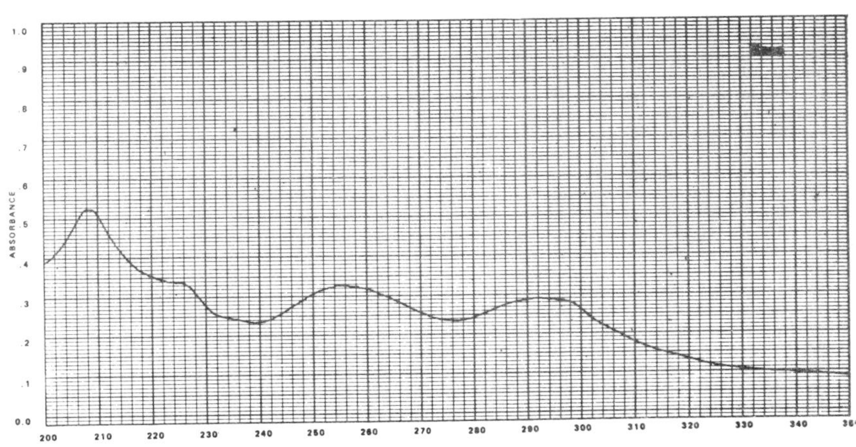

THIOACETIC ACID 2609

C_2H_4OS

Mol. Wt. 76.12

B.P. 93°C

λ Max. mμ	a_m	Cell mm	Conc. g/L

Pure sample not available.

THIOBENZOIC ACID 2610

C_7H_6OS

Mol. Wt. 138.19

Solvent: Methanol

λ Max. mμ	a_m	Cell mm	Conc. g/L
414	78	20	0.100
289	7460	1	0.100
241	10900	1	0.100
x	x	1	0.100

THIOBENZOIC ACID 2610

C_7H_6OS

Mol. Wt. 138.19

Solvent: Methanol KOH

λ Max. mμ	a_m	Cell mm	Conc. g/L
282	7200	1	0.100
x	x	0.5	0.100

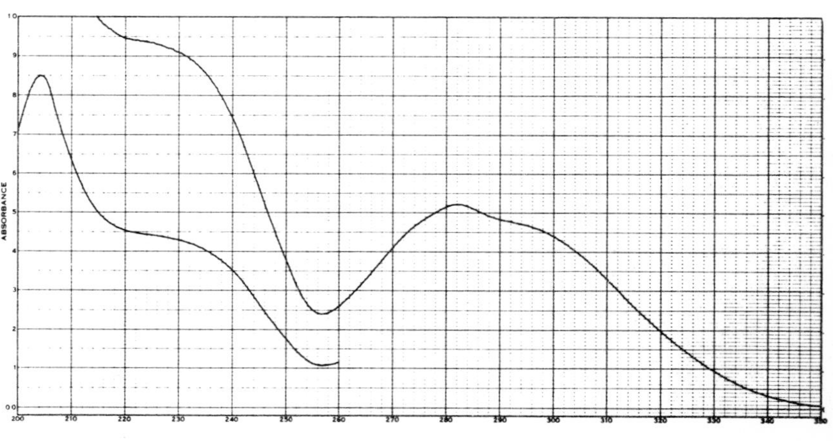

2611

λ Max. mμ	a_m	Cell mm	Conc. g/L

The alkyl amino acids (compounds 2611 through 2632) do not display any maxima in the near UV.

GLUTAMIC ACID, 5-BENZYL ESTER

2633

$C_{12}H_{15}NO_4$

Mol. Wt. 237.26

M.P. 181-182°C

Solvent: Methanol

λ Max. mμ	a_m	Cell mm	Conc. g/L
266	139	40	0.100
260	219	40	0.100
256	267	40	0.100
250	241	40	0.100
244	261	40	0.100

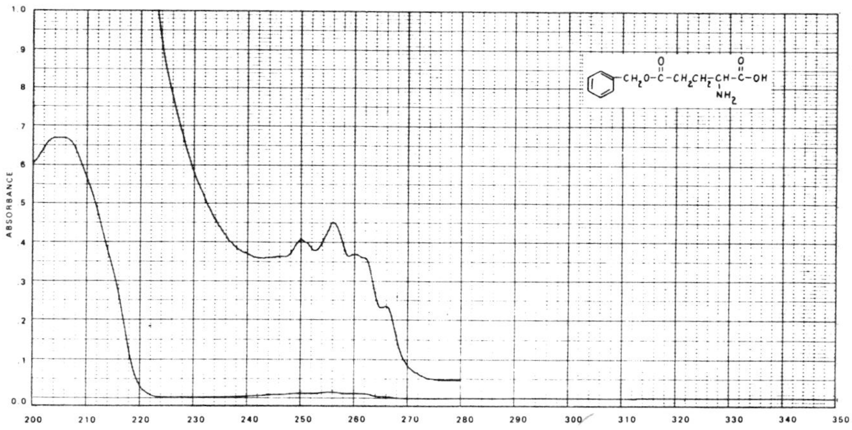

λ Max. mμ	a_m	Cell mm	Conc. g/L

N-PHENYLGLYCINE 2634

$C_8H_9NO_2$

Mol. Wt. 151.17

Solvent: Methanol

λ Max. mμ	a_m	Cell mm	Conc. g/L
292	2030	4	0.100
243	9060	1	0.100

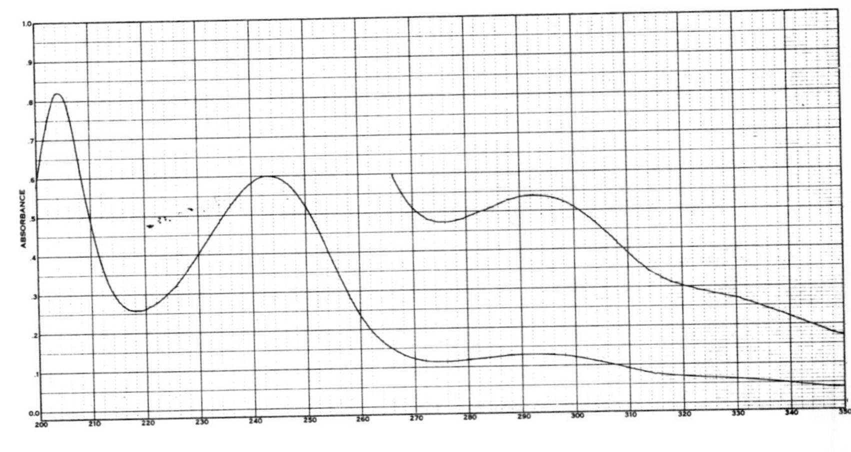

N-PHENYLGLYCINE 2634

$C_8H_9NO_2$

Mol. Wt. 151.17

Solvent: Methanol HCl

λ Max. mμ	a_m	Cell mm	Conc. g/L
312	1140	4	0.100
238	2860	4	0.100
x	x	1	0.100

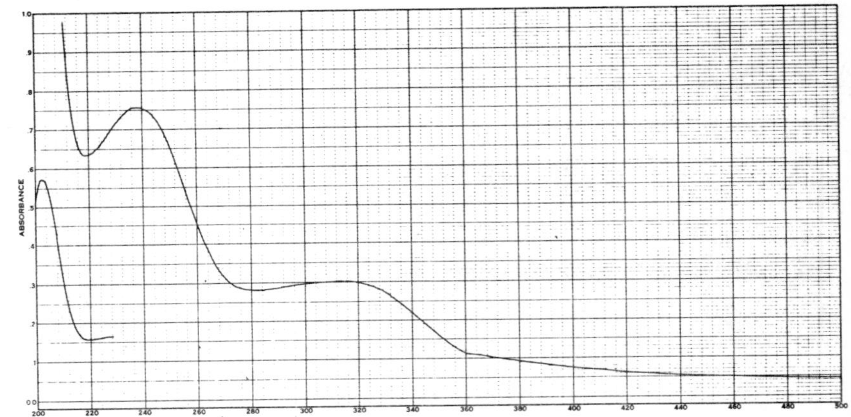

2,2-DIPHENYLGLYCINE 2635

$C_{14}H_{13}NO_2$

Mol. Wt. 227.27

Solvent: Methanol

λ Max. mμ	a_m	Cell mm	Conc. g/L
258.5	1020	20	0.100
210.5	21100	1	0.100

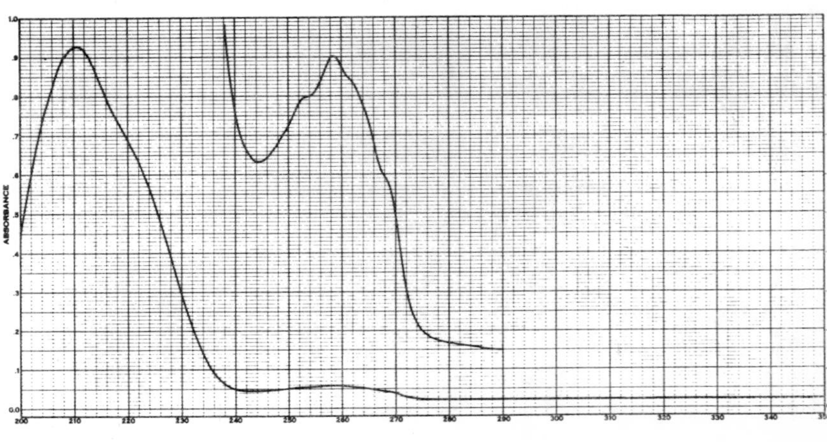

λ Max. mμ	a_m	Cell mm	Conc. g/L

The aliphatic amino acids (compounds 2636 through 2646) do not display any maxima in the near UV.

λ Max. mμ	a_m	Cell mm	Conc. g/L

λ Max. mμ	a_m	Cell mm	Conc. g/L

NOTES

THE SALTS OF CARBOXYLIC ACIDS

Aliphatic Compounds

The aliphatic carboxylic acid salts do not display any maxima in the near ultraviolet region and thus there are no spectra in this section for compounds 2647 through 2668.

Olefinic Compounds

The salts of acrylic acid, maleic acid and their longer chain analogs such as 10-undecenoic acid, potassium salt (compound 2670) do not produce any maxima in the near UV region.

The sorbates show an absorbance band at 249 mμ (ϵ_{max} = 25500) which shifts to longer wavelength upon the addition of acid to their methanol solutions (compound 2671).

Aromatic Compounds

The salts of benzoic acid display two major bands which absorb at slightly shorter wavelengths than the parent compounds.

Upon the addition of acid, the bands undergo a bathochromic shift returning to the positions occupied by the corresponding acids.

Several examples of these salt - acid conversions are listed below.

Compound	$\lambda_{max}(\epsilon_{max})$	$\lambda_{max}(\epsilon_{max})$	Solvent	Spectrum
Benzoic acid	228 (11900)	272 (893)	Methanol	2566
Benzoic acid	222 (8890)	269 (598)	Methanol/KOH	2566
—, Sodium salt	224 (7620)	269 (546)	Water	2675
—, Ammonium salt	225 (8890)	270 (594)	Methanol	2683
—, Ammonium salt	228 (11100)	272 (878)	Methanol/HCl	2683

ACRYLIC ACID, CALCIUM SALT

2669

$C_6H_6CaO_4$
Mol. Wt. 182.19
Solvent: Methanol

λ Max. mμ	a_m	Cell mm	Conc. g/L
x	x	10	0.100
x	x	1	0.100

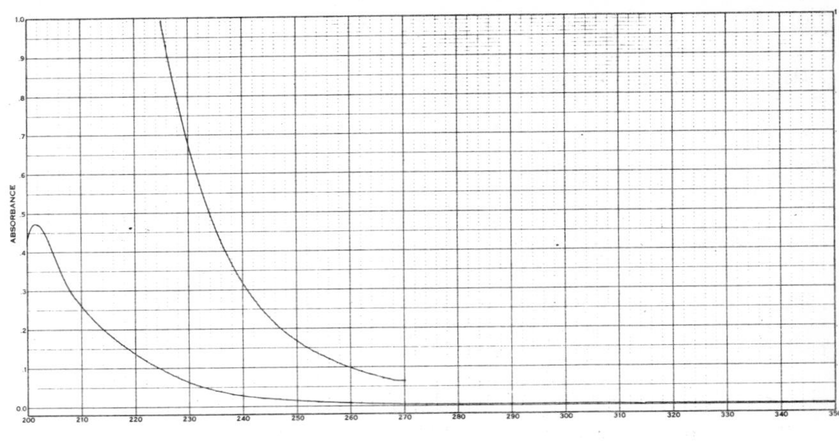

ACRYLIC ACID, CALCIUM SALT

2669

$C_6H_6CaO_4$
Mol. Wt. 182.19
Solvent: Methanol HCl

λ Max. mμ	a_m	Cell mm	Conc. g/L
x	x	4	0.100
x	x	1	0.100

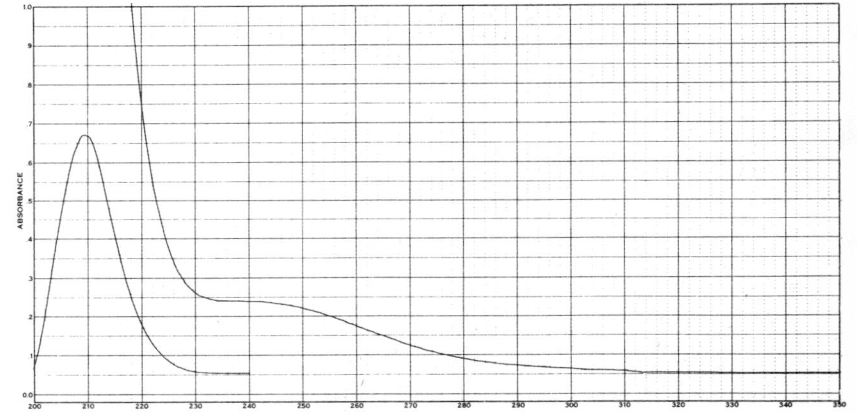

10-UNDECENOIC ACID, POTASSIUM SALT

2670

$C_{11}H_{19}KO_2$
Mol. Wt. 222.37

λ Max. mμ	a_m	Cell mm	Conc. g/L

10-Undecenoic acid, potassium salt does not display any maxima in the near UV.

SORBIC ACID, POTASSIUM SALT

2671

$C_6H_7KO_2$

Mol. Wt. 150.22

Solvent: Methanol

λ Max. mμ	a_m	Cell mm	Conc. g/L
248.5	25500	0.5	0.100

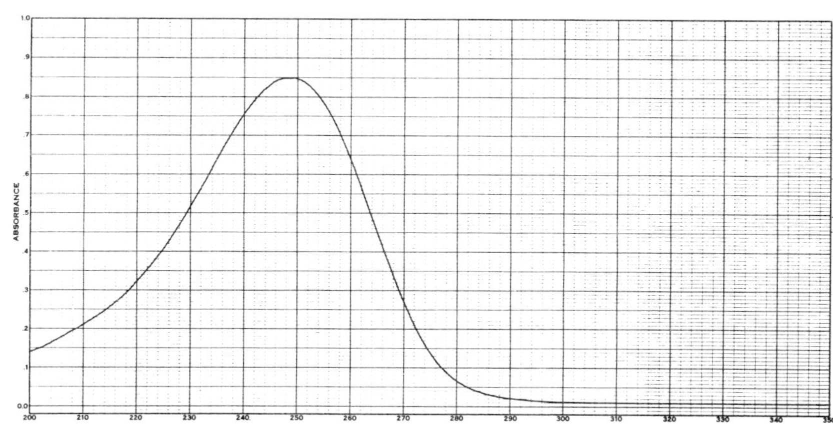

SORBIC ACID, POTASSIUM SALT

2671

$C_6H_7KO_2$

Mol. Wt. 150.22

Solvent: Methanol HCl

λ Max. mμ	a_m	Cell mm	Conc. g/L
257	26400	0.5	0.100

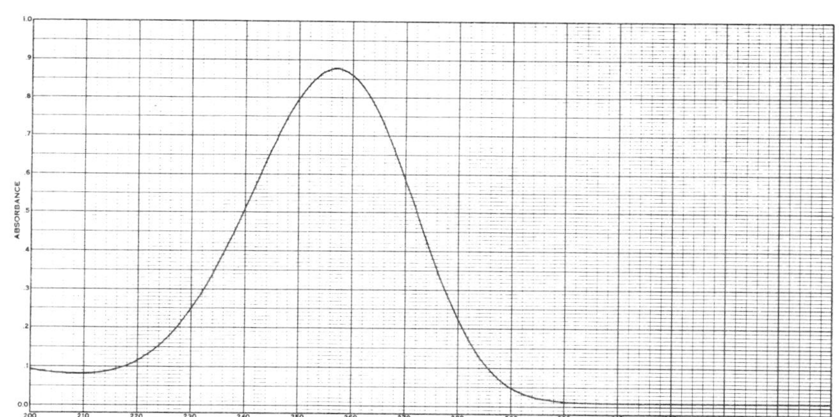

MALEIC ACID, SODIUM SALT

2672

$C_4H_2Na_2O_4$

Mol. Wt. 160.04

Solvent: Methanol

λ Max. mμ	a_m	Cell mm	Conc. g/L
x	x	1	0.100

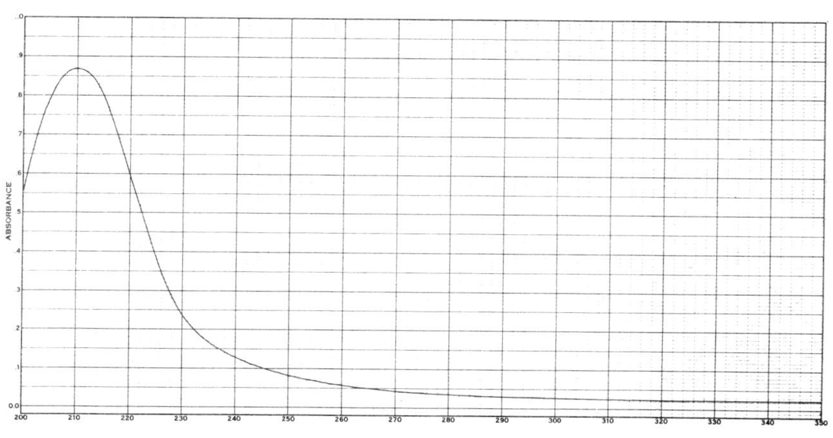

PHENYLACETIC ACID, SODIUM SALT

2673

$C_8H_7O_2Na$

Mol. Wt. 158.13

Solvent: Methanol

λ Max. mμ	a_m	Cell mm	Conc. g/L
268.5	131	10	2.100
268.5	127	10	1.049
265	153	10	1.049
259	207	10	1.049
253.5	173	10	1.049
248.5	130	10	1.049
x	x	10	0.105
x	x	10	0.011

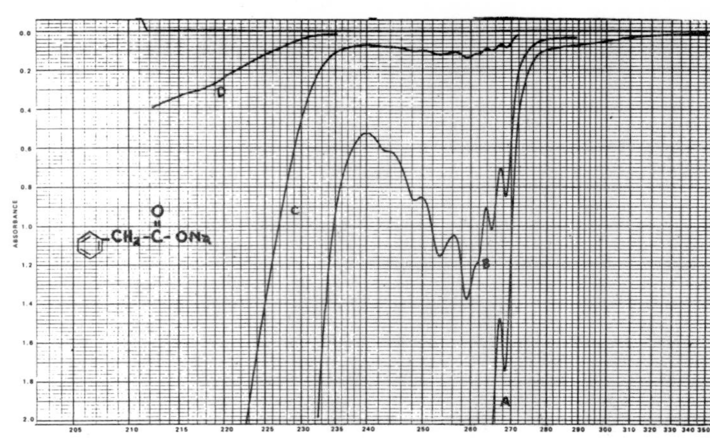

1-NAPHTHALENEACETIC ACID, SODIUM SALT

2674

$C_{12}H_9NaO_2$

Mol. Wt. 208.19

Solvent: Methanol

λ Max. mμ	a_m	Cell mm	Conc. g/L
282	6760	2	0.100
273	5730	2	0.100
223.5	72000	0.5	0.050

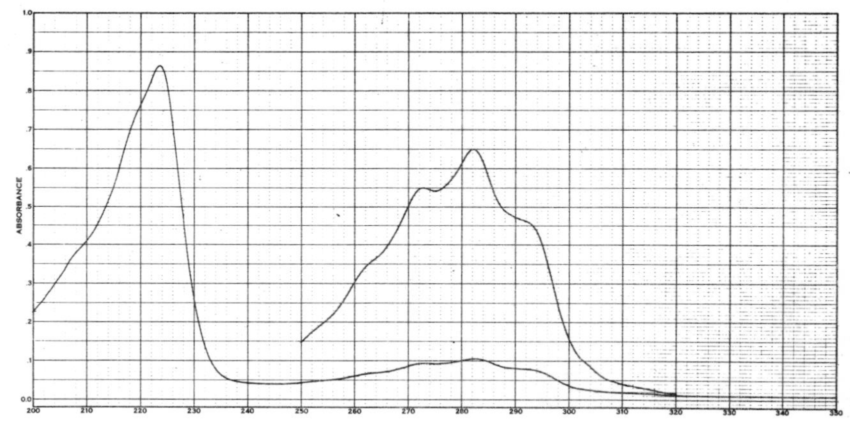

BENZOIC ACID, SODIUM SALT

2675

$C_7H_5NaO_2$

Mol. Wt. 144.11

Solvent: Water

λ Max. mμ	a_m	Cell mm	Conc. g/L
x	x	10	1.780
269	546	10	0.356
223.5	7620	10	0.032

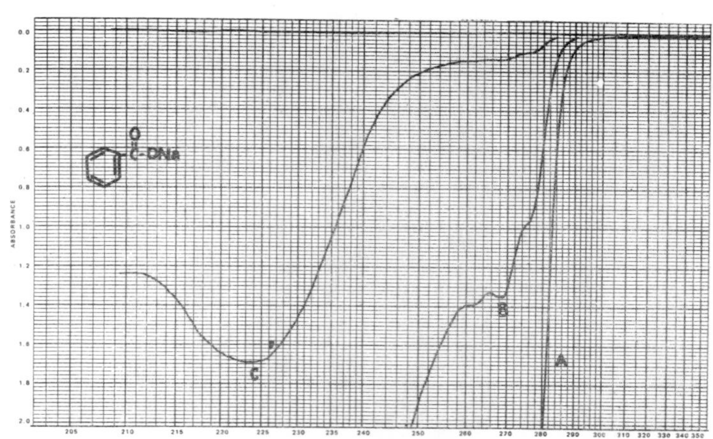

m-AMINOBENZOIC ACID, SODIUM SALT

2676

$C_7H_6NNaO_2$

Mol. Wt. 159.12

Solvent: Methanol

λ Max. mμ	a_m	Cell mm	Conc. g/L
303	1650	5	0.100
208.5	23800	0.5	0.100

m-AMINOBENZOIC ACID, SODIUM SALT

2676

$C_7H_6NNaO_2$

Mol. Wt. 159.12

Solvent: Methanol HCl

λ Max. mμ	a_m	Cell mm	Conc. g/L
277.5	673	10	0.100
270.5	796	10	0.100
223.5	10200	1	0.100

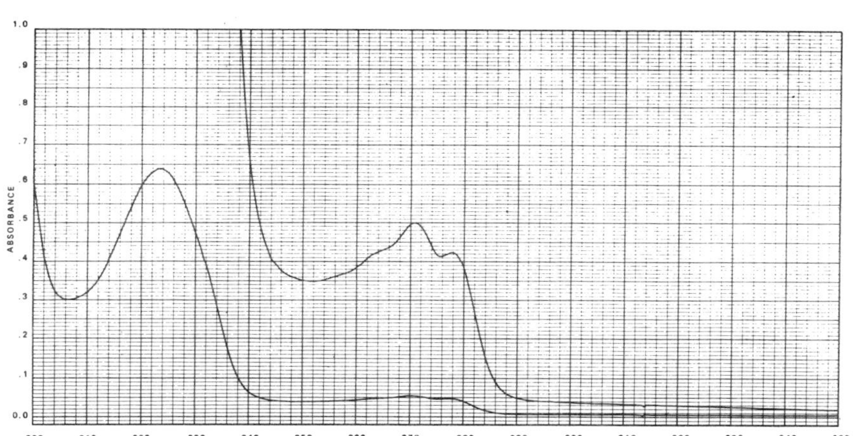

λ Max. mμ	a_m	Cell mm	Conc. g/L

2677

p-AMINOBENZOIC ACID, SODIUM SALT

$C_7H_6NNaO_2$

Mol. Wt. 159.12

Solvent: Methanol

λ Max. mμ	a_m	Cell mm	Conc. g/L
269	14800	1	0.100

2677

p-AMINOBENZOIC ACID, SODIUM SALT

$C_7H_6NNaO_2$

Mol. Wt. 159.12

Solvent: Methanol HCl

λ Max. mμ	a_m	Cell mm	Conc. g/L
288	971	10	0.100
276	1400	10	0.100
269	1360	10	0.100
224.5	12000	1	0.100

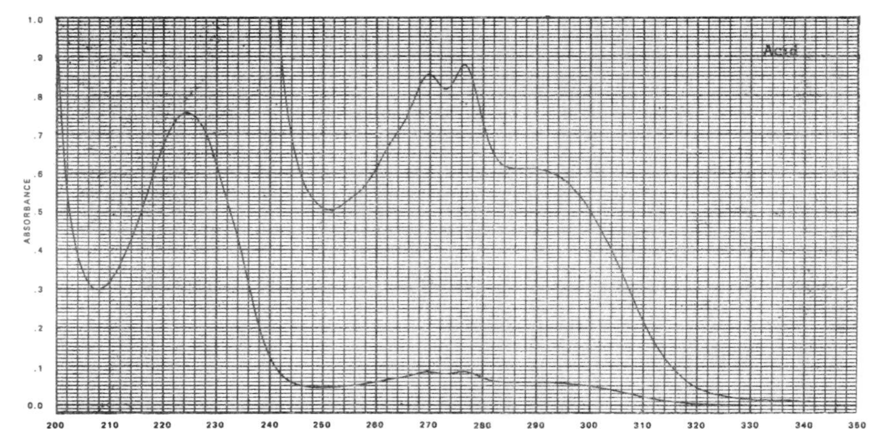

2678

SODIUM SALICYLATE

$C_7H_5NaO_3$

Mol. Wt. 160.11

Solvent: Methanol

λ Max. mμ	a_m	Cell mm	Conc. g/L
296.5	3740	2	0.100
228	6470	2	0.100

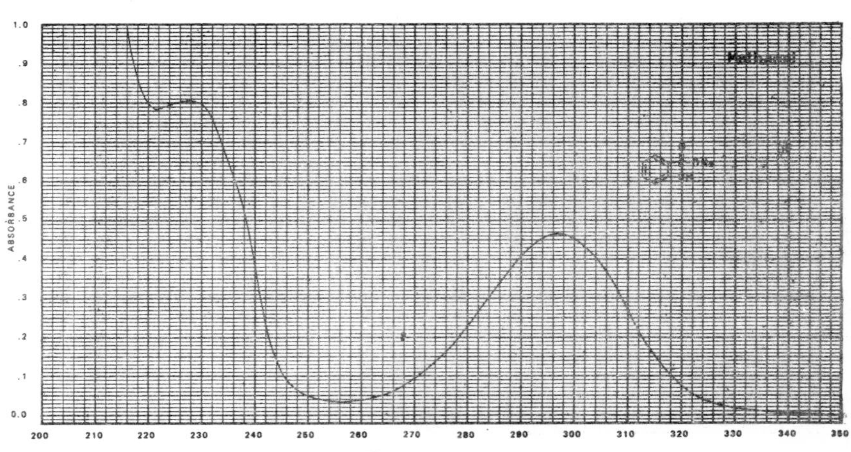

SODIUM SALICYLATE 2678

$C_7H_5NaO_3$

Mol. Wt. 160.11

Solvent: Methanol KOH

λ Max. mμ	a_m	Cell mm	Conc. g/L
296	3630	2	0.100

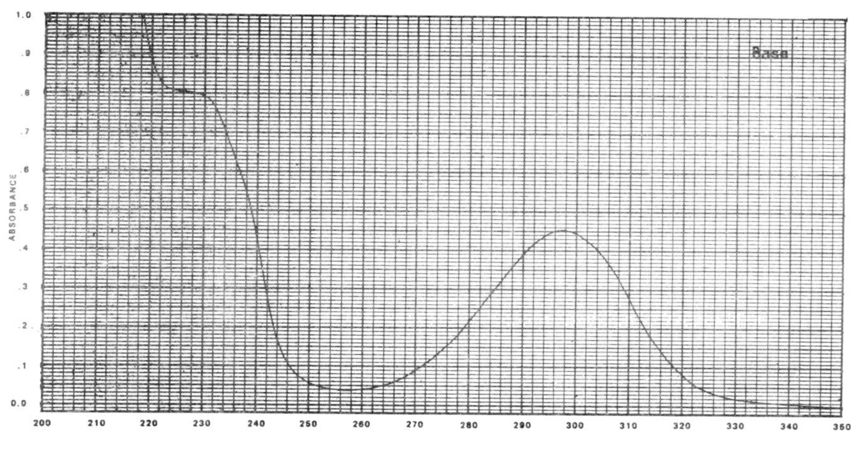

SODIUM SALICYLATE 2678

$C_7H_5NaO_3$

Mol. Wt. 160.11

Solvent: Methanol HCl

λ Max. mμ	a_m	Cell mm	Conc. g/L
304	3810	2	0.100
236	7530	2	0.100

λ Max. mμ	a_m	Cell mm	Conc. g/L

p-HYDROXYBENZOIC ACID, MONOSODIUM SALT

2679

$C_7H_5NaO_3$
Mol. Wt. 160.11
Solvent: Methanol

λ Max. mμ	a_m	Cell mm	Conc. g/L
281	1050	10	0.100
245	13400	1	0.100

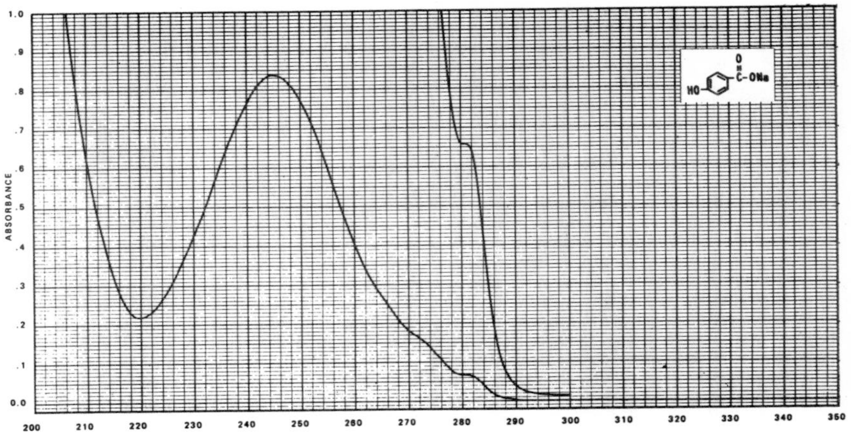

p-HYDROXYBENZOIC ACID, MONOSODIUM SALT

2679

$C_7H_5NaO_3$
Mol. Wt. 160.11
Solvent: Methanol HCl

λ Max. mμ	a_m	Cell mm	Conc. g/L
253	15500	1	0.100

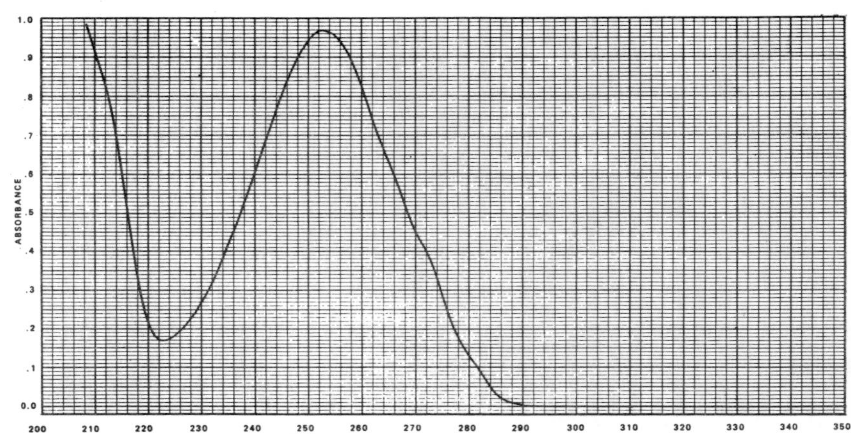

PHTHALIC ACID, MONOPOTASSIUM SALT

2680

$C_8H_5KO_4$
Mol. Wt. 204.23
Solvent: Methanol

λ Max. mμ	a_m	Cell mm	Conc. g/L
285	2160	5	0.100
233	9190	1	0.100

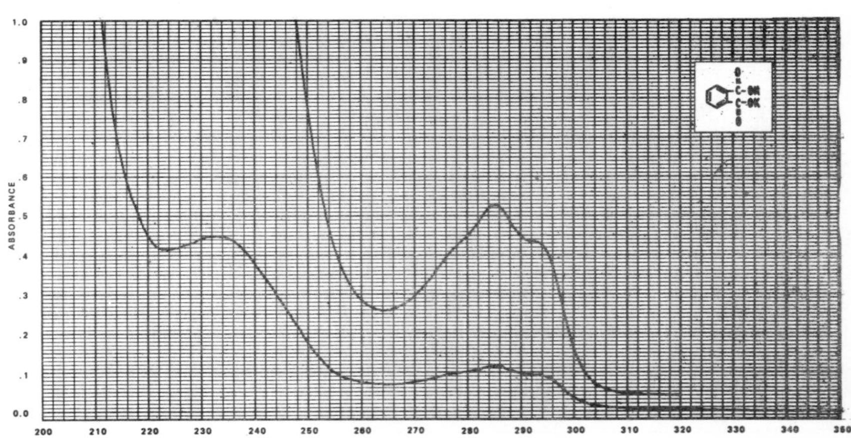

PHTHALIC ACID, MONOPOTASSIUM SALT

2680

$C_8H_5KO_4$

Mol. Wt. 204.23

Solvent: Methanol KOH

λ Max. mμ	a_m	Cell mm	Conc. g/L
273	942	10	0.100
265	911	10	0.100
x	x	1	0.100

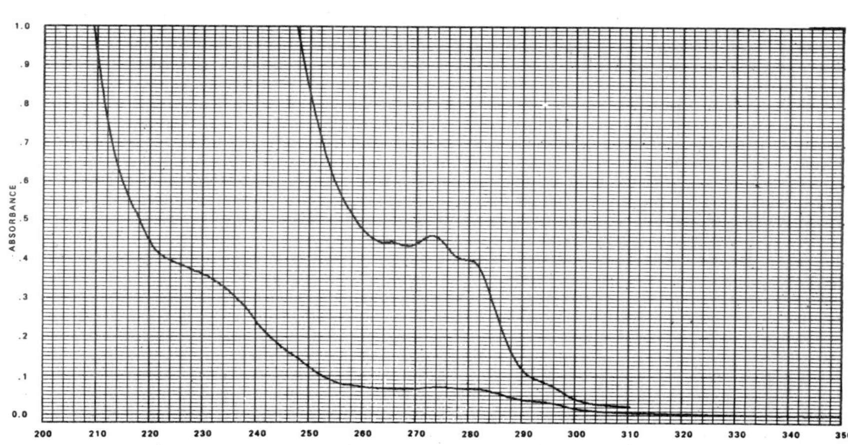

2-FUROIC ACID, POTASSIUM SALT

2681

$C_5H_3KO_3$

Mol. Wt. 150.18

Solvent: Methanol

λ Max. mμ	a_m	Cell mm	Conc. g/L
240.5	10700	1	0.0800

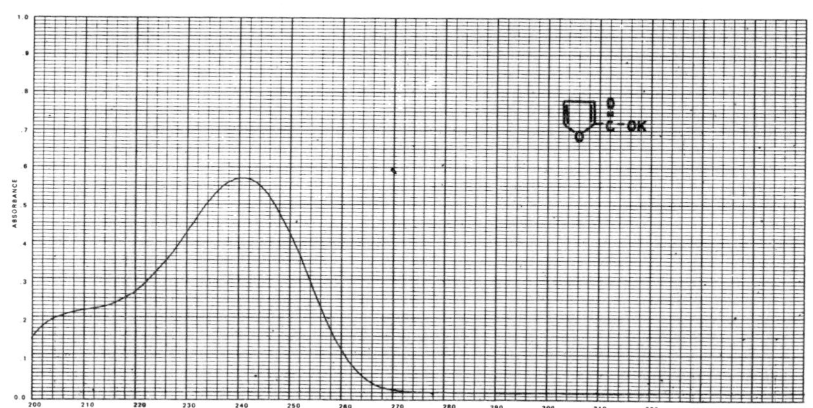

2-FUROIC ACID, POTASSIUM SALT

2681

$C_5H_3KO_3$

Mol. Wt. 150.18

Solvent: Methanol HCl

λ Max. mμ	a_m	Cell mm	Conc. g/L
248	12200	1	0.0800

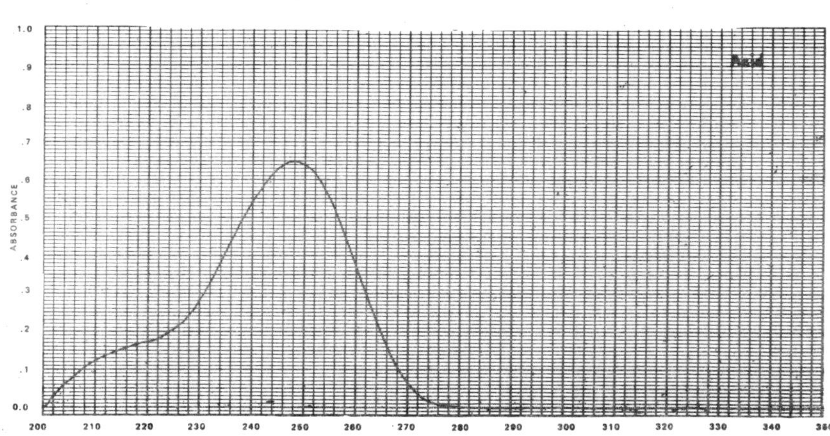

SUCCINIC ACID, DIAMMONIUM SALT 2682

$C_4H_{12}N_2O_4$

Mol. Wt. 152.15

λ Max. mμ	a_m	Cell mm	Conc. g/L

Succinic acid, diammonium salt does not display any maxima in the near UV.

BENZOIC ACID, AMMONIUM SALT 2683

$C_7H_9NO_2$

Mol. Wt. 139.16

M.P. 200°C (dec.)

Solvent: Methanol

λ Max. mμ	a_m	Cell mm	Conc. g/L
269.5	594	20	0.100
263	581	20	0.100
224.5	8890	1	0.100

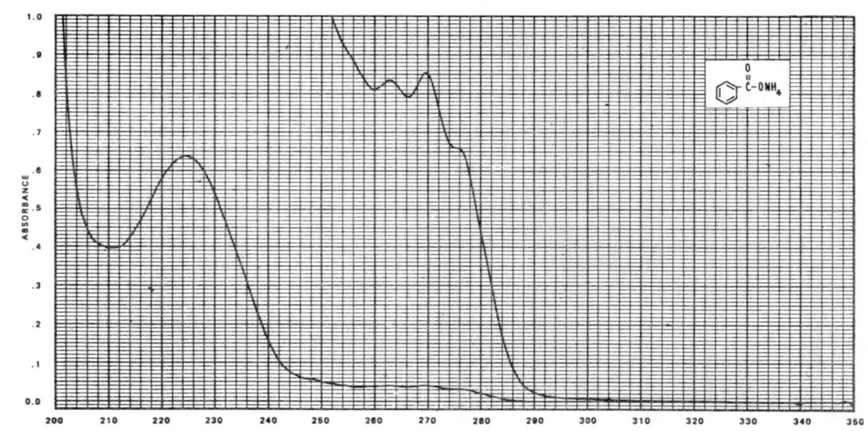

BENZOIC ACID, AMMONIUM SALT 2683

$C_7H_9NO_2$

Mol. Wt. 139.16

M.P. 200°C (dec.)

Solvent: Methanol HCl

λ Max. mμ	a_m	Cell mm	Conc. g/L
279.5	722	10	0.100
272	878	10	0.100
228	11100	1	0.100

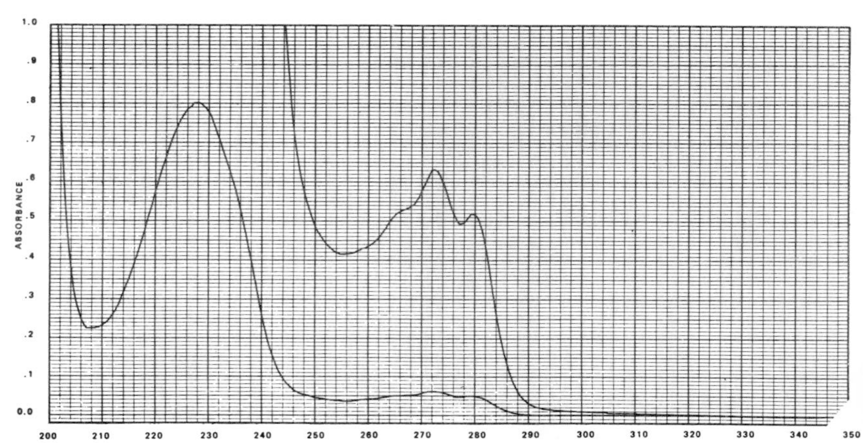

2684

SALICYLIC ACID, AMMONIUM SALT

$C_7H_9NO_3$

Mol. Wt. 155.15

Solvent: Methanol

λ Max. mμ	a_m	Cell mm	Conc. g/L
x	x	10	0.400
294	3900	10	0.040
225.5	6800	10	0.040

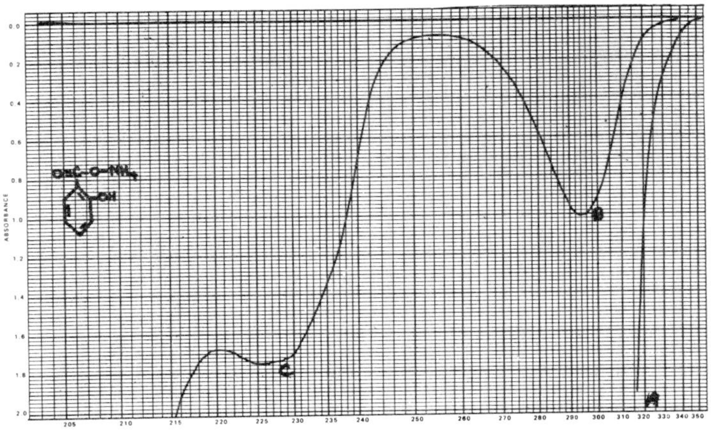

2685

λ Max. mμ	a_m	Cell mm	Conc. g/L

The aliphatic amine salts of aliphatic carboxylic acids (compounds 2685 through 2687) do not display any maxima in the near UV.

λ Max. mμ	a_m	Cell mm	Conc. g/L

N,N-DIMETHYL-p-PHENYLENEDIAMINE, OXALATE (2:1) 2688

$C_{16}H_{24}N_4 \cdot C_2H_2O_4$
Mol. Wt. 362.43
Solvent: Methanol

λ Max. mμ	a_m	Cell mm	Conc. g/L
306	4260	5	0.100
255	27580	1	0.100

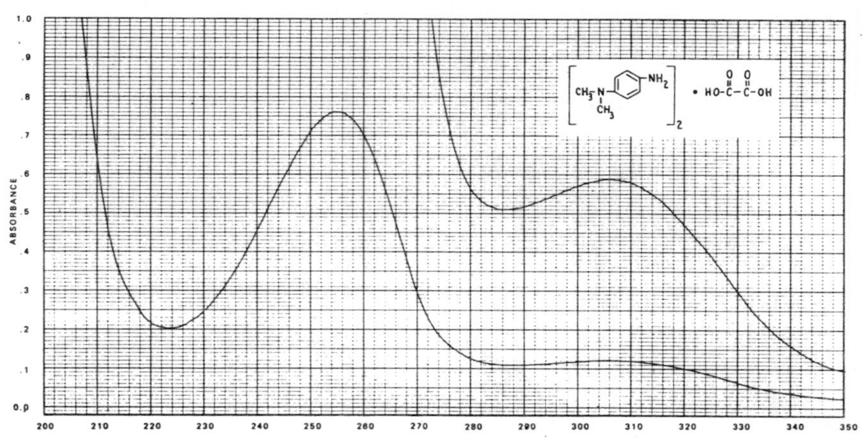

N,N-DIMETHYL-p-PHENYLENEDIAMINE, OXALATE (2:1) 2688

$C_{16}H_{24}N_4 \cdot C_2H_2O_4$
Mol. Wt. 362.43
Solvent: Methanol KOH

λ Max. mμ	a_m	Cell mm	Conc. g/L
309	4110	5	0.100
251	26200	1	0.100

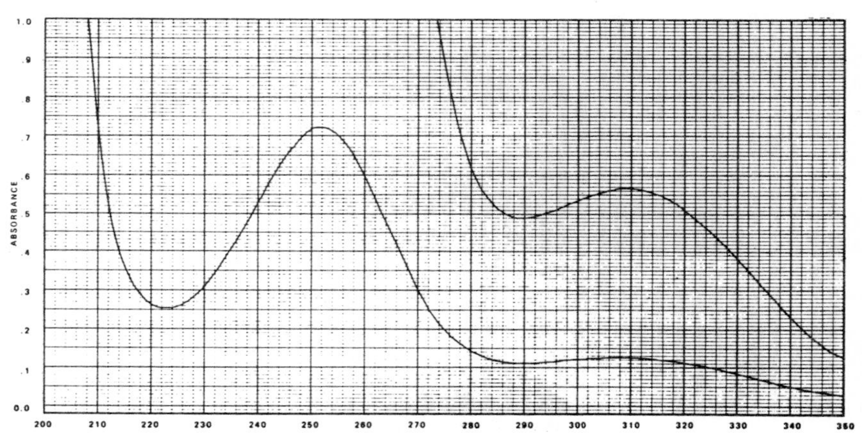

λ Max. mμ	a_m	Cell mm	Conc. g/L

THE ESTERS OF CARBOXYLIC ACIDS

Aliphatic Compounds

The aliphatic esters of aliphatic carboxylic acids do not produce any maxima over the near ultra-violet region. As a consequence, there are no spectra in this section for compounds 2689 through 2827 except for 2799, 2805, 2809, 2812, 2814, 2815 and 2826 which represent the olefinic esters discussed below.

Olefinic Esters

The esters of acrylic, fumaric and maleic acid and their alkyl substituted derivatives generally do not produce any maxima in the near UV, although a shoulder or weak maximum may be observed in the methanol solvent cut-off region from 200 - 220 mμ.

Aromatic Compounds

The benzyl and other aromatic esters in which the aromatic ring is insulated from the ester group by one or more saturated carbon atoms, give rise to UV spectra containing one major band near 258 mμ with benzenoid fine structure.

The aliphatic esters of benzoic acid produce spectra in the near UV quite similar to those of the benzoic acid salts i.e. a relatively strong absorption band near 225 mμ with a weaker benzenoid absorption near 270 mμ.

The esters of phthalic, isophthalic and terephthalic acid (compounds 2896 - 2909) illustrate the effect of substituent position on the intensity and wavelength of the major bands as shown in the following table.

Compound	$\lambda_{max}(\epsilon_{max})$	$\lambda_{max}(\epsilon_{max})$	Solvent	Spectrum
Dipentyl phthalate	226 (8070)	275 (1210)	Methanol	2897
Dimethyl isophthalate	228 * (12000)	280 (917)	Methanol	2901
Diethyl terephthalate	240 (22500)	284 (1960)	Cyclohexane	2907

*Shoulder

The addition of acid or base to the solutions of the esters does not result in any significant change in the spectra unless a different functional group is present that is sensitive to changes in pH.

2-HEXENOIC ACID, METHYL ESTER

2799

$C_7H_{12}O_2$

Mol. Wt. 128.17

Solvent: Methanol

λ Max. mμ	a_m	Cell mm	Conc. g/L
x	x	1	0.100

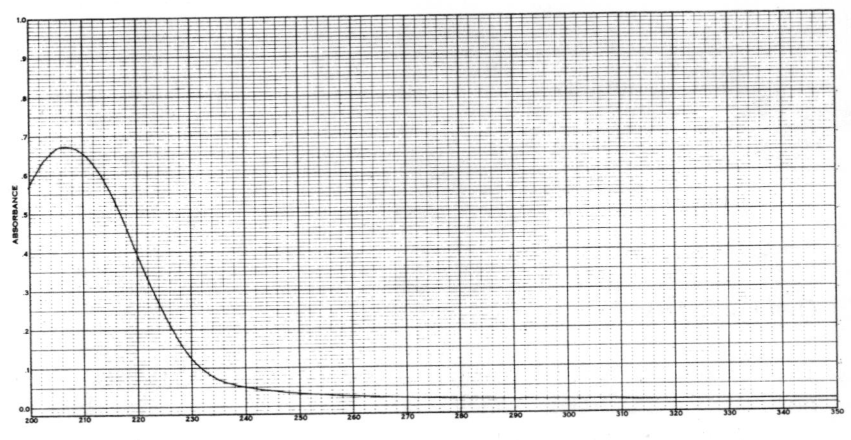

OXALIC ACID, DIALLYL ESTER

2805

$C_8H_{10}O_4$

Mol. Wt. 170.17

Solvent: Methanol

λ Max. mμ	a_m	Cell mm	Conc. g/L
x	x	10	0.100

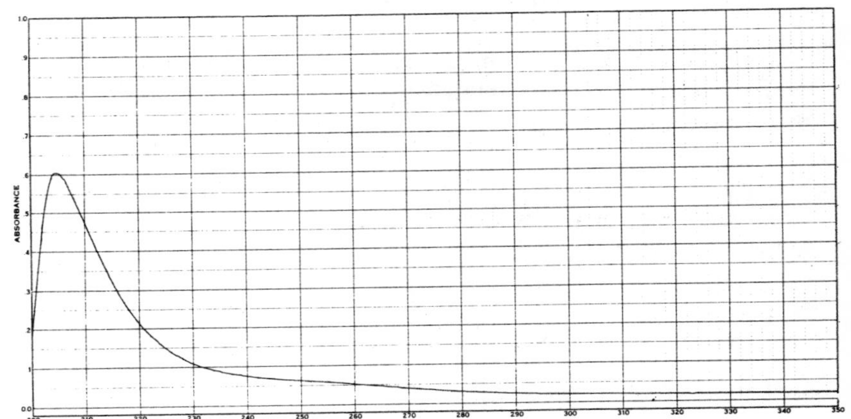

ACRYLIC ACID, DODECYL ESTER

2809

$C_{15}H_{28}O_2$

Mol. Wt. 240.39

Solvent: Isooctane

λ Max. mμ	a_m	Cell mm	Conc. g/L
243	75.0	10	1.890
x	x	10	0.189

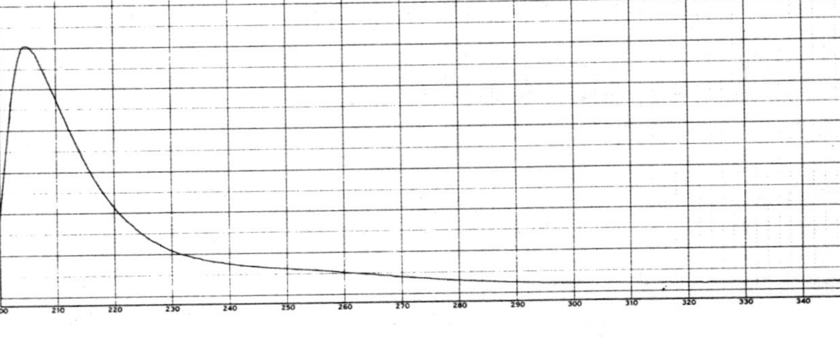

METHACRYLIC ACID, ISOBUTYL ESTER

2812

$C_8H_{14}O_2$
Mol. Wt. 142.20
Solvent: Methanol

λ Max. mμ	a_m	Cell mm	Conc. g/L
216.5	2700	5	0.100

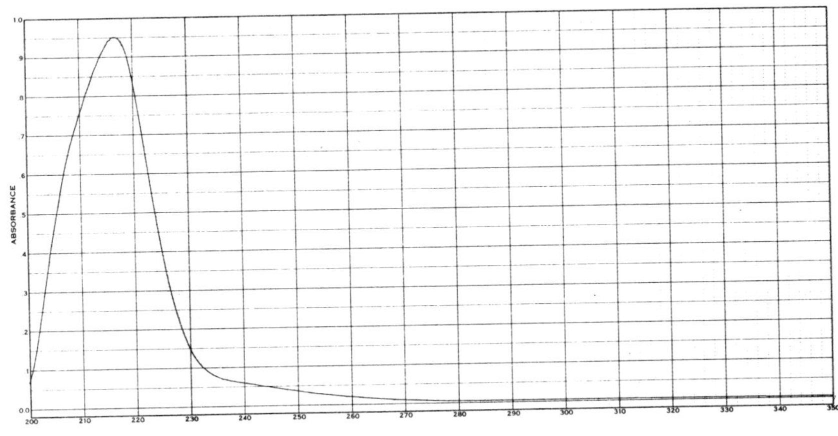

CROTONIC ACID, ETHYL ESTER

2814

$C_6H_{10}O_2$
Mol. Wt. 114.15
Solvent: Methanol

λ Max. mμ	a_m	Cell mm	Conc. g/L
x	x	1	0.100

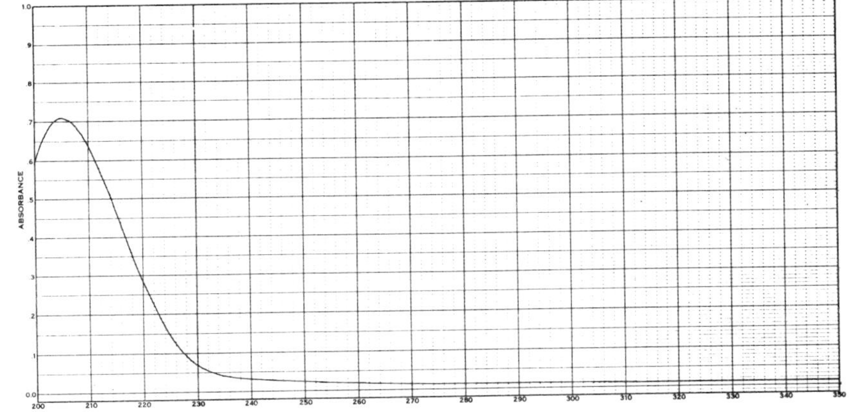

2-DECENOIC ACID, METHYL ESTER

2815

$C_{11}H_{20}O_2$
Mol. Wt. 184.28
Solvent: Methanol

λ Max. mμ	a_m	Cell mm	Conc. g/L
x	x	1	0.100

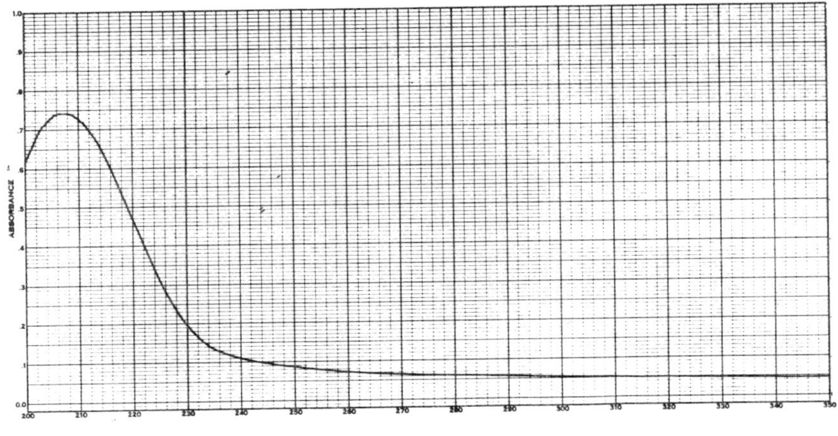

FUMARIC ACID, DIISOPROPYL ESTER

2826

$C_{10}H_{16}O_4$
Mol. Wt. 200.24
B.P. 108-109°C/10mm
Solvent: Methanol

λ Max. mμ	a_m	Cell mm	Conc. g/L
209	19300	2	0.0490

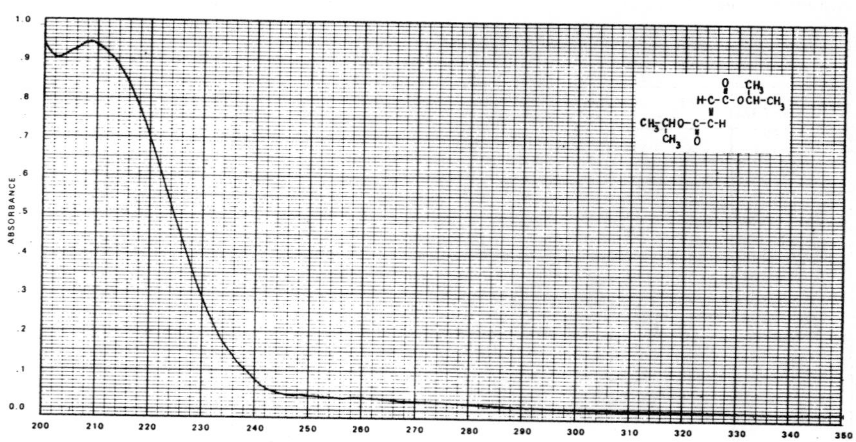

MALEIC ACID, DIALLYL ESTER

2829

$C_{10}H_{12}O_4$
Mol. Wt. 196.20
Solvent: Methanol

λ Max. mμ	a_m	Cell mm	Conc. g/L
213.5	3450	5	0.100

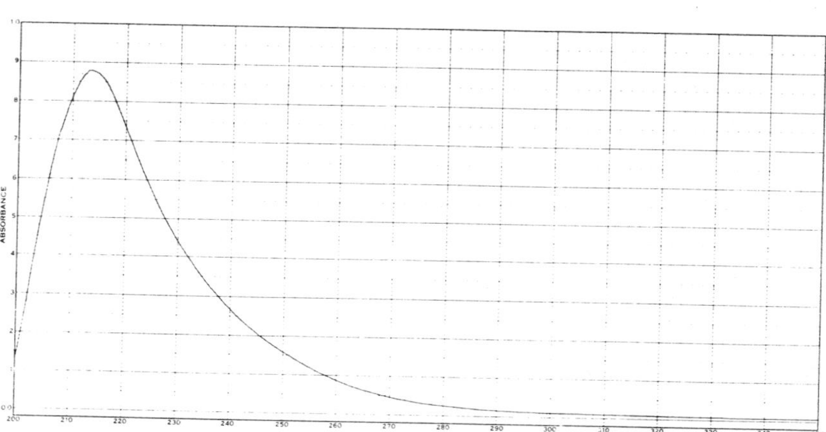

ETHENETETRACARBOXYLIC ACID, TETRAETHYL ESTER

2830

$C_{14}H_{20}O_8$
Mol. Wt. 316.31
Solvent: Cyclohexane

λ Max. mμ	a_m	Cell mm	Conc. g/L
x	x	10	1.830
x	x	10	0.183
x	x	10	0.018

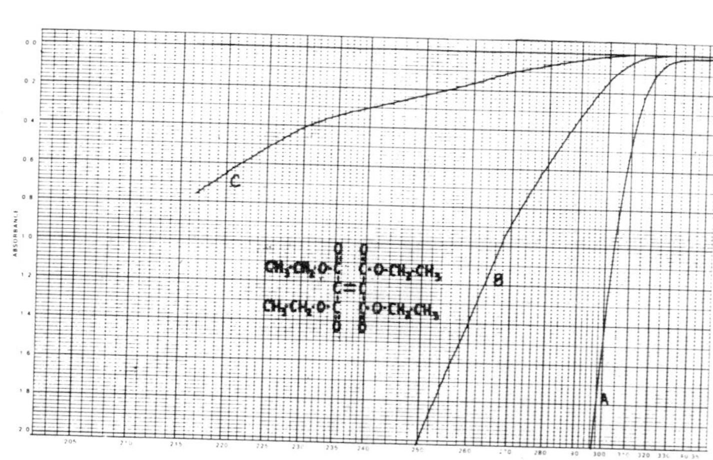

FORMIC ACID, PHENETHYL ESTER

2831

$C_9H_{10}O_2$

Mol. Wt. 150.18

Solvent: Cyclohexane

λ Max. mμ	a_m	Cell mm	Conc. g/L
x	x	10	1.876
267.5	98.7	10	0.563
264	155	10	0.563
258	192	10	0.563
252.5	152	10	0.563
247.5	109	10	0.563
237.5	60.8	10	0.563

ACETIC ACID, BENZYL ESTER

2832

$C_9H_{10}O_2$

Mol. Wt. 150.18

B.P. 213-215°C

Solvent: Methanol

λ Max. mμ	a_m	Cell mm	Conc. g/L
267	114	10	0.376
263	174	10	0.376
257	214	10	0.376
251.5	174	10	0.376
x	x	1	0.376

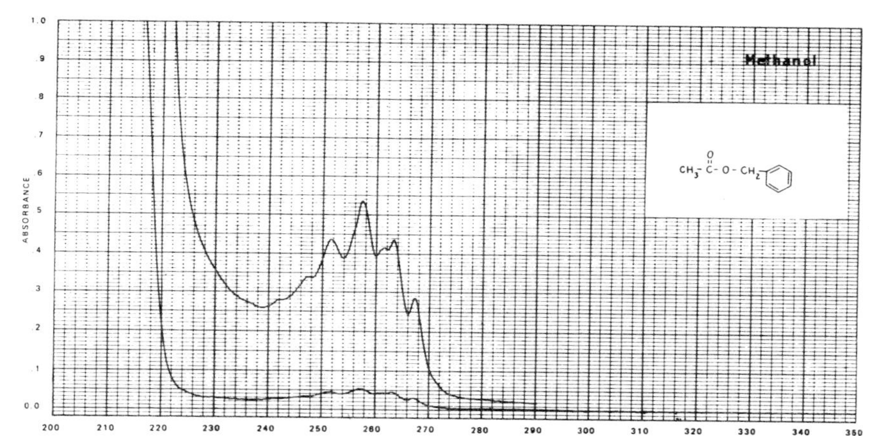

ACETIC ACID, PHENETHYL ESTER

2833

$C_{10}H_{12}O_2$

Mol. Wt. 164.20

B.P. 90-92°C/5mm

Solvent: Methanol

λ Max. mμ	a_m	Cell mm	Conc. g/L
264.5	207	40	0.100
259	264	40	0.100
253.5	238	40	0.100
x	x	1	0.100

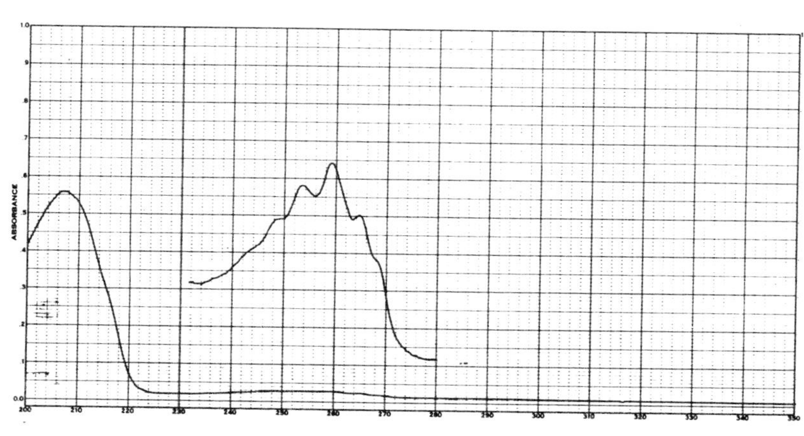

α-METHYLBENZYL ALCOHOL, ACETATE

2834

$C_{10}H_{12}O_2$
Mol. Wt. 164.21
Solvent: Methanol

λ Max. mμ	a_m	Cell mm	Conc. g/L
263	159	10	0.671
257.5	213	10	0.671
251	195	10	0.671
246	166	10	0.671

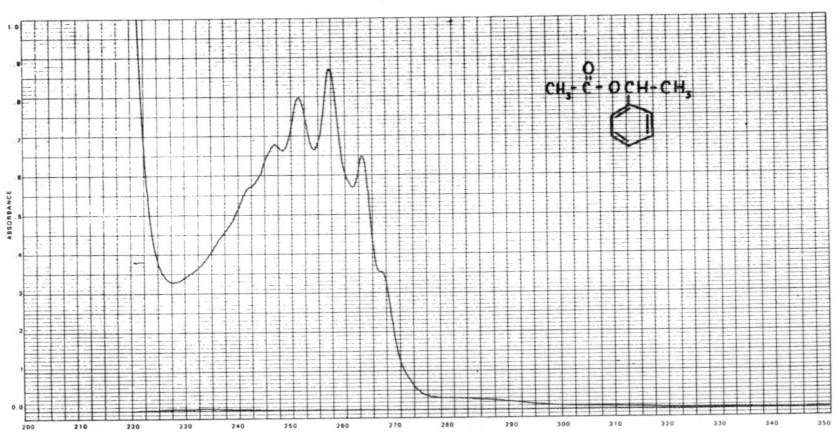

PROPIONIC ACID, PHENETHYL ESTER

2835

$C_{11}H_{14}O_2$
Mol. Wt. 178.22
Solvent: Cyclohexane

λ Max. mμ	a_m	Cell mm	Conc. g/L
266.5	113	10	1.040
263.5	163	10	1.040
257.5	218	10	1.040
252	166	10	1.040
247	115	10	1.040

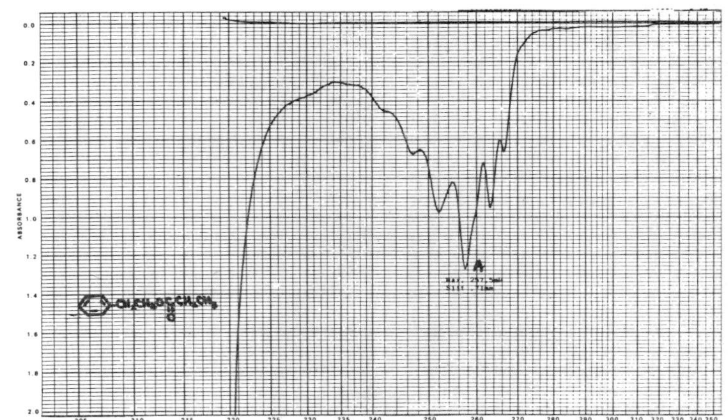

ISOBUTYRIC ACID, PHENETHYL ESTER

2836

$C_{12}H_{16}O_2$
Mol. Wt. 192.25
Solvent: Cyclohexane

λ Max. mμ	a_m	Cell mm	Conc. g/L
267.5	108	10	1.677
264	150	10	1.677
258	189	10	1.677
252.5	156	10	1.677
247.5	116	10	1.677
242	86.0	10	1.677
236.5	75.7	10	1.677
x	x	10	0.134

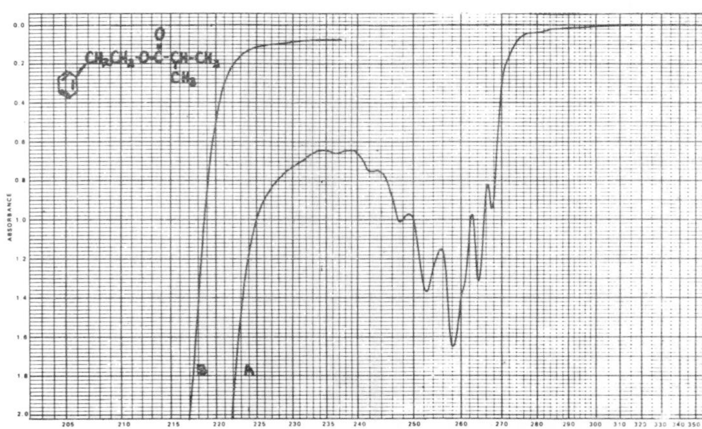

ISOVALERIC ACID, BENZYL ESTER

2837

$C_{12}H_{16}O_2$
Mol. Wt. 192.26
Solvent: Methanol

λ Max. mμ	a_m	Cell mm	Conc. g/L
263	211	20	0.100
257.5	244	20	0.100
252	200	20	0.100
x	x	2	0.100

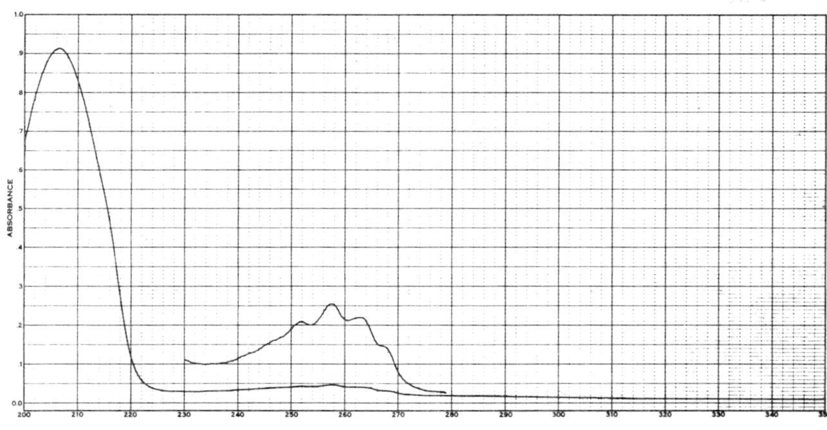

ISOVALERIC ACID, PHENETHYL ESTER

2838

$C_{13}H_{18}O_2$
Mol. Wt. 206.28
Solvent: Methanol

λ Max. mμ	a_m	Cell mm	Conc. g/L
266.5	127	20	0.276
263	172	20	0.276
257	229	20	0.276
251.5	215	20	0.276
246.5	191	20	0.276
240.5	176	20	0.276
x	x	1	0.276

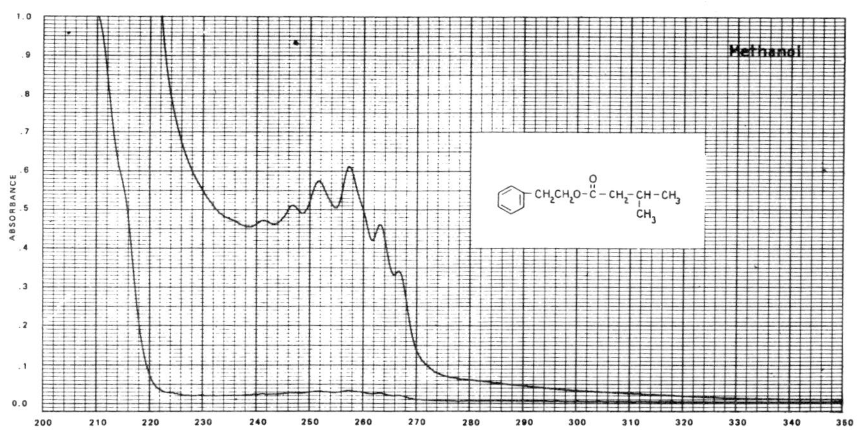

p-METHOXYBENZYL ALCOHOL, ACETATE

2839

$C_{10}H_{12}O_3$
Mol. Wt. 180.21
B.P. 110-117°C
Solvent: Methanol

λ Max. mμ	a_m	Cell mm	Conc. g/L
280	1320	5	0.178
273.5	1520	5	0.178
226.5	13000	1	0.0890

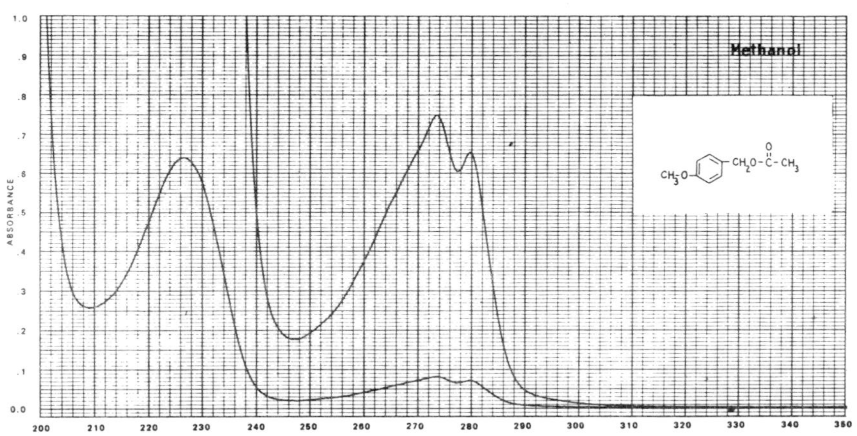

ACETIC ACID, PHENACYL ESTER

2840

$C_{10}H_{10}O_3$
Mol. Wt. 178.19
M.P. 47-48°C
Solvent: Methanol

λ Max. mμ	a_m	Cell mm	Conc. g/L
279.5	11500	1	0.100
242	13000	1	0.100

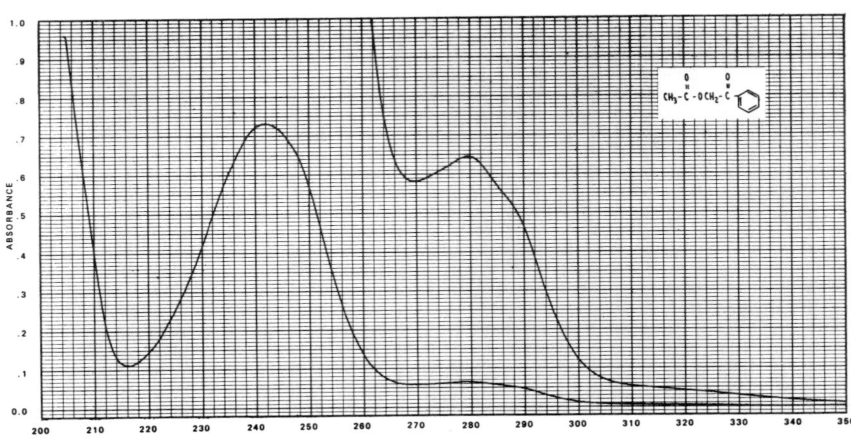

ACETIC ACID, CINNAMYL ESTER

2841

$C_{11}H_{12}O_2$
Mol. Wt. 176.22
B.P. 122-124°C/5mm
Solvent: Methanol

λ Max. mμ	a_m	Cell mm	Conc. g/L
291	1130	5	0.188
282	1440	5	0.188
250	17100	1	0.0938
215	13000	1	0.0938

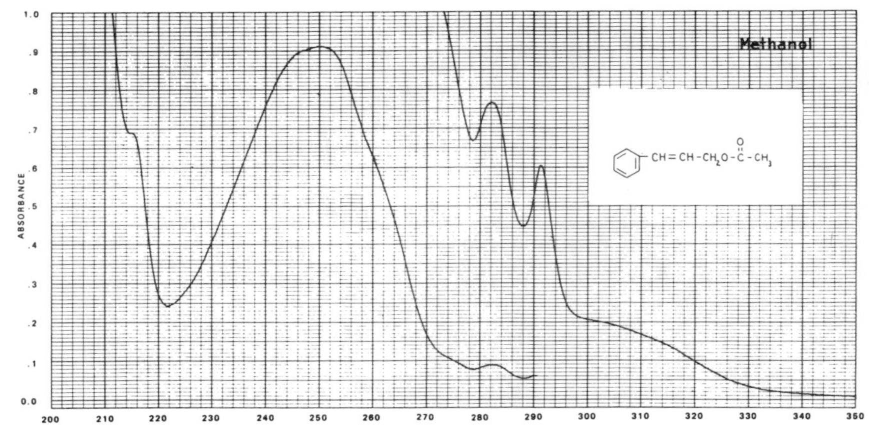

BUTYRIC ACID, CINNAMYL ESTER

2842

$C_{13}H_{16}O_2$
Mol. Wt. 264.27
Solvent: Methanol

λ Max. mμ	a_m	Cell mm	Conc. g/L
286	940	10	0.104
277	1350	10	0.104
244.5	17600	1	0.104

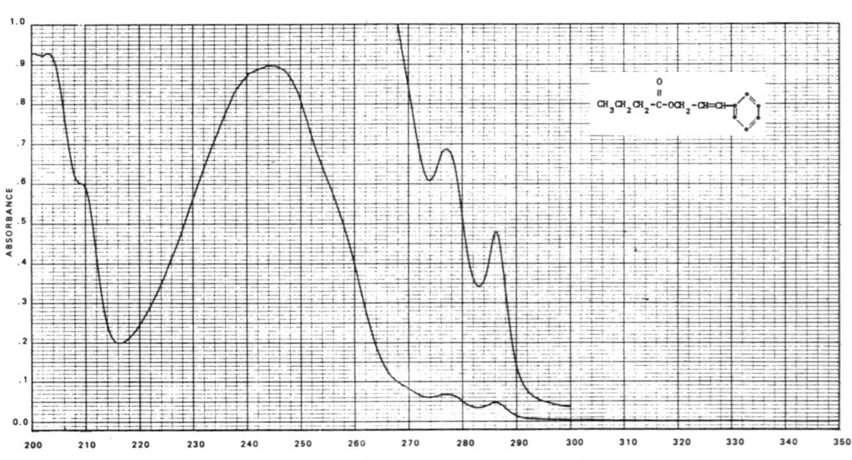

ISOVALERIC ACID, CINNAMYL ESTER

2843

$C_{14}H_{18}O_2$
Mol. Wt. 218.28
Solvent: Cyclohexane

λ Max. mμ	a_m	Cell mm	Conc. g/L
x	x	10	2.180
280.5	428	10	0.653
273	475	10	0.653
230.5	3790	10	0.065

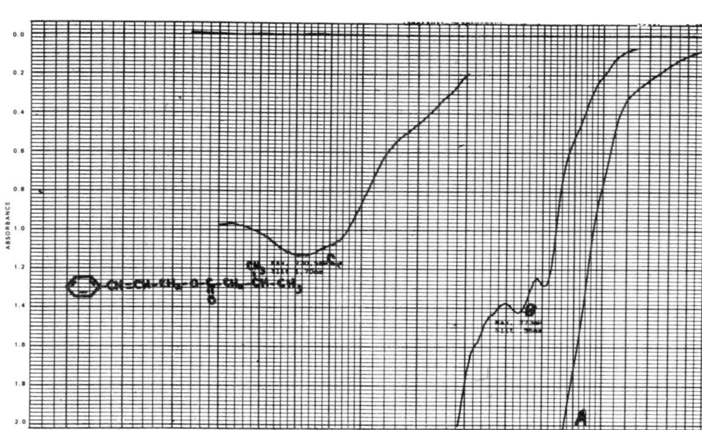

BROMOACETIC ACID, BENZYL ESTER

2844

$C_9H_9BrO_2$
Mol. Wt. 229.09
Solvent: Methanol

λ Max. mμ	a_m	Cell mm	Conc. g/L
x	x	10	2.312
267.5	139	10	0.694
263	214	10	0.694
262	211	10	0.694
257.5	276	10	0.694
251	264	10	0.694
x	x	10	0.139

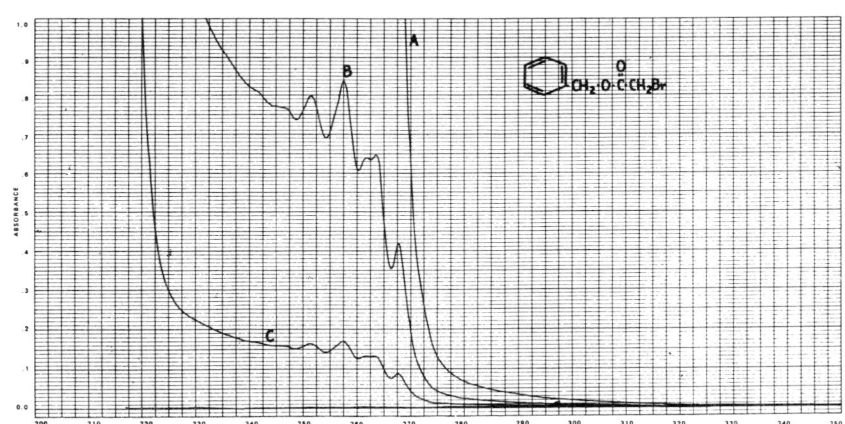

ACRYLIC ACID, BENZYL ESTER

2845

$C_{10}H_{10}O_2$
Mol. Wt. 162.19
B.R. 110-111°C/8mm (lit.)
Solvent: Cyclohexane

λ Max. mμ	a_m	Cell mm	Conc. g/L
267	137	10	2.250
263.5	224	10	0.674
257	276	10	0.674
251	245	10	0.674
x	x	10	0.007

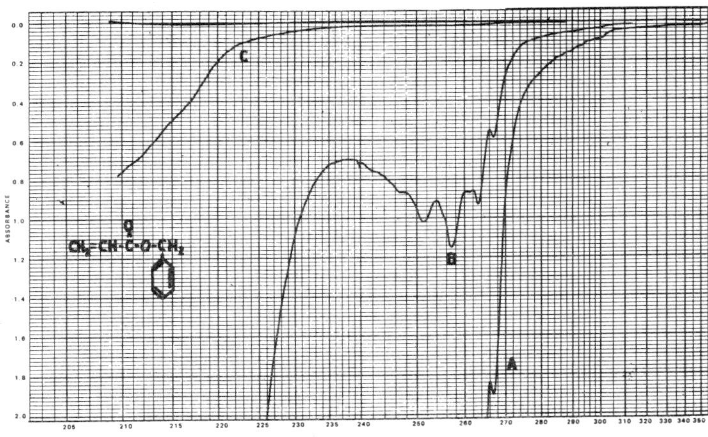

METHACRYLIC ACID, BENZYL ESTER

2846

$C_{11}H_{12}O_2$
Mol. Wt. 176.22
B.P. 231-233°C
Solvent: Methanol

λ Max. mμ	a_m	Cell mm	Conc. g/L
266.5	152	20	0.195
260	232	20	0.195
256.5	299	20	0.195
250.5	294	20	0.195
207.5	13000	0.5	0.195

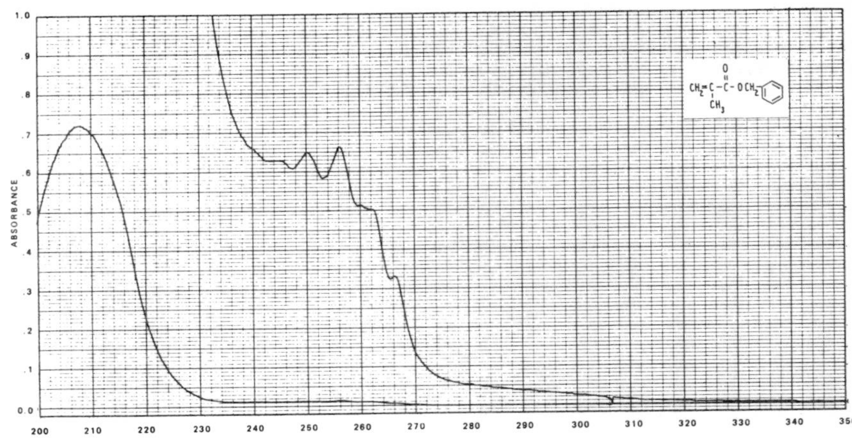

PHENYLACETIC ACID, BUTYL ESTER

2847

$C_{12}H_{16}O_2$
Mol. Wt. 192.25
Solvent: Cyclohexane

λ Max. mμ	a_m	Cell mm	Conc. g/L
x	x	10	1.840
264	224	10	0.736
257.5	336	10	0.736
252	329	10	0.736
247	295	10	0.736
x	x	10	0.184

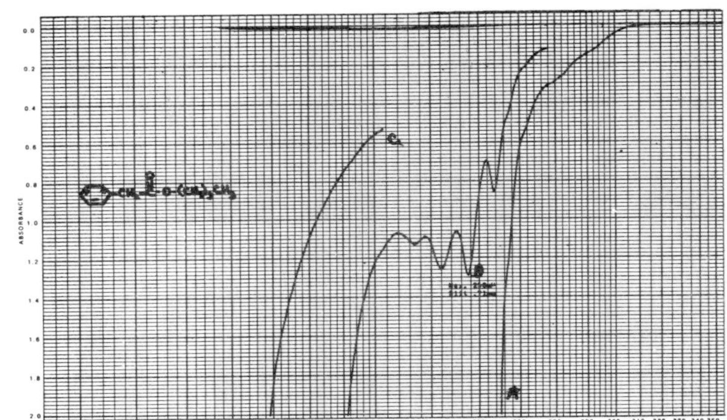

PHENYLACETIC ACID, OCTYL ESTER

2848

$C_{16}H_{24}O_2$
Mol. Wt. 248.37
Solvent: Methanol

λ Max. mμ	a_m	Cell mm	Conc. g/L
263	286	40	0.100
257	346	40	0.100
251	310	40	0.100
246	279	40	0.100
x	x	1	0.100

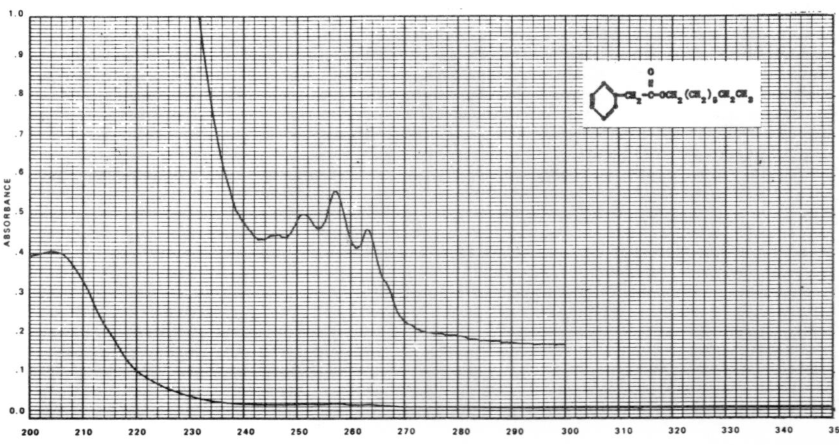

4-PHENYLBUTYRIC ACID, METHYL ESTER 2849

$C_{11}H_{14}O_2$
Mol. Wt. 178.23
Solvent: Methanol

λ Max. mμ	a_m	Cell mm	Conc. g/L
267	276	20	0.100
257	461	20	0.100
251.5	519	20	0.100
247	508	20	0.100
x	x	1	0.100

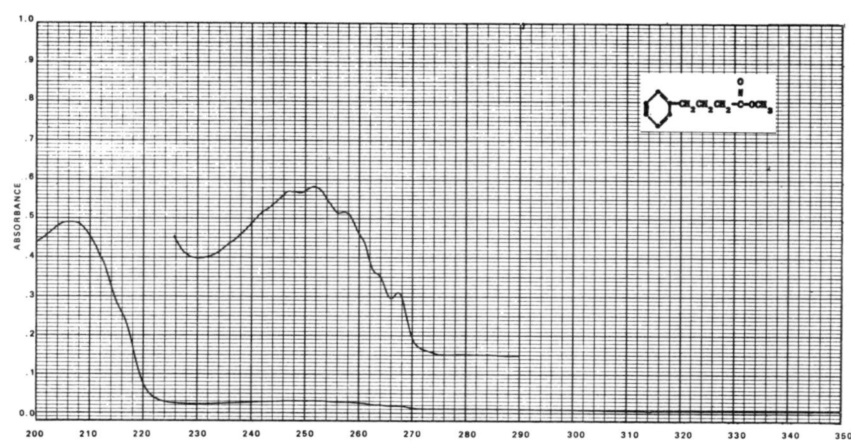

3-PHENYLHYDRACRYLIC ACID, ETHYL ESTER 2850

$C_{11}H_{14}O_3$
Mol. Wt. 194.23
Solvent: Methanol

λ Max. mμ	a_m	Cell mm	Conc. g/L
270.5	6150	10	0.021
265.5	6300	10	0.021
261.5	6600	10	0.021
255.5	6750	10	0.021
249.5	6550	10	0.021

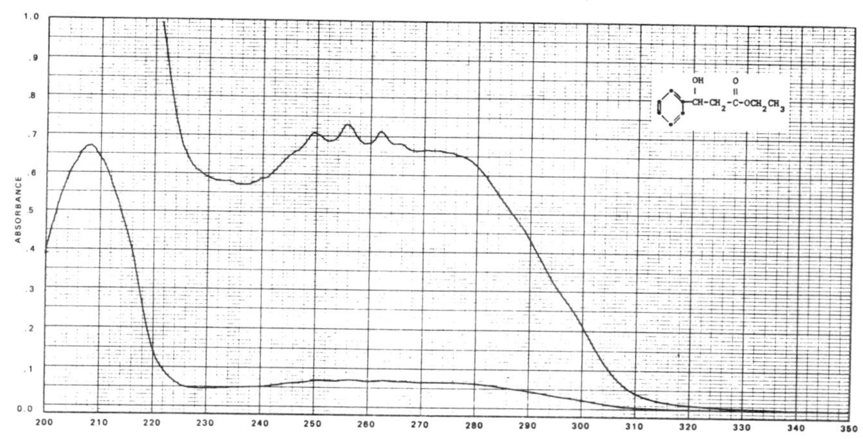

HIPPURIC ACID, METHYL ESTER 2851

$C_{10}H_{11}NO_3$
Mol. Wt. 193.20
M.P. 80°C
Solvent: Methanol

λ Max. mμ	a_m	Cell mm	Conc. g/L
226.5	11500	1	0.100

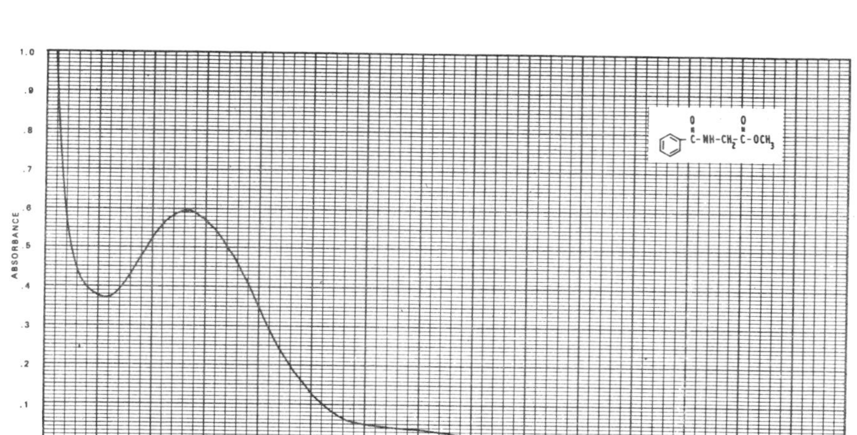

METHYLPHENYLMALONIC ACID, DIETHYL ESTER 2852

$C_{14}H_{18}O_4$
Mol. Wt. 250.30
Solvent: Methanol

λ Max. mμ	a_m	Cell mm	Conc. g/L
338	10.1	10	1.036
264	169	10	1.036
258	199	10	1.036
251.5	174	10	1.036
207	11700	10	0.010

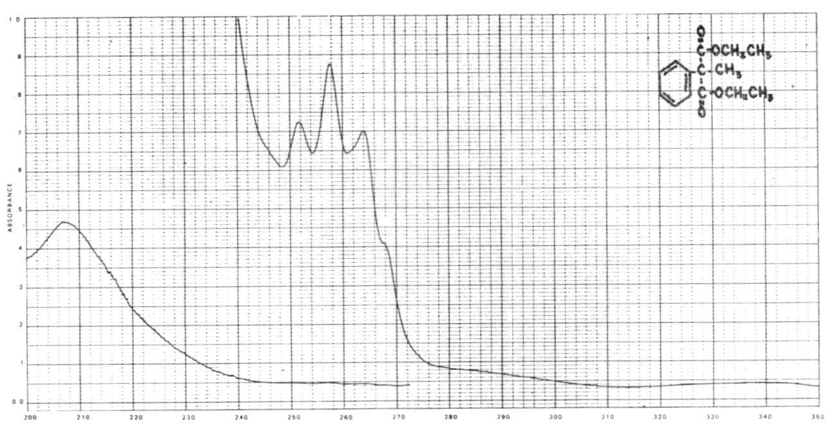

3,3′-(BENZYLIMINO)DIPROPIONIC ACID, DIETHYL ESTER 2853

$C_{17}H_{25}NO_4$
Mol. Wt. 307.39
Solvent: Methanol

λ Max. mμ	a_m	Cell mm	Conc. g/L
280	328	10	0.524
268	339	10	0.524
264	374	10	0.524
258	397	10	0.524
252	382	10	0.524

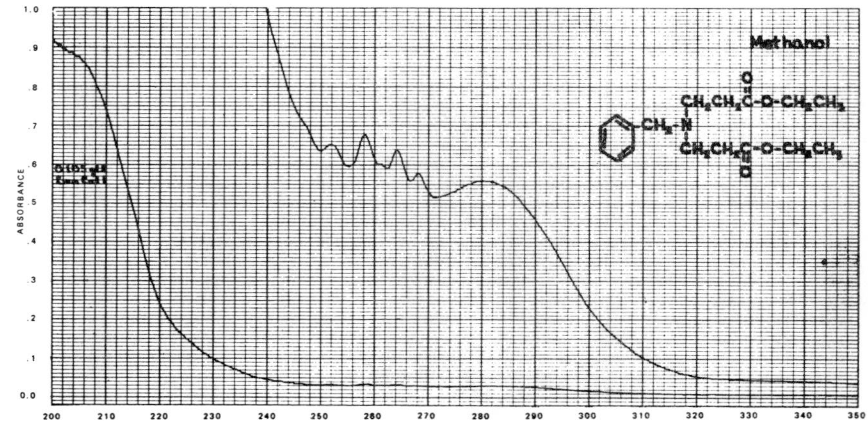

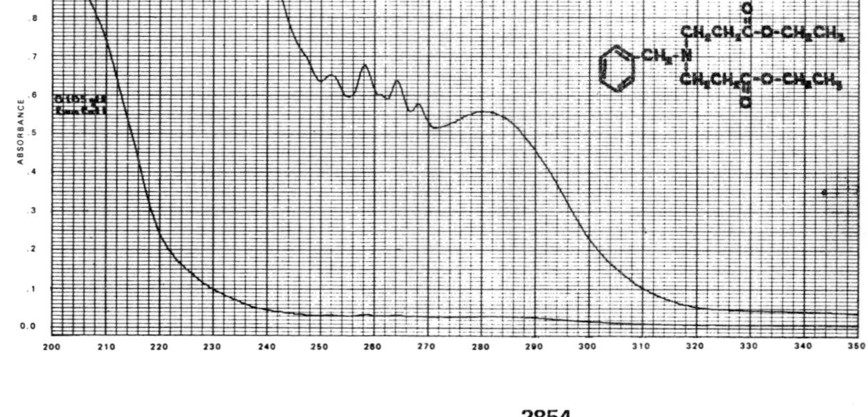

o-TOLYLACETIC ACID, ETHYL ESTER 2854

$C_{11}H_{14}O_2$
Mol. Wt. 178.23
Solvent: Methanol

λ Max. mμ	a_m	Cell mm	Conc. g/L
271	251	20	0.100
263	315	20	0.100
x	x	2	0.100

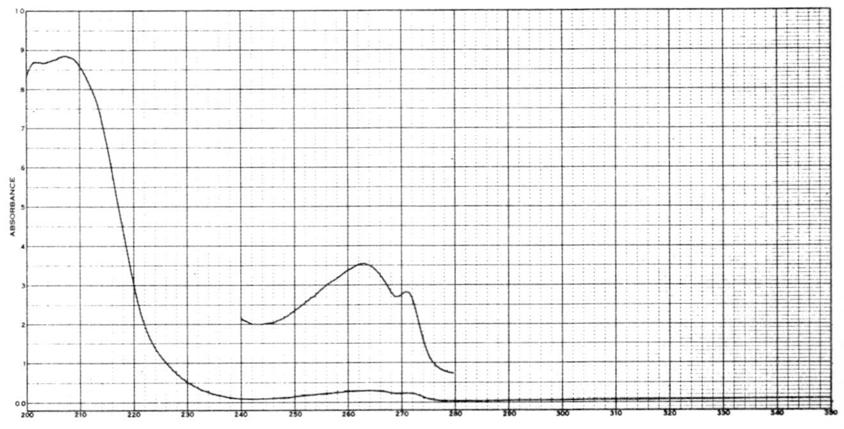

FLUORENE-9-CARBOXYLIC ACID, METHYL ESTER

2855

$C_{15}H_{12}O_2$
Mol. Wt. 224.26
M.P. 66-68°C
Solvent: Methanol

λ Max. mμ	a_m	Cell mm	Conc. g/L
301	3630	1	0.100
289.5	3660	1	0.100
265	18000	1	0.100
229	8840	1	0.100

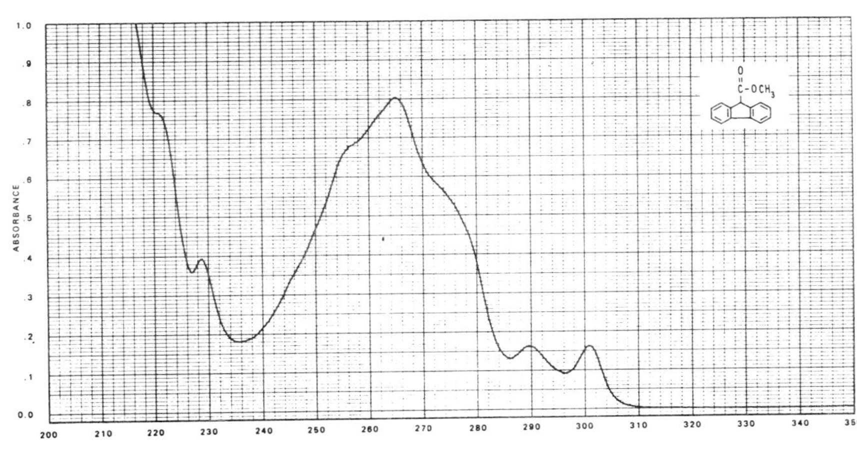

β-METHYLCINNAMIC ACID, ETHYL ESTER

2856

$C_{12}H_{14}O_2$
Mol. Wt. 190.24
B.P. 123-125°C/6mm
Solvent: Methanol

λ Max. mμ	a_m	Cell mm	Conc. g/L
262.5	14700	1	0.105
206.5	13600	1	0.105

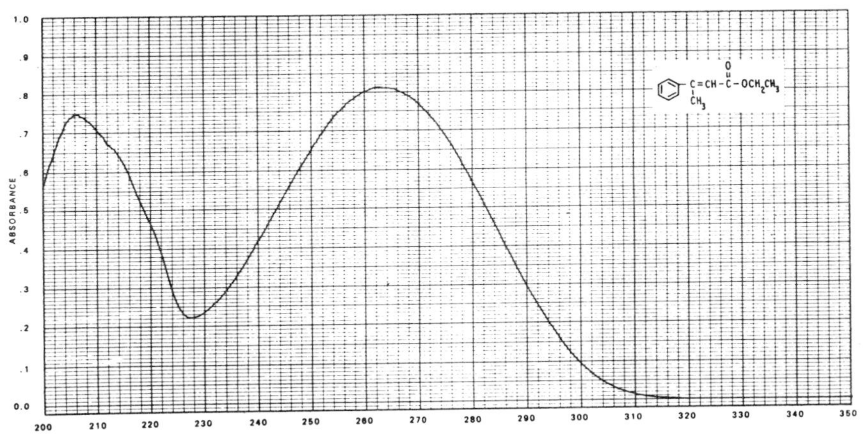

CINNAMIC ACID, CYCLOHEXYL ESTER

2857

$C_{15}H_{18}O_2$
Mol. Wt. 230.31
Solvent: Methanol

λ Max. mμ	a_m	Cell mm	Conc. g/L
275	22100	1	0.0800
221.5	13600	1	0.0800
216	16100	1	0.0800
204.5	14700	1	0.0800

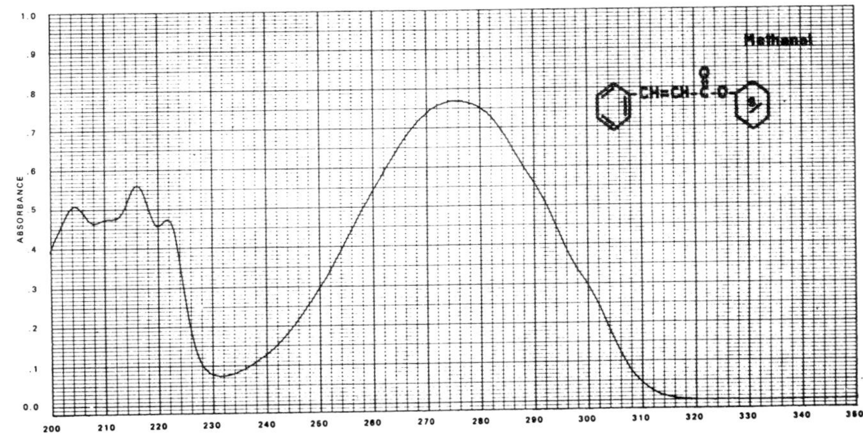

α-CYANOCINNAMIC ACID, ETHYL ESTER

2858

$C_{12}H_{11}NO_2$
Mol. Wt. 201.23
M.P. 48.5-49.5°C
Solvent: Methanol

λ Max. mμ	a_m	Cell mm	Conc. g/L
302	21300	1	0.050
228	8610	1	0.050
223	9140	1	0.050

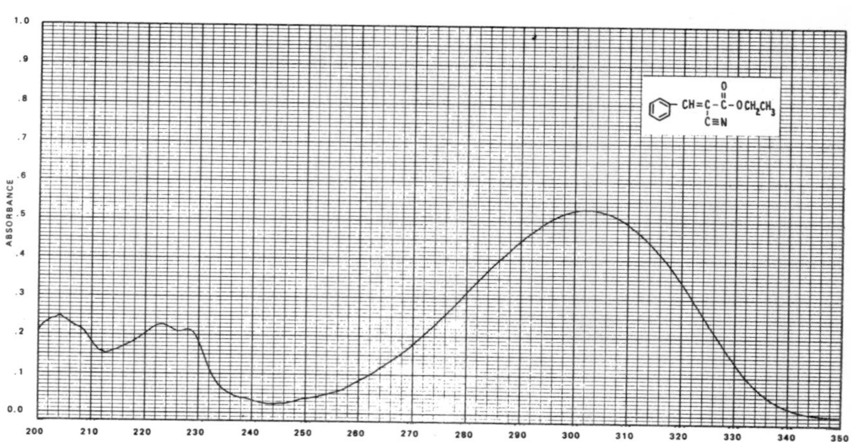

(TRIPHENYLPHOSPHORANYLIDENE)ACETIC ACID, METHYL ESTER

2859

$C_{21}H_{19}O_2P$
Mol. Wt. 334.36
M.P. 170-172°C
Solvent: Methanol

λ Max. mμ	a_m	Cell mm	Conc. g/L
272	1770	10	0.100
265.5	2090	10	0.100
259.5	1610	10	0.100
223	26100	1	0.100

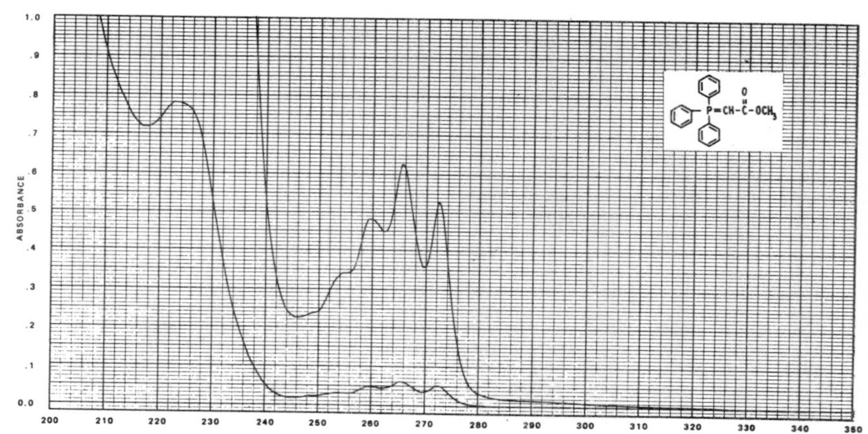

PHENYLACETIC ACID, PHENETHYL ESTER

2860

$C_{16}H_{16}O_2$
Mol. Wt. 240.30
Solvent: Methanol

λ Max. mμ	a_m	Cell mm	Conc. g/L
264	299	10	0.452
258	397	10	0.452
252	345	10	0.452
247	300	10	0.452
x	x	1	0.452

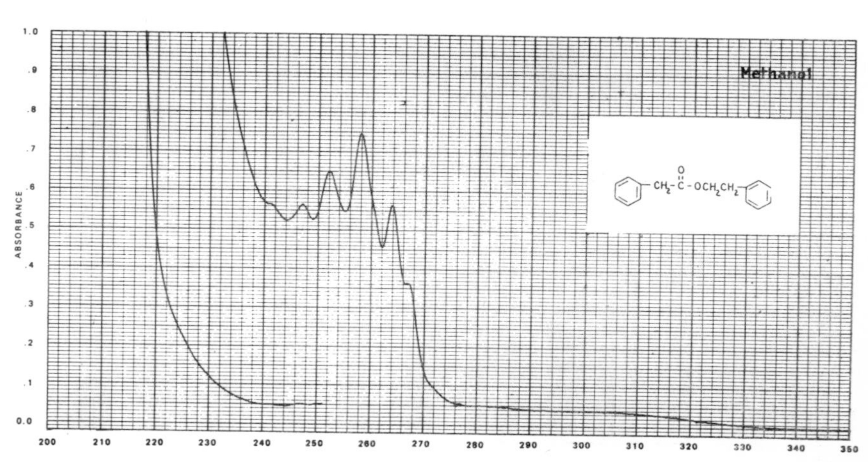

CINNAMIC ACID, BENZYL ESTER

2861

$C_{16}H_{14}O_2$

Mol. Wt. 238.27

M.P. 39°C B.P. 244°C/25mm

Solvent: Methanol

λ Max. mμ	a_m	Cell mm	Conc. g/L
280	23900	10	0.008
225	15700	10	0.008
218.5	21300	10	0.008
208	22000	10	0.008

CINNAMIC ACID, PHENETHYL ESTER

2862

$C_{17}H_{16}O_2$

Mol. Wt. 252.32

M.P. 56-57°C

Solvent: Methanol

λ Max. mμ	a_m	Cell mm	Conc. g/L
276.5	24100	1	0.100
221.5	14800	1	0.100
215.5	20500	1	0.100
204.5	24500	1	0.100

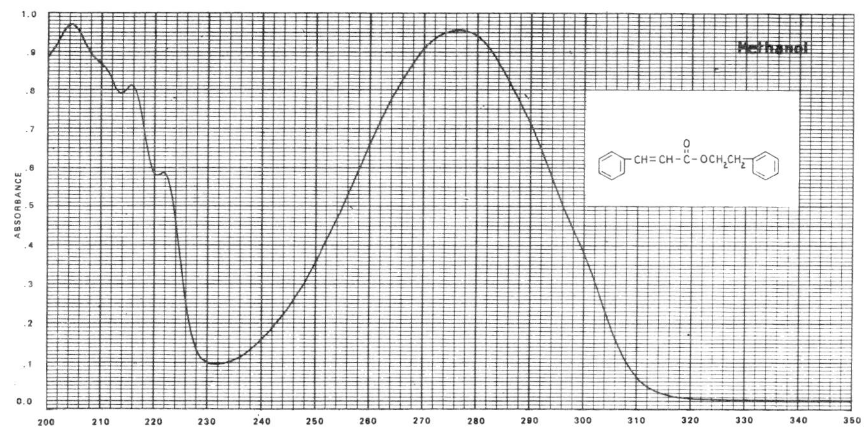

BENZOIC ACID, PROPYL ESTER

2863

$C_{10}H_{12}O_2$

Mol. Wt. 164.21

B.P. 227-228°C

Solvent: Methanol

λ Max. mμ	a_m	Cell mm	Conc. g/L
277.5	707	5	0.2663
271	881	5	0.2663
226	11500	0.5	0.2663

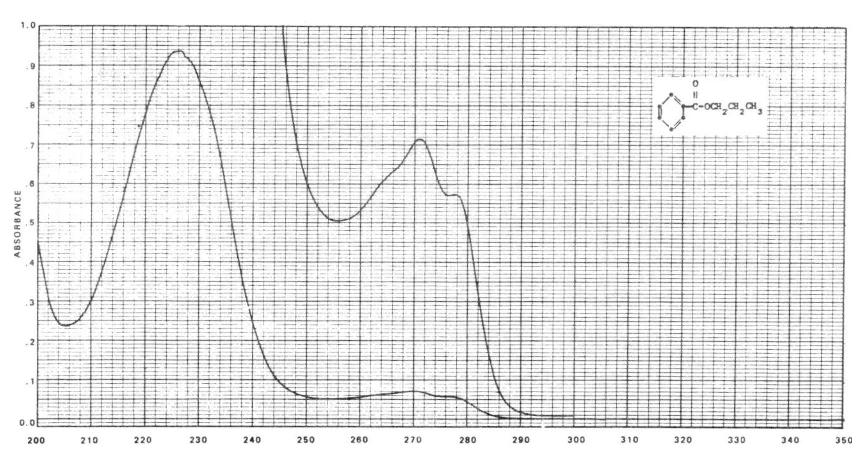

BENZOIC ACID, ISOBUTYL ESTER

2864

$C_{11}H_{14}O_2$

Mol. Wt. 178.23

Solvent: Methanol

λ Max. mμ	a_m	Cell mm	Conc. g/L
306	89.0	20	0.159
280	175	5	0.159
272.5	213	5	0.159
228.5	28200	2	0.0159

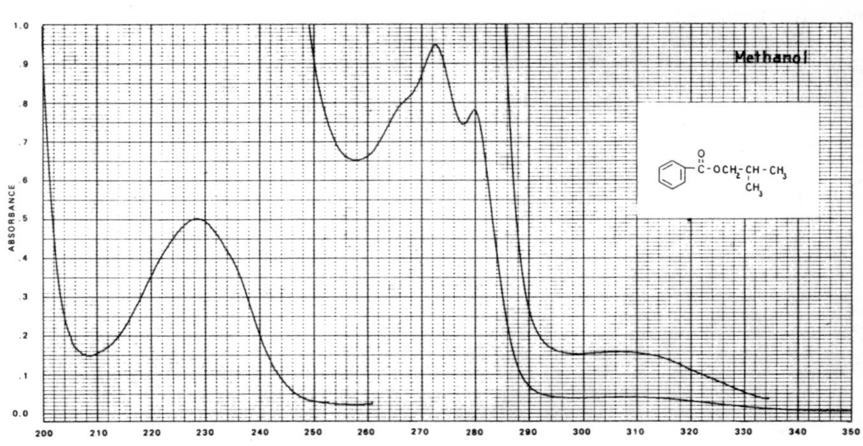

BENZOIC ACID, 2-(DIMETHYLAMINO)ETHYL ESTER

2865

$C_{11}H_{15}NO_2$

Mol. Wt. 193.25

B.P. 132-133°C/9mm

Solvent: Methanol

λ Max. mμ	a_m	Cell mm	Conc. g/L
278	383	10	0.348
271.5	505	10	0.348
226.5	13100	1	0.087

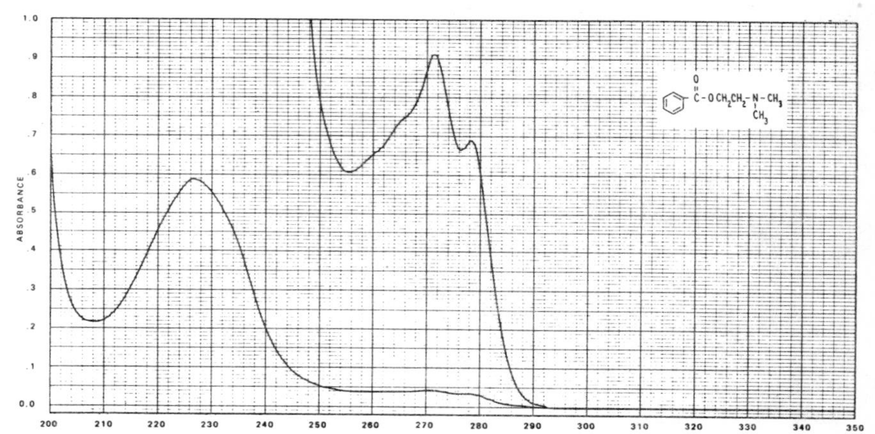

BENZOIC ACID, PHENETHYL ESTER

2866

$C_{15}H_{14}O_2$

Mol. Wt. 226.28

Solvent: Methanol

λ Max. mμ	a_m	Cell mm	Conc. g/L
272	923	10	0.1275
267	907	10	0.1275
263	903	10	0.1275
257	932	10	0.1275
228	13500	1	0.1275

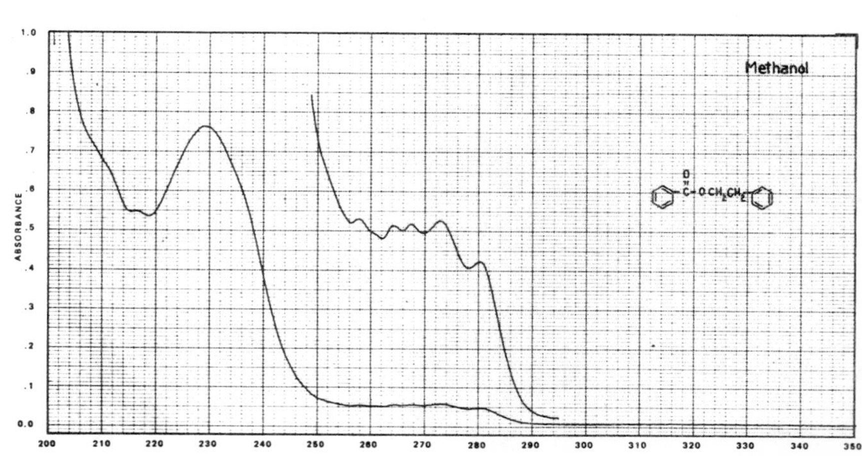

DIETHYLENE GLYCOL, DIBENZOATE 2867

$C_{18}H_{18}O_5$
Mol. Wt. 314.34
B.P. 200-205°C
Solvent: Methanol

λ Max. mμ	a_m	Cell mm	Conc. g/L
281.0	1520	1	1.00
273.0	1850	1	1.00
228.5	25600	1	0.100

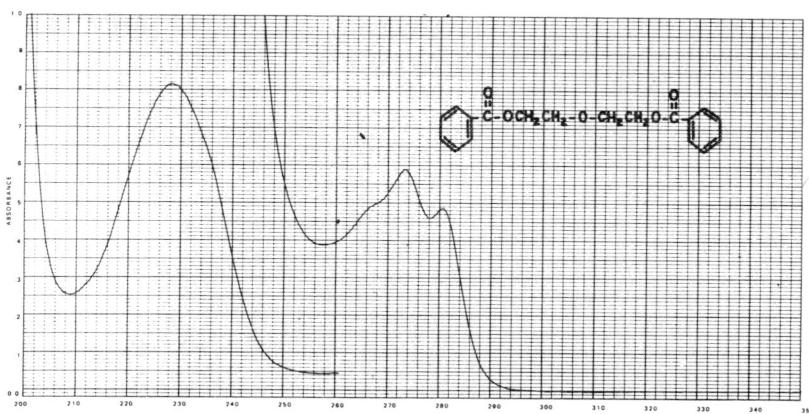

8-QUINOLINOL, BENZOATE 2868

$C_{16}H_{11}NO_2$
Mol. Wt. 249.27
Solvent: Methanol

λ Max. mμ	a_m	Cell mm	Conc. g/L
310	3250	4	0.100
280	2870	4	0.100
272	2910	4	0.100
240	39200	0.5	0.100

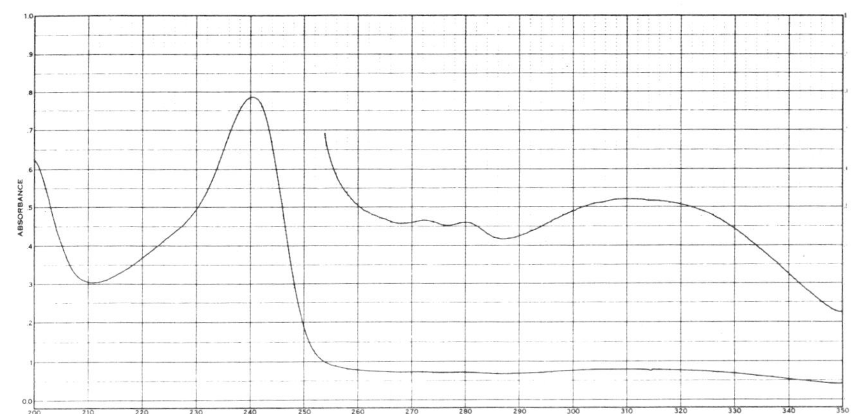

8-QUINOLINOL, BENZOATE 2868

$C_{16}H_{11}NO_2$
Mol. Wt. 249.27
Solvent: Methanol HCl

λ Max. mμ	a_m	Cell mm	Conc. g/L
362	1670	10	0.100
319	1280	10	0.100
308	1340	10	0.100
217	1250	10	0.100
253	38800	0.5	0.100
223	15800	0.5	0.100

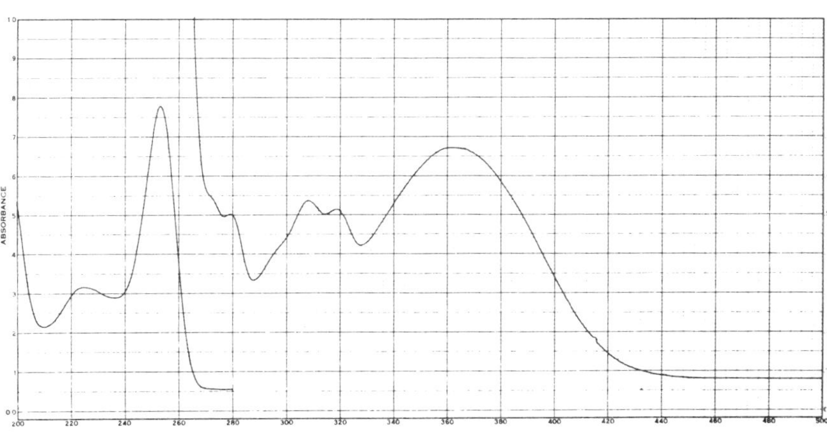

o-TOLUIC ACID, METHYL ESTER

2869

$C_9H_{10}O_2$

Mol. Wt. 150.18

B.P. 97-99°C/15mm

Solvent: Methanol

λ Max. mμ	a_m	Cell mm	Conc. g/L
279	1190	5	0.149
230	8160	1	0.149

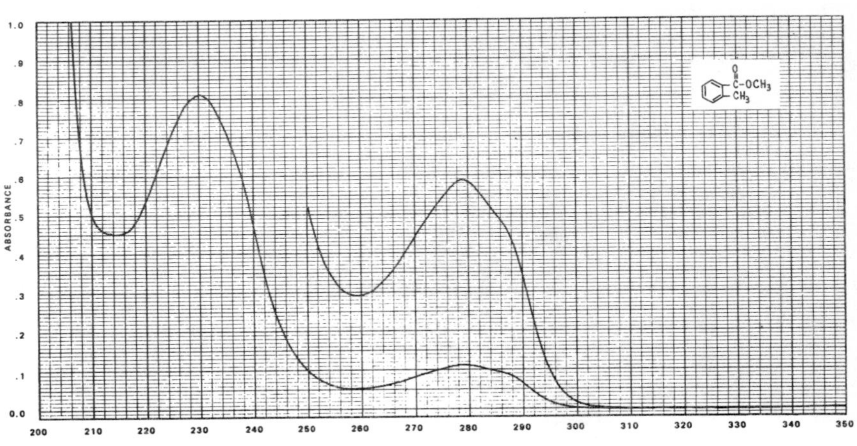

p-tert-BUTYLBENZOIC ACID, ETHYL ESTER

2870

$C_{13}H_{18}O_2$

Mol. Wt. 206.29

Solvent: Methanol

λ Max. mμ	a_m	Cell mm	Conc. g/L
238	46300	2.5	0.010

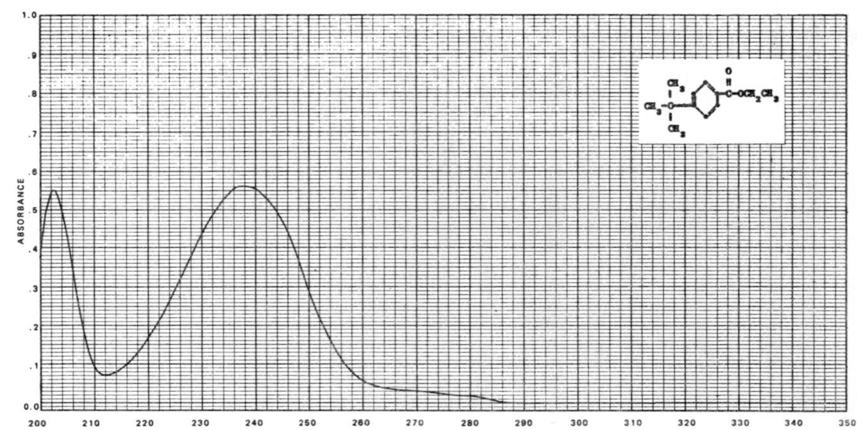

m-FLUOROBENZOIC ACID, ETHYL ESTER

2871

$C_9H_9FO_2$

Mol. Wt. 168.17

B.P. 94-95°C/16mm

Solvent: Methanol

λ Max. mμ	a_m	Cell mm	Conc. g/L
283.5	1440	1	1.00
276	1670	1	1.00
226	1120	1	0.0800

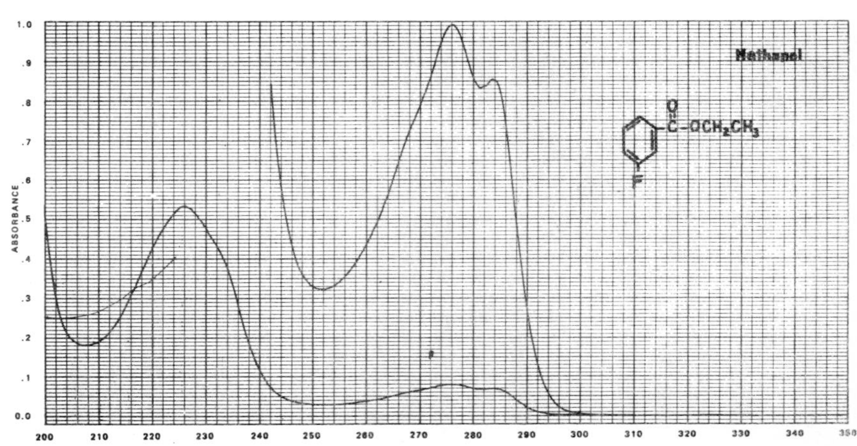

o-CHLOROBENZOIC ACID, METHYL ESTER

2872

$C_8H_7ClO_2$

Mol. Wt. 170.60

B.P. 110-112°C/10mm

Solvent: Methanol

λ Max. mμ	a_m	Cell mm	Conc. g/L
281	795	5	0.21050
227	54	1	0.21050
x	x	1	0.04210

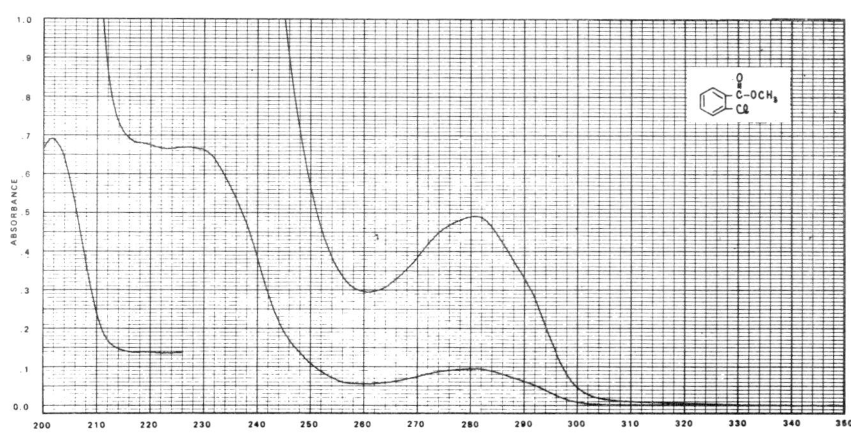

m-CHLOROBENZOIC ACID, METHYL ESTER

2873

$C_8H_7ClO_2$

Mol. Wt. 170.60

M.P. 18-19°C

Solvent: Methanol

λ Max. mμ	a_m	Cell mm	Conc. g/L
289.5	1020	2	0.439
281.5	1170	2	0.439
229.5	9870	1	0.088

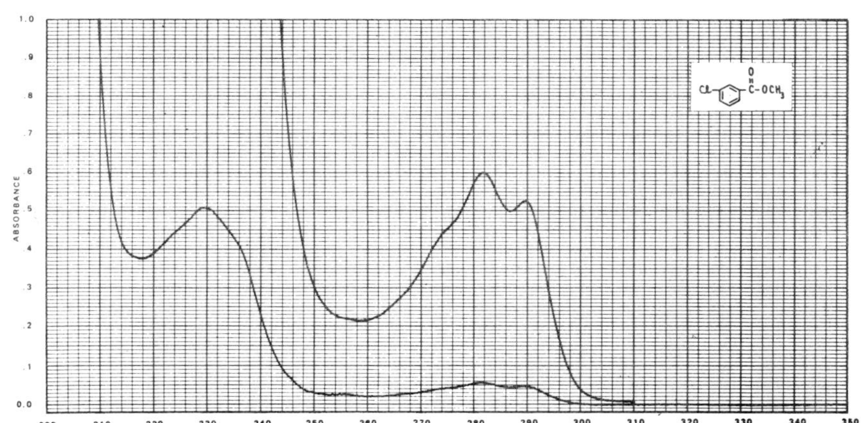

p-CHLOROBENZOIC ACID, METHYL ESTER

2874

$C_8H_7ClO_2$

Mol. Wt. 170.60

Solvent: Methanol

λ Max. mμ	a_m	Cell mm	Conc. g/L
281.5	568	10	0.100
238.5	17400	0.5	0.100

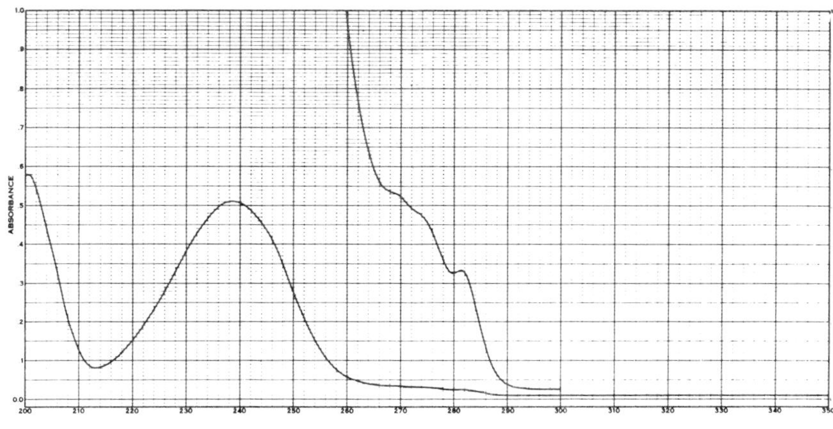

p-BROMOBENZOIC ACID, ETHYL ESTER 2875

$C_9H_9BrO_2$

Mol. Wt. 229.08

B.P. 115-116°C/5mm

Solvent: Methanol

λ Max. mμ	a_m	Cell mm	Conc. g/L
282	604	5	0.31170
243	18300	1	0.062340

m-IODOBENZOIC ACID, METHYL ESTER 2876

$C_8H_7IO_2$

Mol. Wt. 262.05

M.P. 48-50°C

Solvent: Methanol

λ Max. mμ	a_m	Cell mm	Conc. g/L
288	968	20	0.100
219	26200	1	0.0500

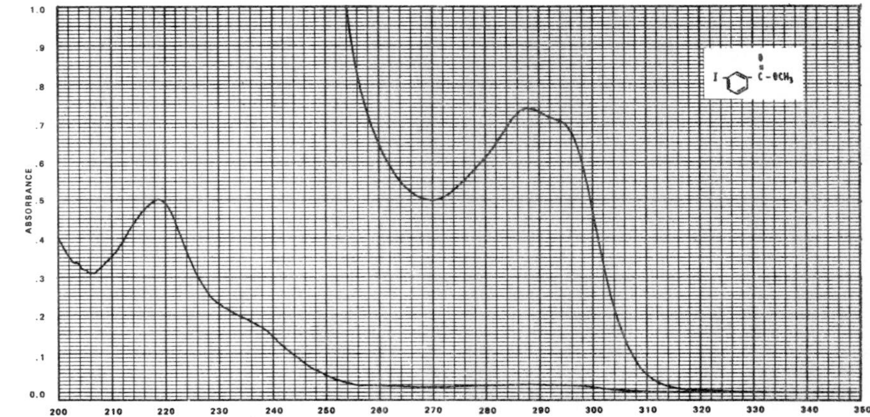

ANTHRANILIC ACID, HEXYL ESTER 2877

$C_{13}H_{19}NO_2$

Mol. Wt. 221.30

B.P. 194-195°C @ 16mm

λ Max. mμ	a_m	Cell mm	Conc. g/L

Pure sample not available.

ANTHRANILIC ACID, CYCLOHEXYL ESTER

2878

$C_{13}H_{17}NO_2$
Mol. Wt. 219.29
Solvent: Methanol

λ Max. mμ	a_m	Cell mm	Conc. g/L
334	4800	2	0.100
245	7130	2	0.100

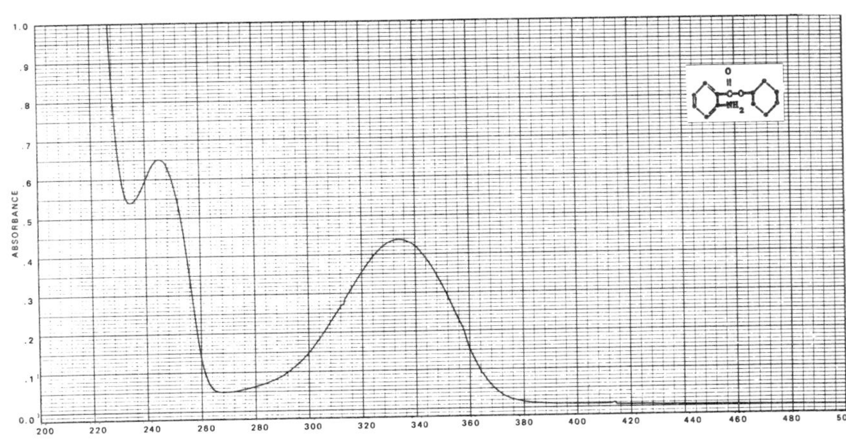

ANTHRANILIC ACID, CYCLOHEXYL ESTER

2878

$C_{13}H_{17}NO_2$
Mol. Wt. 219.29
Solvent: Methanol HCl

λ Max. mμ	a_m	Cell mm	Conc. g/L
333	1110	10	0.100
270	789	10	0.100
221	13400	1	0.100

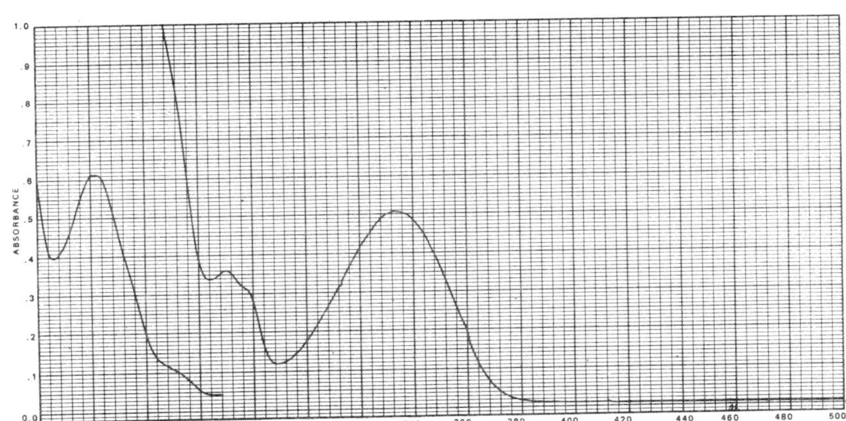

λ Max. mμ	a_m	Cell mm	Conc. g/L

ANTHRANILIC ACID, PENTYL ESTER

2879

$C_{12}H_{17}NO_2$

Mol. Wt. 207.27

Solvent: Methanol

λ Max. mμ	a_m	Cell mm	Conc. g/L
334	18400	0.5	0.100
245	26600	0.5	0.100

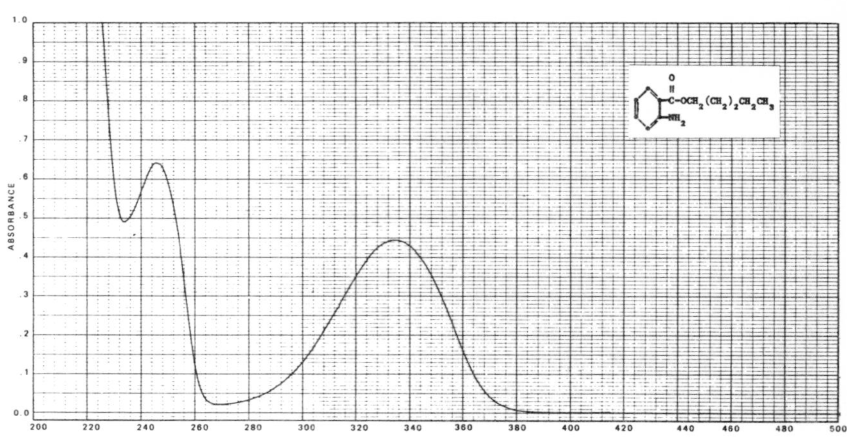

ANTHRANILIC ACID, PENTYL ESTER

2879

$C_{12}H_{17}NO_2$

Mol. Wt. 207.27

Solvent: Methanol HCl

λ Max. mμ	a_m	Cell mm	Conc. g/L
335	4420	2.5	0.100
271	2980	2.5	0.100
x	x	0.5	0.100

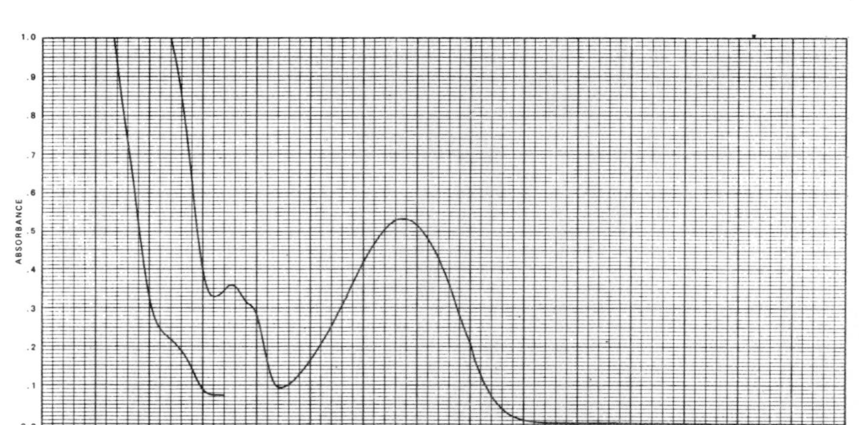

m-AMINOBENZOIC ACID, METHYL ESTER

2880

$C_8H_9NO_2$

Mol. Wt. 151.17

M.P. 52-54°C

Solvent: Methanol

λ Max. mμ	a_m	Cell mm	Conc. g/L
302	2330	5	0.100
219.5	2280	0.5	0.100

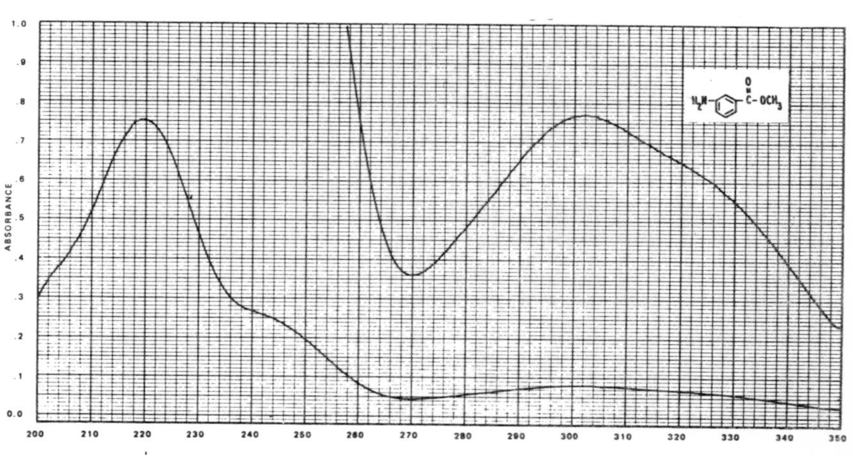

m-AMINOBENZOIC ACID, METHYL ESTER 2880

$C_8H_9NO_2$

Mol. Wt. 151.17

M.P. 52-54°C

Solvent: Methanol HCl

λ Max. mμ	a_m	Cell mm	Conc. g/L
278	961	10	0.100
271	1010	10	0.100
223	10900	1	0.100

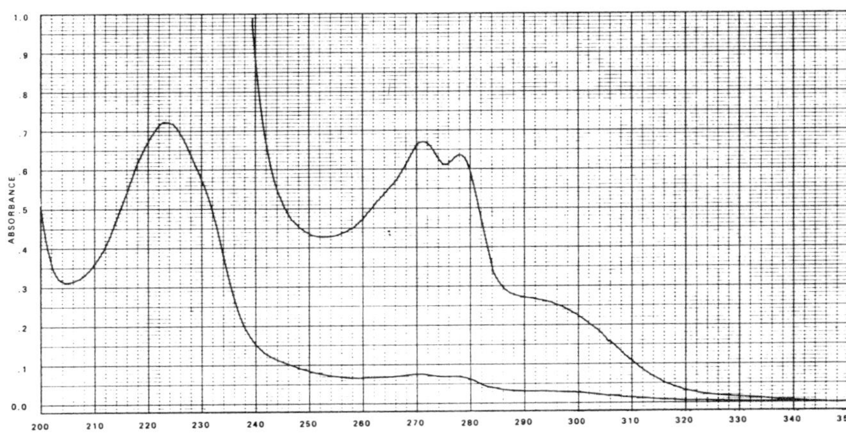

p-AMINOBENZOIC ACID, METHYL ESTER 2881

$C_8H_9NO_2$

Mol. Wt. 151.16

B.P. 111-112°C (lit.)

Solvent: Methanol

λ Max. mμ	a_m	Cell mm	Conc. g/L
x	x	10	0.190
291	19000	10	0.010
219.5	8400	10	0.010

λ Max. mμ	a_m	Cell mm	Conc. g/L

p-AMINOBENZOIC ACID, ISOPROPYL ESTER 2882

$C_{10}H_{13}NO_2$
Mol. Wt. 179.22
M.P. 85-86°C
Solvent: Methanol

λ Max. mμ	a_m	Cell mm	Conc. g/L
292	21200	2	0.0200
219.5	10100	2	0.0200

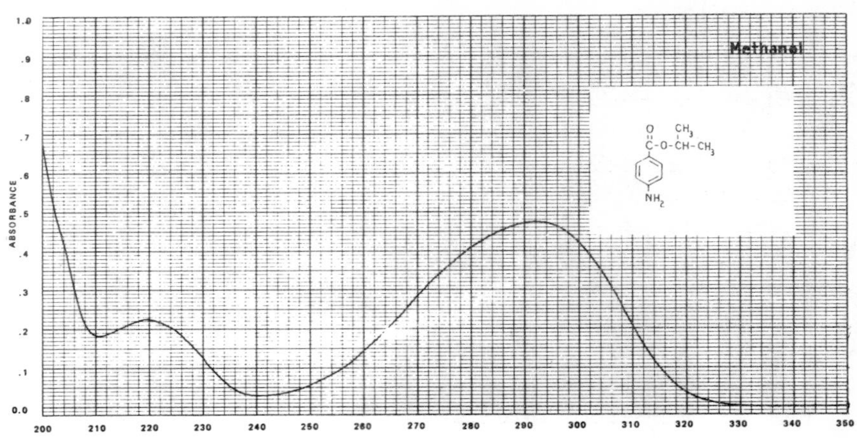

p-AMINOBENZOIC ACID, ISOPROPYL ESTER 2882

$C_{10}H_{13}NO_2$
Mol. Wt. 179.22
M.P. 85-86°C
Solvent: Methanol HCl

λ Max. mμ	a_m	Cell mm	Conc. g/L
292	1690	5	0.100
277.5	1950	5	0.100
271	1780	5	0.100
226	13500	1	0.100

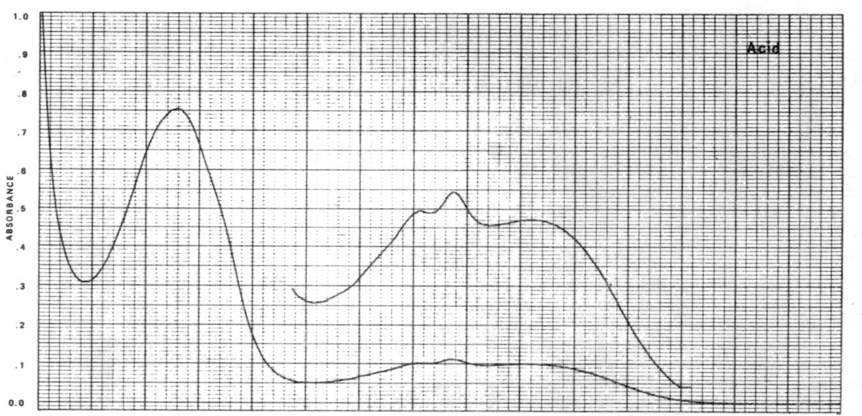

p-NITROSOBENZOIC ACID, ETHYL ESTER 2883

$C_9H_9NO_3$
Mol. Wt. 179.18
M.P. 79-81°C
Solvent: Methanol

λ Max. mμ	a_m	Cell mm	Conc. g/L
306.5	7080	1	0.100
287.5	13000	1	0.100
219	6310	1	0.100

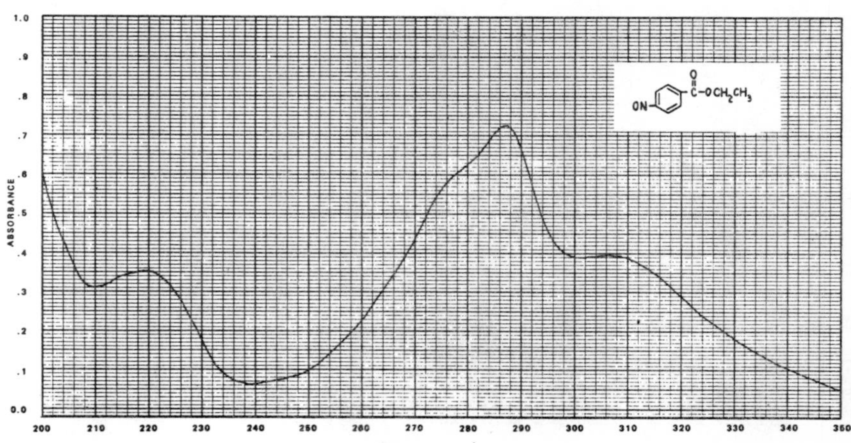

p-ISOCYANATOBENZOIC ACID, ETHYL ESTER 2884

$C_{10}H_9NO_3$

Mol. Wt. 191.19

M.P. 27-29°C

Solvent: Cyclohexane

λ Max. mμ	a_m	Cell mm	Conc. g/L
251	17500	1	0.100
x	x	1	0.100

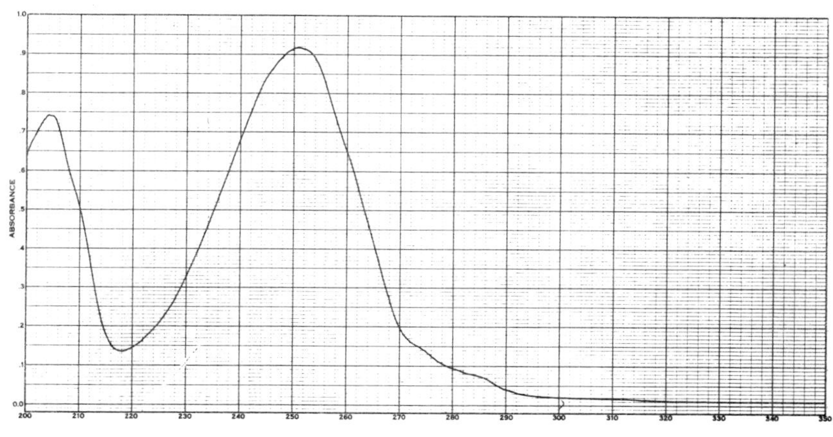

m-NITROBENZOIC ACID, ETHYL ESTER 2885

$C_9H_9NO_4$

Mol. Wt. 195.18

M.P. 41-43°C

Solvent: Methanol

λ Max. mμ	a_m	Cell mm	Conc. g/L
255	7410	2	0.100
217.5	27900	2	0.0200

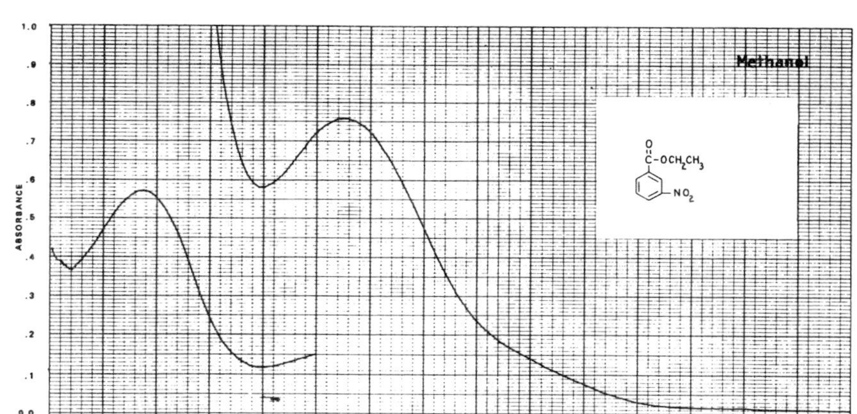

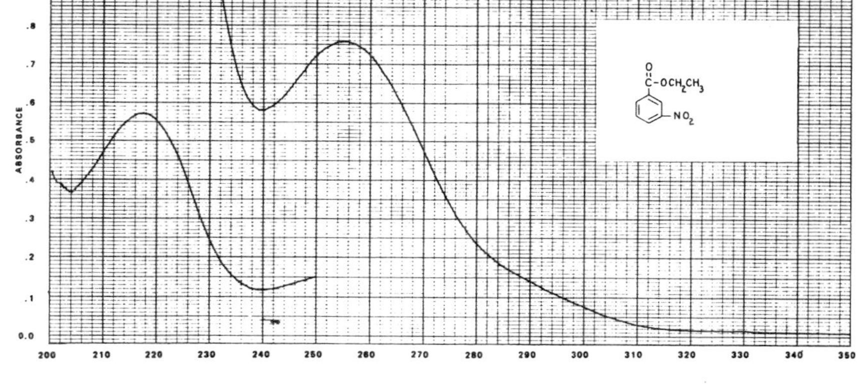

p-NITROBENZOIC ACID, METHYL ESTER 2886

$C_8H_7NO_4$

Mol. Wt. 181.15

M.P. 94-96°C

Solvent: Methanol

λ Max. mμ	a_m	Cell mm	Conc. g/L
257.5	12000	1	0.100

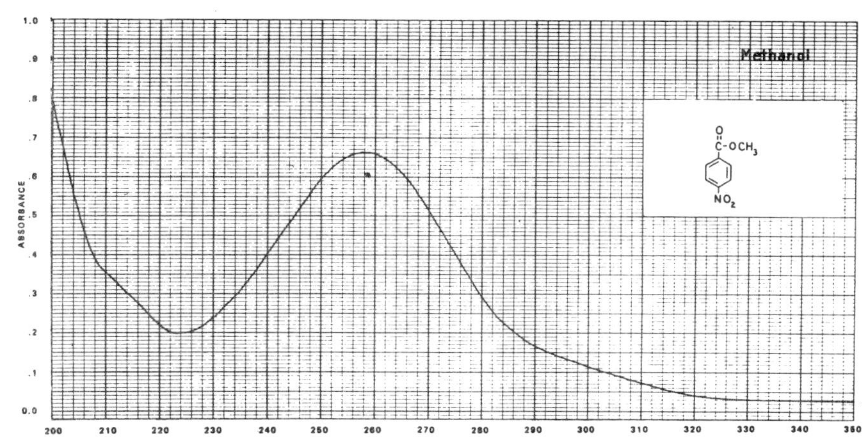

o-ANISIC ACID, METHYL ESTER

2887

$C_9H_{10}O_3$

Mol. Wt. 166.18

B.P. 117-118°C/8mm

Solvent: Methanol

λ Max. mμ	a_m	Cell mm	Conc. g/L
294.5	3330	1	0.16250
234	7080	1	0.16250
x	x	1	0.03250

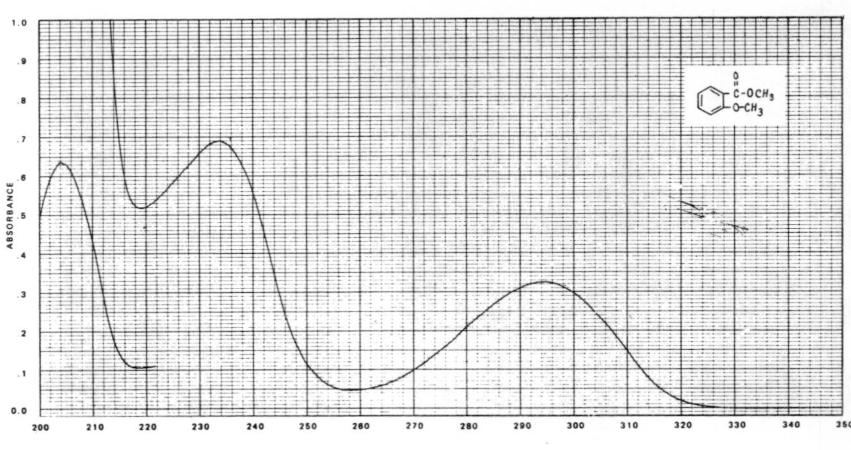

p-ANISIC ACID, METHYL ESTER

2888

$C_9H_{10}O_3$

Mol. Wt. 166.18

M.P. 49.5-50.5°C

Solvent: Methanol

λ Max. mμ	a_m	Cell mm	Conc. g/L
255	19200	1	0.0500
207	17000	1	0.0500

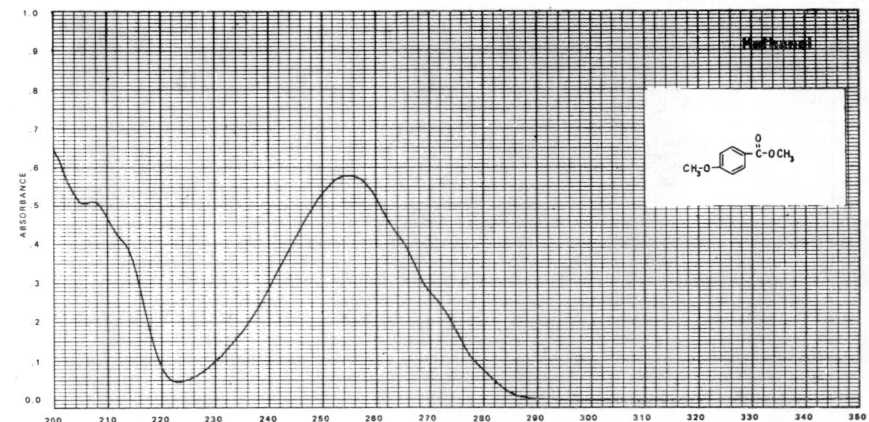

SALICYLIC ACID, ISOPROPYL ESTER

2889

$C_{10}H_{12}O_3$

Mol. Wt. 180.21

Solvent: Methanol

λ Max. mμ	a_m	Cell mm	Conc. g/L
306	4160	1	0.117
238	9030	1	0.117

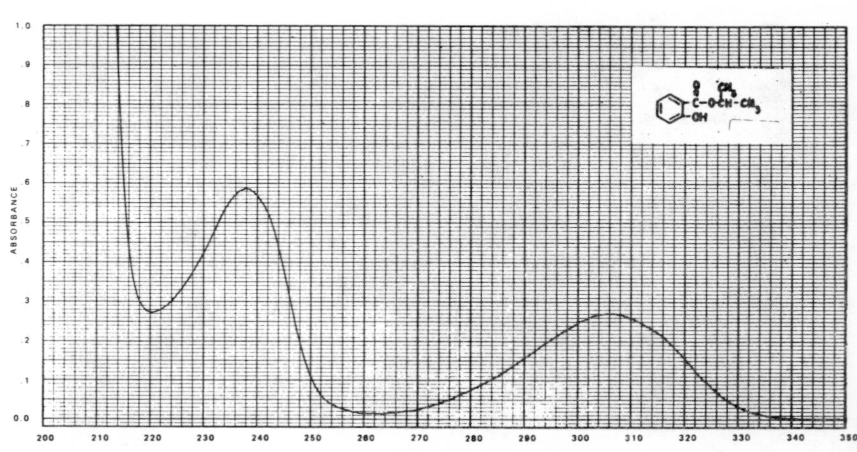

SALICYLIC ACID, ISOPROPYL ESTER 2889

$C_{10}H_{12}O_3$

Mol. Wt. 180.21

Solvent: Methanol KOH

λ Max. mμ	a_m	Cell mm	Conc. g/L
313	2570	2	0.117
238.5	7590	2	0.117
x	x	1	0.117

SALICYLIC ACID, BUTYL ESTER 2890

$C_{11}H_{14}O_3$

Mol. Wt. 194.23

B.P. 132-133°C/0.5mm

Solvent: Methanol

λ Max. mμ	a_m	Cell mm	Conc. g/L
306	4210	2	0.0526
237.5	8990	2	0.0526

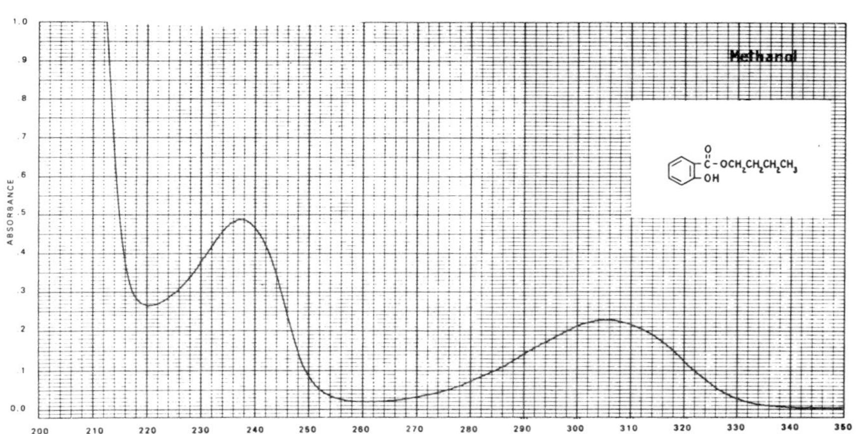

SALICYLIC ACID, BUTYL ESTER 2890

$C_{11}H_{14}O_3$

Mol. Wt. 194.23

B.P. 132-133°C/0.5mm

Solvent: Methanol KOH

λ Max. mμ	a_m	Cell mm	Conc. g/L
314	3470	2	0.0526
238.5	7440	2	0.0526

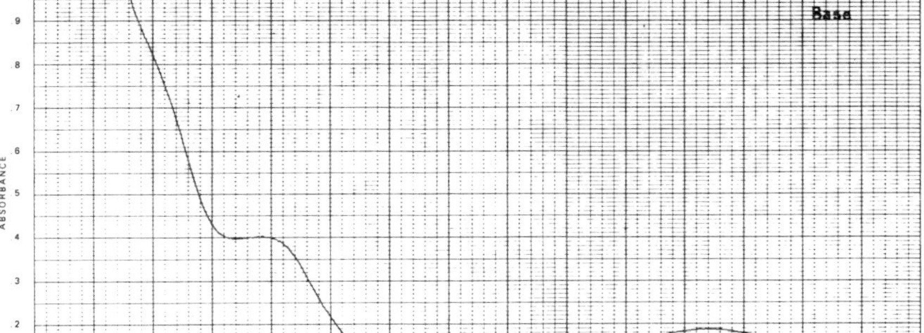

SALICYLIC ACID, PHENETHYL ESTER

$C_{15}H_{14}O_3$
Mol. Wt. 242.28
Solvent: Methanol

λ Max. mμ	a_m	Cell mm	Conc. g/L
306	4360	2	0.100
264	508	20	0.100
238	9680	2	0.100

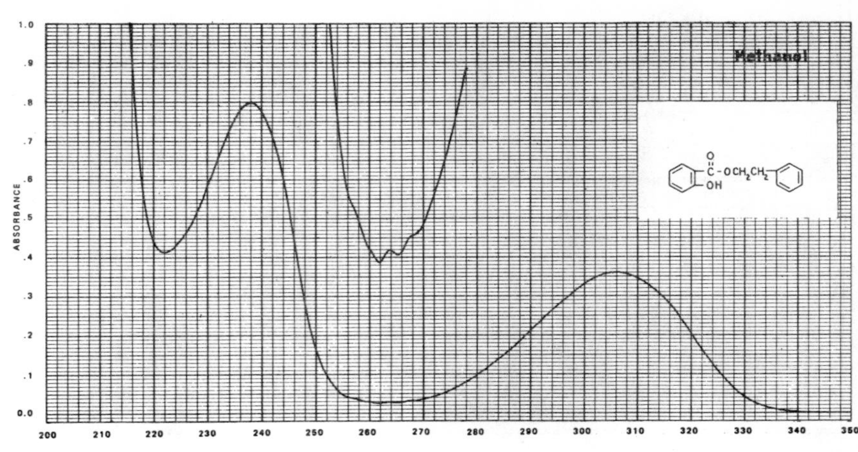

SALICYLIC ACID, PHENETHYL ESTER

2891

$C_{15}H_{14}O_3$
Mol. Wt. 242.28
Solvent: Methanol KOH

λ Max. mμ	a_m	Cell mm	Conc. g/L
331	3780	2	0.100
241	7110	2	0.100
x	x	20	0.100
x	x	1	0.100

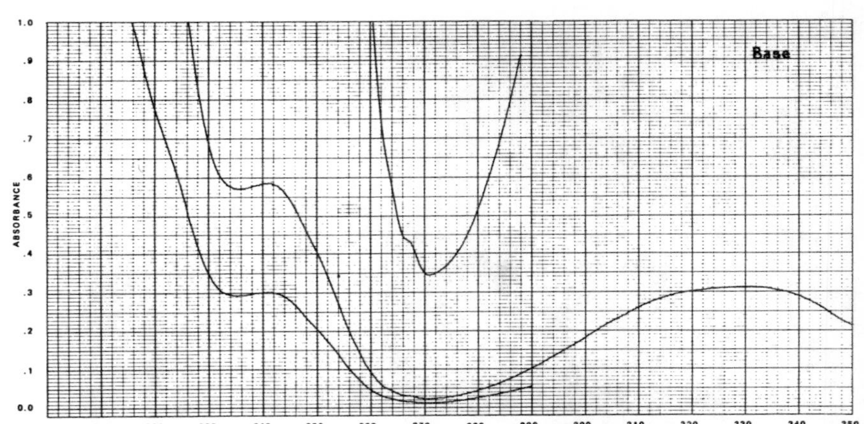

m-HYDROXYBENZOIC ACID, METHYL ESTER

2892

$C_8H_8O_3$
Mol. Wt. 152.15
M.P. 131°C B.P. 270-280°C (dec.) (lit.)
Solvent: Methanol

λ Max. mμ	a_m	Cell mm	Conc. g/L
298.5	2940	2	0.100
236	7460	2	0.100
208.5	31200	2	0.0200

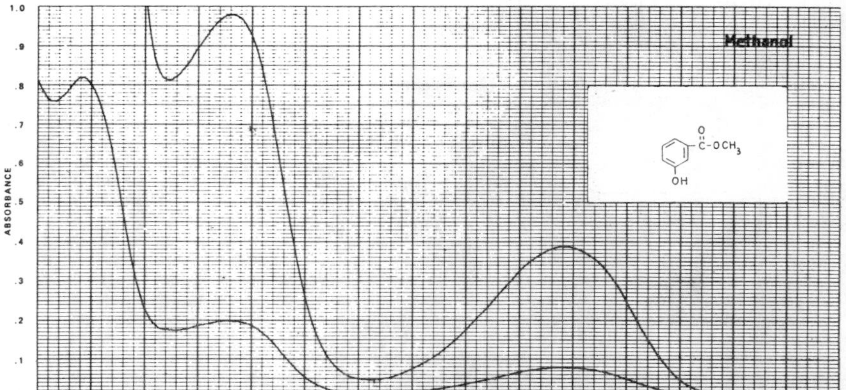

m-HYDROXYBENZOIC ACID, METHYL ESTER

2892

$C_8H_8O_3$
Mol. Wt. 152.15
M.P. 131°C B.P. 270-280°C (dec.) (lit.)
Solvent: Methanol KOH

λ Max. mμ	a_m	Cell mm	Conc. g/L
328	3190	2	0.100
224	29800	2	0.0200

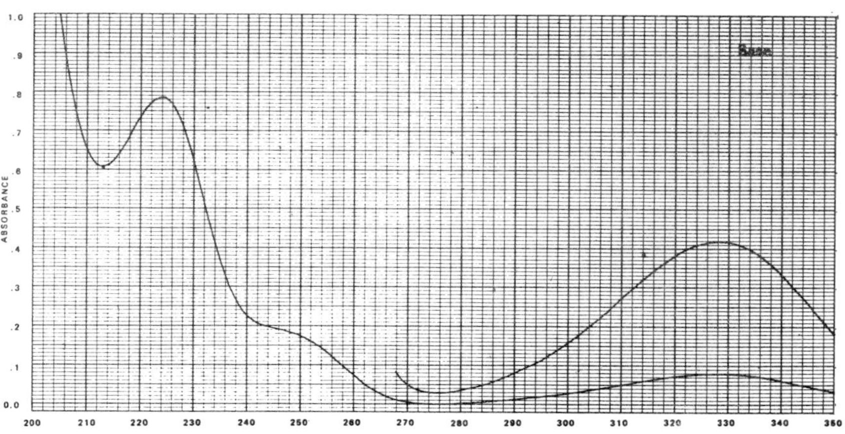

p-HYDROXYBENZOIC ACID, ISOPROPYL ESTER

2893

$C_{10}H_{12}O_3$
Mol. Wt. 180.21
M.P. 86°C (lit.)
Solvent: Methanol

λ Max. mμ	a_m	Cell mm	Conc. g/L
256	18600	0.5	0.100

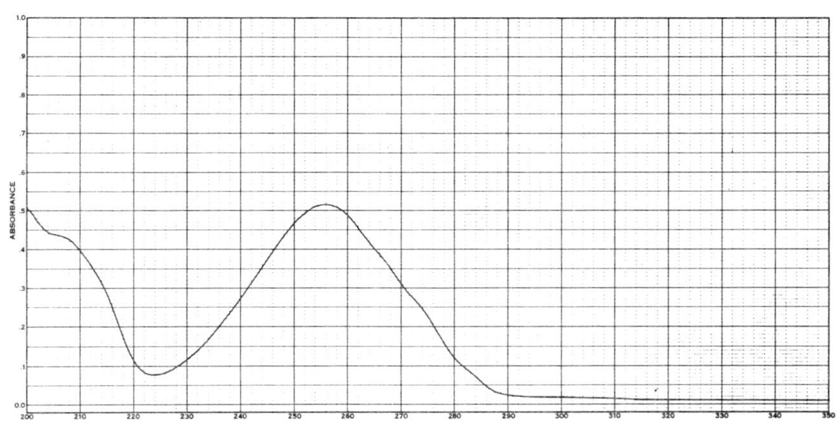

p-HYDROXYBENZOIC ACID, ISOPROPYL ESTER

2893

$C_{10}H_{12}O_3$
Mol. Wt. 180.21
M.P. 86°C (lit.)
Solvent: Methanol KOH

λ Max. mμ	a_m	Cell mm	Conc. g/L
297	27400	0.5	0.100
x	x	0.5	0.100

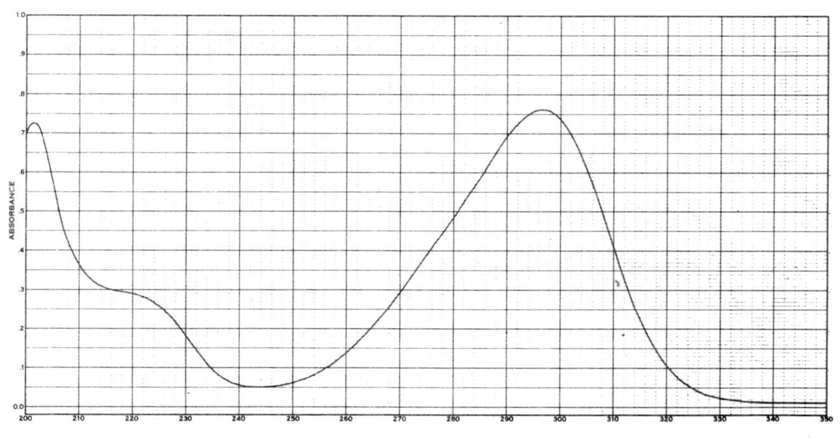

p-HYDROXYBENZOIC ACID, BUTYL ESTER 2894

$C_{11}H_{14}O_3$

Mol. Wt. 194.22

M.R. 67-69°C (lit.)

Solvent: Methanol

λ Max. mμ	a_m	Cell mm	Conc. g/L
x	x	10	2.00
256	20600	10	0.010

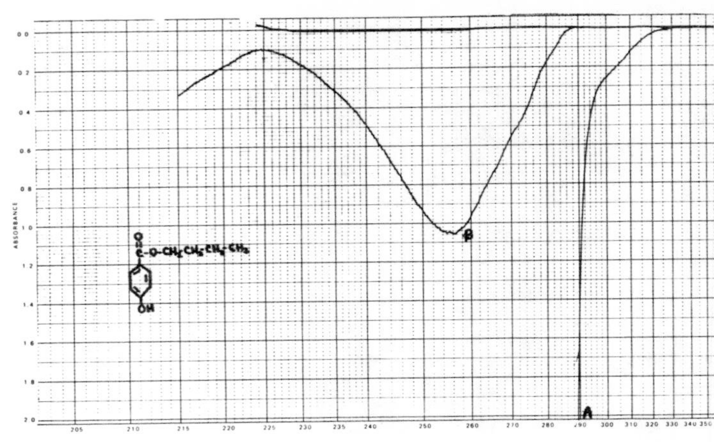

p-HYDROXYBENZOIC ACID, BUTYL ESTER 2894

$C_{11}H_{14}O_3$

Mol. Wt. 194.22

M.R. 67-69°C (lit.)

Solvent: Methanol KOH

λ Max. mμ	a_m	Cell mm	Conc. g/L
297	18600	10	0.010

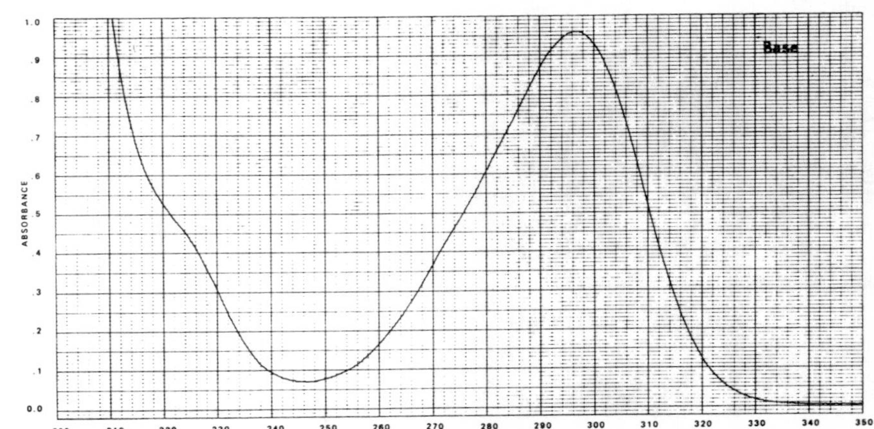

p-HYDROXYBENZOIC ACID, DODECYL ESTER 2895

$C_{19}H_{30}O_3$

Mol. Wt. 306.45

Solvent: Methanol

λ Max. mμ	a_m	Cell mm	Conc. g/L
256	16900	1	0.100

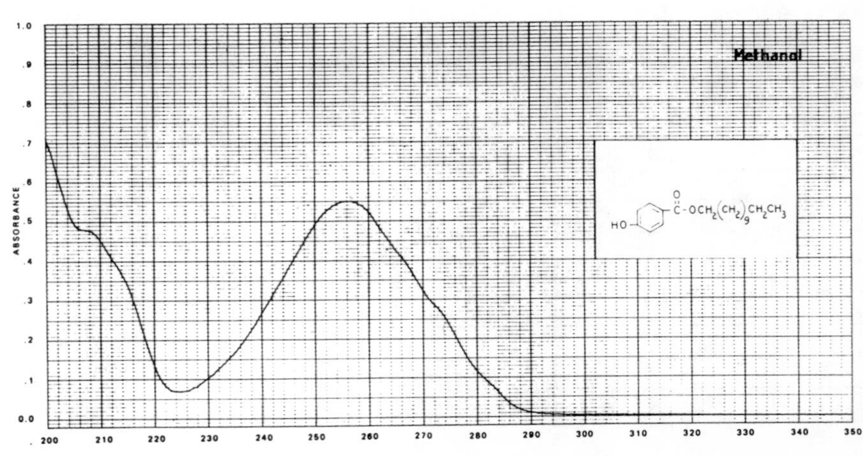

p-HYDROXYBENZOIC ACID, DODECYL ESTER

2895

$C_{19}H_{30}O_3$
Mol. Wt. 306.45
Solvent: Methanol KOH

λ Max. mμ	a_m	Cell mm	Conc. g/L
296.5	25800	1	0.100
220	9220	1	0.100

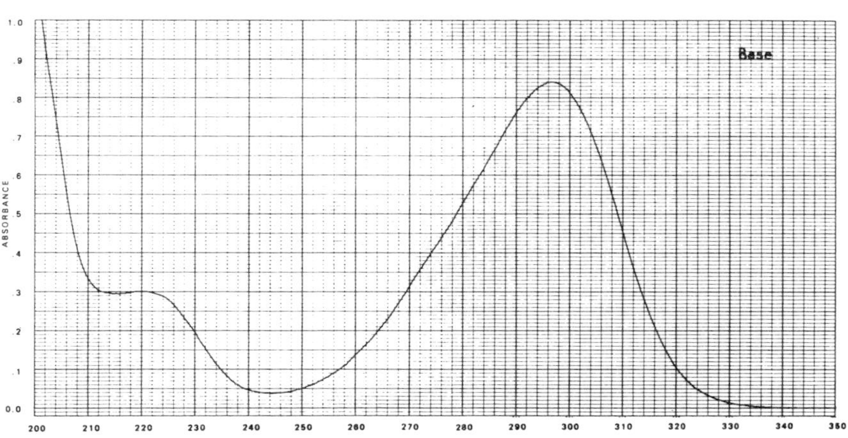

PHTHALIC ACID, MONOBUTYL ESTER

2896

$C_{12}H_{14}O_4$
Mol. Wt. 222.24
M.P. 73-78°C
Solvent: Methanol

λ Max. mμ	a_m	Cell mm	Conc. g/L
274.5	1220	10	0.122
223.5	8450	1	0.122

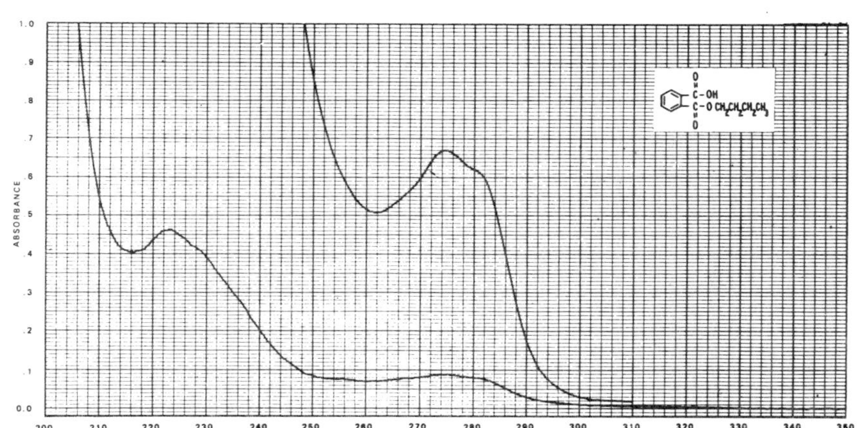

PHTHALIC ACID, MONOBUTYL ESTER

2896

$C_{12}H_{14}O_4$
Mol. Wt. 222.24
M.P. 73-78°C
Solvent: Methanol KOH

λ Max. mμ	a_m	Cell mm	Conc. g/L
280.5	1200	10	0.122
x	x	1	0.122

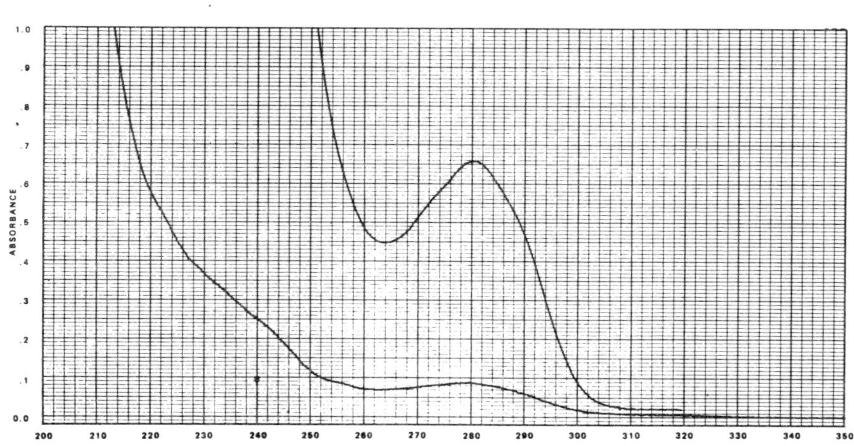

PHTHALIC ACID, DIPENTYL ESTER

2897

$C_{18}H_{26}O_4$
Mol. Wt. 306.41
B.P. 204-206°C/11mm
Solvent: Methanol

λ Max. mμ	^{a}m	Cell mm	Conc. g/L
275	1210	10	0.248
225.5	8070	1	0.248

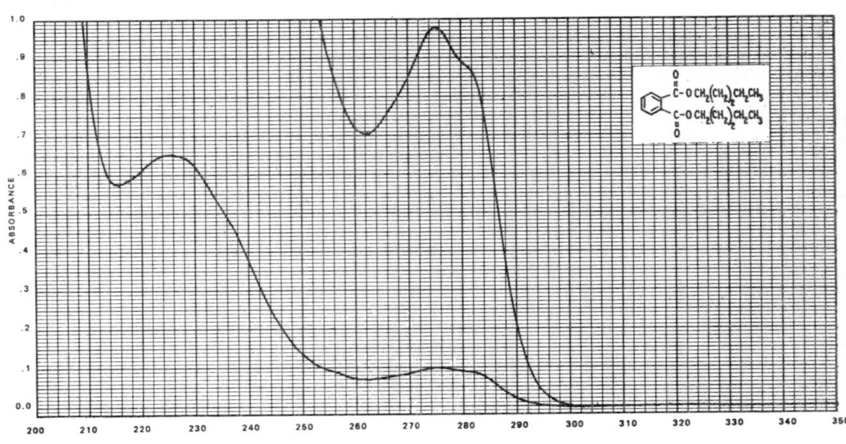

PHTHALIC ACID, BIS(2-ETHYLHEXYL) ESTER

2898

$C_{24}H_{38}O_4$
Mol. Wt. 390.57
B.P. 384°C
Solvent: Methanol

λ Max. mμ	^{a}m	Cell mm	Conc. g/L
275	1240	20	0.142
225	8310	2	0.142

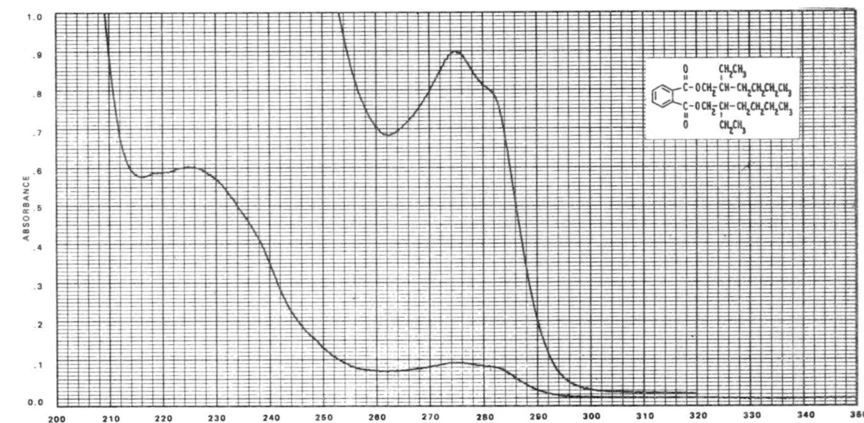

PHTHALIC ACID, DIALLYL ESTER

2899

$C_{14}H_{14}O_4$
Mol. Wt. 246.24
B.P. 160-163°C/4mm (lit.)
Solvent: Methanol

λ Max. mμ	^{a}m	Cell mm	Conc. g/L
x	x	10	1.664
275	1270	10	0.250
225.5	8490	10	0.050

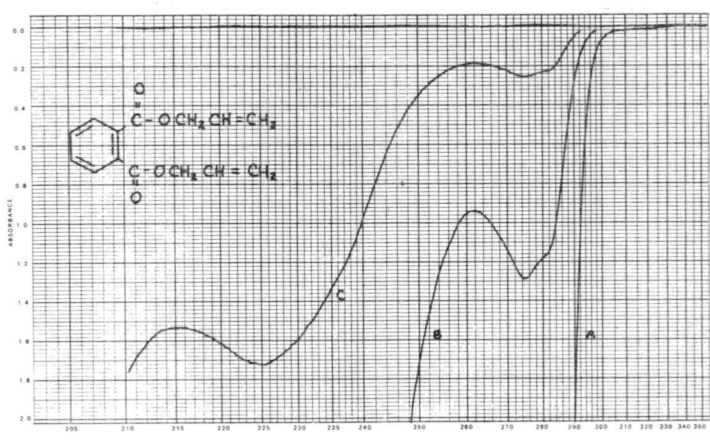

TETRACHLOROPHTHALIC ACID, DIPROPYL ESTER

2900

$C_{14}H_{14}Cl_4O_4$

Mol. Wt. 388.08

M.P. 24-27°C

λ Max. mμ	a_m	Cell mm	Conc. g/L

Pure sample not available.

ISOPHTHALIC ACID, DIMETHYL ESTER

2901

$C_{10}H_{10}O_4$

Mol. Wt. 194.19

M.P. 66.5-67.5°C

Solvent: Methanol

λ Max. mμ	a_m	Cell mm	Conc. g/L
288	873	10	0.100
280	917	10	0.100
x	x	10	0.010

ISOPHTHALIC ACID, DI-BUTYL ESTER

2902

$C_{16}H_{22}O_4$

Mol. Wt. 278.34

B.R. 191-193°C (lit.)

Solvent: Cyclohexane

λ Max. mμ	a_m	Cell mm	Conc. g/L
x	x	10	2.220
286.5	953	10	0.444
279	943	10	0.444
272	708	10	0.444
x	x	10	0.044
x	x	10	0.004

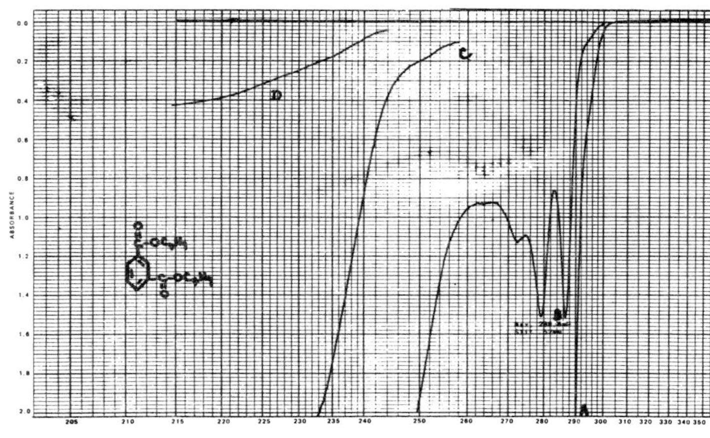

ISOPHTHALIC ACID, DI-(2-ETHYLHEXYL) ESTER

2903

$C_{24}H_{38}O_4$

Mol. Wt. 390.57

B.P. 224-226°C/3mm (lit.)

Solvent: Cyclohexane

λ Max. mμ	a_m	Cell mm	Conc. g/L
x	x	10	2.044
286.5	937	10	0.613
279	919	10	0.613
272	691	10	0.613
x	x	10	0.043

ISOPHTHALIC ACID, DI-ALLYL ESTER

2904

$C_{14}H_{14}O_4$

Mol. Wt. 246.26

B.R. 176-177°C/5mm (lit.)

Solvent: Cyclohexane

λ Max. mμ	a_m	Cell mm	Conc. g/L
x	x	10	2.020
287	1010	10	0.404
279.5	1000	10	0.404
272.5	728	10	0.404
x	x	10	0.020

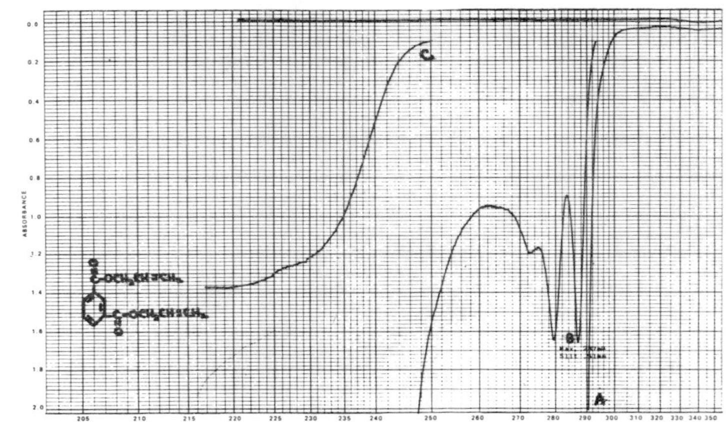

5-AMINOISOPHTHALIC ACID, DIMETHYL ESTER

2905

$C_{10}H_{11}NO_4$

Mol. Wt. 209.20

M.P. 179.5-181°C

Solvent: Methanol

λ Max. mμ	a_m	Cell mm	Conc. g/L
343	2010	5	0.100
268	2360	5	0.100
225	20300	1	0.100

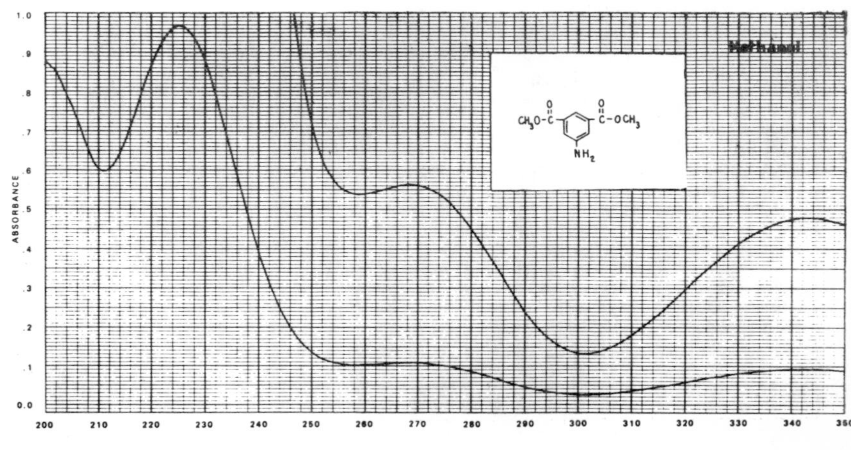

5-AMINOISOPHTHALIC ACID, DIMETHYL ESTER

2905

$C_{10}H_{11}NO_4$

Mol. Wt. 209.20

M.P. 179.5-181°C

Solvent: Methanol HCl

λ Max. mμ	a_m	Cell mm	Conc. g/L
342.5	203	10	0.100
288	833	10	0.100
279.5	923	10	0.100
x	x	2	0.100
x	x	1	0.100

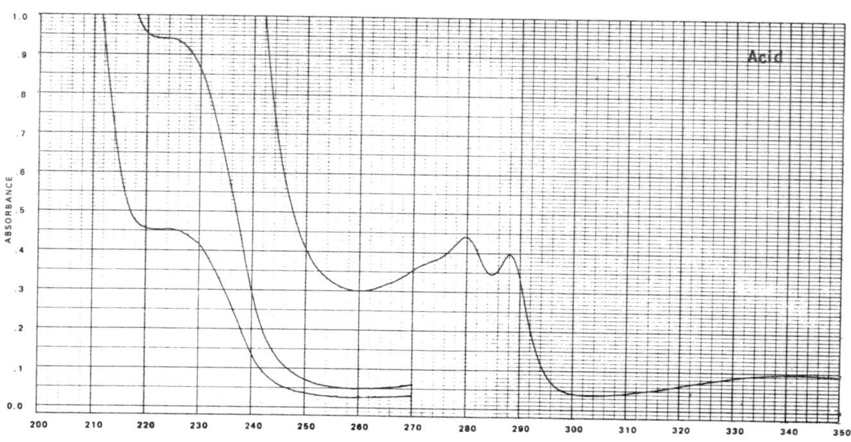

5-NITROISOPHTHALIC ACID, DIMETHYL ESTER

2906

$C_{10}H_9NO_6$

Mol. Wt. 239.19

M.P. 122-124°C

Solvent: Methanol

λ Max. mμ	a_m	Cell mm	Conc. g/L
x	x	5	0.0500
221	28300	1	0.0500

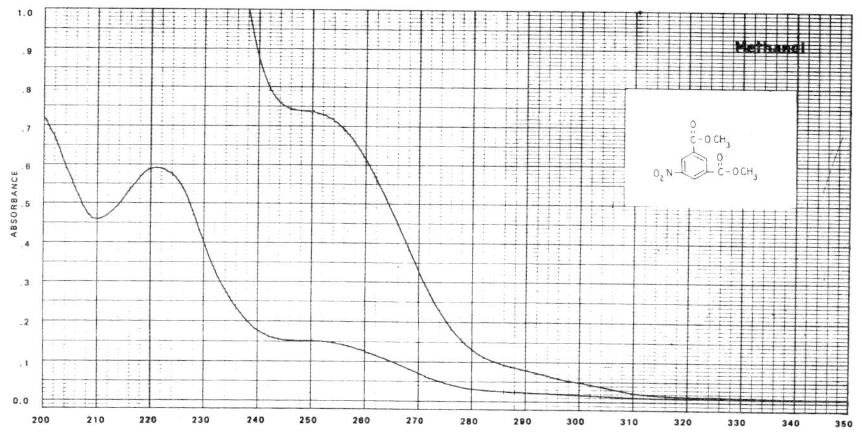
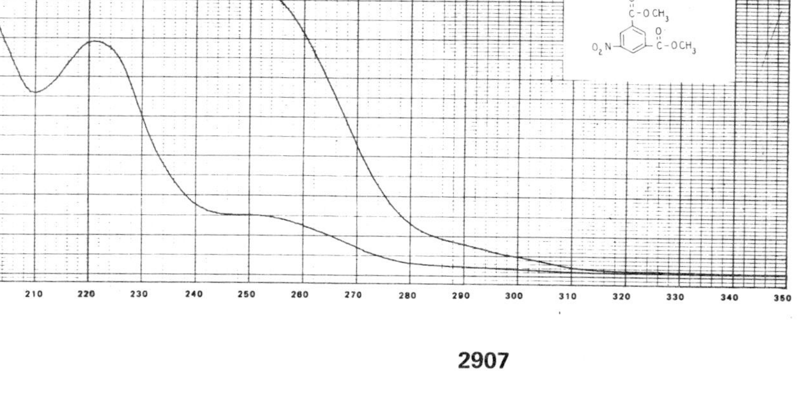

TEREPHTHALIC ACID, DIETHYL ESTER

2907

$C_{12}H_{14}O_4$

Mol. Wt. 222.24

M.R. 38-40°C (lit.)

Solvent: Cyclohexane

λ Max. mμ	a_m	Cell mm	Conc. g/L
x	x	10	2.00
293.5	1580	10	0.200
283.5	1960	10	0.200
240.5	22500	10	0.014

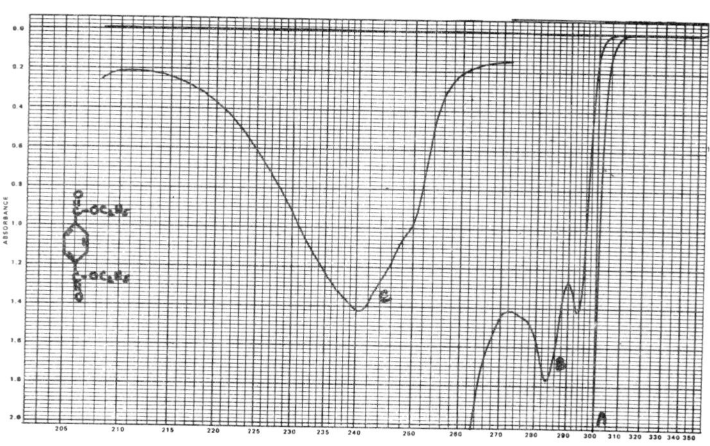

TEREPHTHALIC ACID, DIBUTYL ESTER

2908

$C_{16}H_{22}O_4$

Mol. Wt. 278.34

B.R. 194-196°C/8mm (lit.)

Solvent: Cyclohexane

λ Max. mμ	a_m	Cell mm	Conc. g/L
x	x	10	1.990
294	1480	10	0.199
284	1790	10	0.199
241	23700	10	0.020

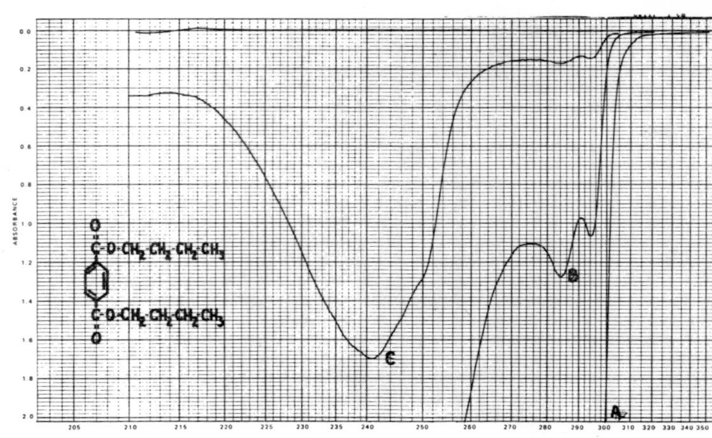

TEREPHTHALIC ACID, DIOCTYL ESTER

2909

$C_{24}H_{38}O_4$

Mol. Wt. 390.57

M.P. 42.5-43.5°C

Solvent: Methanol

λ Max. mμ	a_m	Cell mm	Conc. g/L
285	1660	10	0.200
241	21100	10	0.010

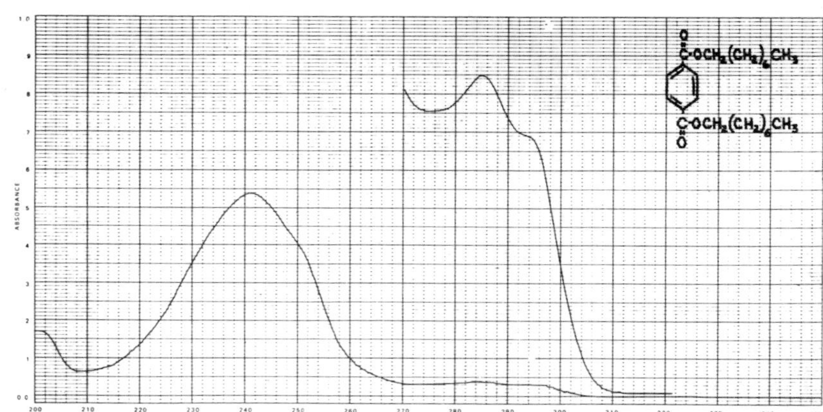

2-AMINOTEREPHTHALIC ACID, DIMETHYL ESTER

2910

$C_{10}H_{11}NO_4$

Mol. Wt. 209.20

M.P. 133-135°C

Solvent: Methanol

λ Max. mμ	a_m	Cell mm	Conc. g/L
366	5240	2	0.100
229	36800	1	0.050

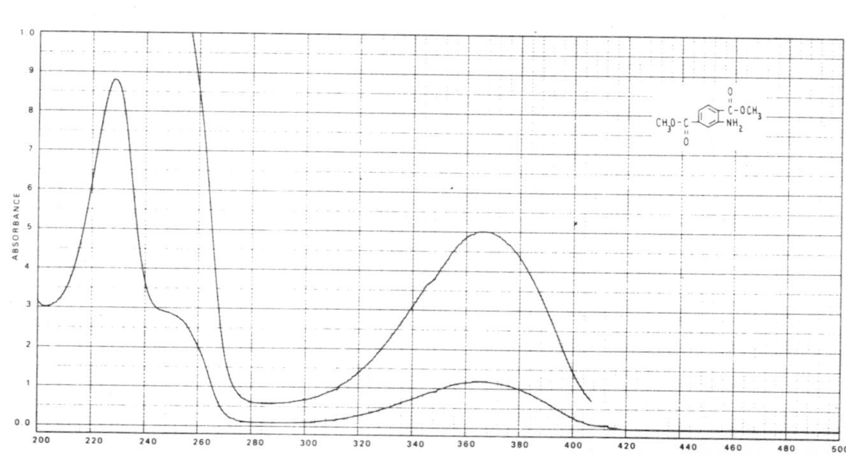

2-AMINOTEREPHTHALIC ACID, DIMETHYL ESTER

2910

$C_{10}H_{11}NO_4$

Mol. Wt. 209.20

M.P. 133-135°C

Solvent: Methanol HCl

λ Max. mμ	a_m	Cell mm	Conc. g/L
365	2850	10	0.050
281	669	10	0.050
229	28600	1	0.050

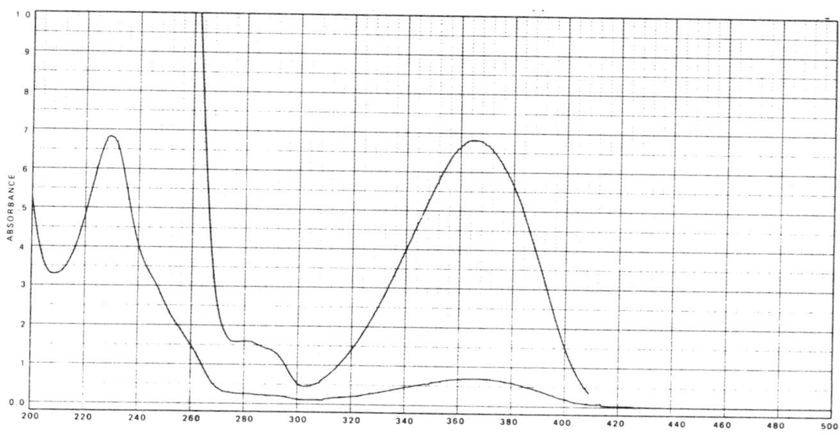

3,5-DINITROBENZOIC ACID, ETHYL ESTER

2911

$C_9H_8N_2O_6$

Mol. Wt. 240.18

M.P. 90-92°C

Solvent: Methanol

λ Max. mμ	a_m	Cell mm	Conc. g/L
x	x	1	0.100

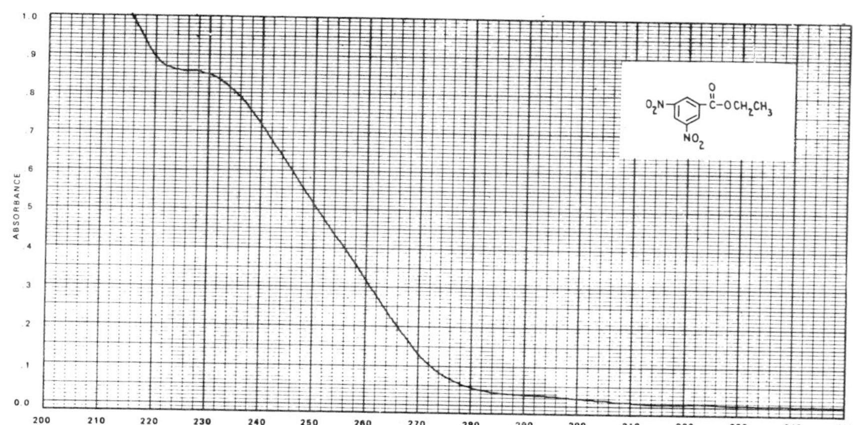

3,5-DINITROBENZOIC ACID, CYCLOHEXYL ESTER

2912

$C_{13}H_{14}N_2O_6$

Mol. Wt. 294.27

M.P. 87°C

Solvent: Methanol

λ Max. mμ	a_m	Cell mm	Conc. g/L
209	27000	1	0.100

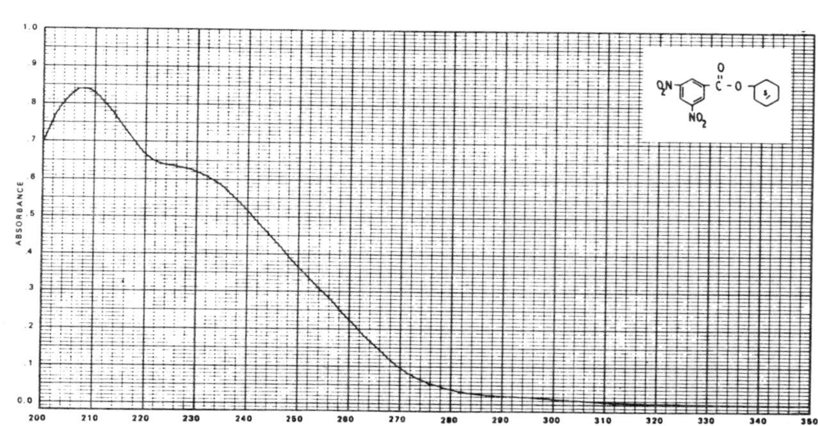

3,5-DINITROBENZOIC ACID, BENZYL ESTER

2913

$C_{14}H_{10}N_2O_6$
Mol. Wt. 302.25
M.P. 115.5°C (lit.)
Solvent: Dioxane

λ Max. mμ	a_m	Cell mm	Conc. g/L
x	x	10	2.390
x	x	10	0.239
x	x	10	0.024
x	x	10	0.012

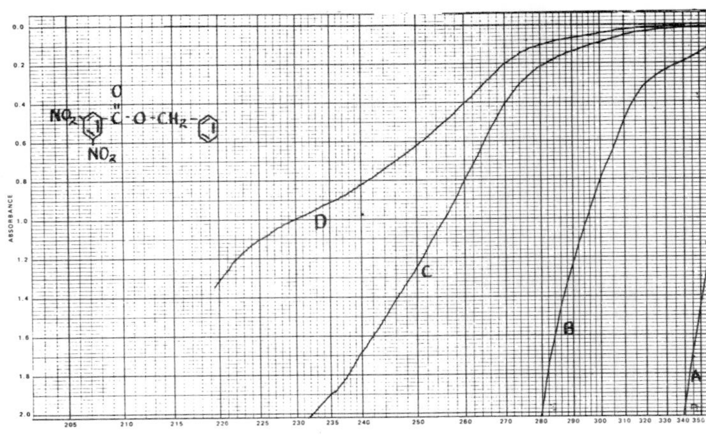

α-RESORCYLIC ACID, METHYL ESTER

2914

$C_8H_8O_4$
Mol. Wt. 168.15
M.P. 164-166°C
Solvent: Methanol

λ Max. mμ	a_m	Cell mm	Conc. g/L
310	2690	2	0.100
251	6190	2	0.100
206	26300	1	0.0500

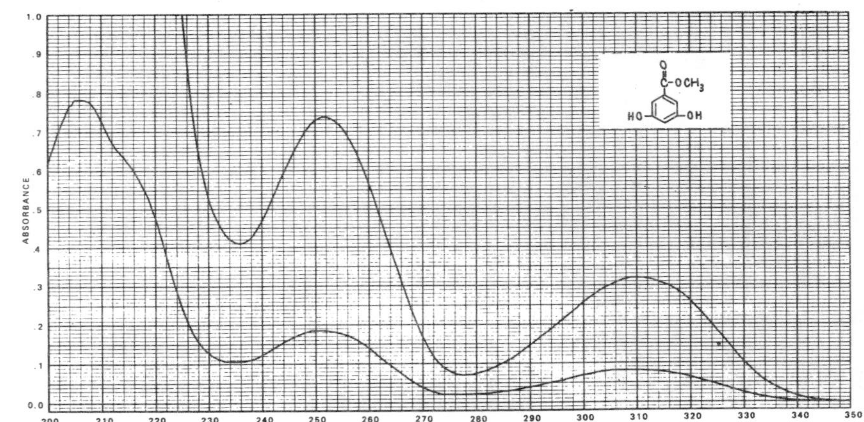

α-RESORCYLIC ACID, METHYL ESTER

2914

$C_8H_8O_4$
Mol. Wt. 168.15
M.P. 164-166°C
Solvent: Methanol KOH

λ Max. mμ	a_m	Cell mm	Conc. g/L
331	2860	5	0.0500
265	4130	5	0.0500
229	21000	1	0.0500

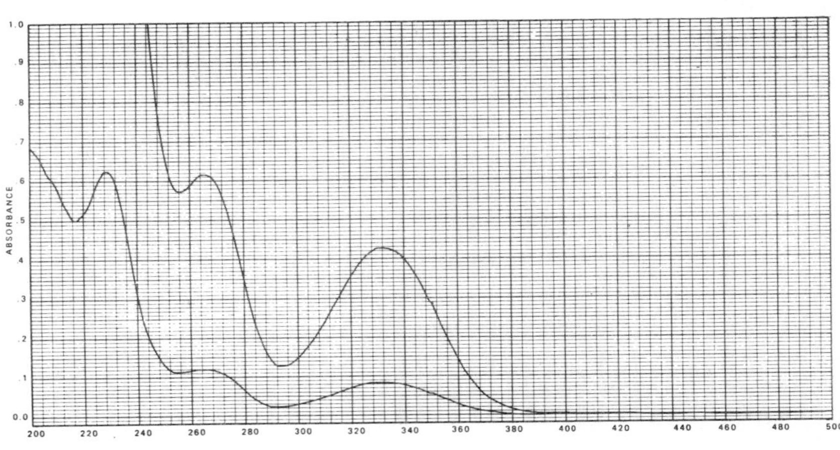

3,5-DIMETHOXY-4-HYDROXYBENZOIC ACID, METHYL ESTER

2915

$C_{10}H_{12}O_5$
Mol. Wt. 212.19
M.P. 107°C
Solvent: Methanol

λ Max. mμ	a_m	Cell mm	Conc. g/L
275.5	10900	10	0.006
218	25200	10	0.006

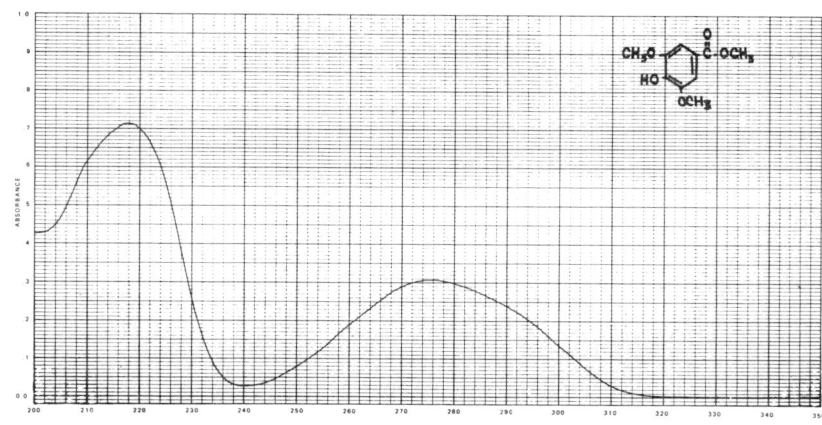

GALLIC ACID, METHYL ESTER

2916

$C_8H_8O_5$
Mol. Wt. 184.15
M.P. 201-203°C
Solvent: Methanol

λ Max. mμ	a_m	Cell mm	Conc. g/L
275	10400	1	0.0500
218.5	27200	1	0.0500

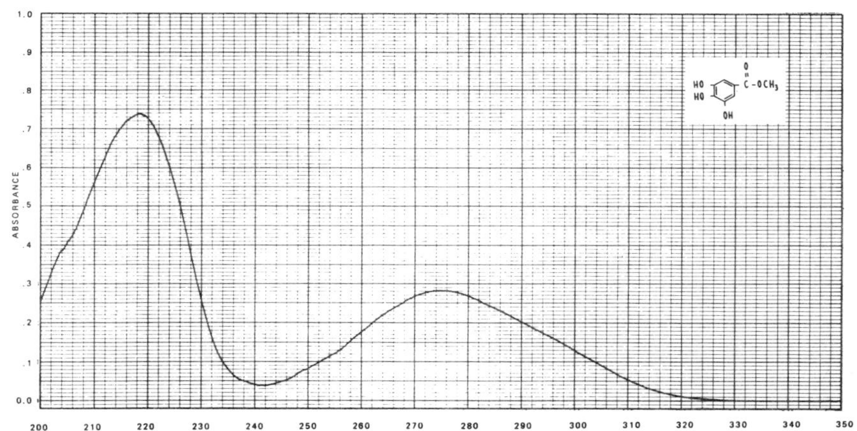

GALLIC ACID, METHYL ESTER

2916

$C_8H_8O_5$
Mol. Wt. 184.15
M.P. 201-203°C
Solvent: Methanol KOH

λ Max. mμ	a_m	Cell mm	Conc. g/L
318	8070	1	0.100
278	6410	1	0.100
239	9020	1	0.100

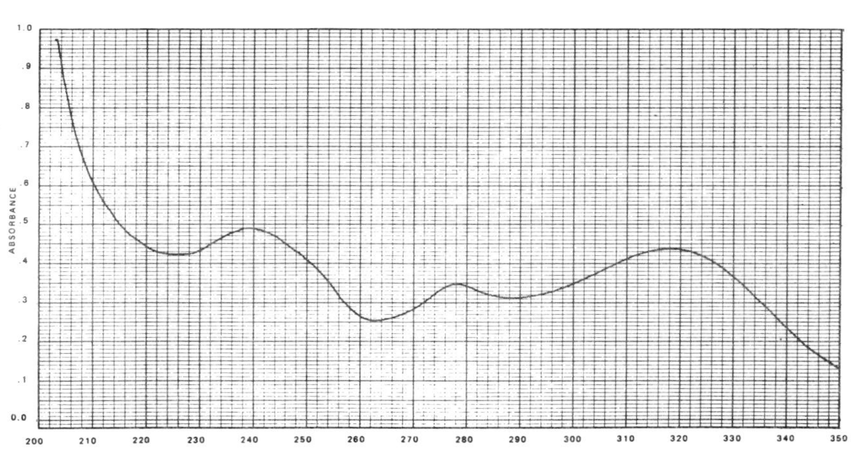

GALLIC ACID, BUTYL ESTER

$C_{11}H_{14}O_5$
Mol. Wt. 226.23
M.P. 134°C
Solvent: Methanol

λ Max. mμ	a_m	Cell mm	Conc. g/L
274	11400	1	0.0500
218	28600	1	0.0500

GALLIC ACID, BUTYL ESTER

$C_{11}H_{14}O_5$
Mol. Wt. 226.23
M.P. 134°C
Solvent: Methanol KOH

λ Max. mμ	a_m	Cell mm	Conc. g/L
240	9390	2	0.0500
276	7420	2	0.0500
317	7760	2	0.0500

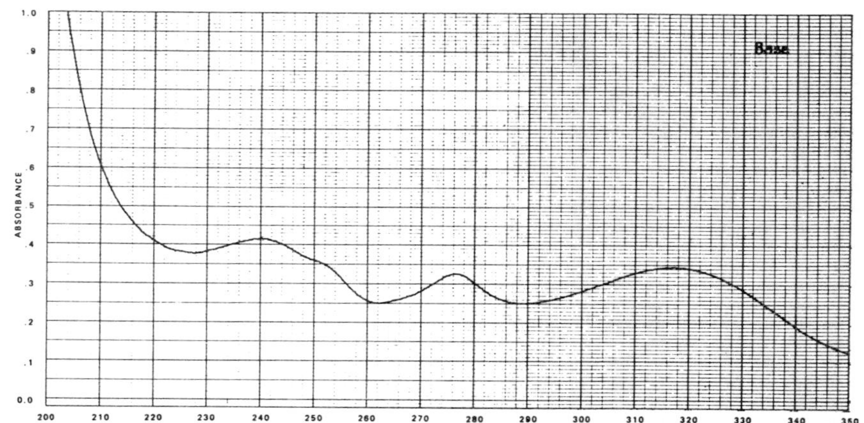

GALLIC ACID, ISOBUTYL ESTER

$C_{11}H_{14}O_5$
Mol. Wt. 226.23
M.P. 129°C
Solvent: Methanol

λ Max. mμ	a_m	Cell mm	Conc. g/L
274	9500	1	0.0500
218	24100	1	0.0500

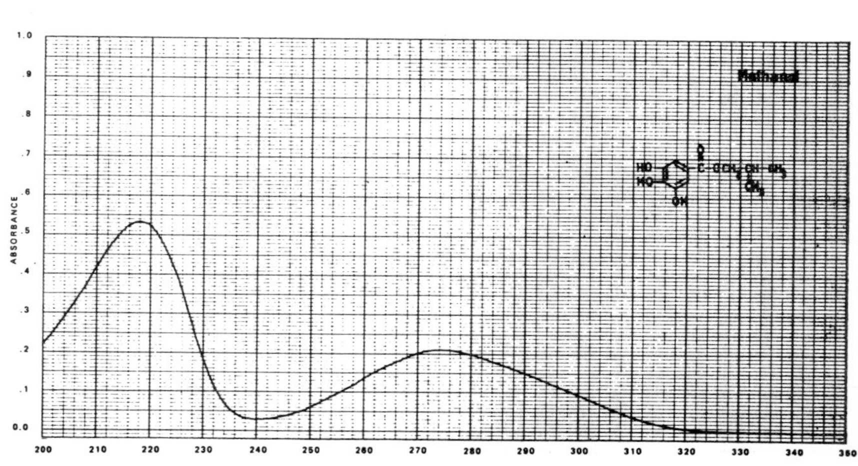

GALLIC ACID, ISOBUTYL ESTER

2918

$C_{11}H_{14}O_5$
Mol. Wt. 226.23
M.P. 129°C
Solvent: Methanol KOH

λ Max. mμ	a_m	Cell mm	Conc. g/L
318	4530	5	0.0500
276	3980	5	0.0500
240	6260	5	0.0500

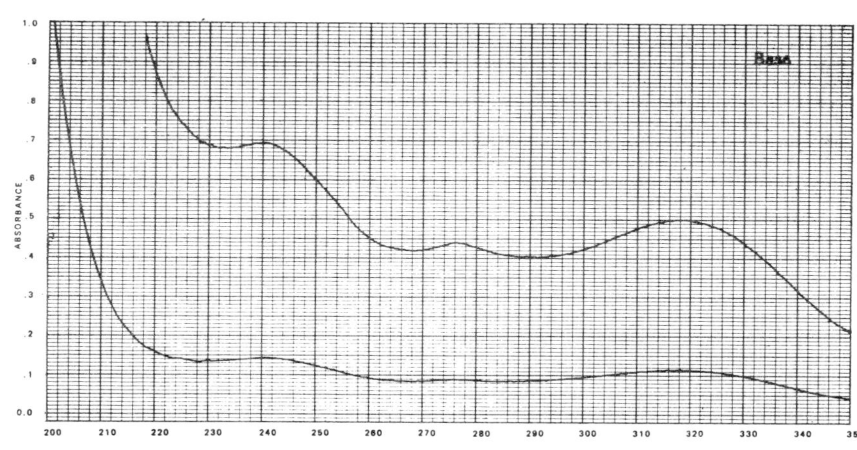

GALLIC ACID, DODECYL ESTER

2919

$C_{19}H_{30}O_5$
Mol. Wt. 538.45
Solvent: Methanol

λ Max. mμ	a_m	Cell mm	Conc. g/L
275	10100	1	0.100
218	23700	1	0.100

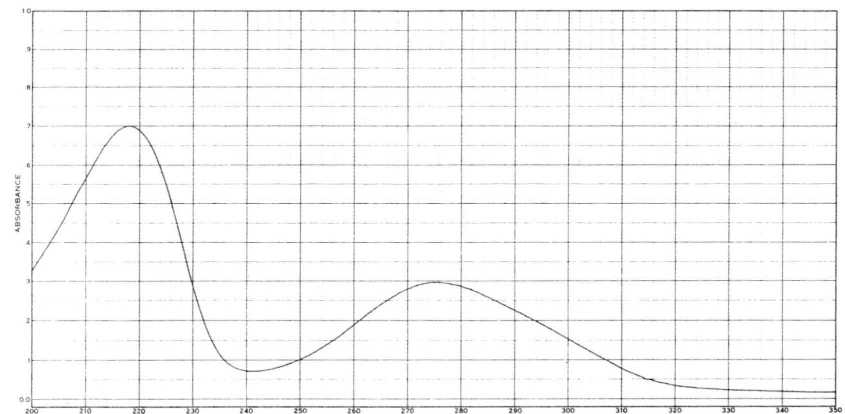

GALLIC ACID, DODECYL ESTER

2919

$C_{19}H_{30}O_5$
Mol. Wt. 538.45
Solvent: Methanol KOH

λ Max. mμ	a_m	Cell mm	Conc. g/L
316	7970	2	0.100
286	7400	2	0.100
237	11900	2	0.100
x	x	1	0.100

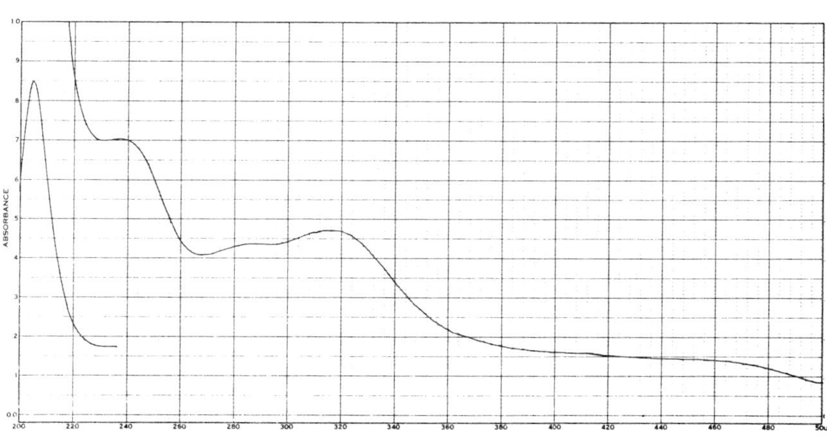

1,2,4,5-BENZENETETRACARBOXYLIC ACID, TETRAMETHYL ESTER 2920

$C_{14}H_{14}O_8$
Mol. Wt. 310.26
Solvent: Methanol

λ Max. mμ	a_m	Cell mm	Conc. g/L
290.5	2700	10	0.100
x	x	1	0.1

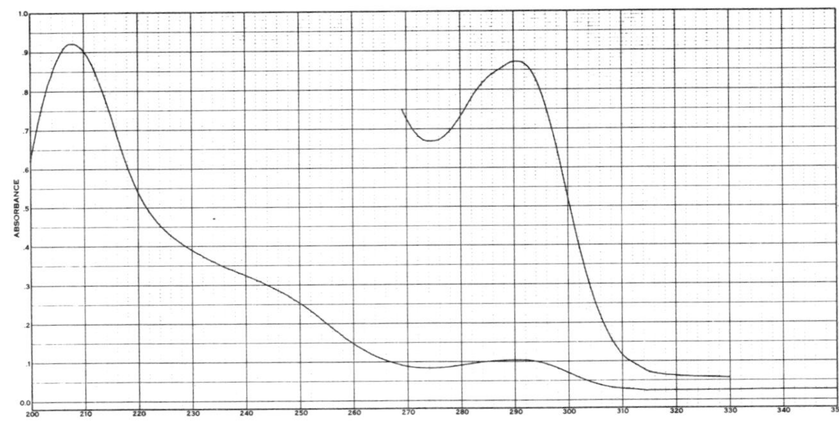

PROPIONIC ACID, PHENYL ESTER 2921

$C_9H_{10}O_2$
Mol. Wt. 150.18
B.P. 75-77°C/4mm
Solvent: Methanol

λ Max. mμ	a_m	Cell mm	Conc. g/L
265	316	2	0.882
x	x	1	0.0882

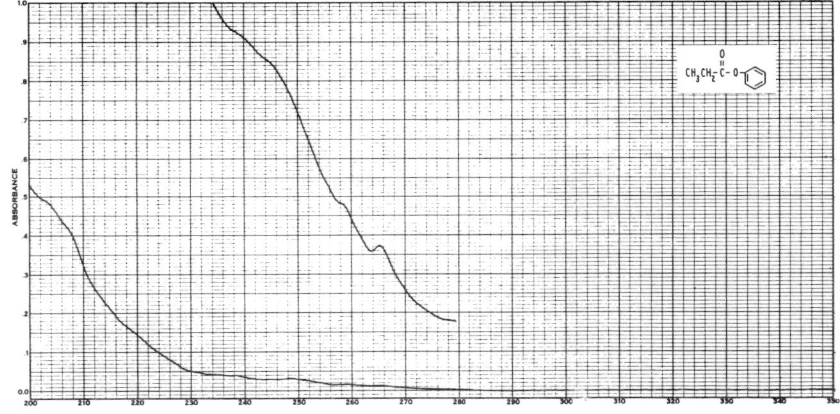

PIVALIC ACID, PHENYL ESTER 2922

$C_{11}H_{14}O_2$
Mol. Wt. 178.23
B.P. 85-87°C/5mm

λ Max. mμ	a_m	Cell mm	Conc. g/L

Pure sample not available.

TRIFLUOROACETIC ACID, PHENYL ESTER

2923

$C_8H_5F_3O_2$
Mol. Wt. 190.12
B.P. 145-147°C
Solvent: Methanol

λ Max. mμ	a_m	Cell mm	Conc. g/L
266.5	1160	5	0.180
212.5	3730	5	0.090
208	3710	5	0.090

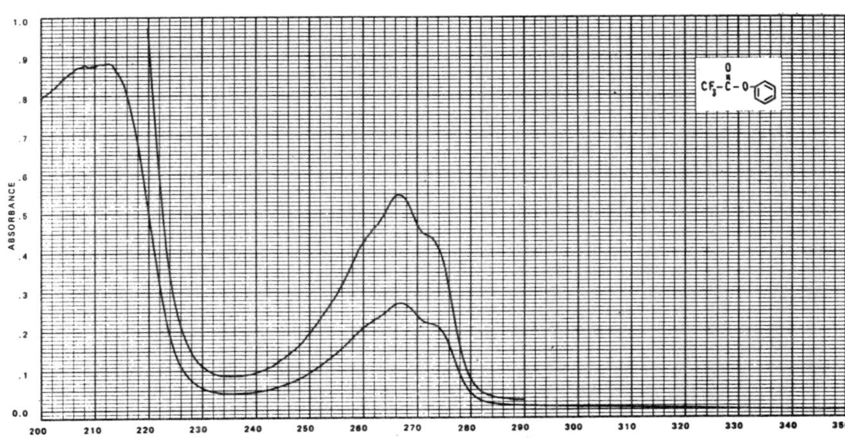

ACETIC ACID, p-TOLYL ESTER

2924

$C_9H_{10}O_2$
Mol. Wt. 150.18
B.P. 212-214°C
Solvent: Cyclohexane

λ Max. mμ	a_m	Cell mm	Conc. g/L
272.0	1290	8	0.10
266.2	1260	8	0.10
214	13100	1	0.10

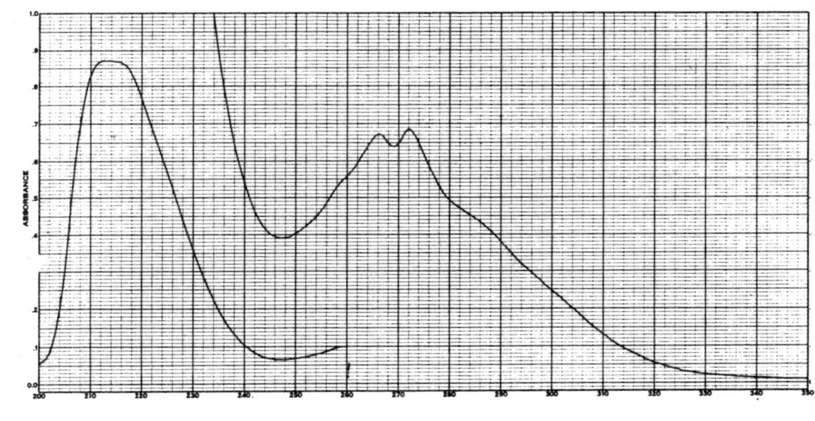

OCTANOIC ACID, p-TOLYL ESTER

2925

$C_{15}H_{22}O_2$
Mol. Wt. 234.34
Solvent: Methanol

λ Max. mμ	a_m	Cell mm	Conc. g/L
271	508	40	0.100
265	569	40	0.100
257	535	40	0.100
x	x	2	0.100

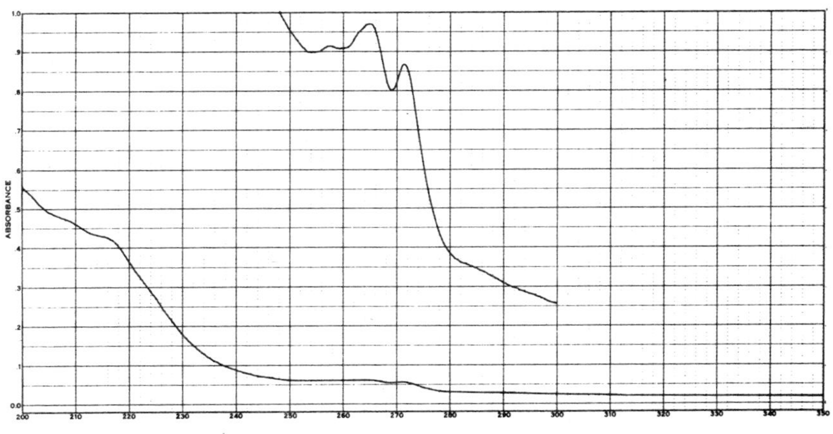

2926

ACETIC ACID, p-NITROPHENYL ESTER

$C_8H_7NO_4$
Mol. Wt. 181.15
M.P. 80°C
Solvent: Methanol

λ Max. mμ	a_m	Cell mm	Conc. g/L
271	7230	2	0.100

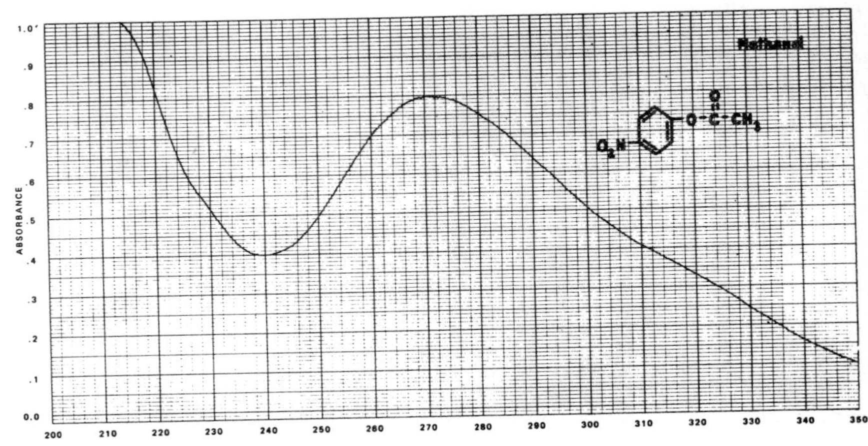

2927

PIVALIC ACID, p-NITROPHENYL ESTER

$C_{11}H_{13}NO_4$
Mol. Wt. 223.23
M.P. 92-95°C
Solvent: Methanol

λ Max. mμ	a_m	Cell mm	Conc. g/L
269	9110	1	0.100
211.5	7810	1	0.100

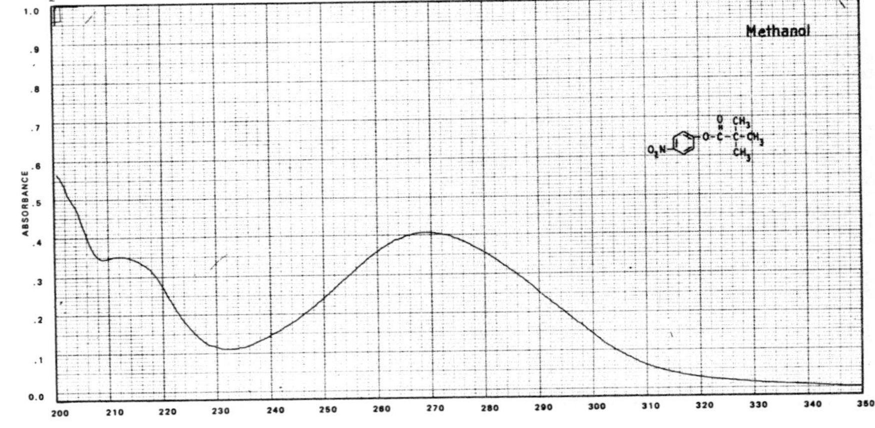

2928

RESORCINOL, DIACETATE

$C_{10}H_{10}O_4$
Mol. Wt. 194.19
B.P. 150°C/10mm (lit.)
Solvent: Methanol

λ Max. mμ	a_m	Cell mm	Conc. g/L
316	103	20	0.425
259.5	574	5	0.425
x	x	1	0.0850

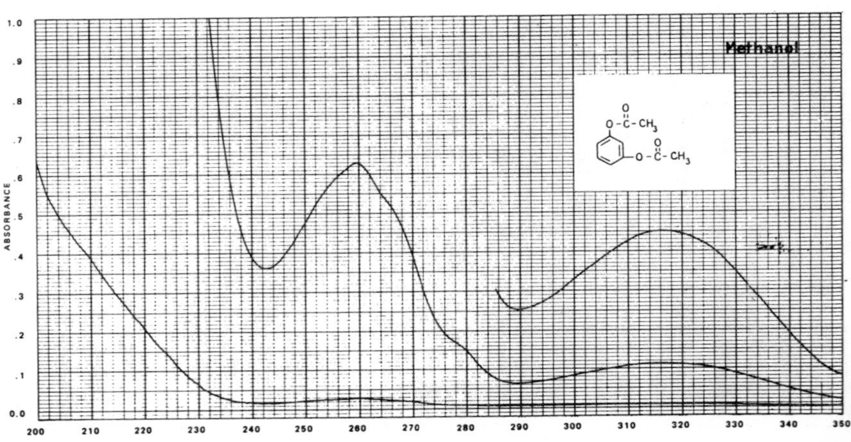

PHLOROGLUCINOL, TRIACETATE

2929

$C_{12}H_{12}O_6$

Mol. Wt. 252.23

M.P. 105°C

Solvent: Methanol

λ Max. mμ	a_m	Cell mm	Conc. g/L
269	629	20	0.100
x	x	1	0.100

2-NAPHTHOL, ACETATE

2930

$C_{12}H_{10}O_2$

Mol. Wt. 186.21

M.P. 68-68.5°C

Solvent: Methanol

λ Max. mμ	a_m	Cell mm	Conc. g/L
318	497	10	0.030
310.5	434	10	0.030
304.5	528	10	0.030
286	3630	10	0.030
275.5	5360	10	0.030
266	4860	10	0.030
222.5	81800	10	0.002

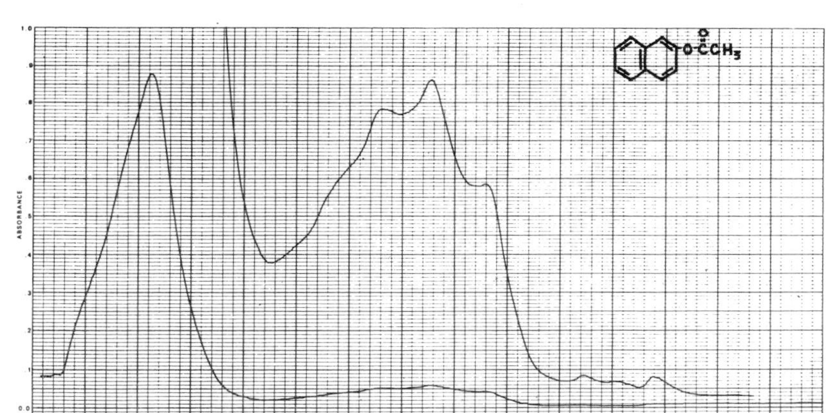

FURFURYL ALCOHOL, ACETATE

2931

$C_7H_8O_3$

Mol. Wt. 140.14

Solvent: Methanol

λ Max. mμ	a_m	Cell mm	Conc. g/L
271.5	94.5	20	0.223
216	9040	1	0.111

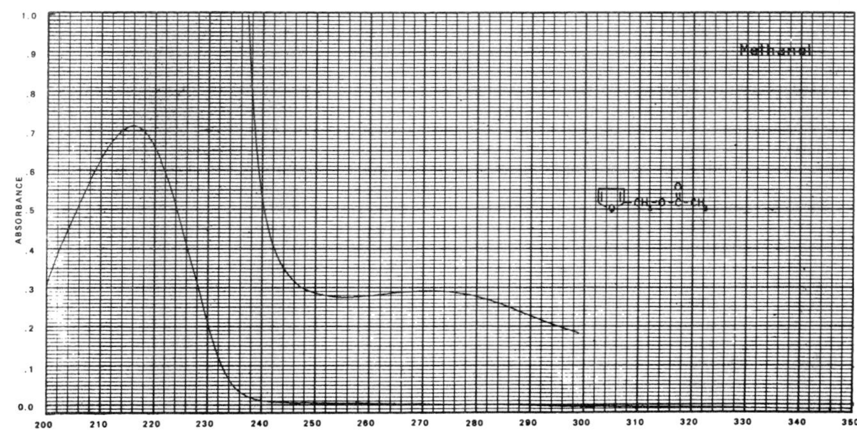

2932

PHENYLACETIC ACID, m-TOLYL ESTER

$C_{15}H_{14}O_2$
Mol. Wt. 226.28
M.P. 50°C
Solvent: Methanol

λ Max. mμ	a_m	Cell mm	Conc. g/L
268	364	20	0.100
263	497	20	0.100
257	520	20	0.100
252	455	20	0.100
x	x	1	0.100

2933

PHENYLACETIC ACID, p-TOLYL ESTER

$C_{15}H_{14}O_2$
Mol. Wt. 226.26
Solvent: Methanol

λ Max. mμ	a_m	Cell mm	Conc. g/L
x	x	10	2.00
270	499	10	0.400
264	667	10	0.400
257	591	10	0.400
251.5	467	10	0.400
x	x	10	0.040

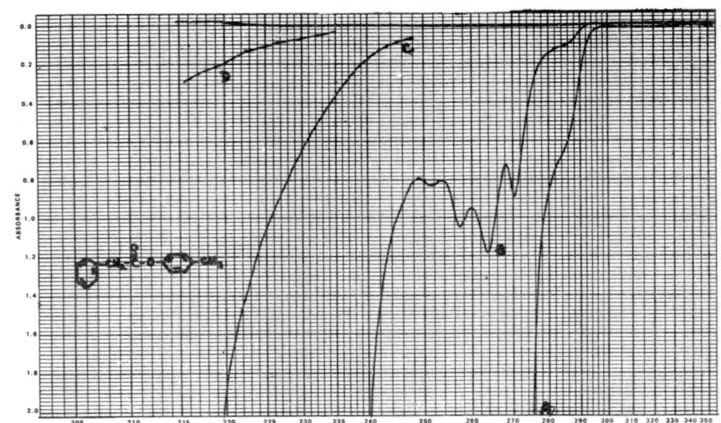

2934

2-FURANACRYLIC ACID, ETHYL ESTER

$C_9H_{10}O_3$
Mol. Wt. 166.18
Solvent: Methanol

λ Max. mμ	a_m	Cell mm	Conc. g/L
302	20100	10	0.005

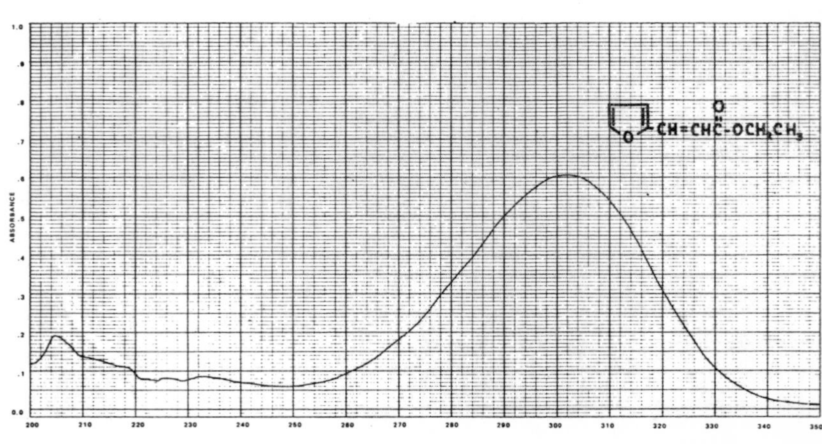

2-FUROIC ACID, PROPYL ESTER

2935

$C_8H_{10}O_3$

Mol. Wt. 154.17

B.P. 211°C (lit.)

Solvent: Methanol

λ Max. mμ	a_m	Cell mm	Conc. g/L
249	13300	2	0.0492

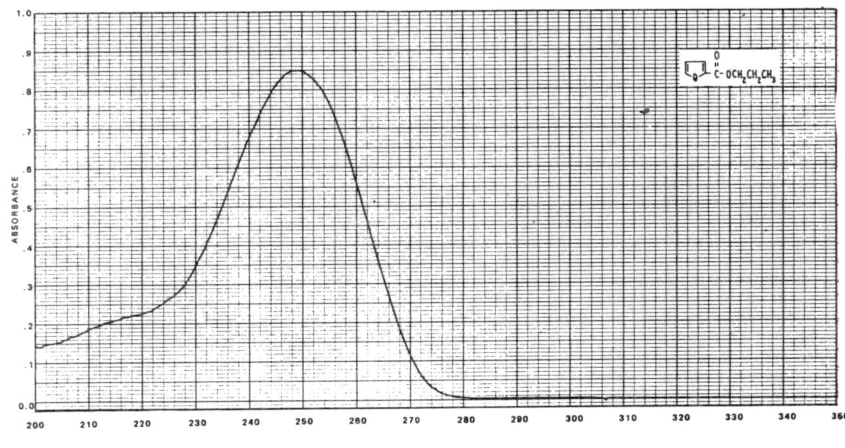

2-FUROIC ACID, PENTYL ESTER

2936

$C_9H_{14}O_3$

Mol. Wt. 170.21

Solvent: Methanol

λ Max. mμ	a_m	Cell mm	Conc. g/L
249	12000	1	0.100

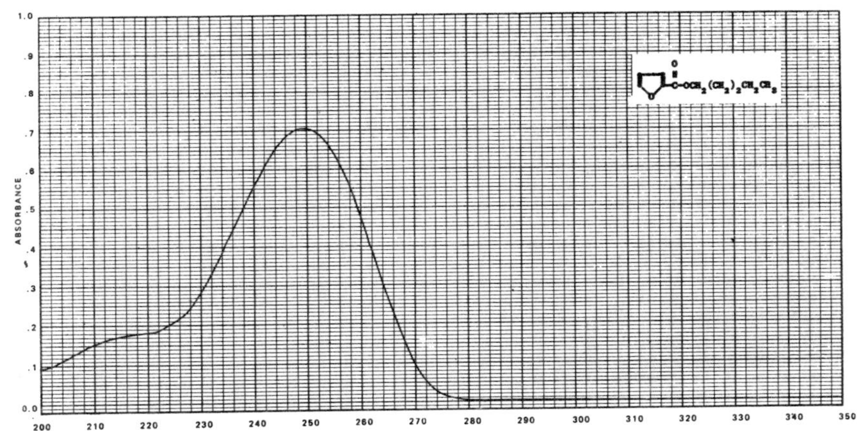

5-NITRO-2-FUROIC ACID, ETHYL ESTER

2937

$C_7H_7NO_5$

Mol. Wt. 185.14

Solvent: Methanol

λ Max. mμ	a_m	Cell mm	Conc. g/L
295	12300	1	0.100
211.5	11800	1	0.100

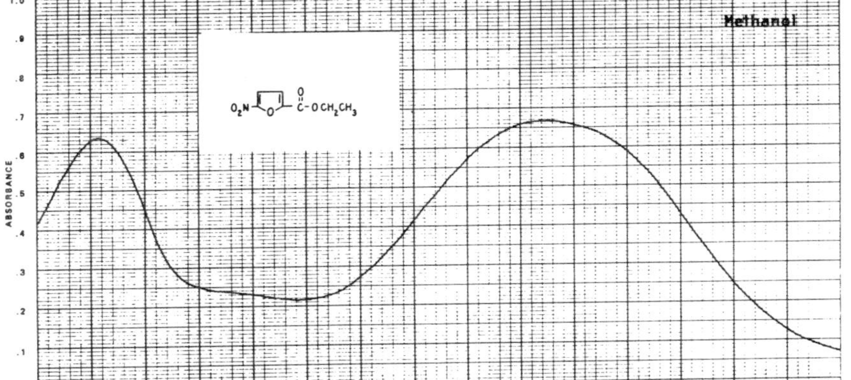

2-PYRIDINEACETIC ACID, METHYL ESTER

2938

$C_8H_9NO_2$
Mol. Wt. 151.17
Solvent: Methanol

λ Max. mμ	a_m	Cell mm	Conc. g/L
266.5	2610	2	0.1764
260	3540	2	0.1764
254.5	3060	2	0.1764

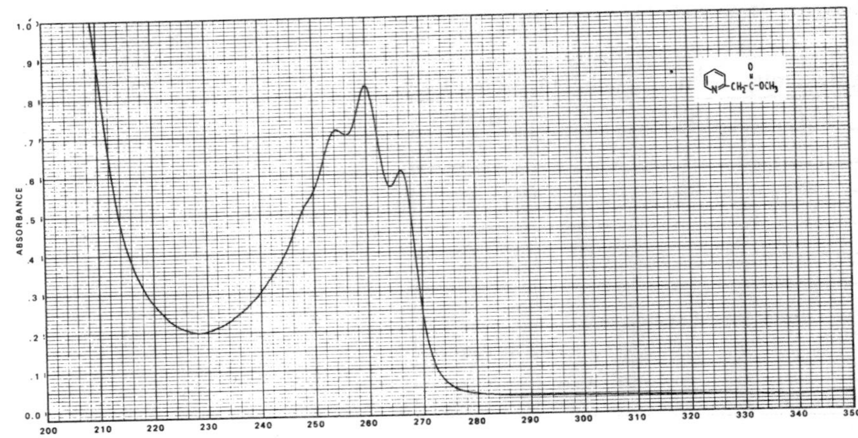

2-PYRIDINEACETIC ACID, METHYL ESTER

2938

$C_8H_9NO_2$
Mol. Wt. 151.17
Solvent: Methanol HCl

λ Max. mμ	a_m	Cell mm	Conc. g/L
261.5	7120	1	0.1764

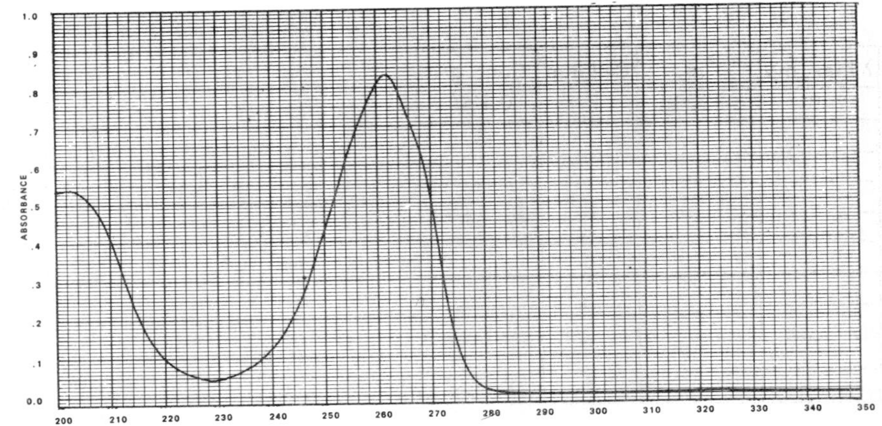

NICOTINIC ACID, NONYL ESTER

2939

$C_{15}H_{23}NO_2$
Mol. Wt. 249.36
B.P. 118-120°C/1mm
Solvent: Methanol

λ Max. mμ	a_m	Cell mm	Conc. g/L
262.5	3380	1	0.189
217	19900	1	0.189

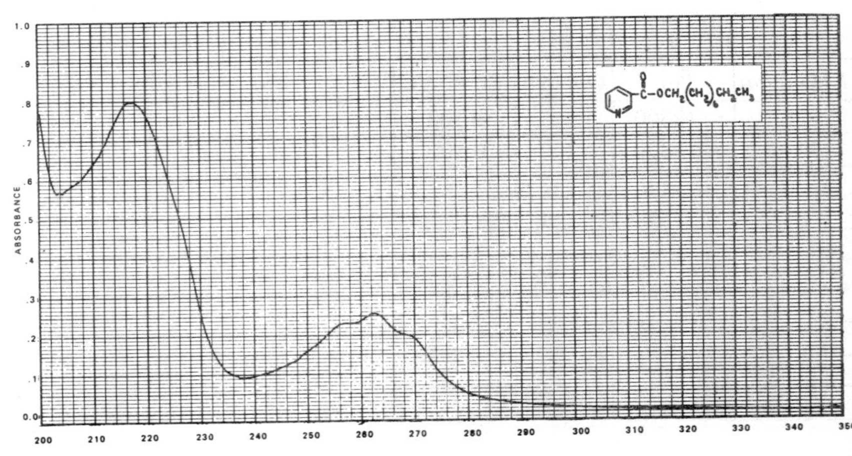

NICOTINIC ACID, NONYL ESTER

2939

$C_{15}H_{23}NO_2$
Mol. Wt. 249.36
B.P. 118-120°C/1mm
Solvent: Methanol HCl

λ Max. mμ	a_m	Cell mm	Conc. g/L
261	5780	1	0.189

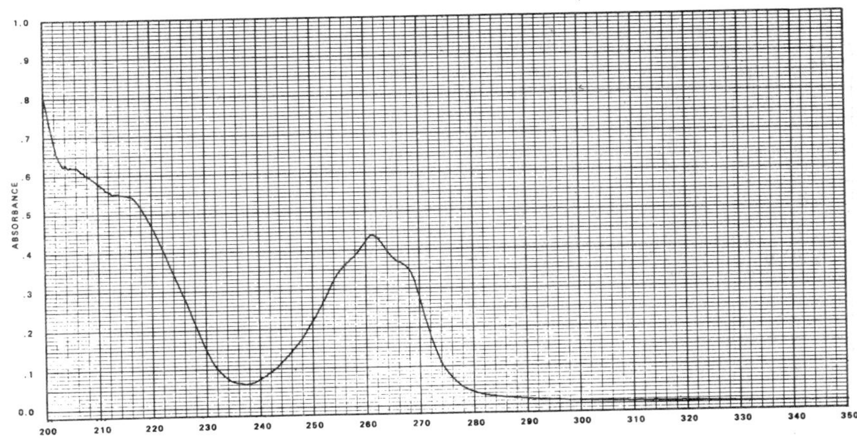

CARBONIC ACID, DI-p-TOLYL ESTER

2940

$C_{15}H_{14}O_3$
Mol. Wt. 242.28
M.P. 110-112°C
Solvent: Methanol

λ Max. mμ	a_m	Cell mm	Conc. g/L
270	814	20	0.100
264	945	20	0.100
216.5	16200	1	0.100
208.5	18100	1	0.100

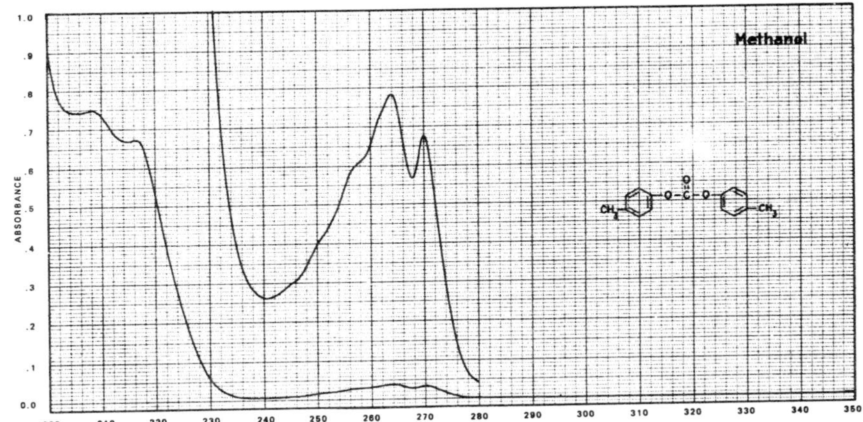

CARBONIC ACID, BIS(p-CHLOROPHENYL) ESTER

2941

$C_{13}H_8Cl_2O_3$
Mol. Wt. 283.11
M.P. 149-151°C
Solvent: Methanol

λ Max. mμ	a_m	Cell mm	Conc. g/L
282	1640	10	0.100
275	1610	10	0.100
251	674	10	0.100
220.5	18400	1	0.100

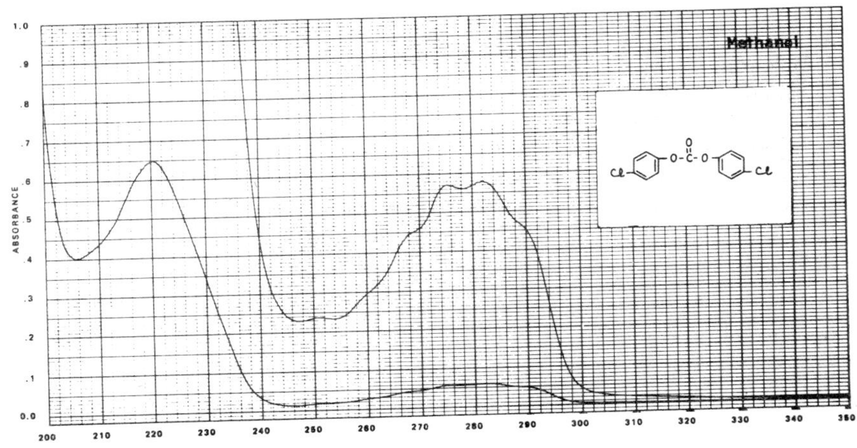

BENZOIC ACID, BENZYL ESTER

2942

$C_{14}H_{12}O_2$

Mol. Wt. 212.25

Solvent: Methanol

λ Max. mμ	a_m	Cell mm	Conc. g/L
279.5	771	5	0.268
272	968	5	0.268
267	954	5	0.268
263	952	5	0.268
257	952	5	0.268
229.5	1470	1	0.134

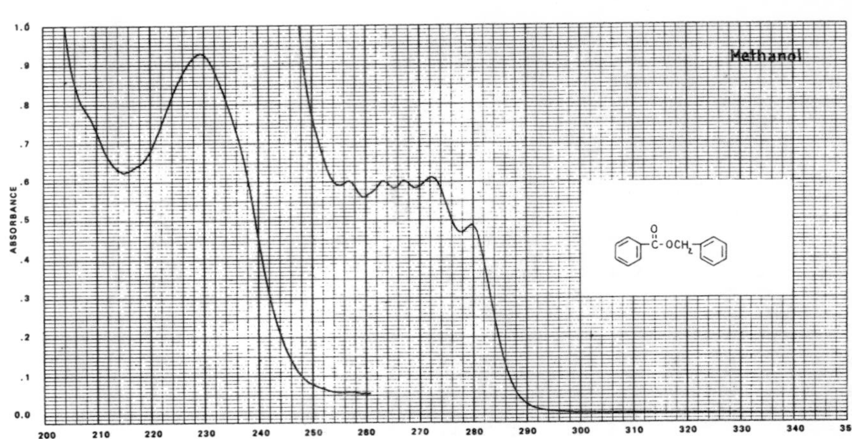

BENZOIC ACID, p-TOLYL ESTER

2943

$C_{14}H_{12}O_2$

Mol. Wt. 212.25

Solvent: Methanol

λ Max. mμ	a_m	Cell mm	Conc. g/L
270.5	2580	5	0.100
231	17100	1	0.100

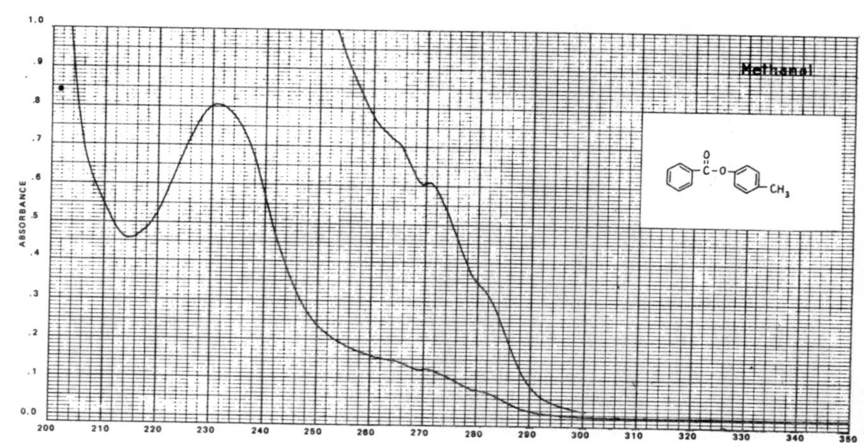

ETHYLENE GLYCOL, DIBENZOATE

2944

$C_{16}H_{14}O_4$

Mol. Wt. 270.28

M.P. 72°C

Solvent: Methanol

λ Max. mμ	a_m	Cell mm	Conc. g/L
280.5	1610	10	0.100
273	1950	10	0.100
228.5	23500	1	0.100

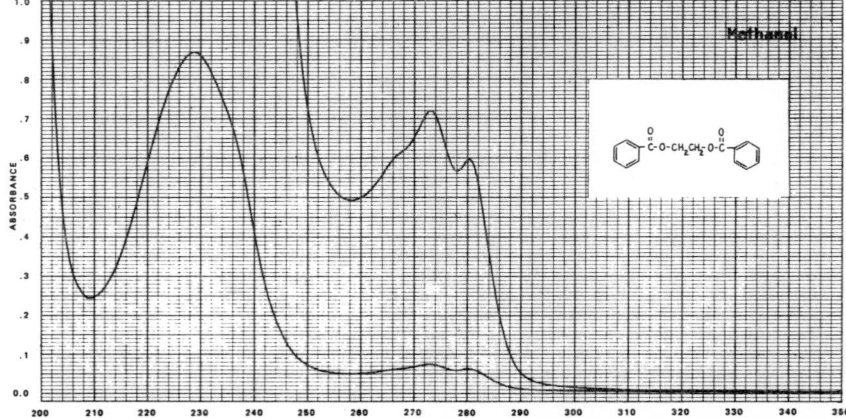

PYROCATECHOL, DIBENZOATE 2945

$C_{20}H_{14}O_4$
Mol. Wt. 318.33
M.P. 82-83°C
Solvent: Methanol

λ Max. mμ	a_m	Cell mm	Conc. g/L
230	33100	1	0.0500

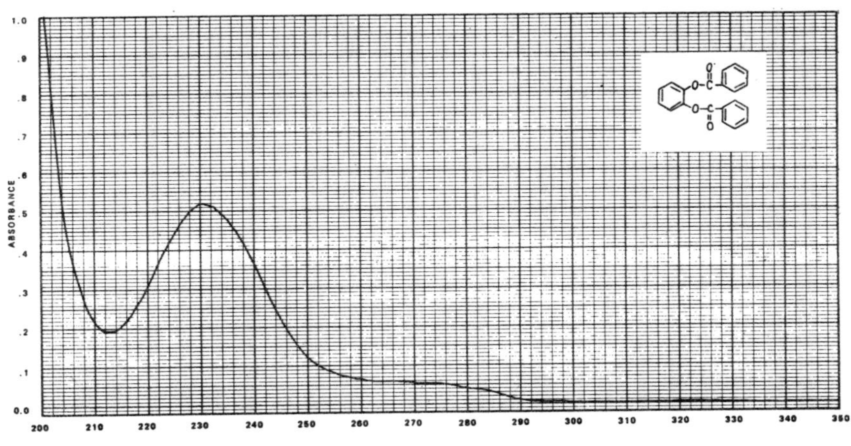

2946

λ Max. mμ	a_m	Cell mm	Conc. g/L

The saturated lactones (compounds 2946 through 2949) do not display any maxima in the near UV.

3-ACETYL-4,5-DIHYDRO-2(3H)-FURANONE 2950

$C_6H_8O_3$
Mol. Wt. 128.13
B.P. 107-108°C/5mm
Solvent: Methanol

λ Max. mμ	a_m	Cell mm	Conc. g/L
252	1190	2	0.2200

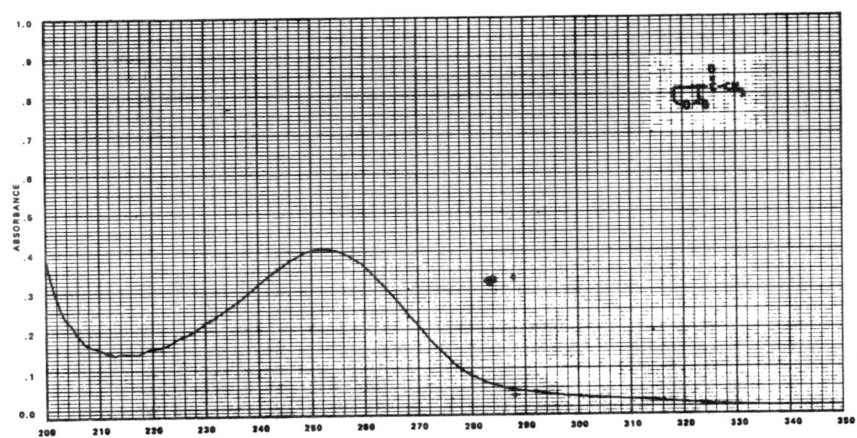

DIHYDRO-4-PHENYL-2(3H)-FURANONE 2951

$C_{10}H_{10}O_2$

Mol. Wt. 162.19

Solvent: Methanol

λ Max. mμ	a_m	Cell mm	Conc. g/L
256.5	528	20	0.100
251	485	20	0.100
x	x	1	0.100

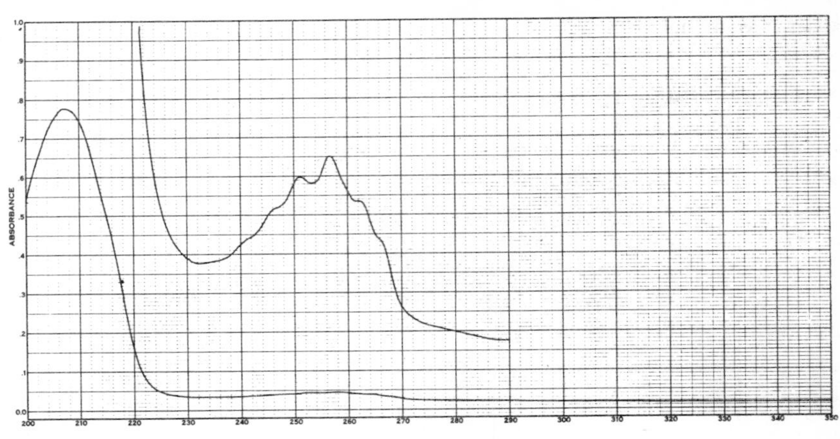

2952

λ Max. mμ	a_m	Cell mm	Conc. g/L

The saturated lactones (compounds 2952 and 2953) do not display any maxima in the near UV.

5-METHYL-2(3H)-FURANONE 2954

$C_5H_6O_2$

Mol. Wt. 98.10

B.R. 58-60°C (lit.)

Solvent: Methanol

λ Max. mμ	a_m	Cell mm	Conc. g/L
x	x	10	2.45
x	x	10	0.245
x	x	10	0.025

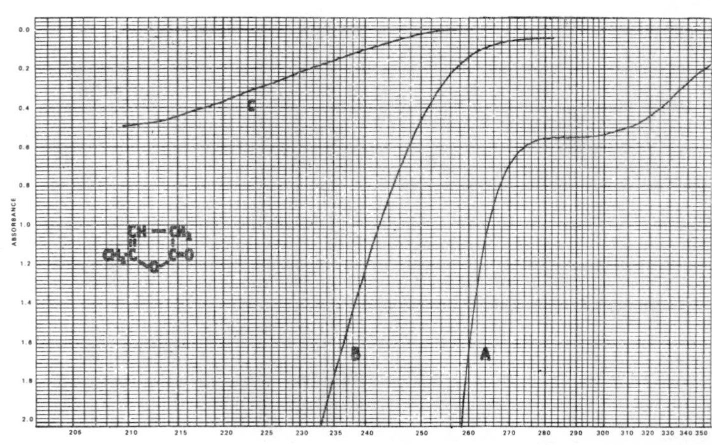

(o-HYDROXYPHENYL)ACETIC ACID, γ-LACTONE

2955

$C_8H_6O_2$
Mol. Wt. 134.14
M.P. 49-51°C
Solvent: Methanol

λ Max. mμ	a_m	Cell mm	Conc. g/L
276	1190	10	0.100
269.5	1210	10	0.100
x	x	1	0.100

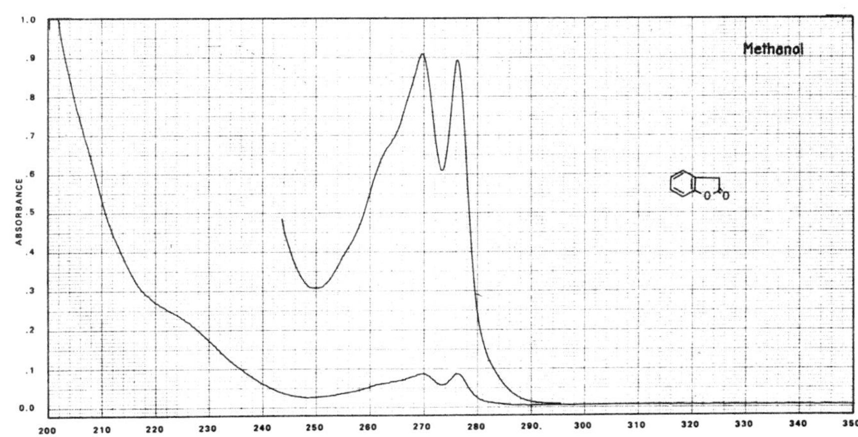

(o-HYDROXYPHENYL)ACETIC ACID, γ-LACTONE

2955

$C_8H_6O_2$
Mol. Wt. 134.14
M.P. 49-51°C
Solvent: Methanol KOH

λ Max. mμ	a_m	Cell mm	Conc. g/L
292.5	2440	5	0.100
238.5	5490	1	0.100

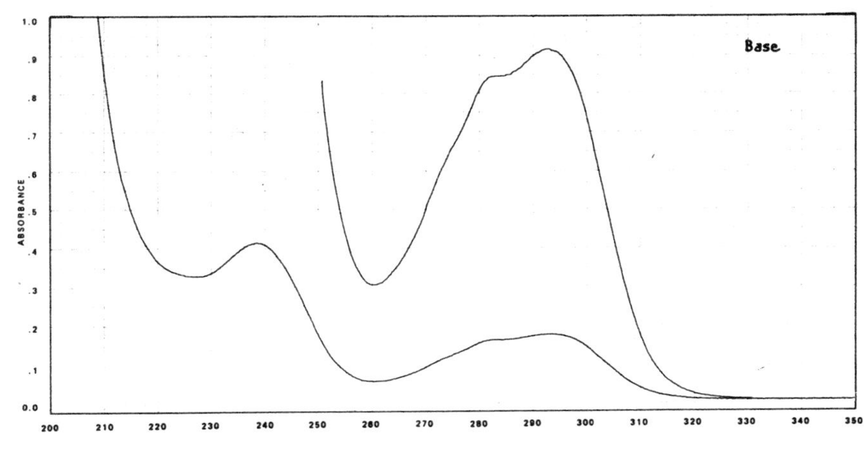

6-NITROPHTHALIDE

2956

$C_8H_5NO_4$
Mol. Wt. 179.13
M.P. 139-141°C
Solvent: Methanol

λ Max. mμ	a_m	Cell mm	Conc. g/L
259	7520	1	0.0500
218	24300	1	0.0500

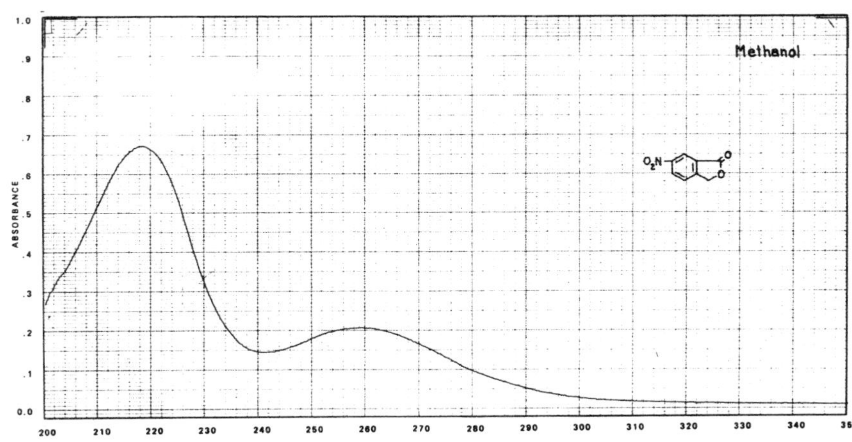

3-CHLOROCOUMARIN 2957

$C_9H_5ClO_2$

Mol. Wt. 180.60

Solvent: Methanol

λ Max. mμ	a_m	Cell mm	Conc. g/L
283	12500	10	0.010

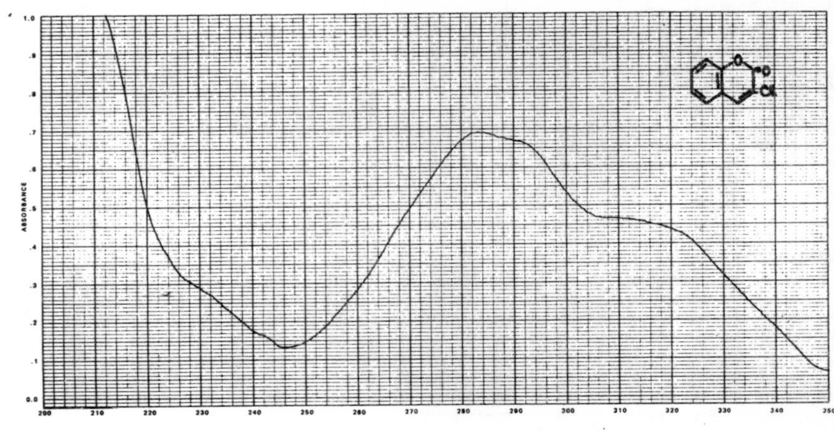

4-HYDROXYCOUMARIN, ACETATE 2958

$C_{11}H_8O_4$

Mol. Wt. 204.18

Solvent: Methanol

λ Max. mμ	a_m	Cell mm	Conc. g/L
303	8040	1	0.0500
279	11800	1	0.0500
267	10800	1	0.0500
211.5	24100	1	0.0500

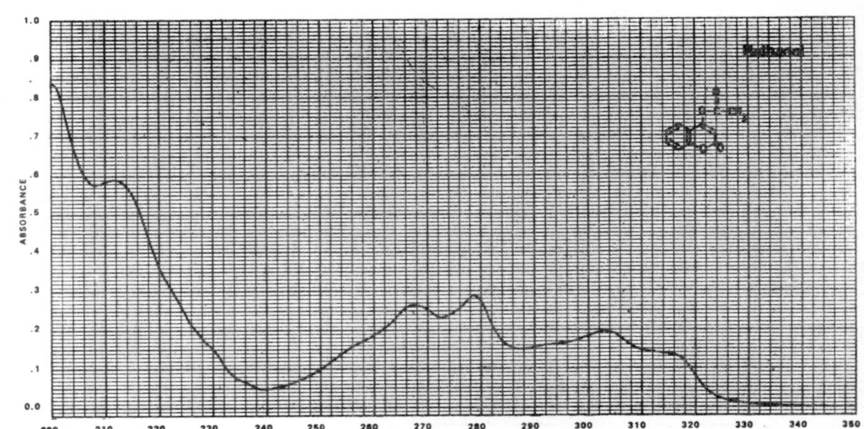

λ Max. mμ	a_m	Cell mm	Conc. g/L

THE ESTERS OF CHLOROFORMIC ACID

Aliphatic and Olefinic Compounds

The aliphatic and olefinic chloroformates do not give rise to any maxima in the near ultraviolet region and thus there are no spectra included in this section for compounds 2959 through 2966.

Aromatic Compounds

The phenyl ester of chloroformic acid (compound 2968, page 836) produces a near UV spectrum containing one major band at 256 mμ with a great deal of superimposed vibrational bands. This spectrum and that of its 4-nitro derivative are not significantly different in either band intensity or wavelength from those of the corresponding aliphatic carboxylic acids.

The spectra of the chloroformates do not change significantly upon the addition of either acid or base.

THE CARBAMATES

The phenyl esters of the carbamic acids produce spectra displaying significantly different intensities depending upon the degree of substitution of the carbamate nitrogen atom. The table given below lists two examples.

Compound	λ_{max} (ϵ_{max})	Solvent	Spectrum
Carbamic acid, phenyl ester	255 (23100)	Methanol	2978
Dimethylcarbamic acid, phenyl ester	260 (387)	Methanol	2991

The carbanilates, which contain the phenyl group bonded to the nitrogen atom (compounds 2987, 2988, 2990 and 2994) produce UV spectra containing one major band in the region from 229 - 236 mμ. They may also display one or more inflections or weak maxima near 270 mμ.

The aromatic derivatives of carbamic acid are not sensitive to changes in pH and their UV spectra are not significantly affected by the addition of either acid or base.

THE ESTERS OF PHOSPHORUS ACID

The diesters of vinylphosphonic acid (compound 2996) display one major band near 256 mμ (ϵ_{max} = 3360) unlike their carboxylic acid counterparts which do not display any maxima in the near UV.

The spectrum of the tribenzyl ester of phosphoric acid (compound 3000) gives rise to a typical benzyl spectrum consisting of one major band near 260 mμ with associated fine structure.

p-NITROBENZYL CHLOROFORMATE

2967

$C_8H_6ClNO_4$
Mol. Wt. 215.59
M.P. 32.5-34°C
Solvent: Cyclohexane

λ Max. mμ	a_m	Cell mm	Conc. g/L
256	7420	2	0.100
x	x	2	0.100

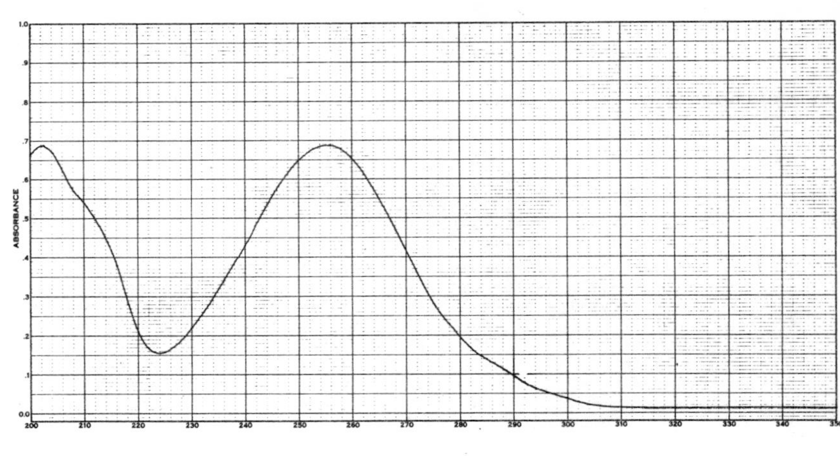

CHLOROFORMIC ACID, PHENYL ESTER

2968

$C_7H_5ClO_2$
Mol. Wt. 156.57
B.P. 192°C (lit.)
Solvent: Cyclohexane

λ Max. mμ	a_m	Cell mm	Conc. g/L
277	72.0	10	2.260
270	856	10	0.260
261	187	10	1.130
256	200	10	1.130
250.5	163	10	1.130
x	x	10	0.113
x	x	10	0.011

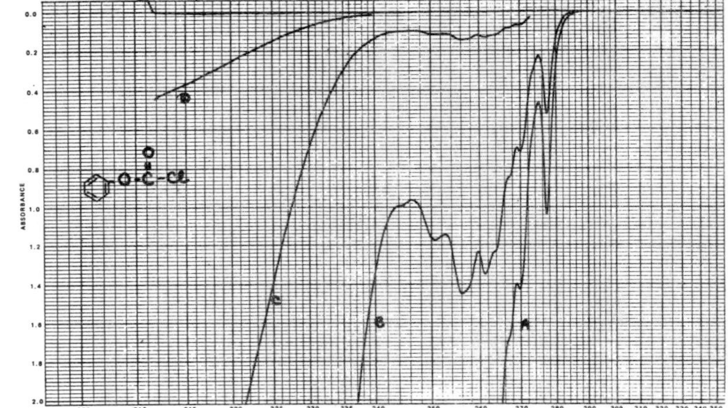

CHLOROFORMIC ACID, p-NITROPHENYL ESTER

2969

$C_7H_4ClNO_4$
Mol. Wt. 201.57
M.P. 77-79°C
Solvent: Methanol

λ Max. mμ	a_m	Cell mm	Conc. g/L
269	8050	2	0.100

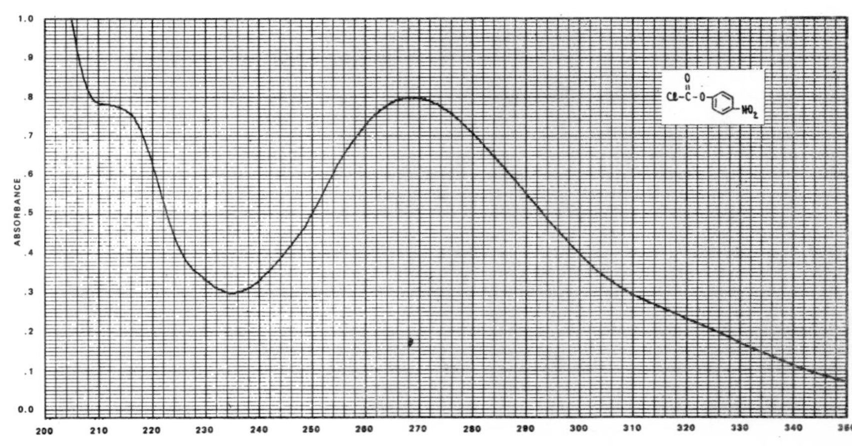

CHLOROFORMIC ACID, p-NITROPHENYL ESTER 2969

$C_7H_4ClNO_4$
Mol. Wt. 201.57
M.P. 77-79°C
Solvent: Methanol KOH

λ Max. mμ	a_m	Cell mm	Conc. g/L
392	17800	1	0.100
300	1150	10	0.100
290	1190	10	0.100
226	6450	1	0.100

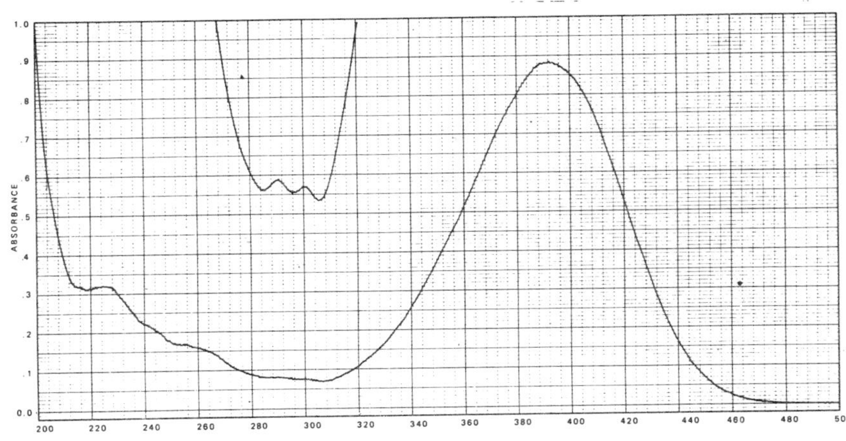

THIOACETIC ACID S-ETHYL ESTER 2970

C_4H_8OS
Mol. Wt. 104.17
B.P. 115-117°C

λ Max. mμ	a_m	Cell mm	Conc. g/L

Pure sample not available.

THIOBENZOIC ACID, S-BENZYL ESTER 2971

$C_{14}H_{12}OS$
Mol. Wt. 228.29
Solvent: Cyclohexane

λ Max. mμ	a_m	Cell mm	Conc. g/L
x	x	10	2.00
267	9020	10	0.040
233.5	17500	10	0.008

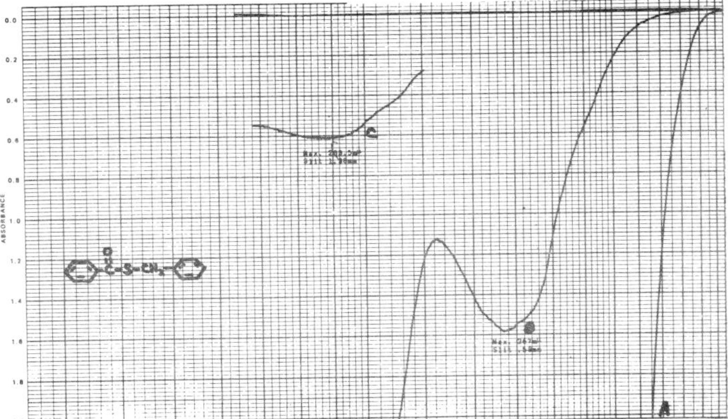

THIOCARBONIC ACID, o-ETHYL S-(2-HYDROXYETHYL) ESTER 2972

$C_5H_{10}O_3S$

Mol. Wt. 150.20

B.P. 109-112°C/5mm

λ Max. mμ	a_m	Cell mm	Conc. g/L

The esters of thiocarbonic acid do not display any maxima in the near UV.

2973

λ Max. mμ	a_m	Cell mm	Conc. g/L

The aliphatic carbamates (compounds 2973 through 2977) do not display any maxima in the near UV.

CARBAMIC ACID, PHENYL ESTER 2978

$C_7H_7NO_2$

Mol. Wt. 137.13

M.P. 241°C (lit.)

Solvent: Methanol

λ Max. mμ	a_m	Cell mm	Conc. g/L
x	x	10	0.404
255	23100	10	0.008

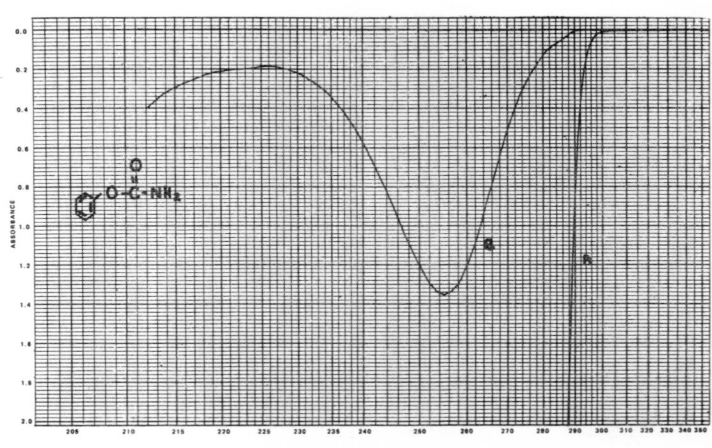

CARBAMIC ACID, p-TOLYL ESTER

2979

$C_8H_9NO_2$

Mol. Wt. 151.17

M.P. 163-164°C

Solvent: Methanol

λ Max. mμ	a_m	Cell mm	Conc. g/L
271	527	10	0.100
265	575	10	0.100

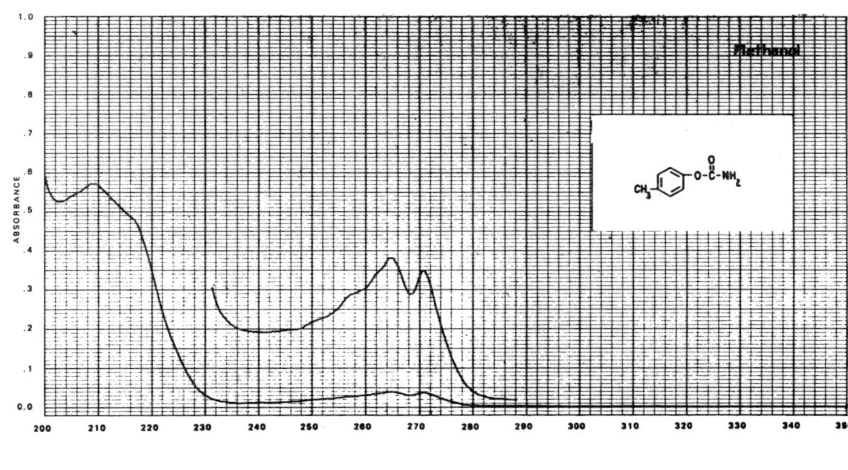

2980

λ Max. mμ	a_m	Cell mm	Conc. g/L

The aliphatic carbamates (compounds 2980 through 2985) do not display any maxima in the near UV.

PHENETHYLCARBAMIC ACID, ETHYL ESTER

2986

$C_{11}H_{15}NO_2$

Mol. Wt. 193.25

Solvent: Methanol

λ Max. mμ	a_m	Cell mm	Conc. g/L
258	427	40	0.100
252.5	373	40	0.100
215.5	3510	5	0.100

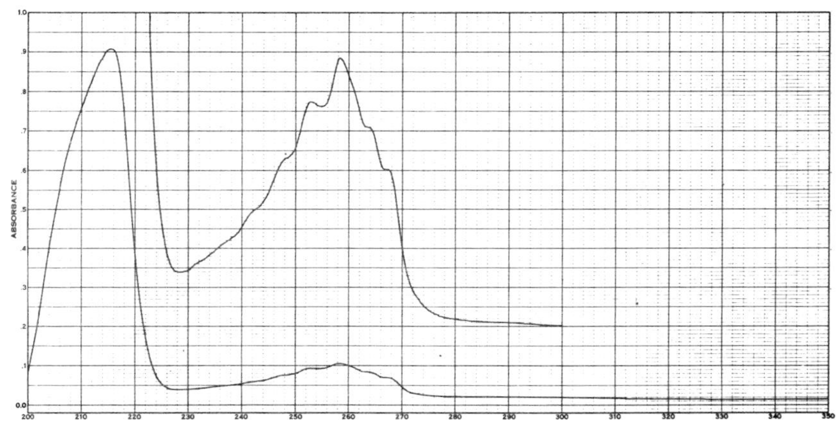

CARBANILIC ACID, PROPYL ESTER

2987

$C_{10}H_{13}NO_2$
Mol. Wt. 179.22
Solvent: Methanol

λ Max. mμ	a_m	Cell mm	Conc. g/L
234	17000	1	0.100
x	x	1	0.100

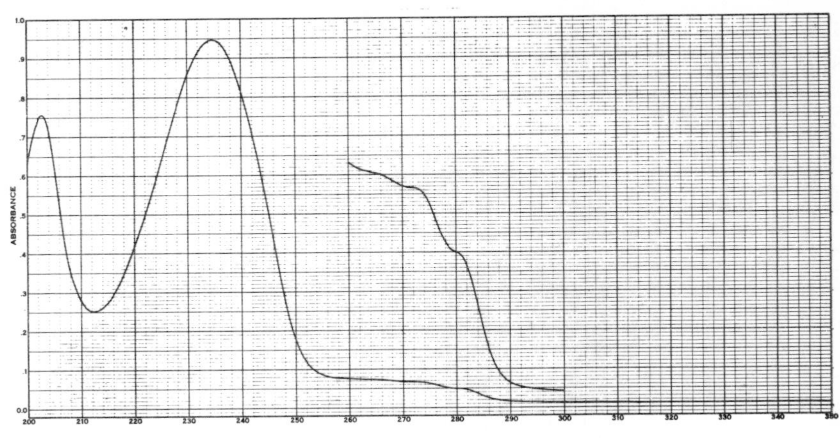

CARBANILIC ACID, CYCLOHEXYL ESTER

2988

$C_{13}H_{17}NO_2$
Mol. Wt. 219.29
Solvent: Methanol

λ Max. mμ	a_m	Cell mm	Conc. g/L
234	15800	1	0.100
x	x	1	0.100

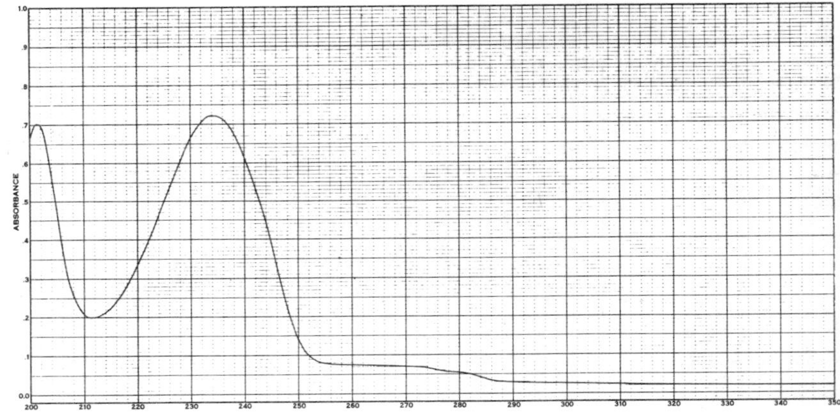

CARBANILIC ACID, DIPHENYLMETHYL ESTER

2989

$C_{20}H_{17}NO_2$
Mol. Wt. 303.36
M.P. 140°C
Solvent: Methanol

λ Max. mμ	a_m	Cell mm	Conc. g/L
280	637	20	0.100
264	1260	20	0.100
234	19700	1	0.100

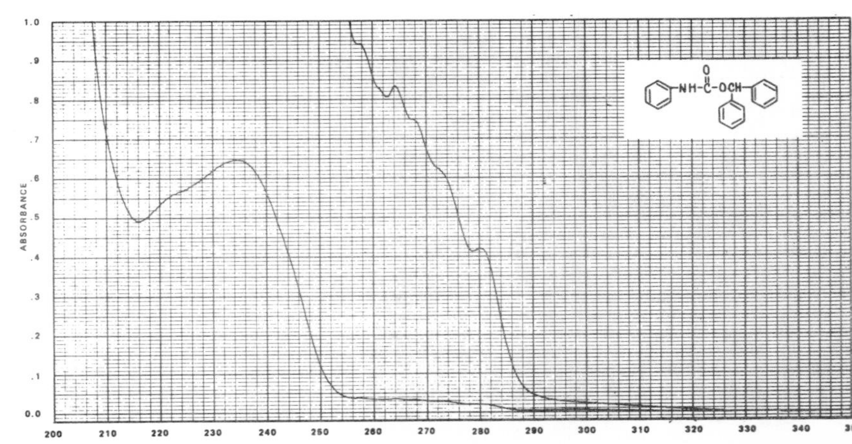

BUTYLPHENYLCARBAMIC ACID, ETHYL ESTER 2990

$C_{13}H_{19}NO_2$
Mol. Wt. 221.30
Solvent: Methanol

λ Max. mμ	a_m	Cell mm	Conc. g/L
229	6170	10	0.020

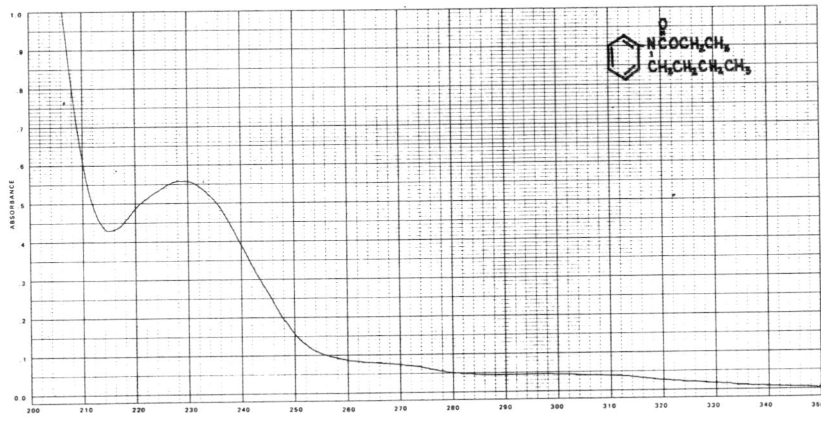

DIMETHYLCARBAMIC ACID, PHENYL ESTER 2991

$C_9H_{11}NO_2$
Mol. Wt. 165.19
M.P. 45-46°C
Solvent: Methanol

λ Max. mμ	a_m	Cell mm	Conc. g/L
265.5	318	20	0.100
259.5	387	20	0.100
x	x	1	0.100

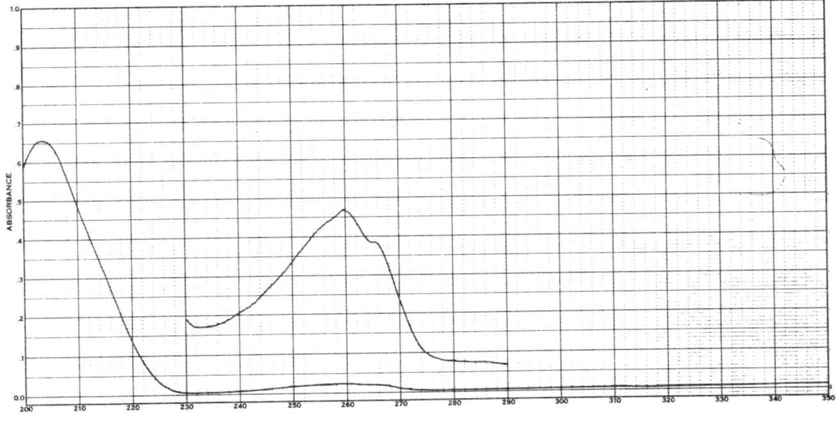

2992

λ Max. mμ	a_m	Cell mm	Conc. g/L

The alicyclic carbamates (compounds 2992 and 2993) do not display any maxima in the near UV.

3-PHENYL-2-OXAZOLIDINONE

2994

$C_9H_9NO_2$
Mol. Wt. 163.18
Solvent: Methanol

λ Max. mμ	a_m	Cell mm	Conc. g/L
278	572	20	0.100
271	774	20	0.100
264.5	713	20	0.100
236	16400	1	0.050

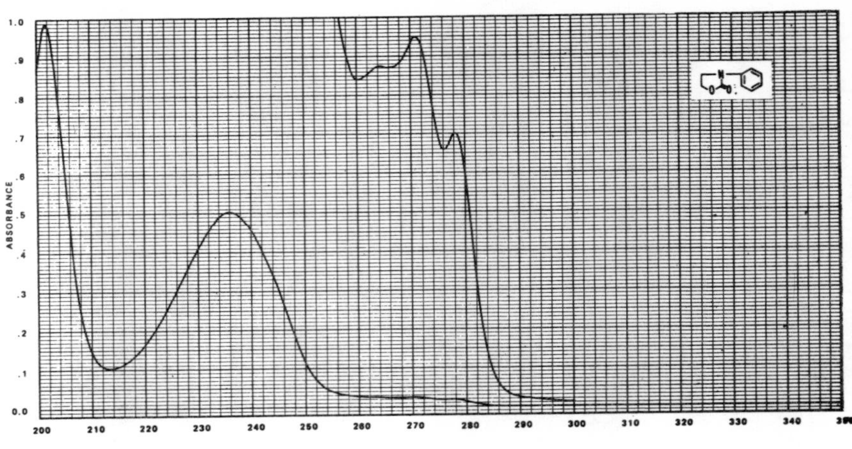

BENZOYL PEROXIDE

2995

$C_{14}H_{10}O_4$
Mol. Wt. 242.22
Solvent: Dioxane

λ Max. mμ	a_m	Cell mm	Conc. g/L
275	2540	10	0.083
235	23000	10	0.008

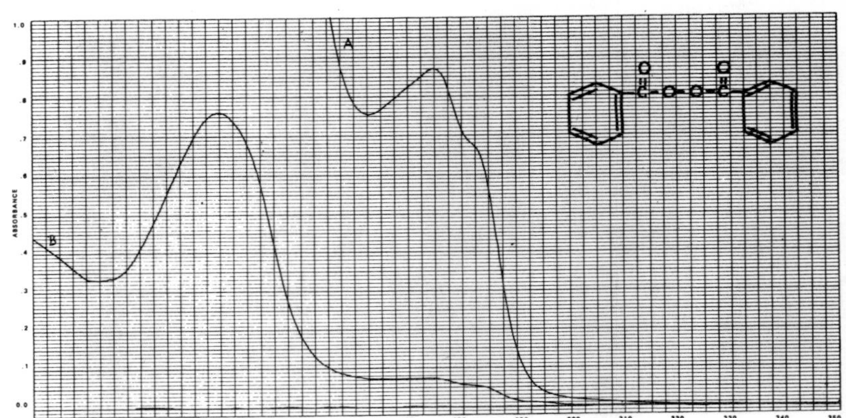

VINYLPHOSPHONIC ACID, BIS(2-CHLOROETHYL) ESTER

2996

$C_6H_{11}Cl_2O_3P$
Mol. Wt. 233.03
Solvent: Methanol

λ Max. mμ	a_m	Cell mm	Conc. g/L
255.5	3360	40	0.100
x	x	20	0.100

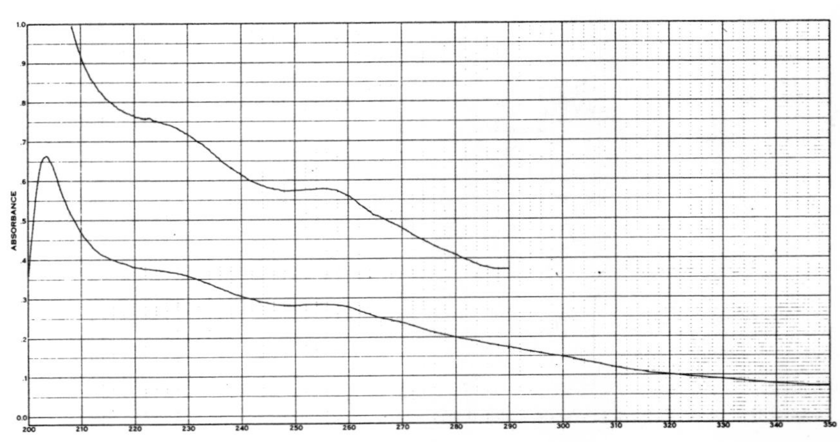

2997

λ Max. mμ	a_m	Cell mm	Conc. g/L

The aliphatic esters of phosphoric and phosphoramidic acid do not display any maxima in the near UV.

PHOSPHORIC ACID, TRIBENZYL ESTER **3000**

$C_{2}IH_{21}O_{4}P$

Mol. Wt. 368.37

Solvent: Methanol

λ Max. mμ	a_m	Cell mm	Conc. g/L
267	584	20	0.1
261.5	805	20	0.100
256.5	862	20	0.100
251	733	20	0.100
214.5	6760	5	0.100

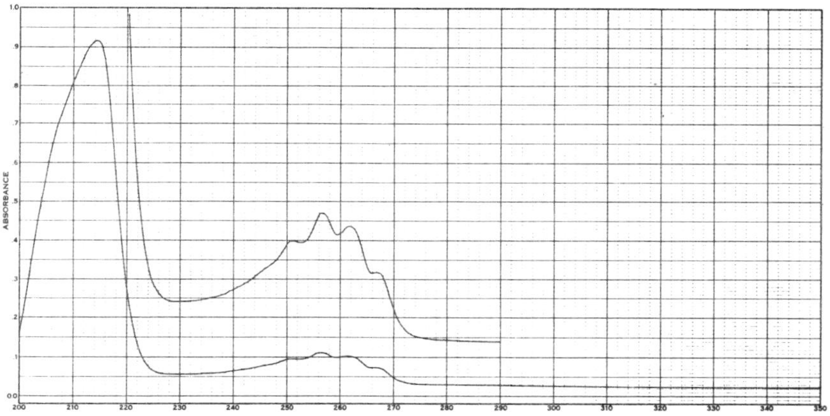

λ Max. mμ	a_m	Cell mm	Conc. g/L

* No spectrum is included for this compound (see Preface).

* No spectrum is included for this compound (see Preface).

* No spectrum is included for this compound (see Preface).

SPECTRUM NO. NAME

MONOCYCLIC AROMATICS

* No spectrum is included for this compound (see Preface).

* No spectrum is included for this compound (see Preface).

SPECTRUM NO.	NAME
221	α-FLUOROTOLUENE
222	α,α,α-TRIFLUOROTOLUENE
223	FLUOROBENZENE
224	o-FLUOROTOLUENE
225	m-FLUOROTOLUENE
226	p-FLUOROTOLUENE
227	o,α,α,α-TETRAFLUOROTOLUENE
228	m,α,α,α-TETRAFLUOROTOLUENE
229	p,α,α,α-TETRAFLUOROTOLUENE
230	o-DIFLUOROBENZENE
231	m-DIFLUOROBENZENE
232	p-DIFLUOROBENZENE
233	1-FLUORONAPHTHALENE
234	2-FLUORONAPHTHALENE

CHLORINATED HYDROCARBONS

SPECTRUM NO.	NAME
* 235	1-CHLOROPROPANE
* 236	1-CHLOROBUTANE
* 237	2-CHLOROBUTANE
* 238	1-CHLORO-2-METHYLPROPANE
* 239	2-CHLORO-2-METHYLPROPANE
* 240	1-CHLOROPENTANE
* 241	2-CHLORO-2-METHYLBUTANE
* 242	1-CHLOROHEPTANE
* 243	1-CHLORODECANE
* 244	1-CHLOROUNDECANE
* 245	1-CHLORODODECANE
* 246	1-CHLOROTETRADECANE
* 247	1-CHLOROHEXADECANE
* 248	1-CHLOROOCTADECANE
* 249	DICHLOROMETHANE
* 250	CHLOROFORM
* 251	1,1-DICHLOROETHANE
* 252	1,2-DICHLOROETHANE
* 253	1,1,1-TRICHLOROETHANE
* 254	1,1,2-TRICHLOROETHANE
* 255	1,1,2,2-TETRACHLOROETHANE
* 256	PENTACHLOROETHANE
* 257	2-DICHLOROPROPANE
* 258	2,2-DICHLOROPROPANE
* 259	1,2,3-TRICHLOROPROPANE
* 260	1,1,1,2-TETRACHLOROPROPANE
* 261	1,1,2,3,3-PENTACHLOROPROPANE
* 262	1,2-DICHLOROBUTANE
* 263	1,4-DICHLOROBUTANE
* 264	1,5-DICHLOROPENTANE
* 265	1,1-DICHLORO-3,3-DIMETHYLBUTANE
* 266	CHLOROCYCLOPENTANE

* No spectrum is included for this compound (see Preface).

* No spectrum is included for this compound (see Preface).

SPECTRUM NO.	NAME
313	1,2,4-TRICHLOROBENZENE
314	1,3,5-TRICHLOROBENZENE
315	1,2,4,5-TETRACHLOROBENZENE
316	1-(CHLOROMETHYL)NAPHTHALENE
317	1-CHLORONAPHTHALENE
318	2-CHLORONAPHTHALENE

BROMINATED HYDROCARBONS

SPECTRUM NO.	NAME
* 319	BROMOETHANE
* 320	1-BROMOPROPANE
* 321	2-BROMOPROPANE
* 322	1-BROMOBUTANE
* 323	2-BROMOBUTANE
* 324	1-BROMO-2-METHYLPROPANE
* 325	2-BROMO-2-METHYLPROPANE
* 326	1-BROMOPENTANE
* 327	2-BROMOPENTANE
* 328	1-BROMO-3-METHYLBUTANE
* 329	1-BROMO-2,2-DIMETHYLPROPANE
* 330	1-BROMOHEXANE
* 331	3-BROMOHEXANE
* 332	1-BROMOHEPTANE
* 333	1-BROMOOCTANE
* 334	2-BROMOOCTANE
* 335	1-BROMOUNDECANE
* 336	1-BROMODODECANE
* 337	1-BROMOTETRADECANE
* 338	1-BROMOPENTADECANE
* 339	1-BROMOHEXADECANE
* 340	1-BROMOHEPTADECANE
* 341	1-BROMONONADECANE
* 342	BROMODICHLOROMETHANE
* 343	1-BROMO-2-CHLOROETHANE
* 344	1-BROMO-3-CHLORO-2-METHYLPROPANE
* 345	1-BROMO-2-CHLORO-1,1,2-TRIFLUOROETHANE
* 346	DIBROMOMETHANE
* 347	TRIBROMOMETHANE
* 348	1,2-DIBROMOETHANE
* 349	1,2-DIBROMO-1,1-DIFLUOROETHANE
* 350	1,2-DIBROMO-1,1-DICHLOROETHANE
* 351	1,1,2-TRIBROMOETHANE
* 352	1,1,2,2-TETRABROMOETHANE
* 353	1,2-DIBROMOPROPANE
* 354	1,3-DIBROMOPROPANE
* 355	1-CHLORO-2,3-DIBROMOPROPANE
* 356	1,2,3-TRIBROMOPROPANE
* 357	1,2-DIBROMOBUTANE

* No spectrum is included for this compound (see Preface).

* No spectrum is included for this compound (see Preface).

* No spectrum is included for this compound (see Preface).

SPECTRUM NO.	NAME
* 447	tert-PENTYLAMINE
* 448	1,2,2-TRIMETHYLPROPYLAMINE
* 449	1-METHYLPENTYLAMINE
* 450	1,3-DIMETHYLBUTYLAMINE
* 451	HEPTYLAMINE
* 452	1,1-DIMETHYLPENTYLAMINE
* 453	1,4-DIMETHYLPENTYLAMINE
* 454	2-ETHYLHEXYLAMINE
* 455	1-BUTYLPENTYLAMINE
* 456	1,1-DIBUTYLPENTYLAMINE
* 457	ETHYLENEDIAMINE
* 458	1,3-PROPANEDIAMINE
* 459	1,2-PROPANEDIAMINE
* 460	2-METHYL-1,2-PROPANEDIAMINE
* 461	1,4-BUTANEDIAMINE
* 462	1,12-DODECANEDIAMINE
* 463	N-ETHYLETHYLENEDIAMINE
* 464	N-METHYL-1,3-PROPANEDIAMINE
* 465	N,N-DIBYTYL-1,3-PROPANEDIAMINE
* 466	3,3′-DIAMINODIPROPYLAMINE
* 467	4-DODECYLDIETHYLENETRIAMINE
* 468	CYCLOPENTYLAMINE
* 469	CYCLOHEXANEMETHYLAMINE
* 470	CYCLOHEXYLAMINE
* 471	4-METHYLCYCLOHEXYLAMINE
* 472	CYCLOHEPTYLAMINE
* 473	1-ADAMANTANEMETHYLAMINE
* 474	ALLYLAMINE
* 475	2-METHYLALLYLAMINE
476	BENZYLAMINE
477	PHENETHYLAMINE
478	DL-α-METHYLBENZYLAMINE
479	β-METHYLPHENETHYLAMINE
480	α,α-DIMETHYLBENZYLAMINE
481	3-PHENYLPROPYLAMINE
482	4-PHENYLBUTYLAMINE
483	o-METHYLBENZYLAMINE
484	m-METHYLBENZYLAMINE
485	p-METHYLBENZYLAMINE
486	p-ISOPROPYLBENZYLAMINE
487	ANILINE
488	o-TOLUIDINE
489	m-TOLUIDINE
490	p-TOLUIDINE
491	o-ETHYLANILINE
492	m-ETHYLANILINE

* No spectrum is included for this compound (see Preface).

* No spectrum is included for this compound (see Preface).

* No spectrum is included for this compound (see Preface).

TERTIARY AMINES

* No spectrum is included for this compound (see Preface).

SPECTRUM NO.	NAME
* 629	N,N-DIMETHYL-N'-(1-METHYLDODECYL)-1,3-PROPANEDIAMINE
* 630	N,N'-METHYLENEBISDIMETHYLAMINE
* 631	N,N,N',N'-TETRABUTYLMETHANEDIAMINE
* 632	N,N-DIETHYL-N',N'-DIMETHYLETHYLENEDIAMINE
* 633	N,N'-DIETHYL-N,N'-DIMETHYLETHYLENEDIAMINE
* 634	N,N,N',N'-TETRAMETHYL-1,3-PROPANEDIAMINE
* 635	N,N-DIETHYLCYCLOHEXYLAMINE
* 636	1-METHYLPYRROLIDINE
* 637	1-METHYLPIPERIDINE
* 638	1,1'-METHYLENEDIPIPERIDINE
639	1-(DIPHENYLMETHYL)-4-METHYLPIPERAZINE
640	1-PHENYLPIPERAZINE
641	2-METHYL-1-PHENYLPIPERAZINE
* 642	N,N-DIMETHYLALLYLAMINE
* 643	N,N,2-TRIMETHYLPROPENYLAMINE
644	N,N-DIMETHYLBENZYLAMINE
645	N,N-DIETHYLBENZYLAMINE
646	N-ETHYLDIBENZYLAMINE
647	TRIBENZYLAMINE
648	N,N-DIMETHYLANILINE
649	N,N-DIETHYLANILINE
650	N,N-DIPROPYLANILINE
651	N,N-DIBUTYLANILINE
652	N-BENZYL-N-METHYLANILINE
653	N-ETHYL-N-PHENYLBENZYLAMINE
654	N,N-DIBENZYLANILINE
655	N,N-BIS(2-CHLOROETHYL)ANILINE
656	N,N-DIALLYLANILINE
657	TRIPHENYLAMINE
658	N,N-DIMETHYL-o-TOLUIDINE
659	N,N-DIMETHYL-m-TOLUIDINE
660	N,N-DIMETHYL-p-TOLUIDINE
661	N,N-DIETHYL-o-TOLUIDINE
662	N,N-DIETHYL-m-TOLUIDINE
663	N,N-DIETHYL-p-TOLUIDINE
664	N,N-DIETHYL-2,5-XYLIDINE
665	N,N-DIMETHYL-2,6-XYLIDINE
666	4,4'-METHYLENEBIS[N,N-DIMETHYLANILINE]
667	4,4',4''-METHYLIDYNETRIS[N,N-DIMETHYLANILINE]
668	p-BROMO-N,N-DIMETHYLANILINE
669	N,N-DIMETHYL-p-PHENYLENEDIAMINE
670	N,N-DIETHYL-p-PHENYLENEDIAMINE
671	N,N-DIMETHYL-1-NAPHTHYLAMINE
672	N,N-DIETHYL-1-NAPHTHYLAMINE
* 673	1-METHYL-1,2,3,6-TETRAHYDROPYRIDINE

* No spectrum is included for this compound (see Preface).

* No spectrum is included for this compound (see Preface).

* No spectrum is included for this compound (see Preface).

* No spectrum is included for this compound (see Preface).

OXIMES

* No spectrum is included for this compound (see Preface).

* No spectrum is included for this compound (see Preface).

* No spectrum is included for this compound (see Preface).

SPECTRUM NO.	NAME
933	ISOTHIOCYANIC ACID, HEPTYL ESTER
* 934	ISOTHIOCYANIC ACID, OCTADECYL ESTER
935	ISOTHIOCYANIC ACID, 1-ADAMANTYL ESTER
936	ISOTHIOCYANIC ACID, ALLYL ESTER
* 937	ISOTHIOCYANIC ACID, BENZYL ESTER
938	ISOTHIOCYANIC ACID, PHENYL ESTER
939	ISOTHIOCYANIC ACID, o-FLUOROPHENYL ESTER
940	ISOTHIOCYANIC ACID, m-FLUOROPHENYL ESTER
941	ISOTHIOCYANIC ACID, p-FLUOROPHENYL ESTER
* 942	ISOTHIOCYANIC ACID, o-CHLOROPHENYL ESTER

NITRILES

SPECTRUM NO.	NAME
* 943	ACETONITRILE
* 944	BUTYRONITRILE
* 945	ISOBUTYRONITRILE
* 946	VALERONITRILE
* 947	ISOVALERONITRILE
* 948	PIVALONITRILE
* 949	HEXANENITRILE
* 950	HEPTANENITRILE
* 951	OCTANENITRILE
* 952	DECANENITRILE
* 953	PALMITONITRILE
* 954	3-CHLOROPROPIONITRILE
* 955	4-CHLOROBUTYRONITRILE
* 956	3-BROMOPROPIONITRILE
* 957	7-BROMOHEPTANONITRILE
* 958	4-(DIISOPROPYLAMONO)BUTYRONITRILE
* 959	4-(DIBUTYLAMONO)BUTYRONITRILE
* 960	3,3′-IMINODIPROPIONITRILE
* 961	MALONONITRILE
* 962	SUCCINONITRILE
* 963	PIMELONITRILE
* 964	CYCLOHEXANECARBONITRILE
* 965	trans-1,4-CYCLOHEXANEDICARBONITRILE
966	ACRYLONITRILE
* 967	2-METHYLACRYLONITRILE
* 968	3-BUTENENITRILE
969	(AMINOMETHYLENE)MALONONITRILE
* 970	3-CYCLOHEXENE-1-CARBONITRILE
971	1-CYCLOHEXENE-1-CARBONITRILE
972	PHENYLACETONITRILE
973	HYDROCINNAMONITRILE
* 974	β,β-DIMETHYLHYDROCINNAMONITRILE
975	(DIMETHYLAMONO)PHENYLACETONITRILE
976	3,3′-(PHENYLIMONO)DIPROPIONITRILE
977	2,2-DIPHENYLBUTYRONITRILE

* No spectrum is included for this compound (see Preface).

CYANAMIDES

THIOCYANATES

* No spectrum is included for this compound (see Preface).

SPECTRUM NO.	NAME
NITROSO COMPOUNDS	
*1021	2-METHYL-2-NITROSOPROPANE
1022	4-NITROSODIPHENYLAMINE
1023	N,N-DIMETHYL-p-NITROSOANILINE
1024	N,N-DIETHYL-4-NITROSOANILINE
N-NITROSO COMPOUNDS	
1025	N-NITROSODIMETHYLAMINE
1026	N-NITROSODIETHYLAMINE
*1027	N-NITROSODIPROPYLAMINE
*1028	N-NITROSODICYCLOHEXYLAMINE
*1029	1-NITROSOPYRROLIDINE
1030	1-NITROSOPIPERIDINE
1031	N-METHYL-N-NITROSOANILINE
1032	N-NITROSODIPHENYLAMINE
NITRITES	
*1033	PROPYL NITRITE
*1034	sec-BUTYL NITRITE
*1035	ISOBUTYL NITRITE
*1036	tert-BUTYL NITRITE
*1037	ISOPENTYL NITRITE
1038	OCTYL NITRITE
NITRO COMPOUNDS	
1039	NITROMETHANE
1040	NITROETHANE
1041	1-NITROPROPANE
1042	2-NITROPROPANE
*1043	2-METHYL-2-NITROPROPANE
1044	1-CHLORO-1-NITROETHANE
*1045	NITROCYCLOHEXANE
1046	o-NITROTOLUENE
1047	m-NITROTOLUENE
1048	p-NITROTOLUENE
1049	1-ETHYL-2-NITROBENZENE
1050	1-ETHYL-4-NITROBENZENE
1051	2-NITROBIPHENYL
1052	3-NITROBIPHENYL
1053	4-NITROBIPHENYL
1054	1-FLUORO-2-NITROBENZENE
1055	1-FLUORO-4-NITROBENZENE
1056	1-CHLORO-2-NITROBENZENE
1057	1-CHLORO-3-NITROBENZENE
1058	1-CHLORO-4-NITROBENZENE
1059	1-BROMO-2-NITROBENZENE
1060	1-IODO-3-NITROBENZENE
1061	1-IODO-4-NITROBENZENE

* No spectrum is included for this compound (see Preface).

* No spectrum is included for this compound (see Preface).

SPECTRUM NO.	NAME
1102	METHYLTRIPHENYLPHOSPHONIUM BROMIDE
*1103	DIMETHYLDODECYLPHOSPHINE OXIDE
*1104	DIMETHYLHEXADECYLPHOSPHINE OXIDE
1105	TRI-o-TOLYLPHOSPHINE OXIDE
1106	TRI-m-TOLYLPHOSPHINE OXIDE

SULFIDES

*1107	ETHYL METHYL SULFIDE
*1108	ETHYL SULFIDE
*1109	PROPYL SULFIDE
*1110	BUTYL SULFIDE
*1111	ISOBUTYL SULFIDE
*1112	ISOPENTYL SULFIDE
*1113	BIS(2-ETHYLHEXYL) SULFIDE
*1114	HEXYL SULFIDE
*1115	HEPTYL SULFIDE
*1116	DODECYL METHYL SULFIDE
*1117	DODECYL ETHYL SULFIDE
*1118	DODECYL SULFIDE
*1119	ETHYL OCTADECYL SULFIDE
*1120	BIS(CHLOROMETHYL) SULFIDE
*1121	3-(METHYLTHIO)PROPYLAMINE
*1122	3,3'-THIODIPROPIPNITRILE
*1123	1,2-BIS(ETHYLTHIO)ETHANE
*1124	1,2-BIS(PROPYLTHIO)ETHANE
*1125	1,4-BIS(ETHYLTHIO)BUTANE
*1126	1,4-BIS(PROPYLTHIO)BUTANE
*1127	1,6-BIS(METHYLTHIO)HEXANE
*1128	TRITHIOORTHOFORMIC ACID, TRIETHYL ESTER
*1129	TRIMETHYLENE SULFIDE
*1130	TETRAHYDROTHIOPHENE
*1131	TETRAHYDRO-2H-THIOPYRAN
*1132	m-DITHIANE
*1133	p-DITHIANE
*1134	2-METHYL-2-THIAZOLINE
1135	2-(BENZYLAMINO)-2-THIAZOLINE
1136	THIOPHENE
1137	3-METHYLTHIOPHENE
1138	2-CHLOROTHIOPHENE
1139	2,5-DICHLOROTHIOPHENE
1140	2-BROMOTHIOPHENE
1141	3-BROMOTHIOPHENE
1142	2,5-DIBROMOTHIOPHENE
1143	2-IODOTHIOPHENE
1144	2-THIOPHENECARBONITRILE
1145	2-THIOPHENECARBOXALDEHYDE, anti-OXIME

* No spectrum is included for this compound (see Preface).

SPECTRUM NO.	NAME
1146	3-NITROTHIOPHENE
1147	2,2'-METHYLENEDITHIOPHENE
*1148	3-METHYLISOTHIAZOLE
1149	4-METHYLISOTHIAZOLE
1150	4-PHENYLISOTHIAZOLE
1151	4,5-DIPHENYL-2-METHYLTHIAZOLE
1152	2-BROMOTHIAZOLE
1153	2-AMINOTHIAZOLE
1154	2-AMINO-4-METHYLTHIAZOLE
1155	2-AMINO-5-ETHYL-1,3,4-THIADIAZOLE
1156	2-(ETHYLAMINO)-1,3,4-THIADIAZOLE
1157	2,5-DIPHENYL-p-DITHIIN
1158	BENZYL METHYL SULFIDE
1159	BENZYL ETHYL SULFIDE
1160	p-BROMOPHENYL METHYL SULFIDE
1161	o-(METHYLTHIO)ANILINE
1162	BENZYL p-TOLYL SULFIDE
1163	PHENETHYL PHENYL SULFIDE
1164	PHENYL 3-PHENYLPROPYL SULFIDE
1165	BENZYL p-CHLOROPHENYL SULFIDE
1166	2,2-DIPHENYLVINYL PHENYL SULFIDE
1167	BIS(PHENYLTHIO)METHANE
*1168	TETRATHIOORTHOCARBONIC ACID, TETRAPHENYL ESTER
1169	PHENYL SULFIDE
1170	DI-p-TOLYL SULFIDE
1171	BIS(p-CHLOROPHENYL)SULFIDE
1172	4-(PHENYLTHIO)PYRIDINE
1173	BENZYL 2-NAPHTHYL SULFIDE
1174	2-(PHENYLTHIO)QUINOLINE
1175	2-METHYLBENZOTHIAZOLE
1176	2-PHENYLBENZOTHIAZOLE
1177	5-CHLORO-2-METHYLBENZOTHIAZOLE
1178	2,1,3-BENZOTHIADIAZOLE
1179	3-DIBENZOTHIOPHENAMINE
*1180	3,7-DINITRODIBENZOTHIOPHENE
1181	PHENOTHIAZINE
1182	3-CHLOROPHENOTHIAZINE

DISULFIDES

SPECTRUM NO.	NAME
1183	BUTYL DISULFIDE
*1184	sec-BUTYL DISULFIDE
1185	ISOBUTYL DISULFIDE
*1186	tert-BUTYL DISULFIDE
1187	PENTYL DISULFIDE
1188	ISOPENTYL DISULFIDE
*1189	DODECYL DISULFIDE
*1190	ALLYL DISULFIDE

* No spectrum is included for this compound (see Preface).

* No spectrum is included for this compound (see Preface).

*** No spectrum is included for this compound (see Preface).**

SPECTRUM NO. NAME

SULFONYL HALIDES

SPECTRUM NO.	NAME
1279	α-TOLUENESULFONYL FLUORIDE
*1280	1-PROPANESULFONYL CHLORIDE
*1281	1-BUTANESULFONYL CHLORIDE
*1282	2-CHLOROETHANESULFONYL CHLORIDE
*1283	p-TOLUENESULFONYL CHLORIDE
1284	2,5-XYLENESULFONYL CHLORIDE
1285	o-NITROBENZENESULFONYL CHLORIDE
1286	1-NAPHTHALENESULFONYL CHLORIDE

SULFONIC ACIDS, SALTS AND ESTERS

SPECTRUM NO.	NAME
*1287	ETHANESULFONIC ACID
*1288	N-METHYLTAURINE
1289	4-BIPHENYLSULFONIC ACID
1290	6-AMINO-m-TOLUENESULFONIC ACID
1291	3-AMINO-p-TOLUENESULFONIC ACID
1292	1-NAPHTHALENESULFONIC ACID, DIHYDRATE
1293	2-AMINO-1-NAPHTHALENESULFONIC ACID
*1294	1-PENTANESULFONIC ACID, SODIUM SALT, HYDRATE
*1295	1-HEPTANESULFONIC ACID, SODIUM SALT, HYDRATE
*1296	2-BROMOETHANESULFONIC ACID, SODIUM SALT
*1297	2-CYANOETHANESULFONIC ACID, SODIUM SALT
*1298	1,2-ETHANEDISULFONIC ACID, DISODIUM SALT
*1299	2-PROPENE-1-SULFONIC ACID, SODIUM SALT
1300	BENZENESULFONIC ACID, SODIUM SALT
1301	2,4-XYLENESULFONIC ACID, SODIUM SALT
1302	p-TOLUENESULFONIC ACID, BARIUM SALT, HYDRATE
1303	p-BROMOBENZENESULFONIC ACID, SODIUM SALT
1304	SULFANILIC ACID, SODIUM SALT, DIHYDRATE
1305	p-(PHENYLAZO)BENZENESULFONIC ACID, SODIUM SALT
1306	2-ANILINO-5-NITROBENZENESULFONIC ACID, SODIUM SALT
1307	2,4-DINITROBENZENESULFONIC ACID, SODIUM SALT
1308	1,3,5-BENZENETRISULFONIC ACID, TRISODIUM SALT, TRIHYDRATE
1309	2-NAPHTHALENESULFONIC ACID, SODIUM SALT
1310	4-AMINO-1-NAPHTHALENESULFONIC ACID, SODIUM SALT, HEMIHYDRATE
1311	2,7-NAPHTHALENEDISULFONIC ACID, DISODIUM SALT
1312	1-DODECYLPYRIDINIUM p-TOLUENESULFONATE
1313	PHENYLTRIMETHYLAMMONIUM BENZENESULFONATE
*1314	SULFURIC ACID, MONOMETHYL ESTER, POTASSIUM SALT
*1315	METHANESULFONIC ACID, BUTYL ESTER
*1316	ETHANESULFONIC ACID, METHYL ESTER
*1317	METHANESULFONIC ACID, DECYL ESTER
*1318	1,2-OXATHIOLANE, 2,2-DIOXIDE
*1319	1,2-OXATHIANE, 2,2-DIOXIDE
1320	METHANESULFONIC ACID, PHENYL ESTER
1321	p-TOLUENESULFONIC ACID, ISOPROPYL ESTER
1322	p-TOLUENESULFONIC ACID, BUTYL ESTER

* No spectrum is included for this compound (see Preface).

* No spectrum is included for this compound (see Preface).

SPECTRUM NO.	NAME
1363	p-TOLUENESULFONAMIDE
1364	2-MESITYLENESULFONAMIDE
1365	SULFANILAMIDE
1366	N^4-BENZYLIDENESULFANILAMIDE
1367	2-NAPHTHALENESULFONAMIDE
1368	ETHANESULFONO-p-TOLUIDIDE
1369	N-(2-HYDROXYETHYL)-N-(3-HYDROXYPROPYL)-p-TOLUENESULFONAMIDE
1370	p-TOLUENESULFONANILIDE
1371	BENZENESULFONO-o-TOLUIDIDE
1372	p-TOLUENESULFONO-2′,6′-XYLIDIDE
*1373	N,N-DIMETHYLMETHANESULFONAMIDE
*1374	N,N,N′,N′-TETRAMETHYL-1,4-PIPERAZINEDISULFONAMIDE
1375	N,N-DIMETHYL-p-TOLUENESULFONAMIDE
1376	1,3-BIS(PHENYLSULFONYL)IMIDAZOLIDINE

SULFAMIDES

*1377	N,N′-DICYCLOHEXYLSULFAMIDE
1378	4,4′-DIBROMOSULFANILIDE

ETHERS

*1379	ETHYL ETHER
*1380	BUTYL METHYL ETHER
*1381	PROPYL ETHER
*1382	BUTYL ETHYL ETHER
*1383	ETHYL ISOBUTYL ETHER
*1384	BUTYL ETHER
*1385	ISOPENTYL ETHER
*1386	HEXYL ETHER
*1387	BIS(2-ETHYLHEXYL) ETHER
*1388	OCTYL ETHER
*1389	DECYL ETHER
*1390	ETHYL OCTADECYL ETHER
*1391	HEXADECYL ETHER
*1392	OCTADECYL ETHER
*1393	(2-CHLORO-1,1,2-TRIFLUOROETHYL) ETHYL ETHER
*1394	ISOPROPYL PROPYL ETHER
*1395	ISOPROPYL ETHER
*1396	tert-BUTYL METHYL ETHER
*1397	tert-BUTYL ETHYL ETHER
*1398	tert-BUTYL ISOPROPYL ETHER
*1399	BIS(CHLOROMETHYL) ETHER
*1400	3-ISOPROPOXYPROPIONITRILE
*1401	2-ETHOXYETHANETHIOL
*1402	2,2′-OXYDIETHANETHIOL
*1403	ALLYL ETHYL ETHER
*1404	BUTYL VINYL ETHER
*1405	ISOBUTYL VINYL ETHER

* No spectrum is included for this compound (see Preface).

SPECTRUM NO.	NAME
*1406	N,N-DIMETHYL-2-(VINYLOXY)ETHYLAMINE
*1407	ALLYL ETHER
*1408	ETHYL PROPENYL ETHER
*1409	DIMETHOXYMETHANE
*1410	DIETHOXYMETHANE
*1411	BIS(2-CHLOROETHOXY)METHANE
*1412	1,2-DIETHOXYETHANE
*1413	1,2-DIBUTOXYETHANE
*1414	2-BUTOXYETHYL VINYL ETHER
*1415	BIS(2-METHOXYETHYL)ETHER
*1416	BIS(2-ETHOXYETHYL)ETHER
*1417	BIS(2-BUTOXYETHYL)ETHER
*1418	BIS[2-VINYLOXY)ETHYL] ETHER
*1419	1,2-BIS(2-METHOXYETHOXY)ETHANE
*1420	BIS[2-(2-METHOXYETHOXY)ETHYL] ETHER
*1421	5,8,11,14,17-PENTAOXAHENEICOSANE
*1422	ACETALDEHYDE, DIMETHYL ACETAL
*1423	ACETALDEHYDE, DIETHYL ACETAL
*1424	ACETALDEHYDE, DIBUTYL ACETAL
*1425	ACROLEIN, DIETHYL ACETAL
*1426	BROMOACETALDEHYDE, DIETHYL ACETAL
*1427	AMINOACETALDEHYDE, DIMETHYL ACETAL
*1428	AMINOACETALDEHYDE, DIETHYL ACETAL
*1429	MALONALDEHYDE, BIS(DIMETHYL ACETAL)
*1430	(METHYLIMINO)DIACETALDEHYDE, BIS(DIMETHYLACETAL)
*1431	N-METHYL-2,2,2',2'-TETRAETHOXYDIETHYLAMINE
*1432	METALDEHYDE
*1433	ACETONE, DIMETHYL ACETAL
*1434	ACETONE, DIALLYL ACETAL
*1435	ORTHOFORMIC ACID, TRIMETHYL ESTER
*1436	ORTHOFORMIC ACID, TRIETHYL ESTER
*1437	ORTHOACETIC ACID, TRIMETHYL ESTER
*1438	PROPYLENE OXIDE
*1439	1,2-EPOXYBUTANE
*1440	1,2-EPOXYOCTANE
*1441	1,2-EPOXYDECANE
*1442	1,2-EPOXYDODECANE
*1443	1-CHLORO-2,3-EPOXYPROPANE
*1444	1-BROMO-2,3-EPOXYPROPANE
*1445	1,2-EPOXY-3-ISOPROPOXYPROPANE
*1446	3,4-EPOXY-1-BUTENE
1447	(EPOXYETHYL)BENZENE
*1448	7-OXABICYCLO[4.1.0] HEPTANE
*1449	2,3-EPOXYPINANE
*1450	8-OXABICYCLO[5.1.0] OCTANE
*1451	9-OXABICYCLO[6.1.0] NONANE

*** No spectrum is included for this compound (see Preface).**

SPECTRUM NO.	NAME
*1452	5,10-DIOXATRICYCLO[7.1.0.0^{4,6}] DECANE
1453	1,2-EPOXY INDAN
*1454	2-CHLORO-1,3-EPOXYPROPANE
*1455	TETRAHYDROFURAN
*1456	2-METHYLTETRAHYDROFURAN
*1457	2-(METHOXYMETHYL)TETRAHYDROFURAN
*1458	1,3-DIOXOLANE
*1459	2-ETHYL-2-METHYL-1,3-DIOXOLANE
*1460	TETRAHYDROFURFURYL TETRAHYDRO-2H-PYRAN-2-YL ETHER
*1461	3,6-DIHYDRO-2H-PYRAN
*1462	MORPHOLINE
*1463	2,6-DIMETHYLMORPHOLINE
*1464	4-ETHYLMORPHOLINE
*1465	4-ALLYLMORPHOLINE
*1466	4-(3-AMINOPROPYL)MORPHOLINE
*1467	α,α-DIMETHYL-4-MORPHOLINEACETONITRILE
1468	4-m-TOLYLMORPHOLINE
*1469	MORPHOLINE, HYDROBROMIDE
*1470	1,4-OXATHIANE
*1471	p-DIOXANE
*1472	5,5-DIMETHYL-2-HEXYL-m-DIOXANE
*1473	2,5-BIS(MORPHOLINOMETHYL)-p-DIOXANE
*1474	2,4,8,10-TETRAOXASPIRO[5.5] UNDECANE
*1475	3,9-DIMETHYL-2,4,8,10-TETRAOXASPIRO[5.5] UNDECANE
*1476	3,9-DIETHYL-2,4,8,10-TETRAOXASPIRO[5.5] UNDECANE
*1477	s-TRIOXANE
*1478	1,3-DIOXEPANE
1479	BENZYL METHYL ETHER
1480	4-ETHOXY-4-PHENYLBUTYRONITRILE
1481	ETHYL TRITYL ETHER
1482	BENZYL ETHER
1483	BIS(α-METHYLBENZYL) ETHER
1484	METHYL PHENETHYL ETHER
1485	ACETALDEHYDE, DIPHENETHYL ACETAL
1486	DIMETHOXYDIPHENYLMETHANE
1487	ORTHOBENZOIC ACID, TRIMETHYL ESTER
1488	ANISOLE
1489	PHENETOLE
1490	PHENYL PROPYL ETHER
1491	β-BROMOPHENETOLE
1492	(2-METHOXYETHOXY)BENZENE
1493	ORTHOFORMIC ACID, DIETHYL PHENYL ESTER
1494	o-METHYLANISOLE
1495	m-METHYLANISOLE
1496	p-METHYLANISOLE
1497	p-ETHYLANISOLE

* No spectrum is included for this compound (see Preface).

* No spectrum is included for this compound (see Preface).

* No spectrum is included for this compound (see Preface).

SPECTRUM NO.	NAME
1588	1,3-BENZODIOXOLE
1589	ISOCHROMAN
1590	1,4-BENZODIOXAN
1591	DIBENZO-p-DIOXIN
*1592	HYPOCHLOROUS ACID, tert-BUTYL ESTER

SILICON ETHERS

*1593	ETHOXYTRIMETHYLSILANE
1594	DIMETHOXYDIPHENYLSILANE
*1595	METHYLTRIETHOXYSILANE
*1596	ETHYLTRIETHOXYSILANE
*1597	3-(TRIETHOXYSILYL)PROPYLAMINE
*1598	SILICIC ACID, TETRAMETHYL ESTER
*1599	SILICIC ACID, TETRABUTYL ESTER
*1600	PENTYL SILICATE
*1601	SILICIC ACID, TETRAKIS(2-ETHYLBUTYL)ESTER
*1602	SILICIC ACID, TETRAKIS(2-ETHYLHEXYL)ESTER
*1603	HEXAMETHYLDISILOXANE
*1604	1,3-BIS(CHLOROMETHYL)-1,1,3,3-TETRAMETHYLDISILOXANE
*1605	OCTAMETHYLCYCLOTETRASILOXANE

PHOSPHORUS ETHERS

*1606	2-ETHYL-1-HEXANOL, PHOSPHITE
*1607	2-CHLOROETHANOL, PHOSPHITE (3:1)
1608	PHOSPHOROUS ACID, TRIPHENYL ESTER

PEROXIDES

*1609	tert-BUTYL PEROXIDE
*1610	1,4-EPIDIOXY-p-MENTH-2-ENE

PRIMARY ALCOHOLS

*1611	METHANOL
*1612	ETHYL ALCOHOL
*1613	PROPYL ALCOHOL
*1614	BUTYL ALCOHOL
*1615	ISOBUTYL ALCOHOL
*1616	PENTYL ALCOHOL
*1617	(–)-2-METHYL-1-BUTANOL
*1618	3-METHYL-1-BUTANOL
*1619	HEXYL ALCOHOL
*1620	3-METHYL-1-PENTANOL
*1621	4-METHYL-1-PENTANOL
*1622	2-ETHYL-1-BUTANOL
*1623	HEPTYL ALCOHOL
*1624	2,2-DIMETHYL-1-PENTANOL
*1625	5-METHYL-1-HEXANOL
*1626	1-OCTANOL
*1627	2-ETHYL-4-METHYL-1-PENTANOL

* No spectrum is included for this compound (see Preface).

* No spectrum is included for this compound (see Preface).

SPECTRUM NO.	NAME
*1674	2-[2-(ETHOXY)ETHOXY] ETHANOL
*1675	2-[2-(BUTOXY)ETHOXY] ETHANOL
*1676	2,2'-(2–BUTYNYLENEDIOXY)DIETHANOL
*1677	2,3-EPOXY-1-PROPANOL
1678	2-THIOPHENETHANOL
*1679	2,2-DIMETHYL-1,3-DIOXOLANE-4-METHANOL
*1680	CYCLOHEXANEMETHANOL
*1681	4-METHYLCYCLOHEXANEMETHANOL
*1682	CYCLOHEXANEETHANOL
*1683	3-PIPERIDINEMETHANOL
*1684	1-ADAMANTANEMETHANOL
*1685	ALLYL ALCOHOL
*1686	2-BUTEN-1-OL
*1687	3-BUTEN-1-OL
*1688	cis-3-HEXEN-1-OL
*1689	cis-9-OCTADECEN-1-OL
*1690	PHYTOL
*1691	2-(ALLYLOXY)ETHANOL
*1692	3,4-DIHYDRO-2,5-DIMETHYL-2H-PYRAN-2-METHANOL
*1693	2-PROPYN-1-OL
*1694	2-BUTYN-1-OL
*1695	3-BUTYN-1-OL
*1696	2-PENTYN-1-OL
*1697	2-NONYN-1-OL
*1698	3-NONYN-1-OL
*1699	3-DECYN-1-OL
1700	BENZYL ALCOHOL
1701	PHENETHYL ALCOHOL
1702	3-PHENYL-1-PROPANOL
1703	2-(BENZYLMETHYLAMINO)ETHANOL
1704	2-(DIBENZYLAMINO)ETHANOL
1705	2-(BENZYLOXY)ETHANOL
1706	2-(N-ETHYLANILINO)ETHANOL
1707	2-[(p-CHLOROBENZYLIDENE)AMINO] ETHANOL
1708	2-(p-TOLYLTHIO)ETHANOL
1709	(p-TOLYLSULFONYL)METHANOL
1710	2-PHENOXYETHANOL
1711	CINNAMYL ALCOHOL
1712	3-PHENYL-2-BUTEN-1-OL
1713	p-METHYLBENZYL ALCOHOL
1714	p-CYMEN-7-OL
1715	o-FLUOROBENZYL ALCOHOL
1716	p-FLUOROBENZYL ALCOHOL
1717	o-CHLOROBENZYL ALCOHOL
1718	p-AMINOPHENETHYL ALCOHOL
1719	o-NITROBENZYL ALCOHOL

* No spectrum is included for this compound (see Preface).

SECONDARY ALCOHOLS

* No spectrum is included for this compound (see Preface).

SPECTRUM NO.	NAME
*1765	trans-2-METHYLCYCLOPENTANOL
*1766	CYCLOHEXANOL
*1767	trans-2-METHYLCYCLOHEXANOL
*1768	trans-4-METHYLCYCLOHEXANOL
*1769	cis-4-METHYLCYCLOHEXANOL
*1770	2-ETHYLCYCLOHEXANOL
*1771	2,4-DIMETHYLCYCLOHEXANOL
*1772	(–)-MENTHOL
*1773	[BICYCLOHEXYL]-2-OL
1774	trans-2-PHENYLCYCLOHEXANOL
1775	cis-2-PHENYLCYCLOHEXANOL
1776	2,2-DIPHENYLCYCLOHEXANOL
*1777	CYCLOHEPTANOL
*1778	DECAHYDRO-2-NAPHTHOL
*1779	BORNEOL
*1780	CHOLESTEROL
*1781	TETRAHYDRO-2H-THIOPYRAN-3-OL
*1782	3-METHYL-3-BUTEN-2-OL
*1783	1-HEPTEN-3-OL
*1784	1-HEPTEN-4-OL
*1785	1,5-HEXADIEN-3-OL
*1786	2,3-DICHLORO-1-PROPEN-1-OL
*1787	5-NONYN-3-OL
1788	α-ETHYLBENZYL ALCOHOL
1789	α-CYCLOPROPYLBENZYL ALCOHOL
1790	BENZHYDROL
1791	1,2-DIPHENYLETHANOL
1792	1-PHENOXY-2-PROPANOL
1793	2,5-DICHLORO-α-METHYLBENZYL ALCOHOL
1794	QUININE

TERTIARY ALCOHOLS

SPECTRUM NO.	NAME
*1795	tert-BUTYL ALCOHOL
*1796	2-METHYL-2-BUTANOL
*1797	2-METHYL-2-PENTANOL
*1798	2-METHYL-2-HEXANOL
*1799	2,5-DIMETHYL-2-HEXANOL
*1800	2-METHYL-2-OCTANOL
*1801	3,6-DIMETHYL-3-HEPTANOL
*1802	3,7-DIMETHYL-3-OCTANOL
*1803	3,4-DIETHYL-3-HEXANOL
*1804	14-TRIDECYL-14-HEPTACOSANOL
*1805	2-METHYL-1,1,1-TRIBROMO-2-PROPANOL
*1806	2-METHYLLACTONITRILE
*1807	2-HYDROXY-2-PROPANESULFONIC ACID, SODIUM SALT
*1808	p-MENTH-1-EN-8-OL
*1809	1-METHYLCYCLOHEXANOL

* No spectrum is included for this compound (see Preface).

SPECTRUM NO.	NAME
*1810	1-ETHYLCYCLOHEXANOL
*1811	1-METHYLCYCLOHEPTANOL
*1812	2-METHYL-3-BUTEN-2-OL
*1813	2-METHYL-3-BUTYNE-2-OL
*1814	3-METHYL-1-PENTYN-3-OL
*1815	2,4,7,9-TETRAMETHYL-5-DECYNE-4,7-DIOL
*1816	1-ETHYLNYLCYCLOHEXANOL
1817	α,α-DIMETHYLBENZYL ALCOHOL
*1818	α,α-DIETHYLBENZYL ALCOHOL
1819	2-PHENYL-3-BUTYN-2-OL
1820	α-OCTYLBENZHYDROL
1821	1-p-TOLYLCYCLOHEXANOL
1822	TRIPHENYLMETHANOL

DIOLS

SPECTRUM NO.	NAME
*1823	ETHYLENE GLYCOL
*1824	1,3-PROPANEDIOL
*1825	1,5-PENTANEDIOL
*1826	1,6-HEXANEDIOL
*1827	1,16-HEXADECANEDIOL
*1828	1,2-PROPANEDIOL
*1829	1,2-BUTANEDIOL
*1830	2,4-PENTANEDIOL
*1831	2-METHYL-2,4-PENTANEDIOL
*1832	3-METHYL-1,5-PENTANEDIOL
*1833	2,5-HEXANEDIOL
*1834	2,3-DIMETHYL-2,3-BUTANEDIOL, HYDRATE
*1835	2,2-DIETHYL-1,3-PROPANEDIOL
*1836	2-ETHYL-1,3-HEXANEDIOL
*1837	2,4,4-TRIMETHYL-1,2-PENTANEDIOL
*1838	2,4,4-TRIMETHYL-2,3-PENTANEDIOL
*1839	2-BUTYL-2-ETHYL-1,3-PROPANEDIOL
*1840	3-CHLORO-1,2-PROPANEDIOL
*1841	2,2-BIS(BROMOMETHYL)-1,3-PROPANEDIOL
*1842	2,2′-IMINODIETHANOL
*1843	2,2′-(ETHYLENEDIIMINO)DIETHANOL
*1844	3-AMINO-1,2-PROPANEDIOL
*1845	DIETHYLENE GLYCOL
*1846	TRIETHYLENE GLYCOL
*1847	TETRAETHYLENE GLYCOL
*1848	GLYCEROL
*1849	1,4,7-HEPTANETRIOL
*1850	2,2′,2′′-NITRILOTRIETHANOL
*1851	1,1′,1′′-NITRILOTRI-2-PROPANOL
*1852	2,2′,2′′-NITRILOTRIETHANOL, HYDROCHLORIDE
*1853	PENTAERYTHRITOL

* No spectrum is included for this compound (see Preface).

SPECTRUM NO.	NAME
* 1854	2,2′,2″,2‴-(ETHYLENEDINITRILO)TETRAETHANOL
* 1855	cis-CYCLOHEXANE-1,2-DIOL
* 1856	1,4-CYCLOHEXANEDIOL
* 1857	cis-1,5-CYCLOOCTANEDIOL
* 1858	2-BUTYNE-1,4-DIOL
1859	2,7-DIMETHYL-3,5-OCTADIYNE-2,7-DIOL
1860	p-XYLENE-α,α'-DIOL

CARBOHYDRATES

SPECTRUM NO.	NAME
* 1861	ERYTHRITOL
* 1862	XYLITOL
* 1863	GALACTITOL
* 1864	D-GLUCITOL
* 1865	D-(–)-MANNITOL
* 1866	D-RIBOSE
* 1867	1-ARABINOPYRANOSE
* 1868	D-(+)-XYLOSE
* 1869	L-(+)-RHAMNOSE, HYDRATE
* 1870	D-(–)-FRUCTOSE
* 1871	D-(+)-GLUCOSE
* 1872	D-(+)-MANNOSE
* 1873	D-(+)-GALACTOSE
* 1874	SUCROSE

PHENOLS

SPECTRUM NO.	NAME
1875	PHENOL
1876	o-CRESOL
1877	m-CRESOL
1878	p-CRESOL
1879	o-ETHYLPHENOL
1880	m-ETHYLPHENOL
1881	p-ISOPROPYLPHENOL
1882	o-tert-BUTYLPHENOL
1883	p-tert-BUTYLPHENOL
1884	p-PENTYLPHENOL
1885	p-tert-PENTYLPHENOL
1886	p-(1,1,3,3-TETRAMETHYLBUTYL)PHENOL
1887	p-CYCLOHEXYLPHENOL
1888	4,4′-METHYLENEDIPHENOL
1889	p-PHENYLPHENOL
1890	o-FLUOROPHENOL
1891	p-FLUOROPHENOL
1892	o-CHLOROPHENOL
1893	p-CHLOROPHENOL
1894	o-BROMOPHENOL
1895	p-BROMOPHENOL
1896	o-IODOPHENOL

* No spectrum is included for this compound (see Preface).

*** No spectrum is included for this compound (see Preface).**

SPECTRUM NO.	NAME
1943	2,6-DICHLOROHYDROQUINONE
1944	2-NITRORESORCINOL
1945	PYROGALLOL
1946	1,2,4-BENZENETRIOL
1947	PHLOROGLUCINOL
1948	4-INDANOL
1949	FLUOREN-2-OL
1950	1-NAPHTHOL
1951	2-NAPHTHOL
1952	2-METHYL-1-NAPHTHOL
1953	6-AMINO-1-NAPHTHOL
1954	2-HYDROXY-1-NAPHTHALENEPROPIONITRILE
1955	1-NITROSO-2-NAPHTHOL
1956	1,3-NAPHTHALENEDIOL
1957	1,5-NAPHTHALENEDIOL
1958	2,7-NAPHTHALENEDIOL
1959	3-PYRIDINOL
1960	2-PYRIMIDINOL
1961	CARBOSTYRYL
1962	8-QUINOLINOL
1963	4-METHYLCARBOSTYRIL
1964	4-NITRO-1(2H)-ISOQUINOLONE
*1965	PHOSPHOROUS ACID, DIBUTYL ESTER
*1966	PHOSPHORUS ACID, BIS(2-ETHYLHEXYL) ESTER

KETONES

SPECTRUM NO.	NAME
1967	ACETONE
*1968	2-BUTANONE
*1969	2-HEXANONE
*1970	3-HEXANONE
1971	4-METHYL-2-PENTANONE
*1972	4-HEPTANONE
*1973	4,4-DIMETHYL-2-PENTANONE
*1974	2-OCTANONE
1975	3-OCTANONE
*1976	6-METHYL-2-HEPTANONE
*1977	2,2,4-TRIMETHYL-3-PENTANONE
*1978	5-NONANONE
1979	2,6-DIMETHYL-4-HEPTANONE
*1980	3-DECANONE
*1981	4-DECANONE
*1982	2-METHYL-3-NONANONE
*1983	6-HENDECANONE
*1984	4-DODECANONE
*1985	6-DODECANONE
*1986	6-TRIDECANONE
*1987	7-TRIDECANONE

* No spectrum is included for this compound (see Preface).

SPECTRUM NO.	NAME
* 1988	3-TRIDECANONE
* 1989	2-TETRADECANONE
* 1990	1,3-DIFLUORO-2-PROPANONE
* 1991	3-CHLORO-2-BUTANONE
* 1992	3-BROMO-2-BUTANONE
* 1993	3-HYDROXY-3-METHYL-2-BUTANONE
* 1994	4-HYDROXY-3-METHYL-2-BUTANONE
1995	2,5-HEXANEDIONE
1996	CYCLOPROPYL KETONE
* 1997	1-CYCLOPENTYL-2-PROPANONE
* 1998	METHYL 2-NORBORNYL KETONE
* 1999	CYCLOPENTANONE
2000	CYCLOHEXANONE
* 2001	2-METHYLCYCLOHEXANONE
* 2002	3-METHYLCYCLOHEXANONE
2003	4-METHYLCYCLOHEXANONE
* 2004	4-tert-BUTYLCYCLOHEXANONE
* 2005	3-HEXYL-5-METHYLCYCLOHEXANONE
* 2006	1,3,3-TRIMETHYL-2-NORBORNANONE
* 2007	DL-2-OXO-10-BORNANESULFONIC ACID, SODIUM SALT
* 2008	2,5-BORNANEDIONE
* 2009	CYCLOHEPTANONE
* 2010	CYCLOTRIDECANONE
* 2011	CYCLOPENTADECANONE
* 2012	2-ADAMANTONE
* 2013	2,2,6,6-TETRAMETHYL-4-PIPERIDONE
2014	1-PHENETHYL-4-PIPERIDONE
2015	1-BENZYL-4-PIPERIDONE
* 2016	TETRAHYDROTHIOPYRAN-4-ONE
2017	3-BUTEN-2-ONE
2018	3-PENTEN-2-ONE
* 2019	5-HEXEN-2-ONE
2020	4-METHYL-3-PENTEN-2-ONE
2021	5-ETHYL-3-HEPTEN-2-ONE
2022	1-CYCLOHEXEN-1-YL METHYL KETONE
2023	FUROIN
* 2024	3-CHLORO-2-CYCLOPENTEN-1-ONE
2025	2-CYCLOHEXEN-1-ONE
2026	3-CHLORO-2-CYCLOHEXEN-1-ONE
2027	3,5-DIMETHYL-2-CYCLOHEXEN-1-ONE
* 2028	3-CHLORO-2-METHYL-2-CYCLOHEXEN-1-ONE
2029	3-CHLORO-5,5-DIMETHYL-2-CYCLOHEXEN-1-ONE
2030	p-TOLUQUINONE
2031	2,5-DI-tert-PENTYL-p-BENZOQUINONE
2032	TETRAMETHYL-p-BENZOQUINONE
2033	PHENYL-p-BENZOQUINONE

* No spectrum is included for this compound (see Preface).

* No spectrum is included for this compound (see Preface).

* No spectrum is included for this compound (see Preface).

ALDEHYDES

*** No spectrum is included for this compound (see Preface).**

SPECTRUM NO.	NAME
2170	p-(DIMETHYLAMINO)BENZALDEHYDE
2171	m-NITROBENZALDEHYDE
2172	p-NITROBENZALDEHYDE
2173	p-PROPOXYBENZALDEHYDE
2174	p-(PENTYLOXY)BENZALDEHYDE
2175	p-(ALLYLOXY)BENZALDEHYDE
2176	2,5-DIMETHYLBENZALDEHYDE
2177	3,4-DICHLOROBENZALDEHYDE
2178	6-HYDROXY-m-ANISALDEHYDE
2179	5-INDANCARBOXALDEHYDE
2180	FLUORENE-2-CARBOXALDEHYDE
2181	3-PYRENECARBOXALDEHYDE
2182	PYRROLE-2-CARBOXALDEHYDE
2183	3-QUINOLINECARBOXALDEHYDE
2184	5-METHYL-2-THIOPHENECARBOXALDEHYDE
2185	5-NITROFURFURAL
2186	PIPERONAL

ACID HALIDES

SPECTRUM NO.	NAME
*2187	PROPIONYL CHLORIDE
*2188	BUTYRYL CHLORIDE
*2189	3,3-DIMETHYLBUTYRYL CHLORIDE
*2190	2,2-DIMETHYLVALERYL CHLORIDE
*2191	2-PROPYLVALERYL CHLORIDE
*2192	DECANOYL CHLORIDE
*2193	LAUROYL CHLORIDE
*2194	STEAROYL CHLORIDE
*2195	4-CHLOROBUTYRYL CHLORIDE
*2196	3-BROMOPROPIONYL CHLORIDE
*2197	6-BROMOHEXANOYL CHLORIDE
*2198	SUCCINYL CHLORIDE
*2199	ADIPOYL CHLORIDE
*2200	PIMELOYL CHLORIDE
*2201	AZELAOYL CHLORIDE
*2202	SEBACOYL CHLORIDE
*2203	CYCLOPENTANEPROPIONYL CHLORIDE
*2204	CYCLOPENTANECARBONYL CHLORIDE
*2205	CYCLOHEXANECARBONYL CHLORIDE
*2206	10-UNDECENOYL CHLORIDE
*2207	OLEOYL CHLORIDE
2208	SORBOYL CHLORIDE
2209	FUMAROYL CHLORIDE
2210	1-CYCLOHEXENE-1-CARBONYL CHLORIDE
*2211	3-CYCLOHEXENE-1-CARBONYL CHLORIDE
2212	HYDROCINNAMOYL CHLORIDE
2213	CHLOROPHENYLACETYL CHLORIDE
*2214	BROMODIPHENYLACETYL BROMIDE

* No spectrum is included for this compound (see Preface).

* No spectrum is included for this compound (see Preface).

* No spectrum is included for this compound (see Preface).

* No spectrum is included for this compound (see Preface).

* No spectrum is included for this compound (see Preface).

* No spectrum is included for this compound (see Preface).

* No spectrum is included for this compound (see Preface).

* No spectrum is included for this compound (see Preface).

* No spectrum is included for this compound (see Preface).

SPECTRUM NO.	NAME
2575	o-IODOBENZOIC ACID
2576	m-IODOBENZOIC ACID
2577	p-IODOBENZOIC ACID
2578	p-AMINOBENZOIC ACID
2579	N-PHENYLANTHRANILIC ACID
2580	m-CYANOBENZOIC ACID
2581	o-NITROBENZOIC ACID
2582	p-NITROBENZOIC ACID
2583	m-ANISIC ACID
2584	p-ANISIC ACID
2585	o-ETHOXYBENZOIC ACID
2586	p-PROPOXYBENZOIC ACID
2587	SALICYLIC ACID
2588	p-HYDROXYBENZOIC ACID
2589	4,4′-OXYDIBENZOIC ACID
2590	PHTHALIC ACID
2591	ISOPHTHALIC ACID
2592	TEREPHTHALIC ACID
2593	2,6-DIMETHYLBENZOIC ACID
2594	2,4-DINITROBENZOIC ACID
2595	6-AMINO-m-ANISIC ACID
2596	2,4-CRESOTIC ACID
2597	3-NITROSALICYLIC ACID
2598	VANILLIC ACID
2599	β-RESORCYLIC ACID
2600	PROTOCATECHUIC ACID
2601	4-NITROPHTHALIC ACID
2602	5-NITROISOPHTHALIC ACID
2603	1,3,5-BENZENETRICARBOXYLIC ACID
2604	3-FUROIC ACID
2605	2-FURANACRYLIC ACID
2606	NICOTINIC ACID, HYDROCHLORIDE
2607	3-INDOLEACETIC ACID
2608	PIPERONYLIC ACID
2609	THIOACETIC ACID
2610	THIOBENZOIC ACID
AMINO ACIDS	
*2611	GLYCINE
*2612	SARCOSINE
*2613	N-(2-CYANOETHYL)GLYCINE
*2614	L-ALANINE
*2615	dl-2-AMINOBUTYRIC ACID
*2616	2-METHYLALANINE
*2617	β-ALANINE
*2618	DL-NORVALINE

* No spectrum is included for this compound (see Preface).

SALTS OF CARBOXYLIC ACIDS

* No spectrum is included for this compound (see Preface).

SPECTRUM NO.	NAME
*2664	SUCCINIC ACID, DISODIUM SALT
*2665	NITRILOTRIACETIC ACID, DISODIUM SALT, HYDRATE
*2666	NITRILOTRIACETIC ACID, TRISODIUM SALT, HYDRATE
*2667	POTASSIUM CITRATE, HYDRATE
*2668	(ETHYLENEDINITRILO)TETRAACETIC ACID, DIPOTASSIUM SALT, DIHYDRATE
2669	ACRYLIC ACID, CALCIUM SALT
2670	10-UNDECENOIC ACID, POTASSIUM SALT
2671	SORBIC ACID, POTASSIUM SALT
2672	MALEIC ACID, SODIUM SALT
2673	PHENYLACETIC ACID, SODIUM SALT
2674	1-NAPHTHALENEACETIC ACID, SODIUM SALT
2675	BENZOIC ACID, SODIUM SALT
2676	m-AMINOBENZOIC ACID, SODIUM SALT
2677	p-AMINOBRNZOIC ACID, SODIUM SALT
2678	SODIUM SALICYLATE
2679	p-HYDROXYBENZOIC ACID, MONOSODIUM SALT
2680	PHTHALIC ACID, MONOPOTASSIUM SALT
2681	2-FUROIC ACID, POTASSIUM SALT
*2682	SUCCINIC ACID, DIAMMONIUM SALT
2683	BENZOIC ACID, AMMONIUM SALT
2684	SALICYLIC ACID, AMMONIUM SALT
*2685	DECYLAMINE, ACETATE (1:1) (SALT)
*2686	DODECYLAMINE, ACETATE
*2687	HYDROXYLAMINE, ACETATE (SALT)
2688	N,N-DIMETHYL-p-PHENYLENEDIAMINE, OXALATE (2:1)
*2689	PIPERAZINE, ADIPATE (1:1)
*2690	ETHYLENEDIAMINE, MONO-(+)-TARTRATE

ESTERS

SPECTRUM NO.	NAME
*2691	2-ETHYL-1-BUTANOL, FORMAT
*2692	FORMIC ACID, HEPTYL ESTER
*2693	FORMIC ACID, OCTYL ESTER
*2694	ACETIC ACID, METHYL ESTER
*2695	ACETIC ACID, 2-ETHYLBUTYL ESTER
*2696	ACETIC ACID, 2-ETHYLHEXYL ESTER
*2697	ACETIC ACID, DODECYL ESTER
*2698	PROPIONIC ACID, sec-BUTYL ESTER
*2699	ISOVALERIC ACID, METHYL ESTER
*2700	BUTYRIC ACID, ISOPROPYL ESTER
*2701	VALERIC ACID, ETHYL ESTER
*2702	ISOBUTYRIC ACID, BUTYL ESTER
*2703	PIVALIC ACID, ETHYL ESTER
*2704	OCTANOIC ACID, METHYL ESTER
*2705	VALERIC ACID, PENTYL ESTER
*2706	ISOVALERIC ACID, PENTYL ESTER
*2707	DECANOIC ACID, METHYL ESTER

*** No spectrum is included for this compound (see Preface).**

* No spectrum is included for this compound (see Preface).

* No spectrum is included for this compound (see Preface).

* No spectrum is included for this compound (see Preface).

* **No spectrum is included for this compound (see Preface).**

* No spectrum is included for this compound (see Preface).

SPECTRUM NO.	NAME
2935	2-FUROIC ACID, PROPYL ESTER
2936	2-FUROIC ACID, PENTYL ESTER
2937	5-NITRO-2-FUROIC ACID, ETHYL ESTER
2938	2-PYRIDINEACETIC ACID, METHYL ESTER
2939	NICOTINIC ACID, NONYL ESTER
2940	CARBONIC ACID, DI-p-TOLYL ESTER
2941	CARBONIC ACID, BIS(p-CHLOROPHENYL) ESTER
2942	BENZOIC ACID, BENZYL ESTER
2943	BENZOIC ACID, p-TOLYL ESTER
2944	ETHYLENE GLYCOL, DIBENZOATE
2945	PYROCATECHOL, DIBENZOATE

CYCLIC ESTERS (LACTONES)

SPECTRUM NO.	NAME
*2946	4-HYDROXY-2-METHYLBUTYRIC ACID, γ-LACTONE
*2947	4-HYDROXYOCTANOIC ACID, γ-LACTONE
*2948	3-BROMODIHYDRO-2(3H)-FURANONE
*2949	2,4-DIHYDROXY-3,3-DIMETHYLBUTYRIC ACID, γ-LACTONE
2950	3-ACETYL-4,5-DIHYDRO-2(3H)-FURANONE
2951	DIHYDRO-4-PHENYL-2(3H)-FURANONE
*2952	2-OXEPANONE
*2953	OXACYCLOPENTADECAN-2-ONE
2954	5-METHYL-2(3H)-FURANONE
2955	(o-HYDROXYPHENYL)ACETIC ACID, γ-LACTONE
2956	6-NITROPHTHALIDE
2957	3-CHLOROCOUMARIN
2958	4-HYDROXYCOUMARIN, ACETATE

CHLOROFORMATES

SPECTRUM NO.	NAME
*2959	CHLOROFORMIC ACID, BUTYL ESTER
*2960	CHLOROFORMIC ACID, 2-ETHYLHEXYL ESTER
*2961	CHLOROFORMIC ACID, DODECYL ESTER
*2962	CHLOROFORMIC ACID, 2-CHLOROETHYL ESTER
*2963	CHLOROFORMIC ACID, 2,2,2-TRICHLOROETHYL ESTER
*2964	2,2-DIMETHYL-1,3-PROPANEDIOL, BIS(CHLOROFORMATE)
*2965	CHLOROFORMIC ACID, ALLYL ESTER
*2966	CHLOROFORMIC ACID, 9-OCTADECENYL ESTER
2967	CHLOROFORMIC ACID, p-NITROBENZYL ESTER
2968	CHLOROFORMIC ACID, PHENYL ESTER
2969	CHLOROFORMIC ACID, p-NITROPHENYL ESTER

ESTERS OF THIO-ACIDS

SPECTRUM NO.	NAME
*2970	THIOACETIC ACID S-ETHYL ESTER
2971	THIOBENZOIC ACID, S-BENZYL ESTER
*2972	THIOCARBONIC ACID, o-ETHYL S-(2-HYDROXYETHYL) ESTER

CARBAMATES

SPECTRUM NO.	NAME
*2973	CARBAMIC ACID, ISOPROPYL ESTER

* No spectrum is included for this compound (see Preface).

* No spectrum is included for this compound (see Preface).

* No spectrum is included for this compound (see Preface).

ALPHABETICAL INDEX

* No spectrum is included for this compound (see Preface).

ALPHABETICAL INDEX

NAME	SPECTRUM NO.
* ACETIC ACID, m-FLUOROPHENYL-,	2559
ACETIC ACID, o-FLUOROPHENYL-,	2558
* ACETIC ACID, HYDROXY-,	2492
ACETIC ACID, (o-HYDROXYPHENYL)-,	2955
* ACETIC ACID, IMINODI-, DIETHYL ESTER	2789
* ACETIC ACID, IODO-,	2488
* ACETIC ACID, IODO-, ETHYL ESTER	2734
* ACETIC ACID, IODO-, SODIUM SALT	2656
* ACETIC ACID, MERCAPTO-, SODIUM SALT	2658
* ACETIC ACID, METHOXY-,	2491
* ACETIC ACID, METHOXY-, METHYL ESTER	2739
ACETIC ACID, 2-METHOXY-2-PHENYL-,	2552
* ACETIC ACID, NITRILOTRI-, DISODIUM SALT, HYDRATE	2665
* ACETIC ACID, NITRILOTRI-, TRISODIUM SALT, HYDRATE	2666
* ACETIC ACID, NITRILOTRI-, TRIETHYL ESTER	2794
ACETIC ACID, (p-NITROPHENYL)-,	2561
ACETIC ACID, PHENOXY-,	2553
ACETIC ACID, PHENYL-,	2539
ACETIC ACID, PHENYL-, BUTYL ESTER	2847
ACETIC ACID, PHENYL-, PHENETHYL ESTER	2860
ACETIC ACID, PHENYL-, SODIUM SALT	2673
ACETIC ACID, PHENYL-, m-TOLYL ESTER	2932
ACETIC ACID, PHENYL-, p-TOLYL ESTER	2933
ACETIC ACID, PHENYL-, OCTYL ESTER	2848
ACETIC ACID, (p-PHENYLENEDIOXY)DI-,	2565
ACETIC ACID, (PHENYLIMINO)DI-,	2548
ACETIC ACID, STYRYL-,	2549
ACETIC ACID, THIO-,	2609
* ACETIC ACID, THIO-, S-ETHYL ESTER	2970
ACETIC ACID, o-TOLYL-, ETHYL ESTER	2854
ACETIC ACID, p-TOLYL-,	2557
* ACETIC ACID, TRICHLORO-, ETHYL ESTER	2723
* ACETIC ACID, TRICHLORO-, METHYL ESTER	2722
ACETIC ACID, TRIFLUORO-, PHENYL ESTER	2923
ACETIC ACID, TRIPHENYL-,	2547
ACETIC ACID, (TRIPHENYLPHOSPHORANYLIDENE)-, METHYL ESTER	2859
* ACETIC ACID, TRIFLUORO-, PENTYL ESTER	2721
* ACETIC ANHYDRIDE	2247
* ACETIN, 1-MONO-,	2718
* ACETOACETAMIDE, N,N-DIETHYL-,	2358
ACETOACETANILIDE	2319
* ACETOACETIC ACID, BUTYL ESTER	2743
* ACETOACETIC ACID, METHYL ESTER	2742
* ACETOACETIC ACID, 2-ETHYL-, ETHYL ESTER	2744
ACETOACETIC ACID, 2-(2-HYDROXY-ETHYL)-, γ-LACTONE	2950

* No spectrum is included for this compound (see Preface).

* No spectrum is included for this compound (see Preface).

NAME	SPECTRUM NO.
ACETOPHENONE, 2-PHENOXY-,	2089
ACETOPHENONE, 2-PHENYL-,	2085
ACETOPHENONE, 2′,3′,5′,6′-TETRAMETHYL-,	2058
m-ACETOTOLUIDIDE	2322
o-ACETOTOLUIDIDE	2321
p-ACETOTOLUIDIDE	2323
ACETOXYLIDIDE, 2′,4′-,	2338
ACETOXYLIDIDE, 2′,5′-,	2339
* ACETYL BROMIDE, BROMODIPHENYL-,	2214
ACETYL CHLORIDE, CHLOROPHENYL-,	2213
ACETYL CHLORIDE, (p-CHLOROPHENYL)-,	2217
ACETYL CHLORIDE, PHENOXY-,	2215
ACETYLENE, DIPHENYL-,	169
ACETYLENE, PHENYL-,	166
ACRIDINE	746
ACRIDINE, 9-AMINO-,	747
* ACROLEIN, DIETHYL ACETAL	1425
ACRYLAMIDE, N-ALLYL-,	2306
ACRYLAMIDE, N-tert-BUTYL-,	2304
ACRYLAMIDE, N-(1,1,3,3-TETRAMETHYLBUTYL)-,	2305
ACRYLIC ACID, BENZYL ESTER	2845
ACRYLIC ACID, CALCIUM SALT	2669
ACRYLIC ACID, DODECYL ESTER	2809
* ACRYLIC ACID, 2-ETHYLHEXYL ESTER	2808
* ACRYLIC ACID, ISOBUTYL ESTER	2807
* ACRYLIC ACID, 2-CHLORO-, ETHYL ESTER	2820
ACRYLIC ACID, 3-CHLORO-, cis-,	2531
ACRYLIC ACID, 3-PHENYL-,	2550
ACRYLONITRILE	966
ACRYLOPHENONE, 3-(2-FURYL)-,	2091
ACRYLOPHENONE, 3-PHENYL-,	2092
* 1-ADAMANTANAMINE, N,N-DIMETHYL-, HYDROCHLORIDE	813
* ADAMANTANE, 1-CHLORO-,	268
* ADAMANTANE, 2-CHLORO-,	269
ADAMANTANE, 1-ISOTHIOCYANATO-,	935
* 1-ADAMANTANECARBOXAMIDE, N,N-DIMETHYL-,	2359
* 1-ADAMANTANEMETHANOL	1684
* 1-ADAMANTANEMETHYLAMINE	473
* 2-ADAMANTONE	2012
* ADIPIC ACID	2499
* ADIPIC ACID, DIETHYL ESTER	2777
* ADIPIC ACID, DIHYDRAZIDE	2404
* ADIPIC ACID, DIISOBUTYL ESTER	2778
ADIPIC ACID, 2,5-DIPHENYL-,	2542

*** No spectrum is included for this compound (see Preface).**

ALPHABETICAL INDEX

* No spectrum is included for this compound (see Preface).

* No spectrum is included for this compound (see Preface).

* No spectrum is included for this compound (see Preface).

* No spectrum is included for this compound (see Preface).

ALPHABETICAL INDEX

* No spectrum is included for this compound (see Preface).

* No spectrum is included for this compound (see Preface).

* No spectrum is included for this compound (see Preface).

* No spectrum is included for this compound (see Preface).

* No spectrum is included for this compound (see Preface).

ALPHABETICAL INDEX

* No spectrum is included for this compound (see Preface).

* No spectrum is included for this compound (see Preface).

* No spectrum is included for this compound (see Preface).

* No spectrum is included for this compound (see Preface).

ALPHABETICAL INDEX

* No spectrum is included for this compound (see Preface).

* No spectrum is included for this compound (see Preface).

* No spectrum is included for this compound (see Preface).

* No spectrum is included for this compound (see Preface).

* No spectrum is included for this compound (see Preface).

* No spectrum is included for this compound (see Preface).

*** No spectrum is included for this compound (see Preface).**

* No spectrum is included for this compound (see Preface).

ALPHABETICAL INDEX

NAME	SPECTRUM NO.
* CYCLOHEXANECARBONITRILE	964
* CYCLOHEXANECARBONYL CHLORIDE	2205
* CYCLOHEXANECARBOXALDEHYDE	2155
* CYCLOHEXANECARBOXYLIC ACID	2514
* 1,4-CYCLOHEXANEDICARBONITRILE, trans-,	965
* 1,2-CYCLOHEXANEDICARBOXYLIC ACID, BIS(2-ETHYLHEXYL ESTER)	2788
* 1,3-CYCLOHEXANEDICARBOXYLIC ACID, DIMETHYL ESTER	2787
* 1,4-CYCLOHEXANEDICARBOXYLIC ACID	2515
* 1,2-CYCLOHEXANEDICARBOXYLIC ANHYDRIDE	2261
* 1,2-CYCLOHEXANEDIOL, cis-,	1855
* 1,4-CYCLOHEXANEDIOL	1856
1,2-CYCLOHEXANEDIONE, DIOXIME	865
1,3-CYCLOHEXANEDIONE, 2-ACETYL-,	2145
1,3-CYCLOHEXANEDIONE, 5,5-DIMETHYL-,	2144
* CYCLOHEXANEETHANOL	1682
* CYCLOHEXANEMETHANOL	1680
* CYCLOHEXANEMETHANOL, α-METHYL-,	1762
* CYCLOHEXANEMETHANOL, 4-METHYL-,	1681
* CYCLOHEXANEMETHYLAMINE	469
* CYCLOHEXANOL	1766
* CYCLOHEXANOL, 2-CYCLOHEXYL-,	1773
* CYCLOHEXANOL, 2,4-DIMETHYL-,	1771
CYCLOHEXANOL, 2,2-DIPHENYL-,	1776
* CYCLOHEXANOL, 1-ETHYL-,	1810
* CYCLOHEXANOL, 2-ETHYL-,	1770
* CYCLOHEXANOL, 1-ETHYNYL-,	1816
* CYCLOHEXANOL, 2-ISOPROPYL-5-METHYL-,	1772
* CYCLOHEXANOL, 1-METHYL-,	1809
* CYCLOHEXANOL, 2-METHYL-, trans-,	1767
* CYCLOHEXANOL, 4-METHYL-, cis-,	1769
* CYCLOHEXANOL, 4-METHYL-, trans-,	1768
CYCLOHEXANOL, trans-2-PHENYL-,	1774
CYCLOHEXANOL, 2-PHENYL-, cis-,	1775
CYCLOHEXANOL, 1-p-TOLYL-,	1821
CYCLOHEXANONE	2000
* CYCLOHEXANONE, 4-tert-BUTYL-,	2004
* CYCLOHEXANONE, 5-HEXYL-3-METHYL-,	2005
* CYCLOHEXANONE, 2-METHYL-,	2001
* CYCLOHEXANONE, 3-METHYL-,	2002
CYCLOHEXANONE, 4-METHYL-,	2003
* CYCLOHEXENE	99
* CYCLOHEXENE, 1,2-DIMETHYL-,	104
* CYCLOHEXENE, 1-ETHYL-,	103
* CYCLOHEXENE, 4-ISOPROPENYL-1-METHYL-,	111
* CYCLOHEXENE, 1-METHYL-,	102

*** No spectrum is included for this compound (see Preface).**

ALPHABETICAL INDEX

* No spectrum is included for this compound (see Preface).

* No spectrum is included for this compound (see Preface).

* No spectrum is included for this compound (see Preface).

* No spectrum is included for this compound (see Preface).

* No spectrum is included for this compound (see Preface).

* No spectrum is included for this compound (see Preface).

* No spectrum is included for this compound (see Preface).

* No spectrum is included for this compound (see Preface).

ALPHABETICAL INDEX

* No spectrum is included for this compound (see Preface).

* No spectrum is included for this compound (see Preface).

* No spectrum is included for this compound (see Preface).

* No spectrum is included for this compound (see Preface).

ALPHABETICAL INDEX

* No spectrum is included for this compound (see Preface).

*** No spectrum is included for this compound (see Preface).**

* No spectrum is included for this compound (see Preface).

*** No spectrum is included for this compound (see Preface).**

ALPHABETICAL INDEX

* No spectrum is included for this compound (see Preface).

ALPHABETICAL INDEX

* No spectrum is included for this compound (see Preface).

* No spectrum is included for this compound (see Preface).

ALPHABETICAL INDEX

	NAME	SPECTRUM NO.
	ISOTHIOCYANIC ACID, p-FLUOROPHENYL ESTER	941
	ISOTHIOCYANIC ACID, HEPTYL ESTER	933
*	ISOTHIOCYANIC ACID, METHYL ESTER	930
*	ISOTHIOCYANIC ACID, OCTADECYL ESTER	934
	ISOTHIOCYANIC ACID, PHENYL ESTER	938
	ISOVALERIC ACID, BENZYL ESTER	2837
	ISOVALERIC ACID, CINNAMYL ESTER	2843
*	ISOVALERIC ACID, CYCLOHEXYL ESTER	2715
*	ISOVALERIC ACID, METHYL ESTER	2699
*	ISOVALERIC ACID, PENTYL ESTER	2706
	ISOVALERIC ACID, PHENETHYL ESTER	2838
*	ISOVALERONITRILE	947
	ISOXAZOLE, 3-METHYL-,	1579
	ITACONIC ANHYDRIDE	2258
	KETONE, 1-CYCLOHEXENYL METHYL,	2022
	KETONE, CYCLOHEXYL PHENYL,	2084
	KETONE, CYCLOPENTYL PHENYL,	2083
	KETONE, DICYCLOPROPYL,	1996
	KETONE, HEXYL PHENYL,	2049
	KETONE, 5-INDANYL METHYL,	2108
*	KETONE, METHYL ETHYL,	1968
*	KETONE, METHYL HEXYL,	1974
*	KETONE, METHYL 2-NORBORNYL,	1998
	KETONE, METHYL 6-METHYL-2-PYRIDYL	2111
	KETONE, METHYL PHENYL,	2045
	KETONE, METHYL 4-PHENYL-4-PIPERIDYL, HYDROCHLORIDE	144
	KETONE, METHYL 2-PYRIDYL,	2110
	KETONE, METHYL 2-PYRIDYL, PHENYL HYDRAZONE	878
	KETONE, PHENYL 3-PYRIDYL,	2112
*	LACTAMIDE	2283
*	LACTAMIDE, N,N-DIMETHYL-,	2357
*	LACTIC ACID	2493
*	LACTIC ACID, METHYL ESTER	2740
*	LACTIC ACID, SODIUM SALT, DL-,	2659
*	LACTONITRILE	1758
*	LACTONITRILE, 2-METHYL-,	1806
*	LAURAMIDE, N,N-DIETHYL-,	2356
*	LAURIC ACID	2480
*	LAURIC ACID, DODECYL ESTER	2711
*	LAURIC ACID, SODIUM SALT	2652
*	LAUROYL CHLORIDE	2193
	LEPIDINE	720
*	L-LEUCINE, N-ACETYL-,	2621
*	LEVULINIC ACID	2494
*	LEVULINIC ACID, ISOPENTYL ESTER	2747
*	LEVULINIC ACID, METHYL ESTER	2746

* No spectrum is included for this compound (see Preface).

* No spectrum is included for this compound (see Preface).

* No spectrum is included for this compound (see Preface).

ALPHABETICAL INDEX

* No spectrum is included for this compound (see Preface).

* No spectrum is included for this compound (see Preface).

ALPHABETICAL INDEX

*** No spectrum is included for this compound (see Preface).**

* No spectrum is included for this compound (see Preface).

ALPHABETICAL INDEX

* No spectrum is included for this compound (see Preface).

* No spectrum is included for this compound (see Preface).

* No spectrum is included for this compound (see Preface).

NAME	SPECTRUM NO.
* 2-PENTYNE, 4,4-DIMETHYL-,	126
* 1-PENTYN-3-OL, 3-METHYL-,	1814
* 2-PENTYN-1-OL	1696
PHENACYL BROMIDE	2053
PHENACYL CHLORIDE	2051
PHENANTHRENE	214
PHENANTHRENE, 9-AMINO-,	541
PHENANTHRENE, 9,10-DIHYDRO-,	211
PHENANTHRENE, 7-ISOPROPYL-1-METHYL-,	216
PHENANTHRENE, 2-METHYL-,	215
9-PHENANTHRENECARBONITRILE	1001
PHENANTHROLINE, 1,10-, HYDRATE	750
PHENANTHROLINE, 2,9-DIMETHYL-1,10-,	751
PHENETHYL ALCOHOL	1701
PHENETHYL ALCOHOL, p-AMINO-,	1718
PHENETHYLAMINE	477
PHENETHYLAMINE, p-AMINO-,	529
PHENETHYLAMINE, p-CHLORO-α,α-DIMETHYL-, HYDROCHLORIDE	786
PHENETHYLAMINE, DL-N,α-DIMETHYL-, HYDROCHLORIDE	804
PHENETHYLAMINE, β-METHYL-,	479
PHENETHYLENE	156
m-PHENETIDINE	1522
m-PHENETIDINE, N,N-DIETHYL-,	1525
PHENETOLE	1489
PHENETOLE, β-BROMO-,	1491
PHENETOLE, o-BROMO-,	1517
PHENETOLE, p-BROMO-,	1518
PHENETOLE, o-CHLORO-,	1512
PHENETOLE, p-CHLORO-,	1513
PHENETOLE, 2,4-DINITRO-,	1557
PHENETOLE, m-METHYL-,	1499
PHENETOLE, o-METHYL-,	1498
PHENETOLE, p-METHYL-,	1500
PHENETOLE, p-NITRO-,	1533
PHENOL	1875
PHENOL, PROPIONATE	2921
PHENOL, 4-ALLYL-2-METHOXY-,	1924
PHENOL, m-AMINO-,	1899
PHENOL, 4,4'-BIS(2,6-DI-tert-BUTYL-,	1934
PHENOL, o-BROMO-,	1894
PHENOL, p-BROMO-,	1895
PHENOL, o-tert-BUTYL-,	1882
PHENOL, p-tert-BUTYL-,	1883
PHENOL, o-CHLORO-,	1892
PHENOL, p-CHLORO-,	1893

*** No spectrum is included for this compound (see Preface).**

* No spectrum is included for this compound (see Preface).

* No spectrum is included for this compound (see Preface).

* No spectrum is included for this compound (see Preface).

* No spectrum is included for this compound (see Preface).

* No spectrum is included for this compound (see Preface).

* No spectrum is included for this compound (see Preface).

* No spectrum is included for this compound (see Preface).

* No spectrum is included for this compound (see Preface).

	NAME	SPECTRUM NO.

*** No spectrum is included for this compound (see Preface).**

* No spectrum is included for this compound (see Preface).

* No spectrum is included for this compound (see Preface).

* No spectrum is included for this compound (see Preface).

* No spectrum is included for this compound (see Preface).

* No spectrum is included for this compound (see Preface).

* No spectrum is included for this compound (see Preface).

* No spectrum is included for this compound (see Preface).

* No spectrum is included for this compound (see Preface).

* No spectrum is included for this compound (see Preface).

* No spectrum is included for this compound (see Preface).

* No spectrum is included for this compound (see Preface).

* No spectrum is included for this compound (see Preface).

* No spectrum is included for this compound (see Preface).

* No spectrum is included for this compound (see Preface).

ULTRAVIOLET SPECTRA LOCATOR

Ultraviolet spectra are a very useful analytical tool in illustrating important structural features and identifying unknown compounds. The spectroscopist frequently requires comparison spectra of known compounds for evaluation and it is to this end that the Sadtler Ultraviolet Locator has been devised. Using the Locator it is possible to rapidly retrieve those spectra which most closely resemble an unknown spectrum. The retrieval method is based upon the wavelength location and absorptivity of the peaks in the ultraviolet spectra.

The Locator consists of up to five pairs of columns containing the spectral information; the sixth column shows the total number of absorption peaks exhibited in the region 200 - 350 mμ (some into the visible region), followed by the UV Handbook spectrum number. The last column headed 'NAB' indicates whether the corresponding data was obtained from a spectrum determined in a neutral (N), acidic (A) or basic (B) medium. Since many compounds possessing ionizable functional groups exhibit spectral shifts and changes in absorptivity dependent on the pH of the solvent system, it is desirable to have this information as a further means of locating an unknown spectrum. It is also evident that often more than one spectrum will fulfill the requirements exacted by an unknown. The purpose of the Locator is to minimize the number of spectra to be examined for comparison purposes, it should not be considered as an absolute identification in itself.

The Locator relies principally upon the first five pairs of columns for its operation. The first four digits of the first column pair denote the position of the peak of maximum absorption (highest absorptivity) to the nearest one half mμ. The second set of four digits within the first column gives the value of the absorptivity (a) of that peak. To facilitate the use of the Locator with unknown compounds the absorptivity rather than the molar absorptivity has been used. The absorptivity has been calculated from.

$$a = \frac{A}{bC}$$

where a = absorptivity
A = absorbance (also known as optical density or extinction)
b = optical path length in cm
C = concentration in grams per liter

In order to convert values of absorptivity (a) to molar absorptivity (ϵ) simply multiply by the molecular weight of the compound.

The entries in column pairs 2 through 5 have the same designation as the first column pair and are arranged in order of descending absorptivity. If there are less than five column pairs for a spectrum entry this indicates that the compound exhibits fewer than five absorption peaks in the 200 - 350 mμ range. Should all five column pairs be filled then the compound has five or more peaks in the 200 - 350 mμ region and the total number of peaks is given in the column labelled "PEAKS." The arbitrary decision to include specified values for a maximum of five peaks was made following a survey of the complete Sadtler Ultraviolet Spectra collection which showed that less than 10% of the spectra exhibited more than five peaks.

USE OF THE LOCATOR

There are two methods of locating unknown spectra for comparison. Firstly, comparing on λ values only taking the λ values of the five strongest peaks without calculating the absorptivities. This method gives a rapid preliminary screening for possible matching spectra. The second and more precise method entails the calculation of absorptivity values and more detailed searching for spectra which match on both wavelength and absorptivity values.

During the searching procedure it is advisable to look at spectra within ±0.5 mμ if an exact match cannot be found, this allows for instrument variation.

The example shown below illustrates the composition of the Ultraviolet Locator. On the following page a worked example of an actual spectrum is illustrated.

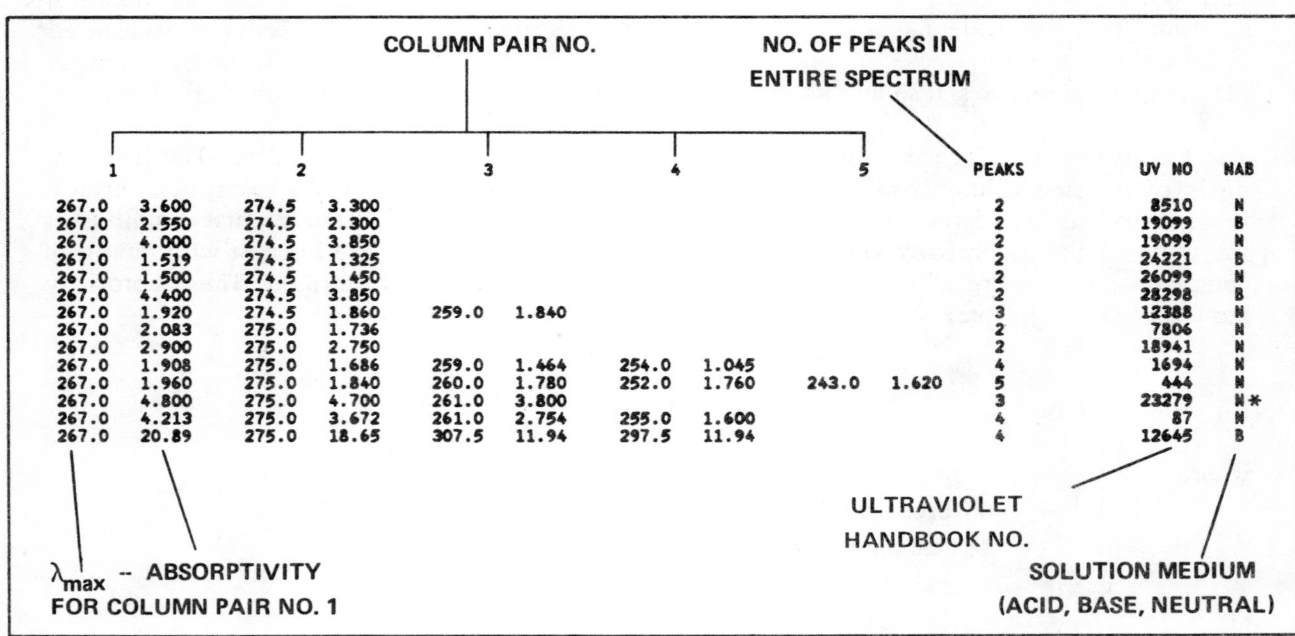

1		2		3		4		5		PEAKS	UV NO	NAB
267.0	3.600	274.5	3.300							2	8510	N
267.0	2.550	274.5	2.300							2	19099	B
267.0	4.000	274.5	3.850							2	19099	N
267.0	1.519	274.5	1.325							2	24221	B
267.0	1.500	274.5	1.450							2	26099	N
267.0	4.400	274.5	3.850							2	28298	B
267.0	1.920	274.5	1.860	259.0	1.840					3	12388	N
267.0	2.083	275.0	1.736							2	7806	N
267.0	2.900	275.0	2.750							2	18941	N
267.0	1.908	275.0	1.686	259.0	1.464	254.0	1.045			4	1694	N
267.0	1.960	275.0	1.840	260.0	1.780	252.0	1.760	243.0	1.620	5	444	N
267.0	4.800	275.0	4.700	261.0	3.800					3	23279	N*
267.0	4.213	275.0	3.672	261.0	2.754	255.0	1.600			4	87	N
267.0	20.89	275.0	18.65	307.5	11.94	297.5	11.94			4	12645	B

EXAMPLE

1. Examine the spectrum (see illustration below) for all maxima and list them.

2. Calculate the absorptivity for each peak using the equation: $$a = \frac{A}{bc}$$

3. Arrange the peak data in sequence according to decreasing absorptivity, listing both the $\lambda_{max.}$ and absorptivity values. This sequence will indicate which column pairs the data will fall into in the Locator.

4. Compare the data obtained from No. 3 above with the Locator, bearing in mind that the Locator is arranged according to increasing value of $\lambda_{max.}$

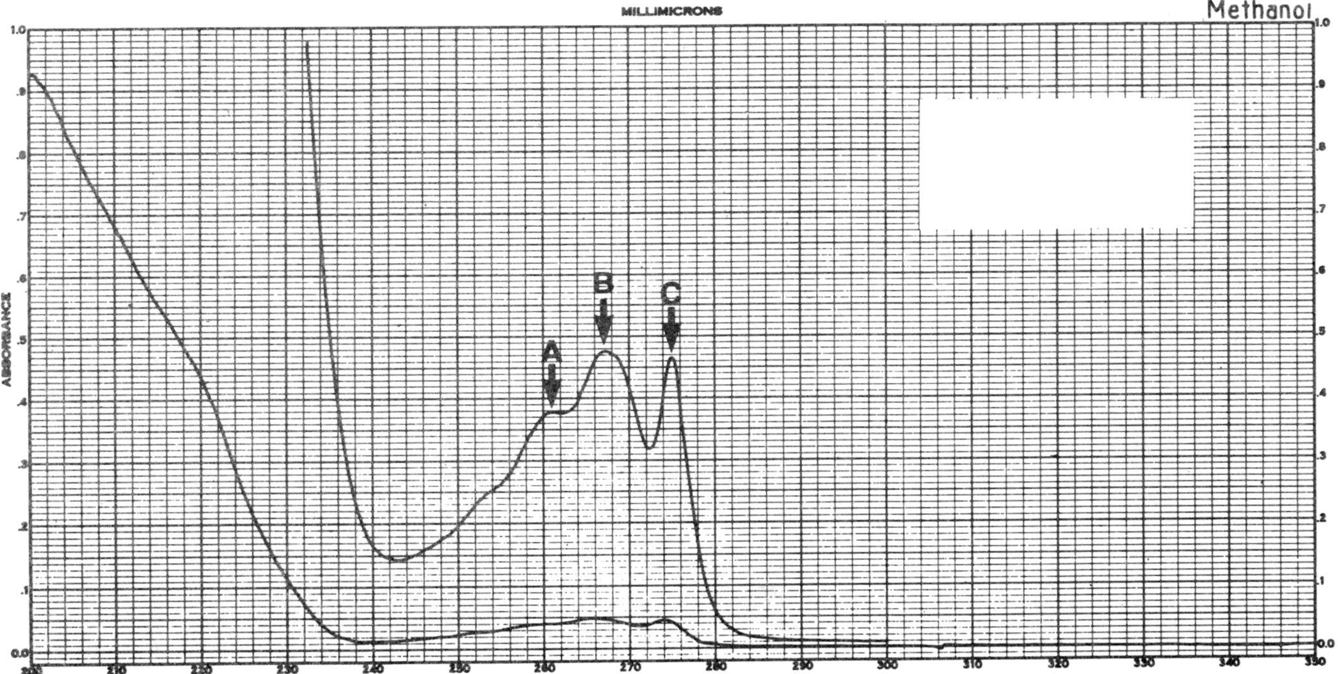

Absorption Maxima	Absorptivity	Column Pair No.
λ_{max} (mμ)	a	
A·261.0	3.800	3
B·267.0	4.800	1
C·275.0	4.700	2

1		2		3		4		5		PEAKS	UV NO	NAB
201.0	155.6	248.0	70.53	296.0	11.20					3	585	N
202.0	48.00									1	2604	B
204.0	68.00	218.0	44.00	252.5	2.150	258.5	2.100	264.5	1.700	1	841	N
204.0	54.62	248.5	12.40	265.0	4.074	303.0	2.193			4	507	A
204.0	136.0	250.0	102.0	283.0	3.750	292.0	2.500			4	2549	N
204.0	146.0	275.0	1.960							2	395	N
204.5	94.79	257.0	30.20							2	1049	N
204.5	106.2	321.5	78.75	232.5	57.50					3	897	A
205.0	65.75	228.0	57.53	276.5	9.815	283.0	8.673			4	1539	N
205.0	325.0	228.0	290.0	316.0	28.50	278.0	27.00	302.5	25.00	5	721	N
205.0	293.7	229.0	253.1	225.5	243.7	232.0	225.0	317.5	28.12	8	722	N
205.0	193.9	249.0	53.78	300.5	14.24					3	601	N
205.0	255.0	257.0	4.500	251.0	3.900	246.0	3.650	263.0	3.500	6	2445	N
205.0	48.00	258.0	1.320	251.5	1.160	264.0	1.040			4	2552	N
205.0	47.00	262.0	5.400	268.0	5.000					3	2558	N
205.0	118.0	314.0	56.00							2	1960	A
205.0	108.7	321.0	78.75	232.5	58.75					3	897	N
205.5	56.00									1	2267	N
205.5	117.1	210.5	108.5	254.5	104.2	216.5	68.57	282.5	10.71	6	1257	N
205.5	70.00	248.0	31.00							2	2407	N
205.5	107.4	250.0	90.12							2	884	A
205.5	265.0	251.5	7.400	259.0	6.900	264.0	4.900			4	2405	A
205.5	155.1	252.0	108.1	292.0	7.767					3	852	N
205.5	65.68	258.5	3.112	253.0	3.112	287.5	.6615	303.0	.4669	5	529	A
205.5	31.16	262.0	6.495	268.5	5.965					3	1715	N
206.0	86.91									1	2264	N
206.0	264.2	235.0	47.96	286.5	16.26					3	1522	N
206.0	140.0	246.0	46.00	302.0	11.20					3	796	N
206.0	150.0	248.0	70.00	306.0	10.20					3	522	N
206.0	52.38	249.5	2.333	245.0	2.333	257.5	2.285	266.5	1.761	5	493	A
206.0	48.06	251.0	2.869	257.0	2.781	247.0	2.693	263.0	2.119	5	1480	N
206.0	156.0	251.0	37.00	310.0	16.00					3	2914	N
206.0	51.00	258.0	4.500	250.0	4.400	246.5	4.300	265.5	3.650	5	492	A
206.0	50.37	260.0	24.43	266.5	23.68					3	690	N
206.5	170.0	234.0	106.0	284.0	23.50					3	492	N
206.5	172.1	235.0	54.91	301.0	21.31					3	1161	N
206.5	64.95	260.5	2.735	267.5	2.564	256.0	2.478			4	589	A
206.5	75.00	262.5	62.00							2	2453	N
207.0	124.0									1	2533	N
207.0	64.00									1	2265	N
207.0	291.4	239.0	92.00	288.0	20.00					3	499	N
207.0	194.0	240.5	160.0	231.0	140.0	339.0	30.50	314.0	21.00	5	764	N
207.0	280.0	242.0	95.00	283.0	49.00					3	2334	N
207.0	91.00	252.0	89.00	289.0	6.500					3	1707	N
207.0	1.880	257.5	1.020	251.5	.8600	263.0	.8000	247.0	.6800	6	804	N
207.0	44.00	258.5	1.100	260.5	1.000	252.5	.9800	264.0	.8600	8	785	N
207.0	39.71	261.0	20.21	257.5	20.21					3	694	N
207.0	3.850	261.0	2.600	268.0	2.300	259.0	2.150	255.0	1.900	8	133	N
207.0	182.0	264.5	126.0							2	667	N
207.0	50.00	268.5	4.300	262.8	3.050	259.8	1.100			4	904	A
207.0	50.00	272.0	37.00							2	2456	N
207.5	40.48	251.0	2.428	246.5	2.428	257.0	2.063	263.0	1.416	7	1775	N
207.5	61.18	257.5	1.494	252.0	1.221	264.0	1.157	247.0	.9053	6	973	N
208.0	124.0	232.0	72.00	324.0	24.00	337.0	17.50	311.0	15.50	5	726	A
208.0	57.23	246.0	3.894	250.5	3.684	257.0	3.052	263.0	2.105	5	1789	N
208.0	65.00	252.0	14.20	291.0	6.000					3	1059	N
208.0	26.00	255.0	16.50	292.0	14.50					3	2608	B
208.0	319.0	255.5	34.76	261.5	33.80	249.5	33.80	265.5	32.38	6	2850	N
208.0	12.38	258.0	7.738							2	2108	N
208.0	63.82	261.5	2.819	268.5	2.606	322.0	.4255			4	590	A
208.0	71.00	263.0	7.500	271.5	7.400					3	665	A
208.0	136.0	323.0	17.40	310.0	13.80	297.0	10.40	302.5	10.20	5	726	N
208.5	42.50									1	1579	N
208.5	56.12	234.5	4.000	257.0	2.709	331.5	2.645	267.0	1.677	5	592	A
208.5	205.0	236.0	49.00	298.0	19.50					3	2892	N
209.0	100.0									1	575	N
209.0	92.00									1	2912	N
209.0	95.91									1	2826	N
209.0	190.0	230.0	43.50	294.0	16.00					3	2583	N
209.0	170.0	243.5	50.00	309.5	17.00					3	517	N
209.0	61.85	258.5	1.649	260.5	1.608	253.0	1.422	267.5	1.299	7	139	N
209.0	58.00	259.5	1.900	268.0	1.400					3	1718	A
209.0	51.99	261.0	1.303	258.5	1.282	253.0	1.132	268.0	1.025	8	482	N
209.0	53.12	261.0	1.583	259.0	1.479	268.0	1.291	255.0	1.291	8	141	N
209.0	49.33	261.5	1.466	259.0	1.366	268.5	1.200	264.0	1.066	5	142	N
209.0	18.40	262.5	.9800	257.0	.8100	268.5	.7900	251.5	.5700	5	839	N
209.5	91.00	251.0	23.00							2	1056	N
209.5	176.0	256.0	84.00	295.0	36.80					3	2599	N
210.0	38.84	217.0	34.53	281.0	23.74					3	1891	N
210.0	198.0	244.0	96.00	277.0	6.100	285.0	4.800			4	2329	N
210.0	97.00	248.0	54.00							2	1096	N
210.0	166.6	248.0	59.25	294.0	10.74					3	2057	N
210.0	289.3	251.0	85.53	340.0	45.28					3	1241	B
210.0	22.92	253.5	19.51	260.0	14.63					3	686	N
210.0	89.00	261.0	21.50							2	665	N
210.0	78.22	261.0	1.900	263.0	1.750	257.5	1.650	271.0	1.300	5	499	A
210.0	55.00	264.0	2.100	271.5	1.800					3	178	N
210.0	40.00	267.0	4.842	277.0	4.105	263.0	3.578			4	391	N
210.0	47.00	270.0	32.50							2	1146	N
210.0	53.75	276.0	8.625	269.0	8.375					3	304	N
210.0	88.00	290.0	10.00							2	2920	N

1		2		3		4		5		PEAKS	UV NO	NAB
210.5	78.00									1	1135	A
210.5	118.0	252.5	76.00	304.0	36.50					3	1529	N
210.5	188.0	257.0	19.50	251.0	19.50	283.5	16.50	292.0	15.00	5	1159	N
210.5	52.37	267.5	30.21	275.0	22.96					3	691	N
210.5	174.0	281.5	39.20	246.0	38.40	275.5	35.20			4	739	N
211.0	89.33	227.0	69.33	267.0	40.00	325.0	13.60			4	1531	N
211.0	136.0	238.0	36.50	296.0	12.50					3	525	N
211.0	120.0	238.5	64.00							2	1354	N
211.0	139.5	242.0	31.25	272.0	12.70					3	758	A
211.0	78.00	256.5	54.00							2	1559	N
211.0	78.00	257.5	14.50							2	519	A
211.0	93.00	258.5	4.500							2	2635	N
211.0	59.00	262.0	38.00							2	2409	N
211.0	275.0	263.0	77.00	349.0	61.00					3	1174	A
211.0	53.00	264.5	6.800	271.0	5.800	258.5	4.900			4	302	N
211.0	50.00	275.0	4.931	266.0	4.794	268.5	4.452	262.0	3.493	5	664	A
211.0	128.9	294.0	3.094	270.5	2.693	266.0	2.636	260.5	2.636	5	486	A
211.5	34.00									1	820	N
211.5	200.0	232.0	197.5	265.0	24.25	297.5	20.50	325.5	13.25	5	1952	N
211.5	114.2	241.0	112.8	326.0	11.85	399.0	5.285			4	826	N
211.5	297.9	243.0	193.7	317.5	35.62					3	539	N
211.5	341.1	247.0	117.6	331.0	37.64					3	600	N
211.5	73.75	261.5	1.560	269.0	1.220					3	502	A
211.5	67.33	262.0	4.641	257.5	4.641	271.0	3.209			4	486	N
211.5	39.50	273.0	8.300	267.5	8.000					3	1493	N
211.5	147.8	276.0	131.0							2	186	N
211.5	118.0	279.0	58.00	267.0	54.00	303.0	20.00			4	2958	N
211.5	178.0	293.0	11.40							2	794	B
211.5	156.0	299.5	8.200	292.0	8.100					3	2400	B
212.0	16.40									1	2523	B
212.0	95.00									1	2520	N
212.0	245.0	207.0	240.0	301.0	15.00					3	2402	B
212.0	288.3	231.0	209.3	293.0	37.99	306.0	25.02	320.0	15.75	5	1569	N
212.0	31.00	237.0	18.50	325.0	17.50	286.0	15.00			4	1564	N
212.0	225.0	243.0	210.0	350.0	28.50					3	727	N
212.0	311.5	248.0	107.6	332.0	42.30	416.0	.6538			4	599	N
212.0	116.9	250.0	57.21							2	1233	N
212.0	35.12	251.0	2.616	257.5	2.437	263.5	1.756			4	1704	N
212.0	75.34	253.5	20.54							2	664	N
212.0	17.20	259.0	1.425	253.0	1.300	264.0	1.125	247.0	1.125	5	379	N
212.0	148.0	261.0	84.00	370.0	32.00					3	1955	N
212.0	60.00	263.0	3.900							2	763	A
212.0	56.00	263.0	1.750	270.0	1.300					3	1717	N
212.0	167.6	266.5	84.84							2	1535	B
212.0	202.5	290.5	26.00							2	1342	N
212.0	240.0	293.0	16.00	262.0	9.400					3	2402	N
212.5	19.55	208.0	19.55	266.5	6.111					3	2923	N
212.5	152.0	242.0	43.00	332.0	20.50					3	2079	N
212.5	210.0	256.0	97.50	338.0	32.50					3	1174	N
212.5	125.9	259.5	62.96	300.0	37.50					3	1525	N
213.0	106.0									1	1574	N
213.0	17.60									1	2829	N
213.0	16.80	252.0	1.825	258.0	1.775	247.0	1.750	268.0	1.300	5	155	N
213.0	16.40	266.0	2.400	274.5	1.920					3	515	A
213.0	36.44	267.0	8.222	274.0	7.666					3	1502	N
213.0	40.81	273.0	14.45	279.5	13.26	245.0	4.761			4	1882	B
213.0	76.55	273.5	5.454	266.5	4.976					3	196	N
213.0	42.50	279.0	26.50							2	2457	N
213.0	200.0	282.5	17.15	290.0	14.73					3	1535	N
214.0	240.5	242.5	51.13	329.0	41.66					3	2293	B
214.0	18.40	256.0	2.350	262.0	2.200	251.0	2.000			4	3000	N
214.0	74.00	259.0	41.00							2	2601	N
214.0	74.00	263.5	3.200	258.5	2.800	270.0	2.440	252.5	2.040	5	1594	N
214.0	245.0	269.0	37.50	278.5	36.25	275.5	36.25	286.5	31.87	5	610	A
214.0	87.00	272.0	8.625	266.0	8.375					3	2924	N
214.0	116.0	305.0	42.00							2	1960	N
214.5	134.2									1	2398	N
215.0	69.00									1	677	N
215.0	154.1	243.5	36.97	295.0	10.08					3	526	N
215.0	134.0	245.0	74.00	330.0	31.50					3	1310	N
215.0	40.00	261.0	22.50							2	2606	N
215.0	12.40	262.5	3.850							2	1365	A
215.0	48.00	266.5	2.400	275.0	2.200					3	1290	A
215.0	28.00	272.0	13.00							2	1581	N
215.0	54.16	273.5	15.95							2	1879	N
215.0	42.85	278.0	3.257	269.0	2.800	264.0	1.885			4	299	N
215.0	125.0	292.0	4.674							2	2067	N
215.0	65.00	293.0	52.00	253.0	33.00					3	1557	N
215.3	53.00	240.0	40.50	322.5	21.50					3	1943	B
215.5	208.0	229.0	88.00	237.0	60.80	290.5	9.400			4	2380	N
215.5	18.60	257.0	1.400	263.5	1.000					3	2446	N
215.5	18.20	258.0	2.200	253.0	1.925					3	2986	N
215.5	318.8	302.0	28.98							2	671	N
216.0	19.00									1	2812	N
216.0	62.00									1	2266	N
216.0	43.00	210.0	41.00	258.0	4.200					3	1304	A
216.0	80.70	245.0	3.111	251.0	2.814	265.0	2.482	258.5	2.202	8	189	N
216.0	97.00	246.0	27.00	353.0	18.80					3	2595	N
216.0	113.3	252.5	34.42							2	1175	A
216.0	151.6	255.0	16.27	274.0	7.400					3	2379	N
216.0	30.00	258.0	2.500	263.0	2.200	253.0	2.200	269.5	1.500	5	1313	N
216.0	38.50	258.5	9.500	252.5	8.300	265.5	7.100	246.0	6.700	5	821	B

ULTRAVIOLET LOCATOR INDEX

1		2		3		4		5		PEAKS	UV NO	NAB
216.0	97.43	263.5	23.45	258.0	21.75	270.0	17.43			4	1002	N
216.0	820.0	270.0	23.00	278.0	19.00	263.0	16.00	256.0	9.500	6	306	N
216.0	64.86	271.5	.6950							2	2931	N
216.0	49.50	271.5	27.00							2	702	N
216.0	51.02	271.5	14.28	278.0	13.26					3	1494	N
216.0	38.77	273.0	14.96	279.5	13.26					3	1882	N
216.0	27.24	274.0	15.57	279.0	13.62					3	1880	N
216.0	174.0	293.5	21.00	286.5	18.50					3	1587	N
216.5	57.02	223.0	56.17	282.5	19.26	275.0	18.23			4	1509	N
216.5	240.0	247.0	64.00	317.0	22.40					3	994	N
216.5	544.9	268.0	28.74	319.5	24.25	306.0	19.16	314.0	17.96	5	728	N
216.5	57.50	270.0	.5325							2	1733	N
216.5	210.0	278.5	35.00	272.0	33.75	288.0	28.12			4	610	N
216.5	105.0	294.5	4.600							2	2384	N
217.0	98.00									1	2576	N
217.0	138.0	248.0	22.00	268.0	7.000	276.0	6.600	316.0	5.300	5	994	A
217.0	230.0	248.5	115.0	280.0	102.5	285.5	95.00	244.0	67.50	8	1541	N
217.0	190.0	254.0	89.00	286.0	30.00	292.5	29.00			4	1563	N
217.0	42.32	262.5	13.75							2	2939	N
217.0	64.00	265.0	40.00							2	2408	N
217.0	74.00	265.0	6.300	273.0	5.100					3	1713	N
217.0	44.00	270.0	12.80	276.0	11.80					3	1526	N
217.0	50.00	271.0	14.43	276.0	13.40	306.0	1.443			4	1504	N
217.0	21.41	271.5	9.271	278.5	8.830					3	1540	N
217.0	55.88	273.0	13.23	280.5	11.91					3	1505	N
217.0	118.1	277.0	48.52							2	1232	B
217.0	77.00	277.0	32.00	348.0	15.40					3	1922	N
217.5	210.2	238.5	48.78	293.0	8.746					3	2393	N
217.5	182.0	253.0	112.0	283.0	35.50	322.0	4.350	338.0	3.450	5	1173	N
217.5	142.5	255.0	38.00							2	2885	N
217.5	106.2	256.5	36.25							2	758	N
217.5	68.00	259.0	22.25							2	842	N
217.5	320.0	271.5	27.50	283.0	23.00	321.0	21.00	310.0	19.00	5	729	N
217.5	236.2	275.5	39.91	265.5	35.08	307.5	1.885			4	201	N
217.5	120.0	276.0	51.66							2	2915	N
217.5	48.12	280.0	11.42	273.0	11.27					3	1499	N
217.5	88.00	288.5	7.733							2	2069	N
217.5	211.7	292.0	8.528	263.5	3.972	257.0	3.972			4	2396	N
218.0	56.73	213.5	54.80	262.5	2.548	258.0	2.307	271.5	1.730	5	1714	N
218.0	265.0	231.0	100.0	240.0	71.00	292.5	5.800			4	2391	N
218.0	210.0	231.0	70.00	240.0	50.00	293.0	8.500			4	2392	N
218.0	154.0	246.0	46.41	287.0	9.282	279.0	8.860	296.0	7.805	5	1232	N
218.0	40.48	251.0	32.68							2	686	A
218.0	285.0	251.0	83.16	336.0	37.50	289.0	22.00			4	604	N
218.0	40.79	258.0	10.19	288.0	1.031					3	843	N
218.0	136.0	259.0	42.00							2	2956	N
218.0	79.00	259.5	67.00	339.0	18.80					3	709	A
218.0	63.00	262.0	1.950	271.0	1.100					3	1860	N
218.0	62.00	262.5	1.500	257.0	1.300	269.0	1.200			4	837	N
218.0	174.0	271.0	144.0	275.0	142.0					3	750	A
218.0	463.6	272.0	32.56	268.0	32.56	263.0	29.35	278.0	27.06	10	234	N
218.0	126.0	274.0	50.00							2	2917	N
218.0	106.0	274.0	42.00							2	2918	N
218.0	70.00	275.0	30.00							2	2919	N
218.0	41.81	278.0	18.18	284.0	16.36					3	1590	N
218.0	60.62	279.0	43.75							2	1959	N
218.0	56.00	295.0	1.300	268.0	1.050					3	1291	N
218.5	184.0									1	2524	B
218.5	54.00	213.5	26.00							3	2041	N
218.5	46.00	222.0	38.50	272.0	1.933	263.0	1.866	265.0	1.800	6	183	N
218.5	50.00	223.0	49.09	278.0	14.00	284.0	12.54			4	1552	N
218.5	206.0	250.0	43.81	283.0	8.890	294.0	8.823	274.5	7.018	5	1175	N
218.5	36.00	259.0	11.40							2	1312	N
218.5	78.03	264.0	2.291	271.0	1.860	257.0	1.759	261.0	1.569	9	291	N
218.5	148.0	275.0	56.00							2	2916	N
219.0	64.44									1	1575	N
219.0	192.0	232.0	63.00	240.5	46.00	293.0	8.700			4	2394	N
219.0	210.0	250.5	90.00	306.0	67.00					3	2334	B
219.0	88.00	253.5	47.00	309.0	31.00					3	2033	N
219.0	98.60	264.5	4.019	260.0	3.751	271.0	3.161	254.5	2.733	5	1084	N
219.0	88.00	266.0	2.100	259.5	1.800	275.0	1.500			4	786	N
219.0	84.00	270.0	7.800	276.5	6.400	264.5	5.800			4	1491	N
219.0	82.25	270.5	17.74	277.0	14.83					3	1492	N
219.0	33.50	271.0	8.300	278.0	7.100	265.0	6.500	218.0	1.300	5	905	A
219.0	23.00	272.0	4.750	278.0	3.850					3	2554	N
219.0	7.317	273.0	3.677	278.0	3.546	269.0	3.339	282.0	2.908	5	294	N
219.0	282.3	277.0	23.66	288.0	20.71	323.0	20.11	311.5	15.68	5	731	N
219.0	426.5	278.0	28.32	276.0	28.32	269.0	27.27	286.0	20.62	5	233	N
219.0	36.00	281.5	18.00							2	2600	N
219.0	116.6	284.0	71.66	349.0	33.33					3	2579	N
219.0	100.0	288.0	3.700							2	2876	N
219.0	178.0	293.5	7.900	269.0	6.900					3	2397	N
219.5	62.77	224.0	51.09	269.0	2.251	277.0	2.076	262.0	1.666	6	305	N
219.5	62.50	224.5	46.15	261.0	1.365	255.0	1.163	267.0	.9519	6	300	N
219.5	14.20	252.0	2.950	248.0	2.800	243.0	2.700	259.5	2.500	7	2212	N
219.5	141.6	261.0	43.33	296.0	38.33					3	2608	N
219.5	61.39	270.0	11.98	277.0	10.29					3	1710	N
219.5	47.92	274.5	13.89	282.0	12.77					3	1510	N
219.5	150.0	302.0	15.40							2	2880	N
220.0	96.00									1	2534	N
220.0	10.00									1	1225	B
220.0	85.00	232.5	30.00	241.0	22.00	293.0	3.800			4	2399	N

ULTRAVIOLET LOCATOR INDEX

1		2		3		4		5		PEAKS	UV NO	NAB
220.0	121.2	252.0	31.25							2	2602	N
220.0	46.85	253.0	37.71							2	685	A
220.0	134.0	255.0	52.00	296.0	8.900					3	1234	N
220.0	27.18	259.0	2.672	253.0	2.565	266.0	2.089	269.0	1.305	5	1247	N
220.0	43.50	259.0	3.300	264.5	3.050					3	2213	N
220.0	50.00	265.0	2.771	271.5	2.751	259.0	2.500	287.5	1.492	5	287	N
220.0	47.27	270.5	13.27	275.5	12.90					3	1722	N
220.0	53.52	270.5	11.12	277.5	9.436					3	1792	N
220.0	46.36	277.0	13.73	283.0	13.55	270.5	9.554			4	1883	N
220.0	260.1	299.0	40.25							2	1241	N
220.5	40.50	228.5	40.00	287.0	15.00					3	1919	N
220.5	222.5	261.5	6.700	268.0	5.800	256.0	5.400	273.5	3.800	5	1302	N
220.5	58.00	262.0	1.200	255.0	1.150	268.0	.8500			4	1291	A
220.5	66.00	265.0	33.00							2	2408	A
220.5	190.0	271.5	42.00	278.5	34.00					3	1490	N
220.5	39.27	278.0	11.34	284.5	10.32	275.0	9.454	272.0	8.727	6	1887	N
220.5	188.0	279.0	34.30	273.5	32.44	289.0	28.98			4	2607	N
220.5	65.00	282.0	5.800	275.0	5.700	251.0	2.400			4	2941	N
221.0	48.00									1	1577	N
221.0	118.0									1	2906	N
221.0	196.5	217.5	191.3	269.0	2.645	277.0	2.525	262.5	2.013	6	384	N
221.0	59.00	225.0	52.00	272.5	1.300	280.0	1.100	265.0	1.100	5	314	N
221.0	114.0	227.5	112.0	209.5	110.0	234.0	106.0			4	2395	N
221.0	110.0	233.0	91.00	343.0	42.00					3	1964	N
221.0	48.50	245.0	34.00							2	1250	N
221.0	15.60	268.0	10.20	275.0	8.400	262.5	8.000			4	2215	N
221.0	630.0	272.0	30.00	264.5	29.00	245.5	22.00			4	540	A
221.0	42.64	278.0	11.39	285.0	11.01					3	1885	N
221.0	390.0	278.0	32.80	285.0	28.80	268.0	28.00			4	1342	A
221.0	53.33	279.5	14.28							2	2116	N
221.0	282.3	279.5	36.62	269.5	32.55	287.0	27.90	302.0	8.023	7	600	A
221.0	543.6	279.5	36.89	270.5	33.00	302.0	4.385	311.5	2.409	6	671	A
221.0	198.5	281.5	67.56	271.0	66.66					3	940	N
221.0	164.0	299.5	10.20	290.5	10.00					3	2380	B
221.0	523.0	311.0	71.15	316.0	60.57	279.0	3.461	504.0	1.000	5	599	A
221.0	61.00	333.0	5.100	270.0	3.600					3	2878	A
221.0	6.300	355.0	.3400	343.0	.3000	369.0	.2900	333.0	.2200	6	1038	N
221.5	196.0									1	2524	N
221.5	150.8	241.5	49.64	312.0	20.98					3	672	N
221.5	46.09	252.0	30.46							2	688	A
221.5	68.27	265.0	2.882							2	285	N
221.5	53.50	280.5	16.55	287.0	15.77	274.0	11.55			4	1881	N
221.5	234.2	281.0	71.10	270.5	65.46	286.0	6.772			4	939	N
221.5	145.7	289.0	10.08	299.5	9.059	280.0	8.376			4	1177	A
221.5	162.7	289.5	8.376	300.0	8.290					3	1177	N
221.5	.3550	291.5	.1621							2	2003	N
222.0	44.50									1	2306	N
222.0	81.00									1	889	N
222.0	134.0	253.0	44.00	300.0	14.80					3	816	B
222.0	66.00	265.0	5.200	272.0	4.300	259.5	4.000			4	1659	N
222.0	380.6	269.0	34.82	276.0	34.50	313.0	16.61	300.0	15.33	5	720	N
222.0	90.00	273.5	12.60	303.5	1.100	335.0	.1500			4	989	N
222.0	136.0	298.0	44.00							2	1960	B
222.0	206.5	298.0	17.60							2	1237	N
222.0	103.7	304.5	100.0	311.0	98.75					3	1178	N
222.2	73.00	261.5	5.300	268.5	4.900	276.0	3.500			4	2566	B
222.5	62.00									1	677	A
222.5	58.76	242.0	24.57							2	1709	N
222.5	55.00	246.0	54.00							2	1370	B
222.5	49.00	257.0	4.700	262.0	4.600					3	668	A
222.5	19.20	271.5	6.400							2	2018	N
222.5	66.66	272.0	14.95	278.0	13.17					3	1522	A
222.5	60.00	274.5	10.20	281.0	8.800					3	791	N
222.5	440.0	275.5	28.66	266.0	26.00	286.0	19.66	304.5	3.000	7	2930	N
223.0	148.0									1	1076	N
223.0	27.00									1	378	N
223.0	78.00									1	2021	N
223.0	35.00									1	2365	N
223.0	1.223	220.0	1.156	269.0	.1779					3	1995	N
223.0	9.874	230.0	8.463	281.5	1.536	273.5	1.536			4	987	N
223.0	72.00	261.0	2.500	255.0	2.250	271.5	1.500			4	388	N
223.0	140.0	262.0	60.00	406.0	54.00					3	2178	B
223.0	73.00	262.5	39.00							2	1100	N
223.0	38.00	265.5	3.500	259.0	2.850	272.0	2.800			4	1376	N
223.0	78.00	265.5	6.300	272.0	5.300	259.5	4.800			4	2859	N
223.0	42.00	267.0	1.950	271.0	1.750	276.0	1.700			4	1301	N
223.0	65.51	268.5	2.241	277.0	1.422					3	1225	N
223.0	42.95	270.0	3.943	264.5	3.943					3	432	N
223.0	72.00	271.0	6.700	278.0	6.400					3	2880	A
223.0	822.2	274.5	37.77	318.0	3.600	304.0	3.500	310.5	2.200	5	202	N
223.0	114.0	276.0	60.00							2	158	N
223.0	270.0	282.0	43.00	290.0	36.00					3	607	N
223.0	830.0	283.5	46.00	273.0	40.50	290.5	32.50	310.0	2.700	7	317	N
223.0	192.0	289.0	4.900	297.0	4.200					3	2081	N
223.5	39.50									1	2363	N
223.5	60.00									1	1370	N
223.5	58.00	237.0	56.00	300.0	6.000					3	2224	N
223.5	51.43	262.0	2.046	267.0	1.918	273.0	1.649	256.5	1.560	5	1322	N
223.5	52.81	268.0	3.792							2	2675	N
223.5	64.00	270.5	5.000	277.5	4.200					3	2676	A
223.5	270.0	274.0	250.5	282.5	28.50	312.5	2.000	317.0	1.600	5	1292	N
223.5	67.00	274.5	11.00							2	2569	N

ULTRAVIOLET LOCATOR INDEX

1		2		3		4		5		PEAKS	UV NO	NAB
223.5	37.70	274.5	5.491							2	2896	N
223.5	670.0	275.0	29.50	267.0	27.00	284.5	20.00			4	998	N
223.5	73.78	276.5	14.17	283.0	11.65					3	1497	N
223.5	37.50	278.0	8.000							2	1886	N
223.5	38.75	288.5	10.37							2	1921	N
223.5	127.7	300.0	18.75							2	504	N
224.0	98.75									1	2288	N
224.0	66.25									1	2344	N
224.0	250.0	219.0	250.0	296.0	45.00	308.5	32.50	322.3	14.50	5	999	N
224.0	240.0	227.0	237.5	289.0	21.50					3	1591	N
224.0	67.00	261.0	3.600	272.0	2.300					3	1267	N
224.0	66.50	261.5	2.600	256.0	2.160	267.0	2.140	272.0	1.680	5	1363	N
224.0	100.0	262.5	2.782	257.5	2.631	250.0	1.992	270.0	1.654	5	988	N
224.0	69.00	271.0	1.940	279.0	1.580					3	1793	N
224.0	15.40	272.0	9.400	279.0	8.000					3	1524	A
224.0	66.00	273.0	2.079	272.0	1.800	265.0	1.729	281.0	1.717	5	394	N
224.0	46.29	274.0	12.59	280.0	11.48					3	1525	A
224.0	42.58	275.0	10.22							2	874	A
224.0	60.67	277.0	12.13	284.0	10.18					3	1501	N
224.0	98.00	279.0	23.00							2	2038	N
224.0	44.38	279.5	10.71							2	1884	N
224.0	59.75	279.5	14.21	286.0	13.30	276.0	12.71			4	1500	N
224.0	195.0	328.0	21.00							2	2892	B
224.5	253.3									1	2150	B
224.5	184.0	243.5	82.00	283.0	26.40	313.0	3.200	318.0	3.000	5	1293	N
224.5	77.27	267.0	8.863	274.0	7.613	260.5	6.477			4	1102	N
224.5	36.57	267.0	2.879	274.0	2.373	261.0	2.373	292.0	.2690	5	289	N
224.5	64.00	269.5	4.250	263.0	4.200					3	2683	N
224.5	672.0	273.0	30.09	263.0	26.53	284.0	19.00	329.0	13.36	6	1951	N
224.5	115.0	273.5	4.025	282.0	3.450	266.0	2.725	268.0	2.400	7	307	N
224.5	109.7	281.0	13.15	272.0	10.31	275.0	8.711			4	984	N
224.5	283.0	285.0	5.142	275.0	4.238	291.0	3.476	296.5	3.333	7	400	N
224.5	116.0	285.0	12.80	318.0	2.350					3	1293	A
224.5	230.2	287.5	30.69	277.5	26.51	299.0	21.86	316.0	2.511	5	438	N
224.5	69.50	293.0	30.50							2	1912	N
224.5	190.0	293.5	35.20	284.0	28.00	304.0	24.80			4	402	N
224.5	220.0	296.0	36.80							2	2274	B
225.0	42.71									1	371	N
225.0	8.500									1	2025	N
225.0	52.00									1	1568	N
225.0	82.00									1	2342	N
225.0	263.3	219.0	253.3	301.0	33.00	312.0	32.00	337.0	15.50	5	2136	N
225.0	70.00	225.0	70.00							1	2531	N
225.0	104.9	230.0	97.16	276.0	59.21	268.5	57.44	263.5	42.55	5	983	N
225.0	46.00	255.0	2.000	260.5	1.966					3	639	N
225.0	172.0	261.0	39.50	283.0	30.00	290.5	26.50			4	606	N
225.0	97.00	268.0	11.20	343.0	9.600					3	2905	N
225.0	76.05	274.0	11.61	280.0	10.07					3	1822	N
225.0	21.12	275.0	3.169							2	2898	N
225.0	34.46	275.0	5.168							2	2899	N
225.0	58.00	277.5	11.71							2	1902	N
225.0	637.5	278.0	31.87	268.0	30.62	288.0	20.62	305.5	2.850	7	203	N
225.0	73.00	279.0	4.100	287.0	3.750					3	2580	N
225.0	26.00	286.0	6.300							2	2565	N
225.0	70.00	289.0	23.00							2	1547	N
225.0	241.1	333.0	41.00	480.0	2.000					3	752	A
225.5	140.0									1	2073	N
225.5	75.20	204.5	49.58							2	436	N
225.5	93.43	232.5	84.67	282.0	9.124	274.0	7.883	267.0	5.109	5	985	N
225.5	112.0	250.0	47.50	368.5	32.50					3	2079	B
225.5	114.0	265.0	30.50	302.0	19.50	291.5	19.00	312.0	10.00	5	742	N
225.5	102.0	272.0	1.610	264.5	1.250	280.5	1.230			4	312	N
225.5	26.20	275.0	3.951							2	2897	N
225.5	620.0	277.0	32.00	266.5	29.00	306.5	2.300	320.5	2.100	5	318	N
225.5	257.5	285.0	27.00	314.0	2.500					3	1310	A
225.5	95.00	296.0	90.00	255.0	37.50	247.0	37.50			4	1176	N
225.5	545.0	298.0	53.00	330.0	46.00	316.0	45.00			4	1957	N
225.5	178.0	309.0	32.00	301.0	31.60	323.0	31.20	338.0	28.80	5	2274	N
225.5	78.00	329.0	23.00							2	2597	N
226.0	39.50									1	2305	N
226.0	58.59									1	2361	N
226.0	62.00									1	376	N
226.0	86.00	254.0	73.00							2	2388	N
226.0	105.0	255.0	46.25							2	2080	N
226.0	5.500	261.5	1.350	278.5	1.250					3	2560	N
226.0	32.79	262.0	1.862							2	290	N
226.0	186.0	262.0	64.00	290.0	52.00	425.0	45.00	372.0	36.00	5	1955	B
226.0	94.00	269.0	7.300	276.5	5.100					3	912	N
226.0	83.00	270.5	9.100	277.5	7.300					3	916	N
226.0	42.00	271.0	21.50	261.0	20.00	282.0	14.60	327.0	9.000	7	1726	N
226.0	83.58	274.0	9.477	280.5	8.358					3	2839	N
226.0	75.62	275.0	12.82	282.0	11.03					3	1723	N
226.0	66.25	276.0	9.900	283.5	8.500					3	2871	N
226.0	84.00	276.0	6.000	285.5	5.800	268.0	5.300	294.0	5.100	6	1273	N
226.0	61.00	276.5	9.500	283.0	8.250					3	2563	N
226.0	75.00	277.5	10.80	271.0	10.00	292.0	9.400			4	2882	A
226.0	62.50	278.0	3.485	286.0	3.464	269.5	2.157			4	313	N
226.0	50.00	279.0	4.800	287.0	3.400					3	2562	N
226.0	4058.	290.0	471.9	318.0	47.19					3	922	N
226.0	43.75	294.0	25.25							2	2684	N
226.0	76.00	302.0	68.00							2	2054	B
226.0	1.160	303.0	.2400	282.0	.1800	341.5	.1500			4	2142	N

ULTRAVIOLET LOCATOR INDEX

1		2		3		4		5		PEAKS	UV NO	NAB
226.5	39.00									1	2304	N
226.5	60.00									1	2851	N
226.5	259.0	231.0	222.7	277.0	27.67	313.0	27.23	288.8	25.89	7	718	N
226.5	67.81	271.5	2.614	278.0	1.982					3	2865	N
226.5	93.12	272.0	7.354	279.0	5.978					3	2566	N
226.5	440.0	274.0	22.00	305.0	2.500	319.5	2.400	312.0	2.100	5	1309	N
226.5	74.00	275.5	11.40	282.0	9.600					3	1503	N
226.5	65.77	279.0	15.79							2	1908	N
226.5	192.0	281.0	40.00							2	611	N
226.5	84.00	289.0	35.00							2	1558	N
226.5	72.00	295.0	6.400							2	1938	N
226.5	338.4	296.0	35.38							2	734	N
227.0	49.00									1	2321	N
227.0	134.0									1	864	N
227.0	98.00									1	1335	B
227.0	43.20	223.0	43.20	277.0	12.80	284.0	11.20			4	1897	N
227.0	547.3	223.5	410.0	280.5	43.15	281.5	40.00	270.5	34.21	5	2287	N
227.0	54.00	262.0	3.400	273.0	2.900					3	1264	N
227.0	73.51	263.5	3.512	269.5	2.258					3	2570	N
227.0	82.00	272.0	7.500	265.0	7.000	280.0	6.000			4	2085	N
227.0	82.68	272.0	5.474	279.0	4.916	265.0	4.245			4	2864	N
227.0	75.00	272.5	6.900	280.5	6.400	265.0	6.200			4	430	N
227.0	60.00	273.0	1.416	265.0	1.383	257.5	1.233	281.0	.9000	5	398	N
227.0	41.50	280.0	16.50	287.0	14.50					3	1896	N
227.0	82.75	280.5	12.75	288.0	10.17					3	1511	N
227.0	31.82	281.0	4.655							2	2872	N
227.0	67.08	282.0	9.493	290.0	8.417					3	1516	N
227.0	41.25	296.0	24.77							2	2678	N
227.0	341.3	332.0	34.13	274.0	16.76	266.0	16.16			4	728	A
227.5	65.00									1	1075	N
227.5	54.00									1	674	A
227.5	27.56									1	377	N
227.5	74.00	256.0	3.550							2	429	N
227.5	78.00	265.5	2.650	262.5	2.600	255.5	2.200	273.5	2.150	5	1263	N
227.5	93.75	270.0	8.937	277.0	7.687					3	2270	N
227.5	64.00	274.0	2.750							2	2157	N
227.5	794.7	274.0	32.21	325.0	8.734	310.0	5.805	317.0	3.974	6	204	N
227.5	44.00	281.0	22.00							2	1924	N
227.5	65.15	282.5	8.401	290.5	7.384					3	1518	N
227.5	109.4	285.0	6.080	296.0	4.395					3	1067	N
228.0	18.50									1	2037	N
228.0	41.00									1	2338	N
228.0	222.5	232.5	210.0	316.0	22.00	278.0	21.00	303.0	19.25	6	1731	N
228.0	59.72	233.0	59.25	258.5	3.611	276.0	2.268			4	427	N
228.0	87.09	238.0	82.25	257.0	4.274	263.0	3.669			4	426	N
228.0	260.0	248.0	65.00	279.5	5.100	287.5	4.500	303.5	1.800	5	2150	N
228.0	144.0	257.0	58.00	358.0	31.60					3	2178	N
228.0	46.50	264.5	1.050	258.0	1.000	270.5	.7000			4	1303	N
228.0	630.0	270.0	29.00	276.0	28.00	308.5	3.500	322.5	3.300	5	205	N
228.0	75.64	272.0	4.775	279.0	4.359	266.0	4.294	263.0	4.294	7	2942	N
228.0	80.00	272.0	6.300	279.5	5.200					3	2683	A
228.0	82.00	273.0	5.900	281.0	4.900					3	2867	N
228.0	19.86	274.0	15.23	320.0	14.40	210.0	13.24	307.0	11.92	5	725	N
228.0	58.00	277.5	3.350							2	1368	N
228.0	74.25	279.0	17.26							2	1888	N
228.0	67.79	279.0	12.54	271.0	12.37					3	1548	N
228.0	72.00	284.0	14.00							2	1893	N
228.0	230.0	284.0	46.00	292.0	40.00					3	609	N
228.0	87.91	289.0	32.89							2	1070	N
228.0	34.50	294.0	12.50							2	2595	A
228.0	58.00	390.0	13.80							2	1074	N
228.5	57.00	215.0	55.00	256.0	24.00	322.0	14.00			4	1938	B
228.5	333.3	271.0	20.50	261.0	20.25	252.0	16.25	282.0	13.00	8	1572	N
228.5	88.13	282.0	13.05	290.0	11.69					3	1513	N
228.5	600.0	289.0	38.77	279.0	38.77	300.0	27.80	306.5	18.36	10	207	N
229.0	67.00									1	2381	N
229.0	28.57									1	2990	N
229.0	38.50									1	913	N
229.0	57.00	224.0	57.00	279.5	5.500	287.5	5.000	272.5	3.800	5	993	N
229.0	257.1	226.0	252.3	233.0	242.8	316.0	33.17	303.0	27.10	9	719	N
229.0	73.00	235.0	62.00	289.0	10.60	278.0	10.60			4	990	N
229.0	33.75	238.0	33.12	286.5	8.250					3	1886	B
229.0	200.0	244.0	56.00	325.0	33.50	267.0	31.00	275.0	27.50	5	1963	N
229.0	92.00	256.0	40.00	524.0	4.400	341.0	4.300			4	2149	N
229.0	61.53	260.0	3.601	269.0	3.216	277.5	2.272			4	428	N
229.0	19.20	260.5	1.800	267.5	1.650	255.0	1.600	276.0	1.200	5	2217	N
229.0	55.00	262.0	2.850	273.0	1.400					3	1375	N
229.0	245.0	263.0	155.0							2	750	N
229.0	126.0	265.0	24.80	331.0	17.20					3	2914	B
229.0	63.84	267.5	33.84							2	2110	N
229.0	234.9	268.0	45.22	327.0	43.31					3	1961	N
229.0	69.00	268.0	43.00	329.0	14.50					3	1904	N
229.0	59.60	273.0	4.078	257.5	4.078	267.5	4.000	264.0	4.000	5	2866	N
229.0	491.6	275.0	1.908	283.5	1.576	268.0	1.452			4	311	N
229.0	77.50	276.0	7.050							2	2289	N
229.0	236.6	279.0	24.33	291.0	20.33	268.0	19.00	335.0	12.66	6	1954	N
229.0	104.0	325.0	55.00							2	2043	N
229.0	136.0	365.0	13.60	281.0	3.200					3	2910	A
229.0	176.0	366.0	25.00							2	2910	N
229.5	55.00									1	2411	A
229.5	67.51	235.5	65.98	245.0	63.95	315.0	58.88			4	760	N
229.5	149.2	237.0	133.3	265.5	4.549	257.5	3.981	260.0	3.886	11	986	N

ULTRAVIOLET LOCATOR INDEX

1		2		3		4		5		PEAKS	UV NO	NAB
229.5	39.19	277.0	12.06	285.0	11.55					3	1519	N
229.5	57.95	281.5	6.833	289.5	6.036					3	2873	N
229.5	55.00	291.0	15.71							2	510	N
230.0	48.50									1	525	A
230.0	46.00									1	1137	N
230.0	104.0									1	2945	N
230.0	91.00	209.5	88.00	272.0	57.00	305.0	32.00			4	2109	N
230.0	82.85	246.0	80.00	300.0	11.42	313.0	10.28	352.0	9.142	5	826	B
230.0	43.50	260.0	17.00							2	1061	N
230.0	196.0	261.0	78.00	284.5	52.00	310.5	31.00	299.0	28.00	5	2373	N
230.0	61.00	276.0	29.00							2	1903	B
230.0	42.40	278.0	16.80							2	1561	A
230.0	43.50	278.5	16.50							2	1527	N
230.0	54.36	279.0	7.919							2	2869	N
230.0	44.89	280.0	16.46							2	1560	N
230.0	33.50	280.0	9.500							2	2560	B
230.0	49.00	282.5	6.600	274.5	6.300					3	1364	N
230.0	52.00	302.0	9.600							2	1556	N
230.5	75.78	281.0	18.15	285.0	17.63					3	1549	N
230.5	110.0	312.0	57.50	272.0	47.50					3	2186	N
231.0	82.00									1	1051	N
231.0	72.07									1	679	N
231.0	90.00									1	1369	N
231.0	62.12	263.0	8.181	271.0	7.727	279.5	5.909			4	1538	N
231.0	82.00	264.5	5.500							2	2567	B
231.0	83.00	266.5	5.300							2	2571	B
231.0	65.42	267.5	9.719							2	2063	N
231.0	41.50	274.5	33.00							2	2111	N
231.0	31.50	283.0	12.00							2	824	N
231.0	475.0	285.0	21.00	328.0	19.50	313.0	15.00	319.5	12.00	5	1958	N
231.0	296.6	291.0	24.66	303.0	22.00	315.5	16.33			4	723	N
231.0	17.00	359.0	.6500	308.0	.4750					3	1334	N
231.5	40.68									1	372	N
231.5	62.93									1	2362	N
231.5	50.00									1	2512	N
231.5	62.00	210.0	36.00	258.0	26.00					3	1060	N
231.5	281.2	235.5	265.6	210.5	103.1	256.0	84.37	286.0	51.87	7	1179	A
231.5	1.663	253.5	1.178	247.0	1.156	259.5	.8921	278.5	.0220	5	788	N
231.5	27.50	280.0	17.50							2	904	N
231.5	76.00	283.0	38.00							2	1151	N
231.5	89.00	292.5	83.00							2	2341	A
231.5	54.00	293.5	6.100	284.0	5.500	279.0	2.800	275.5	2.700	5	315	N
232.0	80.86									1	1072	N
232.0	109.0									1	176	N
232.0	176.0									1	850	N
232.0	25.00									1	2604	N
232.0	63.00									1	2410	N
232.0	52.00	227.0	50.00	237.0	43.00	280.5	8.300	288.5	8.000	5	992	N
232.0	66.00	230.0	66.00	255.0	60.00	313.5	38.00			4	1335	N
232.0	170.0	242.0	132.0	287.0	122.0	363.0	88.00	394.0	48.00	5	2181	N
232.0	39.20	264.0	3.045	271.0	2.954					3	431	N
232.0	740.0	271.0	105.0							2	2943	N
232.0	39.28	272.5	7.142							2	914	N
232.0	67.58	272.5	61.88							2	2145	N
232.0	70.00	273.0	6.666							2	1251	N
232.0	213.2	273.0	2.174	281.0	1.960					3	2843	N
232.0	46.39	275.0	5.463							2	919	N
232.0	49.00	276.5	4.350	285.5	3.550					3	1266	N
232.0	35.50	281.0	11.00							2	823	N
232.0	84.67	282.0	17.13	392.0	.2822					3	508	N
232.0	44.80	293.0	16.63							2	511	N
232.0	190.0	338.0	54.00	276.0	22.00	442.0	4.700			4	752	N
232.0	91.25	339.0	13.40							2	2333	N
232.0	152.0	362.0	78.00	476.0	8.000					3	752	B
232.5	138.0									1	2171	N
232.5	51.00									1	528	A
232.5	54.16									1	526	A
232.5	57.00									1	527	A
232.5	245.0	213.0	120.0	273.0	26.00	264.5	24.00	329.5	5.900	5	825	N
232.5	70.00	228.5	67.00	225.0	64.00	249.0	44.00	301.5	15.80	9	602	N
232.5	54.78	276.0	6.782							2	2271	N
232.5	69.36	282.5	6.576							2	1898	N
232.5	73.33	286.0	11.42							2	493	N
232.5	42.30	294.0	18.37							2	2585	N
232.5	227.5	295.5	33.33	308.0	26.86	323.0	20.64			4	1950	N
233.0	48.00									1	2390	N
233.0	50.00									1	2265	B
233.0	46.00									1	1678	N
233.0	71.42	237.0	66.66							2	1136	N
233.0	273.3	255.5	120.0	291.5	110.0	321.5	21.33	335.0	18.66	5	612	N
233.0	79.00	280.5	6.200							2	1521	N
233.0	114.0	285.0	29.39							2	488	N
233.0	45.00	285.0	10.60							2	2680	N
233.0	43.88	301.0	21.58							2	1891	B
233.0	23.66	301.0	2.166							2	1260	N
233.0	250.0	317.0	28.00	304.0	21.00	310.0	17.00	297.0	16.50	5	724	N
234.0	72.00									1	2988	N
234.0	103.3									1	2027	N
234.0	50.00									1	2368	N
234.0	74.00									1	889	A
234.0	95.00									1	2987	N
234.0	65.00	264.0	4.150	280.0	2.100					3	2989	N

ULTRAVIOLET LOCATOR INDEX

1		2		3		4		5		PEAKS	UV NO	NAB
234.0	510.0	281.0	40.00	271.0	36.00	330.0	9.700	315.0	8.000	7	1000	N
234.0	59.00	284.0	13.00							2	788	B
234.0	58.75	288.0	15.00							2	502	N
234.0	42.46	294.5	20.30							2	2887	N
234.0	64.00	299.0	13.80							2	791	B
234.0	76.00	418.0	28.00	281.0	19.60					3	1922	B
234.5	107.0									1	2290	N
234.5	77.00									1	2210	N
234.5	53.00	265.5	6.700	260.0	5.700	273.0	4.600			4	1272	N
234.5	76.25	267.0	39.75							2	2971	N
234.5	94.00	275.0	49.00							2	2341	N
234.5	70.05	284.5	21.94							2	491	N
234.5	108.6	286.0	21.06	282.5	20.34	289.0	19.04	280.0	18.75	5	487	N
234.5	64.48	287.0	15.40							2	496	N
234.5	21.34	287.5	20.50							2	2039	N
234.5	118.5	296.0	42.22							2	706	N
235.0	87.00									1	2467	B
235.0	84.00									1	1147	N
235.0	226.6	229.0	196.6	261.0	110.0	293.0	90.00	287.5	56.66	7	744	N
235.0	18.18	245.0	16.45	240.0	13.41	269.0	5.021	262.0	4.935	8	166	N
235.0	62.00	259.0	5.700							2	1271	N
235.0	66.00	260.0	6.200	266.0	5.300	274.0	3.300			4	1270	N
235.0	139.7	269.0	4.121	261.5	3.510	275.0	3.215	281.0	2.943	5	991	N
235.0	91.56	275.0	10.48							2	2995	N
235.0	67.35	278.0	7.823	270.0	7.772	267.0	7.668	288.5	4.041	5	1542	N
235.0	27.50	285.5	25.00							2	1734	N
235.0	85.00	286.0	17.60	275.0	13.40	398.0	4.750	456.0	.9500	5	533	A
235.0	43.50	287.0	13.00							2	792	B
235.0	293.3	287.0	30.50	297.0	28.00	336.0	16.00	326.0	15.50	5	1956	N
235.0	55.00	300.0	29.50							2	2293	N
235.0	55.00	302.5	29.50							2	2587	N
235.5	65.54									1	1138	N
235.5	45.50	284.5	8.000							2	763	N
235.5	66.00	287.5	12.60							2	793	N
235.5	81.00	302.5	21.75	321.0	16.25					4	1286	N
236.0	50.49									1	1140	N
236.0	59.00									1	2594	N
236.0	58.77									1	172	N
236.0	142.5	221.5	90.00	292.0	18.33					3	1586	N
236.0	9.600	254.0	5.600	260.0	3.700	284.0	1.600			4	787	N
236.0	146.0	268.0	50.00	334.0	48.00					3	764	A
236.0	100.0	271.0	4.750	264.5	4.350	278.0	3.500			4	2994	N
236.0	40.00	272.0	9.500							2	2225	N
236.0	100.0	279.5	36.00							2	2567	N
236.0	87.00	285.5	15.00							2	2227	N
236.0	69.00	285.5	33.00	279.5	32.00	275.5	31.00	270.0	23.00	5	1585	N
236.0	50.00	287.0	10.40							2	790	B
236.0	65.77	287.0	20.88							2	497	N
236.0	262.0	287.0	250.0	276.0	122.4	282.0	93.10	253.0	74.13	11	212	N
236.0	70.00	289.0	10.80							2	1718	N
236.0	83.50	290.0	23.84							2	512	N
236.0	87.00	314.0	15.25							2	2183	A
236.0	12.40	321.0	5.800							2	2141	N
236.0	59.00	350.0	38.00	298.0	17.00					3	1941	N
236.5	45.55									1	865	N
236.5	114.0	206.0	68.00	290.0	43.00	336.5	9.000	323.0	8.100	5	745	N
236.5	81.00	233.0	70.00	243.0	63.00	291.0	16.33	281.5	13.66	5	997	N
236.5	39.20	283.0	5.360							2	2064	N
236.5	90.52	283.5	16.63							2	509	N
236.5	62.43	286.0	16.20							2	495	N
236.5	44.94	293.0	15.73							2	518	N
236.5	55.71	314.0	16.42							2	2071	A
237.0	119.2									1	2020	N
237.0	67.61									1	2371	N
237.0	49.56	232.5	46.08	262.5	2.604	258.0	2.534	272.0	2.447	6	433	N
237.0	15.96	245.0	15.82	281.0	2.773	290.0	1.764			4	2841	N
237.0	66.66	276.0	6.600	316.5	6.400	281.0	6.200			4	2070	A
237.0	73.89	277.0	7.881	270.0	7.635					3	1228	N
237.0	88.00	282.0	3.450							2	2571	N
237.0	91.00	292.5	18.00	294.5	17.75	288.0	17.25			4	490	N
237.0	35.00	316.0	23.50	286.0	22.00					3	2919	B
237.5	114.0	207.0	72.00	289.5	43.50	336.0	9.000	322.5	8.100	5	745	A
237.5	76.21	237.5	76.21	277.0	5.996	277.0	5.820	285.0	5.687	2	1230	N
237.5	77.60	279.0	6.628	286.0	5.323	322.0	.3549			4	2046	N
237.5	8.530	287.0	1.966							2	489	N
237.5	63.33	293.0	28.66							2	533	N
237.5	69.68	293.0	15.77							2	498	N
237.5	74.01	295.0	17.35							2	506	N
237.5	122.0	332.0	8.300							2	2103	N
238.0	67.00									1	2367	N
238.0	55.71									1	680	N
238.0	67.00									1	2406	N
238.0	65.00									1	1371	B
238.0	50.68									1	1192	N
238.0	122.0									1	2467	N
238.0	280.0									1	2870	N
238.0	3.250	261.0	2.150	268.5	1.850	286.0	.5500			4	790	N
238.0	50.70	282.0	18.30							2	1876	B
238.0	57.07	282.5	4.203							2	1231	N
238.0	42.00	287.0	14.50							2	1914	B
238.0	71.92	290.0	12.93							2	529	N
238.0	40.65	299.0	12.08							2	521	N

ULTRAVIOLET LOCATOR INDEX

1		2		3		4		5		PEAKS	UV NO	NAB
238.0	39.05	306.0	19.05							2	2891	N
238.0	50.42	306.0	23.07							2	2889	N
238.0	19.00	312.0	7.500							2	2634	A
238.5	28.40									1	2366	N
238.5	57.93									1	1193	N
238.5	84.95									1	105	N
238.5	93.00									1	717	N
238.5	275.0	235.5	275.0	316.0	13.40	309.0	12.00	267.5	6.500	6	602	A
238.5	5.463	260.0	1.876	266.0	1.696	287.0	1.311	279.0	1.311	5	2034	N
238.5	55.00	286.0	11.60							2	1885	B
238.5	41.50	287.0	15.50							2	1284	N
238.5	46.11	291.0	16.33	321.0	.2489					3	503	N
238.5	41.00	292.5	18.40							2	2955	B
238.5	45.60	294.0	17.60							2	1561	N
238.5	42.30	313.0	19.65							2	2889	B
238.5	38.02	314.0	18.06							2	2890	B
238.5	330.0	315.5	55.00							2	721	A
239.0	57.98									1	1229	N
239.0	106.0									1	2435	N
239.0	71.00									1	2450	N
239.0	52.00									1	888	A
239.0	4.227	234.0	4.105	263.5	2.357	271.0	2.154			4	434	N
239.0	80.00	276.0	7.600							2	2327	N
239.0	100.0	278.0	5.728	286.0	4.422	325.0	.3719			4	2048	N
239.0	118.0	279.0	6.900							2	2423	N
239.0	68.49	285.5	7.123							2	2065	N
239.0	57.40	289.0	19.39							2	1880	B
239.0	14.80	293.0	6.600							2	2391	B
239.0	36.50	295.0	13.50							2	1291	B
239.0	52.58	307.5	24.41							2	2890	N
239.0	262.5	316.5	48.75							2	722	A
239.0	49.00	318.0	44.00	278.0	35.00					3	2916	B
239.5	118.6									1	1576	N
239.5	84.00	229.0	83.00	288.0	23.00					3	2038	B
239.5	89.10	250.5	85.14	272.0	6.237	265.0	5.940	279.0	5.148	5	168	N
239.5	26.00	280.5	14.60							2	1913	B
239.5	46.00	292.0	18.50							2	1907	B
239.5	87.00	292.0	28.00							2	519	N
240.0	71.06									1	1194	N
240.0	52.00									1	2427	N
240.0	132.8									1	918	N
240.0	59.00	218.0	50.00							2	2086	N
240.0	78.00	266.0	10.00	274.0	5.600					3	1268	N
240.0	64.00	276.5	5.500							2	2049	N
240.0	47.72	277.0	3.422							2	2050	N
240.0	259.3	282.0	76.56							2	1179	N
240.0	46.00	285.0	17.00							2	1527	B
240.0	60.00	288.0	11.60							2	712	N
240.0	66.00	290.5	8.900							2	2405	N
240.0	82.05	291.0	18.80							2	589	N
240.0	51.25	296.0	23.00							2	1894	B
240.0	59.00	308.0	28.00							2	2596	N
240.0	42.00	317.0	34.00	276.0	33.00					3	2917	B
240.0	27.60	318.0	20.00	276.0	17.60					3	2918	B
240.5	114.2									1	2080	B
240.5	142.0									1	1338	N
240.5	26.50	218.5	22.50	257.5	19.00	264.0	12.50			4	821	N
240.5	100.0	272.0	14.50	279.0	11.50					3	2326	N
240.5	63.00	275.5	4.950							2	1378	N
240.5	14.80	278.0	12.80							2	1916	B
240.5	28.00	283.5	15.50							2	1917	B
240.5	101.4	283.5	8.900	293.0	7.100					3	2907	N
240.5	105.0	285.5	11.87							2	2592	N
240.5	36.25	286.0	8.625							2	2592	B
240.5	50.00	287.0	6.415							2	2068	N
241.0	87.11									1	157	N
241.0	71.25									1	2681	N
241.0	62.50									1	297	N
241.0	77.14									1	1196	N
241.0	37.00									1	2088	N
241.0	79.83									1	2052	N
241.0	223.6	214.0	216.3	281.0	44.56	291.0	35.86	320.0	6.630	6	1242	N
241.0	2.300	229.0	2.200	218.5	1.700	254.0	1.450			4	1859	N
241.0	325.0	248.0	267.5	281.0	50.50	271.5	44.00	291.0	36.50	7	2340	N
241.0	77.00	268.5	75.00							2	1150	N
241.0	77.90	278.0	6.453							2	2047	N
241.0	9.044	278.5	7.113							2	2045	N
241.0	108.6	281.0	9.883							2	2220	N
241.0	80.50	282.0	2.850							2	2574	N
241.0	85.42	284.0	6.432	294.0	5.326					3	2908	N
241.0	54.00	285.0	4.250							2	2909	N
241.0	96.00	289.0	10.40							2	2425	N
241.0	79.00	289.0	54.00	414.0	.5500					3	2610	N
241.0	50.36	295.0	12.26							2	1884	B
241.0	90.14	295.5	16.33							2	515	N
241.0	41.00	298.0	20.00							2	1896	B
241.0	68.00	301.0	23.00							2	537	N
241.0	42.50	303.0	.2300							2	2130	N
241.0	300.0	315.0	43.33							2	723	A
241.0	29.50	331.0	15.50							2	2891	B
241.5	121.4	234.0	121.4	227.5	111.4	209.5	108.5	266.0	98.57	7	1278	A
241.5	74.00	277.5	5.700							2	2083	N

1		2		3		4		5		PEAKS	UV NO	NAB
241.5	64.00	278.0	5.200							2	2084	N
241.5	147.5	278.0	11.45	288.0	9.708	338.5	.2729	328.0	.2632	8	2163	N
241.5	82.00	279.5	4.100							2	2317	N
241.5	70.37	285.5	10.92							2	2055	N
241.5	110.0	287.5	28.00							2	1908	B
241.5	45.16	293.0	14.83							2	1897	B
241.5	79.00	294.5	21.00							2	591	N
241.5	987.5	334.0	650.0	272.0	637.5	231.5	537.5	318.5	368.7	8	217	N
242.0	213.6									1	95	N
242.0	82.35									1	859	N
242.0	.3175									1	2809	N
242.0	6.634									1	933	N
242.0	105.0									1	2315	N
242.0	240.0	214.0	140.0	262.0	91.00	391.0	35.00			4	727	A
242.0	2.834	251.0	2.677	257.0	2.244	255.0	2.165	263.0	1.535	7	975	N
242.0	77.00	274.0	59.00							2	697	N
242.0	73.00	279.5	65.00							2	2840	N
242.0	60.18	282.0	12.50							2	658	N
242.0	35.00	282.0	10.00							2	823	B
242.0	70.00	294.0	15.00							2	513	N
242.0	52.29	301.5	15.29							2	1054	N
242.0	60.00	307.5	11.80							2	795	B
242.0	32.50	328.0	16.00							2	2595	B
242.5	51.33									1	936	B
242.5	10.10									1	2316	N
242.5	61.00									1	2372	N
242.5	70.45	238.0	68.63							2	435	N
242.5	66.16	250.5	62.62	293.0	8.669	302.0	6.955			4	2230	N
242.5	54.00	285.0	7.200							2	1948	B
242.5	49.52	294.0	35.23							2	2184	A
242.5	365.0	342.5	25.00	293.0	22.50	283.0	22.50			4	1958	B
243.0	38.50									1	2440	N
243.0	88.00									1	437	N
243.0	40.00									1	1143	N
243.0	75.00									1	2103	A
243.0	27.50									1	1152	N
243.0	87.00	235.5	62.00	301.0	43.00					3	876	A
243.0	64.00	276.0	11.40							2	2089	N
243.0	91.19	281.0	24.21	274.5	22.01	269.0	15.72			4	1584	N
243.0	80.25	282.0	2.630							2	2875	N
243.0	49.00	284.0	2.300							2	2387	B
243.0	44.50	285.0	14.50							2	1290	B
243.0	110.0	289.0	15.80							2	530	N
243.0	50.78	289.5	6.042							2	2167	N
243.0	60.00	292.0	13.50							2	2634	N
243.0	74.00	292.0	16.25							2	595	N
243.0	52.00	294.0	25.00							2	1554	N
243.0	960.0	296.0	126.7							2	514	N
243.0	101.0	308.0	16.90							2	535	N
243.0	296.4	317.0	15.81							2	1962	N
243.5	99.00									1	1712	N
243.5	72.00									1	1238	A
243.5	76.00									1	184	N
243.5	57.00									1	2468	N
243.5	70.00									1	1155	A
243.5	36.50	269.0	34.00							2	2409	B
243.5	85.00	292.0	14.00							2	794	N
243.5	78.00	294.0	16.00							2	1902	B
243.5	79.16	296.5	12.01							2	592	N
243.5	93.82	301.5	21.28							2	708	N
243.5	120.8	307.5	26.01							2	707	N
244.0	49.00									1	899	N
244.0	98.00									1	2322	N
244.0	118.0									1	2323	N
244.0	75.53									1	2319	N
244.0	71.00									1	2318	N
244.0	78.00									1	1536	N
244.0	85.00									1	1237	A
244.0	68.67									1	146	N
244.0	244.0	218.0	80.00	282.5	31.20	272.5	27.60	294.0	18.00	5	1293	B
244.0	82.00	222.0	45.00	274.5	4.800					3	1269	N
244.0	80.67	229.5	66.66	281.0	7.180	290.0	6.527	300.0	4.656	6	296	N
244.0	5.681	255.5	4.139	261.5	2.922					3	1320	N
244.0	91.92	260.0	77.99							2	1144	N
244.0	85.00	280.5	13.40							2	2054	N
244.0	84.11	292.0	13.92							2	594	N
244.0	74.00	292.5	11.20							2	2548	N
244.0	47.50	295.0	7.400							2	795	N
244.0	73.00	297.0	8.500							2	520	N
244.0	42.50	370.0	40.00							2	2104	A
244.5	.4240									1	1009	N
244.5	86.53	277.0	6.634	286.0	4.615					3	2842	N
244.5	67.00	285.5	15.80							3	2237	N
244.5	90.00	299.5	15.80							2	1895	B
244.5	67.00	305.0	15.60							2	516	N
245.0	88.77									1	2051	N
245.0	84.00									1	373	N
245.0	95.00									1	2324	N
245.0	88.00									1	2325	N
245.0	130.6									1	2320	N
245.0	61.00									1	1536	B
245.0	79.04									1	2060	N

1		2		3		4		5		PEAKS	IR NO	NAB
245.0	65.00									1	20994	B
245.0	54.00									1	21082	N
245.0	48.00									1	32109	N
245.0	16.40									1	49950	N
245.0	6.200	227.5	2.250	266.0	2.250	307.0	1.700			4	46091	N
245.0	84.00	281.0	6.600							2	46503	N
245.0	74.00	283.0	21.33	290.0	19.33					3	19561	N
245.0	104.4	293.0	17.44							2	6365	N
245.0	137.5	299.0	6.000							2	9535	N
245.0	81.00	305.0	19.40							2	17468	B
245.0	77.00	307.0	11.60							2	40632	N
245.0	60.00	310.0	16.00							2	50305	N
245.0	42.00	317.0	11.20							2	46029	B
245.0	32.50	334.0	22.00							2	50322	N
245.5	8.398									1	1603	N
245.5	530.0									1	8030	N
245.5	59.16									1	18083	N
245.5	104.0									1	34472	N
245.5	18.60									1	47486	N
246.0	144.8									1	19440	N
246.0	.2500									1	24239	N
246.0	80.00									1	49787	N
246.0	600.0	238.5	506.2	281.0	66.25	291.0	52.50	288.0	52.50	8	1245	N
246.0	2.776	251.0	2.634	257.0	2.209	263.0	1.473	280.0	.4532	5	32250	N
246.0	72.00	251.0	70.00	264.0	60.00	332.0	11.20			4	19483	N
246.0	6.400	262.0	3.100	266.0	2.200	278.5	1.380			4	15402	A
246.0	60.62	283.5	24.40							2	44983	N
246.0	80.54	293.0	12.64	303.5	9.886	301.0	9.886			4	625	N
246.0	53.00	294.0	28.00							2	3880	B
246.0	64.22	294.0	10.48							2	13702	N
246.0	91.00	295.0	17.00							2	9167	N
246.0	21.00	306.5	4.300	281.0	2.900					3	23709	A
246.0	63.00	308.0	23.00							2	1315	B
246.5	128.0									1	15402	N
246.5	.6300									1	20002	N
246.5	74.00									1	42774	N
246.5	58.00	285.0	16.00	393.0	9.200					3	19974	B
246.5	70.00	294.5	11.40							2	10644	B
246.5	79.78	295.0	15.10							2	46008	N
246.5	56.00	300.0	16.20	279.5	10.80					3	38681	N
247.0	115.6									1	783	N
247.0	165.2									1	17423	N
247.0	76.36									1	19864	N
247.0	49.50									1	40761	N
247.0	74.00									1	41504	N
247.0	2.560	243.0	2.508	252.0	2.318	257.5	1.937	261.0	1.833	7	1651	N
247.0	83.00	282.0	5.500							2	43897	B
247.0	107.0	287.0	3.891	315.0	.3969					3	872	N
247.0	69.00	296.0	9.100							2	11627	N
247.0	54.00	307.0	11.20							2	23709	N
247.0	248.5	341.0	11.03	327.0	11.03	312.5	7.971	320.0	4.697	6	15224	N
247.5	81.39									1	9239	N
247.5	131.4									1	20340	N
247.5	112.5									1	41888	N
247.5	138.5	206.5	111.4	313.0	20.28					3	13294	N
247.5	118.0	213.0	58.00							2	22153	N
247.5	90.00	277.0	57.50	226.0	52.50					3	4875	N
247.5	83.00	294.0	13.40							2	50586	N
247.5	350.0	340.0	18.00							2	37742	N
248.0	13.97									1	866	N
248.0	46.96									1	1809	N
248.0	81.25									1	1980	A
248.0	70.00									1	21488	N
248.0	90.00									1	22087	N
248.0	48.00									1	49899	N
248.0	11.04	253.5	1.341	257.5	1.104	263.5	.7889			4	216	A
248.0	87.00	264.0	67.00	331.0	12.80					3	8154	N
248.0	153.0	280.0	8.012	285.0	3.132					3	1012	N
248.0	145.9	281.0	8.918	272.0	8.828	289.0	6.396			4	241	N
248.0	55.00	287.0	5.400							2	19813	B
248.0	6.100	293.0	.9000							2	10644	N
248.0	84.31	297.0	14.70							2	44872	N
248.0	56.00	332.0	17.20							2	21019	A
248.5	54.00									1	16309	N
248.5	35.00									1	49893	N
248.5	3.950	244.0	3.950	254.0	3.400	260.0	2.400			4	2731	A
248.5	2.941	254.0	2.843	260.0	2.156	316.0	1.666			4	44872	A
248.5	41.00	297.0	6.300							2	46977	N
248.5	65.00	302.0	10.25							2	46052	N
248.5	51.87	310.5	15.00							2	22392	B
249.0	128.0									1	8130	B
249.0	14.52									1	8378	N
249.0	50.87									1	9773	B
249.0	86.38									1	10517	N
249.0	76.50									1	14255	N
249.0	41.22									1	18491	N
249.0	58.00									1	41528	N
249.0	33.50									1	46044	B
249.0	71.00									1	50308	N
249.0	70.00	214.0	35.00							2	46466	A
249.0	119.5	253.0	118.7	244.0	115.7	263.5	102.2	328.0	14.67	5	8077	N
249.0	84.00	289.0	11.00							2	38720	N

1		2		3		4		5		PEAKS	UV NO	NAB
249.0	50.90	296.0	7.748							2	527	N
249.0	82.88	297.0	9.909							2	1898	B
249.0	64.62	297.0	9.556							2	586	N
249.0	64.31	299.0	10.70							2	654	N
249.0	89.00	310.0	.0950							2	2331	N
249.5	86.00									1	1341	N
249.5	29.00									1	1366	A
249.5	31.50	279.0	6.000							2	917	N
249.5	138.0	285.0	19.40							2	1468	N
249.5	66.00	292.5	9.000							2	976	N
249.5	71.92	301.5	12.80							2	2115	N
249.5	63.00	312.0	11.60							2	524	N
250.0	55.88									1	670	N
250.0	88.48									1	2328	N
250.0	41.25									1	1046	N
250.0	1.760									1	1187	N
250.0	34.54									1	1142	N
250.0	88.00									1	762	A
250.0	75.00									1	1348	N
250.0	46.00									1	2087	N
250.0	217.5	209.0	160.0	221.0	127.5	312.0	41.00			4	541	N
250.0	4.200	256.0	3.850							2	1703	N
250.0	37.60	281.0	7.253							2	2164	N
250.0	5.800	282.0	4.200	224.0	3.600	372.0	2.700			4	870	A
250.0	1066.	339.5	38.00							2	746	N
250.5	1.760									1	1188	N
250.5	8.300									1	935	N
250.5	11.40									1	932	N
250.5	.1400									1	971	N
250.5	194.0	222.0	48.00	317.0	19.40					3	1182	N
250.5	90.00	282.0	12.80	291.0	10.00					3	1711	N
250.5	73.14	289.0	10.00							2	507	N
250.5	72.00	310.5	17.20							2	709	N
250.5	150.0	336.0	35.00							2	1952	B
251.0	30.88									1	670	A
251.0	79.38									1	2099	N
251.0	1.960									1	1183	N
251.0	43.50									1	1149	N
251.0	72.00									1	860	N
251.0	92.00									1	2884	N
251.0	71.00									1	2388	B
251.0	73.00									1	2029	N
251.0	70.00	232.0	36.52	277.0	31.30					3	1169	N
251.0	365.0	243.5	270.0	210.0	160.0	218.5	120.0	273.0	63.00	12	541	A
251.0	37.44	256.5	3.640	246.5	3.597	241.5	3.383	262.5	2.441	5	580	N
251.0	1.800	257.0	1.775	246.0	1.725	241.5	1.625	263.0	1.225	5	578	N
251.0	6.166	257.0	5.849	266.0	4.189					3	1821	N
251.0	62.00	275.0	29.00							2	1170	N
251.0	58.00	282.0	47.00	224.0	41.00					3	869	A
251.0	83.33	290.0	24.83							2	1900	N
251.0	76.31	297.0	9.824							2	817	N
251.0	72.00	309.0	11.40							2	2688	B
251.0	57.00	311.0	8.300							2	818	B
251.0	95.00	348.0	21.00	314.0	13.60					3	1794	A
251.5	42.62									1	1161	A
251.5	2.900	247.0	2.850	257.0	2.600	267.0	1.550			4	2849	N
251.5	8.400	256.0	8.100							2	977	N
252.0	9.318									1	2950	N
252.0	176.0									1	2098	N
252.0	9.800									1	861	N
252.0	1.900									1	1185	N
252.0	10.74									1	298	N
252.0	35.71									1	1926	B
252.0	66.00									1	2577	N
252.0	21.60									1	288	N
252.0	51.00									1	1141	N
252.0	42.00									1	1097	N
252.0	90.00									1	717	A
252.0	17.50									1	661	N
252.0	390.0	212.5	170.0	275.5	80.00	294.5	60.00	282.0	60.00	5	215	N
252.0	74.00	232.5	44.00							2	1275	N
252.0	363.6	245.0	278.7	221.0	127.2	293.0	78.04	275.0	76.82	11	214	N
252.0	81.00	257.5	8.100							2	424	N
252.0	2.275	258.0	2.200	248.0	2.175					3	1820	N
252.0	2.009	258.5	1.845	262.5	1.261					3	644	N
252.0	2.955	258.5	2.680	263.5	1.890					3	646	N
252.0	73.33	286.0	9.787							2	640	N
252.0	83.33	302.5	13.44							2	2176	N
252.5	76.00									1	1304	N
252.5	82.00									1	2589	B
252.5	91.11									1	678	N
252.5	100.9									1	2059	N
252.5	116.0									1	2106	N
252.5	2.944	258.0	2.894	264.0	2.095	268.0	1.297			4	647	N
252.5	113.3	270.0	21.25	277.0	6.387	281.0	4.625			4	2888	N
252.5	78.88	303.0	23.33							2	669	N
253.0	250.0									1	2584	N
253.0	222.8									1	2530	N
253.0	107.8									1	2588	N
253.0	67.00									1	1378	B
253.0	110.0									1	2127	N
253.0	97.00									1	2679	A
253.0	385.0	212.0	165.0	305.0	70.00					3	206	N

ULTRAVIOLET LOCATOR INDEX

1		2		3		4		5		PEAKS	UV NO	NAB
253.0	132.0	227.0	114.0	351.0	52.00					3	1947	B
253.0	1483.	246.0	750.0	337.5	33.00	321.0	17.25	307.5	7.500	5	213	N
253.0	1.975	257.0	1.925	247.0	1.600	263.5	1.300			4	840	N
253.0	23.50	261.0	2.700	257.0	2.700	268.0	1.900	325.0	.3500	5	596	A
253.0	46.17	262.5	44.70	312.5	18.08	325.0	16.02			4	900	N
253.0	12.58	275.5	5.862	297.0	2.068					3	2176	A
253.0	46.50	298.0	8.750							2	761	N
253.0	84.87	299.0	14.20							2	653	N
253.0	83.00	300.0	13.00							2	652	N
253.0	73.00	320.0	17.00							2	173	N
253.0	64.58	334.0	.6715							2	2112	N
253.5	38.00									1	1708	N
253.5	2.270	248.0	2.243	259.5	1.729	263.0	1.162			4	648	A
253.5	5.809	268.0	3.817							2	154	N
253.5	81.37	298.5	1.386							2	656	N
254.0	71.00									1	1355	N
254.0	67.00									1	2389	B
254.0	60.00									1	1155	N
254.0	40.50									1	1162	N
254.0	44.00	219.0	38.50							2	1729	A
254.0	43.79	227.5	38.56	285.0	9.281					3	1923	N
254.0	1.871	248.0	1.812	244.0	1.666	257.5	1.520	264.0	1.081	5	650	A
254.0	1.900	248.5	1.769	238.0	1.539	260.0	1.507			4	587	A
254.0	1.327	248.5	1.244	244.0	1.078	238.5	1.037	260.0	.9958	5	585	A
254.0	41.50	296.0	28.50							2	2033	B
254.0	211.7	317.0	23.39							2	1181	N
254.5	10.50									1	688	N
254.5	33.69									1	1164	N
254.5	96.00									1	2586	N
254.5	1.331	249.0	1.228	260.5	1.023	244.5	1.023	239.0	.9215	5	586	A
254.5	77.00	296.5	10.00							2	655	N
254.5	84.00	301.5	12.00							2	2548	B
254.5	182.0	306.5	60.00							2	2125	N
255.0	167.9									1	2978	N
255.0	112.0									1	399	N
255.0	44.44									1	669	A
255.0	31.52									1	2072	N
255.0	41.12									1	1163	N
255.0	79.61									1	885	A
255.0	58.00									1	1343	N
255.0	27.00									1	862	A
255.0	54.95	247.0	33.88	291.5	17.82	305.0	10.27	320.0	6.435	5	2122	N
255.0	1.550	259.0	1.400	249.5	1.300	264.5	.9500			4	2466	N
255.0	17.14	261.5	13.14							2	685	N
255.0	21.37	262.0	17.13							2	684	N
255.0	2.350	265.0	2.100	250.0	2.050	267.0	1.150			4	594	A
255.0	1.350	270.0	.7880							2	483	N
255.0	227.5	273.0	77.50	327.0	22.50					3	2126	N
255.0	76.00	306.0	11.80							2	2688	N
255.5	1.450									1	2996	N
255.5	78.00									1	1289	N
255.5	1.368	250.0	1.368	244.0	1.263	264.0	.7895			4	229	N
256.0	34.50									1	2967	N
256.0	66.00									1	1153	N
256.0	115.1									1	2231	N
256.0	55.00									1	2895	N
256.0	12.80									1	2894	N
256.0	115.7									1	698	N
256.0	160.0									1	2144	N
256.0	49.00									1	872	A
256.0	93.87									1	852	B
256.0	463.2	248.0	308.8	292.0	19.11					3	2123	N
256.0	.9250	251.0	.7500							2	979	N
256.0	14.96	260.0	14.72							2	711	N
256.0	2.120	261.0	1.960	250.5	1.640	267.0	1.400			4	805	N
256.0	1.283	261.0	1.194	250.5	1.044	269.5	.6327	277.0	.4602	5	2968	N
256.0	11.96	261.5	11.60	268.0	8.159					3	689	N
256.0	25.54	262.0	25.00	268.0	13.58					3	713	N
256.0	72.34	292.5	55.31							2	1238	N
256.0	128.3	295.0	10.66							2	2082	N
256.0	67.00	296.5	2.400							2	2031	N
256.5	20.00									1	1729	N
256.5	57.00	222.0	57.00	280.5	29.00					3	1171	N
256.5	1.692	250.5	1.666	260.0	1.307	266.5	.8461			5	2846	N
256.5	6.600	250.5	5.400	262.5	5.200	260.0	4.800	246.5	4.300	6	784	N
256.5	31.37	251.0	27.20	262.0	23.77					3	681	N
256.5	1.425	251.0	1.275	265.5	1.000					3	1484	N
256.5	1.776	260.5	1.731	266.5	1.412	250.5	1.366			4	579	A
256.5	2.350	261.0	2.150	250.5	1.950	267.0	1.600			4	221	N
256.5	1.340	263.0	1.040	251.0	1.040	246.5	.7200			4	1819	N
256.8	1.652	251.0	1.611	245.5	1.528	262.0	1.363	266.5	1.157	5	2014	N
257.0	68.30									1	1047	N
257.0	46.00									1	1057	N
257.0	182.0									1	894	N
257.0	47.00									1	1167	N
257.0	59.63									1	1172	N
257.0	55.00	227.0	51.00							2	2411	N
257.0	3.250	251.0	3.000							2	2951	N
257.0	1.834	251.0	1.809	246.5	1.683	263.0	1.281			4	577	N
257.0	3.187	251.0	3.187	247.0	3.047	263.0	2.290			4	581	N
257.0	1.400	251.0	1.250	263.0	1.150	246.0	1.125			4	2848	N
257.0	1.706	251.0	1.513	263.0	1.379	267.0	.8754			4	2845	N

ULTRAVIOLET LOCATOR INDEX

1		2		3		4		5		PEAKS	UV NO	NAB
257.0	1.594	251.5	1.571	247.0	1.480	241.5	1.366	263.0	1.116	5	579	N
257.0	1.297	251.5	1.192	247.0	1.013	263.0	.9690			4	2834	N
257.0	2.295	251.5	2.193	247.0	1.887	263.5	1.760	242.0	1.709	6	1483	N
257.0	1.550	251.5	1.400	263.0	1.200	246.0	1.200	266.5	.9500	5	2422	N
257.0	1.840	251.5	1.600	263.0	1.380	247.0	1.340			4	805	B
257.0	1.180	251.5	1.020	263.0	.8800	247.0	.8400	241.0	.7200	6	2310	N
257.0	1.450	251.5	1.241	263.0	1.100	247.0	.9667	267.0	.7500	5	478	N
257.0	.9600	252.0	.8200	263.0	.7400	246.5	.7000	241.0	.6700	6	2311	N
257.0	1.515	252.0	1.206	263.0	1.092	266.5	.8711	247.0	.8351	5	140	N
257.0	1.937	259.5	1.875	263.0	1.787	267.0	1.737	253.0	1.525	5	2540	N
257.0	1.480	261.5	1.220	263.0	1.200	251.0	1.200	267.0	.8600	5	782	N
257.0	21.84	262.0	20.87							2	2346	N
257.0	1.631	262.0	1.087	251.5	.8995	267.5	.7112	298.0	.2144	5	1279	B
257.0	1.400	263.0	1.150							2	2448	N
257.0	1.555	263.0	1.174	251.5	1.174	246.5	.7937			4	972	N
257.0	1.318	263.0	1.059	252.0	.9852	267.0	.6593			4	2832	N
257.0	1.800	263.5	1.200							2	2447	N
257.0	3.750	263.5	3.600	270.5	2.600	216.5	2.550			4	1361	B
257.0	98.00	264.0	96.00	237.0	48.00	291.5	7.600			4	2400	N
257.0	319.5	285.0	13.26	295.0	8.260					3	380	N
257.0	93.33	293.0	13.00							2	1019	N
257.0	79.00	304.0	12.80							2	816	N
257.0	67.00	306.0	8.800							2	818	N
257.5	162.7									1	2124	N
257.5	.9100									1	1016	N
257.5	94.73	221.5	52.63							2	2134	N
257.5	293.3	250.5	233.3	213.5	153.3	299.5	63.33	279.0	62.66	9	216	N
257.5	1.900	251.5	1.850							2	1705	N
257.5	1.793	251.5	1.793	248.0	1.659	263.5	1.300	267.0	.8520	5	1479	N
257.5	1.380	251.5	1.180	263.5	1.040	247.0	.9600	241.0	.8800	5	2307	N
257.5	.8494	251.5	.6950	264.0	.6757					3	2852	N
257.5	1.752	252.0	1.712	247.0	1.548	264.0	1.168			4	2847	N
257.5	1.221	252.0	.9327	263.0	.9135	247.0	.6442	266.5	.6346	5	2835	N
257.5	1.313	252.0	1.029	263.0	.9608	247.0	.7255	266.5	.7059	5	2833	N
257.5	1.788	252.0	1.585	263.0	1.361	247.0	1.361	267.5	.8943	5	480	N
257.5	1.049	252.0	.8843	263.0	.8094	247.0	.6745	267.5	.5396	6	2313	N
257.5	6.100	252.0	5.300	263.5	4.500	247.0	4.400	242.0	3.600	7	784	B
257.5	1.211	252.0	1.153	263.5	.9371	262.0	.9227	268.0	.6055	5	2844	N
257.5	2.550	252.0	2.175	264.0	2.050					3	2556	N
257.5	1.280	252.0	1.040	264.0	1.000	247.0	.8000			4	2539	N
257.5	1.340	252.0	1.100	264.0	1.040	247.0	.9200			4	2542	N
257.5	1.280	252.0	1.060	264.0	.9600	247.0	.8600			4	2286	N
257.5	1.283	252.0	1.016	264.0	1.000	247.0	.7500	267.0	.5833	6	2312	N
257.5	1.394	252.0	1.129	267.0	.9134	263.5	.8413	247.0	.8173	5	479	N
257.5	32.16	252.5	28.03	264.0	22.05					3	699	N
257.5	1.750	260.0	1.562	252.5	1.375	263.5	1.312	267.0	1.125	6	1701	N
257.5	1.250	263.0	1.100	252.0	1.050					3	2837	N
257.5	3.450	263.5	3.000	266.5	2.700	295.0	2.600			4	2385	N
257.5	94.59	301.0	13.33							2	1706	N
257.5	8.434	303.0	1.123							2	651	N
257.5	83.00	306.0	32.00							2	1157	N
258.0	77.61									1	1055	N
258.0	67.00									1	2886	N
258.0	87.00									1	2463	B
258.0	64.00									1	1154	N
258.0	95.00									1	2030	B
258.0	40.00									1	1307	N
258.0	67.00									1	1732	A
258.0	6.500	252.0	6.500	247.0	6.000					3	1791	N
258.0	1.301	252.0	1.149	247.0	.9761	264.0	.9544			4	2541	N
258.0	1.850	252.0	1.800	248.0	1.700	263.5	1.500	267.5	1.400	5	1774	N
258.0	1.075	252.0	.9250	263.5	.8250					3	2314	N
258.0	1.983	252.0	1.786	264.0	1.575					3	1482	N
258.0	2.211	252.0	2.211	264.0	1.759					3	2015	N
258.0	2.229	252.0	1.944	264.0	1.743	247.0	1.715	268.0	1.129	5	1005	N
258.0	1.297	252.0	1.240	264.0	1.221	268.0	1.106	280.0	1.068	5	2853	N
258.0	1.300	252.5	1.200	247.0	1.033	264.5	.9667	242.0	.8833	6	1817	N
258.0	1.849	252.5	1.698	263.5	1.547	248.0	1.509	267.5	1.358	5	1218	N
258.0	2.350	252.5	2.100	263.5	1.900	267.5	1.550	302.0	.3000	5	2432	N
258.0	2.566	253.0	2.466	264.5	1.900					3	374	N
258.0	48.00	253.0	48.00	275.0	39.00					3	741	N
258.0	3.050	253.5	2.900	267.5	1.900					3	1481	N
258.0	2.058	261.0	2.026	253.0	1.960	247.5	1.764	267.5	1.699	6	2159	N
258.0	1.549	261.0	1.383	253.0	1.346	264.0	1.217	247.5	1.051	6	1485	N
258.0	2.300	263.5	2.200	252.5	2.000	268.5	1.600			4	2932	N
258.0	1.279	264.5	1.012	252.5	1.012	247.5	.7285	267.5	.6574	6	2831	N
258.0	3.176	281.0	1.996							2	2035	N
258.0	61.06	289.5	31.63							2	2598	N
258.0	84.07	321.5	62.83							2	1530	N
258.5	195.0	229.5	195.0	269.0	90.00	268.0	84.00	311.0	70.00	8	1001	N
258.5	98.75	235.5	63.75							2	1537	N
258.5	3.600	252.5	3.600	247.5	3.500	264.5	3.000			4	2308	N
258.5	1.568	252.5	1.308	264.5	1.207	247.0	1.150	307.5	.1850	5	2860	N
258.5	1.240	252.5	1.009	264.5	.9352	247.5	.8148	242.0	.7222	5	375	N
258.5	3.800	253.0	3.650							2	2040	N
258.5	.9840	253.0	.8170	264.5	.7872	247.5	.6023	267.5	.5606	7	2836	N
258.5	1.360	253.0	1.180	264.5	1.040	248.0	.9800	242.5	.8000	6	782	B
258.5	2.126	253.0	1.810	265.0	1.674	248.5	1.470	279.0	1.108	5	2546	N
258.5	.9112	253.5	.7710	264.0	.7126	268.0	.6542			4	2309	N
258.5	1.160	261.0	1.040	252.5	1.000	264.0	.9000	247.5	.8000	7	804	B
258.5	7.789	265.0	7.684	253.5	6.210					3	509	A
258.5	1.600	266.5	1.390	283.0	.1500					3	789	N

1		2		3		4		5		PEAKS	UV NO	NAB
258.5	95.29	304.5	13.17							2	650	N
259.0	13.78									1	1506	N
259.0	78.00									1	2582	N
259.0	84.14									1	2454	N
259.0	30.50									1	895	N
259.0	27.50									1	845	N
259.0	39.00									1	2389	N
259.0	96.00									1	1360	N
259.0	79.00	217.0	29.00							2	1154	A
259.0	1.900	252.0	1.850							2	2545	N
259.0	1.777	253.0	1.466	264.5	1.400	248.0	1.111	268.0	1.022	5	2544	N
259.0	1.604	253.0	1.350	265.0	1.258	248.0	1.015	268.5	.8223	5	1700	N
259.0	.9556	253.0	.7481	265.0	.7333	268.0	.5185	248.0	.5185	5	2838	N
259.0	2.833	253.5	2.250	264.5	2.050	268.5	1.833	249.0	1.533	5	149	N
259.0	2.383	253.5	2.166	265.0	1.900	249.0	1.666			4	1790	N
259.0	2.700	253.5	2.450	268.0	2.100					3	481	N
259.0	3.256	254.0	3.173	264.0	3.118	274.0	2.124	297.0	.1545	5	484	N
259.0	1.250	254.0	1.050	268.0	.9500					3	147	N
259.0	6.000	254.5	4.900	264.5	4.800					3	230	N
259.0	1.884	261.0	1.833	253.0	1.615	264.0	1.435	268.0	1.397	6	477	N
259.0	4.100	261.5	4.000	253.0	3.800	269.0	3.700	298.0	3.500	5	151	N
259.0	2.684	262.0	2.617	254.0	2.483	265.0	2.013	269.0	1.862	7	153	N
259.0	3.777	265.0	3.092	253.0	2.667	249.0	1.605			4	222	N
259.0	1.315	265.0	.9720	253.0	.8290	268.0	.8287	248.5	.8195	5	2673	N
259.0	5.700	265.0	4.800	254.0	4.500					3	231	N
259.0	1.523	265.0	1.301	263.0	1.291	253.0	1.248	269.0	.9735	5	1090	N
259.0	97.01	293.0	47.76							2	211	N
259.0	96.55	304.0	14.65							2	649	N
259.0	15.57	324.0	11.23							2	1534	N
259.0	93.00	328.0	1.450							2	2100	N
259.0	31.50	353.0	.5500							2	1334	A
259.5	68.00									1	2292	N
259.5	3.850									1	2547	N
259.5	90.00									1	2589	N
259.5	4.191									1	1017	N
259.5	102.0									1	1901	B
259.5	25.00									1	705	N
259.5	1.100	253.0	1.050	267.5	.9500					3	143	N
259.5	2.480	253.5	2.080	265.0	1.960	268.5	1.640	249.0	1.560	5	152	N
259.5	48.91	256.0	48.36	216.5	48.36					3	713	A
259.5	7.500	265.0	6.774	255.0	5.725	392.0	.3225			4	508	A
259.5	2.350	265.5	1.950							2	2991	N
259.5	18.40	265.5	16.40	253.5	12.80	248.0	6.400			4	223	N
259.8	5.307	266.2	4.804	253.0	4.357	246.0	4.022			4	1453	N
260.0	38.00									1	1719	N
260.0	62.00									1	2062	N
260.0	45.00									1	1099	N
260.0	5.000									1	1308	N
260.0	45.00									1	1165	N
260.0	326.6	218.0	100.0	310.5	7.500	325.0	7.100			4	747	A
260.0	310.0	218.5	100.0	332.0	5.400	315.0	3.300			4	747	N
260.0	118.0	235.5	70.00	312.0	48.00					3	871	N
260.0	1.976	253.0	1.860	244.0	1.860	269.0	1.366	328.0	.9883	5	593	A
260.0	1.578	253.5	1.491	265.0	1.081	269.0	.9064	325.0	.1169	5	663	A
260.0	3.050	254.0	2.900							2	1776	N
260.0	23.52	254.5	20.12	266.5	17.29					3	2938	N
260.0	2.170	258.0	2.036	267.0	1.803	254.0	1.719	252.5	1.719	10	134	N
260.0	1.320	258.5	1.312	253.0	1.128	267.0	1.024	263.5	.9920	6	145	N
260.0	1.612	265.5	1.435	253.0	1.335	271.0	.6981			4	284	N
260.0	3.400	266.5	2.200							2	1191	N
260.0	6.400	267.0	4.800							2	1371	N
260.0	1.348	270.5	1.011	292.0	.7865					3	518	A
260.0	67.00	316.0	8.400							2	819	B
260.0	91.00	323.0	4.150	309.0	3.750					3	1508	N
260.0	70.00	397.0	3.150	422.0	2.900					3	2095	N
260.5	106.6									1	1889	N
260.5	80.00									1	2102	N
260.5	50.00									1	2110	A
260.5	14.25									1	696	N
260.5	4.100	254.0	3.700							2	667	A
260.5	1.563	256.5	1.469	263.0	1.374	267.0	1.279	250.5	1.137	6	1487	N
260.5	1.992	258.0	1.992	253.0	1.897	254.0	1.878	264.0	1.366	8	136	N
260.5	2.645	267.5	2.376							2	489	A
260.5	2.650	269.0	2.050							2	148	N
261.0	123.0									1	1365	N
261.0	54.37									1	1276	N
261.0	82.97									1	1160	N
261.0	32.50									1	2602	B
261.0	23.28									1	2939	A
261.0	54.00									1	1262	N
261.0	2.026	255.0	1.666	266.0	1.634	272.0	1.209			4	1321	N
261.0	1.850	255.0	1.552	267.0	1.358	250.5	1.313			4	1447	N
261.0	3.100	255.0	2.850	270.0	2.200					3	530	A
261.0	31.27	255.5	27.04	267.0	22.40					3	1728	N
261.0	41.73	256.0	35.65	268.0	30.86					3	682	N
261.0	.8800	256.5	.8600	251.0	.6400	267.0	.6300			4	2272	N
261.0	3.950	256.5	3.700	267.5	3.100					3	595	A
261.0	1.561	258.5	1.561	267.5	1.343	264.0	1.343	253.0	1.324	8	2036	N
261.0	18.09	259.0	17.79	253.0	17.48	268.0	14.41			4	135	N
261.0	1.508	259.0	1.508	264.0	1.377	255.0	1.210	268.0	1.201	7	138	N
261.0	1.838	259.0	1.739	268.0	1.503	255.0	1.490	253.0	1.490	7	137	N
261.0	1.788	263.5	1.605	255.5	1.459	270.0	1.441	266.5	1.368	6	144	N

1		2		3		4		5		PEAKS	UV NO	NAB
261.0	3.634	265.0	3.501	267.5	3.368	271.5	2.925	254.5	2.570	5	1091	N
261.0	9.142	267.0	8.285	255.5	7.428					3	510	A
261.0	6.492	267.0	6.175	256.0	4.592					3	980	N
261.0	3.101	268.5	2.848							2	659	A
261.0	3.111	268.5	2.518							2	187	N
261.0	2.484	268.5	2.212	235.0	2.121	315.0	.3030			4	601	A
261.0	112.9	300.0	53.35	289.0	36.58	294.0	30.18	320.0	.1828	6	208	N
261.0	152.7	302.0	22.71							2	662	N
261.0	90.00	310.0	10.00							2	668	N
261.0	31.00	394.0	3.300	376.0	2.750	482.0	2.100	450.0	1.650	5	761	A
261.0	48.00	511.0	5.700	551.0	4.300					3	598	A
261.5	99.00									1	1909	N
261.5	47.05									1	2938	A
261.5	48.87	213.0	33.83							2	690	A
261.5	18.40	256.0	18.28	267.5	13.31					3	687	N
261.5	1.120	256.0	.9400	267.5	.8800	251.0	.6600			4	838	N
261.5	5.800	256.0	5.000	268.0	4.500					3	836	N
261.5	1.527	256.5	1.443	267.5	1.108	251.0	1.004			4	1279	N
261.5	3.466	268.0	3.200							2	227	N
262.0	68.75									1	1032	N
262.0	68.00									1	890	A
262.0	79.00									1	847	N
262.0	46.90									1	1720	N
262.0	2.195	255.0	1.837	266.0	1.718	275.0	1.527	291.0	.6205	5	485	A
262.0	19.80	258.0	18.20	268.5	17.60	243.0	17.00	321.0	1.800	5	1468	A
262.0	6.100	268.5	5.600							2	224	N
262.0	6.750	268.5	6.250							2	228	N
262.0	2.600	269.0	2.400							2	661	A
262.0	6.800	269.5	6.200	257.0	5.600					3	225	N
262.0	112.0	300.0	14.52							2	666	N
262.0	78.94	312.0	10.81							2	663	N
262.5	99.00									1	847	B
262.5	60.86									1	1728	A
262.5	81.55									1	885	N
262.5	94.00									1	1901	N
262.5	77.14	206.5	71.42							2	2856	N
262.5	3.150	256.0	2.650	269.5	2.250					3	150	N
262.5	18.00	257.0	16.40							2	2606	B
262.5	32.19	257.0	27.85	269.0	23.05					3	683	N
262.5	3.700	268.0	2.400							2	2570	B
262.5	2.209	269.5	1.479							2	1224	N
262.5	1.955	271.0	1.515							2	174	N
263.0	95.00									1	598	N
263.0	79.00									1	2343	N
263.0	90.50									1	1340	N
263.0	92.50									1	2551	N
263.0	2.050									1	2593	B
263.0	33.00									1	1195	N
263.0	29.41	257.0	24.50	270.0	20.58					3	700	N
263.0	1.750	271.0	1.400							2	2854	N
263.0	2.087	271.0	1.937	265.0	1.825	257.0	1.675			4	2557	N
263.0	84.00	309.0	10.40	566.0	1.650	612.0	1.550			4	819	N
263.0	113.4	344.0	1.850							2	2107	N
263.5	46.22									1	1934	N
263.5	6.497									1	1608	N
263.5	95.06									1	884	N
263.5	60.00									1	1930	N
263.5	2.950	257.0	2.625	270.5	2.225	251.5	2.075			4	2933	N
263.5	4.075	270.5	3.250	257.0	2.900	253.0	1.875			4	1361	N
263.5	20.00	318.0	4.250							2	1544	N
264.0	105.0									1	2101	N
264.0	80.00									1	888	N
264.0	57.00									1	1156	N
264.0	70.21	218.0	62.12							2	1048	N
264.0	2.004	259.0	1.718	270.5	1.675	253.0	1.217	247.0	.7302	5	1300	N
264.0	1.284	261.0	1.154	257.5	1.146	251.0	.9024	271.0	.8943	7	381	N
264.0	6.281	269.5	6.112	265.0	5.772					3	511	A
264.0	21.80	270.0	15.86							2	703	N
264.0	3.750	270.0	3.300							2	2940	N
264.0	1.386	270.0	1.119	258.0	1.119					3	190	N
264.0	1.974	271.5	1.692	257.5	1.519	268.0	1.475			4	179	N
264.5	44.66									1	1068	N
264.5	70.00									1	2172	N
264.5	29.81									1	695	N
264.5	70.00									1	2452	N
264.5	6.011	271.0	5.204							2	1716	N
264.5	.6566	271.0	.6378	208.0	.5722	258.5	.5065			4	301	N
264.5	6.037	271.0	5.660	258.5	4.056					3	389	N
264.5	62.00	306.0	50.00							2	1529	B
265.0	146.0									1	1331	N
265.0	88.00									1	165	N
265.0	2.097									1	2921	N
265.0	64.00									1	743	N
265.0	62.00	207.0	60.00							2	2455	N
265.0	100.0	220.5	86.00	300.0	36.00	228.0	34.00	289.0	28.00	5	1727	N
265.0	114.0	221.5	108.0	276.0	78.00	305.0	45.00	293.5	35.00	6	209	N
265.0	80.00	229.0	39.00	301.0	16.00	289.5	16.00			4	2855	N
265.0	44.00	239.0	39.00							2	1073	N
265.0	5.538	258.0	5.346	272.5	5.076	316.0	1.307	302.0	1.015	8	603	N
265.0	6.400	259.0	6.300	272.0	6.000					3	2387	N
265.0	3.800	271.0	3.500							2	2979	N
265.0	2.600	271.5	2.250							2	2925	N

ULTRAVIOLET LOCATOR INDEX

1		2		3		4		5		PEAKS	UV NO	NAB
265.0	3.106	272.0	2.613	268.0	2.405	259.5	2.253			4	177	N
265.0	64.00	335.0	23.00							2	2105	N
265.5	125.4									1	2145	B
265.5	2.150	250.5	2.050	272.5	2.000	256.0	1.950			4	591	A
265.5	20.00	271.5	16.92	260.0	13.84	262.5	13.40	257.5	11.42	6	232	N
265.5	1.893	273.0	1.582	259.0	1.408					3	382	N
266.0	100.0									1	2097	N
266.0	62.00									1	1069	N
266.0	68.00									1	1332	N
266.0	79.00									1	890	N
266.0	17.25									2	1311	N
266.0	94.00									1	1523	N
266.0	56.00	216.0	42.00	316.0	29.00					3	1334	A
266.0	132.8	228.0	102.8	236.0	88.57	287.0	38.57	315.5	18.85	5	1278	N
266.0	1.950	257.0	1.813	275.0	1.758	299.0	.8516			4	521	A
266.0	130.0	259.0	126.0							2	2032	N
266.0	1.252	262.0	.9820	274.0	.9099					3	309	N
266.0	6.400	272.5	5.700							2	2568	B
266.0	6.541	272.5	6.090	259.0	4.210					3	390	N
266.0	2.267	273.5	1.904	259.0	1.613					3	295	N
266.0	2.880	274.0	2.471	259.0	1.964					3	292	N
266.0	3.627	274.0	3.534	298.0	.0837	304.0	.0558	318.0	.0279	5	198	N
266.0	166.0	343.0	11.00							2	969	N
266.3	33.00	286.5	18.00							3	608	A
266.5	100.0									1	1231	B
266.5	73.00									1	1145	N
266.5	20.40									1	2291	N
266.5	95.00	220.0	76.00	300.5	75.00	289.0	56.00	315.0	37.00	5	2180	A
266.5	720.0	256.5	400.0	219.5	166.0	241.0	96.00	319.0	54.00	9	218	N
266.5	3.450	260.0	3.350	254.0	2.650	271.0	2.300			4	1088	N
266.5	57.14	261.0	55.02	279.0	47.08	287.0	35.97			4	605	N
266.5	114.0	272.0	108.1	237.0	16.29					3	2246	N
266.5	2.594	273.5	2.280	259.5	1.903	220.0	1.548	253.0	1.359	5	293	N
267.0	4.150									1	1565	N
267.0	5.700									1	1945	N
267.0	19.97	261.0	19.14	274.0	14.87					3	701	N
267.0	3.653	261.5	3.253	275.5	3.167	292.0	.0913			4	485	N
267.0	9.543	273.0	9.128	261.0	6.224	259.0	5.809	253.0	3.526	5	226	N
267.0	1.908	275.0	1.686	259.0	1.464	254.0	1.045			4	981	N
267.5	1.160	260.5	1.020	274.5	.8400					3	783	B
267.5	17.00	262.0	15.00	275.0	12.50					3	704	N
267.5	28.86	275.0	22.16							2	692	N
268.0	108.0									1	2578	B
268.0	15.70									1	693	N
268.0	2.800	272.0	2.400							2	1947	N
268.0	22.85	272.0	6.628	280.0	6.400					3	310	N
268.0	128.5	272.0	7.857	280.0	6.825	267.0	6.269			4	2944	N
268.0	5.900	275.0	5.400							2	1362	N
268.0	2.112	275.0	1.815	261.0	1.600	254.5	1.188			4	383	N
268.0	32.50	288.0	17.00							3	608	N
268.5	1.296									1	387	N
268.5	5.700									1	2568	N
268.5	48.45	217.0	19.58							2	696	A
268.5	8.700	261.5	7.000	255.0	4.300					3	863	N
268.5	1.400	262.0	1.160	275.5	1.060	248.0	.7200			4	783	N
268.5	3.350	273.0	2.900	277.0	2.800					3	192	N
268.5	7.600	295.0	1.100							2	2569	B
269.0	13.50									1	1890	N
269.0	40.00									1	2969	N
269.0	8.600									1	2216	N
269.0	2.500									1	2929	N
269.0	78.00									1	1352	B
269.0	23.75									1	736	N
269.0	41.00	211.5	35.00							2	2927	N
269.0	106.0	228.5	25.50							2	2459	N
269.0	7.600	262.0	6.500	253.5	5.200					3	863	B
269.0	8.750	276.0	7.800	263.0	7.000					3	2553	N
269.5	64.00									1	2345	N
269.5	9.100	276.0	8.900							2	2955	N
269.5	5.800	277.0	5.700							2	1948	N
269.5	1.250	277.0	1.000	262.5	1.000	256.0	.7917			4	392	N
269.5	90.00	298.5	70.00	230.5	67.00					3	2599	B
270.0	83.00									1	1058	N
270.0	.2760									1	1967	N
270.0	51.00									1	2561	N
270.0	54.63									1	1031	N
270.0	107.5	217.0	77.50							2	2075	N
270.0	87.12	217.0	59.40							2	2077	N
270.0	28.00	260.0	26.00	280.0	18.00	325.0	15.00	312.0	10.20	8	1571	N
270.0	2.100	275.5	1.850	279.0	1.700					3	194	N
270.0	12.60	277.0	12.40							2	1550	N
270.0	8.800	277.0	8.300							2	824	B
270.0	1.079	278.0	.7619							2	396	N
270.0	25.22	279.0	22.03	264.0	15.80					3	1875	N
270.0	6.400	280.5	6.200							2	1901	A
270.0	36.00	286.0	35.00							2	887	A
270.5	54.00									1	2111	A
270.5	57.00	214.0	43.00							2	1721	N
270.5	16.92	277.0	14.51							2	1488	N
270.5	17.30	277.0	15.57	264.5	11.53					3	1489	N
271.0	.8000									1	924	N
271.0	92.50									1	2677	N

1		2		3		4		5		PEAKS	UV NO	NAB
271.0	40.00									1	2926	N
271.0	88.00									1	866	A
271.0	49.00									1	1946	B
271.0	91.53	216.0	87.83	227.5	64.55					3	2862	N
271.0	67.44	229.0	51.74							2	1333	N
271.0	3.450	263.5	3.450	278.0	2.350					5	167	N
271.0	5.332	277.5	4.280							3	2863	N
271.0	9.700	278.5	9.200							2	1106	N
271.0	10.00	278.5	9.625							2	1105	N
271.0	2.589	278.5	2.410							2	1553	N
271.0	2.062	278.5	1.538	263.5	1.433	257.0	.9440	249.0	.7692	5	393	N
271.0	133.3	305.5	33.50	314.0	32.50					3	1949	N
271.5	58.48									1	694	A
271.5	98.52	217.5	70.58							2	2076	N
271.5	1.602	264.0	1.243	279.0	1.215	257.5	.8839			4	397	N
271.5	13.92	277.5	13.17							2	1498	N
271.5	8.915	278.0	8.072							2	2928	N
272.0	12.00									1	1916	N
272.0	18.30									1	1876	N
272.0	46.50									1	756	N
272.0	152.0									1	2550	N
272.0	70.00									1	1352	N
272.0	2.300									1	1227	N
272.0	173.4	216.0	130.6	221.5	110.2	210.5	104.0	204.5	100.0	5	982	N
272.0	95.00	221.0	83.00							2	2078	N
272.0	4.285	264.5	4.114	258.5	3.257					3	1589	N
272.0	12.71	266.0	11.18	260.0	7.457					3	195	N
272.0	48.00	272.0	45.00	345.0	24.00					2	1903	N
272.0	2.300	280.5	2.000	306.0	.7000					3	522	A
272.5	7.050									1	2590	N
272.5	118.0									1	2588	B
272.5	103.9									1	879	N
272.5	41.00	234.0	25.50							2	1023	N
272.5	3.850	263.5	3.450	267.0	3.300	236.0	3.000	259.0	2.650	5	792	N
272.5	3.550	264.0	3.100	266.5	3.000	258.5	2.300			4	182	N
272.5	7.500	283.5	5.200							3	2223	N
273.0	34.00									1	756	A
273.0	1.948									1	286	N
273.0	31.66	236.5	16.66							2	1024	N
273.0	4.600	265.0	4.500							2	2680	B
273.0	3.700	268.0	3.600							2	2593	N
273.0	14.55	279.0	13.02							2	1877	N
273.0	16.78	279.5	15.14							2	1546	N
273.5	13.20									1	1913	N
273.5	86.00									1	732	N
273.5	15.00	264.0	13.50	329.5	13.25	319.5	10.00			5	730	N
273.5	101.5	268.0	89.11	265.0	84.97	259.5	65.28	262.0	54.40	7	181	N
274.0	15.95									1	1879	B
274.0	17.40									1	1907	N
274.0	98.19									1	874	N
274.0	83.00									1	1351	N
274.0	5.100									1	2339	N
274.0	142.0	215.0	106.0							2	1050	N
274.0	225.0	218.0	90.00							2	996	N
274.0	3.300	267.0	3.300	263.5	3.300	257.0	3.300	251.0	3.200	5	2543	N
274.0	36.00	280.5	34.00	244.0	29.50					3	1730	N
274.5	315.0	219.0	265.0	344.5	160.0	331.0	95.00			4	1357	N
274.5	15.16	281.0	13.34							2	1906	N
275.0	38.00									1	1098	N
275.0	52.80									1	2146	N
275.0	96.25	216.0	70.00	204.5	63.75	210.5	60.00	221.5	58.75	5	2857	N
275.0	.1951	229.0	.0346							2	1996	N
275.0	17.00	251.0	13.00							2	1925	N
275.0	51.21	265.0	45.12	285.0	32.92	296.0	32.57	283.0	32.11	10	200	N
275.0	27.00	265.0	26.50	307.0	2.500	321.0	1.950			5	1367	B
275.0	49.00	269.0	45.00	237.0	22.00					3	1730	A
275.0	19.18	282.0	16.48							2	1911	N
275.0	13.20	282.5	12.07							2	1514	N
275.0	12.09	282.5	10.93							2	1515	N
275.0	24.00	323.0	4.000	308.0	3.400	312.5	2.900			5	1367	N
275.5	15.00									1	1917	N
275.5	56.00	269.5	48.00	239.5	26.00					3	739	A
275.5	16.75	282.5	15.00							2	1517	N
275.5	16.45	283.0	15.45							2	1512	N
276.0	2.150									1	2375	N
276.0	10.20									2	2219	N
276.0	30.00									1	674	N
276.0	2.663	268.5	2.391	284.0	2.065					3	2573	B
276.0	8.800	269.0	8.600	224.5	7.600	288.0	6.200			4	2677	A
276.5	15.50									1	1894	N
276.5	185.7									1	1235	B
276.5	5.300									1	2058	N
276.5	47.00									1	1582	N
276.5	64.00	214.0	46.00							2	2173	N
276.5	76.78	216.5	51.78							2	2023	N
276.5	57.00	227.0	51.00							2	887	N
276.5	39.00	245.0	39.00	282.5	37.50					3	740	N
276.5	4.007	267.5	3.947							2	188	N
277.0	.2780									1	1040	N
277.0	.3025									1	1039	N
277.0	18.35									1	1918	N
277.0	47.00									1	1582	A

ULTRAVIOLET LOCATOR INDEX

1		2		3		4		5		PEAKS	UV NO	NAB
277.0	19.43	272.5	18.45	282.0	14.26					3	1545	N
277.0	10.70	284.5	10.00							2	1520	N
277.0	3.100	285.5	2.650							2	1018	N
277.5	29.33	267.0	26.33	270.5	25.00	288.5	18.33	307.0	2.000	6	401	N
277.5	5.400	268.5	5.200	272.0	4.800					3	191	N
278.0	.2690									1	1042	N
278.0	18.03									1	1878	N
278.0	24.11									1	1910	N
278.0	62.55									1	735	N
278.0	121.2									1	505	N
278.0	57.00	242.5	50.00	271.0	49.00	248.0	45.00	265.0	34.00	5	738	N
278.0	5.154	269.0	4.896							2	193	N
278.0	57.00	273.0	57.00	218.5	50.00					3	1528	A
278.0	15.18	285.0	12.65							2	1496	N
278.0	5.000	285.5	4.800	270.5	4.000					3	2580	B
279.0	2.160									1	2158	N
279.0	92.39	269.0	89.67							2	938	N
279.0	10.70	270.5	10.21	273.5	10.05					3	1551	N
279.0	15.81	285.0	15.14							2	1914	N
279.5	.3036									1	1041	N
279.5	4.700									1	2572	N
279.5	8.700									1	1928	N
279.5	14.56	272.0	14.17							2	1495	N
279.5	5.246	287.5	5.061							2	2591	N
279.5	4.400	288.0	4.000							2	2905	A
280.0	.5200									1	2153	N
280.0	1.673									1	675	N
280.0	48.00									1	1581	A
280.0	12.82									1	2585	B
280.0	82.95									1	1233	B
280.0	134.0	203.0	100.0	213.0	90.00					3	2269	N
280.0	100.0	219.0	90.00	225.0	66.25					3	2861	N
280.0	3.480	271.5	2.889	289.0	2.714					3	2177	N
280.0	51.33	273.5	49.33	265.5	34.66	243.0	28.00			4	740	A
280.0	4.700	288.0	4.500							2	2901	N
280.5	5.409									1	2896	B
280.5	3.585	272.0	3.389							2	386	N
280.5	240.0	298.0	208.3	273.0	186.6	265.0	173.3	289.0	170.0	8	169	N
281.0	.2478									1	1044	N
281.0	14.87									1	1927	N
281.0	16.00									1	1936	N
281.0	122.0									1	2332	N
281.0	12.00									1	757	A
281.0	13.00	271.0	11.00	288.0	9.000					4	1725	N
281.0	19.07	273.0	18.26							2	1892	N
281.0	4.583	273.0	4.351	267.0	2.731					3	308	N
281.0	4.728	288.0	4.130							2	2573	N
281.5	119.0									1	597	N
281.5	3.300									2	2874	N
281.5	158.9	219.0	66.22							2	2160	N
281.5	89.77	244.0	74.43	237.0	74.43					3	716	N
282.0	110.0									1	532	N
282.0	2.897									1	2603	N
282.0	17.50									2	2221	N
282.0	52.00									1	2610	B
282.0	97.13	253.0	64.01	225.0	55.18					3	2160	A
282.0	32.50	273.0	27.50							3	2674	N
282.0	12.00	275.5	12.00							2	1915	N
282.0	108.3	276.0	108.3	220.0	77.77					3	2175	N
282.0	15.46	317.0	.7129							2	1929	N
282.5	118.0									1	2332	B
282.5	26.51	231.0	25.11							2	1588	N
283.0	15.27									1	501	N
283.0	69.00									1	2957	N
283.0	24.66									1	1926	N
283.0	114.8	220.0	52.70							2	2161	N
283.0	.1948	232.0	.1732							2	1971	N
283.0	.1629	232.0	.0748							2	1975	N
283.0	17.45	234.0	5.785							2	500	N
283.5	41.50									2	316	N
283.5	143.3	220.0	93.33	207.5	81.66	225.5	80.00			4	2564	N
283.5	86.85	220.5	60.57							2	2174	N
284.0	14.86									1	1933	N
284.0	132.7									1	531	N
284.0	102.2									1	807	N
284.0	57.00									2	787	B
284.0	30.50	301.0	24.00	315.0	17.50					5	2183	N
285.0	10.40									1	1895	N
285.0	93.61	224.5	72.34							2	906	N
285.0	50.00	258.0	31.00							2	1234	B
285.0	17.60	303.0	14.80							2	1936	B
285.5	.4904									1	645	N
285.5	7.200	296.0	4.900							3	2236	N
286.0	14.20									1	1920	N
286.0	21.25									2	2239	N
286.0	17.16	235.0	7.735							2	494	N
286.5	5.700									1	2575	N
286.5	3.423	279.0	3.400	272.0	2.545					3	2902	N
286.5	2.413	279.0	2.348	272.0	1.761					3	2903	N
287.0	.1573									1	2000	N
287.0	19.30									1	1899	N
287.0	.1635	233.5	.1009							2	1979	N